Perazzi Introduce:

MX11-MX14   WITH ADJUST

They have been designed to improve your performanc
Drop out Trigger, Adjustable Stock-
All Styles available: Combo

MX11 COMBO

MX14 COMBO

MX11 SPORTING

PERAZZI U.S.A. Inc. 1207 S. Shamrock Ave.MONROVIA, CA 91016 U.S.A. Tel.818 303 0068 Fax 818 303 208

Contact PERAZZI U.S.A. or your nearest PERAZZI Dealer for more information.

the New Models

BLE COMB ON THE STOCK

erazzi features and quality at competitive prices.

tandard, Choice of Single or Un-Single

ingle—Sporting—Skeet—Trap.

Black's
WING & CLAY

is really three

directories in one.

Use the thumb tabs

to turn right

to the section

you want...

or turn the page

to find a more

detailed listing of

each section.

PUBLISHING STAFF

James F. Black, Jr.	*Publisher*
Raymond Goydon	*Associate Publisher*
Lois A. Ré	*Editor*
Amanda Santos	*Assistant to the Publisher*
Ann N. Edmonds	*Director of Research*
David G. Hanson	*Copywriter*
Glenn J. J. Davidson	*Database Support*

About our cover: Top Photo: Courtesy of Joe Prather, Griffin & Howe.

Wings Photo: "Mission Accomplished" - Springer Spaniel and Pheasant by Wayne Dowdy. Available through Bennett Publishing, 328 Ponderilla, Polson, MT 59860. (406) 883-3108.

Clays Photo: Courtesy of Kaltron-Pettibone, Importer of Vihtavuori Smokeless Powder.

THE SHOTGUNNER'S SOURCE

A reference guide to equipment and services.

Begins on page 10

WINGS
HUNTING

A nationwide guide to hunting destinations, outfitters and hunting preserves.

Begins on page 255

CLAYS
SPORTING, TRAP & SKEET LOCATIONS

A nationwide guide to sporting clays, trap and skeet locations.

Begins on page 407

Turn to the expanded table of contents on the following pages.

SHOTGUNNER'S SOURCE 10

A Word Of Thanks

The publication of Wing & Clay would not be possible without the support of hundreds of companies and individuals. Though it would be impossible to thank each and every one in this limited space, the publisher would be remiss in not singling out Jerry Allen & Tina Sidwell, Quail Unlimited; Al Anglace, CTSCA; Rudy Bechtel, B-SQUARE; Bill Binnian, COSCA; David Bopp, ATA; Larry Cero, Hunters Pointe; Fred Collins,

SCA; Joe Daniel, DBC Direct; Richard Frisella, Sr., NESCA; Mike Hampton, NSCA and NSSA; Sue King, WSSF; Bill Kinsala, Americase; Robert R. Knopf, Outdoor Mgmt. Network; Dave Lyon, Buick; Todd MacCoy, Pinkerton; Rebecca Maddy, NASGW; Peggy Mullin-Boehmer & John Mullin, Wildlife Harvest; Gary Rogers, UST; Dick Welch, Griffin & Howe. To all, a sincere thank you. And a special thanks to Susan Bernard, Bernard & Associates.

Improve Your Shooting in Record Time.

Now, Remington® offers the very best in shotgun instruction on clays. The new Remington Shooting School features $2^{1}/_{2}$-day sessions for beginners through experienced shooters—including special classes for trap, skeet, sporting clays, women and youths.

The Shooting School opens May 31 and runs through mid-October. It's located in New York's scenic Mohawk Valley at Ilion—historic home of Remington Arms.

To register or for more details, call (315) 895-3574 today.

WINGS   255

CLAYS   407

INDEXES

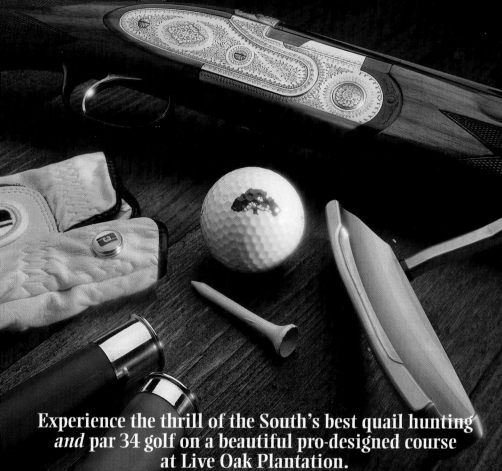

THE SHOTGUNNER'S SOURCE

A FEW FACTS ABOUT SHOTGUNS

Before you buy and shoot a shotgun you should understand the equipment you're shooting with: how it works, how to care for it and how to handle it safely. Today's shotgun is a high quality instrument designed to function flawlessly year after year. Understand your gun. Handle it safely. And the sport of shotgunning will offer a lifetime of enjoyment. (Note: Terms appearing in *italicized* type below may be found on the accompanying illustrations or defined in the Shotgunning Terms section.)

A Basic Distinction

Other types of firearms fire single projectiles. The shotgun, with one exception, fires a number of projectiles--from 45 to almost 1,170—called *shot* . The shot begins to spread as soon as it is discharged from the gun's *muzzle*. Obviously, the area the shot covers--the *shot pattern*--increases as the shot moves away from the gun and towards the target. This explains why the shotgun rather than the single projectile rifle is preferred for shooting a moving target.

Most shotguns have a constriction, or *choke*, at the muzzle that controls the shot pattern. The tighter the constriction, the greater the effective range of the shot. Many shotguns have changeable chokes that allow the gun's shot pattern to be customized for different situations.

The Right Gun

Choosing the right shotgun can be an intimidating experience for the new shooter. Doing a little homework can make it less so: Read as much as you can about shotgunning in general and about specific

manufacturers; also, seek the advice of an experienced shooter or a shotgun professional before you make a purchase.

Here are some basics to get you started: There are three basic types of shotgun used today: the *pump*, the *hinge*--most often double-barreled guns in either a *side by side* or *over and under* configuration--and the *semi-automatic*. The *action*, or the moving parts that allow you to load, fire and unload the shotgun, are different in each type.

Shotguns are further distinguished by the length of their barrels--usually 26 to 30 inches long, and their diameter, or *bore*, which varies according to the gun's design and intended use. The size of the bore is indicated by the term *gauge*: the smaller the gauge number, the larger the bore size. Modern shotguns are available in 10, 12, 16, 20, and 28 gauge. An exception is the .410 bore shotgun, which is actually a 67 gauge.

Which gauge is right for you? Unfortunately, there's no easy answer to that question. To a great extent it depends on you and the primary type of shooting you'll be doing. In the long run, if you're like most shooters, you'll end up owning two or more shotguns of various gauges.

A Word About Fit

Much of what is said today about gun fit is highly technical and not particularly helpful to the novice. The essential point is this: Proper fit depends largely on the length of the gun's *stock*. And most manufacturers tailor their gunstocks to fit the average size adult. So, if you're more or less an average size shooter, an off the shelf shotgun will provide a more-or-less average fit. Shorter or taller shooters --especially youngsters--usually require some stock adjustments, which should be done by a competent gunsmith.

SHOTGUN ACTIONS

BREAK ACTION, over-and-under, double barrel

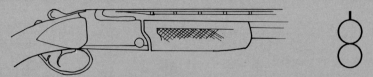

BREAK ACTION, side-by-side, double barrel

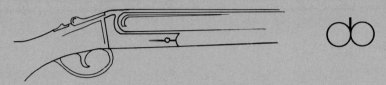

PUMP ACTION, single barrel repeater

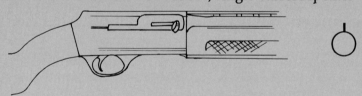

SEMI-AUTOMATIC ACTION, single barrel repeater

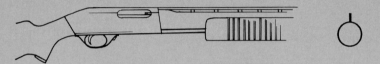

STANDARD BORE DIAMETERS

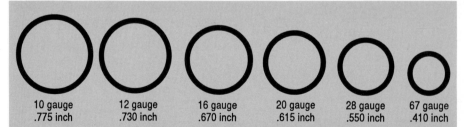

| 10 gauge | 12 gauge | 16 gauge | 20 gauge | 28 gauge | 67 gauge |
| .775 inch | .730 inch | .670 inch | .615 inch | .550 inch | .410 inch |

(subject to variations of a few thousandths of an inch under manufacturing tolerances)

THE MAIN PARTS OF AN OVER-AND-UNDER SHOTGUN

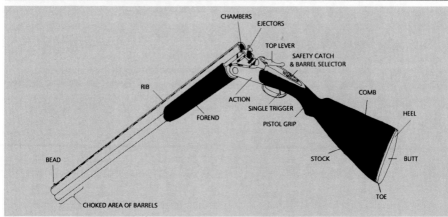

BASIC SHOTGUN STOCK GRIPS AND FOREND STYLES

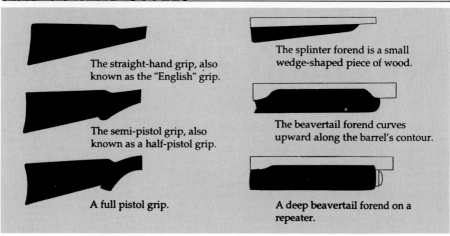

The straight-hand grip, also known as the "English" grip.

The semi-pistol grip, also known as a half-pistol grip.

A full pistol grip.

The splinter forend is a small wedge-shaped piece of wood.

The beavertail forend curves upward along the barrel's contour.

A deep beavertail forend on a repeater.

SHOTGUN RIB STYLES

FLAT RIB

CONCAVE RIB

CHURCHILL STYLE RIB

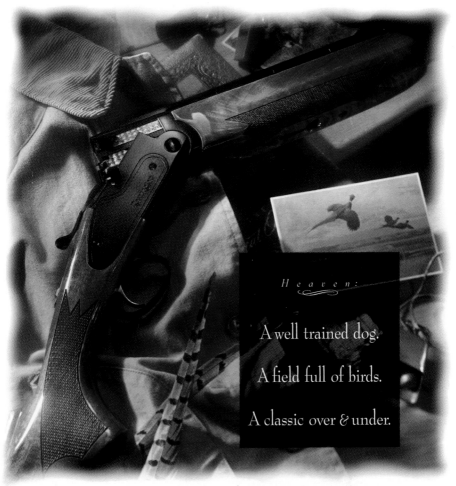

H e a v e n :

A well trained dog.

A field full of birds.

A classic over & under.

P e e r l e s s

Push-pull automatic safety and barrel selector.

20-line checkering.

Removable side plates.

12 ga. 3" chambers and elongated forcing cones.

Vent rib over hammer-forged light contour barrels.

20", 28" or 30" barrels with Rem™ Choke tubes.

Few things in life are as satisfying as the feel of a finely crafted over-and-under. Consider, for example, the Peerless® from Remington,® a shotgun evolved through almost 200 years of gun-making. Its look is classic. Its feel is light and agile. And its pointability, like that of its renowned predecessors, is the stuff legends are made of. Peerless. It's your gun. Life is good in a place we call Remington Country.

Remington.
C O U N T R Y

A Safety Reminder: Always keep the muzzle pointed in a safe direction.

SHOTGUN TERMS

action - the moving parts that allow you to load, fire and unload your shotgun. (See Breech, Chamber, Trigger)

barrel selector - detemines which barrel of a double barrel gun will fire first.

blacking/blueing - the blue coloration applied to protect gun barrels.

bore - in simple terms the interior diameter of a gun barrel, which will vary according to the gun's design and intended use. The size of the bore is indicated by the term gauge. Also someone who goes on interminably about shooting to the exclusion of all other subjects.

box-lock - a type of gun action, often recognizeable by its squared appearance.

breech - the end of the barrel nearest the stock.

broken gun - in a hinge type gun, where the barrels are dropped open and clear of the action, exposing the chambers to view.

butt - the rear of the shoulder end of the gun's stock.

comb - the side of the stock that fits against your cheek.

chamber - the part of the action, at the breech end of the barrel, into which the shot shell is placed.

choke - the degree of narrowing or constriction of the bore at the muzzel end of the barrel, intended to increase the effective range of the gun. (See Full, Modified, and Improved Cylinder)

ejector - the mechanism on shotguns by which spent shot cases are automatically ejected from the gun when it is opened after firing.

forearm - the part of the stock that lies under the barrel.

full choke - the tightest constriction or narrowing of the bore, producing the greatest effective range.

grip - the narrow portion of the stock held with the trigger hand.

gauge - the term used to describe the interior diameter of the bore. The smaller the gauge number, the larger the bore size. Modern shotguns are available in 10, 12, 16, 20 and 28 gauge. An exception is the .410 bore shotgun, which is actually a 67 gauge.

hinge - a type of action in which a hinge mechanism separates the barrel from the standing breech block, providing access to the chamber.

improved cylinder - Least constricted or narrowed choke causing shot pattern to widen relatively quickly.

modified choke - moderate constriction or narrowing of the bore.

muzzle - the end of the barrel from which the shot exits.

over-and-under - a two-barrelled shotgun with one barrel placed over the other. (The American version of the standard British game shooting weapon.)

pump - a type of action that loads and ejects shells by "pumping" the forearm of the stock back and forth.

recoil - force with which the gun moves backwards into the shoulder when fired.

safety - a safety device that, in the "on" position, prevents the gun from firing. In many field guns the safety is automatically engaged when the gun is opened; in other guns, particularly competition grades, the safety must be manually engaged.

semi automatic - a type of action in which gas from the burning gunpowder in the shell automatically ejects the spent shell and loads another. Semi-automatics are noted for minimal recoil.

shot - round projectiles, usually of lead or steel. Depending on shot size and load, a shell can contain from 45 to 1,170 shot.

shot pattern - The concentration of shot measured in a circle at a given range, usually 30 to 40 yards.

side-by-side - a shotgun with two barrels sitting side by side. In Great Britain, the standard game shooting weapon.

stock - The "handle" of the shotgun, the part held to the shoulder, comprising the butt, comb, grip and forearm.

shotshell or *shell* - the ammunition fired by shotguns, consisting of five components: the case, primer, powder charge, wad, and shot.

trigger - finger-pulled lever--single, double and release-- that drives the firing point forward and fires the gun.

Year-Round Guns for Year-Round Hunters.

New 425 Sporting Clays

Whether your quarry is a clay bird or live game bird, you'll benefit from the natural shooting qualities of a Browning sporting clays shotgun. The 425 moves and points smoothly and precisely with the hands — putting you on target instantly. A low, 10mm wide rib allows you to pick up targets quickly and with little effort. An optional adjustable comb allows a custom fit. Available in 12 or 20 gauge.

New Ultra Sporter

The GTI with a new name and features. The rib tapers from 13mm to 10mm for a wide sighting plane and quick target acquisition — benefiting the sporting clays shooter and hunter. A ventilated side rib ensures a smooth swing. A trim forearm promotes exceptional hand-eye coordination for quick shots at departing game or a fast double. Choose a blued or grayed receiver.

Visit your Browning dealer for a free 1995 Hunting & Shooting catalog full of information on Browning firearms and accessories, clothing, boots, knives and gun safes. For $3.00 we'll send you a catalog by priority mail. Call 1-800-333-3504 to order by credit card, or send payment to Browning, Dept. M3, One Browning Place, Morgan, Utah 84050-9326. If you have questions on Browning products, please call 1-800-333-3288.

THE BEST THERE IS.

SHOTGUN SAFETY

It's Largely Common Sense

Imagine that firearms have just been invented, and you're one of the first to be introduced to the shotgun. What precautions would you take to avoid accidental injury to humans or animals, or accidental damage to objects? What, in other words, would common sense suggest?

Because that's what safe shotgun handling and shooting largely consists of. Good old common sense, applied over and over and over again until it becomes pure instinct. And if you're an old pro to whom safety rules are second nature, why not review them anyway? Like chicken soup, if it doesn't help, it couldn't hurt. And the few minutes youspend could keep you from getting careless or falling into bad habits.

Safe Handling

In simplest terms, safe handling of your shotgun is whatever prevents you from firing accidentally, or prevents injury or damage if such a discharge does occur:

- Keep the muzzle pointed in a safe direction. Never point the muzzle at any person, animal or object you don't intend to shoot. The safest directions: upward, or toward the ground (but not toward your foot).

- Keep your finger off the trigger. Fight the natural tendency to put your finger on the trigger when you hold a shotgun. If you must curl it around something, use the trigger guard. The only time your finger should touch the trigger is when you're ready to shoot.

- Keep the gun unloaded, with the action open. Make it a reflex to open the action and check the chamber whenever you pick up a shotgun. And keep the gun empty and open until you're ready to use it.

Safe Shooting

Like safe handling, safe shooting depends on-- you guessed it-- common sense:
- Know your shotgun. Familiarity with your gun's basic parts and how they function is a prerequisite for safe shooting. Know how to open and close the action, for example, and how to remove ammunition.

- Don't depend on the safety. This may be the cardinal rule of safe shooting. Remember, the safety is a mechanical device. And, while the likelihood is remote, it can malfunction. The safety is not a replacement for safe handling and shooting practices.

- Make sure gun and ammunition match. If there is any question about compatibility between shot shell and gun, don't fire! The gauge of the shell must match the gauge of the shotgun. The gauge of the gun is likely to be stamped on the barrel. The gauge of the shell will be indicated on the box, and on each shell.

- Don't carry shells of mixed gauge. Whenever you're through shooting, immediately remove unfired shells from your clothing. It's a good way to avoid mixing ammunition, and slipping the wrong size shell in the chamber your next time out. The drawings that follow illustrate the explosive—and potentially disastrous— effect of placing both a 20 and a 12 gauge shell in the same gun. Remember your fingers would have been placed directly over the blown out portion of the forearm!

Mixed Shells in Chamber

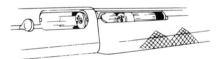

Disastrous Results!

- Be sure before you shoot. If you're not absolutely certain that you've identified your target, don't shoot! And be equally aware of what's beyond your target. If it's another person, or an object that shouldn't be hit -- no matter how far -- don't shoot!

- Protect your eyes and ears. Guns make noise. Noise affects your hearing. Guns also emit debris and gases that can injure your eyes. Ear protectors and safety glasses are a must. [more >]

Now bag both birds with one gun.

686 Onyx Hunter Sport

To win at sporting clays, start with the Beretta Hunter Sport.

You're getting into sporting clays and you want that winning edge. But you want your gun to be at home in the field, too. You're the reason Beretta created our Hunter Sport class of over-and-unders.

Their light weight, perfect balance and low profile receiver give them the legendary Beretta swing and pointability hunters have long relied on. But the Hunter Sport has been refined still further for the quick action of the range.

Get the QStar Advantage with Beretta's super-

QSTAR – Quick Sighting Target Acquisition Rib – with a wide, scored face, contrasting central channel and prominent bead, the new "Strada" ventilated rib guides the eye for maximum pointability and target acquisition.

wide ventilated "Strada" rib featuring a 12.5mm sighting plane, with a center groove and white bead that help you "lock on" to targets even faster. Cut checkered American walnut stock, special grooved fore-end and recoil pad are designed especially for sporting clays. Barrels are hard chromed in 28" or 30" lengths and are chambered for 2¾" or 3" shells. Mobilchoke® screw-in choke tubes are standard.

For a gun that will bag any bird, ask about the new Hunter Sport shotguns at your nearest Beretta dealer, or contact Beretta U.S.A. Corp., 17601 Beretta Drive, Accokeek, MD 20607. (301) 283-2191.

686 Silver Perdiz Hunter Sport

687 Silver Pigeon Hunter Sport

Beretta U.S.A.

- If your senses are impaired, don't go shooting! Among the world's worst combinations are firearms and alcohol, and firearms and drugs.

- Don't run the risk of a clogged barrel. Barrel obstructions can cause gun bursts. If you've stumbled and jabbed the barrel into the ground, or crawled to surprise your quarry, unload and check the barrel for mud or snow.

- Don't rest your gun on your feet to keep it out of mud or snow.

Field Etiquette

In any human situation, etiquette is just good manners. In shooting, etiquette also introduces another element of safety. Practice shooting etiquette in the field and you'll be a safe -- and a popular -- shooting companion.

- Never shoot across another shooter.

- Don't interfere with another hunter's dog. Period!

- Never put your gun off safety until game has flushed.

- Don't shoot if a dog is directly behind low flying birds.

- Make sure every member of your is wearing an article of blaze orange clothing.

- Agree prior to going into field what are the safe zones of fire.

- Always maintain a "straight line" when hunting with a partner and/or guide.

- If you don't know where your partner and guide are, don't shoot!

SHOTGUN SHELLS & CHOKES

Clays, upland birds, waterfowl, big game, small game—- you can shoot or hunt them all with a shotgun. Even a single shotgun with choke tubes, thanks to the variety of specialized ammunition available.

It's the shotshell's unique design that allows individual components [see Shotshell illustration below] to be adapted for specific purposes. That means manufacturers can match the type of case, powder charge, shot size and wad to suit your needs.

Of course the shotgun has something to do with all of this. Ammunition chosen for a fixed choke model should be compatible with that choke. However, the ammunition options available for shotguns fitted with choke tubes are seemingly endless.

Chokes range from cylinder, which means no constriction or reduction of muzzle diameter, for the largest possible shot patterns, to full choke with the greatest amount of muzzle constriction and the tightest patterns. Between these extremes

fall seven additional graduated choke constrictions.

Basically, the key to shooting success is matching ammunition and choke to provide a dense enough pattern for effective shooting at the ranges chosen for each species or clay target.

Ammunition selection depends on several factors: The first choice is between lead or steel shot. In the U.S., steel shot is for waterfowl hunting [see Steel Shot article]. Because it is harder than lead shot, steel shot deforms less readily and produces a denser pattern. That means for most hunting a larger shot size and a more open choke is suggested than for lead.

Standard shot sizes range from No. 9 to BB in lead, from number 6 to T in steel [see Ammo & Choke Suggestion Chart]. Buckshot, available only in lead, is yet another category of shot, used, as the name would indicate, largely for deer (buck) hunting.

Sound complicated? It's not really if you take it one step at a time. The accompanying articles and charts, while not the final word on the subtleties and nuances of shot and choke selection, should prove helpful in answering your questions.

SHOTSHELL PARTS

HULL
The outer container of a shotgun shell, typically made of plastic or paper with a metal base

WAD
Plastic or fiber separating powder and shot that forms a seal so that gasses eject shot uniformly down the barrel

PRIMER
A compound contained in the middle of the base of a shotgun shell, where the firing pin strikes

SHOT
Round projectiles, usually of lead or steel. Depending on shot size and load, a shell can contain from 45 to 1,170 shot.

POWDER
Gun powder situated above the primer where it will be ignited by flames caused by the detonation of the primer compound.

How Do You Get 27 Yards Out Of 2³/4 Inches?

WINCHESTER® DOUBLE A®

Simple. You count on the shotshells that will go the distance: Winchester Double A target loads. It all adds up. Superior, one-piece plastic hulls for consistent reloadability. Winchester primers and custom blended, BALL POWDER® propellant for swift, sure ignition. And Double A wads and hardened shot for tight patterns that smoke birds out to 27 yards. All manufactured by Winchester, for Winchester, under the industry's toughest quality control standards - <u>our own</u>.

They're the perfect loads, made from 100% superior Winchester components, and proven through decades of tough competition and consistently superior scores. Winchester Double A. Add it up and you'll understand why Winchester is America's ammunition leader. And why Double A is the way American trap shooters gauge performance.

The Winchester Double A family. From Xtra-Lite™ to Super-Handicap®

WINCHESTER®
AMMUNITION

What America Shoots.™

PATTERN/PELLET DENSITY & ENERGY GUIDE

Look up distance to your game for recommended pellet. Pellets appropriate for longer distances may also be used at shorter range. Use of pellets at distances surpassing their listing is not recommended

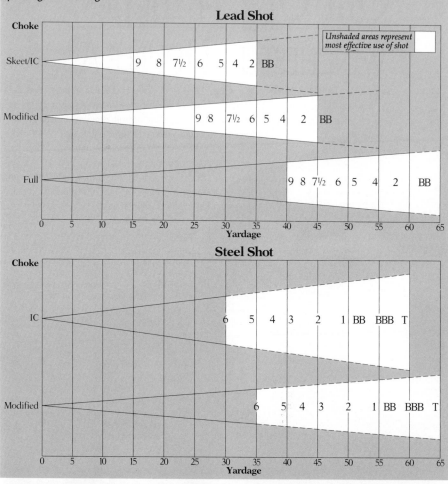

APPROXIMATE NUMBER OF SHOTS IN VARIOUS LOADS

Shot Size	Shot Diameter	2 oz.	1⅞ oz.	1⅝ oz.	1½ oz.	1⅜ oz.	1¼ oz.	1⅛ oz.	1oz.	⅞ oz.	¾ oz.	½ oz.
#9	.08	1170	1097	951	877	804	731	658	585	512	439	292
#8	.09	820	769	667	615	564	513	462	410	359	308	205
#7½	.095	700	656	568	525	481	437	393	350	306	262	175
#6	.11	450	422	396	337	309	281	253	225	197	169	112
#5	.12	340	319	277	255	234	213	192	170	149	128	85
#4	.13	270	253	221	202	185	169	152	135	118	101	67
#2	.15	180	169	158	135	124	113	102	90	79	68	45

AMMUNITION & CHOKE SUGGESTIONS

GAME	SUGGESTED SHOT SIZE	SUGGESTED CHOKES	WHAT EXPERIENCED SHOTGUNNERS SAY...
DUCKS	BB, 1, 2, 3 *	Modified--for pass shooting Improved Cylinder-- over decoys	Use BB shot for long range and pass shooting. For normal range--No. 1 or No. 2 shot while some hunters use No. 3 shot for closer range shooting over decoys.
GEESE	T, BBB, BB, 1*	Modified	Goose hunters need wallop so they use the big loads with large shot. Many hunters prefer No. 1 shot for a denser pattern at shorter ranges over decoys.
PHEASANTS	5, 6, 7½	Improved Cylinder-- for close cover Modified or Full-- for long cornfield shots	For cornfield shooting where long shots are usual - better use No. 5. On a normal rise over dogs and for all around use, No. 6 is the favorite.
GROUSE OR PARTRIDGE	5, 6, 7½, 8	Improved Cylinder or Modified--for brush work Full--for open ranges	On the smaller birds such as ruffed grouse or Hungarian Partridge, use the smaller shot. The big western grouse (sage, sooty, and blue) call for heavier loads and larger shot.
QUAIL	7½, 8, 9	Cylinder Improved Cylinder Modified	For early season shooting on bobwhites when feathers are light, some hunters use No. 9 shot. Later they switch to No. 7½ or 8. On the running or wild flushing type of quail, such as the Gambel's, larger shot is sometimes used.
DOVES AND PIGEONS	6, 7½, 8, 9	Modified Improved Cylinder	Use lighter loads and No. 7½ or No. 8 shot on mourning doves at normal ranges--for longer ranges use the heavy loads and No. 6 or No. 7½. Use the same load on band tailed pigeons and white wings.
WOODCOCK	7½, 8, 9	Improved Cylinder Modified	The choice of shot size here will depend on ranges at which the game is shot. For fast shooting in the alder thickets, No. 8 shot is a good choice.
TURKEY	BB, 2, 4, 5, 6, 7½	Full	Choice of shot size depends on the range. If you're a good caller, No. 6 or No. 7½ shot makes a clean kill. BBs, No. 2s, 4s, 5s, are best for long shots.
TRAP	7½, 8	Full or Modified	In most cases, No. 7½ is used for trap. Check the Official Rulebook.
SKEET	8, 9	Skeet Choke Improved Cylinder	In most cases, No. 9 is used for skeet, check the Official Rulebook.
SPORTING CLAYS	7½, 8, 9	Any choke (Depends on practice desired)	For targets at close range use a more open choke, at longer distances tighten the chokes.

SOURCE: NRA THE BASICS OF SHOTGUN SHOOTING   * Steel Shot [See Steel Shot article for add'l. info]

New Nitro 27
Because at Handic
No Such Thing as

'arget Loads
p Yardage, There's
a Lucky Break.

Back where you shoot, trap is reduced to its basic elements: concentration and consistency. It's just you, your gun

and a target headed the other way. We can't do anything for your concentration. But now, there's a brand new shot-

A new powder blend produces consistent ignition & velocity. Reduces felt recoil, too.

Our exclusive one-piece Figure 8™ wad cushions and protects shot.

Ultra-round shot helps produce dense patterns with no lost pellets. In #7-1/2 or #8.

Our #209 Premier® primer means fast, consistent ignition– shot after shot.

Mouth design has been improved for easier reloading in all reloading machines.

The sleek-looking gold hull is built with our Hardbody™ construction for extended reloading life.

Brass head is easily resized.

shell that takes consistency to new levels. It's the Remington® Nitro 27, and it was designed and built

especially for the handicap shooter. Inside the Nitro 27's gold hull, every component has been pushed to peak

performance. The shot, for example, is triple-tabled for near-perfect roundness. The powder blend

was specially formulated to work with our #209 primer. It's slower burning to produce a more gentle

acceleration of shot, bringing you enhanced performance with less shot deformation, and reduced recoil

sensation. Each component is balanced with the others to produce a noticeably tighter pattern. It's a pattern that

stays tighter longer, and hits targets harder. So the leads you establish are the leads you can stay with. And win with.

This weekend try the new Nitro 27 target load. It could be that the

Remington.
C O U N T R Y

only thing standing between you and a better average is a better shell.

A Safety Reminder: Safe reloading is your responsibility.

STEEL SHOT

Some years back, the ammunition industry funded a study to find a replacement for lead shot. The study found that the only substitute combining reasonable cost and ballistic performance was a form of soft iron or steel.

Selecting Steel Shot Loads

An early "rule of thumb" suggested going two shot sizes larger when substituting steel loads for lead. This guideline was selected because a steel pellet two sizes larger than a lead counterpart is approximately equal in individual pellet energy at normal hunting ranges.

Further experience indicates that, for longer ranges such as pass shooting, steel pellets three sizes larger may be a more effective replacement. For example, use No. 4 or 3 steel to replace No. 6 lead, or No. 2 or 1 steel to replace No. 4 lead.

Since individual pellet energy and total pattern energy increase directly and progressively for both lead and steel as pellet size increases, the largest pellet sizes would always seem to be better than smaller sizes. However, experience indicates that effective hunting at selected

STEEL VS. LEAD SHOT

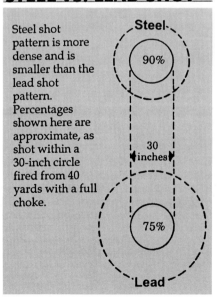

Steel shot pattern is more dense and is smaller than the lead shot pattern. Percentages shown here are approximate, as shot within a 30-inch circle fired from 40 yards with a full choke.

ranges depends on a balanced combination of both pellet energy (based on size) and pattern density. As a result, the steel loads recommended on the chart represent the best combination of steel pellet energy and pattern density for effective performance.

Chokes & Patterns With Steel

In choosing the proper choke constriction for steel shot, waterfowlers should give careful consideration to several factors:

- The harder steel pellets deform less than their lead counterparts. The result is less erratic pellet flight with steel, fewer pellets straying from the pattern, and denser patterns than those normally produced by lead shot.

- In most cases, waterfowlers can use more open choke constrictions with steel than they did with lead. For example, substitute a modified choke with steel for situations that previously called for a full choke with lead; or an improved cylinder choke for previous modified choke situations.

- Research indicates that steel shot in sizes of BB and larger should not be shot through previously produced full chokes, even in modern and recently-manufactured shotguns. Shooting steel shot sizes of BB and larger through full chokes can cause bulging of barrels in the choke area and "seizing" of screw-in choke tubes so that they cannot be removed. For shot sizes BB and larger, use a modified choke tube.

- A wise practice when learning to hunt with steel shot is to first pattern your loads at various ranges with different choke constrictions. Evaluate patterns for sufficient pattern density and even pellet distribution.

Determining Lead With Steel Shot

Most steel loads start out with greater velocity than comparable lead loads. But because steel, being lighter, slows down more quickly than lead, it loses that velocity superiority downrange -- generally at about 40 yds. Much has been written about learning "to shoot differently" when replacing lead loads with steel. In practice, the differences in necessary lead between lead and steel are minimal and, in many cases, insignificant.

SHOTGUN DISCIPLINES & GAMES

Layout of a trap field

Disciplines

Classifying and defining the various shotgun disciplines and clay target games is no easy task. There are almost as many out there as there are shotgunners to shoot them. And new ones spring up all the time. What follows then is not meant to be the final word on the topic--just a helpful guide to the most prominent games played and disciplines followed today.

Trap Disciplines

1. American Trap (ATA) - The most basic of all the trap disciplines. Standard targets are thrown as singles. The horizontal direction is randomized with a maximum angle of 22 degrees measured from a line from the trap to the middle station. The height at which the targets are thrown is constant. The distance is constant at 50 yards. A squad of five shooters shoot in rotation from five positions arrayed in an arc located 16 yards behind the traphouse, with five targets thrown at each station before the shooters change. A round is 25 targets with one shot allowed at each target. An English variation is called Down-The-Line, a two-barrel discipline that allows two shots at a single target with a scoring penalty for a second-barrel hit.

Handicap Trap - The same as ATA singles, except the shooter stands further back than 16 yards -- but no longer than 27 yards. The ATA reviews handicap yardage for shooters every 1000 targets as part of their handicap system.

Doubles Trap - As the name implies, two targets are launched simultaneously from one machine. Squads of five shooters rotate the five positions on the 16 yard line. Shooting events consist of 25 or 50 pairs. Like 16 yard and handicap, scoring is one point per target hit.

SHOTGUN DISCIPLINES & GAMES

TRAP/GOVERNING BODY	SKEET /GOVERNING BODY
1. American Trap/ATA	1. American Skeet/ NSSA
2. Olympic Trap/UIT, USA Shooting	2. English Skeet/ CPSA
3. Olympic Trap Doubles/UIT, USA Shooting	3. International Skeet /UIT, USA Shooting
4. Automatic Ball Trap/UIT	**SPORTING/GOVERNING BODY**
5. Universal Trench/UIT	1. English Sporting/CPSA
6. ZZ/FITASC	American Sporting /NSCA, SCA
	2. FITASC or International Sporting/FITASC, NSCA

GAMES	
1. Crazy Quail	13. Modern Skeet ®, Modern Sporting Skeet ®
2. Two-Man Flush	and Modern Trap ®
3. Trap House Sporting Clays	14. Lasersport
4. 5-STAND SPORTING ®	15. AmericanZZ
5. Quail Walk	16. Scrap/Chinese Trap
6. Supersport	17. Follow the Leader
7. Tower Shooting	18. Riverside Skeet
8. Pro-Sporting	19. Skeet Doubles
9. Sub-Trap	20. Rabbit Run
10. Flushes, Flurries & Mixed Bag (Team Events)	21. Annie Oakley or Shooting Down the Line
11. Starshot	22. Buddy Shoot or Back-Up Trap
12. Double Rise	

TO ATTAIN PEAK PERFORMANCE, SMOOTH HANDLING AND A QUIET RIDE . . . YOU NEED THE RIGHT VEHICLE.

And now the choice is even easier. Whether you're shooting for fun or in competition, Lincoln has a model to suit your demands. Constructed to be reliably consistent, whisper quiet, and weather resistant, Lincoln's design and style combine all of these features to offer easy cocking and superb control. Protected by a unbeatable warranty and built in America with pride. Optional accessories and equipment are available. Call your Lincoln dealer for details and *Discover the Difference* the right vehicle can make.

LINCOLN

1009 South Lincoln Avenue
Lebanon, PA 17042-7166
717-274-8676

2. Olympic Trap/Olympic Bunker/Olympic Trench - An international discipline that incorporates fifteen machines. Targets have a minimum height of 1.5 meters and a maximum height of 3.5 meters as measured 10 meters in front of the bunker. Targets are thrown up to 110 mph depending on the target height to get the 70 to 75 meter variable distance required. The maximum target angle is 45 degrees. There are nine set programs for the fifteen traps that are used in all countries of the world. A squad of six shooters take turns shooting from five stations. Shooters move to the next station after each target in a shoot-and-move rotation. The shooting stations are located in a straight line. On the call "pull" (phono-pull release system is utilized to insure equitable target releases), a clay is thrown from one of three fixed traps directly in front of each of five shooters. Two shots may be used for each target with no penalty in scoring. Each shooter gets two lefts, two rights, and one straightaway target from

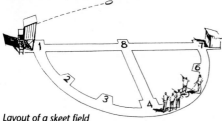

Layout of a skeet field

each station. Shot charge is restricted to 24 Grams (approx. 7/8 oz.) using any safe powder charge (plated shot is allowed). Also, the Olympic target is made harder, to handle the higher target speed and is slightly smaller than the standard American trap target.

3. Olympic Trap Doubles/Olympic Bunker Doubles/Olympic Trench Doubles - Here, two targets are launched simultaneously from two traps of station three's set of three fixed traps. As in Olympic singles, squads of six shooters shoot in rotation from five stations, shooting a round of 20 or 25 pairs (40 or 50 targets). Scoring is one point per target hit.

4. Automatic Ball Trap (ABT)/Wobble/Continental - Like ATA trap, the horizontal direction is randomized, but also the target vertical height is varied from 1.5 to 3.5 meters. The horizontal throwing angle is widened from the ATA

22 degrees to 45 degrees. The distance is set at 75 meters. Squads of six shooters shoot in rotation as in Olympic Trap. Two shots are allowed at each target with no penalty scoring. A phono-pull system may be used.

5. Universal Trench - This form of International trapshooting is also referred to as "Five Trap"; it is a variation of Olympic Trap using only five machines. Squads of six take turns shooting from each of five stations. UT is very similar to Olympic Trap in the speeds, heights and angles of targets. Trap position sequences for a round of 25, though predetermined, are unknown to the squad. Each squad member is allowed two shots at each target, with no penalty in scoring. Computer and phono-pull system for target selection are the same as in Olympic Trap.

6. ZZ/Electrocibles - A world-wide trap discipline, the target is a two or three bladed plastic propeller with a detachable (breakable) center. One of five traps in front of the shooter releases the target on call; two shots are allowed at each target. To score a "kill", the shooter must knock the center out of the target so that it lands within the confines of a circular fence.

SKEET DISCIPLINES

1. American Skeet - A round of skeet consists of 25 targets in a set sequence of singles and simultaneous doubles. Squads of five shooters take their turns from eight shooting stations. Each squad member takes two singles and one double from stations 1, 2, 6 & 7. Two singles are taken from stations 3, 4, 5 & 8. The 25th target is taken after the first target is missed, or as a final target (low house #8) after 24 kills. Targets are thrown a distance of 60 yards. Variations in the angles of the targets presented from the "high" and "low" house result from the shooter moving from station to station. American Skeet is the only discipline that has regular, specific tournament events for sub-bore shotguns: 20, 28,and .410.

Skeet Doubles - Shooters, in squads of five, start on station 1, shooting one pair of doubles each to station 7. Then they reverse, shooting one pair each from stations 7 through 1. On station 4, shooters must shoot the high house target first. On reversing, (shooting 7 through 1), they must shoot the low house target first. In tourna-

You can customize all of our safes with a variety of available features. Shown here: The Premier with optional door mounted pistol racks.

Something That Helps You Relax This Much Usually Requires A Prescription.

If you're looking for a worry-free place to store firearms and other valuables, your timing couldn't be better. You see, after 179 years of making the best-selling guns in the world, Remington® is now making a place to put them. Our new gun safes are built Remington tough, with the finest, performance-tested security features. And while that's good for your gun collection, it does wonders for your peace of mind. For a brochure describing our complete line, call 1-800-479-2563.

Remington.
C O U N T R Y

ments, the events are on a total of 50 (or 100) targets with the last pair shot on station 1. Scoring is one point per hit target.

2. English Skeet - A seven station version of American Skeet, substituting the singles thrown on station 8 with a double on station 4.

3. International Skeet - An eight station format like that of American Skeet with faster targets thrown at 72 meters. The shooter is required to hold the butt of the gun at hip level until the target is seen, which may be delayed for up to 3.5 seconds after the "pull" request. Single and double target sequences are slightly different from American Skeet with a high single and one pair of doubles from Stations #1 & #2; high and low singles and one pair of doubles from Stations #3, #4 and #5 (on Station #4, the high bird must be attempted first in doubles); a single low and a double from Station #6; one pair of doubles from Station #7; a single high and a single low from Station #8. A round is 25 targets (no option shot). Like Olympic Trap, shot charge is restricted to 24 grams (approx. 7/8 oz.), with any safe powder charge. For tournaments, all shells must be of the same type and load.

Layout of a sporting course

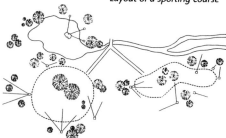

SPORTING DISCIPLINES

1. English or American Sporting - Sporting Clays, like Trap and Skeet, uses traps and clay targets to duplicate, as far as possible, conditions and presentations you would normally find while hunting. A typical sporting course is laid out over a 10, 20 or 30 acre site, ideally in rough, hilly terrain. Usually, the path the shooters follow will take a circular or horse-shoe shape enabling shooters to start and finish in roughly the same place. Along the path targets are thrown from 10 to 14 shooting stations. Courses can be laid out with either automatic or manual traps, usually set

out-of-sight. Six different types of targets can be used: standard, midi, mini, battue, rocket or rabbit. Target sequence may incorporate singles, report pairs, following pairs and true (simultaneous) pairs. A round usually consists of 50 or 100 targets. The shooter's gun must be visible below the armpit and may not be mounted until the target is visible.

2. FITASC Sporting/International Sporting - The most challenging form of sporting shooting, it is the French version of practice for field shooting. Unlike the free and easy format of English or American Sporting, FITASC Sporting is shot in squads of up to six with a fixed order of stands (*parcours*, in French) that are shot in strict rotation. A competition normally consists of 200 targets shot over three days in eight rounds of 25. In each round of 25, shots are taken from at least three different stands. The shooter is required to hold the butt of the gun below armpit level until the target is seen. Great variety and lack of repetition is accomplished by use of a number of traps. Single targets are first shot by the entire squad. After the entire squad has completed the singles, combinations of the singles are presented as doubles. Here, as in English Sporting, all six types of clays are used. Generally speaking, targets tend to be at longer ranges with the added challenge of a continual variation of speeds, angles, distances and target combinations.

GAMES

1. Crazy Quail - This game simulates quail rising from cover. The trap used is hidden in a pit to prevent shooters from anticipating the flight direction of the target. Targets fly straight away, to the side, or directly toward the shooter, because the trap and the trapper's seat rotate 360 degrees. Automatic machines on special rotating bases can also be used.

2. Two-Man Flush - Using an International "Wobble" trap, the targets are launched and fly in all directions away from the trap house. Two shells are loaded in each shotgun, and a rail holding 10 shotgun shells is set in front of each shooter to make reloading quicker. Targets (24 total) will be launched at 1.5 second intervals. Shooter one will take the first two and shooter two the next two, and so on.

PLUGGED
OR
UNPLUGGED

WHEN CHOOSING AN AUTOMATIC OR MANUAL TRAP, WE PUT THE POWER AT YOUR FINGERTIPS.

At Shyda's Services we are committed to selling only the finest clay target traps in the industry. Automatic or manual, new or used, whatever your specific needs, we offer a full line of traps, accessories and service. Searching for automatic machines? We carry the quality lines of Parker Boss, Super Star, and Winchester by Laporte, along with a wide range of accessories, including wireless release systems. In manual traps, targets are limited only by your imagination with our complete line of durable Lincoln Traps and accessories. Discover the Difference...

SHYDA'S
SERVICES INC.
HOME OF LINCOLN TRAPS

1009 South Lincoln Avenue • Lebanon, PA 17042 • (717) 274-8676 • Fax (717) 274-8672

3. Trap-House Sporting Clays - A self-contained transportable unit holding 15 traps presents all the angles, shots and target capabilities seen on a "traditional" sporting clays course. 13 shooting stations, separated by safety screens are positioned around the periphery of the unit. This game can be set up in the woods, in an open field or on a skeet field. [See Ad Pg. 239 for more information.]

NSCA 5-STAND SPORTING
National Sporting Clays Association

4. 5-STAND SPORTING® - Sometimes overlayed on a trap or skeet field this game utilizes 6-8 automatic traps. There are 3 levels of difficulty: Level I, 5 single targets with full use of the gun for scoring; Level II, 3 single and a simultaneous pair; Level III, 1 single and 2 simultaneous pairs. Shooters (squad of five) can move from station to station with a predetermined menu of shots and combinations, or in a sequence unknown to the shooters. 5-STAND SPORTING® is a registered trademark of Clay-Sport International, Inc. , Alberta, Canada. In the U.S., 5-STAND is licensed by the NSCA.

targets presented and the degree of difficulty desired. As the shooter walks the course, sensors located on the course pick up signals from transmitters worn by individual shooters. These are relayed to the course control computer which adjusts the machines, angles, and the number of targets. A noise simulating the particular bird (target(s)) is generated prior to use. Less sophisticated Supersport courses attempt to achieve similar results without using the control computer, i.e. a control tower in the middle of the course. The automatic traps will present targets from all angles, heights and directions thus providing the element of surprise found in true hunting.

7. Tower Shooting - This game simulates pass shooting of dove or a driven pheasant shoot (which, depends on how the shooters are positioned around a tower equipped with one or two traps). Traps may be manual, but the best installations use automated equipment controlled from the ground.

8. Pro-Sporting - A game of 25 targets for squads of six shooters. Shooters stand in one position to attempt killing targets from five traps.

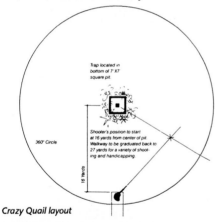

Trap located in
bottom of 7' X7'
square pit.

Shooter's position to start
at 16 yards from center of pit.
Walkway to be graduated back to
27 yards for a variety of shooting and handicapping.

360° Circle

16 Yards

Crazy Quail layout

5. Quail Walk - Another version of sporting shooting. A quail walk or walk-up involves the shooter walking down a path in a "more-or-less" straight line. Just as in "rough" shooting in the field, the shooter carries a loaded gun in anticipation of targets being presented while walking. Manual traps or automatic traps can be utilized.

6. Supersport - This game uses 15 to 30 automatic trap machines spread over 10 - 30 acres and buried in bunkers, on top of hills, placed behind trees or bushes, or up in towers. It is the ultimate simulation of a live bird hunt. The shooter uses a controlling computer to indicate the number of

9. Sub-Trap - A game where a squad of shooters attempt targets thrown manually from a machine blocked from sight. Shooters take turns at five positioned pegs or stations. A total of 25 targets (5 at each peg) are randomly released in sequences of singles or doubles. The fun and frustration of the game is that the shooter must have his gun loaded with two cartridges at all times in anticipation of a simultaneous pair.

10. Flushes, Flurries, And Mixed Bag - A "Flush" begins at the call of "pull" and 5 clay targets are launched in crossing and going way flight patterns, with another bird in the air about every second, until 50

STRICTLY FOR THE BIRDS

Vihtavuori introduces SPORTING LITE (N3SL), a shotgun powder for shooters with a big appetite for clay birds. Not the typical trap and skeet fare, but a full course of those tricky clay fowl known as minis, midis, rockets, battues and rabbits.

Formulated from ribbon extrusions of pure nitrocellulose, it is produced and tested for reliability, consistency and overall performance in 12 gauge 1⅛ oz. and lighter loads. And SPORTING LITE gives new meaning to the words, "clean burning," light recoil and economy.

So next time you have a craving for shooting clays, use the powder that keeps you hungry for more, Vihtavuori N3SL. Also try our new N3SM and N3SH powders for upland game and magnum field loads.

For a free Reloading Guide with recipes for all Vihtavuori Powders, contact: Kaltron-Pettibone, U.S. Importer, Dept. GW, 1241 Ellis St., Bensenville, IL 60106 (800) 683-0464.

VIHTAVUORI OY

Flush & Mixed Bag

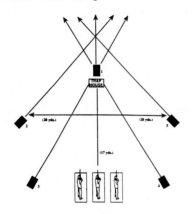

birds have been thrown. A "Flurry" begins the same way, but the 5 targets are all traveling towards and over the shooting stations, like a covey rise. A target is released from one of five traps until 50 birds have been launched in under one minute. In a "Mixed Bag" targets can simulate a high flying pheasant, a bouncing rabbit, a darting woodcock, a springing teal , or crossing doves, or any combination of the above. At each call of "pull", a double is shot. This scenario is repeated 8 times per shooter, with the first shooter attempting a 9th pair for a total of 50 birds. Emphasis is on the individual shooter. There is a 3 minute time limit for this event. [These games are offered as part of the "Chevy Truck Sportsman's Team Challenge" All-Around Shooting Tournament.]

11. Starshot - A game of clay pigeon shooting invented primarily for easy viewing by spectators and the television audience.The layout consists of an upright semi-circular tubular steel framework. From the shooters' and viewers' perspectives the steel framework appears to be divided into pie slices. Each "slice" is further divided by smaller semi-circular arcs that make the structure look similar to a large dart board half-sunk in the ground. The sections of the framework are numbered 1 to 12. At the base of the structure, i.e. the dart board bulls-eye, is a large pit containing four traps that release targets at different speeds across the face of the structure. The number of points scored for each target "killed" depends on the sector in which the target is broken. The highest scores come by "killing" clays within the lower, narrower sectors of

the pie slices. Numerous games can be played in Starshot by teams.

12. Double Rise - Involves the shooting of two ATA targets launched simultaneously from the same trap. Squads of six shooters shoot in rotation from five stations. Competitors may only fire one shot at each bird of the pair, scoring five points for a pair killed and two points for one "kill".

13. Modern Skeet ®, Modern Sporting Skeet ®, and Modern Trap ® - Developed by Quack Sporting Clays, Inc., these new shotgun games combine the low cost of skeet (and trap) and the variable birds of sporting clays. The target's movement simulates shooting conditions (ranging from a slight breeze to gales) found on a windy day. Modern Skeet and Sporting Skeet are basically the same shotgun game. In Modern Skeet, the shooter attemps to hit 25 oscillating birds on 8 regular skeet field stations. Modern Sporting Skeet presents the shooter with a variety of close birds on the regular skeet stations and far crossing targets from 8 yards back of stations 3,4, and 5. Modern Trap uses the Quack Oscillator to present trap targets that curl rather than fly straight. [Available through Quack Sporting Clays, Cumberland, RI; (401) 723-8202.].

14. Lasersport - A true simulation of Clay Pigeon Shooting that uses deactivated shotguns to fire harmless infrared beams at plastic clay targets. 5, 10, 15 or 20 shooters, experience full sound simulation, shot pattern spread and simulation of all types and sizes of targets. Each player's progress is displayed on a large scoreboard.[Available through Intermark, Cedar Crest, NM, (800) 386-4861.]

15. AmericanZZ - America's version of the European "ZZ" Bird. AmericanZZ provides an effective simulation of the zig-zagging, unpredictable flight of a live pigeon.[Available through AmericanZZ, Trumbull, CT; (203) 261-1058.]

16. Scrap/Chinese Trap - Using a skeet/trap field overlay and stations #1 through #7, squads of shooters shoot ATA trap birds. Generally, a low-gun mount is used and two shots may be taken without scoring penalty.

17. Follow the Leader - Played either on a trap or skeet field, but preferably on a field with both layouts. Shooters draw lots to de-

AMERICA'S BEST™

AMERICA'S BEST CHEW™
RED MAN
CHEWING TOBACCO
NET WT. 3 OZ.

RED MAN
GOLDEN BLEND™
NET WT. 3 OZ

RED MAN®

© 1995 Pinkerton Group, Inc.

termine order. Shooter #1 calls the shot to be attempted--any shot combination from any position. If he is successful, all shooters must attempt to duplicate the shot(s). Shooters who fail to match the leader's score are eliminated. The last shooter remaining wins.

18. Riverside Skeet - A game of 25 targets played on a skeet/trap overlay field. A squad of 5 shooters shoot 3 singles and 1 double from each of the arc-layout positions in ATA. The targets are launched from the skeet high and low houses with adjusted tragjectories that have been angled out. 3 singles (a left single, a right single, a "puller's option" single) are presented to each shooter before proceeding to the next shooter. After the 5th position has shot at the singles, shooter #1 is presented a simultaneous pair, and so on down the line. After completing 5 shots, all the shooters rotate.

19. Skeet Doubles - Doubles are shot at each of the regular 8 skeet stations, making a round of 16. Usually, the shooter is eliminated from the round when he misses a target.

20. Rabbit Run - Played on a trap field, the trap is set to launch targets as close to the ground as possible. The shooter stands either behind the trap house or on top of it, shooting a round of 25 "rabbits".

21. Annie Oakley or Shooting Down the Line - Shooters--as many as safety dictates is prudent--line up shoulder-to-shoulder on the 27 yard line of a ATA trap field in an order determined by lot. Shooters fire in groups of three. The first shooter calls for and fires at the target. If he misses, the second shooter fires. If he misses, then the third shooter fires. The shooter scoring the hit eliminates the pre-

Flurry

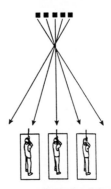

ceeding shooter (s) of the group. If all miss, none are eliminated. The first group consists of shooters 1, 2, 3. The second group becomes shooters 2, 3, and 4, and so on. The shooting continues down the line until only one winning shooter remains. When only 2 or 3 shooters remain a winner may be more quickly determined by increasing the distance from the trap and moving to the extreme stations 1 or 5.

22. Buddy Shoot or Back-up Trap - A team of two shooters stand shoulder to shoulder at the 27 yard line of a ATA trap field--the total number of teams dictated by safety considerations. When the target is launched, the shooter on the left fires; the second shooter can hit it for a score, if the first shooter misses. However, if second shooter shoots after the first shooter has hit the target, a "miss" is scored for the team. Each team member, in turn, calls for the target. The teams shoot down the line. High score wins. [Portions of this article were written by Joseph J. Rusin, M.D. and Willam Bartell.]

VESTED INTEREST!

OUR **SHOOTING VEST** PERFORMS ON COURSE, OR OFF.

OLYMPIA CARTRIDGES

EXPERIENCE

THE SPIRIT

OF OLYMPIA

- HIGH PERFORMANCE

- LOW RECOIL

- LOW COST

1996 CALENDAR OF EVENTS

January

SHOT SHOW.
Shooting, Hunting, Outdoor Trade Show and Conference

Jan. 11-14
18th Annual
S.H.O.T. Show
Dallas Convention Center,
Dallas, TX
(203) 840-5600
Reed Exhibition Companies
383 Main Ave.
Norwalk, CT 06851
The SHOT SHOW is the world's
largest showcase of shooting,
hunting, and outdoor-related
merchandise, with more than
1,300 exhibitors and 17,000 dealer
attendees sponsored by the
National Shooting Sports
Foundation, Inc. For information
call 203-840-5600.

Jan. 24-27
Safari Club International
Convention
Reno Hilton, Reno, NV
(602) 620-1220
Contact: Safari Club International
4800 W. Gates Pass Rd.
Tuscon, AZ 86745

Jan. 25-28
10th Annual Quail Unlimited
Celebrity Hunt
Albany, GA
(803) 637-5731
Contact: Scott Henson, Ext. 32
Quail Unlimited
PO Box 610
Edgefield, SC 29824

Jan. 26-28
12th National Custom
Gunmakers Guild and
Engravers Exhibition
Sands Hotel, Reno, NV
(319) 752-6114
Contact: Jan Billeb
American Custom Gun Makers Guild
PO Box 812
Burlington, IA 52601

JANUARY

S	M	T	W	T	F	S
			1	2	3	4	5	6
7	8	9	10	(11)	12	13
14	15	16	17	18	19	20
21	22	23	24	25	26	27
28	29	30	31			

FEBRUARY

S	M	T	W	T	F	S
				1	2	3
4	5	6	7	8	9	10
11	12	13	14	15	16	17
18	19	20	21	22	23	24
25	26	27	28	29		

MARCH

S	M	T	W	T	F	S
					1	2
3	4	5	6	7	8	9
10	11	12	13	14	15	16
17	18	19	20	21	22	23
24	25	26	27	28	29	30
31						

Jan. 29-Feb. 1
North American Gamebird
Assoc. Annual Convention &
Short Course
Omni Hotel, Atlanta, GA
(803) 796-8163
Contact: Walter Walker
North American Gamebird Assoc.
PO Box 2105
Cayce-West Columbia, SC 29171

February

Feb. 9-11
Rocky Mountain Elk
Foundation Eastern
Rendezvous
Rochester Riverside Convention
Center-Hyatt Regency, Rochester, NY
(800) CALL-ELK
Conventions Mgr: Carrie Cummings
Rocky Mountain Elk Foundation
PO Box 8249
Missoula, MT 59807

Feb. 23-24
Quail Invitational
Championship Trial
(317) 839-4059
Contact: National Shoot to
Retrieve Field Trial Assoc.
226 North Mill St., #2
Plainfield, IN 46168

Feb. 29
Pheasants Forever West Metro
Annual Banquet
Sheraton Park Place Hotel,
St. Louis Park, MN
(612) 481-7142
Contact: Pheasants Forever
PO Box 75473
St. Paul, MN 55175

Feb. 29-March 3
Rocky Mountain Elk
Foundation Elk Camp and
Exposition
Reno Hilton, Reno, NV
(800) CALL-ELK
Conventions Mgr: Carrie Cummings
Rocky Mountain Elk Foundation
PO Box 8249, Missoula, MT 59807

March

March
9th Annual Quail Unlimited
Dog of the Year Field Trial
Come Away Plantation, Norwood,GA
(803) 637-5731
Contact: Scott Henson, Ext. 32
Quail Unlimited
PO Box 610, Edgefield, SC 29824

March 7-10
Alabama Governor's Cup
March 7-8
Rockfence Station, Alabama
March 9
White Oak Plantation, Alabama
March 10
Seven Bridges, Alabama
 (800) 627-2606
Contact: Trey McClendon
Rockfence Station
4388 Chambers Cty. Rd. 160
Lafayette, AL 36862

March 8-11
IWA-International Trade Fair
for Hunting and Sporting
Arms and Accessories
Nuremberg Fair Grounds,
Nuremberg, Germany
(508) 371-2203
Contact: Dianna Hallett
Concord Expo Group
PO Box 677
Concord, MA 01742

March 14-17
The Schwarzkopf Cup
Tampa, FL
(813) 229-2145
Contact: Mary Buckley
400 North Ashley Street
Suite 3050
Tampa, FL 33602

Park Avenue's back seats don't take a back seat to most other cars' front seats.

Remember legroom? Well, Buick Park Avenue

provides its back-seat drivers with nearly the

same legroom, headroom, shoulder room

and hip room as its own front seats.

And Park Avenue's front seats sit

you firmly in the lap of luxury. There

is no second class seating here.

To learn more, call 1-800-4A-BUICK.

BUICK
The New Symbol For Quality
In America.

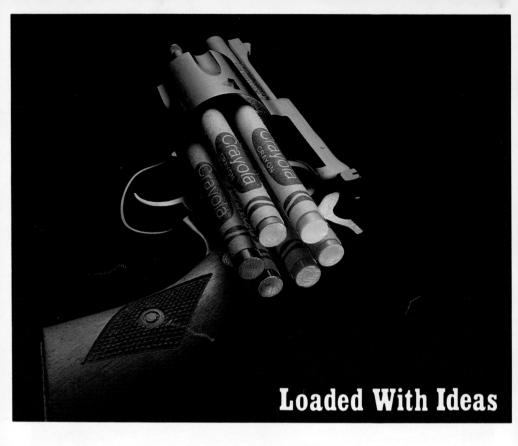

Loaded With Ideas

Creative,
Hard-Hitting,
Effective,
On-Target
Advertising Design

NICHOLS BOYESEN & ZINO

ADVERTISING
DESIGN
MARKETING
SERVICES

194 Valley View Road   New Hartford, NY 13413   Ph 315 797-0700   Fax 315 738-0224

March 27-29
Firearms Trade Expo (FTE)
Atlantic City Convention Hall,
Atlantic City, NJ
(305) 561-3505
Contact: Andrew Molchan
American Firearms Industry
2245 E. Sunrise Blvd., #916
Fort Lauderdale, FL 33304

March 28-30
8th Annual Chevy Truck
Sportsmen's Team Challenge
National Championships
Markham Regional Range,
Sunrise, FL
(203) 426-1320
Contact: National Shooting Sports
Foundation
Flintlock Ridge Office Center
11 Mile Hill Rd.
Newtown, CT 06470

March 29-April 7
USA Shooting Olympic Trials
Wolf Creek Olympic Shooting
Complex, Atlanta, GA
(719) 578-4670
USA Shooting
One Olympic Plaza
Colorado Springs, CO 80909

April

April 5-8
10th Annual Ducks Unlimited
Continental Fun Shoot
Wolf Creek Sport Shooting,
Atlanta, GA
(901) 758-3816
Contact: Gary Goodpaster
Ducks Unlimited
Special Projects Department
One Waterfowl Way
Memphis, TN 38120

April 11-14
11th Annual U.S. Open
Pheasant Championship
Minnesota Horse & Hunt Club,
Prior Lake, MN
(612) 447-2272
Contact: Terry Correll
Minnesota Horse & Hunt Club
PO Box 482
Prior Lake, MN 55372

April 17
Pheasants Forever
Annual Banquet
Radisson Hotel,
St. Paul, MN
(612) 481-7142
Contact: Pheasants Forever
PO Box 75473
St. Paul, MN 55175

APRIL

S	M	T	W	T	F	S
	1	2	3	4	5	6
7	8	9	10	11	12	13
14	15	16	17	18	(19)	20
21	22	23	24	25	26	27
28	29	30				

MAY

S	M	T	W	T	F	S
			1	2	3	(4)
5	6	7	8	9	10	11
12	13	14	15	16	17	18
19	20	21	22	23	(24)	25
26	27	28	29	30	31	

JUNE

S	M	T	W	T	F	S
						1
2	3	4	5	6	(7)	8
9	10	11	12	13	14	15
16	17	18	19	20	21	22
23	24	25	26	27	28	29
30						

April 17-21
Association of College Unions -
International Clay Target
Championship
Wolf Creek Sport Shooting,
Atlanta, GA
(513) 529-3355
Contact: John Walker
Manager of Special Events
Miami University
Millett Hall
Oxford, OH 45056

April 19-23
NRA Annual Meetings
& Exhibits
Dallas, TX
(703) 267-1000
Contact: National Rifle Association
11250 Waples Mill Rd.
Fairfax, VA 22030

April 22-27
NSTRA Champion of
Champions
Conservation Bird Dog Club,
Amo, IN
(317) 839-4059
Contact: National Shoot to
Retrieve Field Trail Assoc.
226 North Mill St., #2
Plainfield, IN 46168

April 22-29
UIT World Cup USA
Wolf Creek Olympic Shooting
Complex, Atlanta, GA
(719) 578-4670
USA Shooting
One Olympic Plaza
Colorado Springs, CO 80909

May

May 4-5
WSSF Ladies Charity
Classic "Mother Shoot"
American Shooting Center,
Houston, TX
(713) 584-9907
Contact: Sue King
Women's Shooting Sports
Foundation
1505 Hwy. 6 South, Suite 101
Houston, TX 77077

May 13-17
Ducks Unlimited
National Convention
Ceaser's Palace, Las Vegas, NV
(901) 758-3716
Contact: Convention Central
Ducks Unlimited
One Waterfowl Way
Memphis, TN 38120

May 18-19
Quail Unlimited/ Redman
National Sporting Clays
Tournament
Wolf Creek, Atlanta, GA
(803) 637-5731
Contact: Scott Henson, Ext. 32
Quail Unlimited
PO Box 610
Edgefield, SC 29824

May 19
Lew Horton's Great Eastern
Sporting Clays Classic
Addieville East Farm,
Mapleville, RI
(401) 568-3185
Contact: Geoff Gaebe
Addieville East Farm
200 Pheasant Drive
Mapleville, RI 02839

HOMESTEAD.
1766

May 24-27
The Homestead Cup
The Homestead,
Hot Springs, VA
(800) 838-1766
(540) 839-1766
Contact: The Shooting Club
The Homestead
PO Box 2000
Hot Springs, VA 24445
See Our Ad Across

June

June 7-9
The Big Pig
Hillside Hunting Preserve &
Sporting Clays
Berlin, PA
(301) 293-1936
Contact: Mid-Maryland Outfitters
3000 E. Ventrie Ct.
Myersville, MD 21773

June 16-20
OWAA Annual Conference
Duluth Entertainment
Convention Center, Duluth, MN
(814) 234-1011
Contact: Eileen King
Outdoor Writers Association of
America
2017 Cato Ave., Suite 101
State College, PA 16801-2768

JULY

S	M	T	W	T	F	S
	1	2	3	4	5	6
7	8	9	10	11	12	13
14	15	16	17	18	19	20
21	22	23	24	25	26	27
28	29	30	31			

AUGUST

S	M	T	W	T	F	S
				1	2	3
4	5	6	7	8	9	10
11	12	13	14	15	16	17
18	19	20	21	22	23	24
25	26	27	28	29	30	31

SEPTEMBER

S	M	T	W	T	F	S
1	2	3	4	5	6	7
8	9	(10)	11	12	13	14
15	16	17	18	19	20	21
22	23	24	(25)	26	27	28
29	30					

June 29-30
The Ohio Cup
Mad River Sportsmen's Club,
Bellefontaine, OH
(513) 593-8245
Contact: Tony Stratton
Mad River Sportsmen's Club
One Hunter Place
Bellefontaine, OH 43311

July

July
NSCA U.S. Open
(210) 688-3371
Contact: National Sporting Clays
Association
5931 Roft Rd.
San Antonio, TX 78253
This annual event is held at
different locations throughout the
U.S. each year. Please watch
Sporting Clays Magazine for details
on the 1996 location and date.

July 20-27
Olympic Games Shooting
Events
Wolf Creek Olympic Shooting
Complex, Atlanta, GA
(404) 548-1842

Shooting Competition Mgr: Gary L.
Anderson
Atlanta Committee for the
Olympic Games
270 Peachtree St. R,
Atlanta, GA 30303
See Events Schedule Pg. 53

July 25-28
Quail Unlimited National
Convention & Sportsmen's Expo
Opryland Hotel, Nashville, TN
(803) 637-5731
Contact: Scott Henson, Ext. 32
Quail Unlimited
PO Box 610
Edgefield, SC 29824

August

August
NESCA Make-A-Wish Sporting
Clays Family Day
(603) 878-1257
Contact: Tony Haigh
New England Sporting Clays Assoc.
PO Box 137
New Ipswich, NH 03071

HOMESTEAD.
1766

August
The Homestead
Sporting Clays Golf
Championship
The Homestead, Hot Springs, VA
(800) 838-1766
(540) 839-1766
Contact: The Shooting Club
The Homestead
PO Box 2000
Hot Springs, VA 24445
See Our Ad Across

August
SCA National
Championship/U.S. SCI
Championship
Addieville East Farm,
Mapleville, RI
(203) 831-8483
Contact: Fred Collins
Sporting Clays of America
33 South Main St.
Norwalk, CT 06854

HOMESTEAD.
1766

AMERICA'S PREMIER MOUNTAIN RESORT

Home of

The Homestead Cup Sporting Clays Championship
–Memorial Day Weekend, May 24-27, 1996–

The Homestead Sporting Clays Golf Championship
–Annually in August–

And Former Host Of

- The 1992 United States Open Sporting Clays Championship
- 1992, 1993 & 1994 Land Rover Challenge for the Virginia Cup
- 5 United States Golf Association Championships
- The 1995 Merrill Lynch Senior PGA TOUR Shoot-Out Championship

Visit The Homestead and experience the ultimate sporting vacation. Located on 15,000 acres in the Allegheny Mountains of Virginia, the resort offers 521 rooms, sporting clays, skeet, trap, golf, tennis, fly fishing, horseback and carriage rides, 100 miles of hiking and mountain bike trails, complete children's program and a European style spa. Enjoy fine or casual dining and browse through 18 sport shops and boutiques.

LEVEL I and III N.S.C.A. INSTRUCTION AVAILABLE
Specializing in Corporate Meetings
Featuring Sporting Clays and Golf Outings

For More Information or Reservations Call:

The Homestead
P.O. Box 2000 • Hot Springs, VA 24445
800-838-1766 • 540-839-1766

CLUB RESORTS.
Where every guest is a Member

OCTOBER

S	M	T	W	T	F	S
	1	2	3	4	5	
6	7	8	9	10	11	12
13	14	15	16	17	18	19
20	21	22	23	24	25	26
27	28	29	30	31		

NOVEMBER

S	M	T	W	T	F	S
					1	2
3	4	5	6	7	8	9
10	11	12	13	14	15	16
17	18	19	20	(21)	22	23
24	25	26	27	28	29	30

DECEMBER

S	M	T	W	T	F	S
1	2	3	4	5	6	7
8	9	10	11	12	13	14
15	16	17	18	19	20	21
22	23	24	25	26	27	28
29	30	31				

August
97th Grand American Amateur Trapshooting Association, Vandalia, OH
(513) 898-4638
Amateur Trapshooting Association
601 W. National Rd.
Vandalia, OH 45377

August
NSCA/FITASC Nationals
(210) 688-3371
Contact: National Sporting Clays Association
5931 Roft Rd.
San Antonio, TX 78253
This annual event is held at different locations around the country. Watch Sporting Clays Magazine for the 1996 location and date of this exciting event typically held in August.

Aug. 4-11
USA Shooting National Championships
Wolf Creek Olympic Shooting Complex, Atlanta, GA
(719) 578-4882
Contact: Randy Moeller
USA Shooting
One Olympic Plaza
Colorado Springs, CO 80909

Aug. 31-Sept. 2
NSTRA Purina Hi-Pro National Endurance Classic
(317) 839-4059
Contact: National Shoot to Retrieve Field Trial Association
226 North Mill St., #2
Plainfield, IN 46168

September

Sept. 6-11
International Association of Fish and Wildlife Agencies Annual Meeting
Phoenix, AZ
(202) 624-7890
International Association of Fish and Wildlife Agencies
444 North Capitol St., NW
Suite 544
Washington, DC 20001

Sept. 10-15
NSCA National Sporting Clays Championship
National Gun Club,
San Antonio, TX
(210) 688-3371
Contact: National Sporting Clays Association
5931 Roft Rd.
San Antonio, TX 78253
Come enjoy the world's finest in sporting clays in September at the National Gun Club in San Antonio, TX. Take your chance at $25,000 in guaranteed cash and $125,000 in prizes and products to be given away.

Sept. 21
National Hunting & Fishing Day
(203) 426-1320
Contact: Gary Kolesar
National Hunting & Fishing Day Headquarters
c/o NSSF
11 Mile Hill Rd.
Newtown, CT 06470

Sept. 25
7th Annual Congressional Sportsmen's Foundation Annual Banquet
Hyatt Regency Washington, On Capitol Hill, Washington, DC
(202) 785-9153
President: Dallas Miner
Congressional Sportsmen's Foundation
1730 K St., NW, Suite 1300
Washington, DC 20006
See Our Ad Pg. 67

October

October
National All-Around Shotgun Championships
(210) 688-3371
Contact: Mike Hampton
NSSA/NSCA, 5931 Roft Rd.
San Antonio, TX 78253
This event is a test of one's ability to shoot a variety of different clay target games. Each year it proves to be more challenging. Watch Skeet Shooting Review and Sporting Clays Magazine for details on date and location.

October
NSSA World Skeet Championship
National Gun Club,
San Antonio, TX
(210) 688-3371
Contact: National Skeet Shooting Association
5931 Roft Rd.
San Antonio, TX 78253
Held annually at the National Gun Club in San Antonio, TX, this event draws shooters from around the world for a week of shooting and fun for everyone.

October
3rd Annual Louise Mandrell Celebrity Shoot
Nashville Gun Club, Nashville, TN
(615) 822-7200
Contact: Matt Dudney
PO Box 800
Hendersonville, TN 37077-0800

Oct. 21-26
NSTRA Dog of the Year
Conservation Bird Dog Club,
Amo, IN
(317) 839-4059
Contact: National Shoot to
Retrieve Field Trial Association
226 North Mill St., #2
Plainfield, IN 46168

November

Nov. 2-3
Pheasant Festival U.S.A.-
Make A Wish Foundation
Mitchell, SD
(414) 554-0800
Contact: Phil Murray
Kolar Arms
1925 Roosevelt Ave.
Racine, WI 53406

Nov. 9-11
Waterfowl Festival
Easton, MD
(410) 822-4567
Contact: Waterfowl Festival
PO Box 929
Easton, MD 21601

Nov. 20-23
61st Annual World
Championship Duck Calling
Contest & Wings Over the
Prairie Festival
Stuttgart, Arkansas
(501) 673-1602
Stuttgart Chamber of Commerce
PO Box 932
Stuttgart, AR 72160

Nov. 21-23
National Association
Sporting Goods
Wholesalers Hunting
Show
Tarrant County Convention
Center, Ft. Worth, TX
(312) 565-0233
Contact: Rebecca Maddy
National Association Sporting
Goods Wholesalers
PO Box 11344
Chicago, IL 60611

Calling for more info?
Great! And whenever you
contact the sponsors of one
of the events listed on this
calendar, don't forget to say
"I read it in Wing & Clay!"

1996 OLYMPIC SHOOTING EVENTS SCHEDULE

The first medal of the 1996 Olympic Games will be awarded in shooting, where the competition is as varied as it is difficult. Fifteen medal events are featured in four disciplines; rifle, pistol, running target and clay target. The dime-sized rifle bull's eyes are 50 meters away; the clay targets fly through the air, one after another, at 65 miles per hour. Concentration and control are paramount to athletes, who remain steady by firing shots between heartbeats and reducing gun movements to fractions of a millimeter. Electronic target monitors instantly show competitors and spectators the location and score of every shot fired. Each daily ticket will allow an entire day's access to all four ranges at the Wolf Creek Shooting Complex. ✍

Date	Day	Shooting Event	Ticket Code	Price
7/20/96	Saturday	W-10m Air Rifle M-10m Air Pistol	SH001	$24.00
7/21/96	Sunday	W-10m Air Pistol M-Trap	SH002	$24.00
7/22/96	Monday	M-10m Air Rifle	SH003	$24.00
7/23/96	Tuesday	W-Double Trap M-50m Free Pistol	SH004	$24.00
7/24/96	Wednesday	W-50m 3x20 Rifle M-Double Trap M-25m Rapid Pistol	SH005	$24.00
7/25/96	Thursday	M-50m Prone M-25m Rapid Fire Pistol	SH006	$24.00
7/26/96	Friday	W-25m Sport Pistol M-10m Running Target	SH007	$24.00
7/27/96	Saturday	M-50m 3x40 Rifle M-Skeet	SH008	$24.00

IMPORTANT: This was the schedule as of Spring, 1995.
Daily events may change, but days of shooting should remain the same.
One ticket is good for all of the shooting events scheduled that day.
Tickets are sold only through the Atlanta Olympic Ticket office.

✍ Reprinted from the 1996 Centennial Olympic Games Ticket Request Form

ACCESSORIES/
BAGS, POUCHES & SOFT GUN CASES

10x Products Group
2915 LBJ Freeway, Suite 133
Dallas, TX 75234
(800) WEAR 10X
(214) 243-4016
FAX: (214) 243-4112
Contact: Tom Carlson
Available: Retail
Since 1934, 10x has maintained a proud American tradition of making clothes for the Great Outdoors. The 10x line of high-tech hunting apparel includes: lightweight and insulated Gore-Tex fabric garments; upland hunting clothes; and coveralls, jackets, bibs and pants in a variety of camouflage patterns. 10x also offers a wide range of shooting vests, jackets, shirts and accessories for sporting clays and trap & skeet enthusiasts.
See Our Ad Pg. 61

Bob Allen
Companies
214 S.W. Jackson St.
PO Box 477
Des Moines, IA 50315
(800) 685-7020
FAX: (515) 283-0779
Est.: 1946   Staff: 150
Ch. Board: Bob Allen
President: Matt Allen
Nat'l. Sales Mgr: Pam Bradford
Available: Retail & Direct
Bob Allen Sportswear is a premier manufacturer of shooting wear for sporting clays, trap and skeet as well as gun cases, gloves and accessories.
See Our Ad Below

Bianchi International
100 Calle Cortez
Temecula, CA 92590
(909) 676-5621
FAX: (909) 676-6777
Est.: 1958   Staff: 200
President: Gary French
VP/Sales: Tom Frederick
Dir. of Mktg: Hope Bianchi Sjursen
Available: Retail
Sporting Clays collection of shotgun cases, bags & pouches, constructed from fine English Bridle Leather. Handgun holsters,

belts, accessories in leather & nylon. Call us for the retailer nearest you.

The Boyt Company
509 Hamilton
PO Box 668
Iowa Falls, IA 50126
(515) 648-4626
FAX: (515) 648-2058
Est.: 1901   Staff: 300
VP/Sptg. Goods: Tony Caligiuri
Admin. Ass't: Lacey Kifer
Available: Retail
Nation's oldest manufacturer of quality gun cases and shooting accessories, specializing in canvas and leather breathable cases. Traditional leather & canvas gun cases and shooting accessories since 1901. "NO NONSENSE" lifetime guarantee. We specialize in durable canvas, breathable gun cases with over 30 styles available. Luggage and field bags, shell bags, new trap & tackle bag, leather slings & holsters. Dealer custom

cases available. North American distributors for Brett Parsons & Sons —fine English shooting accessories.

Brauer Brothers Mfg. Co.
2020 Delmar
St. Louis, MO 63103
(314) 231-2864
FAX: (314) 241-4952
VP: Teresa E. Downs
Gun cases, gun sleeves and accessories.

Chasse L'Etang
P.L. Gordon Imports
66 Golf Lane
Ridgefield, CT 06877
(203) 431-1553
FAX: (203) 431-1554
Est.: 1992   Staff: 1
President: Pierette Gordon
Available: Direct
Handcrafted leather shooting & hunting accessories.

CHIMERE, inc.
Chimere, Inc.
3435 Enterprise Ave., #44-7
Naples, FL 33942
(813) 643-4222
FAX: (813) 643-5807
President: C.K. "Casey" Koehler
VP/Sales: Mike Boyer
Available: Retail
Competition clothing and accessories; vests, shirts, rainwear, sweaters, gloves, glasses and bags of every kind.
See Our Ad Pg. 56

Crane & Crane, Ltd.
105 N. Edison Way, Unit 6
Reno, NV 89502
(702) 856-1516
FAX: (702) 856-1616
Contact: Jim & Harriet Crane
Crane & Crane manufactures the most versatile Sporting Clays Range and Upland Game Bags on the market. Designed and constructed here in the USA for strength and durability, our bags come in several different models and a variety of colors. Custom embroidery is available for individuals and clubs. Visa and MasterCard accepted. Dealer, pro shop and club inquiries welcome.
See Our Ad Right

Fieldline
The Outdoor Recreation Group
1919 Vineburn Ave.
Los Angeles, CA 90032
(213) 226-0830
FAX: (213) 226-0831
Contact: Joel Altshule
Gen. Mgr: Algird J. Kavalauskas
Available: Retail
For over 2 decades, outdoor enthusiasts have come to rely on us for quality American made outdoor gear and accessories. Call for our catalog.

Galco International
2019 West Quail Ave.
Phoenix, AZ 85027
(602) 258-8295

FAX: (602) 582-6854
President: Rick Gallagher
Exec. VP: Lisa Des Camps
Galco International's Sporting Collection uses only the finest materials available, from rich California latigo leather and rugged waxed canvas, right down to our solid brass hardware handmade in our in-house foundry, to create a full line of gun cases, shell bags, game bags, sporting clays pouches, trap and skeet pouches, belts, leg o'mutton cases, etc.

Hafner Creations, Inc.
PO Box 1987
Lake City, FL 32056
(904) 755-6481
FAX: (904) 755-6595
Est.: 1985   Staff: 15
Contact: John Hafner
Available: Retail & Direct
Nylon gun cases, bags, vests & cartridge belts.

Hip-Hopper
H&H Marketing, Inc.
PO Box 1481
East Stroudsburg, PA 18301
(800) 297-1334
FAX: (610) 366-9680
Contact: Dana Hardy
Available: Retail & Direct
"Hip-Hopper" is a functionally designed shotgun shell carrier.

Holland Sport
190 Napoleon St.
San Francisco, CA 94124
(415) 824-5995
FAX: (415) 824-0265
Est.: 1984   Staff: 180
Contact: Jay Holland
Available: Retail
Holland Sport embraces the return of the by-gone era of American Craftsmanship with its fine line of products. Produced in our own factory, with meticulous attention to every detail. Holland Sport products use prime Latigo leather, with solid brass or gold plate fixtures at the core of each basic piece. Like a well-worn saddle, our leather products improve with age.

Hunter Company, Inc.
3300 West 71st Ave.
PO Box 467
Westminster, CO 80030-9977
(303) 427-4626
FAX: (303) 428-3980
VP/Sales & Mktg: Jim Holtzclaw
Available: Retail
Call for our catalog of leather accessories.

On Point Sportswear
PO Box 18474
Reno, NV 89511
(800) 297-6468 (Orders)
Contact: Russ Carpenter
Dealer Inquiries Welcome

Perazzi USA Inc.
1207 South Shamrock Ave.
Monrovia, CA 91016
(818) 303-0068
FAX: (818) 303-2081
Vice President: Lucio Sosta
Available: Through our Dealers
Perazzi offers a selection of quality bags, cases and clothing. Call for the dealer nearest you.

Ed Scherer's
Custom Leathercraft
W30059 Woodcrest Dr.
Waukesha, WI 53188
(800) 451-1253
(414) 640-5845 (Mobile)
FAX: (414) 968-3048
Contact: Ed Scherer
Available: Direct
Ed Scherer has been producing his custom leathercraft items for over three decades. His handcrafted shell pouch is the perfect setup for warm weather shooting. His pouch takes the weight off the shoulders, producing a smooth swing. Also available is a double pouch with two compartments that holds 75-12 ga. shells. A special zipper pocket holds valuables. Hand stamped initials included. Plain pouch and belt set (no carving) only $99.95. Completely hand carved pouch & belt set. . .$149.95. Call today (800) 451-1253. Credit cards accepted.
See Our Ad Pg. 179

SHOOTING SYSTEMS GROUP INC.

Shooting Systems Group
1075 Headquarters Park
Fenton, MO 63026-2478
(800) 325-3049
(314) 343-3575
FAX: (314) 349-3311
President: Bruce Bogue
Shooting Systems has been servicing discerning sportsmen for more than two decades. Our handsome, black ballistic nylon sporting clays bag was developed to meet your exacting needs, including quick access provided by "zipcords"; two movable, adjustable inside walls; four exterior pockets and free choke tube box. Call today to order yours! Pro shop inquiries welcome.

See Our Ad Below

Sporting Bag Specialties
7300 North 101st St.
White Bear Lake, MN 55110
(612) 429-5272
Contact: Mimi Ward
Distinctive sport bags with classic British styling. Special & multi-purpose bags made in canvas & leather. Ask about our customizing options.

TSA Manufacturing, Inc.
129 State St.,St. Paul, MN 55107
(612) 222-2220
Contact: Jim Thomas
Available: Retail
Cordura luggage & shooting bags.

WILD·HARE International
PO Box 11943, Memphis, TN 38111
(800) 523-9453
Est.: 1992
Contact: Paul Brown
Available: Retail & Direct
Get in gear this season with WILD-HARE's complete shotgunning accessory system. From our SHOT SHELL APRON to our "QUICK-SNAP" GUNBOY, WILD-HARE manufactures the best in affordable, high quality products designed by competition shooters for the sporting clay enthusiast. Available through your local dealer and catalogues.

See Our Ad Pg. 43

Wilderness Pride
2562 East 7th Ave.
North St. Paul, MN 55109
(612) 773-5887
Est.: 1980   Staff: 10
Sales Mgr: Vicki McGinty
Available: Retail & Direct
Wilderness Pride can manufacture your next line of leather and canvas shooting accessories. Retail and commercial inquiries only–thank you.

ACCESSORIES/GUN

B.A.T. Products, Inc.
Fischer Gunsmithing, Inc.
Box 55-8266, 4235 S.W. 75 Ave.
Miami, FL 33155
(305) 261-4454
Contact: Steve Fischer
Titainium firing pins. Lifetime warranty. Dealer inquiries invited. Call for catalog.

Barrel Button
All Sport Tech
2606 Alden Ct.
West Bloomfield, MI 48324
(810) 360-7118
Est.: 1990   Staff: 2
Contact: Ira Place
Available: Retail & Direct
Washable long-lasting button for your shoe to rest your gun barrel on.

Beamer Line
Phase Laser Systems, Inc.
14255 N 79th St., Suite 6
Scottsdale, AZ 85260
(602) 998-4828
President: Michael J. Brubacher
Available: Direct
The Impact Laser 12/20 enables you to see precisely what your shotgun barrel "sees" without firing a round. It's compact, light and slides into the muzzle and projects a continuous pattern 100 ft.

BRILEY

Briley Manufacturing
1230 Lumpkin, Houston, TX 77043
(800) 331-5718 (Cust. Svc.)
(713) 932-6995
Contact: Chuck Webb
Available: Retail & Direct
Full line of BRILEY products made by shooters for shooters. Unique accessories include choke cases, choke and bore gauge, Turbo-choke cleaner, Speed Wrench, Unilube choke tube grease, Sport-lube pump action lubricant, the best chamber brush you've ever used, and for tube sets, our Power Knockout tool for the easiest insertion or removal of any tube set. Call for brochure.

See Our Ad Pg. 27

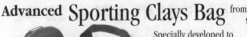

GALAZAN

GALAZAN
A Division of Connecticut Shotgun
Manufacturing
PO Box 1692
New Britain, CT 06051-1692
(203) 225-6581
FAX: (203) 832-8707
Est.: 1967   Staff: 20
Contact: Dick Perrett
Available: Direct
Our new catalog, "GALAZAN -
Things for fine guns....and more" is
now available for $5.00. You can
order our entire line of fine gun
products directly from us. Included
are many hard-to-get items including recoil pads and butt plates,
gun parts (including all of the Winchester Model 21 parts), hard
leather gun cases and shooting
bags, gun case accessories, snap
caps, shooting accessories,
gauges, Turkish Circassian Walnut
gunstock wood and tools.

HOPPE'S ⑨™
A DIVISION OF PENGUIN INDUSTRIES, INC.

Hoppe's
Airport Industrial Mall
Coatesville, PA 19320
(610) 384-6000
FAX: (610) 857-5980
Contact: Patricia Lucas

Available: Retail
Shooter's screwdriver–tough lightweight set with storage chambers
and spanner handle contains 2 Phillips head bits, 7 slotted head bits
and 5 Allen wrenches in the most
often needed sizes. May be purchased at your local gun dealer.
See Our Ad Below

Magic Dot Corporation
PO Box 513
Elm Grove, WI 53122
(414) 546-1399
(414) 245-5013
FAX: (414) 546-1105
Est.: 1984   Staff: 6
President: Hugh Brown
Contact: Robert P. Ryan or
Rich Stpniewksi
Available: Retail & Direct
Using Magic Dot on your shooting
glasses, to correct cross domi-
nance, double vision, and ghost
image, lets you shoot with both
eyes opened.

Meadow Industries
PO Box 754
Dept. WC
Locust Grove, VA 22508
(703) 972-2175 (Phone/Fax)
Contact: Ken Vickers
Available: Retail & Direct
Accessories for your gun: "Brite-Site
Crossfire"-Eliminator; Soft-Comb
Shock Absorber System; Convert-A-
Stock Pad; 12 Ga. Barrel-Buddy.

New England
Custom Gun Service
Brook Rd., RR#2
Box 122W
W. Lebanon, NH 03784
(603) 469-3450
Est.: 1986   Staff: 3
Contact: Dietrich Apel
We stock an assortment of gun accessories including leather shotgun
hand guards, shotgun snap caps
made of chrome & aluminum, hardwood snap cap blocks, and
engraved grip caps which can be personalized. Please request brochure.

Quality Arms, Inc.
PO Box 19477
Houston, TX 77224
(713) 870-8377
FAX: (713) 870-8524
Contact: John Boyd
Available: Direct
Fine imported accessories for the
serious sportsman: European snap
caps; oil bottles; English cleaning
rods or complete sets; handguards;
English oils and European cartridge
boxes; Trunk style cases; European
shotshells.
See Our Ad Pg. 112

Shell D-Jammer
Kiwi Sales
PO Box 349
Tustin, CA 92681
(800) 832-9026
(714) 972-0388
FAX: (714) 972-1667
Contact: Tom Hippensteel
Available: Direct

Tasco Sales, Inc.
PO Box 520080
7600 Northwest 26 St.
Miami, FL 33152-0080
(305) 591-3670 (Ext. 315)
FAX: (305) 592-5895
Contact: George Edwards
Available: Retail
Bantom scopes & PRO-point sighting device for shotguns can
improve turkey hunters' performance and is excellent for other
shotgun shooting applications.

ACCESSORIES/
SLINGS & CARRIERS

Butt Buddy Holster
The Long Gun Holster Co.
Box 225
Olpe, KS 68865
(800) 345-2195
Est.: 1989
Contact: Jerry Gerleman
Available: Retail & Direct
A leather belt holster that allows
the hunter to carry his gun at the
ready and do away with the fa-
tigue that sets in after carrying a
shotgun/rifle for a long time.

Michaels of Oregon Co.
(Uncle Mike's)
PO Box 13010
Portland, OR 97213
(503) 255-6890
FAX: (503) 255-0746
Available: Retail
Firearm/hunting accessories: sling
swivels, leather and nylon slings, re-
coil pads, and gun cases.

**The Safety Connection
Gun Cling**
Hard Target, Inc.
PO Box 652
Corbin, KY 40702
(800) 887-1799
(606) 528-1799
FAX: (606) 528-8794
Pres: Harold W. Turner
Available: Retail & Direct
The Cling's unique design gives a
hands-free carrying system and prevents the muzzle of the gun from
being pointed at the head or torso
if the hunter should fall or drop
the gun. Dealer inquiries also welcomed.

Universal Gun Caddy
Sooner Marketing
PO Box 271593
Oklahoma City, OK 73137
(800) 495-3260
The Universal Gun Caddy takes the
load off your arms and places the
weight on your shoulders. Greater
safety, better gun balance and easily accessible for firing.

APPAREL/
CLOTHING

For related products & services see:

- *Mail Order Catalogs, Pg. 131*
- *Accessories, Pg. 54*

*Every sport has its look, and
hunting and shooting are no
exceptions. The apparel manufacturers in the section that
follows produce clothing and
accessories for all tastes and
budgets. If you're a retailer
or a pro-shop manager,
write or call them directly for
information. Individuals
interested in a particular
company should check with
that company to see if it
sells direct to the consumer;
or, if it doesn't, to get a list
of nearby retailers that carry
its product line.*

10x Products Group
2915 LBJ Freeway, Suite 133
Dallas, TX 75234
(800) WEAR 10X
(214) 243-4016
FAX: (214) 243-4112
Contact: Tom Carlson
Available: Retail
Since 1934, 10x has maintained a
proud American tradition of making clothes for the Great Outdoors.
The 10x line of high-tech hunting
apparel includes: lightweight and
insulated Gore-Tex fabric garments; upland hunting clothes;
and coveralls, jackets, bibs and
pants in a variety of camouflage
patterns. 10x also offers a wide
range of shooting vests, jackets,
shirts and accessories for sporting
clays and trap & skeet enthusiasts.
See Our Ad Pg. 61

Bob Allen
Companies
214 S.W. Jackson St.
PO Box 477
Des Moines, IA 50315
(800) 685-7020
FAX: (515) 283-0779
Est.: 1946   Staff: 150
Ch. Board: Bob Allen
President: Matt Allen
Nat'l. Sales Mgr: Pam Bradford
Available: Retail & Direct
Bob Allen Sportswear is a premier
manufacturer of shooting wear for
sporting clays, trap and skeet as
well as gun cases, gloves and acces-
sories.
See Our Ad Pg. 54

Barbour, Inc.
55 Meadowbrook Dr.
Milford, NH 03055
(800) 338-3474
FAX: (603) 673-6510
Gen. Mgr: Tom Hooven
Sales Manager: Tom Sobolewski
Available: Retail
Waxed cotton jackets, shooting
vests and country clothing & acces-
sories.

Beretta U.S.A.
c/o Beretta Gallery
New York:
718 Madison Ave.
New York, NY 10021
(212) 319-6614
Alexandria:
317 S. Washington St.
Old Town Alexandria, VA 22314
(703) 739-0596
Beretta Sport casual, travel and
hunting apparel plus shooting
vests and shooting accessories.

Browning
One Browning Place
Morgan, UT 84050
(800) 333-3288 (Customer)
(801) 876-2711 (General)
FAX: (801) 876-3331
Est.: 1878   Staff: 350
Available: Retail
Waterproof fleece, insultated outer-
wear, Dura-wax, down garments,
rainwear, shirts, pants, underwear
& socks.

Carhartt, Inc.
PO Box 600, Dearborn, MI 48121
(800) 833-3118
(800) 358-3825 (Retail)
Est.: 1889   Staff: 2000
Contact: Customer Service
Available: Retail
All cotton rugged hunting and
outerwear.

Columbia Sportswear
6600 N. Baltimore
Portland, OR 97203
(800) MAB-OYLE (Retail)
(503) 286-3676
Est.: 1938   Staff: 800
PR Coordinator: Angela Peets
Available: Retail
Manufacturer of high quality, value-priced outdoor apparel and footwear.

Christopher Dawes Countrywear
Chapel Field Barn, 2 Old Bank
Ripponden, Sowerby Bridge, West
Yorkshire HX6 4DG England
011-44-42-282-4600
FAX: 011-44-42-282-2401
Contact: Christopher Dawes
Available: Retail
Exclusive range of men's and ladies' country clothing for all field sports.

C.C. Filson Company
PO Box 34020
Seattle, WA 98124
(206) 624-4437
FAX: (206) 624-4539
Est.: 1897
Contact: Steve Matson
Available: Retail & Direct
C.C. Filson is a manufacturer of quality outdoor clothing, luggage and hats.

Hatch Gloves & Accessories
1445 Donlon St., Bldg. 12
Ventura, CA 93003
(800) 767-1343 (Cust. Service)
(805) 642-0170
FAX: (805) 642-0224
Est.: 1964   Staff: 12
Contact: Lisa Hatch Sciuto
Pres/CEO: Robert J. Hatch
VP/Sales & Mktg: Joshua Cranford
Available: Retail
Clay target shooting and all weather hunting gloves. Distributor & dealer inquiries welcome.

Holland & Holland, Ltd.
31-33 Bruton St.
London, W1X 8JS England
011-44-171-499-4411
Est: 1835
Chairman: Alain Drach
Contact: Jeannie Perkins
80 Winding Lane
Greenwich, CT
(203) 622-6844
FAX: (203) 622-6844
Contact: Nina Rumbough Craig
Available: Direct
Superb country clothing, silks and accessories available by mail order.

Hunting World, Inc.
PO Box 5981,
Sparks, NV 89432
(702) 331-0414
FAX: (702) 331-1130
President: Robert M. Lee
Available: Retail
Clothing & accessories of classic design.

Lewis Creek Company
2065 Shelburne Rd.
Shelburne, VT 05482
(800) 336-4884
(802) 985-1099
FAX: (802) 985-1097
President: Jeff Pratt
Available: Retail
Outerwear, shooting apparel and accessories. Traditional American designs as well as classic European influence.

Marathon Apparel
621 N. 31st St.
Birmingham, AL 35203
(205) 251-4735
FAX: (205) 251-1286
Est.: 1991   Staff: 40
Dir. of Advtg: Louise Gaither
Available: Retail
Men's sportswear-with "Country Gentleman" look.

Mossy Oak
Haas Outdoors, Inc.
200 East Main St.
PO Box 757
West Point, MS 39773
(601) 494-8859
Contact: Toxey Haas
Available: Retail
Camouflage hunting apparel and accessories.

Norton & Sons, Inc.
16 Savile Row
London W1X 1AE England
011-44-71-437-0829
FAX: 011-44-71-287-4764
Managing Dir: John Granger
Available: Direct
Traditional Scottish tweeds. Savile Row designed field sports clothing enhanced with breathable Gortex for all weather protection.

PAST Sporting Goods, Inc.
PO Box 1035
Columbia, MO 65205
(314) 445-9200
Est.: 1980   Staff: 12
President: Dick Leeper
The finest in wearable recoil protection and accessories for all shooting sports–RECOIL SHIELDS-SHOOTING VESTS- SHOOTING GLOVES-GUN VISE-TUMBLER HUNTING VEST-SHOOTING ACCESSORIES-SHOOTING GLASSES-SHOOTING SHIRTS-AND MORE. Full line available for all ages. To purchase any of our fine products please contact your local shooting sports retailer or gun club manager. Available in both right and left handed. 100% U.S. made.
See Our Ad Pg. 64

Pendleton Woolen Mills
220 N.W. Broadway
Portland, OR 97208
(503) 226-4801
Contact: Lynnette Loop
Available: Retail
Full clothing line for men and women: shirts, pants, vests, hats.

Spartan-RealTree Products, Inc.
1390 Box Circle
Columbus, GA 31907
(706) 569-9101
Contact: Bill Jordan
Available: Retail
Hunting clothes: Bill Jordan's RealTree camouflage clothing includes clothing in the RealTree All-Purpose pattern. Fabrics include 100% cotton ripstop, 50/50 brushed twill, 100% cotton knits, Polar Tuff, several types of netting and other; products include 100% cotton tees, coats, pants, shorts, netting items, hats, sports shirts, western shirts, bib overalls, and a complete line of youth clothing.

Steinman's
2908 South Santa-Fe
Chanute, KS 66720
(316) 431-1936
Est.: 1995   Staff: 12
Contact: Donna Steinman
Available: Retail & Direct
Shooting shirts–100% cotton twills and denims

Storm Shooting Apparel
320 E. 14th St.
Wahoo, NE 68066
(402) 443-3720
Est.: 1990
Pres: John Storm
Available: Retail & Direct
Shooting jacket-short & regular sizes.

Walls Industries, Inc.
PO Box 98
Cleburne, TX 76033
(817) 645-4366
FAX: (817) 645-7946
Est.: 1943   Staff: 1500
Contact: Jim Lowstetter
Available: Retail
Outdoor & workwear catalog &
shirts. Rugged outdoor apparel in-
cluding camouflage, blaze orange,
insulated and non-insulated outer-
wear, coveralls, overalls,
Water-Pruf breathables, shirts,
pants and accessories.

Woolrich, Inc.
1 Mill St.
Woolrich, PA 17779
(800) 995-1299
(717) 769-6464
FAX: (717) 769-6234
Est.: 1830   Staff: 2150
Prod. Mgr. Hunting Wr: Rick Insley
Available: Retail
Manufacturers of rugged outdoor
sportswear & hunting wear. Consumer may call to find local retailer
information.

APPAREL/ FOOTWEAR

LE CHAMEAU

Bottes Le Chameau
14690 Pont-D'Ouilly
Cahan France
Est.: 1927
011-33-31-698045
FAX: 011-33-697979
Contact: Astrid Judmaier and
Ghislain Pages
Available: Retail
Le Chameau has been hand-mak-
ing boots since 1927 and is known
for using the very best raw materials. It has been the first company
to use leather and Neoprene as a
lining, and as such is considered to
offer "The Ultimate Boot". Main
models: the Leather lined Zip boot
and the Neoprene lined boot. See
the list of retailers in our ad.

See Our Ad Across

Chippewa Boot Company
PO Box 548
Fort Worth, TX 76101
(817) 332-4385
FAX: (817) 390-2566

Est.: 1901
Contact: Don Honeycutt
Available: Retail
Work sport and utility boots. We
put only the finest elements into
Chippewas. Call for the retailer
nearest you.

Danner Shoe Mfg. Co.
12722 NE Airport Way
PO Box 30148, Portland, OR 97230
(800) 345-0430
FAX: (503) 251-1119
Est.: 1932   Staff: 160
President: Eric Merk, Sr.
Ass't. Nat'l. Sales Mgr: Eric Merk, Jr.
Available: Retail & Direct
Mfg. of quality rugged footwear.
Guaranteed against defects and
leakage for 2 years.

Herman Survivors
Joseph M. Herman Shoe Corp.
200 Business Park Dr.
Suite 100, Armonk, NY 10504
(800) 962-4007
(914) 273-4499
FAX: (914) 273-6980
Vice President: Anthony DiPaolo
Available: Retail
The Herman Survivors outdoor
boot line has been designed to
meet the quality, value and innova-
tion that today's outdoorsmen
demands. Herman Survivors waterproof collection has been
expanded to meet all the expectations of today's consumer. For over
115 years Herman Survivors has
been dedicated to making the ab-
solute best product at a fair price.
Call (800) 962-4007.
See Our Ad Left

Irish Setter Sport Boots
314 Main St.,
Red Wing, MN 55066
(612) 388-8211
FAX: (612) 388-7415
Est.: 1948   Staff: 1500
Div. Mgr: John DePalma
Available: Retail
Leading manufacturer of outdoor
footwear – over 20 styles.

LaCrosse Footwear, Inc.
1319 St. Andrew St.
PO Box 1328, LaCrosse, WI 54603
(800) 323-2668
Est.: 1897   Staff: 1300
Contact: Tiffany Schilla
Available: Retail
General outdoor and hunting
footwear.

Rocky Shoes & Boots, Inc.
294 Harper St.
Nelsonville, OH 45764
(800) 848-9452
(614) 753-1951
FAX: (614) 753-4024

W.C. Russell Moccasin Co.
285 S.W. Franklin
Berlin, WI 54923
(414) 361-2252
FAX: (414) 361-3274
Est.: 1889　　Staff: 30
Pres: Ralph Fabricius
Available: Direct
Hand lasted custom made hunting and shooting boots and shoes. Any size, any width, color, height. Specializing in special orders and hard to fit boots. Sporting clays shoes, bird hunting boots, safari shoes & boots, big game hunting boots.

Timberland Company
PO Box 5050
Hampton, NH 03842
(800) 445-5545
(603) 926-1600
Available: Retail
Consumer can call 800# to find local retailers carrying apparel.

B.B. Walker Company
414 East Dixie Dr.
PO Box 1167
Asheboro, NC 27204
(800) 334-1242
(910) 625-1380
FAX: (910) 625-8125
Customer Svc. Mgr: Betty Howard
Sales Mgr: Norman Miller
Available: Retail
Golden Retriever Rugged Outdoor Footwear.

APPAREL/ VESTS

10x Products Group
2915 LBJ Freeway, Suite 133
Dallas, TX 75234
(800) WEAR 10X
(214) 243-4016
FAX: (214) 243-4112
Contact: Tom Carlson
Available: Retail
Since 1934, 10x has maintained a proud American tradition of making clothes for the Great Outdoors.

The 10x line of high-tech hunting apparel includes: lightweight and insulated Gore-Tex fabric garments; upland hunting clothes; and coveralls, jackets, bibs and pants in a variety of camouflage patterns. 10x also offers a wide range of shooting vests, jackets, shirts and accessories for sporting clays and trap & skeet enthusiasts.
See Our Ad Pg. 61

A.D.S. Vest
1605 Sunset Dr.
Louisville, CO 80027
(303) 665-7369
FAX: (303) 666-4806
Est.: 1979　　Staff: 2
Contact: Alberto DeSimone
Available: Direct
Custom made shooting vests of supreme quality.

Bob Allen Companies
214 S.W. Jackson St.
PO Box 477
Des Moines, IA 50315
(800) 685-7020
FAX: (515) 283-0779
Est.: 1946　　Staff: 150
Pres: Matt Allen
Nat'l. Sales Mgr: Pam Bradford
Available: Retail & Direct
Full line of vest for men & women. Premier manufacturer of shooting wear for sporting clays, trap and skeet as well as gun cases, gloves and accessories.
See Our Ad Pg. 54

B.T.P. Sports
10 Elm St., W.
Valhalla, NY 10595
(914) 949-8183
Contact: Dick Thomas
Available: Direct
The ultimate shooting sweaters:
Skookum and sporting clays models available.

Barbour, Inc.
55 Meadowbrook Dr.
Milford, NH 03055
(800) 338-3474
FAX: (603) 673-6510
Gen. Mgr.: Tom Hooven
Sales Manager: Tom Sobolewski
Available: Retail
Ganton vest line: all Barbour shooting vests are available in sizes 34"
to 52". Functional features vary from
vest to vest. Call for a brochure.

Beretta U.S.A.
c/o Beretta Gallery
New York:
718 Madison Ave.
New York, NY 10021
(212) 319-6614
Alexandria:
317 S. Washington St.
Old Town Alexandria, VA 22314
(703) 739-0596
Available: Retail
Competition and hunting vests

British Sporting Vest
British Sporting Arms
RR1, Box 193A
Millbrook, NY 12545
(914) 677-8303
Contact: Margaret Schneible
Available: Direct
Customized vests available in many
colors. Special features include
mesh backs, left hand, and custom
embroidery.

Browning
One Browning Place
Morgan, UT 84050
(800) 333-3288 (Customer)
(801) 876-2711 (General)
FAX: (801) 876-3331
Est.: 1878   Staff: 350
Available: Retail
"REACTAR" Technical shooting
vests and upland "Dura-Wax" vests

CHIMERE, inc.

Chimere, Inc.
3435 Enterprise Ave., #44-7
Naples, FL 33942
(813) 643-4222
FAX: (813) 643-5807
President: C.K. "Casey" Koehler
VP/Sales: Mike Boyer
Available: Retail
Competition clothing
and accessories: vests,
shirts, rainwear, sweaters, gloves, glasses and
bags of every kind.
See Our Ad Pg. 56

**Columbia
Sportswear**
PO Box 83239
Portland, OR 97283
(800) 547-8066
Est.: 1938   Staff: 800
PR Coordinator: Angela
Peets
Available: Retail
Columbia's "Quick
Loader" vest is available
in either 12 or 20
gauge.

**Custom
Sportswear &
Optical**
11658 Walnut Hill Dr.
Baltimore, OH 43105
(800) 745-6066
Est.: 1983   Staff: 6
Owner: Clarence Willis
Available: Direct
Our custom tailored waterproof shooting coats
have been designed by
shooters for shooters.
They are the lightest all
weather coats made
and ensure ease of
swing and movement.

C.C. Filson Company
PO Box 34020
Seattle, WA 98124
(206) 624-4437
FAX: (206) 624-4539
Est.: 1897
Contact: Steve Matson
Available: Retail & Direct
Hunting vests available in oil finish
duck and 100% cotton poplin.

Game Winner, Inc.
2625 Cumberland Pkwy., #220
Atlanta, GA 30339
(404) 434-9210
FAX: (404) 434-9215
Sales Mgr: Robert Ingram
Available: Direct
Upland shooting vests in a variety
of fabrics. Call for information.

El Gavilan
11059 S.W. 70th Terrace
Miami, FL 33173
(305) 595-4321
FAX: (305) 598-7654
Contact: David Feldman
The Pro Sporting Clays shirt and
shooting vests are available in
100% cotton. Club and dealer inquiries invited.

Lady Clays
PO Box 457
Shawnee Mission, KS 66201
Est.: 1991   Staff: 2
Contact: Becky Bowen
Available: Direct
Custom designed shooting vests
for ladies & men.

Mack-Jac Vest
The Audio Protection Co.
Sportsmen's Closet
365 W. 19th St.,

Houston, TX 77008
(713) 802-1840
Contact: Tim Holt
The MACK-JAC was designed with
the competitive shooter in mind
who demands both performance
and style.

PAST Sporting Goods, Inc.
PO Box 1035
Columbia, MO 65205
(314) 445-9200
Est.: 1980   Staff: 12
Pres: Dick Leeper
Available: Retail & Direct
The finest in wearable recoil protec-
tion and accessories for all
shooting sports–RECOIL SHIELDS-
SHOOTING VESTS-SHOOTING
GLOVES-GUN VISE-TUMBLER-HUNT-
ING VEST-SHOOTING
ACCESSORIES- SHOOTING
GLASSES-SHOOTING SHIRTS-AND
MORE. Full Line available for all
ages. To purchase any of our fine
products please contact your local
shooting sports retailer or gun club
manager. Available in both right
and left handed. 100% U.S. made.

See Our Ad Pg. 64

The Quilomene
All Day Vest
3042 Kincaid Rd.
Billings, MT 59101
(800) 585-8804 (Orders)
(406) 254-0003
Contact: Steve Owen
Available: Retail & Direct

A wingshooting vest featuring the
new "Camelbak" water system. Call
for more information. 24 hr. order
service.

Shoot the Moon
3400 16th St.
Bldg. 1N, Suite DD
Greeley, CO 80631
(303) 356-5148
FAX: (303) 353-7393
Est.: 1992
Contact: Susan Carter/ S.LeGate
Available: Retail & Direct
Female apparel – shooting vests, re-
laxed shooting shirt, quilted
Bomber jacket, brush pants, an-
aorack - special orders.

Top Line
Company, Inc.
600 N. Broad St.
Suite 7, Dept. WC
Middletown, DE 19709
(800) 538-0888 (Orders Only)
(302) 378-2113
FAX: (302) 378-2201
Est.: 1970
Contact: Jane Ritter
Available: Direct
Top Line offers the best designs in
shooting vest wear. We will custom make any vest. Our vests are
made of durable and sturdy fabric
of 50% cotton and 50% polyester
sail cloth or you can provide your
own fabric. We have 25 years of experience in manufacturing
shooting vests. We offer quality,
comfort, durability and good looks.
Please call for our catalog.

See Our Ad Below

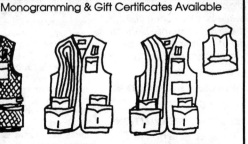

Vermont Vest
RR1, Box 4231
Bennington, VT 05201
(802) 442-4250
Contact: Tom Crowley
Available: Direct
A New England tradition of quality
and workmanship. Men's and
ladies' shooting vests for sporting
clays, trap or skeet. Custom fitting

WILD-HARE, International
PO Box 11943
Memphis, TN 38111
(800) 523-9453
Est.: 1992
Contact: Paul Brown
Available: Retail & Direct
Our SHOOTING VEST features
large double bellow pockets allowing for plenty of shell space. Our
distinctive logo is embroidered into
the regulation FITASC line. Button
tab adjustments along the back
allow for a proper fit at the waist,
as well as a double brass zippered
front. Made of supple cognac pig-
skin and a durable cotton blend,
our vest cuts a stylish appearance
both on and off the course. We
also offer our SHOOTER'S WAIST-
COAT and FIELDCOAT made to the
same exacting standards as our
VEST. Available through your local
dealer and catalogues.
See Our Ad Pg. 43

ASSOCIATIONS

The interests of America's
sportsmen and sports-
women are served by a large
number of associations and
organizations. You will find
valuable information about
the largest and most influen-
tial of these groups In the
five sections that follow:

- *CONSERVATION GROUPS*
- *DOG CLUBS & ASSOCIATIONS*
- *GUN RIGHTS GROUPS*
- *SHOOTING ORGANIZATIONS*
- *TRADE ASSOCIATIONS*

CONSERVATION GROUPS

American Forests
Association
PO Box 2000
Washington, DC 20013
(202) 667-3300
Est.: 1875   Staff: 30
Members: 148,000
Exec. VP: R. Neil Sampson

The American Friends of
the Game Conservancy
910 Pierremont Rd., Suite 250
Shreveport, LA 71106
(318) 868-3631
FAX: (318) 861-4000
Est.: 1986
Exec. Dir: Don Evans

Boone and Crockett Club
250 Station Dr.
Old Milwaukee Depot
Missoula, MT 59801-2753
(406) 542-1888
Est.: 1887   Staff: 6
Members: 128
Dir. of Records: Jack Reneau

Congressional
Sportsmen's Foundation
1730 K St., NW
Washington, DC 20006
(202) 785-9153
FAX: (202) 785-9155
Est.: 1989
Members: 600
Chairman: Sharon Borg Wall
President: Dallas Miner
The Congressional Sportsmen's
Foundation is dedicated to "preserving and promoting our Nation's
outdoor heritage, in particular
sport hunting and angling." The
Foundation's programs closely par-
allel those of the Congressional
Sportsmen's Caucus which is com-
prised of more than 40 percent of
the U.S. Congress. Referred to as
"the sportsmen's link to Congress,"
the Foundation works to ensure
that sportsmen have a strong voice
in the Nation's capital. The CSF is
supported through membership
dues.
See Our Ad Across

Delta Waterfowl
Foundation
102 Wilmot Rd., Suite 410
Deerfield, IL 60015
(708) 940-7776
Est.: 1911   Staff: 4
President: Daniel W. LeBland
Mission: Help reverse the decline in
No. Amer. waterfowl populations

Ducks Unlimited
One Waterfowl Way
Memphis, TN 38120
(901) 758-3825
Est.: 1937   Staff: 270
Members: 550,000
Exec. VP: Matthew B. Connolly, Jr.
Chrmn: Donald L. Rollins
Pres: Gene Henry
Tr: Charles H. Wright
Membership Mgr: J. William
Straughan

Foundation for North
American Wild Sheep
720 Allen Ave.
Cody, WY 82414
(307) 527-6261
Est.: 1981   Staff: 6
Members: 5,000
Exec. Dir: Karen Werbelow

Game Conservation
International
PO Box 17444
San Antonio, TX 78217
(210) 824-7509
Est.: 1967   Staff: 2
Members: 1,000
Exec. Dir: Larry Means

Geese Unlimited
2820 S. Hwy. 169
Grand Rapids, MN 55744
(218) 327-0774
FAX: (218) 327-1349
Est.: 1984   Staff: 1
Members: 1,000
Contact: Shawn McDowell
Conservation organization dedicated to the proper management
of the Canada goose functioning
through relocation, habitat enhancement and legislation.

International Association
of Fish & Wildlife Agencies
444 N. Capitol St., NW #544
Washington, DC 20001
(202) 624-7890
Est.: 1902   Staff: 12
Members: 450
Exec. VP: R. Max Peterson

Izaak Walton League
of America
707 Conservation Lane
Gaithersburg, MD 20878-2983
(301) 548-0150

Est.: 1922   Staff: 27
Members: 55,000
Exec. Dir: Paul Hansen

Miller's Friends of the Fields
PO Box 93848
Milwaukee, WI 53203-0848
(800) 57F-IELD
FAX: (414) 276-9858
Est.: 1994
Contact: Michael Johnston
The Friends of the Field Fund was created to solidify Miller Brewing Company's commitment to outdoor sports, participants and the conservation of natural habitats. A primary mission of Friends of the Field is to create awareness of the need for responsible behavior in the field and on the waterways.

National Fish and Wildlife Foundation
1120 Connecticut Ave., NW, #900
Washington, DC 20036
(202) 857-0166
Exec. Dir: Amos Eno

National Wild Turkey Federation
PO Box 530
Edgefield, SC 29824
(803) 637-3106
Est.: 1973   Staff: 55
Members: 110,000
Exec. VP: Rob Keck

National Wildlife Federation
1400 16th St., NW
Washington, DC 20036
(202) 797-6800
Est.: 1936   Staff: 650
Members: Over 4 million
Pres: Dr. Jay D. Hair

Orion-The Hunters Institute
PO Box 5088, Helena, MT 59604
(406) 449-2795
Est.: 1993
Contact: Jim Posewitz
Orion-The Hunters Institute is a non-profit organization created to sustain hunting and resources essential to that purpose. National in scope, the institute works to assure ethical and responsible hunting.

Pheasants Forever
PO Box 75473
St. Paul, MN 55175
(612) 481-7142
Est.: 1982   Staff: 30
Members: 70,000
Exec. Dir: Jeffrey S. Finden
Membership Svc: Eliz. A. Whitten
Pres. B/Directors: George A. Wilson

Pope and Young Club
Box 548
Chatfield, MN 55923
(507) 867-4144
Est.: 1961   Staff: 3
Members: 2,800
Exec. Sec: Glen E. Hisey

Putting People First
PO Box 1707
Helena, MT 59624
(406) 442-5700
Est.: 1990   Staff: 8
Members: 45,000
Chairman: Kathleen Marquardt
Putting People First is a non-profit grassroots network of concerned citizens dedicated to human rights, animal welfare and conservation. We are ordinary people who eat meat, drink milk, support biomedical research, wear leather and wool, hunt and fish, own pets, go to zoos, circuses and rodeos, and who benefit from the wise and rational use of the earth's resources. We believe in balancing science, reason, and common sense against the deception, coersion and terrorism of the animal rights and green movements. Putting People First seeks to enhance the quality of life through the responsible use of animals and our environment.

Quail Unlimited
PO Box 610
Edgefield, SC 29824-0610
(803) 637-5731
FAX: (803) 637-0037
Est.: 1981
Members: 45,000
Exec. VP: Rocky Evans
Adm. VP: Jerry Allen
Quail Unlimited is a national non-profit conservation organization dedicated to the wise use and management of America's quail and upland game birds. Primarily a habitat management organization, the organization funds its projects through a network of chapters throughout the country.

Rocky Mountain Elk Foundation
PO Box 8249
Missoula, MT 59807
(800) CAL-LELK
(406) 523-4500

FAX: (406) 523-4550
Est.: 1984   Staff: 106
Members: 95,000
Exec. Dir: Robert W. Munson
Mission to ensure the future of elk and other wildlife by conserving, restoring, enhancing natural habitats. Publish "Bugle" Magazine.

The Ruffed Grouse Society
451 McCormick Rd.
Corapolis, PA 15108
(412) 262-4044
Est.: 1961   Staff: 20
Members: 23,000
Exec. Dir: Samuel Pursglove, Jr.
Dir. of Com: Paul E. Carson
Membership: Roberta Sandell
Formed in 1961, the Ruffed Grouse Society uses education and leadership to enhance habitat for ruffed grouse, woodcock and other forest-dwelling animals.

Safari Club International
4800 W. Gates Pass Rd.
Tucson, AZ 86745
(602) 620-1220
Est.: 1971   Staff: 40
Members: 30,000
Exec. Dir: Philip L. DeLone
Membership Association for Hunters & Conservationists. Non-Profit

United Conservation Alliance
PO Box 610
Edgefield, SC 29824-0610
(803) 637-5731
Est.: 1991
Chairman: Rocky Evans

Waterfowl USA
Box 50
Edgefield, SC 29824
(803) 637-5767
FAX: (803) 637-6983
Est.: 1983   Staff: 10
Members: 20,000
President: Roger White
Grass roots waterfowl conservation organization funding local waterfowl habitat projects.

Whitetails Unlimited
PO Box 720
Sturgeon Bay, WI 54235
(414) 743-6777
Est.: 1982   Staff: 20
Members: 35,000
CEO: Peter J. Gerl

The Wilderness Society
900 17th St., NW
Washington, DC 20006
(202) 429-2637 (Member Serv.)
Est.: 1935   Staff: 108
Members: 260,000
Pres: Jon Roush

Non-profit membership organization devoted to preserving America's wilderness heritage.

Wildlife Habitat Council
1010 Wayne Ave., Suite 920
Silver Spring, MD 20910
(301) 588-8994
Est.: 1988   Staff: 11
Members: 115
Pres: Joyce M. Kelly
Promotes habitat enhancement on private lands.

Wildlife Management Institute
1101 14th St., NW, Suite 801
Washington, DC 20005
(202) 371-1808
Est.: 1911   Staff: 15
Pres: Rollin D. Sparrowe

The Wildlife Society
5410 Grosvenor Lane
Bethesda, MD 20814
(301) 897-9770
Est.: 1937   Staff: 12
Members: 9,000
Exec. Dir: Harry E. Hodgdon

DOG CLUBS & ASSOCIATIONS

American Kennel Club
5580 Centerview Dr.
Raleigh, NC 27606
(919) 233-9767
Est.: 1884   Staff: 400
Association of dog clubs in U.S. devoted to interest of pure bred dogs.

Bird Dog Foundation, Inc.
PO Box 774, 505 West Hwy. 57
Grand Junction, TN 38039
(901) 764-2058
Staff: 40
Pres: Gary Lockee
The National Bird Dog Museum, The National Field Trial Hall of Fame, and The Wildlife Heritage Center are under the auspices of The Bird Dog Foundation, Inc.

Hunting Retriever Club, Inc.
United Kennel Club, Inc.
100 East Kilgore Rd.
Kalamazoo, MI 49001-5592
(616) 343-9020
Est.: 1984   Staff: 35
Editorial Advisor: Michelle O'Malley
Registering dogs, licensing their events, awarding titles dogs have earned

National Shoot-to-Retrieve Field Trial Association (NSTRA)
226 North Mill St., #2

Plainfield, IN 46168
(317) 839-4059
FAX: (317) 839-4197
Est.: 1979   Staff: 2
President: Marvin Spiller
NSTRA is a non-profit service association dedicated to promoting sportsmanship and the enjoyment of pointing breed dogs through recognized field trial competition.

North American Hunting Retriever Association (NAHRA)
PO Box 1590, Stafford, VA 22555
(703) 221-4911
President: Jack Jagoda

North American Versatile Hunting Dog Association (NAVHDA)
PO Box 520
Arlington Heights, IL 60006
(708) 255-1120
FAX: (708) 253-6488
Est.: 1969   Members: 2,500
Merch. Coor. Roberta Applegate
Educational video & correlating training book - $49.95.

GUN RIGHTS GROUPS

American Shooting Sports Council (ASSC)
10 Perimeter Way, #B-250
Atlanta, GA 30339
(404) 933-0200
Exec. Dir: Richard Feldman
Membership Dir: Tracy Gault
Comm. Dir: Dianne Jones
Cal. Legis. Dir: Robert Ricker

Gun Owners of America
8001 Forbes Pl., Suite 102
Springfield, VA 22151
(703) 321-8585
FAX: (703) 321-8408
Est.: 1975   Staff: 10
Exec. Dir.: Larry Pratt
Pres: H.L. Richardson
The only no-compromise gun lobby in Washington. Members receive newsletters & legislative alerts.

The Hunter's Alliance
205 Main St., PO Drawer B
Stevensville, MT 59870
(406) 777-2521
Exec. Dir: Dale Burk

National Rifle Association of America
11250 Waples Mill Rd.
Fairfax, VA 22030
(703) 267-1000
Est.: 1871   Staff: 517
Exec. VP: Wayne R. LaPierre, Jr.

The Wildlife Legislative Fund of America and The Wildlife Conservation Fund of America
801 Kingsmill Pkwy.
Columbus, OH 43229-1137
(614) 888-4868
FAX: (614) 888-0326
Est.: 1978
Members: 1,500,000
Exec. Dir: Rick Story
Sr. VP: James Goodrich
State Svcs. Dir: Thomas B. Addis
Comm. Dir: Page Lewis
Companion non-profit organizations to protect the heritage of the American sportsman to hunt, fish and trap.

SHOOTING ORGANIZATIONS

Amateur Trapshooting Association (ATA)
601 W. National Rd.
Vandalia, OH 45377
(513) 898-4638
FAX: (513) 898-5472
Est.: 1923   Members: 102,360
Executive Dir: David Bopp

The Clay Pigeon Shooting Association (CPSA)
107 Epping New Rd.
Buckhurst Hill
Essex, England 1G9 5TG
Est.: 1928
011-44-081-5056221
Members: 30,000

Connecticut Travelers Sporting Clays Association (CTSCA)
91 Park Lane Rd.
New Milford, CT 06776
(203) 354-9351
FAX: (203) 354-1762
Est.: 1978   Members: 400
Contact: Al Anglace

Federation Internationale de Tir Aux Armes Sportives de Chasse (FITASC)
10 Rue de Lisbonne Paris
75008 France
011-49-89-531012
Est.: 1921

The International Shooting Union (UIT)
Bavariaring 21, D-80336
Munich 1, Germany
011-49-89-531012
FAX: 011-49-89-5309481
Contact: Franz Schreiber

International Sporting Clays Federation (ISCF)
5 Brighton Parade
Southport 4215
Queensland, Australia
011-61-18-783515

National Skeet Shooting Association (NSSA)
5931 Roft Rd.
San Antonio, TX 78253
(210) 688-3371
FAX: (210) 688-3014
Est.: 1947   Staff: 29

Members: 18,000
Exec. Dir: Mike Hampton
Ass't. Dir: Eric Beckmann
National governing body of American Skeet

National Sporting Clays Association (NSCA)
5931 Roft Rd.
San Antonio, TX 78253
(210) 688-3371
FAX: (210) 688-3014
Est.: 1989   Staff: 29
Members: 12,000
Exec. Dir.: Mike Hampton
Member Services: Lois Lessing
Chief Instructor: John Higgins

New England Sporting Clays Association (NESCA)
441 Rose Hill Rd.
Peace Dale, RI 02879

Director: Tony Haigh
(603) 878-1257
President: Richie Frisella
(401) 789-3730
NESCA Shoot Schedule Hotline:
(401) 783-9330

Sporting Clays of America (SCA)
33 South Main St.
Norwalk, CT 06854
(203) 831-8483
FAX: (203) 831-8497
Est.: 1985
Members: 5,000
Pres: Fred G. Collins
VP/Club Div: Meylert Armstrong
VP/Nat'l Tourn. Dir: Timothy Nichols
Treas./Sec: Barbara Schaefer
See Our Ad Below Left

U.S. Shooting Team
Office of Junior Development
PO Box 3207
Brentwood, TN 37024-3207
(615) 831-0485
(615) 834-2632
Director: Leo R. Lujan
Established by USSTF and supported by industry to attract youth to the shooting sports and to assure that they receive competent entry level training.

USA Shooting
One Olympic Plaza
Colorado Springs, CO 80909
(719) 578-4670
Director of Admin.: Ray Carter
USA Shooting is the national governing body for the sport of Olympic style shooting.

Women's Shooting Sports Foundation (WSSF)
1505 Hwy. 6 South, Suite 101
Houston, TX 77077
(713) 584-9907
FAX: (713) 584-9874
Est.: 1993   Staff: 3
Exec. Dir: Sue King
Exec. VP/Programs & Mbrshp:
Glynne Moseley
Exec. VP/Finance: Ann C. Ballard
...to provide information, education, create opportunities, and to serve as the collective voice for women's shooting sports interests.
See Our Ad Right

TRADE ASSOCIATIONS

American Custom Gunmakers Guild
PO Box 812
Burlington, IA 52601
(319) 752-6114 (Phone/Fax)
Est.: 1983
Exec. Dir: Jan Billeb

F.A.I.R. Trade Group
Firearms Importers Roundtable
PO Box 25767
Alexandria, VA 22313
(703) 684-8232
FAX: (703) 684-8233
Est.: 1994   Staff: 1
Deputy Director: Craig Dowd

Firearms Engravers Guild of America
332 Vine St.
Oregon City, OR 97045
(503) 656-5693
Sec: Robert Evans

Hunter Education Association
PO Box 347
Jamestown, CO 80455
(303) 449-0631
FAX: (303) 449-0576

Members: 2,000
Exec. VP: David M. Knotts
To establish safe, responsible and knowledgeable hunters.

National Alliance of Stocking Gun Dealers
PO Box 187
Havelock, NC 28532
(919) 447-1313
Exec. Dir: Bill Bridgewater

National Association of Sporting Goods Wholesalers
PO Box 11344
Chicago, IL 60611
(312) 565-0233
Est.: 1954
Exec. Dir: Rebecca A. Maddy

National Hunters Association, Inc.
9312 US Hwy. 64E
PO Box 820
Knightdale, NC 27545
(919) 365-7157
Est.: 1976
President: D.V. Smith
Education: Hunting Skills; Firearm Safety; Wilderness Survival; Outdoor Ethics.

National Reloading Manufacturers Association
One Centerpointe Dr., #300
Lake Oswego, OR 97035
See Our Ad Pg. 146

National Shooting Sports Foundation
Flintlock Ridge Office Center
11 Mile Hill Rd.
Newtown, CT 06470
(203) 426-1320
Est.: 1961   Staff: 21
Members: 1,200
Pres: Robert T. Delfay
Membership: J. Mannuzza
The NSSF is the shooting industry's trade organization. Since 1961, our mission has been to promote a better understanding of and more active participation in the shooting sports. Through positive publicity and education programs, NSSF strives to present the facts about recreational shooting to the non-shooting public.

(SHOTGUNNER'S SOURCE)

What Makes NAGA Preserves Special?

- NAGA Preserves abide by the Association's "Standards Of Excellence" and "Code of Ethics", making NAGA Preserves the preserves to call first.

- NAGA Preserves are serious about providing quality outdoor experiences. They are professionals continually striving to improve their establishments.

- There is a wide array of NAGA preserves to choose from. Each offers their own unique blend of style and atmosphere, making it easier to find one that suits your individual taste and budget.

WHAT IS NAGA?

The North American Gamebird Association (NAGA) is a non-profit trade organization, established in 1931.

For more than 63 years, NAGA members have "led the field" in improving methods of gamebird production and hunting preserve management.

JOIN TODAY!

Members receive a monthly magazine, "Wildlife Harvest". Each issue (80-88 pages) is filled with timely information, helpful "how to" articles on cover plantings, bird dogs, gamebird production, issues and developments.

Annual dues include, the monthly magazine, a directory of all NAGA members, and for preserves, a free listing in NAGA's Directory of Hunting Resorts.

Note: Special Liability Insurance available exclusively to NAGA preserves and sporting clays ranges.

For FREE Information contact:

NAGA (North American Gamebird Association)
PO Box 2105
Cayce, SC 29171
Phone 803/796-8163

Visa/ Mastercard Service, Phone: Wildlife Harvest Publications 319/242-3046

National Taxidermists Association
108 Branch Dr.
Slidell, LA 70461
(504) 641-4682
Est.: 1971
Exec. Dir: Greg Crain
Official information clearinghouse for the taxidermy industry.

North American Gamebird Association
PO Box 2105
Cayce-West Columbia, SC 29171
(803) 796-8163
FAX: (803) 791-0982
Est.: 1900　　Staff: 2
Exec. Dir.: Walter S. Walker
Pres: Charles Mann
The North American Gamebird Association (NAGA) is a non-profit trade organization, established in 1931. For more than 63 years, NAGA members have "led the field" in improving methods of gamebird production and hunting preserve management. JOIN TODAY! Members receive a monthly magazine, "Wildlife Harvest". Each issue (80-88 pgs.) is filled with timely information, helpful "how to" articles on cover plantings, bird dogs, gamebird production, issues and developments. Annual dues include the monthly magazine, a directory of all NAGA members; and for preserves, a free listing in NAGA's Directory of Hunting Resorts.
See Our Ad Across

Outdoor Guides Assn. of North America
PO Box 12996
Tallahassee, FL 32317-2996
(904) 668-4957
Est.: 1991
Members: 2,000
Exec. Dir.: Casey Madigan

Outdoor Writers Assn. of America (OWAA)
2017 Cato Ave., #101
State College, PA 16801-2768
(814) 234-1011
Est.: 1927　　Staff: 5
Members: 2,000
Exec. Dir: James W. Rainey
Pres: Mark LaBarbera
Public. Editor: C.J. Kersavage

Sporting Arms & Ammunition Manufacturers Institute (SAAMI)
11 Mile Hill Rd.
Flintlock Ridge Office Center
Newtown, CT 06470
(203) 426-4358
Est.: 1926
Pres: Robert T. Delfray
Represents major manufacturers of sporting firearms and ammunition.

BOOKSELLERS

Outdoor writer—and book lover—Tom McIntyre thinks the "serious" hunting book may well be headed the "way of the buffalo and the heath hen". To prove his point he suggests a modest experiment: Walk into your local bookshop and ask for the hunting section. Don't be surprised, McIntyre warns, if your request is met with silence—if not open hostility. Fact is, most bookstores don't have one. Why? Political correctness and anti-hunting sentiment have been suggested as possible explanations. But whatever the reason, fortunately, there is an alternative: the thriving catalog and mail-order sportsman's booksellers. Whether the title's a new one or old, a classic of its genre or a workaday handbook, if the companies listed here can't get it for you, it probably "can't be got".

Angler's & Shooter's Bookshelf
PO Box 178, Goshen, CT 06756
(203) 491-2500
Est.: 1967
Available: Direct
Catalog Available-$5.00. 4,000 hunting & fishing books; new, used, rare & collector's books.

Blacksmith Corporation
830 N. Road 1 East
Box 1752, Chino Valley, AZ 86323
(602) 636-4456
FAX: (602) 636-4457
Est.: 1975　　Staff: 5
Contact: Nancy Padua
Available: Retail & Direct
Books and videos pertaining to guns, hunting & outdoors

Judith Bowman Books
Pound Ridge Rd.
Bedford, NY 10506
(914) 234-7543
Est.: 1979　　Staff: 2
Contact: Judith Bowman
Mail Order Only – Hunting & Fishing Books
See Our Ad Above

Countrysport
15 S. High St.
PO Box 166
New Albany, OH 43054-0166
(800) 367-4114
(615) 855-1000
President: Charles Fry
Dir. of Editorial: Doug Truax
Available: Retail & Direct
Sold through catalog - hard cover hunting classics, historical & geographic
See Our Ad Pg. 131

James Cummins Booksellers

699 Madison Ave.,
New York, NY 10021
(212) 688-6441
Est.: 1978   Staff: 4
Contact: James Cummins
All types of antiquarian & sporting books; Old & new sporting art. Catalogues issued.

Duckett's Sporting Books

1968 E. Carson Dr.,
Tempe, AZ 85282
(602) 345-2698
Est.: 1987   Staff: 2
Contact: Randy Duckett
Firearms; edged weapons; hunting, fishing, out-of-print and new books. Search service. Buy-trade-sell. Catalog $5.00.

Gary L. Estabrook - Books

PO Box 61453
Vancouver, WA 98666
(360) 699-5454
Est.: 1972   Staff: 1
Owner: Gary L. Estabrook
Fine sporting books & fly fishing, salmon fishing, trout fishing, upland shooting, duck shooting, B.G. hunting, etc. Over 30,000 books in stock.

Fair Chase, Inc.

S1118 Hwy. HH
Lyndon Station,
WI 53944
(800) 762-2843
(608) 524-9677
Est.: 1982   Staff: 1
Contact: Carol Lueder
Available: Direct
Fine sporting books, new and out-of-print.
We offer regular cata-

logs and prompt service. Also, Filson and Barbour clothing. Please call us when you are looking for:
* Big Game Hunting Books
* Wingshooting Books
* Sporting Clays and Shotgun Books
* Fine Collector's Editions
See Our Ad Below

Fin & Feather Gallery

PO Box 13
North Granby, CT 06060
(203) 653-6557
Contact: Barry or Jerry Small

David Foley

76 Bonnyview Rd.
West Hartford, CT 06107
(203) 561-0783
Est.: 1987   Staff: 1
Contact: David Foley
Available: Retail & Direct
Catalog available; primarily out-of-print hunting, fishing, archery, and firearms books.

Gunnerman Books

PO Box 214292
Auburn Hills, MI 48321
(810) 879-2779
FAX: (810) 879-3235
Est.: 1978
Contact: Carol Barnes
Hunting, Big Game, Upland, Duck, Gun Books, In Print & Out of Print

Hungry Horse Books

4605 Hwy. 93 South
Whitefish, MT 59937
(406) 862-7997
FAX: (406) 862-6134
Est.: 1992   Staff: 2
Contact: Mike Renner or Patsy Lightner
Books on firearms, edged weap-

ons, gunsmithing, handloading, African safaris, hunting, competition shooting & out-of-print titles.

Inquisitive Sportsman Books

PO Box 1811
Granite Falls, WA 98252
(360) 691-7540 (Phone/Fax)
Contact: Stephen P. Gill
Available: Direct
Fine uncommon, scarce, out-of-print and rare hunting and fishing books. Wingshooting, big game, small game, fly-fishing, deep sea, etc.

Inter-Sports Book & Video

790 W. Tennessee Ave.
Denver, CO 80223
(800) 456-5842
FAX: (800) 279-9196
Marketing: Johnny J. Jones
America's largest assortment of hunting, fly-fishing and archer books, maps and videos. Please call for our 80-page catalog describing 1500 titles (retail outlets only).

Larsen's Outdoor Publishing

2640 Elizabeth Place
Lakeland, FL 33813
(813) 644-3381
Est.: 1986   Staff: 3
Contact: Larry Larsen
Available: Retail & Direct
Publishers of numerous hunting titles; order direct or through retailers.

Pisces & Capricorn Books

514 Linden Ave.
Albion, MI 49224
(517) 629-3267
Est.: 1975   Staff: 1
Contact: Claire & Joe Wilcox

Available: Retail & Direct
Out-of-print books, sporting books, search service, Notable British Trail Series offering 1,000+ entries

Ray Riling Arms Books Co.
6844 Gorsten St.
Philadelphia, PA 19119
(215) 438-2456
Contact: Joseph Riling
Used and rare books

Sunrise Publishing Co.
481 Route 45 South
Austinburg, OH 44010
(216) 275-1310
Est.: 1992
Contact: Duke Biscotti
Available: Direct Mail Order
We specialize in unusual, rare and limited edition sporting books as well as sporting bibliographies. We are active buyers and sellers–send for free catalog: 481 Rt. 45 S., Austinburg, OH 44010 (216) 275-1310.

Wilderness Adventures Sporting Books
PO Box 1410
Bozeman, MT 59771
(800) 925-3339
FAX: (406) 763-4911
Contact: Chuck Johnson
Available: Retail & Direct
Fine sporting books for the collector and enthusiast.

CARTS

Big Shot
Shotgunner's Caddy
3227 Auburn St.
Rockford, IL 61101
(815) 962-6788
Est.: 1979
Contact: Marvin Conrad
Type: Hand
Big Shot shotgunner's caddy looks like a shotgun shell, made of impact resistant PVC with a durable high gloss acrylic finish. Lightweight with 4 compartments; fits most golf carts.

EZ-Shooter Carts
Pavo Welding Shop
N. Main St., PO Box 52
Pavo, GA 31778
(912) 859-2075 (Day)
(912) 859-2162 (Eve.)

Contact: Buddy Lewis
Type: Motorized
EZ-Shooter Carts are 4 wheel golf carts (gas or electric), customized for sporting shooters. Also available- custom built EZ-Load Trailers. Call for more information.

Gun/Buggy

Clay Toons
109.5 Clay St., Suffolk, VA 23434
(800) 677-3201
(804) 934-0136
FAX: (804) 934-6151
Contact: Jennifer Beigle
Available: Direct
Type: Hand
Gun/Buggy is lightweight, holds shotguns, shells, chokes, plus a compartment for miscellaneous items. Standard, oak and walnut models available. Comes with a 3-year limited warranty. Dealer inquiries welcomed.
See Our Ad Below

The Jackass
Ziegel Engineering
2108 Lomina Ave.
Long Beach, CA 90815
(310) 596-9481
FAX: (310) 598-4734
Est.: 1972   Staff: 10
Contact: Dean Ziegel
Available: Retail & Direct
Type: Hand
Heavy duty aluminum field cart for transporting rifles & shotguns. A

must for the competitor. Also the largest manufacturer of aluminum gun cases. Visa/Mastercard accepted.

The Rhino
Sportscar
4960 SW 52nd St., #408
Davie, FL 33314
(800) 226-3613
(305) 797-0600
FAX: (305) 797-9350
Est.: 1988
Contact: Janet Morales or Joe Morales
Available: Direct
Type: Hand
The Rhino Sportscar is made of all-aluminum construction: The base is anodized aluminum in either red, blue or black with a rubber matt on the bottom where shells, a cooler or a shooting bag may be carried. Two shotguns are carried in a vertical coated gun bracket. (the Cart may be converted to carry rifles for the competitive shooter). The tires are all-terrain with zirk fittings to keep them rolling smoothly through any course. The handle is in two parts fastened with wing nuts for easy assembly and storage. The barrels rest in U-brackets with latches attached to the top of the handle. The Sportscar weighs only about 18 pounds fully assembled and pulls easily.
See Our Ad Pg 113

Seminole Chokes & Gun Works

Mitchell Machine & Mfg., Inc.
3049 US 1
Mims, FL 32754
(407) 383-8556
FAX: (407) 383-8532
Est.: 1989   Staff: 6
Contact: Janice Mitchell or Randy Mitchell
Type: Hand
Seminole Travelcarts are made of durable aluminum tread plate, measuring 16"x24"x16". The Travelcart carries two guns and assembles in 60 seconds. In stock and ready for delivery.

J.M. Caldwell Co., Inc's

**ULTIMATE
SHOOTING CART
& TRAILER**

The Ultimate Shooting Cart

J.M. Caldwell Co., Inc.
322 East Turner Lane
West Chester, PA 19380
(800) 890-8872
(610) 436-9997
FAX: (610) 436-9957
President: Jim Caldwell
Available: Direct
Type: Motorized
J.M. Caldwell Co., Inc. understands the needs of the shooting clay sportsman. We have now introduced our customized Ultimate Shooting Cart for those of you who appreciate convenience as well as performance. Designed by Jim Caldwell, a dedicated sporting clays enthusiast, this cart offers you the ability to move with ease between stations, eliminating the need to carry heavy bags. Whether you enjoy sporting clays competition, claybird or range shooting, the Ultimate Shooting Cart is tailored to suit your every need and budget, ranging from $1995 to $4995.

See Our Ad Below

RACKS

The Gun Rest

Vee Dennis Mfg.
620 Park Rd.
Cherry Hill, NJ 08034
(609) 428-7676
Contact: Rich Lang

MTM Case-Gard

PO Box 14117
Dayton, OH 45414
(513) 890-7461
FAX: (513) 890-1747
Contact: Al Minneman
Available: Retail
PRO-1: A portable utility platform designed to hold up to 4 guns, several boxes of shells and various accessories.

VEHICLE ACCESSORIES

Ainley Kennels & Fabrication

1945 Washington St.
Dubuque, IA 52001-3664
(319) 583-7615
Contact: Jane Ainley
Custom dog trucks, trailers, bird boxes & dog crates

Aluma Sport by Dee Zee

PO Box 3090
Des Moines, IA 50316
(800) 798-9899 (Cust. Service)
(515) 265-7331
FAX: (515) 265-7926
Est.: 1978   Staff: 400
Contact: Chuck Long
Available: Retail
Cruise around in the best looking vehicle. From a complete series of Running Boards to Roof Racks, Dee Zee offers you quality products designed to enhance your vehicle's appearance. Style enhancers. Reinforce your truck bed

while adding classic styling to your vehicles with our side bed caps, tailgate protectors and rails. Choose your favorite from our selection of sturdy tube products. To obtain information on a dealer nearest you or a free brochure call 1-800-730-4665.

See Our Ad Below Left

Creative Sports Supply
PO Box 765
Attalla, AL 35954
(205) 442-5244
Est.: 1968
Contact: Jerry Collett
Available: Direct
Aluminum dog crates–designed to last. Custom service available. Write for a free catalog.

Jones Trailer Company
PO Box 288
Woodson, TX 76491
(800) 336-0360
(817) 345-6759
FAX: (817) 345-6505
Contact: Patsy Jones

Quail Buggy
Box 1222
Perry, GA 31069
(800) 27P-EACH
(912) 987-7216
Contact: Vic Correll
Available: Direct
The Quail Buggy is designed with the bird hunter in mind: gun racks, 4-dog compartments, bird box and other features.

Versatile Rack Company
5761 Anderson St.
Vernon, CA 90058
(213) 588-0137
FAX: (213) 588-5067
Est.: 1978
Contact: John Cardenas
Available: Retail & Direct

Shell caddies to organize & transport shells. Our steel wire basket carries up to 4 boxes of 12 gauge shells & over 100 spent shells. Also available are fence mounted shell caddies, which come with a gun receiver to hold your gun between rounds. It also carries up to 4 boxes of 12 gauge shells & has a pouch which holds 100 spent shells. A vehicle gun rack is also available.

See Our Ad Below Right

SHOTGUNNER'S SOURCE

CHOKES

For related products & services
• *See Gunsmiths Pg. 120*

Angle Porting
Ballistic Specialties
100 Industrial Dr.
Batesville, AR 72501
(800) 276-2550
FAX: (501) 793-7933
Est.: 1991   Staff: 4
President: John Clouse
Available: Retail & Direct
Custom chokes built specifically for your gun.

Stan Baker
10000 Lake City Way
Seattle, WA 98125
(206) 522-4575
Contact: Stan Baker
Available: Direct
Barrels with factory screw-in chokes - Browning, Beretta, Rem-ington, etc. converted to our competition choke.

Briley Manufacturing
1230 Lumpkin
Houston, TX 77043
(800) 331-5718 (Cust. Service)
(713) 932-6995
FAx: (713) 932-1043
Est.: 1976   Staff: 65
Contact: Chuck Webb
Available: Retail & Direct
The only source for in-line, concentric, true-to-the-bore installation of chokes. Briley installs the world famous long choke in all makes and gauges using special long geometry for improved patterns. Steel or lead shot capability in nine true constrictions gives all shooters maximum flexibility. For the shooter who has a gun with factory screw-in's, Briley has the answer in their BRC line of factory replacement chokes; Knurled or flush in nine constrictions they will give superior performance at factory prices. In stock for immediate delivery. New for choke designed with the turkey hunter in mind. For all factory guns with screw-in chokes. Call for brochure.
See Our Ad Pg. 27

Clear View Products, Inc.
3021 N. Portland
Oklahoma City, OK 73107
(405) 943-9222
Est.: 1975
Contact: Larry Nailon
Available: Direct
Custom screw in chokes; Load development & Shot string measurement.

The world's finest shotgun screw-in choke tubes.

Name your target or quarry and Colonial has what you're looking for: sporting clay tubes, flushmounted lead shot, extended steel shot, turkey, rifled and cardshooting tubes.

• *Screw-in tubes for 10, 12, 16, 20, 28 and .410 gauges*
• *Flushmounted lead shot (all gauges), knurled end sporting clays (12 & 20 ga.), extended steel shot (10, 12, 16 & 20 ga.), turkey (10, 12 & 20 ga.), cardshooting (12 ga.), rifled (12 & 20 ga.), and gunsmith blank (10, 12, 16 & 20 ga.)*
• *Choke tubes are available in true-size after market (all gauges), thin wall after market (12 ga.), Remington/Remchoke (10, 12 & 20 ga.), Invector/Winchoke (12 & 20 ga.), and various other systems too numerous to list.*

Contact your local dealer for help in choosing the choke tube that's right for your needs. Or, if one is unavailable, call Colonial for direct shipment.

(334) 872-9455 • Fax (334) 872-9540

 P.O. Box 636 • Selma, AL 36702

Colonial Arms, Inc.
1109 C Singleton Dr.
PO Box 636
Selma, AL 36702
(334) 872-9455
FAX: (334) 872-9540
Est.: 1989   Staff: 10
Advtg. Dir: Traci Denson
Available: Retail
Screw-in shotgun choke tubes and installation tooling and accessories. Colonial Arms offers the shooting enthusiast a full line of the world's finest 10, 12, 16, 20, 28, and .410 gauge shotgun screw-in choke tubes. Name your target or quarry and Colonial has what you're looking for: sporting clays tubes, flushmounted lead shot, extended steel shot, turkey, rifled and cardshooting tubes. The knurled ends of our sporting clays tubes extend about 3/8" past the end of the barrel for easy changeability. Available in cylinder, skeet 1, improved cylinder, modified and full constrictions for the 12 gauge true size and thin wall after market installations, Invector, Remington, Invector Plus and Beretta Systems. Also, available for the 20 gauge true size after market installation, Invector and Remington systems. Contact your local dealer or, if one is unavailable, call or write Colonial for a list of dealers in your area.
See Our Ad Left

DAYSON ARMS, LTD.

Dayson Arms, Ltd.
PO Box 532, 511 Willow
Vincennes, IN 47591
(812) 882-8680
FAX: (812) 882-6226
Est.: 1993   Staff: 11
Contact: Gary Ciluffo or
Louie Dayson
Available: Retail & Direct
Patented ABS ventilated chokes
will provide a tighter shot pattern
and reduce recoil and muzzle jump
by up to 25%. Increase recoil reduction up to 60% by using our
patented muzzle break. Our tubes
fit most guns and are available in
12 & 10 gauge.

Pete Elsen, Inc.
Parabolic Chokes
1529 S. 113th St.
West Allis, WI 53214
(414) 476-4660
Est.: 1982
Owner: Pete Elsen
Available: Direct
Screw-in chokes

Hastings

Hastings
320 Court St., PO Box 224
Clay Center, KS 67432
(913) 632-3169
Est.: 1985
President: Robert Rott
Available: Retail
One of the largest selections of
choke tubes on the market; includes standard flush mounted
chokes, Hastings Turkey Chokes;
extended chokes for steel shot;
and the new QC choke line consisting of 13 different constrictions for
precise pattern control. All Hastings chokes are available to fit
most popular choke systems.
See Our Ad Right

Kick's Komps
Kick's Industries, Inc.
698 Magnolia Rd., Rt. 1, Box 71D
Statesboro, GA 30458
(912) 587-2779
FAX: (912) 587-2745
Est.: 1994   Staff: 5
Contact: Bob Bryan or Vickie Deal
Available: Retail & Direct
Featuring angle-ported specialty
screw-in chokes for serious
shotgunning folks.
Our unique directional angled port-

ing markedly improves patterns by
stopping wad spin and by peeling
the wad away from the shot which
allows the shot string to fly less dis-
turbed. Also, because of diffusion
of gasses through the ports the reduction of both muzzle jump and
recoil improve follow-up shots.
Your shooting buddies will appreciate our chokes because there is
less significant side blast than with
chokes that have parts of 90 degrees or less. We offer a complete
line of specialty hunting and clay
target chokes to satisfy even the
most discriminating of sportsmen.
Manufactured in true-to-bore constrictions and available for most
shotgun models.
See Our Ad Following Page

POLY-CHOKE®

Marble Arms/Poly-Choke
CRL, Inc.
PO Box 111
Gladstone, MI 49837
(906) 428-3710
FAX: (906) 428-3711
Est.: 1898   Staff: 15
President: Craig R. Lauerman
Available: Retail (Factory direct on installed products)
If you want nine different choke settings and no loose choke tubes or wrenches, yet spend under $100, look at Poly-Choke, the original adjustable choke tube. Marble Arms will install the Poly-Choke on any 12, 16, 20 or 28-gauge pump, auto or single barrel shotgun. Just twist the sleeve to select chokes from X-Full to Open Cylinder and choose any pattern in between. Great for hunting or sporting clays, trap and skeet. Standard and ventilated styles. Marble Arms also offers a wide selection of shotgun sights for single or double barrel shotguns. High quality front and mid sights are available in bead, Bradley, Xpert and Bev-L-Blok styles in gold, ivory, red and sunspot colors. To improve accuracy, Marble Arms installs anodized, ventilated shotgun ribs for all single and over/under barrels, complete with front and mid sights. Free catalog.

See Our Ad Pg. 79

Kick's Komps™ Angle Ported Screw In Chokes

Featuring Specialty Chokes For SERIOUS Shotgunning Folks.

Offering a full line of hunting and clay target chokes that markedly improve patterns and reduce muzzle jump and recoil.

Hunting chokes available in a matte black finish and a wide range of constrictions: Wing Shooter for small and large game bird hunting; High Flyer steel shot tubes for waterfowl; Gobblin Thunder for turkey hunting; Deer hunting chokes described below.

Smoke
•"Smoke" clay target chokes available in a wide range of constrictions to suit all needs including those for sporting clays, skeet and trap. Angling of parts away from shooter reduces muzzle blast which trap and 5 stand partners will appreciate. Offered in polished stainless steel. Blued finish available.

High Flyer

Wing Shooter

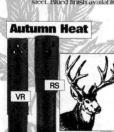

Autumn Heat

Just In Time For The '95 Season

Buckshot Choke

Gobblin' Thunder

• Autumn Heat - a ported rifled choke tube that improves both slug placement & accuracy, available in rifle sight & vent rib models.

•Easily converts most 10 or 12 gauge threaded barrels •No choke tube wrench required for installation •Available for most models including Browning, Beretta, Benelli, Rem-Choke, Win Choke, Mossberg, Ruger, & Krieghoff.

Kicks Industries, Inc.

698 Magnolia Church Road, Route 1, Box 71-D Statesboro, GA 30458

To Order (912) 587•2779   Fax (912) 587•2745
Dealer Inquiries Weclome!

Nuline Guns, Inc.
1053 Caulks Hill Rd.
Dept. 2800
Harvester, MO 63304
(314) 441-4500
FAX: (314) 447-5018
Est.: 1949   Staff: 17
Contact: B.J. Stevens
Available: Retail & Direct
Backed by over 25 years of research and development, our custom designed choke tubes greatly reduce stress on the barrel by placing the actual constriction portion outside of it. These screw-in choke tubes are made from heat-treated stainless steel, colored in "heat treat blue," and will fit most threaded barrels. Designed to provide patterns of such density and uniformity as to meet each hunter's and target shooter's demands, including:

* Duck Hunters
* Turkey Hunters
* Card Shooters
* Skeet, Trap & Sporting Clays Enthusiasts

Call or write today for complete details and ordering information.

RHINO.

Rhino Chokes
4960 SW 52nd, #408
Davie, FL 33314
(800) 226-3613
(305) 797-0600
FAX: (305) 797-9350
Est.: 1988
Contact: Janet Morales or Joe Morales
The Rhino Choke is a revolutionary new design. The unique longer design has a wad stripping action yielding a 20% more effective pattern than a standard screw-in choke. It reduces muzzle jump by 15% and also reduces recoil. Made of high grade stainless steel that will not rust or corrode, no wrench needed. Call for prices and models.

See Our Ad Pg. 113

Seminole Chokes & Gun Works
Mitchell Machine & Mfg., Inc.
3049 US 1
Mims, FL 32754
(800) 980-3344
FAX: (407) 383-8532
Est.: 1989   Staff: 6

Contact: Janice Mitchell or
Randy Mitchell
Available: Retail & Direct
Seminole Chokes: 9 true constric-
tions, each color coded for easy
I.D. Tubes are designed to pre-
cisely fit barrel bore. Reasonably
priced.
See Our Ad Below

Wright's
(The Model 12 Shop)
RR3, Box 414
Pinckneyville, IL 62274
(618) 357-8933
Est.: 1980   Staff: 5
Contact: Stu Wright
Available: Direct
SUPERIOR TRAP CHOKES: the permanent modification of factory
chokes to improve pattern diameters and to even density, also
benefits SKEET and SPORTING
CLAYS. Complete repair and restoration of Winchester shotguns,
Browning Competition shotguns,
and Perazzis. Competition triggers
installed, recoil pads installed, ribs
resoldered, five different blueing
techniques. Reliable service of custom handcrafted quality.

CHOKE WRENCHES

B □ SQUARE

B-SQUARE
2708 St. Louis Ave., PO Box 11281
Forth Worth, TX 76110
(800) 433-2909
(817) 923-0964
Est.: 1957
Contact: Rudy Bechtel
Available: Retail & Direct
Texas Twister speed wrench for
12 gauge shotguns. Call for free
catalog.
See Our Ad Below

**Jeffrey Choke Tube
Wrenches**
PO Box 52, Bradford, OH 45308
(513) 448-2502
Est.: 1991   Staff: 3
Pres: Jeff Fashner
Available: Retail & Direct
Speed wrench for changing choke
tubes. Developed originally with
sporting clays in mind.

K.L. Engineering
1190 Knollwood Circle
Anaheim, CA 92801
(714) 870-8629
FAX: (714) 828-6011
Est.: 1985   Staff: 3
Owner: Ray Longerot
Available: Retail & Direct
All metal wrench/container works
like a screwdriver storing chokes
end to end in its aluminum handle.

Quick-Choke
PO Box 412878
Kansas City, MO 64141
(317) 453-1024
Est.: 1989   Staff: 1
Contact: David Dyer
Available: Retail & Direct
Patented wrench for changing
choke tubes. Universally fits all guns.

**The Royal Choke Tube
Wrench**
9921 4th Ave., Brooklyn, NY 11209
(718) 833-6605
Est.: 1991
President: Stavros Mavraki
Available: Retail & Direct
The Royal Choke Tube Wrench securely locks into the choke tube,
thus eliminating any damage to
the choke tube or gun.

TUBE SETS

BRILEY

Briley Manufacturing
1230 Lumpkin
Houston, TX 77043
(800) 331-5718 (Cust. Service)
(713) 932-6995
Est.: 1976   Staff: 65
Contact: Chuck Webb
Available: Retail & Direct
Tube sets made for any 12 ga. or
20 ga. O/U or SxS. Order by the
pair or in sets. Screw-in chokes included at no additional charge
with 12, 20 & 410. Briley tube sets
have a lifetime warranty and a lifetime choke exchange policy on the
tube set. The exclusive Briley Ultra-
Light tube set, 10 oz. the pair. This
set reduces weight by 30% and improves balance and second shot
recovery. Long forcing cones are a
standard item in Ultra-Lights "Ultimate" as is straight rifling for wad
control and reduced flyer pellets.
Call for brochure. New for 1995–
"Companion" 28 ga. drop-in tube
sets. No fitting required for all 12
ga. O/U or SxS. Sets for 26", 28" &
30" in stock for immediate delivery.
See Our Ad Pg. 31

Kolar Arms
1925 Roosevelt Ave.,
Racine, WI 53406
(414) 554-0800
Est.: 1968   Staff: 46
Partner: Don Mainland
Partner/Pres: John Ramagli
Available: Retail & Direct
Standard or Kolarlite small gauge
tubes available; All popular gauges

COURSE DESIGNERS

The Key To Success

As many a failed operator will attest, the sheer popularity of sporting clays alone will not guarantee the success of any particular course. Nor will a great location and a barrel full of good intentions overcome poor course design. Thus, as a prerequisite for success, the conversion of an old course, or the establishment of a new one, calls for careful choice of a course designer.

Opinions vary about the best time to hire the designer. Some experienced sporting clays owners say that, if possible, the decision to hire a course designer should come only after you have secured--or are reasonably certain of securing--the needed approvals to open your course from local and state authorities . Others point out that in certain areas of the country, it is nearly impossible to get those approvals unless you already have a detailed plan.

What approvals are needed? And how do you make your way through the bureaucratic maze of zoning laws and environmental protection regulations? Pre-planning is critical. Obviously, you must know the local and state rules that govern the operation of a sporting clays course before you can get written approval.

When the time comes to select a designer, how do you pick a good one? The profile of a good designer might include experience, reputation and knowledge of all aspects of a club owner's business. Experience is self-explanatory--almost. At the very least your designer's credentials should include the planning and supervision of other sporting clays projects.

In addition, many course designers can help you secure funds, in many instances outright grants, that are available from federal, state and local governments for shooting fields. Finally, reputation means your designer has worked to the satisfaction of other owners. Ask for references and check them. And, if practical, visit one or two of a candidate's courses in person .

Knowledge of your business is important because a savvy designer will function not only as a course layout expert, but also as a consultant. He'll be able to advise on how to gain market share, how to achieve growth, how to purchase trap machines [see the Trap Manufacturer's Section for more information] and other equipment economically. The designer will also share his knowledge of how to organize leagues and conduct tournaments.

Finally, the more you know, the more you'll get out of your designer. Educate yourself: Read everything you can about the sport and course design [see box below]. Visit and shoot established courses as often as possible. Study their layouts. Attend shoots and tournaments regularly. And then by choosing and collaborating with a qualified designer you'll gain a course that takes full advantage of all topographical features, emphasizes safety and introduces a variety of challenges that make shooting fun for all--and profitable for you.

Books & Manuals That Can Help

Wending your way through the sporting clays course planning and approval process can be daunting. Fortunately, the publications listed below--published by some of the most prestigious organizations associated with the sport--provide much of the information you need to do a thorough job of planning and design.

Developing New Places to Shoot
Published by the National Shooting Sports Foundation, Flintlock Ridge Office Center, 11 Mile Hill Rd., Newtown, CT 06470; (203) 426-1320; Cost: $1.00.

NRA Range Manual
Published by the National Rifle Association, 11250 Waples Mill Road, Fairfax, VA 22030; (800) 336-7402; Order No.: 14840; Cost: $49.95.

Sporting Clays Course Design & Layout Package
Published by *Sporting Clays* magazine, 5211 S. Washington Ave., Titusville, FL 32780; (407) 268-5010; Cost: $59.95 plus shipping.

Sporting Clays Gun Club Manual
Published by the National Sporting Clays Association, P.O. Box 680007, San Antonio, TX 78268; (210) 688-3371; Cost: $25.00 plus shipping and handling.

COURSE DESIGNERS

British Sporting Arms
RR1, Box 193A
Millbrook, NY 12545
(914) 677-8303
Est.: 1988   Staff: 2
Contact: Charles Schneible
10 years experience in the U.K.
and USA in course design.

Neil Chadwick
206 Front St.
Milford, PA 18337
(717) 296-2354
FAX: (717) 296-8639
Contact: Neil Chadwick
Courses built on the European De-

sign. 15 years experience. FITASC
course design.

Clay Games, Inc.
55 Lane 240 Big Otter Lake
Fremont, IN 46737
(219) 833-6645
FAX: (219) 833-6649
Est.: 1993
President: Joel Werner
See Our Ad Pg. 240

Clay-Sport International, Inc.
Box 663, Bragg Creek
Alberta, Canada T0L 0K0
(403) 949-3654
Contact: Raymond Forman
The inventor of 5-STAND SPORT-
ING®, Raymond Forman, gives

advice on the game that no one
else can. With 24 years of international shooting and design
experience, he creates a fun atmosphere to attract shooters and
their families, whether for fun
shoots, corporate days or world
championships. The drawings from
his 3-dimensional computer draw-
ing system have proven highly
successful in eliminating zoning
and construction headaches. He offers advice on the best equipment,
and shows you how to market and
manage your range effectively.
And make a profit!
See Our Ad Below Left

Custom Shooting Sports
6970 Somers-Gratis Rd.
Camden, OH 45311
(513) 787-3352
Est.: 1984
Contact: Jim Arnold

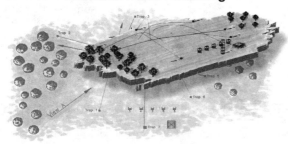

Griffin & Howe

Griffin & Howe
33 Claremont Rd.
Bernardsville, NJ 07924
(908) 766-2287
Contact: Joe Prather
Griffin & Howe's experienced staff
has designed courses in the United
States and Europe. We will be
pleased to discuss your requirements for a first class facility.
See Our Ad Pg. 25

Grinders Switch Club
1608 Chickering Rd.
Nashville, TN 37215
(615) 729-9732
Contact: Barry Claud
John Woolley is recognized as the
world's leading course designer,
having been responsible for numerous World and International
Championship courses, as well as
many private courses.

John Higgins
NSCA - 5931 Roft Rd.
San Antonio, TX 78253
(800) 877-5338 (Ext. 103)
FAX: (210) 688-3014

Holland & Holland
118 North Saint Asaph St.
Alexandria, VA 22314
(703) 549-5540
FAX: (703) 739-8967
Contact: Jan Roosenburg or
Ken Davies

Jon Kruger
Box 213
St. Ansgar, IA 50472
(515) 736-4893
Individual design custom tailored to your specific parcel of land and personal tastes. Courses designed for the recreational shooter yet ideal for hosting tournaments. Recommendations in target and equipment selection.

See Our Ads Pgs. 86 & 163

Patrick LaBoone
The Midwest Shooting School
950 Hwy. 33
Wrenshall, MN 55797
(218) 384-3670
Sporting clays course design, limited to 4 courses/year.

Parker/Boss
Design Team
118 Ira Court
PO Box 309
Andover, KS 67002
(316) 733-2876
Est.: 1985   Staff: 2
Contact: Larry Leatherman
Paker/Boss as an industry leader has recognized that many operators have design questions. These can be answered with a 15 minute conversation or a consultation at your site. Parker/Boss has put together their design team which is headed by Jon Kruger and Doug Fuller. Please call for more information regarding our services and fees.

Gordon C. Philip
1701 Northwest Cookingham
Kansas City, MO 64155
(816) 734-4044
FAX: (816) 734-9650
Est.: 1987   Staff: 1
Your proposed course may be large or small, public or private. In any case, it should have a wide variation of targets. Challenging enough to test the best, yet flexible enough to encourage a beginner. Get the experience of a designer who has worked on 5 World Championship and 5 National Championship courses, who is internationally recognized throughout the industry, and provides his clients with expertise and professionalism at all times.

See Our Ad Below

Quack Sporting Clays, Inc.
PO Box 98, 4 Ann & Hope Way
Cumberland, RI 02864
(401) 723-8202
FAX: (401) 722-5910
Est.: 1986
Pres/CEO: Ken M. Gagnon, Sr.
Quack Sporting Clays, Inc. limits its course designing and building to established gun clubs and game preserves. With 9 years experience in course design/building along with the organization implementation of over 200 shotgun events (6 Int'l) we are definitely the leaders in our field. Always taking advantage of the terrain, always innovative, designing & building a course in a weekend is our specialty. Our solid hands on skills and honesty along with an impeccable track record speaks for itself. A new sporting clays course and a new friendship is as close as your telephone. We will also promote your new range in our national magazine "Modern Skeet & Clays". For more information contact us.

See Our Ads Pgs. 228-229

R&R Sales and Service
9903 Geronimo Oaks
San Antonio, TX 78254
(210) 688-3165
FAX: (210) 688-9048
Est.: 1992
Contact: FM "Butch" Roberson, III
Course design with the owner in
mind. Safety first.

Rock Run Sporting Clays
2708 Edgewood Dr.
Rockford, IL 61114
(815) 633-8870
FAX: (815) 633-8874
Contact: Joe Ongenars
Design English Sporting & FITASC.

The Shooting Academy
8130 E. LaJunta Rd.
Scottsdale, AZ 85255
(602) 585-0882
Contact: Mike Davey

SHOW-ME SPORTS

Show Me Sports Corp.
8267 N. Revere, Dept. WC
Kansas City, MO 64151
(816) 587-9540
FAX: (816) 587-3906
Est.: 1978
President: Andrew Perkins
Complete course design & consulting; Experienced on-staff consulting course designers to serve your needs worldwide. Providing full service detailed information and design. References available upon request.

See Our Ad Pg. 211

Southern Sporting Clays
PO Box 730
Corsicana, TX 75151-0730
(903) 872-5663
FAX: (903) 872-5660
Est.: 1987   Staff: 2
Contact: Steve Stroube
Available: Retail & Direct
Consulting & design of sporting clays courses & hunting preserves.

SportShooting Consultants, Ltd.
PO Box 207
Rincon, GA 31326
(912) 826-0072
Est.: 1992
Contact: Marty Fischer
Recognized across America as one of the foremost authorities on sporting clays course design and marketing and management techniques for shooting facilities and hunting preserves. Below is a list of our various services: Sporting Clays Course Design; Marketing Plans and Business Plans; Management Training and Consultation; Special Event Marketing; Hunting Preserve Consultation; Pro Shop and Retail Design; Shooting Clinics and Instructor Training. Authorized dealer for Lincoln and IBIS automatic traps. Call or write for a brochure describing our services.

Sports Marketing Group
12003 Vanilla Ct.
Orlando, FL 32837
(407) 858-0441
FAX: (407) 858-9904
Contact: Bob Edwards or
Cindy Edwards
Course Design; Management; Consultation; Tournament Coordination; Shooting Instruction

Top Gun Consultants
1142 Draymore Court
Hummelstown, PA 17036
(717) 566-2900
FAX: (717) 566-1399
Contact: Dan Schindler
Experienced, flexible, on-site supervision, start to finish

WILD-HARE, International
PO Box 11943
Memphis, TN 38111
(800) 523-9453
Contact: Paul Brown
WILD-HARE's team of course designers includes landscape and architectural designers, as well as accomplished shooters. We can focus on every aspect of your project from parking to clubhouse to shooting stands. For FITASC parcours, English Sporting, or Five-Stand course designs that are tailored to your project requirements, yet offer flexibility, contact our design staff. We also offer the best in equipment and installation services suited to your needs.

See Our Ad Pg. 43

DOG TRAINERS & BREEDERS

Baier's Den Kennels
Peculiar, MO 64078
(816) 758-5234
Contact: Bud Baier
Over 40 years experience–bird dogs and retrievers trained the old fashioned proven way. Pups & started dogs for sale. Call or write for free folder.
See Our Ad Below

Barn Ridge Kennels
28710 Ropp Rd.
Geneseo, IL 61254
(309) 944-2473
Contact: Mike File
Over 40 years experience in training dogs for hunting, hunting tests & field trials; Labrador Retrievers available.

Bay View Kennels
12 Upton Rd.
LaGrangeville, NY 12540
(914) 223-5546
Contact: Dan Catalano
Linebred for 32 years; Pups & started dogs. References available.

Bramble Creek Kennels
PO Box 1327
Gold Beach, OR 97444
(503) 247-2461
Contact: Randy Barke
Started Cockers and Springs available. Videos & references available. Training of flushing breeds.

Briarstone Sporting Dogs
RR1, Rockford, IA 50468
(515) 756-2327
Contact: Todd Peterson
Wirehaired Pointing Griffons. Quality puppies.

Brigadoon Kennels
High Point, NC 27262
(910) 812-7527
Contact: Phillip H. Hayworth
Field Bred English Pointers & Labs. Started & finished dogs. Gun dog training.

Buck Creek Game Farm & Kennel
PO Box 1114
Laurie, MO 65038
(314) 873-1201
German Shorthair Pointers–puppies & started dogs. Breeding close working dogs from foreign, imported and Champion bloodlines.

Buckeye Kennels
5598 County Rd. 48
Waterloo, OH 45688
(614) 643-0148
Contact: Dick Geswein
English Setters & Pointers–bird dog training seminars. Full-time gun dog training.

Lloyd Budd
PO Box 267
Bellevue, TX 76228
(817) 928-2315
Bird dog training; Brittanys campaigned; Pups & started gun dogs.

Burchett's Bird Dogs
1758 295th St.
Argyle, IA 52619

(319) 838-2822
Contact: Bob Burchett
Classy responsive hunting dogs; Training & handling. Finishing hunting companions for sale. Stud service.

Burnt Creek Setters
1 Kennel Rd., Box 123
Baldwin, KS 58521–123
(701) 258-6373
Contact: Jim Marti
English Setters–Brochure available.

Circle Drive Kennels
Box 50
Hill City, KS 67642
(913) 674-5723
German Shorthairs–pups, started & trained dogs.

Count Kennels
11420 Crawford Rd.
Las Cruces, NM 88005
(505) 526-6504
Breeding for amateur trainable Britts; Field bred pups.

Coyote Creek Retrievers
83574 Territorial Hwy.
Eugene, OR 97405
(503) 485-7887
Linda Fulks
Contact: Jim Fulks or
Obedience & retriever training; all levels of AKC & NAHRA hunting tests. Puppies available.

Crist Culo Kennels
PO Box 602
Minocqua, WI 54548
(715) 356-4772
Silver Labs. Excellent stock, AKC, hips guaranteed.

Dakota Kennels
RR1, Box 47-E
Carthage, SD 57323
(605) 772-4570
Contact: Dennis Lail
Professional training of pointing, retrieving breeds; Pups, started & trained dogs.

R.L. Dalrymple
2640 Springdale Rd.
Ardmore, OK 73401
(405) 223-8782
French Brittanys–Stud service avail..

Danikk Labradors
5162 Union Lake Trail
Lonsdale, MN 55046
(507) 744-2284
Contact: Fran Smith
Producing dual-purpose puppies for conformation, field and the home. Stud service. Personalized training.

Davis' Five Star Kennel
Rt. 1, Box 271
Mt. Vernon, IL 62864
(618) 242-3409
Contact: Bob E. Davis
Complete programs for pointing and retrieving breeds. Call for more information.

Duck's Run Retrievers
PO Box 146
LaFayette, GA 30728
(706) 638-6102
Contact: Calvin & Debbie Almon
Excellent companions, gun dogs or training. Health guaranteed. Pedigrees and references available on request.

Flushing Star Kennel
33665 Henwill Rd.
Columbia Station, OH 44028
(216) 748-1053
Contact: Debbie Karlovec
English Springer & English Cocker Spaniels. Top Quality U.K. & U.S. Breedings; Pups, gun dogs–training & stud service. References & reasonable prices.

John H. Goldsmith, Jr.
3705 Woodsprings Rd.
Jonesboro, AR 72401
(501) 932-5093
Brittany pups–French & Italian bloodlines. Call for information.

The Goodings
Rt. 2, Baldwin, WI 54002
(715) 796-2392
English Setters & Pointers; Labradors. Selected puppies & started dogs available. Professional sporting dog training.

Green Acre Kennels
140 Green Acres
Mt. Sterling, KY 40353
(606) 498-0612
Contact: Bob Adams
Walking gun dogs-finished and started English and Llewellin Setters.

Green Valley Kennels
15437 Derby Grange Rd.
Dubuque, IA 52001
(319) 588-3045
Contact: Bob Iler
Gun dog training, all breeds; seminars & classes.

Grouse Brook Kennels
RD4, Box 585
Middletown, NY 10940
(914) 355-1170
Gun dog training–pointing breeds. Professional training; private lessons; pups & started dogs for sale.

Grouse Ridge Kennels
RD#2, Box 288
Oxford, NY 13830
(607) 334-4920
Contact: Pete Flanagan or Katie Flanagan
English Setters-Hall of fame breeding; Started & trained dogs.

Gun Dog Kennels
PO Box 38
Artesia Wells, TX 78001
(210) 676-3410
Training your started or finished dog.

Gunsmoke Kennels
Rt. 2 Box 15
Union Springs, AL 36089
(334) 738-4642
Herb Holmes
Contact: Bill Holmes or
Quality puppies & well started young dogs; trained gun dogs; stud service; professional training. Call for free brochure.

High Prairie Farms
55552 WCR 23
Carr, CO 80612
(303) 897-2374
Contact: Timothy A. Degroff
Field English Springer Spaniels. Puppies, started & finished dogs. Training, breeding & trial handling.

Highest Retrievers
1021 Lower Honcut Rd.
Oroville, CA 95966
(916) 742-3647
FAX: (916) 742-3653
Contact: John & Debra Folsom
25 years experience-fully trained

shooting dogs available. Labrador puppies. Stud service.

Hunter's Creek Club
675 Sutton Rd.
Metamora, MI 48455
(810) 664-4307
Contact: Charlie Mann or Dale Jarvis
Hunter's Creek takes pride in the quality of it's training program for Pointers, Retrievers and Flushing dogs. Limited numbers of Lab, Brittany & Pointer pups available. Call today.

Hunterhill
23123 Thrush Ave.
Mason City, IA 50401
(515) 696-5925
Quality Brittanys-Pups available.

Intraset Gordons
12273 Hyfield Rd.
DeSoto, MO 63020
(314) 586-6778
Full field strain Gordons-written guarantee.

King Llewellin Setters
27 Gapview Rd.
Conway, AR 72032
(501) 329-7651
Contact: Alfred O. King, Sr.
Breeder for 31 years–references available.

King's Kennels
238 Saunders Rd.
Riverwoods, IL 60015
(708) 945-9592
German Shorthair–Adults & Puppies Started & Finished; Stud service; German Imports are our specialty.

Lehmschlog Kennels
181 McDowell Lane
Selah, WA 98942
(509) 697-8879
Contact: Clay Brown
German Shorthaired & Wirehaired Pointers. Puppies & started dogs available.

Linden Kennels
1657 200th St.
Mt. Pleasant, IA 52641
(319) 986-5589
Contact: Hal Chaney
Field bred English Spring Spaniels–gun dog training, all breeds

Lindley's Kennel
3332 West Georgia Rd.
Piedmont, SC 29673
(803) 243-3583
Contact: Maurice Lindley

Trained dogs, started dogs and puppies available all year.

Taylor & Linda Loop
PO Box 55
Warner, NH 03278
(603) 456-3935
SSK-field trial & hunting labradors. All colors, guaranteed and committed to excellence.

Frank Maple
3520 Ridge Rd.
Zanesville, OH 43701
(614) 453-9614
English Setters; Vizslas; German shorthaired Pointers–Top Bloodlines.

Marks-A-Lot Kennels
RR1, Box 209
Caddo Mills, TX 75135
(903) 527-LABS
Trainer/Handler: Dan Kielty
Full time Retriever training for field trials, hunt tests & gun dogs. Call or write for free brochure.

Mason Creek
126 Erin Rd.
Oconomowoc, WI 53066
(414) 474-7290
Contact: Barbara Grygiel
German Wirehaired Pointers–OFA; Puppies; Stud service.

Mr. Ed's Brittanys
13118 McDougal Rd.
Athens, OH 45701
(614) 448-3881
Contact: David Linscott
Brittanys bred & trained for 36 years.

Mueller's Retriever Kennels
8201 Dutch Rd.
Manitowoc, WI 54220
(414) 758-2262
Contact: Gail Mueller
Training pups & started dogs.

Oak Hill Kennel
Box 1605
Pinehurst, NC 28374
(910) 295-6710
Contact: John Dahl
Complete retriever training including NARHA, AKC & UKC Gun Dog events.

Old South Pointer Farms
Rt. 1, Box 12
Rosanky, TX 78953
(210) 839-4560
Owner/Trainer: Jarrett Thompson
Pups, started and broke dogs for sale from top bloodlines.

Walt Peterson
PO Box 292812
Phelan, CA 92329
(619) 868-1298
Labradors–English/American bloodlines–AKC puppies, family dogs & hunting dogs.

Pheasant Hill Sporting Dogs
709 E. Elizabethtown Rd.
Manheim, PA 17545
(717) 664-4041
FAX: (717) 664-3733
Contact: Judy & Ernie Simmons
Pheasant Hill stands for integrity of the breed. Producing sporting dogs with sound temperament and impeccable conformation, never losing sight of the original purpose of the breed. Our kennel program is about socialization, specialized conditioning and training, all on our private shooting preserve and lake for water work.
- Labrador Retrievers & English Springer Spaniels
- A.K.C. & O.F.A.
- Pedigrees and photos available on request.
See Our Ad Above

Pine Hill Kennels and Sportsmen's Club
8347 Ten Mile Rd.
Rockford, MI 49341
(616) 874-8459
Professional training of all gun dog breeds. Breed top quality German Shorthairs; Stud service & boarding available.

Queensland International Gundog Kennel
160 Maple Hill Rd.
Houlton, WI 54082
(715) 549-6245
British Labradors. Trained Labs, Springers imported from U.K.

Rainwater Kennels
3530 W. Old Hwy. 30
Grand Island, NE 68803
(308) 384-1517
Contact: Larry & Helen Heil
20 years experience in all breed gun dog training. Stud service, puppies & started–Labs, Shorthairs, Pointers.

Ralee's Brittanys
N48 W18424 Lisbon Rd.
Menomonee Falls, WI 53051
(414) 781-1974
Pups, Started Dogs & Studs available. Dual bloodlines.

Rawhide Kennels
1719 Pinecrest Rd.
LaPlatte, NE 68123
(402) 291-6804

Contact: Don Paltani or
Pam Paltani
Call or write for a free brochure.

Joe & Linda Regan
RR1, Box 148
Sherburne, NY 13460
(607) 674-4707
Proven program for all pointing
breeds. Upland for Retrievers, Spaniels & pointing Labs. Modern
kennels.

Robi Lee Setters
397 Valley Rd.
Mason, NH 03048
(603) 878-1923
Irish Red & White Setters–imported
from the best hunting & show
bloodlines in England & Ireland.
Eyes & hips certified. Pups available.

Rockhill Labradors
7119 Labrador Lane
Mechanicsville, VA 23111
(804) 781-0446
Contact: Bert Hill
Yellow, chocolate & black Labs

Rohner Kennel
Rt. 2
Plattsburg, MO 64477
(816) 539-3569
Brittany pups & trained dogs; Field
champions at stud. Call for free information packet.

Royal Flush Kennels
4914 Hwy. G
Eagle River, WI 54521
(715) 479-4188
Contact: Marty & Shelley Knibbs
Specializing in field bred English
Spring Spaniels & Llewellin Setters.
Puppies/started dogs; field trial
prospects; professional training &
handling.

Salt Marsh Kennels
57 Lamberts Lane
Cohasset, MA 02025
(617) 383-1584
Contact: Pat Casey
Gun dog training–pointing and retrieving breeds.

Roland K. Smit
RR3, Box 76
Clark, SD 57225
(605) 532-3717
Drahthaars bred to hunt. Puppies,
started and trained dogs available.
Reasonable. NAVHDA tested.

Snowy Oaks Kennels
Prior Lake, MN
(612) 440-7639
Large Munsterlanders–for the

hunter of upland game & waterfowl. Free video available.

Special K Kennels
Box 286
Riverside, IA 52327
(319) 648-5805
Contact: Mike Kellogg
German Shorthairs, English Setters.
Gun dog training year round. Pups
& started dogs.

Springset Kennels
2715 Skillman Lane
Petaluma, CA 94952
(707) 763-8276
Field proven & adaptable to work
in any type of cover. Call for free
brochure.

Star Lab Kennels
Rt. 1
Lyons, MI 48851
(517) 647-4770
Contact: Stan & Carolyn Krycinski
Superior hunting retrievers for the
marsh and field.

Straight Creek Kennels
Rt. 1, Box 273
West Liberty, KY 41472
(606) 743-4765
Specializing in Llewellin gun dogs.
All phases of training from pup to
finished gun dog.

Sunrise Kennels
6600 County Rt. 69
Canisteo, NY 14823
(607) 776-7349
Contact: Gary Wilson
FC Sired Pups, Started Dogs & Fin-
ished Gun Dogs, Field Trial
Prospects, Training & Handling.

Three Devils Wirehairs
8504 East Scism Rd.
Nampa, ID 83686
(208) 463-2304
NAVHDA tested, truly versatile, satisfaction guaranteed, OFA,
references, pups

Trieven Kennels
3000 N. Phoenix Rd.
Medford, OR 97504
(503) 773-9690
Contact: Tom & Sue Ross
Quality Labrador Retrievers–pups &
started dogs; stud service. Complete professional training (all
breeds). Call or write for brochure.

Trieven Sungold Kennels
1558 Rd. 9 1/2
Lovell, WY 82431
(307) 548-6353
Contact: Jay & Val Walker
Field bred Golden Retrievers from

the best of working bloodlines.
Pups available; working goldens at
stud.

Van Lee Labradors
12997 Bullis Rd.
East Aurora, NY 14052
(716) 652-8979
Contact: Carroll Lewandowski
All breeding stock OFA and CERF.
Written guarantee on hips and
eyes. Pedigrees and pictures upon
request.

LeRoy VanKrik
68437 Bellows Rd.
White Pigeon, MI 49099
(616) 641-7709
English Springer Spaniels–puppies,
started and finished dogs for hunting.

Walters Kennels
Rt. 1, Box 154
LaCygne, KS 66040
(913) 757-6679
Contact: D.L. Walters
Professional retriever trainers. Gun
dogs, hunt test dogs & field trial
dogs. Boarding & obedience.

Whack-A-Quack Kennels
Rt. 5 Box 57
Blanchard, OK 73010
(405) 485-9692
Contact: Brad Smith
Professional retriever training gun
dogs; hunt test young field trial
dogs.

Whisper Oak Kennels
PO Box 2048
Hayden Lake, ID 83835
(208) 772-4504
Contact: Dan Hosford
Professional training staff for point-
ers, flushers & retrievers.

White Birch Kennels
Foxboro Rd.
Lovell, ME 04051
(207) 925-1740
Contact: Capt. Paul R. Bois
English Setters, German
Shorthaired Pointers, Beagles.

Whitehaven Canine Center
5725 Brady St.
Davenport, IA 52806
(319) 388-0004
Full service gun dog kennel. Field &
obedience training. Gun dog pups
& started dogs.

Windy Rock Kennels
Box 438
Rockwell, IA 50469
(515) 822-4905
Contact: Cindy Marsh

HEARING PROTECTION

A"Must" For The Shotgunner

The story is told of three Englishmen—avid shotgunners—whose train was pulling into a station."I say, old chap," the first hrrumphed, "is this Wembley?" "No," said the second, "I believe it's Thursday." "Thirsty? So am I", exclaimed the third. "What say we pop off and have a drink?"

Funny in the telling. But the reality of impaired hearing is far from humorous. And the sad fact is, if you're a shooter who pursues the pastime without adequate ear protection, there's little doubt of the eventual outcome: you'll lose, to a greater or a lesser degree, your ability to hear. And the more shooting you do, the quicker it will happen. The reason lies in human physiology.

The healthy ear is a finely calibrated instrument capable of registering an amazing range of sounds. And every sound, from a soft sigh to a crack of thunder, is transmitted as vibrations to the brain by some 30,000 nerve endings. Damage them and you diminish your ability to hear.

Unfortunately hearing loss can be insidious because it's so often gradual. By the time you're aware of symptoms the damage has been done. Perhaps sounds begin to seem muffled or softer. Or you may have difficulty distinguishing consonant sounds in conversation.Or the warning sign may be tinnitus, a constant ringing, buzzing or whistling in your ears. Any symptom is a call to immediate action. If you fail to employ hearing protection now, the problem can—and probably will—grow worse.

Louder Than A Jet

A decibel (dB) is a unit for measuring the relative level or intensity of sounds. A jet engine at full power generates 130 dB. Each shot from a 12-gauge shotgun generates 150 dB or more! And that, because of the complexities of decibel measurement, is over ten times louder than 85 dB, the level at which most experts suggest ear protectors be worn. So the shooter's need for hearing protection is obvious. But things are seldom simple.

Although common sense suggests the need for hearing protection of some kind when you shoot, it's not uncommon for otherwise practical sportsmen to resist the use of protectors. "Uncomfortable." "Bulky." "It interferes with my shooting." You've heard the objections.Perhaps you've voiced them yourself.

For the most part, however, such objections are considerably less valid than they once were. The variety of hearing protection available today runs from low cost one-size-fits-all plugs to devices that are marvels of electronic sophistication. The type of protection you use will depend on several factors including the shooting situation; the degree to which you are willing to sacrifice comfort for protection; and how much you're willing to spend.

Universal Plugs - available at many pro shops for about $2.00 a pair or less. They are similar to the ear plugs that swimmers wear, and do the job they're meant to do. That is, they muffle sound and protect hearing. If there's a drawback to these inexpensive--often disposable--plugs, it's the fact that fit may not be perfect, since the shape of the ear canal varies considerably from one person to another.

Custom Molded Plugs - The ultimate plug type protector resembles a hearing aid. Many sportsmen express a decided preference for this type of plug because it is considerably less bulky than earmuffs, and more comfortable in hot weather. The simplest type is made of a sound dampening material that is custom-fitted to your ear and sells for up to $60 a pair. A more sophisticated version of the custom molded plug, incorporates electronic circuitry that allows all normal sounds through, and a shut-off switch that is automatically activated by very loud noises—say, a shotgun blast. The cost of this modern technology can be high—up to $675 a pair.

Ear Muffs - Many shooters and more than a few shooting instructors, opt for ear muffs. Available from a number of prominent manufacturers, they come in a broad range of styles and models, and offer a variety of features, including cups and foam- or liquid-filled ear cushions.Prices here range from less than $50 to $200, depending, once again, on the materials and the level of electronic sophistication incorporated into the design.

Plug or muff, plain or fancy, the choice is yours. Protect your hearing now, or most assuredly, pay the price later.

EAR PROTECTION

Action Ear-Bionic Ear
Silver Creek Industries
PO Box 1988
Manitowoc, WI 54221
(800) 533-3277
FAX: (414) 684-6267
Est.: 1959
Contact: Kevin Edgar
Available: Retail
The Action Ear Sport stereo amplifier allows you to hear traps and locate targets faster than single in-the-ear devices. Electronic limiter protects your hearing. FREE Brochure!

The Bilsom Group
5300 Region Court
Lakeland, FL 33801
(800) 733-1177 (Customer)
(813) 683-9164
FAX: (813) 683-9582
Est.: 1976
Marketing Mgr: Joseph A. Gilberti
Available: Retail
Hearing protection, voice amplification, GPT Eye Safety Lenses.

British Sporting Arms
RR1, Box 193A
Millbrook, NY 12545
(914) 677-8303
Contact: Margaret Schneible
Available: Direct
Stereo electronic Ear Defender-manufactured in England.

Cabot Safety Corporation
90 Mechanic St.
Southbridge, MA 01550

---

(800) 327-3431
FAX: (800) 488-8007
Marketing Dir: Joann Waite
Available: Retail
Wide selection of earmuffs, banded hearing protection and earplugs, including the E-A-R Classic foam earplug, which gradually expands and conforms to the size and shape of any ear canal to form a custom fit seal against harmful noise.

E.A.R., Inc.
Insta-Mold Division
PO Box 18888
Boulder, CO 80308
(800) 525-2690
(303) 447-2619
FAX: (303) 447-2637
Nat'l. Sales Mgr.: Garry G. Gordon
Available: Retail
Electronic & non-electronic customized ear protection
Presenting E.A.R., Inc.'s SoundScopes Magnum Ear. Electronic ear plugs that allow shooters the flexibility to enjoy hunting and shooting more than ever. With the Magnum Ear, a shooter can switch from lower output for repetitive target shooting to higher output for enhanced hearing while hunting. Available in custom in-the-ear and behind-the-ear models. Custom fitted Magnum Ear ITEs can be made from acrylics for bowhunters or from softer materials for shooters. The behind-the-ear model comes with tubing attached to a disposable foam ear plug but can be attached to a custom ear mold. Call today for more information.
See Our Ad Pg. 94

E.S.P.
ELECTRONIC SHOOTERS PROTECTION, INC.

Electronic Shooters Protection, Inc.
19423 N. Turkey Creek, Suite E
Morrison, CO 80465
(800) 767-7791
(303) 697-8316
FAX: (303) 697-8396
Est.: 1992
Dir./Cust. Svc: Thomas J. Northey
Available: Retail & Direct
In the field or on the course, the shooter who appreciates quality will appreciate the E.S.P. Competition Series Electronic Earplug. This all-in-the-ear hearing protection amplifies environmental and speech sounds...while simultaneously protecting you from loud noises like gun fire.
See Our Ad Across

HOPPE'S 9™
A DIVISION OF PENGUIN INDUSTRIES, INC.

Airport Industrial Mall
Coatsville, PA 19320
(610) 384-6000
Contact: Patricia Lucas
Available: Retail
Hoppe's Benchrest Sound Mufflers are compact, fully adjustable and may be worn over or behind the head or under the chin. Excellent noise reduction properties make Hoppe's Sound Muffler ideal for the rifle range, shotgun shooting or any other situation where noise protection is advised.
See Our Ad Below

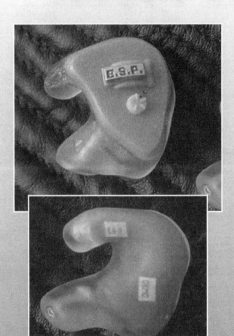

Your choice of three styles

Because one shot is all it takes to ruin your hearing for life, SoundScopes PROTECT as they amplify.

Because some sounds are too important to miss, SoundScopes AMPLIFY as they protect.

SoundScopes hearing protection with amplification.

To order, or for information call:

1 (800) 525-2690

SOUNDSC◉PES™
ELECTRONIC EAR PLUGS

HEARING PROTECTION

Howard Leight Industries
1330 Colorado Ave.
Santa Monica, CA 90404
(800) 327-1110
(310) 396-3838
FAX: (310) 314-3860
Est.: 1978
Contact: Chris Leight
Mktg. Coordinator: Allen McCreight
Available: Retail
HOWARD LEIGHT INDUSTRIES offers the widest selection of hearing protection products available...disposable ear plugs, re-usable earplugs, banded hearing protectors, and quality ear muffs. By following the leader in hearing protection, you can listen to the future. Sell the lead Howard Leight. Call now for more information on how you can offer the fastest growing line of hearing protection in the industry.

North Safety Products
Specialty Products Division
2664 B Saturn St.
Brea, CA 92621
(714) 524-1655

FAX: (714) 524-7944
Est.: 1953   Staff: 30
Contact: Katherine Michalowicz
Available: Retail & Direct
The Sonic II Hearing Protector; The Noise Husher; Foam Ear Plug; The Gun Muffler Ear Muffs; The Com-Fit Multi-Purpose Earplug; Hearing Protectors for Youths.

Peltor Inc.
41 Commercial Way
E. Providence, RI 02914
(401) 438-4800
FAX: (401) 434-1708
Est.: 1952   Staff: 250
Dir. Sales/Mktg.: Frank A. D'Isidoro
Available: Retail
PELTOR offers a complete line of hearing protection that includes ear muffs, ear plugs, and electronic hearing protectors. Recently PELTOR introduced two new products; the Range Partner and the Bull's-Eye Ultimate 10.
The Range Partner is a combo pack containing the PELTOR shotgunner hearing protector and model 2500 amber shooting glasses. The Ultimate 10 has the highest noise reduction rating on the market (29dB) for any ear muff that has been tested in an accredited lab. Other popular PELTOR products include the Tactical 7 electronic hearing protector. The Tactical 7 suppresses sounds above 82 dB, yet still amplifies normal sound such as speech.

Pro-Ears
Ridgeline Products
PO Box 30410
Phoenix, AZ 85046-0410
(800) 888-3277
Contact: Dan Nigro
Available: Direct
Pro-Ears is a new headset that gives superior hearing protection. Available in deep black, cream white or olive green.

Silencio/Safety Direct, Inc.
56 Coney Island Dr.
Sparks, NV 89431
(800) 648-1812
(702) 359-4451
FAX: (702) 359-1074
Contact: Gordon Kramer
Available: Retail
At Team Silencio, customer service and satisfaction are the number

one goal. Earmuffs available in six models; private branding available in certain styles. Electronic earmuff hearing protection - 4 models from which to choose. Earplugs - sound baffler, economy and disposable models available. Call for catalog, (800) 648-1812.
See Our Ad Pg. 97

Sound Scopes
E.A.R., Inc.
PO Box 2146
Boulder, CO 80306
(800) 525-2690
(303) 447-2619
FAX: (303) 447-2637
Nat'l. Sales Mgr.: Garry G. Gordon
Available: Retail
Electronic & non-electronic customized ear protection
See Our Ad Left

Walker's "Game Ear", Inc.
PO Box 1069
Media, PA 19063
(610) 565-8952
FAX: (610) 566-7488
Est.: 1990
President: Bob Walker
Available: Retail & Direct
Using modern hearing aid technology, these products were designed and developed to enhance the user's hearing and offer hearing protection when needed. The "Game Ear"– designed for the hunter with maximum amplification, (49 dB) and hearing protection, (NRR 29 dB). The "Target Ear"– designed for the range with reduced amplification, (23 dB) and maximum hearing protection, (NRR 29 dB). The "Nature Ear"–designed for outdoor enthusiasts and general hearing enhancement with medium amplification (39 dB) and (NRR 27 dB).

Remember your hearing protection. Remember your eye protection. Remember to say: "I saw it in Wing & Clay."

EYE PROTECTION

Shotgunners Should See To It

Think, for a moment, of how much your vision means to you. Then consider the effect on your life if it were impaired. How many activities that you take for granted—like driving—would you have to curtail? How many pleasures—like field hunting or sporting clays—would you have to forsake? As a shotgunner, you owe it to yourself to protect your eyes on every shooting occasion.

If sporting clays are your thing you have little choice in the matter. We're aware of no exceptions to the course management rule that makes eye protection mandatory (and ear protection, too, for that matter).

Why are all sporting clays courses so vision conscious? Because even a partial hit on a target directly overhead will spray shooter and spectator alike with shards of clay. Because pellets ricochet off trees and other objects. Because shooting cages don't entirely prevent the occasional stretch shot that rains pellets on those nearby.

But field hunting also involves hazards that make eye protection a matter of simple common sense. Twigs, saplings, vines and whipping branches are the most obvious examples. A near miss from a springing branch can bring tears. A hit can scratch your eye, resulting in temporary discomfort or serious injury.

Eyeglasses Fill The Bill

Do you wear eyeglasses regularly? Then here's the good news. You're ready to shoot but consider purchasing a large pair of sport glasses that will cover your eyes more for protection and give you better optics when you're mounting your gun. Most prescription lenses are made with optical CR-39 plastic lenses which are less than half the weight of glass and ten times more fog resistant than glass. If your vision is 20/20 perfect. . . protect your precious eyes with some good sport glasses. Consider light to medium shade lenses to keep your pupil small. Why? Your depth of field is improved. . . just like a camera. Lenses are coated with a multitude of colors to ro-

mance the target color besides fading out the background picture. Be sure the shooting glasses ride moderately high on your face, but not so high they deprive you of protection from below. (A vine that gets under your glasses can be nasty.) Also recommended:

- Get a lens that increases visual sharpness by filtering out light's blue wave lengths. Yellow lenses are good for this purpose, although they may be uncomfortable in bright sunlight. Also consider purple lenses. They darken the sky, flatten the green background and illuminate the oranges, green & black targets.

- Select the lightest colored lenses that will do the job. Dark lenses cause your pupils to dilate, diminishing visual acuity.

- Silicone nose pads will prevent annoying slippage when you've worked up a good sweat.

You may even want to consider shooting glasses with interchangeable lenses. Different colors alter contrast, depending on the light, background color and target color. (Many targets stand out distinctly from a green background when seen through vermilion lenses, for example.) And if interchangeable is your choice, why not include clear lenses? They're great for low light levels!

EYE PROTECTION

Bausch & Lomb Sports Optics Division
9200 Cody
Overland Park, KS 66214
(913) 752-3400
FAX: (913) 752-3550
Est.: 1853   Staff: 130
Pub. Rel. Mgr: Barbara Mellman
Available: Retail
Formerly Bushnell Div. of Bausch & Lomb. Marketers of binoculars, rifle scopes, sporting scopes & shooting glasses.

The Bilsom Group
5300 Region Court
Lakeland, FL 33801
(800) 733-1177
(813) 683-9164
FAX: (813) 683-9582
Est.: 1939
Marketing Mgr: Joseph A. Gilberti
Available: Retail
GPT Safety Glasses, hearing protection

Cabot Safety Corporation
90 Mechanic St.
Southbridge, MA 01550
(800) 327-3431
FAX: (800) 488-8007
Marketing Dir: Joann Waite
Available: Retail
Contemporary wraparound styling and tough polycarbonate lenses provide protection against debris from discharged powder and spent shell/cartridge particles; clear, gray and yellow.

Costa Del Mar
123 North Orchard, Bldg. #1
Ormand Beach, FL 32174
(800) 447-3700
FAX: (904) 677-3737
Pres: Ray Ferguson
VP/Mktg: Bill Darby
Available: Retail
Polarized shooting glasses.

Custom Sportswear & Optical
11658 Walnut Hill Dr.
Baltimore, OH 43105
(800) 745-6066
Est.: 1988   Staff: 6
Owner: Clarence Willis
Available: Retail & Direct
Plano & RX customs colors

Decot Hy-Wyd
Sport Glasses
PO Box 15830
Phoenix, AZ 85060
(800) 528-1901
(602) 955-7625
FAX: (602) 955-7151
Est.: 1949   Staff: 11
Contact: Bud Decot
Available: Retail & Direct
Decot Hy-Wyd Sport Glasses-the original since 1949. Many times copied but never duplicated. Our Hy-Wyd frames, both the classic gold II and the satin black teflon Hy-Wyd III, have been the shooters favorite for many years. Our custom coated lenses of various shades bring out the target color like there's nothing else in sight. Our international sport glasses have also been acclaimed to be the "Finest Under the Sun." Champions prefer the best. Dealer Inquiries Welcome. Call us for information.
See Our Ad Pg. 95

Foggles, Inc.
7760 Olentangy River Rd.
Suite 112
Columbus, OH 43235
(800) 521-3001
VP: Mary Betz
Available: Retail & Direct
Foggles eyewear prevents the scattering of glare generated light across the retina of the eye. Our unique and PATENTED design improves visual acuity...targets appear sharper and clearer. We offer the discriminating sportsman the ultimate in quality, target and environmental enhancement and sunlight protection.

HOPPE'S ⑨™
A DIVISION OF PENGUIN INDUSTRIES, INC.

Hoppe's -- Penguin Industries, Inc.
Airport Industrial Mall
Coatesville, PA 19320
(610) 384-6000
FAX: (610) 857-5980
Contact: Patricia Lucas
Available: Retail

Leupold & Stevens, Inc.
PO Box 688
Beaverton, OR 97075
(503) 646-9171
FAX: (503) 526-1455
Contact: Janice Carmen
Available: Retail

Oakley, Inc.
10 Holland
Irvine, CA 92718
(800) 733-6255
(714) 951-0991
Available: Retail

Olympic Optical
3975 Vantech, Suite 2
Memphis, TN 38115
(800) 238-7120 (Cust. Service)
(901) 794-3890
FAX: (800) 748-1669
Est.: 1975   Staff: 50
Contact: Danny Holmes
Available: Retail & Direct
Exclusive licensee of: Remington
shooting and sport eyewear; Smith
& Wesson shooting and sport eye-
wear; Zebco fishing eyewear; Stren
fishing eyewear.

Outdoor Shades, Div. of QT
680 Fargo Ave.
Elk Grove, IL 60007
(800) 262-1180
(708) 228-1180
Est.: 1991   Staff: 15
Contact: Liz Ciprian
Available: Retail & Direct
Protective eyewear and binoculars;
cameras for the outdoors.

Peltor Inc.
41 Commercial Way
E. Providence, RI 02914
(401) 438-4800
FAX: (401) 434-1708
Est.: 1952   Staff: 250
Available: Retail
Bull's-Eye Model 2500 shooting
glasses

Protective Optics, Inc.
1320 W. Winton Ave.
Hayward, CA 94545
(800) 776-7842
(510) 887-2401
FAX: (510) 732-6134
Int'l. Acct. Rep.: Espy Corral
Shatterproof polycarbonate lens –
shooting wrap, wire, clip-on.
Dealer Inquiries Welcome.

RANDOLPH RANGER

Randolph Engineering, Inc.
26 Thomas Patten Dr.
Randolph, MA 02368-3902
(800) 541-1405
(617) 961-6070
FAX: (617) 986-0337

Est.: 1973
VP Sales & Mktg: Richard Thayer
Nat'l. Sales Mgr: Bob Bouchard
Available: Retail & Direct
Manufacturer of the Ranger Shooting Glass. Interchangable
polycarbonate lenses, ophthalmic
frames with spring hinges, made in
the USA. Official sponsors of the
U.S. Shooting Team and The Shooting Federation of Canada.

Rocky Mountain High Sports Glasses
8121 N. Central Park Ave.
Skokie, IL 60007
(708) 679-1012
FAX: (708) 679-0184
Staff: 40
VP: Tibor Grass
Div. Mgr: Eric L. Esson
Available: Retail
Polycarbonate shooting glasses.
Several styles including TED NUG-
ENT BOWHUNTING GLASS,
PATRIOT, CLIP-ONS, also offer po-
larized fishing glasses.

Serengeti Eyewear
PO Box 4000
Corning, NY 14830
(800) 525-4001 (Cust. Service)
(800) 831-8100 (Retail Inquiries)
Available: Retail & Direct
Serengeti Vector lens system.

Silencio/Safety Direct, Inc.
56 Coney Island Dr.
Sparks, NV 89431
(800) 648-1812
(702) 359-4451
FAX: (702) 359-1074
Est.: 1972   Staff: 75
Contact: Gordon Kramer
Available: Retail
From economical shooting glasses
to specialized glasses, Silencio offers real value for shooters. SVS
Shooting glasses - designed to fit
over prescription eyewear, comfort
in an economical one-piece model.
AVI Shooting glasses - popular avia-
tor style offers 99.9% U.V.
blocking with high-impact polycarbonate lens. TRI-LENS glasses - 3
interchangeable polycarbonate
lens sets. WRAPPS Glasses - deluxe,
high impact, 99.9% U.V. blocking
wraparound lense. Also available in
mirrored finishes. Call for catalog,
1-800-648-1812.
See Our Ad Below

SHOTGUNNER'S SOURCE

Simmons Outdoor Corp.
2120 Killearney Way
Tallahassee, FL 32308
(904) 878-5100
FAX: (904) 878-0300
Advtg. Dir: Jerry Cliff
Available: Retail
Wrap-around shooting glasses

Sportsman Eyewear
PO Box 261
Hollister, CA 95024-0261
(408) 637-8271
FAX: (408) 636-9664
Pres: Rudy S. DeLuca
Available: Wholesale
Polycarbonate shooting glasses–rimless, wire frames, wraps, clip-ons, SolarShields–lenses meet FDA &

ANSI standards for impact resistance; U.V. protection; Point-of-Purchase displays.
See Our Ad Pg. 96

Tasco Sales, Inc.
PO Box 520080
7600 Northwest 26 St.
Miami, FL 33152-0080
(305) 591-3670 (Ext. 315)
Contact: Pam Levine
Available: Retail
Shooting glasses, binoculars

Carl Zeiss Optical, Inc.
Sports Optic Division
1015 Commerce St.
Petersburg, VA 23803
(800) 338-2984
(804) 861-0033
FAX: (804) 733-4024

Contact: Joy Prickett
Available: Retail

OPTICIANS/ OPTOMETRISTS/ OPTHALMOLOGISTS

Cobblestone Opticians
PO Box 27532
315 N. Spence Ave.
Goldsboro, NC 27532
(800) 353-1511
(919) 778-1511
Optician: Bobby Raynor
Available: Direct
"Cobblestone" glasses are individually dyed in 4 colors: calichrome; amber gold; clear; and watermelon. Custom work at reasonable prices. Call for details.

Dr. Gilchrist
402 Airport Rd.
Tappahannock, VA 22560
(800) 969-1778
FAX: (804) 443-5389
Staff: 4
Contact: Dr. Gilchrist
Available: Direct

Allan Lehman Optical
3125 N. 34th Place
Phoenix, AZ 85018
(800) 255-0205
FAX: (602) 596-5467
Est.: 1975   Staff: 5
President/Owner: Allan Lehman
Available: Retail & Direct
Manufacturer of plano and prescription sports glasses. We offer quality frames and custom lenses for your frames or ours.

MORGAN OPTICAL

Morgan Optical
912 W. State, PO Box 770
Olean, NY 14760
(800) 803-6117
FAX: (716) 373-1275
Est.: 1962   Staff: 12
Available: Direct
Plano & prescription sport glasses. An experienced shotgunner with over 30 years in the optical business, Harold Morgan knows from personal experience that eyewear can improve shooting performance. He specializes in making prescription glasses for all types of shooters. Call him today with questions about your eyewear needs and problems.
See Our Ad Left

Dr. Frank Rively - Optometrist
100 Northern Blvd.
Clarks Summit, PA 18411
(717) 586-2020
Est.: 1972
Contact: Frank Rively or
Doris Pilling
Available: Direct
Vision consultation and shooting glasses. Ranger and Decot Hy-Wyd frames.

Dr. Jack Wills, O.D.
1823 Charles St.
Fredericksburg, VA 22401
(800) 544-9191
FAX: (703) 373-0017
Contact: Jack Wills, O.D.
Available: Direct
Ranger shooting glasses in stock for immediate delivery.

GAMEBIRD BREEDERS

Eleven Oaks Farm
Rt. 2, Box 318
Hartsville, SC 29550
(803) 331-9191
Est.: 1995   Staff: 3
Contact: Stephen Beasley
Available: Direct
Bobwhite quail for release; Member of N.A.G.A.

Griffin Hill Hunting Preserve
Rt. 3, Box 222
Wadesboro, NC 28170
(704) 694-5086
Contact: Al Griffin or
Phyllis Griffin
Type of Bird(s) Bred: Quail

Hambrook's Quail Farm
PO Box 596
Harrah, OK 73045
(405) 964-2183
Est.: 1989   Staff: 3
Contact: Red Hambrook
Types of Birds Bred: Northern Bobwhite
At Hambrook's Quail Farm, we offer our birds as chicks, flight birds or dressed. For shipping chicks, our minimum order is 500. Our dressed birds are presented whole and are vacuum packages.

Harper's Game Farm
Rt. 2, Box 484WC
Booker, TX 79005
(806) 435-3495 (Information)
(800) 795-7741 (Orders Only)
Contact: Gilbert & Clideene Harper

Type of Bird(s) Bred: Pheasant, Quail, Chukar
* Family owned for 10 years
* Shipping eggs and chicks to all 50 states
* Raising started and adult birds for release
* We also operate Harper's Hunting Preserve–located 130 miles NE of Amarillo, TX.

King Gamebird Farm
Rt. 3, Princeton, MO 64673
(816) 748-3065
Contact: K. King
The King Gamebird Farm has been specializing in raising hard-flying ringneck pheasants and chukars for 25 years. We're geared to servicing the commerical and private preserve operators. Call today–you'll be pleased with our hard-flying birds!

M&M Shooting Preserve
Hook & Winslow Rd.
Pennsville, NJ 08070
(609) 935-1230
Contact: Donna
Type of Bird(s) Bred: Mallards
M&M Hunting Preserve is a major breeder of Mallard Ducks, raising over 140,000 annually. Our ducks are strickly bred for hunting. They are strong, fast flyers, true to size and color. We guarantee top quality ducks and prompt efficient service. Being in the hunting business for over 25 years, we know

what you expect in a mallard Duck–and we deliver it.

Mac Farlane Pheasant Farm, Inc.

MacFarlane Pheasant Farm, Inc.
2821 South US Hwy. 51
Janesville, WI 53546
(800) 345-8348
FAX: (608) 757-7884
Contact: Bill MacFarlane
MacFarlane's has the most modern game hatching facility in the U.S. and is the supplier of choice of the preserve operator interested in premium quality chicks or mature birds. Quick and reliable delivery guaranteed–across the U.S. and to many foreign countries.
See Our Ad Pg. 101

Martz's Game Farm
RD1 Box 85
Dalmatia, PA 17017
(800) 326-8442
FAX: (717) 758-3166
Est.: 1955   Staff: 19
Contact: Don E. Martz
Type of Bird(s) Bred: Pheasants, Chukar, Huns
We hatch over 175,000 gamebirds annually. We sell eggs, day old chicks, started & mature birds. We

SHOTGUNNER'S SOURCE

At Quailco we specialize in day old chicks. We can ship to all 50 states.
See Our Ad Left

Mike Raahauge's Shooting Enterprises
5800 Bluff St.
Norco, CA 91760
(909) 735-2361
FAX: (909) 371-6853
Contact: Mike Raahauge
Type of Bird(s) Bred: Pheasant

Hatchery Gamebirds

Rocky Mountain Hatchery
PO Box 1086
Hamilton, MT 59840
(800) 219-4285
FAX: (406) 642-3253
Est.: 1991
Contact: J.C. or Eileen Jackson
Birds Bred: Ringneck Pheasant, Chukar, Bobwhite Quail
MONTANA HARDY Pheasant, Chukar and Quail are raised at our NPIP and SPF facility. We offer eggs, day-old, started and flight conditioned birds nationwide. A FREE Equipment catalog including incubators, brooders, a unique automatic watering system and nettings is also available upon request with discounts given to our bird customers.

are located in central PA & ship eggs & day old chicks throughout the continental U.S.

Quail Valley
9219 Concord Hwy.
Indian Trail, NC 28079
(800) 443-6391
(704) 753-4464
Contact: Stan Redfern
The Quail Valley Bobwhite stems from production since 1963. We now have our own processing plant to prepare our farm raised quail, carefully selecting only the top quality. We are USDA inspected and can ship throughout

the United States. All packages are vacuum packed to insure freshness. Products available are Whole Bobwhite, Semi-Boneless, Breast Fillets and Legs, and Wings for Hors d'oeuvres.

Quailco
Game Bird Farm

Quailco Game Bird Farm
Box 245, Dora, NM 88115
(800) 315-0016
Contact: Mikel Hays
Type of Bird(s) Bred: Northern Bobwhite, Chukar

Dwayne Sargeant's Gamebirds
R.R. 3, Box 220, Auburn, IL 62615
(217) 438-6582
(217) 438-3114
Contact: Dwayne Sargeant
Type of Bird(s) Bred: Quail, Pheasant, Chukar
We have flight conditioned and meat birds available. We sell to preserves, wholesalers, consumers. We cover the whole U.S.A.

Sharon Pheasant Farm
145 Gay St.
Sharon, CT 06069
(203) 364-5833
Contact: Bob Wilbur
Type of Bird(s) Bred: Pheasant, Chukar
We sell eggs, chicks, started and mature birds. We ship day-old chicks throughout the U.S.

Sumner's Bobwhite Quail
Rt. 2, Box 620
Tifton, GA 31794

(912) 382-1231
Est.: 1979
Contact: Ruth Sumner
Type of Bird(s)Bred: Bobwhite Quail
We offer Bobwhite Quail, flight
conditioned or dressed. Sell to preserves and consumers. We ship to
south Georgia and north Florida;
10,000 to 12,000 yearly.

Top Flight Quail Farm
261 Garrison Rd.
Phillipsburg, NJ 08865
(908) 859-1615
Contact: Shelley MacQueen
Type of Bird(s) Bred: Quail, Pheasant
Weather and flight conditioned
birds available year round. Farm
pickup, National and International
shipping available. Hungarian Partridge, Tennessee Red Quail,
French Redleg Cross also available.
The MacQueen family has been

breeding birds especially for release for over 60 years.

C.D. Wheeler
29519 West Hawthorne Dr.
Spring, TX 77386
(800) 333-9344 (Orders)
(713) 367-1232 (Phone)
Contact: C.D. Wheeler, Sr.
Type of Bird(s) Bred: Pheasant, Chukar, Quail
Producing over 1 million eggs
yearly. Beat the rush—order in January, February, March. Shipping
April to November. All breeds and
ages not available at all times.

**Whistling
Wings, Inc.**
113 Washington St.
Hanover, IL 61041
(815) 591-3512
FAX: (815) 591-3424
Est.: 1954   Staff: 10

Contact: Marianne Murphy
Whistling Wings has hatched over
3 million Flighting Mallards and
been in the business of hatching,
raising and hunting for 40 years.
The experience we have in shipping is unsurpassable.
See Our Ad Pg. 99

Wintergreen
Hunting Preserve
PO Box 981,
Bladenboro, NC 28320
(910) 648-6171
Est.: 1995
Contact: Boyce White
Type of Bird(s) Bred: Bobwhite
Quail
See Our Ad Pg. 100

SHOTGUN CARE

Just A Little "TLC"
Extends Shotgun's Life

That favorite shotgun of yours is a finely crafted mechanism.It provides the pleasures of wing and clay shooting. And it represents an out-of-pocket investment. What better reasons are there to extend its life and dependable performance with regular care? And that's all a shotgun normally requires for a prolonged life.

"TLC"

Cleaning and maintaining your gun demands only a small expenditure of time and effort. But these tasks are important if you want it to remain in peak condition.

Why? For starters, every time you shoot you create a fire inside the weapon. And the resultant soot can foul moving parts, bore and chamber. If you allow this residue to accumulate you get inefficient -- sometimes unsafe -- shooting.

Moisture: An Ancient Enemy

Then there's the old enemy of all metal- moisture, whose sneakiest attack takes the form of condensation. If you carry your weapon from a cold environment to a warm one, condensation begins immediately on all the gun's metal surfaces. Salt water is the most corrosive form of

moisture. You can encounter it in a salty marsh. But it can also be in the air many miles from the nearest seashore.

Furthermore, any foreign substance in your gun's bore will draw moisture like a magnet. And water in any form begins to rust metal within 24 hours of contact. So fouling and moisture are your gun's worst enemies. Regular care and cleaning are its best friends. If you want your shotgun tolast, you must protect it. And only regular cleaning and lubrication will do the trick.

Clean After Each Use

How regular? Ideally, you'll clean your shotgun after each day's use. And you should never fire the weapon after prolonged storage without cleaning it first. Fortunately, the TLC your shotgun needs is neither arduous nor time-consuming. You'll need some inexpensive tools and supplies, of course, and the owner's manual that accompanied your shotgun will recommend specific products. But basically all you need are these:

- A cleaning rod and attachments for reaching inside the barrel. Attachments include a cloth swab, patch holder, and a brush designed to fit your bore.

- Cleaning patches and swabs remove foreign particles from the barrel's interior and are also used to apply solvent or lubricant.

- Bore-cleaning solvent.
- Light gun oil, which serves as a lubricant for your gun's moving parts and a
  protectant for all metal components.
- Clean cloths for wiping down the exterior of your shotgun.
- A small brush for cleaning hard-to-
  reach places. (A toothbrush will do.)

The Most Important Step

Now you're almost ready to clean. Only
the most important step remains: check to be
sure the gun is unloaded before you begin.

All clear? OK, first attach a cloth patch
to the cleaning rod, dip it in bore-cleaning
solvent, and run it— from the action end—
several times down the length of the bore.
Next, dry the bore using clean patches
until one emerges clean after running the
length of the bore. Now use a clean cloth to
remove grease or dirt from all exterior surfaces. Next, check to be sure all removable
parts are securely fastened. Lastly, coat all
metal surfaces -- lightly -- with gun oil.
There. You're finished. And you can be
confident that the next time you're in the
field or on a course, that favorite shotgun
will perform the way it was intended to.

One final tip: If you want to give your
shotgun an occasional extra-special treat,
there are gun stock finishes and easy-to-
use bluing kits available. Try them for a
shotgun that looks like a well groomed
winner.

GUN CARE

B □ SQUARE

B-SQUARE
2708 St. Louis Ave.
PO Box 11281
Forth Worth, TX 76110
(800) 433-2909
(817) 923-0964
Est.: 1957
Contact: Rudy Bechtel
Available: Retail & Direct
"Tube Lube" lubricant for choke
tubes. First non-toxic, non-staining
tube lubricant that prevents gall-
ing, seizing and corrosion. Call for
free catalog.
See Our Ad Pg. 82

Beretta U.S.A.
c/o Beretta Gallery
New York:
718 Madison Ave.
New York, NY 10021
(212) 319-6614
Alexandria
317 S. Washington St.
Old Town Alexandria, VA 22314
(703) 739-0596
Est.: 1977
Available: Retail
Beretta gun cleaning kits, gun oil.

Birchwood Casey
7900 Fuller Rd.
Eden Prairie, MN 55344

(800) 328-6156 (#7933)
FAX: (612) 937-7979
Est.: 1950
Contact: Mike Wenner
Available: Retail
A complete line of high quality gun
care products to clean, protect and
refinish your guns. Prevent stuck
choke tubes caused by erosion,
high stress of shot and extreme
temperatures and pressure from repeated trap, skeet and sporting
clays shooting. Birchwood Casey
also offers a complete line of metal
and fluorescent paper shooting targets. Ask for Choke Tube Lube and
other Birchwood Casey products
by name. Sold at leading shooting
sports retailers. Write or call for a
free catalog.
See Our Ad Above

Break-Free, Inc.
1035 South Linwood Ave.
Santa Ana, CA 92705-4396
(714) 953-1900
FAX: (714) 953-0402
Est.: 1976   Staff: 20
Contact: Customer Service
VP/Gen. Mgr: Dwight B. Woodruff
Available: Retail
Gun cleaning/lubrication/preserv-
ing oils; gun cleaning kits. Powder
Blast is a highly effective gun
cleaner. This environmentally and
user friendlier product cleans without disassembly. Completely. Metal
to metal. Powder Blast is quicker,
easier and safer. It leaves the
metal completely dry and with a
pleasant orange scent. Use Powder
Blast with Break-Free CLP for complete gun maintenance.

Browning
One Browning Place
Morgan, UT 84050
(800) 333-3288 (Customer)
(801) 876-3331 (General)
Est.: 1878   Staff: 350
Available: Retail
Browning oil

chem-pak, Inc.
11 Oates Ave.
PO Box 1685
Winchester, VA 22604

(800) 336-9828
(703) 667-1341
FAX: (703) 722-3993
Est.: 1966
President: George P. "Pete" Duane, Jr.
VP/Sales: Randy Duane
Available: Retail
Gun Sav'r gunstock finishes and
firearm lubricants.

J. Dewey Mfg. Co.
PO Box 2104
Southbury, CT 06488
(203) 598-7912
FAX: (203) 598-3119
Est.: 1975   Staff: 6
Contact: George Dewey
Available: Retail & Direct
Gun cleaning equipment; Nylon
coated gun cleaning rod; "No-
Harm" brass core brush

Du-Lite Corp.
171 River Rd.
Middletown, CT 06457
(203) 347-2505
FAX: (203) 347-9404
Contact: Walt Smith
Lubricants and rust preventative oils.

EZ Oil
Lakos Enterprises, Inc.
PO Box 1747
Cody, WY 82414
(800) 735-9266
(307) 527-7591
FAX: (307) 587-4973
Contact: Bob Zatkos

Firepower Lubricants
Divison of Muscle Dist. Corp.
22 Kirkwood St., PO Box 504
Long Beach, NY 11561-0504
(516) 432-1300
FAX: (516) 432-3866
Est.: 1982
President: Daniel Joffe
Available: Retail
Firepower FP-10 Lubricant; Elite PL-
10 Power-Lift Grease. Firepower
FP-10, is the ONLY product you
need to clean, lubricate, shield and
protect your shotugn...even down
to its Mil. Spec. of -76 degrees.

Flitz International, Ltd.
821 Mohr Ave.,
Waterford, WI 53185
(800) 558-8611
(414) 534-5898
FAX: (414) 534-2991
President: Peter Jentzsch
Available: Retail
Flitz metal polish, Polier natural wax
protectant, FZ liquid metal polish.

Free-Gunn Cleaner
Box 281, 627 W. Crawford
Clay Center, KS 67432
(913) 632-5607
FAX: (913) 632-5609
Contact: A.J. Bloom
Available: Direct
Cleaner for removing lead and plas-
tic wad build-up in chokes &
barrels; "Traveler" cleaning rod;
cleaning kits.

G96 Products Co., Inc.
PO Box 1684, River Street Station
Paterson, NJ 07544
(201) 684-4050
FAX: (201) 684-3848
Contact: Alan Goldman
Available: Retail
Gun care chemicals

HOPPE'S ⑨™
A DIVISION OF PENGUIN INDUSTRIES, INC.
Airport Industrial Mall
Coatsville, PA 19320
(610) 384-6000
FAX: (610) 857-5980
Contact: Patricia Lucas
Available: Retail
Hoppe's No. 9 Nitro Powder Sol-
vent is the most universally used
solvent for removing primer, pow-
der, lead and metal fouling.
Hoppe's solvent has proven itself
over the years and has been the
choice of gun owners for over
ninety years.
See Our Ad Left

A CLEAN GUN IS A SAFE GUN.

Excessive rust or accumulations of an improper lubricant or foreign material inside a firearm may cause serious malfunctions and possible accidental firing. Your shotgun, rifle or handgun, like any precision tool, needs to be cleaned and lubricated frequently. From day one on.

Be sure to follow the manufacturer's instructions exactly, using only the recommended cleaners and lubricants. If your instruction manual is missing, obtain one from the manufacturer.

A change in the operating characteristics of your firearm, such as failure to cock or a noticeable increase in the force needed to open the bolt, operate the safety, or pull the trigger, is a danger signal. Malfunctions may soon occur. If cleaning and lubricating do not restore normal operation, have your firearm checked by a competent gunsmith or the manufacturer—immediately.

Play it safe. Keep your gun clean, inside and out.

Remington®

Hornady Mfg. Co.
Box 1848, Grand Island, NE 68802
(308) 382-1390
FAX: (308) 382-5761
Contact: Doug Engh
Available: Retail
"One Shot" - gun cleaner and dry lube.

International Lubrication Labs
1895 East 56 Rd.
Lecompton, KS 66050
(913) 887-6004
Contact: Glenn Peterson
Available: Retail
"Lube-Shot"–cleans, lubricates, protects against corrosion and rust, friction and wear.

Iosso Products
1485 Lively Boulevard
Elk Grove, IL 60007
(708) 437-8400
FAX: (708) 437-8478
President: Richard Iosso
VP/Sales: Marianne Iosso
Available: Retail
"Gunbrite" gun polish; Iosso bore cleaner; Iosso case cleaner - a liquid immersion cleaner for bullet casings; Iosso case polish - additive to media for cleaning & polishing bullet casings.

Kleen-Bore, Inc.
16 Industrial Pkwy.
Easthampton, MA 01027
(800) 445-0301
(413) 527-0300
FAX: (413) 527-2522
Contact: Paul Judd
Quality gun care products and accessories; deluxe cleaning set. Write for our free fully-illustrated, color brochure.

Krieghoff International, Inc.
7528 Easton Rd., PO Box 549
Ottsville, PA 18942
(610) 847-5173
Chairman: Dieter Krieghoff
President: Jim Hollingsworth
Available: Retail
Gun Care products: Gun Glide and Gun Pro Lubricants. K-80 & KS-5 factory service.

MSR, Inc.
PO Box 1372
Sterling, VA 20167-1372
(800) 822-0258
FAX: (703) 860-0286
Contact: Mike Mueller or Bill Orr
"DSX" firearms maintenance products. Superior cleaners, lubricants and suface treatments. Call for free brochure. Dealer inquiries welcome.

MTM Case-Gard
PO Box 14117
Dayton, OH 45413
(513) 890-7461
FAX: (513) 890-1747
Contact: Al Minneman
Available: Retail
RMC-1 Rifle Maintenance Center for cleaning and maintainance of shotguns & rifles.
See Our Ad Below

Otis Products, Inc.
Rt. 12-D, PO Box 582
Boonville, NY 13309
(800) 684-7486

Outers Gunslick
Blount, Inc., Sporting Equipment Division
PO Box 856
2299 Snake River Ave.
Lewiston, ID 83501
(800) 635-7656
Available: Retail
Solvents, lubricants and protectors, cleaning brushes, tips and patches.

Ox-Yoke Originals
34 West Main St., Milo, ME 04463
(800) 231-8313
FAX: (207) 943-2416
Est.: 1970   Staff: 40
President: C.E. Bottomley
Available: Retail
Quality shotgun rifle & black powder shooting & gun care accessories. Ox-Yoke Products are exclusively used by the U.S. Shooting Team.

Pro-Shot Products, Inc.
PO Box 763, Taylorville, IL 62568
(217) 824-9133
FAX: (217) 824-8861
Contact: John E. Damann

Prolix-Division of ProChemCo
PO Box 1348, Victorville, CA 92393
(619) 243-3129
FAX: (619) 241-0148
Est.: 1984
Sales/Tech: Philip Levy
Available: Retail & Direct
Prolix is #1 in Total Gun Care Products! The pioneers and first on the market with an all-in-one product that works!

Remington Arms Company, Inc.
Delle Donne Corporate Center
1011 Centre Road, Second Floor
Wilmington, DE 19805-1270
(800) 243-9700
(302) 993-8500 (Business Offices)
Est.: 1816
Available: Retail
Remington provides complete shotgun firearm care kits; oils and lubricants; cleaning fluids and supplies; gun parts and accessories.
See Our Ad Pg. 105

Rig Products
87 Coney Island Dr.
Sparks, NV 89431
(702) 331-5666
FAX: (702) 331-5669
Contact: Al Selleck
Available: Retail

Rusteprufe Laboratories
1319 Jefferson Ave.
Sparta, WI 54656
(608) 269-4144
President: Robert Munger
Rust preventing oil; applicator/wiper

Sentry Solutions, Ltd.
111 Sugar Mill Rd.
PO Box 130
Contoocook, NH 03229
(800) 546-8049

(603) 746-5687
FAX: (603) 746-5847
Est.: 1991
Available: Retail & Direct
Manufacturer of high tech dry film lubricants and corrosion inhibitors for all types of firearms and equipment. Mention Wing & Clay for free samples.

Shooter's Choice Gun Care
Venco Industries, Inc.
16770 Hilltop Park Pl.
Chagrin Hills, OH 44023
(216) 543-8808
FAX: (216) 543-8811
Est.: 1983   Staff: 10
Contact: Joseph Ventimiglia
Available: Retail
Constantly searching for a higher standard in firearm care, Shooter's Choice offers a full line of products—cleaners, lubricants and preventatives—backed by the best guarantee in the the business: Complete satisfaction in our products ability to out perform the competition or your money back! Available at your firearms dealer.
See Our Ad Below

Silencio/Safety Direct, Inc.
56 Coney Island Dr.,
Sparks, NV 89431
(800) 648-1812
FAX: (702) 359-1074
President: Gordon Kramer
Marketing Mgr: Howard Levine
Available: Retail
Silencio's TICO Tool will clean and oil your shotgun in 30 seconds. Washable cleaning bar provides years of dependable service. Comes with vinyl storage case.

Sportsman's Rust Guard
Sporting Kare Specialties
PO Box 19229
Minneapolis, MN 55419-9229
(800) 281-8101
(612) 869-2829

TDP Industries
606 Airport Blvd.
Doylestown, PA 18901
(215) 345-8687
Contact: Charles Magee
Cleaners, solvents, lubricants, conditioners.

Tetra Gun Products
Division of FTI, Inc.
1812 Margaret Ave.
Annapolis, MD 21401
(410) 268-6451
FAX: (410) 268-8377
Marketing Mgr: Stephen Meima
Available: Retail
Lubricants and cleaning materials.

TRAVELING WITH YOUR SHOTGUN

Flying With Your Shotgun Is Legal And Easy

Flying within the United States on a commercial airliner with your unloaded shotgun is easy and legal. All airlines require a hard-shell, crush proof, lockable gun case (priced from $150 to $700). And just to be safe, you should allow an additional 15 minutes at check-in.

Each airline has its own rules governing firearms, but they are basically similar. If you follow these steps, you'll breeze through the process and wonder why you ever left your shotgun at home:

- **Step 1:** *Declare Your Firearm* When you check your other luggage, tell the curbside sky-cap or customer service agent at the check-in counter that you are traveling with an *unloaded firearm* and would like to know what you need to do to check it in.

- **Step 2:** *Inspect & Tag* Very often you will be directed to a "semi-private area" at the counter or curb area and asked by an airline employee to unlock the travel case and display the unloaded firearm. After a brief inspection, you will be asked to sign a 3" by 5" *declaration tag*, which attests that you understand that traveling with a loaded firearm violates Federal law and that the firearm you are checking-in is, indeed, unloaded. The tag will then be placed in or on the case.

- **Step 3:** *Lock & Send* The customer service representative will ask you to close and lock your case--the airlines *require* that you alone hold the key or combination-- and it will then be checked through to your final destination.

- **Step 4:** *Pick Up* Very often your gun case will arrive on the luggage carousel along with your other luggage. At some airports, however, the case will be taken to a special pickup area. Just ask one of the sky-caps or customer service reps when you arrive.

A Word About Ammo

Your gun is "one-of-a-kind" and well worth the extra effort to bring it along on business or vacation. But a shotgun shells are readily available in most areas of the U.S. And unless you think you're going to have trouble buying the particular type of shell you like to shoot at your destination, you're better off traveling without them. If you must bring ammo with you, be aware that the airlines generally limit you to 5 pounds of ammo per firearm checked (a maximum of 10 lbs. on some airlines) and require that the ammo be factory boxed and securely packaged.

Another alternative to carrying shells is pre-shipping them to your locations via a common carrier, such as United Parcel Service. Call the carrier you are thinking of using for information.

Gun Cases

from

ALUMA

S P O R T

BY DEE ZEE

GUN CASES

For Soft Gun Cases See:
- *Accessories/ Bags, Pouches & Soft Gun Cases, Pg. 54*

Aluma Sport
by Dee Zee
PO Box 3090, Des Moines, IA 50316
(800) 798-9899 (Cust. Serv.)
(515) 265-7331
FAX: (515) 265-7926
Est.: 1978   Staff: 400
Contact: Chuck Long,
Dean Hulsebuss or
Jeff Johnson
Available: Retail
* Extruded aluminum panels provide strong construction
* Unique gear type hinge for maintenance free operation
* Steel drawlatches offer lockable security
* Full length neoprene gaskets seal out dust and moisture
* Available in black and silver finishes
* Airline approved
See Our Ad Across

Americase Incorporated
1610 E. Main, PO Box 271
Waxahachie, TX 75165
(800) 972-2737

(214) 937-3629
FAX: (214) 937-8373
Est.: 1985   Staff: 30
Contact: Bill Kinsala
Available: Retail & Direct
Want to know more about Americase – our catalog is all you need; it contains complete details and illustrations on our entire line of standard and custom made cases. Americase engineered products combine high strength to weight ratios and classic good looks to suit your every travel need. Approved for air travel. Send for our catalog. You won't be disappointed! Americase also manufactures ATA Spec 300 products.
See Our Ad Below

Beretta U.S.A.
c/o Beretta Gallery
New York:
718 Madison Ave.
New York, NY 10021
(212) 319-6614
Alexandria:
317 S. Washington St.
Old Town Alexandria, VA 22314
(703) 739-0596
Available: Retail
For transporting and protecting your fine Beretta firearms and accessories, we offer a complete line of cases. There are custom-designed Beretta gun cases from

simple soft to molded and aluminum cases. Call for catalog.

Browning
One Browning Place
Morgan, UT 84050
(800) 333-3288 (Customer)
(801) 876-2711 (General)
Est.: 1878   Staff: 350
Available: Retail

Classic Cases
38 Mary Hadge Dr.
Niskayuna, NY 12309-3417
(518) 869-5796
Contact: John Dingman
Available: Direct
Solid oak gun cases, polished brass hardware, padded handle, convoluted foam interior, laquer finish.

ClydesDale
ClydesDale Manufacturing
Box 961, West Chester, OH 45071
(800) 706-6111
FAX: (513) 777-4004
Est.: 1994   Staff: 3
President: Dale Fenn
Available: Retail & Direct
Premium gun cases

Contico International Inc.
1101 Warson Rd.
St. Louis, MO 63132
(314) 997-5900
Est.: 1985   Staff: 2000
Nat'l. Sales Coord.: Jack Berman
Available: Retail
Plastic gun cases, bow cases, ammo boxes, storage bins.

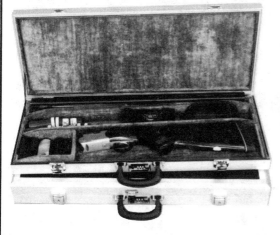

Elk River
PO Box 7321
1225 Paonia St.
Colorado Springs, CO 80933
(719) 574-4407
President: Les Turner
Available: Retail & Direct
Luggage-style gun cases.

Flambo
15981 Valplast, Box 97
Middlefield, OH 44062
(216) 632-1631
Est.: 1994   Staff: 250
Contact: Chris Paradise
Available: Retail
Full line of shotgun, rifle and pistol cases.

Hastings /John™ Hall UNIVERSAL™ GUN CASE

Quite Possibly the Finest Gun Case on the Market!

Designed by All-American Shooting Champion John Hall to be the ultimate gun case. Ultra high impact polycarbonate for extra strength and rigidity makes it the toughest, most durable gun case available. **So strong, it's nearly indestructible.**

The Hastings/John Hall Case . . . used by competitive shooting champions in trap, skeet, live pigeons, and traveling hunters. The universal case is compact and easy to carry. Weighing just eight pounds, it's the maximum in protection with minimum size.

Three models available in choice of black or special order red exterior. **Universal** holds two receivers and three sets of barrels. **Auto** holds two automatic or pump shotguns. **Four Barrel** holds one receiver and four sets of barrels. Available through fine gunshops or contact:

Hastings   **(913) 632-3169**
Box 224 • Clay Center, KS 67432

Luggage by BRILEY®

1-800-331-5718

GALAZAN
GALAZAN
A Division of Connecticut Shotgun Manufacturing
PO Box 1692
New Britain, CT 06051-1692
(203) 225-6581
FAX: (203) 832-8707
Est.: 1967   Staff: 20
Contact: Dick Perrett
- Cases built for double shotguns and rifles. The finest quality traditional leather trunk cases and best oak & leather cases as well as oak & leather ammo boxes and leather shooting bags.
- Gun case accessories. The same high quality snap caps and case accessories furnished by the best English gun companies.
- English style gunmaker trade labels.

Gun Guard/Doskocil
PO Box 1246, Arlington, TX 76004
(817) 467-5116
Contact: Pat Hoffman
Available: Retail
Hard-shell plastic firearm, archery and accessory cases.

Hastings
Hastings/John Hall Gun Cases
320 Court St., PO Box 224
Clay Center, KS 67432
(913) 632-3169
Est.: 1985
President: Robert Rott
Designed by All-American Shooting Champion John Hall to be the ultimate gun case. Ultra high impact polycarbonate for extra strength and rigidity makes the Hastings/John Hall gun case so strong it's nearly indestructible. Available in three configurations to accommodate any gun.
See Our Ad Above Left

Hill Case Co.
806 Brookwood Dr.
Landrum, SC 29356
(803) 457-2694
Est.: 1988
Contact: Lenny Hill
Available: Retail & Direct
Custom made cases for most anything in shooting.
- ATA approved, hand-fitted hard cases
- Airline approved true flight case,

won't dent
- Interior made with super high density foam for maximum protection
- Custom cut-outs for proper fit
- Constructed of 5-ply plywood, laminated with ABS sheets and milled countersink screws, not rivets, for maximum durability.

Hoppe's – Penguin Industries, Inc.
Airport Industrial Mall
Coatesville, PA 19320
(610) 384-6000
FAX: (610) 857-5980
Contact: Patricia Lucas
Available: Retail
Hoppe's Protecto Cases are designed to carry virtually any rifle or shotgun.

Huey Handbuilt Gun Case
PO Box 22456,
Kansas City, MO 64113
(816) 444-1637
Est.: 1976   Staff: 2
Contact: Marvin Huey
Available: Direct
Deluxe oak & leather trunk cases, custom fitted, no two alike.

Hunting Classics, Ltd.
936 N. Marietta St.
PO Box 2089, Gastonia, NC 28054
(704) 867-1307
FAX: (704) 867-0491
Est.: 1912   Staff: 150
Contact: R.B. Jenkins
Customer Service: Jeff Huffstickler
Available: Retail & Direct

ICC,
Impact Case Company
PO Box 9912, Spokane, WA 99209
(800) 262-3322
FAX: (509) 326-5436
Est.: 1985
Contact: Bob Knouff or
Brad Knouff
Available: Retail & Direct
ICC, Impact Case Company Protective Metal Firearms Transport/ Shipping Cases are constructed of either .063 or .080 aluminum, with heli-arc welded corners, full-length staked hinge, Stainless Steel Locking Rod, plus numerous other "toughness" features making it the best Firearms and Archery Transport/Shipping Case available. When the success of your trip depends on your firearms and equipment arriving intact, don't settle for anything less than an ICC transport case. Please call for specifications, test information and easy ordering procedures.
See Our Ad Right

Kalispel Case Line Products
PO Box 267, Hwy. 20
Cusick, WA 99119
(800) 398-0338 (Orders)
(509) 445-1121
FAX: (509) 445-1082
Est.: 1970   Staff: 4
Contact: Jim Sattleen
Available: Retail & Direct
Airline approved aluminum cases.

Kolpin Manufacturing, Inc.
PO Box 107
205 Depot St.
Fox Lake, WI 53933
(800) 556-5746
FAX: (414) 928-3687
Customer Service: Mike Bentz
VP/Mktg: Cole Braun
Available: Retail & Direct
Kolpin Gun Boot III, airline approved; made of HD polyethylen shell.

Kratz Custom Cases
709 S. Adams St.
Arlington, VA 22204-2114
(703) 521-4588
Contact: David A. Kratz
Available: Direct

Mike's Case Company
3901 Nome St., Unit #7
Denver, CO 80239
(800) 847-4002 (Cust. Service)
(303) 371-5659
FAX: (303) 371-5915
Est.: 1994
Contact: Mike Bryant
Available: Retail & Direct
Mike*s Case Company is a small company dedicated to designing and manufacturing the finest in flight style cases. Mike provides the finest quality, appearance and protection at affordable prices. Mike has an excellent line of flight style gun cases now available. These cases offer simply the finest protection, quality and appearance available.
Contact Mike for more information or literature on these excellent cases. Mike*s offers a complete line of simply the finest cases, unique finishes, custom interiors and friendly service.

Nasco Aluminum
14232 McCallum
Alliance, OH 44601
(216) 821-4621
Contact: Otis Lee

Nizzoli of Italy Gun Cases
New England Arms Co. - Sole
Distributor
Box 278, Lawrence Lane
Kittery Point, ME 03905
(207) 439-0593
FAX: (207) 439-6726
Est.: 1975   Staff: 6
Contact: Jim Austin or
Steve McCarthy
Available: Retail & Direct
Hundreds of cases in stock for all
sizes and shapes including double
shotgun cases. Precision leather
fabrication.

Pointer
Specialties
PO Box 152
Wellsville, PA 17365
(717) 292-4776
FAX: (717) 292-0440
Contact: Jim Dickey
Available: Retail & Direct
Makers and distributors of deluxe
cherry hardwood gun cases, protec-
tive vests for dogs and shooting
bench rests.
See Our Ad Below

Quality Arms, Inc.
PO Box 19477
Houston, TX 77224
(713) 870-8377
Est.: 1975   Staff: 3
Contact: John Boyd
Available: Retail & Direct
One of the largest suppliers of
trunk style cases in the U.S. Our
cases are made of aluminum, ABS,
canvas or leather. We can provide
a case for just about every situation. In addition, we can do
custom cases.
See Our Ad Above

Remington
C O U N T R Y

**Remington Arms
Company, Inc.**
Delle Donne Corporate Center
1011 Centre Road, Second Floor
Wilmington, DE 19805-1207
(800) 243-9700
(302) 993-8500 (Business Offices)

Est.: 1816
Available: Retail
Remington provides a full line of
soft gun cases, as well as airline-ap-
proved cases and gun stocks.

RHINO.
GUN CASES, INC.

Rhino Gun Cases, Inc.
4960 SW 52nd, #408
Davie, FL 33314
(800) 226-3613
(305) 797-0600
FAX: (305) 797-9350
Est.: 1988
Contact: Janet Morales or
Joe Morales
Available: Retail & Direct
Retail Outlets: Dealers Worldwide.
Rhino Cases are hand crafted, custom quality manufactured for
airline travel. Exterior material is
.080 marine grade aluminum
welded at the corners for increased strength. Water tight and
dust tight with 1/2" interior to gas-
keting. Interior protection
enhanced with plush padded compartments, closed cell foam with
soft fabrics in a choice of colors.
No cardboard, plastic or wood
used. Custom work available. Call
for sizes & prices.
See Our Ad Across

**Rose Trunk Manufacturing
Co., Inc.**
800 Alabama Ave.
Brooklyn, NY 11207
(800) 221-6737
(718) 257-3131
FAX: (718) 257-0832
Est.: 1945
President: Melvin W. Lapidus

SKB Corporation
434 W. Levers Pl.
Orange, CA 92667
(800) 654-5992
(714) 637-1250
FAX: (714) 637-0491
Est.: 1974   Staff: 500
Contact: Steve Madison
Available: Retail
ATA-rated rifle, shotgun, pistol &
archery cases

Vault Cases, Inc.
Box 684
O'Fallon, IL 62269
(800) 297-1198
FAX: (618) 644-9567
Contact: Frank Gordon
Available: Retail & Direct

Vermont Custom Cases
Rt. 5, Main St., Box 33
Westminster, VT 05158
(800) 952-1215
(802) 722-9019
Est.: 1989   Staff: 4
Contact: Robert L. Byington
Available: Retail & Direct
Premium quality gun cases; complete line of gun cases. Breakdown shotgun, rifle, handgun. Full upholstery with velour, built-in dividers, interior and ext. color choices.

Warrior Luggage
by Briley
1230 Lumpkin
Houston, TX 77043
(800) 331-5718 (Cust. Svc.)
(713) 932-6995

Contact: Chuck Webb
Available: Retail & Direct
The only lightweight stainless steel case on the market. With full welded seams, automotive fabric interior, and coffered corners that defy mistreatment by baggage handlers, this case is built with modern materials to English trunk case quality standards. Also available is an aluminum traditional tube set case for those on a budget; strong, light with all the "right stuff"–in stock for immediate shipment. Call for a brochure.
See Our Ad Pg. 110

Weatherby
2781 Firestone Blvd.
South Gate, CA 92080
(800) 227-2016 (Cust. Svc.)
(213) 569-7186
Est.: 1946   Staff: 65

Available: Retail
Anodized aluminum gun cases and high impact gun guard cases.

Zero Halliburton
200 North 500 West
North Salt Lake, UT 84054
(801) 299-7355
FAX: (801) 299-7350
Contact: Evon Young
Available: Direct
Aluminum gun case

Ziegel Engineering
2108 Lomina Ave.
Long Beach, CA 90815
(310) 596-9481
FAX: (310) 590-4734
Est.: 1972   Staff: 10
Contact: Dean Ziegel
Available: Retail & Direct
Heavy duty aluminum travel gun cases. Visa and Mastercard accepted.

SHOTGUNNER'S SOURCE

GUN CLUB SERVICES

For related prodcuts & services see:

- Carts, Racks..., Pg. 75
- Course Designers, Pg. 83
- Insurance, Pg. 127
- Trap Manufacturers, Pg. 209
- Trap Accessories, Pg. 235

Operating a gun club—hunting preserve, sporting clay, trap or skeet location—is a complex undertaking. Fortunately, in recent years , a growing number of companies have emerged to offer professional assistance to gun clubs. Those listed in the following sections are among them. Call or write each directly for more information.

CLUB SERVICES/ ENVIRONMENTAL

EA Engineering, Science & Technology, Inc.

11019 McCormick Rd.
Hunt Valley, MD 21031
(800) 876-4950
(410) 584-7000
FAX: (410) 771-9148
Contact: Dick Peddicord, Ph.D.
EA is the most experienced U.S. firm providing environmental support to the shooting sports. Our objective is to help your range with proactive and cost-effective compliance with whatever environmental requirements you may face. As the shooting sports face increasing environmental regulation, EA can support you with everything from preliminary evaluation through initial field investigation to full site assessments if warranted, including strategic consultation on the best ways to protect your interests. Offices throughout the United States and Internationally.
See Our Ad Below

CLUB SERVICES/ LEAD SHOT RECLAMATION

B.E.C. Productions
398 Gary Lee Dr.
Gahanna, OH 43230
(614) 475-7122
Est.: 1977
Contact: Fred Bichsel

Eagle Industrial Hygiene Associates
359 Dresher
Horsham, PA 19044
(215) 672-6088
Contact: Alan Okun

Karl & Associates, Inc.
Remediation Contractor
PO Box 645
Shillington, PA 19607
(610) 777-5719
Director: David Shirey

Lead Reclamation
Division of Hardcast Enterprises, Inc.
23128 Wildwood Rd.
Newhall, CA 91321
(805) 259-4796
Est.: 1980
President: Fred W. Wooldridge

MARCOR
PO Box 1043
Hunt Valley, MD 21030-6043
(800) 547-0128
FAX: (410) 771-0348
Project Mgr/Firing Range Remediation: John R. Peterson

National Range Recovery Corporation
735 Fox Chase
Suite 11
Coatesville, PA 19320
(610) 384-6188
FAX: (610) 384-6023
Est.: 1991
Principal: Thomas P. Schafer

Property Solutions, Inc.
10 Tidswell Ave., Bldg. B
Medford, NJ 08055
(609) 953-0003
FAX: (609) 953-0017
VP/Mktg.: Timothy M. Downes

**Gene Sears
Supply Company**
PO Box 38, El Reno, OK 73036
(800) 654-4520
FAX: (405) 262-2811
Contact: Garland Sears

CLUB SERVICES/ MANAGEMENT

Field Sport Concepts, Ltd.
Queen Charlotte Square
256 East High St.
Charlottesville, VA 22902
(804) 979-7522
FAX: (804) 977-1194
Contact: Raymond G. Woolfe, Jr.
Land use planning services.

Marty Fischer
dba SportShooting Consultants, Ltd.
PO Box 207, Rincon, GA 31326
(912) 826-0072
Est.: 1992
Contact: Marty Fischer
Services Provided: Marketing Consultation, Management Consultation & Training, Pro Shop Set Up, Business Plans, Feasibility Studies, Clay Course Design, Clay Course Equipment Sales, Special Event marketing, Hunting Preserve Consultation, NSCA Level III Instruction

**Southeastern
Illinois College**
P.O. Box 200, Vienna, IL 62995
(618) 658-2211
Contact: Bruce Hering
The only program in the U.S. train-

ing hunting preserve managers. Associate Degree Program. Practical technical training. Hands-on, in-the-field internships. Job placement assistance.
See Our Ad Pg. 257

Jimmy Vaughan
1430 Marion Ave.
Tallahassee, FL 32303
(904) 561-5512
Preserve consulting; all phases of your operation from agriculture to office routines, to marketing, to lodging, to guides methods.

CLUB SERVICES/ MARKETING

Nichols Boyesen & Zino
194 Valley View Rd.
New Hartford, NY 13413
(315) 797-0700
FAX: (315) 738-0224
Est.: 1987   Staff: 30
Contact: Hans Boyesen
Creative advertising and marketing services for the outdoor industry.
See Our Ad Pg. 48

Outdoor Management Network
4607 N.E. Cedar Creek Rd.
Woodland, WA 98674
(360) 225-5000
FAX: (360) 225-7616
President: Robert R. Knopf
Specializing in outdoor and travel marketing

CLUB SERVICES/ REFEREES

Sandy Hudson
11120 Augustine Herman Hwy.
Chestertown, MD 21620
(410) 348-2148
Certified FITASC referees

National Sporting Clays Association (NSCA)
5931 Roft Rd.,
San Antonio, TX 78253
(210) 688-3371
FAX: (210) 688-3014
Contact: John Higgins (Ext. 103)

Sporting Clays of America (SCA)
9 Mott Ave., Suite 103
Norwalk, CT 06850
(203) 831-8453
Contact: Timothy Nichols

CLUB SERVICES/ VIDEOS

Hunter's Choice Photography

Hunter's Choice Photography & Video
7615 Columbus Rd.
Lizella, GA 31052-1529
(912) 935-8134 (Phone/Fax)
Est.: 1991   Staff: 4
Contact: Bill M. McLendon
Show what your Facility has to offer, with an ACTION PACKED VIDEO!!!! Specialized Promotional videos, and photography, for Hunting Preserves and Plantations that want to promote their upland gamebird hunting to your potential customers. Projects done by experience hunting personnel who know what to look for when it comes to promoting your Facility. Video and Photography for private hunting groups available. For further information call or write. DEMO VIDEO AVAILABLE. Serious inquiries only!

Sunrise Productions
128 McCullough Dr.,
Cody, WY 82414
(800) 862-6399
(307) 587-3250
Contact: Bruce Scott
Producers of film and video productions for the shooting industry.

GUN SAFES

If you're like most gun owners, you own more than one gun. And if you're like most gun owners--8 out of 10 according to industry experts--you'll wait until after you've been robbed or burgled to buy a safe to protect your guns. Why wait?

The average gun owner pays somewhere in the range of $600 to $3,000 for a safe, with the most popular models selling for between $1,000 and $2,000. These prices do not include shipping costs or options and accessories.

One Time Buy

Safes are built to last. It's that long product life, however, that makes buying a safe interesting: pick the wrong model and you have to deal with the mistake for a long time.

Take storage capacity, for example. It's easy enough for the shotgun owner to anticipate the need for a safe high enough to accomodate his guns' longer barrels. But few first-time safe buyers realize that once the new safe is delivered almost everything of value kept at home--jewelry, documents and so--on will end up in it. So don't discount the salesman's advice when he tells you to "buy as big as you can afford." You'll thank him later.

How Safe Is Safe

Beyond looks and capacity, a good quality safe must be, well, safe. Safe from theives, safe from the corrosive effects of humidity, and to an extent, safe from fire.

Let's start with thieves. It's an industry truism that given enough time, any safe can be cracked. Time then is the critical fac-

tor. And since research shows that a burglar will spend on average only 7-12 minutes as an uninvited guest in your home, you don't need a safe with foot-thick steel walls to protect your guns.

In some sections of the country--especially the Deep-South--the corrosive effects of moisture are far more likely to rob you of your valued guns than a thief. Ventilation is the easiest way to handle the problem, so many manufacturers drill air holes in their safes to allow air to flow around the door, even when it's closed. Others provide built-in dehumidifiers to do the job. Unfortunately, ventilation diminishes a safe's ability to protect against fire. Again, ask your dealer.

Heavy Metal

Most safes are made of metal plate. And, in the simplest terms, the thicker the plate, the more difficult it is to "crack" the safe. The thicker the plate, however, the heavier the safe. Having noted this, don't make the common mistake of buying "by the pound". What you are looking for, they say, is enough metal to discourage the bad guys.

Warranty & Service

Warranties differ in length and conditions from manufacturer to manufacturer, though it isn't uncommon for the bigger names in the industry to offer a life-time replacement guarantee against break-in. More important than warranty, some experts say, are service terms. Who do you turn to when something's not working? And who pays for repairs? Ask before you buy.

GUN SECURITY/ SAFES

American Security Products
11925 Pacific Ave.
Fontana, CA 92337
(909) 685-9680
FAX: (909) 685-9685
Est.: 1948　Staff: 320
Contact: Tracy R. Russell
Available: Retail

Browning
One Browning Place
Morgan, UT 84050
(800) 333-3288 (Customer)
(801) 876-2711 (General)
Est.: 1878　Staff: 350
Available: Retail
Different sizes & interiors, optional fire resistant features

Bulldog Gun Safe Co.
PO Box 240, Syracuse, NY 13206
(800) 933-9115
FAX: (315) 434-9422
Est.: 1995　Staff: 60
Nat'l. Sales Mgr: Mark Koesterer
Available: Retail

Cannon Safe, Inc.
9358 Stephens St.
Pico Rivera, CA 90660
(800) 242-1055
Contact: Jesse Bugarin
Available: Retail

Coach House Antiques
PO Box 118
High Point, NC 27261
(910) 887-4988
Contact: Harriet
Available: Retail & Direct
Beautiful antique reproduction safes that blend-in with furniture; steel construction, wood exterior.

Cobalt Manufacturing, Inc.
1020 Shady Oaks Dr.
Denton, TX 76205
(817) 382-8986
FAX: (817) 383-4281
Est.: 1992　Staff: 25
President: Craig Watkins
Available: Retail
High quality, high gloss, U.L. listed gun safes
Every Cobalt safe has a laser cut 1/4 inch door and front face with a 10 gauge body. Automotive quality paint, polished brass trim, top read key locking dial, easily accessible gun racks and full fire protection are all standard features. Cobalt safes are sold only through store-front dealers.

Decoy Safe Co.
323 North Ivy Lane
Orlando, FL 32811
(800) 972-1850
Est.: 1990　Staff: 16
Contact: Dan Terrico
Available: Retail & Direct
Maker of the STEALTH gun safe.

Fort Knox Security Products
1051 North Industrial Park Rd.
Orem, UT 84057
(800) 821-5216
Est.: 1979　Staff: 60
Mktg. Dir.: T.J. James
Available: Retail & Direct
Fort Knox offers a full line of quality safes. The Chuck Yeager series features concealed hinges, reinforced door, certified 1200 degree fire protection & corner bolts. Executive, Guardian & Protector series offer similar security advantage– include life-time warranty & UL listing.

Frontier Safe Company
3201 S. Clinton St.
Fort Wayne, IN 46806
(800) 461-6131
(219) 744-7233
FAX: (219) 744-6678
President: Marcus Brewer
Sales/Mktg: Fred Caeser
Available: Retail
Manufacturers of laminated steel and hardplate safes. Several models available.

Goldfield Safe Company
PO Box 50805
Provo, UT 84605
(800) 374-6618
FAX: (801) 374-6621
Est.: 1993　Staff: 20
President: G. James Hutchins
Sales Mgr: Dale Kohler
Available: Retail & Direct
Each safe we build meets rigid standards for structural and operational integrity, and for aesthetic appearance. Goldfield takes pride in our smallest Sentry safe as in our most impressive, deluxe Citadel model.

Granite Security Products, Inc.
5216 David Strickland Rd.
Ft. Worth, TX 76119
(817) 561-9095
FAX: (817) 478-3056
Est.: 1991　Staff: 20
Contact: Becky Walters
Available: Retail
Steel body safe – entire safe UL approved. Lifetime warranty on all parts. All safes fully fire-lined.

Heritage Safe Co.
117 South Main, PO Box 349
Grace, ID 83241
(800) 215-SAFE
FAX: (208) 425-3052
Est.: 1993　Staff: 18
Sales Mgr: Shawn McClure
Available: Retail & Direct

Ironman Safes
PO Box 1033, Hayden, ID 83835
(800) 841-8298
(208) 722-7310
FAX: (208) 722-0381
Est.: 1980　Staff: 13
President: Don Clifton
Gen. Sales Mgr: Roy Stallings
Available: Retail

Liberty Safes
1060 N. Spring Creek Place
Springville, UT 84663
(800) 247-5625
Est.: 1989　Staff: 200
Sales: James Stoddard
Mktg. Dir: Jamey Skousen
Available: Retail
Liberty Safes are sold direct to consumers by over 500 dealers and shipped from 13 warehouse locations throughout the US and Canada. Liberty Safes are U.L. listed for security protection. Laboratory tested fire protection is standard on many of the 18 available models. Call for a FREE brochure and dealer nearest you.

National Security Safe Co., Inc.
PO Box 755,
American Fork, UT 84003
(800) 544-3829
FAX: (801) 756-8043
Est.: 1985　Staff: 65
Sales: Todd Atkinson
Available: Retail & Direct
We build gun safes, home safes & vault doors.
See Our Ad Pg.116

Northland Gun Safes
Panel Specialties, Inc.
1720 Madison St., NE
Minneapolis, MN 55413
(612) 789-0925
FAX: (612) 789-0196
Est.: 1985　Staff: 18
Sales Manager: Doug O'Brien
Available: Retail

Remington.
C O U N T R Y

Remington Arms Company, Inc.
Delle Donne Corporate Center
1011 Centre Road, Second Floor
Wilmington, DE 19805-1270
(800) 479-2563
(302) 993-8500 (Business Offices)
Est.: 1816
Available: Retail
If you're looking for a worry-free place to store firearms and other valuables, your timing couldn't be better. You see, after 179 years of making the best-selling guns in the world, Remington is now making a place to put them. Our new gun safes are built Remington tough, with the finest, performance-tested security features. And while that's good for your gun collection, it does wonders for your peace of mind. For a brochure describing our complete line, call 1-800-479-2563.
See Our Ad Pg. 35

Rocky Mountain Safe Co.
PO Box 521
Springville, UT 84663
(800) 787-6259
(801) 798-6364

FAX: (801) 798-9113
Est.: 1994   Staff: 40
Sales Mgr: Lavar Felix
Available: Retail & Direct

Sportsman Steel Safe Co.
6309-6311 Paramount Blvd.
Long Beach, CA 90805
(800) 266-7150
FAX: (310) 984-8116
Est.: 1969   Staff: 45
President: Fred Hand
Contact: Kevin Hand
Available: Direct

Sun Welding Safe Co.
290 Easy St., Suite #3
Simi Valley, CA 93065
(800) 729-SAFE
(805) 584-6678
Est.: 1980
Contact: Mary Simpson
Available: Retail & Direct

Tread Corporation
Treadlok Gun Safes
1764 Granby St., NE
Roanoke, VA 24012
(800) 729-8732
(703) 982-6881
Mkg. Dir: Ken Spratt
Available: Retail & Direct
Steel safes of 10 gauge formed steel channels, 1/4" plate steel door, U.L. listed group 2 combination lock.
See Our Ad Below

United Safe Co.
PO Box 400
400 South 3rd St.
Benton, PA 17814
(800) 505-5085
(717) 925-5684
FAX: (717) 925-2475
Est.: 1992   Staff: 14
Contact: Michael S. Klem
Available: Retail
"America's Safe Manufacturer" continues to set the standard. The Colonial Series combines classic design with unsurpassed quality, security and value. Choose from 8 designer colors. Lifetime warranty.
See Our Ad Pg. 116

Weatherby
2781 Firestone Blvd.
South Gate, CA 92080
(800) 227-2016 (Cust. Svc.)
(213) 569-7186
Est.: 1946   Staff: 65
Available: Retail
Signature Series safes with 10 gauge steel, body construction. A variety of gun storage and shelving options are available.

Winchester Safes
Meilink Safe Co.
111 Security Pkwy.
New Albany, IN 47150
(800) 4WI-NSAF
(812) 941-1655
FAX: (812) 948-0437
Est.: 1994   Staff: 85
President: Van Carlisle
Nat'l. Sales Mgr: Dennis Lindsey
Available: Retail

Wing Sales & Safe Co.
7011 E. Trent
Spokane, WA 99212
(800) 949-4328
FAX: (800) 659-7824
Est.: 1985   Staff: 7
President: Bill Wing
Available: Retail & Direct

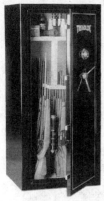

GUN SECURITY/ CABINETS

Aluma Sport by Dee Zee
PO Box 3090
Des Moines, IA 50316
(800) 798-9899 (Cust. Service)
(515) 265-7331
FAX: (515) 265-7926
Est.: 1978   Staff: 400
Contact: Chuck Long,
Dean Hulsebuss or
Jeff Johnson
Available: Retail
The lightweight aluminum Gun
Vault provides security for your
gear. 8 and 10 gun storage units
available.

Crystal Vault
Matrix Technical Engineering
PO Box 11
Greencastle, IN 46135
(800) 678-7233
FAX: (317) 653-7175
Est.: 1992   Staff: 13
President: Terry Moore
Available: Retail & Direct
CRYSTAL VAULT is a museum qual-
ity display safe for home use, clear
as glass, but better protection than
a steel safe.

Hardworks, Inc.
PO Box 159, Nipigon, Ontario
Canada P0T 2J0
(807) 887-2133
FAX: (807) 887-2604
Contact: Bruce Atkinson
Available: Direct

Homak Home Security
3800 W. 45th
Chicago, IL 60632

(800) 874-6625
(312) 523-3100
FAX: (312) 523-9455
Est.: 1945   Staff: 200
VP/Sales: Mike Moser
Available: Retail

Kennedy Mfg. Co.
520 E. Sycamore St.
Box 151
Van Wert, OH 45891-0151
(419) 238-2442
FAX: (419) 238-5644
Est.: 1911
Mktg. Mgr: John Aycock
KenCraft security cabinets

Prototech Industries,Inc.
Rt. 1, Box 81, Delia, KS 66418
(913) 771-3571
Est.: 1961   Staff: 18
Contact: Mike Butler
Available: Retail & Direct
Gun safes and security systems for
vehicles.

Sandusky Cabinets, Inc.
PO Box 1040,
Sandusky, OH 44870
(419) 626-5465
FAX: (419) 626-3308
Est.: 1929   Staff: 300
VP/Nat'l. Sales Mgr: Ronald J.
Nickle
Available: Retail

Se-Cur-All Cabinets
5122 N. State Rd. 39
PO Box 1848
LaPorte, IN 46350-8782
(219) 326-7890
(219) 326-1288
FAX: (219) 324-3780
Est.: 1952   Staff: 65
Creative Director: Sean Rober
Available: Retail

Jim Simmons Company
Security Products Division
952 Main St.
Nashville, TN 37206
(800) 251-4931
(615) 228-4931
FAX: (615) 226-4996
Est.: 1980   Staff: 13
President: Jim Simmons
Available: Retail

Stack-On Products Company
PO Box 489, 1360 N. Old Rand
Wauconda, IL 60084
(800) 323-9601
FAX: (708) 526-6599
Nat'l. Sales Mgr: John Amerine
VP Sale/Mktg: Jon Fiscus
Available: Retail & Direct

GUN SECURITY/ SAFETY DEVICES & GUN LOCKS

GunLoc
Universal GunLoc Industries, Ltd.
525 Highway 97 South
Kelowna, B.C.
Canada V1Z 3J2
(800) 565-4887 (Orders)
FAX: (604) 769-3765
President: Garwood A. Leigh
Vice President: John Upton
Available: Direct
Anti-theft solution-fits all firearms.

Insta Guard
Necessary Concepts, Inc.
PO Box 571
Deer Park, NY 11729
(516) 667-8509
FAX: (516) 667-8688
Est.: 1989
President: Michael Fischer
Available: Retail & Direct
Insta Guard allows keyless access
to firearms in seconds. Fits any
shotgun or handgun. Made of
heavy gauge stainless steel with a
lifetime warranty in workmanship
& materials.

Saf-T-Round
Safety Innovations, Inc.
9208 Kingston Pike, #182
Knoxville, TN 37922-2317
(800) 248-0564
(615) 966-0748
FAX: (615) 671-0372
President: Magalene M. Plummer

SAFE DELIVERY
When arranging for the delivery of a new safe, ask your
salesman the following questions: How long will you have
to wait for delivery? (4-8 weeks is not uncommon.) Where is
the safe coming from and how much will the delivery cost
you? And finally, ask what kind of delivery you can expect.
"Ground or garage" delivery means the mover will drop the
safe in front of your house or in the driveway and you'll have
to take it from there. And that, given the substantial weight of
most safes, can pose a problem.

One final note on weight: The heavier the safe, the more
difficult it is to move it within your home. So before you
buy, consider how far and how often the safe is likely to
be moved. Also, check to make sure that the floor beneath
the safe can handle the load.

GUNSMITHING

That favorite shotgun of yours may need a simple repair or some maintenance work. Or perhaps you've decided the time has arrived for elaborate customizing that will improve your trap, skeet or sporting clays scores, or help you bag more birds in the field. In either case, the person to turn to is the gunsmith, a highly skilled craftsman who specializes in the repair and modification of firearms. How do you find a good one? Ask your fellow shooting enthusiasts for suggestions, inquire at a reputable gun store, or consult the list of top-rated gunsmiths that follows this article.

The following are among the modifications that can boost accuracy -- and scores:

The Barrel

- **Choke Modification:** Replacing or altering your shotgun's fixed choke changes the gun's shot pattern. The option preferred by most sportsmen is an interchangeable choke tube system. Easily removed and replaced, interchangeable chokes let you fine-tune the level of restriction and pellet distribution for particular sporting clays stations or field hunting. The alternative to interchangeable chokes is a fixed choke alteration. Describe the pattern characteristics you want and your gunsmith will recommend the appropriate fixed choke modification .

- **Porting:** Creating small "ports" near the muzzle end of the barrel bleeds off powder gases when the gun is fired, which helps control muzzle jump. Although this does little to reduce rearward thrust, it does lessen felt recoil. And, by keeping the muzzle from jumping upwards, porting permits a faster second shot. On single-barreled pumps and autos the ports are placed on top of the barrel, on either side of the rib. On over-unders it is common to port only the bottom barrel (normally fired first), although some shooters port both.

- **Backboring:** This process enlarges the diameter of the entire barrel, reducing shot pressure, felt recoil & shot deformation.

- **Lengthening The Forcing Cone:** Your factory-supplied forcing cone is an abrupt constriction where the front of the chamber meets the rear portion of the main bore. When it is lengthened (say, from 3/8" to as much as 4"), shot is forced into the barrel more easily, and shot deformation and recoil are reduced. Recoil sharpness is also reduced.

The Trigger

- **Fine-Tuning/Replacement:** A soft, hard or spongy trigger mechanism is bound to adversely affect accuracy. A crisp trigger, with no "creep," is very likely to improve it. Fine-tuning your trigger mechanism is simply polishing and fitting the action parts for smoother, more consistent action. Trigger replacement, on the other hand, is far more costly and it is much more difficult to find a gunsmith willing to do it. Ask your gunsmith for advice.

The Stock

- **Gunfitting:** For shooting efficiency—especially in field hunting or low gun games—your shotgun should fit as comfortably as an old pair of shoes. If the stock is too long you'll shoot high and perceive more recoil; too short and you'll shoot low. The gunsmith can alter the stock or create one that's customized. Other options include alterations or replacement of the forend, and changes to the buttstock to provide a better grip.

- **Recoil Pads:** Many shooters opt to have recoil pads added to the end of the butt to reduce felt recoil.

GUNSMITHS

For related products see:

- Chokes, Pg. 78
- Gunstocks, Pg. 125
- Recoil Products, Pg. 143

Allem's Gun Craft
7937 Sigmund Rd.
Zionsville, PA 18092
(215) 679-9016
FAX: (215) 679-8016
Est.: 1968
Contact: Nancy Allem
Available: Direct
Factory authorized repair center for Krieghoff and Perazzi. Shotgunners. . .improve your scores by reducing recoil and increasing pattern percentages with our Grand Slam Package. For only $199 per barrel, we'll backbore it, put in custom chokes and lengthen your forcing cone. Call today with your questions – we'll be happy to help!

Angle Porting
Ballistic Specialites
100 Industrial Dr.
Batesville, AR 72501
(800) 276-2550
Est.: 1991   Staff: 4
President: John Clouse
Our specialty is angle-porting, which reduces muzzle-jump and felt recoil. These are the cleanest ports you'll ever shoot!

Art's Gun & Sport, Inc.
6008 Hwy. Y, Hillsboro, MO 63050
(314) 944-3630
FAX: (314) 452-3631
Est.: 1972   Staff: 4
President: Art Isaacson
Available: Direct
30 years of experience and factory trained-we specialize in rebuilding Brownings-Superposed, Citori, and BT-99.

B □ SQUARE

B-SQUARE
2708 St. Louis Ave.
PO Box 11281
Forth Worth, TX 76110
(800) 433-2909
(817) 923-0964
Est.: 1957
Contact: Rudy Bechtel
Available: Retail & Direct
One of the largest sources of shotgun tools. Shooter's Tools: Universal Shotgun Spud-centers all bores and chokes; Recoil Pad Jig-in-

stalls recoil pads perfectly; Barrel Press-straightens any shotgun or rifle barrel; Forend Wrench-removes or installs forend slide tube recessed nuts; Rib Center Drill Jig-locates and guides drills on exact center of any rib for sight and mount installation; hammers; punches; screwdrivers; stock wrenches; shell latch; staking tools; & tube dent raiser. Call for free catalog.
See Our Ad Below

Bansner's Gunsmithing Specialties
261 East Main St., PO Box 839
Adamstown, PA 19501
(800) 368-2379
Est.: 1983   Staff: 3
Contact: Mark Bansner

Batesville Gun Works
600 N. Central, Batesville, AR 72501
(501) 793-1122
Contact: Albert R. Dick

Big Ridge Gun Smiths
32801 US 441 N.-68
Okeechobee, FL 34972
(407) 790-2440
Contact: Bill Gillette

Blue Arms Gun Shop
4570 West State
Boise, ID 83703
(208) 336-1661
Owner: Tony Fanelli
Owner: John Person
Shotgun specialists. Repairs of all types. Custom fitting. Chokes, alterations, forcing cones lengthened, stock bending, porting, etc. Professional gunsmithing.

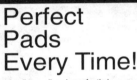

BRILEY

Briley Manufacturing
1230 Lumpkin
Houston, TX 77043
(800) 331-5718 (Cust. Svc.)
(713) 932-6995
Est.: 1976   Staff: 65
Contact: Chuck Webb
Full gunsmithing services include barrel rebuilding, metal refinishing, part fabrications and basic gun services. Full pistol division makes competitive action sport pistols, 10-22 conversions and has a full line of proprietary accessories such as barrels, bushings, comps and scope mounts. Back-boring and long forcing cones are a specialty and can be combined with screw-in choke installation. Call for brochure.
See Our Ad Pg. 27

Burgin's Gun Shop
RD1, Box 66
Sidney Center, NY 13839
(607) 829-8668
Est.: 1960   Staff: 3
Owner/Gunsmith: Bryan B. Burgin
Barrel sleeving, barrel regulating, leather pads, stock bending, custom stocking and fitting, checkering, restorations, blueing, colorcase, chokes permanent and screw-in, brochure available.

Jack Concannon

155 Kings Rd.
Mt. Holly, NJ 08060
(609) 267-8287
Contact: Jack Concannon
Jack Concannon, Gunsmith - Shooting Instructor. Try-gun for gun fitting. Instruction in trap & sporting clays. Custom barrel work, porting, long cones, microhoning, rechoking, fixed chokes & choke tubes, Briley & Rhino dealer. Adj. combs & L.O.P. Adj. pads, all brands; dealer in Terminator, KICK EEZ & Pachmayr pads. One Day Turnaround on most work, (609) 267-8287.
See Our Ad Below Left

Edwards Custom Bores & Ports

12745 Ottawa Ave., S.
Savage, MN 55378
(612) 895-0037
Est.: 1970   Staff: 1
Contact: Leigh Edwards
Custom shotgun boring. European method complete barrel bore system. Re-choking, bore restoration,

---

Question or problem?
Give Wing & Clay a call
9 am - 5 pm E.S.T.
and we'll try to help. Our
number is: (908) 224-8700.

machine porting. Entire system performed by custom crafted machinery. Custom 4-way adjustable stockwork done.

James Flynn Gunsmithing
1932 Viborg Rd.
Solvang, CA 93463
(805) 688-3158
Est.: 1985   Staff: 2
Owner: James Flynn
Repair Tec: Ron Fuakamula
Complete Beretta & Browning repair. Adjustable comb stocks; trap, skeet & sporting clays.

Glen Cove Sports Shop, Inc.
189 Forest Ave.
Glen Cove, NY 11542
(516) 676-7120
Est.: 1971   Staff: 4
Contact: John Cacciola
Custom stock work; barrel work. Specializing in repairing fine double guns.

Griffin & Howe
36 W. 44th St.
New York, NY 10036
(212) 921-0980
Contact: Dick Welch
33 Claremont Road
Bernardsville, NJ 07924
(908) 766-2287
Contact: Joe Prather
Griffin & Howe is dedicated to the legacy of craftmanship begun in 1923 by Seymour Griffin and James Howe. We are equipped to handle stock alterations, engraving, strip cleaning, trigger adjustments, and other custom gunsmithing in our workrooms.
See Our Ad Pg. 25

Paul Jaeger, Inc.
1 Madison Ave.
Grand Junction, TN 38039
(901) 764-6909
Est.: 1935   Staff: 6
Contact: Melissa Quinn (Ext. 247)
Custom gunsmithing

LaBarge-Harkness & Co.
617 E. Broadway
Alton, IL 62002
(800) 562-7980
(618) 465-7247
Est.: 1984
Contact: Paul Fuchs
Complete professional gunsmithing service, offering thirty years in caring for fine firearms. Custom wood fitting, specializing in special dimension stocks, fore arms, fine checkering, and your choice of several finishes. Our metal finishing is mostly hand polished, featuring rust blueing, salt blueing, niter blueing, metal greying and colour case hardening.
See Our Ad Below

LAZER-PORTS™
Lazer-Ports
The Shotgun Shop, Inc.
14145 Proctor Ave., #3
Industry, CA 91746
(800) 833-2737
FAX: (818) 855-2735
Contact: Bill Houston or J.D. Dickman
Lazer Ports * The Ultimate in barrel porting performance. U.S. Patent Number 5243895
- Virtually eliminate muzzle jump and felt recoil
- Quickest recovery for second shot
- Test results prove LAZER-PORTED barrels are quieter than non-ported barrels
- Priority rush service at NO EXTRA CHARGE
The Shotgun Shop, Inc. . . .We Do It All:
- Lengthening & polishing forcing cones (Super long – up to 4")

- BRILEY screw-in chokes
- Custom bluing
- Backboring
- Stock bending
- Custom Stock making
- KICK-EEZ Recoil Pad
See Our Ad Pg. 122

The Lefever Arms Co.
6234 Stokes-Lee Center Rd.
Lee Center, NY 13363
(315) 337-6722
FAX: (315) 337-1543
Owner/Pres: Giacomo Arrighini
General gunsmithing & repair for long guns.

Murray's Gun Shop
14720 NE Sandy Blvd.
Portland, OR 97230
(800) 459-3503
(503) 254-0303
FAX: (503) 254-8191
Est.: 1969   Staff: 4
Contact: Randy Murray
Available: Direct
Custom fit gunstocks of all types; barrel porting; gunsmithing; antique restorations; gunstock duplicating machine work; rust blueing; 25 years same location.
See Our Ad Pg. 126

New England Custom Gun Fitters/ Boyadjian Gun Works
250 County St.
Seekonk, MA 02771
(508) 336-9347
Est.: 1987
Contact: Hagop "Jack" Boyadjian or Gassia Boyadjian
Restoration & repair of quality shotguns, hand crafted custom shotgun stocks. Custom gun fitting & alterations.
See Our Ad Pg. 20

New England Custom Gun Service, Ltd.
Brook Rd., RR#2
Box 122W, W. Lebanon, NH 03784
(603) 469-3450
Est.: 1986   Staff: 3
Contact: Dietrich Apel
Contact: Mark Cromwell
The combined experience in gunmaking, gunsmithing and modern manufacturing enables us to provide you with a wide variety of services in a professinal manner. We have a thorough knowledge of the finest European shotguns, double rifles, drillings and combination guns. We will work on most well made sporting Long Guns, be they foreign or domestic. Our shop is well equuipped to handle both wood and metal work. Tooling and methods are constantly improved and we're open to any suggestions. For the shotgun shooter we offer: stock fitting, stock and alterations, recoil pads, patterning, long forcing cones, choke alterations, screw-in chokes, and porting.
See Our Ad Below

Nuline Guns, Inc.
1053 Caulks Hill Rd., Dept. 2800
Harvester, MO 63304
(314) 441-4500
FAX: (314) 447-5018
Est.: 1949   Staff: 17
Contact: B.J. Stevens
Our outstanding reputation as a complete and quality gunsmithing service is built on 45 years of experience repairing, rebuilding and refurbishing:
* Winchester Model 12
* Super X
* Winchester 42
* Winchester 101
From trigger to barrels, we do it all; repair and sell parts. Call for information on our estimating policy and how to ship and insure your gun. For the "do-it-yourselfers", we offer a gunsmithing video for Winchester M/12 and Super X-1 shooter....only $29.95, plus $5 S/H.

Orvis
Historic Rt. 7A
Manchester, VT 05254
(802) 362-3622
Complete gunsmithing services on all makes; leather covered recoil pads.

P&P Gunsmithing
9324 State Ave., #318
Marysville, WA 98270
(206) 356-7708
Est.: 1987   Staff: 2

Partner: Patrick Gottberg
Custom gunsmiths specializing in competition shotguns.

Precision Porting by Len Evans, III
157 N. Salem Rd.,
Conyers, GA 30208
(404) 922-3480

Pro-Port Limited
41302 Executive Dr.
Harrison Twp., MI 48045
(810) 469-7323
FAX: (810) 469-0425
The company providing porting services utilizing EDM (Electrical Discharge Machining) also offers custom shotgun services. Combined with the world famous porting process services such as lengthening & polishing forcing cones, back-boring, and rechoking. Shotgun shooters can expect nothing but quality services.
See Our Ad Pg. 145

Pylinski Arms
Rt. 2, Box 169
Cumberland, VA 23040
(804) 492-4082
Contact: Laurence Pylinski

R&D Custom Barrel
8423 Terradell St.
Pico Rivera, CA 90660
(310) 923-3608
Contact: Bob Day
Specializing in screw-in chokes for 12, 20 28 ga. and .410 bore. Custom choke work and "Point of Impact" adjustments. Barrel porting and custom stock fitting featuring Airecoil Eliminator pads. All work performed in a timely and professional manner.

Rhino Gun Cases, Inc.
4960 SW 52nd St., #408
Davie, FL 33314
(800) 226-3613
(305) 797-0600
FAX: (305) 797-9350
Contact: Janet or Joe Morales
Our gunsmithing services include custom choke installation and forcing cones. We can tap and thread your barrels for standard or thin wall systems.
See Our Ad Pg. 113

Seminole Chokes
& Gun Works
Mitchell Machine & Mfg., Inc.
3049 US 1
Mims, FL 32754
(800) 980-3344
FAX: (407) 383-8532
Est.: 1989   Staff: 6
Contact: Janice Mitchell or
Randy Mitchell
Available: Retail & Direct
Forcing cones lengthened & polished; barrel porting; barrel boring & threading for screw-in chokes; backboring "Honing"; stock bending; triggers adjusted; custom work on request.

See Our Ad Pg. 81

Sportsman's Haven, Inc.
14695 E. Pike Rd.
Cambridge, OH 43725
(614) 432-7243
FAX: (614) 432-3204
Est.: 1960   Staff: 7
Pres: Brent Umberger
Available: Direct
Complete gunsmithing service-Armorer-specializing in high grade guns-most factory warranty service.

Allen Timney Gunsmith
13524 Edgefield St.
Cerritos, CA 90703
(310) 865-0181
FAX: (909) 877-4713
Contact: Allen Timney

Trulock & Harris Gunsmiths
Corner Farm
Rumburgh, Halesworth
Suffolk 1P19 ORT England
011-44-19-867-81357
Est.: 1991
Contact: Jason Harris
With 13 years experience in gunsmithing, we are now producing an English style game gun in 12 gauge–sidelock and boxlock. We provide specialized tooling and spare parts for gunsmiths.

Doug Turnbull Restoration
6426 County Rd. 30
PO Box 471
Bloomfield, NY 14469
(716) 657-6338
Est.: 1982   Staff: 3
Contact: Doug Turnbull
Bonecharcoal color case hardening; Blueing services include rust, nitro and charcoal blue.

Herbert Weinberger
30 West Prospect St.
Waldwick, NJ 07463
(201) 447-0025
Est.: 1964   Staff: 2
Contact: Herbert Weinberger

Wessel Gun Service, Inc.
4000 E. 9 Mile Rd.
Warren, MI 48091
(810) 756-2660
Est.: 1946   Staff: 6
Contact: Richard A. Cote
Buy, sell & trade guns; Gunsmithing; Browning warranty repair.

Westchester Gun Works
34 Arthur St.
Greenwich, CT 06831
(203) 531-0284
Contact: Nicola DiGualielmo
Master Gunsmith. Trained to work on all types of guns–English guns, Trap guns, Skeet guns.

Woodcock Hill
Thomas Bland & Sons Gunmakers
RD#1, Box 147
Benton, PA 17814
(717) 864-3242
FAX: (717) 864-3232
Contact: Christa Baker or Glenn Baker
Try gun fits; shooting schools; stock bends; all manners of repair work undertaken. Emphasis on quick return to owner.

WRIGHT'S
(THE MODEL 12 SHOP)

Wright's
(The Model 12 Shop)
RR3, Box 414
Pinckneyville, IL 62274
(618) 357-8933
Est.: 1980
Contact: Stu Wright
SUPERIOR TRAP CHOKES: the permanent modification of factory chokes to improve pattern diameters and to even density, also benefits SKEET and SPORTING CLAYS. Complete repair and restoration of Winchester shotguns, Browning Competition shotguns, and Perazzis. Competition triggers installed, Recoil pads installed, Ribs resoldered, Five different blueing techniques. Reliable service of custom handcrafted quality.

GUNSTOCKS & GUNFITTING

• *See Shooting Schools, Pg. 154*

Bell & Carlson, Inc.
101 Allen Rd.
Dodge City Industrial Park
Dodge City, KS 67801
(800) 634-8586 (Orders)
(316) 225-6688
Est.: 1985   Staff: 60
Sales Mgr: Vince Carlson
Cust. Svc./Orders: Lynn Hogg
Available: Retail
Hand laminated synthetic gun stocks and custom fitting services.

Boyd's Gunstocks Industries
PO Box 305
Geddes, SD 57342
(605) 337-2125
FAX: (605) 337-3363
Est.: 1983   Staff: 25
Owner: Randy Boyd
Available: Direct
Production hardwood gunstocks and sole distributor of Bold trigger assemblies-an adjustable trigger for more common bolt action rifles.

Cali'Co Hardwoods, Inc.
1648 Airport Blvd.
Windsor, CA 95492
(707) 546-4045
FAX: (707) 546-4027
Est.: 1960
Contact: Ted Smalley
Available: Retail & Direct

Clove Valley Sports Corp.
Hidden Brook Farm
RR1, Box 110 A
Salt Point, NY 12578
(914) 266-5954
Est.: 1980   Staff: 4
Contact: Charles Conger
Custom stock fitting, alterations, bending, and leather covered recoil pads. Shooting instruction in British C.P.S.A. method.

Dakota Arms, Inc.
HC55, Box 326
Sturgis, SD 57785
(605) 347-4686
FAX: (605) 347-4459
Est.: 1960   Staff: 30
Contact: Norma Allen
Available: Retail & Direct
English, Ciaro & Bastogne Walnut in 2 piece sets or rifle blanks. Stock duplicating machine available.

J.L. Dockwiller Co.
2125 N. Orange St.
PO Box 2028
Redlands, CA 92373
(909) 793-7665
Est.: 1950
Contact: Jack or Lee Dockwiller
Custom exhibition grade stocks on all high grade guns

FIELDSPORT
2581 Hedwidge Dr.
Traverse City, MI 49684
(616) 933-0767
Contact: Bryan Bilinski
FIELDSPORT is an authorized stock fitting agent for AYA, A.H. Fox and will custom fit for any shotgun.
See Our Ad Pg. 133

John R. Frederickson
3934 Carter Mountain Dr.
Cody, WY 82414
(307) 527-4445
Est.: 1970   Staff: 1
Contact: Jack Frederickson
Specializing in custom gunstock work. . .including chasing (re-checkering), checkering, refinishing & stock bending. (Ponsness/Warren sales & repair also offered)

GALAZAN
A Division of Connecticut Shotgun Manufacturing
PO Box 1692
New Britain, CT 06051-1692
(203) 225-6581
FAX: (203) 832-8707
Est.: 1967   Staff: 20

Contact: Dick Perrett
Perazzi MX8 Stocks and America's largest selection of Turkish Circassian Walnut gunstock blanks.

Jim Greenwood Custom Stockmaker
PO Box 183
RR4, Box 2082A
Augusta, KS 67010
(316) 775-0161
Est.: 1986   Staff: 1
Owner: Jim Greenwood
Custom stocks, stock bending, refinishing, leather pads, checkering.

Lee Meadows Custom Gunstocks
6688 Belinda Dr.
PO Box 4264
Riverside, CA 92504
(909) 781-7148
Est.: 1974   Staff: 1
Contact: Lee Meadows or Ray Randel
Custom made stocks. Personal fitting. Stock duplicating, refinishing, checkering, restorations.

Michael Murphy & Sons
6400 S.W. Hunter Rd.
Augusta, KS 67010
(316) 775-2137
Staff: 1
Pres.: Michael Murphy
Custom gun fittings.
See Our Ads Pgs. 169-172

Murray's Gun Shop
14720 NE Sandy Blvd.
Portland, OR 97230

(800) 459-3503
(503) 254-0303
FAX: (503) 254-8191
Est.: 1969   Staff: 3
Contact: Randy Murray
Available: Direct
Custom gunstocks for O/U, doubles, pumps and semi-automatics. Call us for: gunsmithing, stock refinishing, checkering, stock bending, bluing, and antique restorations.
See Our Ad Below

Ram-Line, Inc.
545 Thirty-One Road
Suite 31
Grand Junction, CO 81504
(800) 648-9624
(303) 434-4500
FAX: (303) 434-4004
Ram-Line's new Shot-Tech and Trail-Tech stocks offer the same tough weather-proof features as our classic Syn-Tech stocks. Call for complete information or send $1.00 for catalog.

Reinhart Fajen, Inc.
1000 Red Bud Dr.
PO Box 338, Warsaw, MO 65355
(816) 438-5111
FAX: (816) 438-5175
Est.: 1951   Staff: 115
Mktg. VP: Krista Kellner
Available: Retail & Direct
"Setting the Standard" in drop-in, semi-finished and custom gunstocks.

Shooter's Emporium
606 S.E. 162nd
Portland, OR 97233
(503) 257-0524
Makers of customized stocks

Speedfeed, Inc.
3820 Industrial Way, Suite N
Benicia, CA 94510
(707) 746-1221
FAX: (707) 746-1888
Est.: 1985   Staff: 3
President: Gil Davis
VP: Bill Davis
Manufacturer of synthetic shotgun stock sets for OEM & wholesale accounts.

Stocks by Umberger
14695 E. Pike Rd.
Cambridge, OH 43725
(614) 432-7243
FAX: (614) 432-3204
Est.: 1962   Staff: 6
Pres: Brent Umberger
Available: Direct
High grade custom fitted shotgun stocks; Custom fitting, refinishing & alterations

Wenig Custom Gunstocks
103 N. Market St.
PO Box 249, Lincoln, MO 65338
(816) 547-3334
FAX: (816) 547-2881
Est.: 1993   Staff: 12
President: Fred Wenig
Available: Direct
Custom stock fitting & checkering, machine-inletted stocks

INSURANCE

Carpenter Insurance Service
Friendly service for almost 50 years
134 Holiday Court
Suite 300
Annapolis, MD 21401-7059
(800) 472-7771 (Voice Phone)
FAX: (410) 266-9154
Est.: 1951
Contact: Fred Mann or Bob Mann
Liability insurance for hunting preserves...sporting clays.. .trap and skeet...shooting ranges...shooting clubs...hunting clubs...plus archery, fishing and sportsmen clubs. Amounts of club liability insurance range from $100,000 to $1,000,000. Choice of broad or limited coverage. Extensions for landowners and sponsors. There is no deductible.
All- Risk 3-Year fire, flood, theft, explosion and other accidental damage insurance for sporting guns. Reduced rate All-Risk 3-Year loss or damage insurance for firearm collections used solely for exhibit or personal display.
FREE INFORMATION with no obligation. Prompt, accurate attention to requests and claims.
See Our Ad Below

Joseph Chiarello & Co., Inc.

31 Parker Rd.
Elizabeth, NJ 07308
(800) 526-2199
(908) 352-4444
FAX: (908) 352-8512
Contact: Tina Hegyes or Bob Chiarello
Providing insurance for the firearms industry since 1979. Placed with A++ 15 insurance company licensed in all states. Coverage is comprehensive general liability including products and property including burglary and theft. Additional insureds can be included for vendors and landlords. $1,000,000 limit of liability for firearm retailers and wholesalers; ammo manufacturers; reloaders; gunsmiths; trap, skeet, sporting clays; rifle and pistol ranges. General liability coverage for firearms (shooting) instructors with limits of $250,000, $500,000, or $1,000,000. Umbrella coverage with limits to $15,000,000 is available through the same insurer.
See Our Ad Across

Ferguson & McGuire, Inc.

PO Box 189
Durham, CT 06422
(203) 349-1215
FAX: (203) 349-7799
Est.: 1975
Contact: Gary D'Amico, CIC. CEFS.
Gun club/gun dealers/preserves/range insurance programs for Connecticut, Mass. & Rhode Island. Both NRA and CT state certified firearms instructor.
See Our Ad Pg. 127

Hilb, Rogal & Hamilton Company of Amarillo

1800 Washington, Suite 400
PO Box 1149
Amarillo, TX 79105
(806) 376-4761
FAX: (806) 376-5136
Est.: 1916   Staff: 48
Contact: Judy Hartsock
Specialty markets–trap, skeet, outfitters, guides, guest ranches. Call us.

International Special Events & Recreation Assn. (ISERA)

PO Box 526 148
Salt Lake City, UT 84152-6148
(800) 321-1493
(801) 942-3000
FAX: (801) 942-8095
Est.: 1986   Staff: 4
Program Manager: Rick Lindsey
Non-profit industry trade association specifically set up to provide insurance.

K&K Insurance Group, Inc.

1712 Magnavox Way
PO Box 2338
Ft. Wayne, IN 46801
(219) 459-5000
Contact: Steve Hendricks

Kirke-Van Orsdel, Inc.

99 Canal Center Plaza/Suite 400
Alexandria, VA 22314
(703) 706-9600
Contact: Harry Palmer
Available: Retail & Direct
Insurance coverage provided to NRA members.

Mike Kohout Agency

PO Box 55453
Seattle, WA 98155-0953
(800) 800-4413
FAX: (206) 365-0107
Contact: Mike Kohout

National Sportsman's Alliance

555 W. Granada Blvd., Suite E-11
Ormond Beach, FL 32174
(800) 925-7767
(904) 677-2588
FAX: (904) 677-3292
Contact: Hollis Boss
Specializing in insurance programs for gun clubs, shooting preserves and gun owners. Gun floater insurance on a replacement value basis.

George O'Keefe, Insurance Broker

5516 Northwest Flint Ridge Rd.
Kansas City, MO 64151
(800) 741-2845
Est.: 1980   Staff: 3
Contact: George M. O'Keefe
The "pioneer" in shotgun sports operators "tailored" insurance programs. First offered in 1989 and since that time NO changes in rates, insurance underwriters, or coverages. "A" rated company. Annual policies with installment payment plans available. Comprehensive General Liability Policy format with NO deductible. Land owners (Lessor's) and Members as additional insureds at NO additional premium. Available limits of $300,000; $500,000; $1,000,000 and up to $10,000,000. Excess if needed. Policy on "occurence" basis. Your trap/skeet/sporting clays machines insured under separate policy for physical damage. All Risks and on a REPLACEMENT VALUE basis. Reasonable rates. We offer "QUALITY" insurance products and give prompt, professional and courteous service. Inquiries welcomed.
See Our Ad Below

GUN CLUB OPERATORS
ATTENTION!

Wing & Clay has information on just about every product and service needed by an operator of a hunting preserve, sporting clays, trap or skeet location. In additon to the listings on this page, please refer to:

SECTION	PAGE
Carts, Racks & Vehicle Accessories	.75
Course Designers	.83
Gamebird Breeders	.99
Gun Club Services	114
Trap Manufacturers	209
Trap Accessories	235

The Outdoorsman Agency

126 E. Church St.
PO Box 151
Bishopville, SC 29010
(800) 849-9288
Contact: Steve Murray or Andrew Woodham, Jr.
Specialized commercial insurance programs for hunting preserves and clubs, plantations, lodges, sporting clays, outfitters and guides, and hunting dog field trial clubs.
See Our Ad Pg.128

Woodward Long & Rieger, Inc.

821 Main St.
PO Box 99
Niagara Falls, NY 14302
(716) 285-8441
FAX: (716) 285-8445
Est.: 1916   Staff: 7
Pres: John Long, Sr.
Liability insurance for game preserves and hunting clubs/ NAGA affiliated.

✮ ✮ LIABILITY INSURANCE ✮ ✮

Hunting Preserves and Clay Target Operations

Broad Comprehensive Coverages
Reasonable Rates

Prompt, Professional, and Courteous Service
GEORGE M. O'KEEFE, INSURANCE BROKERS
Association Program Administrators
5516 Northwest Flint Ridge Road - Kansas City, MO 64151 - (800) 741-2845

MAIL ORDER CATALOGS

For related products & services see:

• Accessories, Pg. 54

• Apparel, Pg. 59

Mail order shopping is a time-honored shotgunning tradition. Indeed, the oldest mail order company in the country began serving the hunter five years before Abe Lincoln moved into the White House. Today catalog/mail order houses offer the upland hunter, waterfowler and sporting clays shooter a vast array of functional and reliable products. Before you begin your mail order shopping spree, remember: Safety, Comfort & Personal Style—in that order—should be your prime considerations when choosing your hunting clothing and related items. The companies listed below offer the wingshooting enthusiast a wide range of apparel, accessories, dog training, hunting gear, and gun related equipment.

Atlantic British Ltd.
Box 110, Rover Ridge Dr.
Mechanicville, NY 12118
(800) 533-2208

Contact: Al Buddy
We sell the complete line of Barbour sportswear and accessories.

Ballistic Products, Inc.
20015 75th Ave., N.
Corcoran, MN 55340
(612) 494-9237
Est.: 1975
Contact: Grant Fackler or
Kurt Fackler
Handloading products. Call or write today for our FREE catalog.

Bass Pro Shops
1935 S. Campbell
Springfield, MO 65898-0400
(800) BAS-SPRO
(417) 887-1915
FAX: (417) 887-2531

L.L. Bean, Inc.
Casco St., Freeport, ME
04033-0001
(800) 221-4221
(207) 865-4761
Est.: 1912   Staff: 3500
Pres.: Leon A. Gorman
Tr. Sec./Sr. VP: Norman Poole
Sr. VP/Ops: Lou Zambello

Beretta Gallery
New York:
718 Madison Ave.
New York, NY 10021
(212) 319-6614
Alexandria:
317 S. Washington St.
Old Town Alexandria, VA 22314
(703) 739-0596
Sports and casual wear, hand-tooled luggage, gifts, shooting accouterments, fine art and prints, sportsman's library.

Brownells, Inc.
200 S. Front St., Dept. 910

Montezuma, IA 50171
(515) 623-5401
FAX: (515) 623-3896
Est.: 1939   Staff: 98
Available: Retail & Direct
Gunsmithing tools and custom accessories for shotguns, handguns, rifles; choke tubes and tooling, long forcing cone reamers, sights, recoil pads.

Cabela's
812 13th Ave., Sidney, NE 69160
(800) 237-4444
(308) 254-5505
FAX: (308) 254-2200
Est.: 1961   Staff: 1000
Contact: James W. Cabela

Countrysport, Inc.

Countrysport
15 S. High St., PO Box 166
New Albany, OH 43054-0166
(800) 367-4114
(614) 855-1000
President: Charles Fry
Dir. of Editorial: Doug Truax
Enjoy exciting shopping for quality sporting books, wildlife art, wax cotton outerwear, unique products and gifts designed exclusively for sportsmen by sportsmen. Call for your free catalog.
See Our Ad Below

Dunn's
One Madison Ave.
Grand Junction, TN 38039
(800) 223-8667
FAX: (901) 764-6503
Est.: 1950   Staff: 75
America's best selection of clothing and equipment for wing and clay shooters. Call for free catalog.

FIELDSPORT
Purveyor to the Wingshooter & Angler

FIELDSPORT
2581 Hedwidge Dr.
Traverse City, MI 49684
(616) 933-0767
Contact: Bryan Bilinski
FIELDSPORT specializes in fine clothing, equipment and giftware for the wingshooter and angler.
See Our Ad Across

C.C. Filson Company
PO Box 34020, Seattle, WA 98124
(206) 624-4437
FAX: (206) 624-4539
Est.: 1897
Contact: Steve Matson
Available: Retail & Direct
Manufacturer of quality outdoor clothing, luggage and hats.

Foster & Smith, Inc.
2253 Air Park Rd.,PO Box 100
Rhinelander, WI 54501-0100
(800) 826-7206
Pet supply company owned and operated by veterinarians.

Fox Ridge Outfitters
400 N. Main St., PO Box 1700
Rochester, NH 03867
(800) 243-4570
Contact: Bob Gustafson

Gamaliel Shooting Supply, Inc.
1525 Fountain Run Rd.
Box 156
Gamaliel, KY 42140
(800) 356-6230 (Orders)
(502) 457-2825 (Customer Service)
FAX: (502) 457-3974
Contact: Garon Pare or Geoff Pare

Gander Mountain
PO Box 128
Wilmot, WI 53192
(800) 558-9410 (Cust. Svc.)
(414) 862-2331
FAX: (414) 862-2330
Est.: 1984   Staff: 1750
Chairman: Ralph L. Freitag
President/CEO: Joe Lawler
President-GMO, Inc: John Lappegaard
Pres/GRS, Inc: David W. Reirden

Graf & Sons, Inc.
Rt. 3, Hwy. 54 South
Mexico, MO 65265
(800) 531-2666 (Orders Only)
(314) 581-2266
FAX: (314) 581-2875
Owner: Robert E. Graf
Reloading supplies are our specialty.

Hamilton's
PO Box 2672
S. Vineland, NJ 08360
(800) 292-3695
FAX: (609) 691-0398
Contact: Timothy D. Hamilton
Sportsman's Jacket 100% Egyptian waxed cloth, 5 pockets, two-way brass zipper, snap on hood, tartan lining, olive green. Sizes S-XXL. Price: $139.00 ppd. Call for brochure.
See Our Ad Left

Happy Jack
PO Box 475, Snow Hill, NC 28580
(800) 326-5225
FAX: (919) 747-4111
Est.: 1946
Contact: Ashe Exum, Sr.
Available: Retail & Direct
Dog care products, hunting apparel, hunting art.

Herter's
Waterfowling & Outdoor Specialists
PO Box 1819
Burnsville, MN 55337-0499
(800) 654-3825
(612) 894-9510
FAX: (612) 894-0083

Orvis Company
Historic Rt. 7A
Manchester, VT 05254
(800) 548-9548 (Orders)
(802) 362-3622
Est.: 1865   Staff: 400
CEO: Leigh H. Perkins
VP/Fin.: Thomas Vaccaro
VP/Mktg.: Howard Steere

PAST
Sporting Goods, Inc.
PO Box 1035
Columbia, MO 65205
(314) 445-9200
Est.: 1980   Staff: 12
Pres: Dick Leeper
Available: Retail & Direct
The finest in wearable recoil protection and accessories for all shooting sports–RECOIL SHIELDS-SHOOTING VESTS-SHOOTING GLOVES-GUN VISE-TUMBLER-HUNTING VEST-SHOOTING ACCESSORIES- SHOOTING GLASSES-SHOOTING SHIRTS-AND MORE. Full Line available for all ages. To purchase any of our fine products please contact your local shooting sports retailer or gun club manager. Available in both right and left handed. 100% U.S. made.
See Our Ad Pg. 64

William Powell Catalogue
22 Circle Dr.
Bellmore, NY 11710
(516) 679-1158
FAX: (516) 679-1598
Contact: Mike Patton
Featuring the finest in English guns; specialists in all shooting accessories and country clothing.

Precision Reloading, Inc.
161 Crooked S Rd.
PO Box 122
Stafford Springs, CT 06076
(800) 223-0900
Est.: 1978
Contact: Peter C. Maffei
Precision Reloading, Inc. was established in 1978 and has quickly grown into a Worldwide Mail Order Company. Recent development of many Precision Reloading Products has proven very success-

ful. A free catalog and a fall newsletter are published annually and contain a large selection of reloading equipment and supplies for shotgun, rifle and pistol in addition to other sporting equipment and accessories.

Quality Arms, Inc.
PO Box 19477
Houston, TX 77224
(713) 870-8377
FAX: (713) 870-8524
Contact: John Boyd
We have many accessory items for the serious sportsman: trunk style cases, European shooting items, European cartridge boxes and European shotshells.

Randolph Outfitters
1401 Lavaca
Austin, TX 78701
(800) 856-5161

FAX: (512) 472-5164
Contact: Donald R. Nooner

W.C. Russell Moccasin Co.
285 S.W. Franklin
Berlin, WI 54923
(414) 361-2252
FAX: (414) 361-3274
Est.: 1898
Pres.: Ralph Fabricius
Custom fitted handcrafted moccasin boots and shoes for avid sportsman and women. Dozens of custom options-Thinsulate, Air-Bob Soles, Snake Proof. Fine made-to-measure any size, width or height. Call or write for free color brochure.

Scott's Dog Supply, Inc.
9252 Crawfordsville Rd.
Indianapolis, IN 46234
(800) 966-3647
(317) 293-9850
FAX: (317) 293-9852
Specializing in hunting & training equipment for sporting dogs.

SHYDA'S
Shoe & Clothing Barn
SAVE 30-60%
On American Made Merchandise!
Complete line of trap shooting, sporting clays, hunting and outer wear clothing & accessories.
Call, fax or write for our...

FREE 100+ PAGE CATALOG

Remington • Browning • Bob Allen
10X • Rocky • Columbia • Sorel • Danner
Timberland • Woolrich • Walls • PAST
— BIG & TALL SIZES —
MOSSY OAK • FIELDLINE • MELTON • LACROSS
ROCKPORT • CHIPPEWA • RED BALL
SPARTAN • KELLY • WIGWAM • DUOFOLD
WRANGLER • DUCKS UNLIMITED

717-274-2551 • (Fax) 717-274-6702
1635 South Lincoln Avenue • Lebanon, PA, 17042

SHYDA'S

Shyda's Shoe & Clothing Barn
1635 S. Lincoln Ave.
Lebanon, PA 17042
(717) 274-2551
Est.: 1966   Staff: 8
Complete line of trap & skeet, sporting clays, hunting and fishing outerwear.
See Our Ad Left

The Sportsman's Guide
411 Farwell Ave.
South Saint Paul, MN 55075-0239
(800) 888-3006 (Cust. Svc.)
(612) 686-9000 (Exec. Off.)
FAX: (800) 333-6933

Stafford's
808 Smith St., PO Box 2055
Thomasville, GA 31799-2055
(800) 826-0948
Contact: Warren Stafford

Tidewater Specialties
US Rt. 50, Box 158
Wye Mills, MD 21679
(800) 433-5277 (Orders)
(410) 820-2076
FAX: (410) 364-5215
Est.: 1974
Unique selection of gifts and gear, clothing and home accessories for everyone interested in shotgunn-

ing, wildfowl, field dogs, golf and more.

Tiemann's
PO Box 130, Priddy, TX 76870
(800) 410-3006

Wing Supply
PO Box 367, Greenville, KY 42345
(800) 388-9464 (Orders)
(502) 338-2808
FAX: (502) 338-0057
(502) 338-2808

Wings & Clays, Inc.
24852 Harper Ave.
St. Clair Shores, MI 48080
(800) 746-8486
Est.: 1993
Contact: Larry Woo

Available: Retail & Direct
Michigan's exclusive dealer for K-80, Perazzi, Premium Beretta and Parker Reproductions. Dealer for Lewis Creek, Barbour and Beretta Sport clothing. Also dealer for Wild-Hare Products, Holland Sport, Briley & Kolar products. New Wings & Clays Pro-Shop supply catalog available.
See Our Ad Below

Wingset
61 Central St., PO Box 178
Woodstock, VT 05091
(800) 356-4953
Quality clothing & equipment for waterfowlers & upland hunters.

PUBLICATIONS

The American Field
The American Field Publishing Co.
542 South Dearborn St.
Chicago, IL 60605-1528
(312) 663-9797

FAX: (312) 663-5557
Est.: 1874
Managing Edit.: Bernard J. Matthys
Advtg. Mgr: Ronald Betley
Circulation: 11,000
Frequency: Weekly

American Firearms Industry
2245 E. Sunrise Blvd., #916
Fort Lauderdale, FL 33304
(305) 561-3505
FAX: (305) 561-4129
Est.: 1973   Staff: 14
Publisher: Andrew Molchan
Mgng. Editor: Robert Lesmeister
Advtg: Danny J. Vincent
Trade publication for the firearms industry.

American Hunter
National Rifle Association
11250 Waples Mill Rd.
Fairfax, VA 22030
(703) 267-1300
FAX: (703) 267-3971
Est.: 1973
Exec. Dir: E.G. "Red" Bell, Jr.
Editor: Tom Fulgham
Advertising: Diane Senesac
Circulation: 1,632,900
Frequency: Monthly

Bird Dog News
563 17th Ave., NW
New Brighton, MN 55112
(612) 636-8045
FAX: (612) 636-8045
Est.: 1992
Publisher: Dennis Goldan
Circulation: 2,500
Frequency: 6 Times Per Year plus August & October newsletters
Hunter's guide to hunting upland waterfowl including seasons, trial dates & training tips.

Blue Book Publications

Blue Book Publications, Inc.
One Appletree Square
Dept. WC
Minneapolis, MN 55425
(800) 877-GUNS (4867)
(612) 854-5229
FAX: (612) 853-1486
Est.: 1981   Staff: 13
Publisher: Steven P. Fjestad
Publisher with the following titles in print: 16th Edition *Blue Book of Gun Values*; *The Book of Colt Firearms* by R.L. Wilson; *Mossberg-More Gun for the Money* by Victor & Cheryl Hamlin;

Classic Sporting Collectibles Auctions; CADA Gun Journal (monthly buy/sell/trade gun mag.); The Legend of Little Big Horn by Robert Nightengale.
See Our Ad Above

Ducks Unlimited
One Waterfowl Way
Memphis, TN 38120
(901) 758-3825
Est.: 1937
Publisher: Matthew B. Connolly, Jr.
Editor: Lee D. Salber
Advertising: Beth Bryan
Circulation: 482,750
Frequency: Bimonthly
Ducks Unlimited is a magazine for active outdoor sportsmen and conservationists.

Field & Stream
Times Mirror Magazines, Inc.
2 Park Ave.
New York, NY 10016
(212) 779-5000
FAX: (212) 686-6877
Est.: 1895
Publisher: Michael Rooney
Editor: Duncan Barnes
Circulation: 2,000,000
Frequency: Monthly

Fur-Fish-Game
A.R. Harding Publishing Co.
2878 E. Main St.
Columbus, OH 43209
(614) 231-9585
Est.: 1925

Editor: Mitch Cox
Advertising: Eric R. Schweinhagen
Circulation: 104,106
Frequency: Monthly

Gray's Sporting Journal
North American Publications, Inc.
725 Broad St., Augusta, GA 30901
(706) 722-6060
Est.: 1975
Publisher: William S. Morris, III
Editor: David C. Foster
Advertising: Lea Cockerham
Circulation: 35,000
Frequency: Bimonthly
Literature and Art edited for the advanced angler, hunter, shooter and conservationist.

Gun Dog
The Stover Publishing Co., Inc.
1901 Bell Avenue
Des Moines, IA 50315
(515) 243-2472
Est.: 1981
Publisher: Carrell Bunn
Editor: Bob Wilbanks
Advertising: Mary Stearns
Circulation: 55,718
Frequency: Bimonthly
GUN DOG is edited for sportsmen who own and hunt with upland bird dogs and waterfowl dogs.

Gun List
Krause Publications
700 E. State St., Iola, WI 54990
(715) 445-2214
FAX: (715) 445-4087

Est.: 1952   Staff: 368
Publisher: David Kowalski
Advtr. Mgr: John Kronschnabl
Promotional Mgr: Tom Luba
Circulation: 71,000
Frequency: Every 2 weeks

Hunting
Petersen's Publishing Company
6420 Wilshire Blvd.
Los Angeles, CA 90048
(213) 782-2185
Est.: 1973
VP & Exec. Publisher: Thomas J. Siatos
Editor: Todd Smith
Group Publisher: Ken Elliot
Circulation: 325,000
Frequency: Monthly

The Hunting Report for Birdshooters & Waterfowlers
Oxpecker Enterprises, Inc.
9300 South Dadeland Blvd., #605
Miami, FL 33156
(305) 670-1918 (Order Line)
FAX: (305) 670-1376
Est.: 1989   Staff: 6
Publisher: Don Causey
Adm. Asst.: Christina Muntaneu
Circulation: 2,000
Frequency: 12 Times Per Year

Modern Skeet & Clays Magazine
Quack Sporting Clays, Inc.
4 Ann & Hope Way
PO Box 98
Cumberland, RI 02864
(401) 723-8202
FAX: (401) 722-5910
Est.: 1991
Pub/Edtr: Kenneth Gagnon, Sr.
Ass't. Editor: Joan Mandeville
Frequency: Bi-monthly
Modern Skeet & Clays Magazine, established in 1991, is published bimonthly, promotes and reports news on all the shotgun sports, sporting clays, modern skeet, 5-stand, skeet, trap, modern trap & hunting, both in the USA & Canada. Modern Skeet & Clays is the official magazine for all the "Modern Era Clays" shooting games & the official magazine for the new clays games – Modern Skeet & Modern Trap.
See Our Ads Pg. 228-229

North American Hunter
North American Outdoor Group, Inc.
12301 Whitewater Dr.
Suite 260
Minnetonka, MN 55343
(612) 936-9507
FAX: (612) 936-9169
Est.: 1978
Publisher: Russ Nolan
Editor: Bill Miller
Advertising: Tom Perrier
Circulation: 665,000
Frequency: 7 Times Per Year
Official publication of the North American Hunting Club–not available on newsstands.

Outdoor Life
Times Mirror Magazines, Inc.
2 Park Ave.
New York, NY 10016
(212) 779-5000
FAX: (212) 686-6877
Est.: 1898
Publisher: Michael Rooney
Editor: Vin Sparano
Circulation: 1,350,000
Frequency: Monthly

Pheasants Forever
PO Box 75473
St. Paul, MN 55175
(612) 481-7142
Est.: 1982
CEO: Jeffrey S. Finden
Editor: Dennis Anderson
Advertising: Dill & Associates
Circulation: 72,000
Frequency: 5 Times Per Year

The Pointing Dog Journal
PO Box 968
Traverse City, MI 49685
(616) 946-3712
Est.: 1992
Publisher: David G. Meisner
Editor: David G. Meisner
Advertising: John Shoemaker
Circulation: 30,000
Frequency: Bimonthly
The only full- color magazine in the world devoted totally to pointing dogs.

Q.U. Junior Covey Magazine
PO Box 610
Edgefield, SC 29824-0610
(803) 637-5731
FAX: (803) 637-0037
Est.: 1995   Staff: 3
Publisher: Jerry W. Allen
Editor: Spencer Culp
Advertising: Spencer Culp
Circulation: 35,000
Frequency: Bimonthly

Quail Unlimited
PO Box 610
Edgefield, SC 29824-0610
(803) 637-5731
FAX: (803) 637-0037
Est.: 1981   Staff: 25
Publisher: Jerry W. Allen
Editor: Diana J. Kogon
Advertising: Spencer Culp
Circulation: 45,000
Frequency: Bimonthly

RGS-The Ruffed Grouse Society Magazine
451 McCormick Rd.
Coraopolis, PA 15108
(412) 262-4044
Est.: 1961
Exec. Dir. & VP: Samuel R. Pursglove, Jr.
Editor: Paul E. Carson
Advertising: Paul E. Carson
Circulation: 23,000
Frequency: 5 Times Per Year

Rifle & Shotgun SportShooting
NatCom, Inc.
5300 CityPlex Tower
2448 E. 81st Street
Tulsa, OK 74137-4207
(918) 491-6100
FAX: (918) 491-9424
Est.: 1994
Publisher: Gerald W. Pope
Managing Editor: Lawrence Taylor
Advertising: Ellie Shimer
Circulation: 90,000
Frequency: Bi-Monthly

Shooting Industry
Publisher's Development Corp.
591 Camino de la Reina
Suite 200
San Diego, CA 92108
(619) 297-8520
FAX: (619) 297-5353
Publisher: George Von Rosen
Editor: Russ Thurman
Advtg. Sales Mgr: Anita Carson
Publishers of Guns Magazine and American Handgunner.

Shooting Sports Retailer
130 W. 42nd St., Suite 1804
New York, NY 10036
(212) 840-0660
FAX: (212) 944-1884
Publisher: Bruce Karaban
Editor: Bob Rogers
Advtg: Gina Domanico
Circulation: 16,821
Frequency: 6 Times Per Year

SHOOTING SPORTSMAN
The Magazine of Wingshooting & Fine Guns

Shooting Sportsman
Down East Enterprise, Inc.
PO Box 1357
Camden, ME 04843
(800) 666-4955 (Subscription)
(207) 594-9544
FAX: (207) 594-5144
Est.: 1988
Publisher: H. Allen Fernald
Editor: Ralph P. Stuart
Advertising: Bill Anderson
Circulation: 14,328
Frequency: Bimonthly
Shooting Sportsman brings readers the best in wingshooting and fine shotguns. From upland gunning and waterfowling to sporting clays, the magazine celebrates our sports, their traditions and the people who keep them; the birds and the dogs; and the exciting places we visit - be they around the corner or around the world.
See Our Ad Across

Shot Business
11 Mile Hill Rd.
Flintlock Ridge Office Center
Newtown, CT 06470
(203) 426-1320
FAX: (203) 426-1087
Publisher: Robert T. Delfray
Assoc. Editor: Tim Gorel
Advertising: C. Kenneth Ramage
Circulation: 20,000+
Frequency: Monthly
Official publication of the National Shooting Sports Foundation.

Shotgun News
Snell Publishing Company
PO Box 669
Hastings, NE 68902
(800) 345-6923 (Subscriptions)
(402) 463-4589
FAX: (402) 463-3893
Est.: 1948
Publisher: Robert M. Snell
Advertising: Mary Kriger
Circulation: 142,000
Frequency: 3 Times a Month
It's the leading publication for the sale, purchase and trade of firearms and accessories of all types. Shotgun News has aided thousands of gun enthusiasts to locate firearms, both modern and antique - rifles, shotguns, pistols, revolvers, scopes, mounts...all at money-saving prices.
See Our Ad Pg. 140

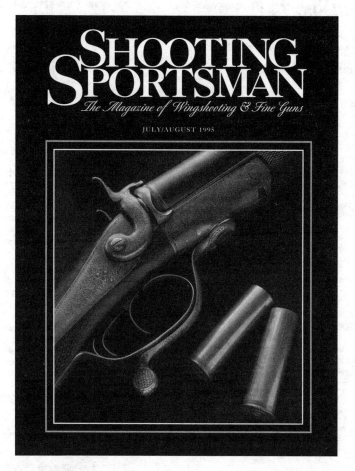

Shotgun Sports MAGAZINE

Shotgun Sports
PO Box 6810, Auburn, CA 95604
(800) 676-8920
FAX: (916) 889-9106
Est.: 1979
Publisher: Frank Kodl
Editor: Frank Kodl
Advertising: Lynn Berger
Circulation: 103,153
Frequency: 11 Times Per Year
Shotgun Sports. . .the magazine
for informed shotgunners. Name
your game, trapshooting, sporting
clays, skeet. . .are you into reload-
ing, patterning or shotgun testing?
Do you live for hunting waterfowl
& upland birds or all of the above!
Whatever your choice, Shotgun
Sports magazine is the nation's
only magazine that delivers it all.
See Our Ad Pg. 137

Skeet Shooting Review
5931 Roft Rd.
San Antonio, TX 78253
(210) 688-3371
FAX: (210) 688-3014
Est.: 1947
Publisher: Mike Hampton
Editor: Susie Fluckiger
Advertising: Jennifer Bittle

Circulation: 17,400
Frequency: Monthly

Southern Outdoors
5845 Carmichael Rd.
Montgomery, AL 36117
(334) 277-3940
Est.: 1968
Publisher: Helen Sevier
Editor: Larry Teague
Advertising: Ken Woodard
Circulation: 249,937
Frequency: 9 Times Per Year

Sporting Classics
PO Box 23707
Columbia, SC 29223
(800) 849-1004
Est.: 1981
Publisher: John Cornett
Editor: Chuck Wechsler
Advertising: Bernard & Associates
(702) 323-6828
Circulation: 31,128
Frequency: Bimonthly

Sporting Clays
Patch Communications
5211 S. Washington Ave.

Titusville, FL 32780
(800) 677-5212 (Subscription)
(407) 268-5010
FAX: (407) 267-7216
Est.: 1989
Publisher: Christi Ashby
Editor: George Conrad
Advertising: Jackie Miller
Circulation: 22,500
Frequency: 12 Times Per Year
Sporting Clays reports on shooting
activities with instructional columns, equipment reviews and
range listings. Each issue features
top tournament coverage as well
as National Sporting Clays Association news, shooter profiles and
hunting and shooting adventure
stories. Special sections on shooting gear, clothing, accessories, and
sporting vehicles are also part of
the Sporting Clays package.
See Our Ad Across

Sporting World International
110 River Bluff
Merry Hill, NC 27957
(919) 356-2662
Est.: 1994   Staff: 4
Publisher: Barry G. Davis
Editor: Barry G. Davis
Hard-hitting, up-to-the-minute, topi-
cal sporting clays newsletter with
worldwide coverage.

Sports Afield
250 W. 55th St.
New York, NY 10019
(212) 649-4302
Est.: 1887
Publisher: Terry McDonell
Editor: Terry McDonell
Associate Publisher: Michael P.
Wade
Circulation: 511,230
Frequency: Monthly
Sportsman's magazine covering:
hunting, fishing, shooting sports,
boating, nature conservation.

Stoeger Publishing Co.
5 Mansard Court
Wayne, NJ 07470
(201) 872-9500
FAX: (201) 872-2230
VP: David C. Perkins
Publishers of the Shooter's Bible
and Gun Trader's Guide and other
outdoor publications.

**Thicket's Hunting and
Fishing Journal**
2100 Riverchase Center
Suite 118
Birmingham, AL 35244
(800) 329-4868
(205) 987-6007
FAX: (205) 987-2882
Est.: 1990   Staff: 33
Publisher: Brock Ray
Editor: Don Kirk
Advertising: Scott Fowler
Circulation: 125,000
Frequency: Bi-Monthly
National publication catering to
the outdoor enthusiast interested
in hunting, fishing and sporting
clays.

Trap & Field
Curtis Magazine Group
1200 Waterway Blvd.
Indianaplis, IN 46202
(317) 633-8802
Est.: 1890
Publisher: Bonnie Nash
Editor: Bonnie Nash
Advertising: Sherry Galbreath
Circulation: 16,284
Frequency: Monthly
Official publication of the Amateur
Trapshooting Association

Turkey & Turkey Hunting
Krause Publications, Inc.
700 E. State St.
Iola, WI 54990
(715) 445-2214
FAX: (715) 445-4087
Est.: 1983   Staff: 24
Publisher: Debbie Knauer
Editor: Jim Casada/Gerry Blair
Advertising: Dave Larsen

Circulation: 98,800
Frequency: Bimonthly
Practical and comprehensive
hunting information for turkey
hunters.

Waterfowl Magazine
Waterfowl U.S.A.
National Headquarters
PO Box 50
Edgefield, SC 29824
(803) 637-5767
FAX: (803) 637-6983
Est.: 1983
Publisher: Roger L. White
Editor: Wayne Waldrop
Advertising: Kim Smith
Circulation: 20,000
Frequency: Bimonthly
Grass roots waterfowl
conservation organization funding
local waterfowl habitat projects

Western Outdoors
3197 E. Airport Dr.
Costa Mesa, CA 92626
(714) 546-4370
Est.: 1960
Publisher: Bob Twilegar
Editor: Jack Brown
Advertising: Joe Higgins
Circulation: 115,000
Frequency: 9 Times Per Year

Wildfowl
The Stover Publishing Co., Inc.
1901 Bell Ave., Suite 4
Des Moines, IA 50315
(515) 243-2472
Est.: 1985
Publisher: Carrell Bunn
Editor: Bob Wilbanks
Advertising: Mary Stearns
Circulation: 34,444
Frequency: Bimonthly
WILDFOWL is edited for and de-
voted to serious duck and goose
hunters.

**Wildlife Harvest
Magazine**
NAGA, Inc.
PO Box 96
Goose Lake, IA 52750
(319) 242-3046
Pub/Editor: John Mullin
Assoc. Editor: Peggy
Mullin-Boehmer
Circulation: 2,500
Frequency: Monthly
The magazine for gamebird produc-
tion and improved hunting.
See Our Ad Pg. 72

Black's
WING
& CLAY
Wing & Clay
43 West Front St., Suite 11
P.O. Box 2029
Red Bank, NJ 07701
(908) 224-8700
FAX: (908) 741-2827
Est.: 1991
Publisher: James F. Black, Jr.
Editor: Lois Re'
Assoc. Publisher: Raymond Goydon
Asst. Publisher: Amanda Santos
Circulation: 60,000
Frequency: Annual

Wing & Shot
Stover Publications, Inc.
1901 Bell Ave., Suite 4
Des Moines, IA 50315
(515) 243-2472
Est.: 1986
Publisher: Carrell Bunn
Editor: Bob Wilbanks
Advertising: Mary Stearns
Circulation: 17,879
Frequency: Bimonthly
WING & SHOT is for outdoorsmen
interested in upland hunting. Each
issue covers pheasant, grouse,
quail, dove and turkey hunting.

Women & Guns
267 Linwood Ave.
PO Box 488, Station C
Buffalo, NY 14209
(716) 885-6408
FAX: (716) 884-4471
Publisher: Julianne Versnel Gòttlieb
Exec. Editor: Peggy Tartaro
Circulation: 18,000
Frequency: 12 Times Per Year

RECOIL REDUCTION PRODUCTS

For related products & services see:

- **Gunsmiths, Pg. 120**

Angle-Ease
Oregon Gun Works
1015 Molalla Ave.
Oregon City, OR 97045
(800) 398-5839
FAX: (503) 657-5529
Est.: 1992   Staff: 3
Contact: Al Peck
Available: Retail & Direct
Hydraulic piston activated recoil reduction system for stocks.

BreakO
Graco Corp.
PO Box 936, Gravette, AR 72736
(501) 787-6520
Contact: Jean Phipps
BreakO Recoil Reduction System;
Graco Adjustable Comb Hardware.

Counter Coil
Danuser Machine Co., Inc.
550 E. Third St., Fulton, MO 65251
(314) 642-2246
FAX: (314) 642-2240
Est.: 1982   Staff: 65
Pres: Jerry Danuser
Contact: Mike Mitchell or
Emery Smola
Available: Retail & Direct
Fully adjustable hydraulic recoil reduction device.

Dead Mule
Recoil-Less Engineering
9 Fox Oaks Court
Sacramento, CA 95831
(916) 391-1242
Contact: Steven J. Jones

Edwards Recoil Reducer
810 Holcomb St.
Watertown, NY 13601
(315) 788-4237
Contact: Kevin Sheff
Adjustable to control barrel bounce and rearward motion on any gun.

G-Squared Air Cushion System
Schroll Shooting Supplies
1320 San Bernardino Rd., #56
Upland, CA 91786
(909) 985-7147
FAX: (909) 981-0436
Pres: Wendell Schroll
Installed in "Stockmaster Stock System".

GALAZAN
A Division of Connecticut Shotgun Manufacturing
PO Box 1692
New Britain, CT 06051-1692
(203) 225-6581
FAX: (203) 832-8707
Est.: 1967   Staff: 20

Contact: Dick Perrett
Available: Direct
Hand finished recoil pads: The original Winchester Patent Date Style, The pre-war Silvers Pad for high grade guns, The HAWKINS Pad, Our Technically Superior Recoil Pad and several other styles.

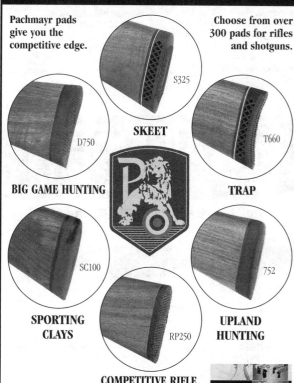

Griggs Recoil Redirector

Griggs Products Factory:
640 N. Main St.
North Salt Lake, UT 84054
(801) 295-9696
FAX: (801) 299-1815
Est.: 1970   Staff: 2
Pres: Jay P. Griggs
Ass't: George Abrams
Available: Retail & Direct
There is nothing...nothing...nothing in this world that treats recoil the same as the Griggs Recoil Redirector, and no phony claims either. Shooters report after using one that it takes all the kick from the face and from 50% to 80% of the kick from the shoulder. Also the Griggs Adjustable system, so great it's patented. Records have been set and are being set, shoots are being won with the Griggs system.

JS Air Cushion Stocks
850 W. Foothill Blvd., #21
Azusa, CA 91702
(818) 334-2563
Est.: 1986   Staff: 1
Contact: Joe Shiozaki
Attention Skeet Shooters: Feel the ultimate in shooting comfort with your different gauge shotguns. New guns shipped direct from manufacturer or send your gun direct.

KICK-EEZ
PO Box 12767
Wichita, KS 67277-2767
(316) 721-9570
FAX: (316) 721-5260
Contact: Robert Pearce or Star Pearce
The Sorbothane® visco-elastic material in KICK-EEZ recoil pads reduces more recoil and does it faster than any other recoil pad. Less recoil reduces flinching, eases sore shoulders or cheeks. Eliminating the rebound effect of the first shot, second shots are quicker and more accurate. Independent lab tests showing these facts are available on request.
See Our Ad Below Left

MGS M-10029
McClelland Gun Shop
1533 Centerville Rd.
Dallas, TX 75228
(214) 321-0231
Est.: 1972
Contact: Joe Ketchum
Available: Retail & Direct
Recoil Reducer; Firearm & accessory sales.

Mercury Inertia Recoil Control
Staub Gun Specialties
261 Herbert, Alton, IL 62002
(618) 465-6286
Contact: Bill Staub

Mercury Recoil Suppressor
C & H Research
115 Sunnyside Dr. Lewis, KS 67552
(316) 324-5445
Est.: 1978
Contact: Frank O'Brien
Available: Retail & Direct
Mercury Recoil Reducer
Your best buy in recoil reduction! The Mercury Recoil Suppressor overcomes the practical limitations of competing spring-weight systems by using liquid mercury to slow down and partially offset apparent recoil. Simple, reliable, easy to install and remove. Complete satisfaction, or your money back! Call or write for free brochure.

Pachmayr®

Pachmayr, Ltd.
1875 South Mountain Ave.
Monrovia, CA 91016
(800) 423-9704
(818) 357-7771
FAX: (818) 358-7251
Contact: Les Whitney
Available: Retail
Pachmayr offers the widest range of recoil pads designed to provide

the competitive edge you need to finish first. Please visit our fully stocked PRO SHOP, located at the Pachmayr Shooting Sports Park, 831 N. Rosemead Blvd., S. El Monte, CA. Our Pro Shop features Perazzi, Browning and Beretta shotguns, reloading supplies and accessories.

See Our Ad Pg. 143

Poorman's Magtube Recoil Reducer
Tom Morton & Company
19309 Gristmill Lane
Knoxville, MD 21758
(800) 382-9691
FAX: (301) 620-1622
Est.: 1975   Staff: 2
Contact: Tom Morton
Available: Direct
Manufacturers of shotgun shooting accessories. Call for free catalog.

Pro-Port Limited
41302 Executive Dr.
Harrison Twp., MI 48045
(810) 469-7323
FAX: (810) 469-0425
Est.: 1980   Staff: 12
Available: Retail & Direct
The one company that has spent years developing a porting process specifically for use on shotguns. Shotgun shooters have benefited from the reduced recoil and muzzle jump provided by the Pro-Port process. The originators of barrel porting used EDM (electrical discharge machining) offering a style of porting suited for all types of shotgun shooters.

See Our Ad Right

Soft Touch
Shooter's Emporium
606 S.E. 162nd
Portland, OR 97233
(503) 257-0524
Est.: 1985   Staff: 4
Owner: Moe Bragg
Available: Retail & Direct
Customize your stock to reduce recoil

SHOTGUNNER'S SOURCE

RELOADING

Why Reload Your Own Shells?

For individuals who love shotgunning, shotshell reloading is a rewarding hobby. It's not surprising then to learn that each year the number of reloads nearly equals the number of new shells manufactured!

Why's reloading so popular? First, you save money. And the more you shoot, the more money you save. The chart [right >] compares the approximate cost of new shells with the cost of reloads. Second, reloading is truly enjoyable hobby, done alone or with a shooting buddy.

Third, for the person who loves shotgun shooting, there's nothing like the satisfaction of breaking a clay target or downing a

Type of Shotshell (Box of 25)	Average Store Price	Handloaded Price (Average price on components)	Savings Per Box
10-ga. 3½" Mag., 2 oz. shot	$19.50	$4.31	$15.19
12-ga. 3" Mag., 1⅞ oz. shot	$12.75	$3.89	$ 8.86
12-ga. 2¾" Mag., 1½ oz. shot	$11.00	$3.47	$ 7.53
12-ga. Target load, 1⅛ oz. shot	$ 5.75	$2.27	$ 3.48
20-ga. 3" Mag., 1¼ oz. shot	$10.50	$3.05	$ 7.45

The price you pay may be more or less depending on your component purchases.

game bird with your own reloads. Interested? Here's what you need to know to get started.

Selecting Components

A shotshell comprises several components--primer, powder, wad, and shot--in various combinations depending on the particular use [see diagram pg. 22]. Each combination has been carefully tested by ballistics experts for maximum effectiveness and safety. Never experiment with combinations of your own. It can be wasteful at best, and very possibly dangerous.

The Hull: An Important Choice

When just getting started as a reloader, it's best to keep things as simple as possible. Not all shells have the same capacity or crimp and you must use a different set of components to reload each. That's why most experts suggest that you begin by choosing your area's most popular low brass or skeet hull and stick with it until you have enough experience to move on to other types of hulls. Consistent use of the same hull permits consistent use of the same components for all your loads. Less chance for confusion. Less chance of error.

A Word About Shot

Both lead and steel shot are easy to reload. But it's imperative that instructions for each type are followed to the letter. Never substitute steel shot for lead. The result could be chamber pressure high enough to burst the gun, causing death or injury to the shooter or bystanders.

Wads that work fine with lead shot will not work with steel shot. If you're using steel shot, employ steel shot components only, and follow the manufacturer's directions religiously.

As shot size increases, fewer pellets can be loaded into the hull. Smaller sizes are used for trap, skeet, sporting clays and small game birds. Larger sizes are suitable for heavier game, such as ducks, geese, and turkeys.

Selecting The Right Wad

The wad is that part of the shotshell between the powder and the shot. A tight seal permits expanding gas from the burning powder to push the shot column from the barrel with maximum velocity. Easy to reload, modern "wad columns" combine cup and wad in a single piece. Use only the specific wad column recommended for the other components you are using.

Powder Precautions

Powders have different burning speeds. The heavier the shot load, the slower the powder must burn, because it takes longer to accelerate such a load than a light one. A fast-burning powder ignited behind a heavy load can cause excessive breech pressure, resulting in gun damage and personal injury. Conversely, a slow-burning powder will not propel a light load effectively. Without proper pressure buildup many powders will fail to burn uniformly, diminishing shot velocity.

When you purchase powder, get--and read-- a Sporting Arms and Manufacturers Association (SAAMI) pamphlet on the properties and proper storage of smokeless powder.

Always store powder in its original container (designed to burst without causing an explosion if the powder is accidentally ignited.) Don't store powder in a glass jar or bottle, or any container that will allow pressure to buildup. Store powder in a

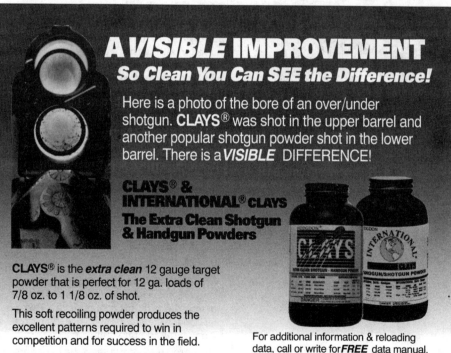

cool, dry, child-safe place where there is no chance of sparks or flame reaching it.

Use The Proper Primer

When you pull the trigger on your shotgun, the hammer falls on the firing pin denting the primer cup. This detonates the primer, which ignites the main powder charge. Primer characteristics vary, depending on their purpose. Always use a primer that is compatible with your other components. Never remove it from its container until you're ready to use it. And store it away from your powder, exercising the same precautions.

Choosing The Right Tool

There are three basic types of reloading tools--manual, semi-automatic/single-stage, and semi-automatic/progressive. The type you choose will depend on cost, convenience and speed.

Manual Reloaders

If low price is your overriding consideration, you can make do with a manual reloader, although speed will be sacrificed and accuracy and uniformity may be somewhat inconsistent. With a manual reloader, care is called for because deviations from the recommended quantities can produce a shell that fails to perform as expected.

Semi-automatic

When the handle of a typical semi-automatic reloader is pulled the tool performs all the reloading steps--depriming, priming, resizing the metal base, measuring the powder, seating the wad column, measuring the shot, and crimping--automatically.

In a single-stage, semi-automatic reloader you manually move the hull from one station to the next. Each shell is processed singly and finished before starting a new one. Completion of eight to ten boxes per hour is not unusual with this type of device. Recommended for the shooter who doesn't require high volume and maximum speed.

Progressive, semi-automatic reloaders process more than one shell simultaneously, and complete a finished shell with each pull of the handle. Skeet and trap enthusiasts, who may run through eight or more boxes of shells in an afternoon, generally prefer progressive reloaders. Hydraulically-operated models eliminate the need to pull a handle.

RELOADERS FOLLOW THE RECIPE EXACTLY.

Reloading ammunition is popular and can save shooters money. But reloading has its responsibilities, too, because you alone control what goes into the reload.

So start with a reputable reloading manual and follow its instructions exactly. Reloading recipes are based upon the interaction between carefully selected components – so substituting components should never be a part of your routine.

Never experiment by deviating from published recipe. Never, ever over-pressure a load in an attempt to boost performance.

Deviating from the exact recipe can cause failure of the firearm and produce disastrous results. An over-pressured shell can cause the firearm to explode and cause serious injury or even death to the shooter and others.

Today's modern powders and primers can lead to higher pressures – so stick to the recipe. If you have any doubts about the quality of the ammunition you have reloaded, get rid of it. It's better to discard possible good ammunition than to chamber possibly bad ammunition.

Remember: load every shell or cartridge as if your safety depends on it – because it does.

Remington®

Published in the interest of Public Safety by Remington Arms Company, Inc.

RELOADING EQUIPMENT

Hornady

Hornady Mfg. Co.
Box 1848
Grand Island, NE 68802
(308) 382-1390
FAX: (308) 382-5761
Contact: Doug Engh
The Hornady APEX Auto comes
loaded with automatic time-saving
features. And no shot or powder
will drop without hulls present.
Hornady Manufacturing offers
shotshell and metallic reloading
equipment and accessories with
lifetime warranties, as well as rifle,
pistol and muzzleloading bullets, ammunition, and shooter accessories.
See Our Ad Below

Lee Precision, Inc.
4275 Highway "U"
Hartford, WI 53027
(414) 673-3075
FAX: (414) 673-9273
Available: Retail & Direct
Load -all II (12, 16 & 20 ga.); Lee
Load Fast (12 ga.).
 Send $1 for complete catalog.

MEC
Mayville Engineering Co.
715 South St.
Mayville, WI 53050
(800) 797-4MEC
(414) 387-4500
FAX: (414) 387-2682
Sales & Mktg: Tom Leigl
Cust. Svc. Mgr: Dave Kern
Single stage and progressive
shotshell reloaders and steel shot
components.

Ponsness/Warren
S. Highway 41
PO Box 8
Rathdrum, ID 83858
(208) 687-2231
FAX: (208) 687-2233
Marketing Mgr: Brian Steele
Available: Retail
Each Ponsness/Warren machine is
hand assembled, thoroughly in-
spected, fully adjusted and put
through the reloading process, pro-
ducing factory looking shells right
out of the box. 4 models of
shotshell reloaders: LS1000; 950
Elite; 900 Elite; Du-O-Matic 375
and hydraulic units.
See Our Ad Pg. 152

Spolar Enterprises
17376 Filbert
Fontana, CA 92335
(800) 227-9667
(909) 350-9667
FAX: (909) 350-4276
Est.: 1990
President: Carter Spolar
VP: Dicksie Spolar
Available: Direct
The new POWER LOAD GOLD PRE-
MIER RELOADER continues our
commitment to providing the re-
loading shooter with innovative
precision crafted, top quality reload-
ing equipment and accessories.
See Our Ad Across Right

RELOADING ACCESSORIES

Hydra-Load, Inc.
3018 D Wildwood Ave.
Jackson, MI 49202
(800) 241-0155
Hydraulic system for progressive
shotshell reloaders.

K&T Company
1027 Skyview Dr.
West Carollton, OH 45449
(513) 859-8414
President: F. Keith Tomlinson
Shell organizing systems, rust inhib-
iting snap caps, gun lubricants

APEX™ 3.0

NEW
PRIMING SYSTEM
Automatically dispenses
primers in the proper upright
position regardless of handle
speed.

NEW
SHELL RETAINER
Holds each shell straight as
they pass through each
station, and lets you remove
shells easily for inspection.

NEW
**SHOT & POWDER
SYSTEM**
Operations take place at the
top and bottom of each
stroke, greatly reducing the
possibility of accidental
double charge.

*Try out the new
APEX 3.0 Automatic at your
Hornady dealer!*

Hornady

Hornady Manufacturing Co.
Box 1848
Grand Island, NE 68802

Kennedy Mfg. Co.
520 E. Sycamore St.
Box 151
Van Wert, OH 45891-0151
(419) 238-2442
FAX: (419) 238-5644
Est.: 1911
Mktg. Mgr: John Aycock
Reloading benches. Compact and deluxe models of industrial grade steel construction with "butcher block" maple tops.

Littleton's Shotmaker
275 Pinedale Ave.
Oroville, CA 95966
(916) 533-6084
Contact: J.F. Littleton
Making shot is easier than reloading. 2 models available to make any one-size shot. Call or write for more information.

MTM Case-Gard
PO Box 14117
Dayton, OH 45414
(513) 890-7461
FAX: (513) 890-1747
Contact: Al Minneman
Available: Retail
Plastic ammo boxes, loading trays, funnels

Multi-Scale Charge Ltd.
PO Box 101, LPO
Niagara Falls, NY 14304
(905) 566-1255
President: Peter Trnkoczy
All metal, fully adjustable charge bars. Models available for lead and steel shot for MEC reloaders.

The Rock
Production Industries, Inc.
240 Teller St., Corona, CA 91719
(909) 272-0555
Contact: Bill Burns or
Greg Burns
Available: Direct
"The Rock" reloading bench with an adjustable height of 36" to 42" and a 60" x 30" work surface; lockable cabinet and drawer. Shipped within 48 hrs. Dealer inquiries also welcomed.

Spolar Enterprises
Spolar Power Load
17376 Filbert, Fontana, CA 92335
(800) 227-9667
(909) 350-9667
FAX: (909) 350-4276
Est.: 1990 Staff: 2
President: Carter Spolar
VP: Dicksie Spolar
Available: Direct
Manufacturers of the superbly designed and precision manufactured Power Load, the industry's most imitated hydraulic. Committed to providing the reloading shooter with innovative, precision crafted, top quality, state of the art reloading accessories and Ponsness/Warren repairs. Selling direct to assure superior quality at fair prices. Spolar Enterprises considers their customers to be their friends and treats them accordingly. All products carry a 100% satisfaction guarantee.
See Our Ad Below

Xavier Products
Box 159, Forestville, NY 14062
(716) 965-2302
President: Tim Noonan
"The Freeloader" frees you from the workbench. Just mount your reloader to the Freeloader for convenience and safety.

RELOADING POWDERS & COMPONENTS

Accurate Arms Co., Inc.
Scot Powders - PO Box 167, Rt. 1
McEwen, TX 37101
(800) 416-3006 (Cust.Service)
(615) 729-4207
FAX: (615) 729-4217

Alliant Techsystems, Inc.
(formerly Hercules Powder)
200 Valley Rd., Suite 305
Mt. Arlington, NJ 07856-1320
(800) 276-9337
(201) 770-2526
FAX: (201) 770-2529
Tech Info Rep: Harry Pascoe
Dir. of Mktg: Donald H. Burton
See Our Ad Pg. 148

Black Magic Wads
1304 North Chestnut
Beloit, KS 67420
(913) 738-5488
Est.: 1994   Staff: 6
Available: Retail & Direct
Quality replacement 1 1/8 oz.
wads for Winchester AA or Remington hulls. Coming fall of '94 - 1 oz.
wads and Federal gold medal replacement wads.

Blount, Inc.
Sporting Equipment Division
PO Box 856
Lewiston, ID 83501
(800) 627-3640
Available: Retail
Primers

Claybuster Wads
Division of C&D Special Products
309 Sequoya Dr.
Hopkinsville, KY 42240
(502) 885-8088
FAX: (502) 885-1951
Est.: 1988   Staff: 7
President: William MacTavish
Claybuster is a line of replacement
shotgun wads designed for economical reloading in the sport of
clay target shooting.

Federal Cartridge Company
Sporting Ammunition & Components
900 Ehlen Dr.
Anoka, MN 55303-7503
(612) 323-2300
Est.: 1922
Available: Retail
Primers & wads

Fiocchi of America, Inc.
5030 Fremont Rd.
Ozark, MO 65721
(417) 725-4118
FAX: (417) 725-1039
CEO: Craig Alderman
Nat'l. Sales Mgr: Dave Thomas
Available: Direct
See Our Ad Pg. 21

Hercules
Incorporated
See **Alliant Techsystems,**
Inc. *listing in this section*
and our ad page 148

Hodgdon Powder Co., Inc.
6231 Robinson
PO Box 2932-Dept. WC
Shawnee Mission, KS 66201
(913) 362-9455
FAX: (913) 362-1307
Est.: 1946   Staff: 50
Chairman: J.B. Hodgdon
President: R.E. Hodgdon
VP/Sales & Mktg: Tom Shepherd
Available: Retail
Hodgdon Powder Company represents the "Visible Improvement". .
.Clays! This powder was developed
especially for 12 gauge clay target
shooters. Clays is an EXTRA CLEEN
burning propellant perfect for trap,
skeet and sporting clays 1-ounce to
11/8th loads! Try clays. . .it's the
"Visible Improvement!"
See Our Ad Pg. 147

IMR Powder Company
1080 Military Tpke., Suite 2
Plattsburgh, NY 12901
(804) 363-2094
Est.: 1987
Mktg. Mgr: Larry Werner
Available: Retail
We sell a complete line of smokeless powders through master distributors to the handloading market.
As the oldest and most experienced powder manufacturer in North America, IMR Powder Company offers shooters the broadest and best-known line of smokeless powders available. Among these are "Hi-Skor" 700-X, an exceptionally clean-burning powder for both field and target loads, as well as a wide range of proven powders for shotshell, rifle & handgun reloading.

Pattern Control
GTM Plastics, Inc.
114 N. Third St., Garland, TX 75040
(214) 494-3551
Contact: Rick Whicker
Makers of P.C. Wads

Polywad Spred-R
PO Box 7916, Macon, GA 31209
(912) 477-0669
Est.: 1986　　Staff: 4
Contact: Jay Menefee
POLYWAD, "Spred-Rs" are the easiest loading, most effective component you can use to improve your close range gunning. Acclaimed by writers and shooters for nearly 10 years, you will always want to have some for upland game and Sporting Clays. Now available in 4 types for handloaders, 12 ga. "3-hole" for all around use, 12 ga. Solid Disc for tight chokes, 16 ga. and 20/28 ga.
See Our Ad Pg. 203

Reloading Specialties, Inc.
Box 1130
Pine Island, MN 55963
(507) 356-8500
FAX: (507) 356-8800
Est.: 1985　　Staff: 15
VP: Mark R. Braaten
CEO: Jon T. Samuelson
Available: Retail
Manufacturers of steel shot and steel shot wads.

Remington Arms Company, Inc.
Delle Donne Corporate Center
1011 Centre Road, Second Floor
Wilmington, DE 19805-1207
(800) 243-9700
(302) 993-8500 (Business Offices)
Est.: 1816
Available: Retail
Shotshell primers and wads for reloading.
See Our Ad Pg.149

Steel Reloading Components, Inc.
Box 812, Washington, IN 47501
(812) 254-3775
Operations Mgr: Doug Abel
Exclusive distribution of Ecoshot soft steel; steel shot wads, card wads, plastic buffer materials, SRC/multi-pax steel shot counter.

Super Hawk Wads
Hawk International
PO Box 219, Gary, SD 57237
(605) 272-5501

Taracorp Industries
1200 16th St.,
Granite City, IL 62040
(618) 451-4400
FAX: (618) 451-9310
Est.: 1870　　Staff: 100
Contact: Bill Schulze
Available: Retail & Direct

Kaltron-Pettibone
1241 Ellis St., Bensenville, IL 60106
(800) 683-0464
(708) 350-1116
FAX: (708) 350-1606
Contact: Bob Trownsell
Kaltron-Pettibone, importers of Vihtavuori Oy shotgun powders: "Sporting Lite", N3SL, is ideal for 12 ga. 1 oz. and 1 1/8 oz. loads for clay shooters. Two other shotshell powders, N3SM & N3SH, are being introduced for medium and heavy loads for upland game and magnum field loads. All are available in 4 lb. plastic bottles. Load & bushing data available Call: 1-800-683-0464.
See Our Ad Below & Pg. 39

W. T. W., Inc.
Englewood, CO 80110
(303) 781-6329
Owner: Dick Loveland

Winchester Ammunition
Olin Corporation - 427 N. Shamrock
East Alton, IL 62024
(618) 258-2000
Primers, wads, "Ball Powder" smokeless propellants and shot.

SHOOTING SCHOOLS

Sharpen Your Skills

So you're a natural shooter, eh? Good technique is just sort of instinctive with you? Could be. But consider, if you will, the concert pianist who repeats scales for hours a day; the top-flight golf pro who practices the same shot, ball after ball after ball.

You get the point. No matter how good you are, there's always room for improvement. And this is just as true of hunting and clay shooting as it is of countless other disciplines. Fact is, every shooter, from enthusiastic beginner to seasoned veteran, can benefit from instruction and plenty of practice.

Fortunately, there is no shortage of professionally run schools, clinics and instructors that can help you hone your skills and break bad shooting habits. The trick is to find the instruction that meets your needs.

Start your search here.

You can start your search right here, with Wing & Clay's detailed listing of shooting schools and instructors. Before you choose, however, a few preliminaries are called for. First, determine the type of shooting that most interests you. Is it trap or skeet? Sporting clays? Upland or driven pheasant hunting? Consider, too, the shooting style you find most compatible:

sustained lead, swing-through, pull-away or instinctive. Next, read ads and articles, and talk to other shooters. Now you can start to zero in. Write or call the shooting schools that appeal to you and ask for more information. Determine if you'll be in a small class with others of similar ability. And don't be shy about discussing costs. Does tuition cover meals and accommodations? Ammunition and clay birds? Are hearing protectors, recoil protectors and shooting glasses provided? Ask for references. Contact them. Finally, select a school that you can return to as your skills improve.

What will you learn?

What you will learn depends to a large degree on the length of the course. A two-hour clinic will differ -- in style and content -- from that of an intensive three-day shooting course. Many schools begin a session with gun-fitting, including pattern board testing. Most precede shooting with a lecture on gun handling and safety. A discussion of shooting concepts and theories is not uncommon. And the fun part -- actual shooting -- may take place on a skeet field or, in some instances, on a specially designed sporting clays course. You can expect instructors to critique your shooting stance and posture, mounting, swing and follow-through, mostly on the spot, sometimes while reviewing videotape playbacks. Be prepared to be critiqued and corrected. And be prepared to advance toward a new level of skill in your favorite sport!

First and Finest
The Orvis Shooting Schools

When you make the decision to invest time and money in improving your shooting, plan to attend the oldest and finest shooting school in the country. Now entering our third decade, the Orvis Shooting Schools, under the direction of 14 year veteran Rick Rishell, use a modified American version of the famed Churchill method of instinctive shooting. This method is based on the combined elements of proper stance, concentration on the target, proper gun mounting, and the acquisition of a properly fitted shotgun. It's an ideal course of instruction for both field shooting and sporting clays.

Locations in Vermont and Florida

•July - October — Two and three day programs in the Green Mountains, Manchester, Vermont, July and August in this 19th century resort town are filled with activities from golf and fine dining, to antiquing and hiking. From September through October, the foliage season and upland game season combine to offer an unparalleled experience for the wing shooter.
• November and December - 2-day sessions at private Mays Pond Plantation (near Tallahasee) in northern Florida's finest quail hunting country. Full and half day private lessons available.

Who Can Benefit

The Orvis Schools are designed to benefit beginners and veteran wing shooters.
•Easy, non-intimidating style
•Professional instructors with years of wing shooting experience.
•Group sizes limited for maximum personal attention.
•Women-only school in August.

The Course of Instruction

•Essential instruction on shotgun safety and etiquette.
•Selection of proper ammunition and patterning.
•Crossing shots, low incomers, high incomers, and pass shooting at our tower station, quail walk, and singles and doubles on the legendary Orvis course which was the precursor to sporting clays courses now showing up all over the country.

What's Included

Students receive comprehensive instruction and will fire hundreds of rounds with an instructor at their side. All clay birds and ammunition are included, as well as the use of an Orvis Custom Shotgun if desired, a complete custom gun fitting, use of hearing protectors, shooting glasses, and recoil pads, daily lunches and a copy of *The Orvis Wing Shooting Handbook.*

How to Register

To register for the Orvis Shooting Schools, or to receive information and a brochure call director Rick Rishell at **1-800-235-9763** or by FAX at **1-802-362-3525.**

SCHOOLS

Addieville
East Farm
200 Pheasant Dr.
Mapleville, RI 02839
(401) 568-3185
FAX: (401) 568-3009
Est.: 1979   Staff: 8
Contact: Geoff Gaebe
Instructors: Jack Mitchell/Russ Jette
Students/yr: 700+
School Location: 35 mi. south of
Boston;
20 mi. north of Providence
Sessions: By appt./1-6 hrs.
Loaner Guns Available
Method Taught: Instinctive;
Pass-through; Pull away
Shooting Taught: SC, WS
Brochure Available
World renowned British shooting
coach Jack Mitchell teaches proven
techniques modified to best suit
each individual.

Bender Shima
Shooting Clinics
217 Linden Ave., Oak Park, IL 60302
(800) 438-7340
FAX: (708) 386-6418
Est.: 1991
Contact: John Shima
Instructors: John Shima & Todd
Bender
Students/Yr: 800
School Location: Entire U.S.
Group Size: Limited-5 students per
instructor
Loaner Guns Available
Method Taught: All methods de-
pending on student's needs
Shooting Taught: SC, SK, Int'l. Skeet
Brochure Available

Bill Yeatts
Instinct Shooting Clinic
7066 Hardisty St.,
Ft. Worth, TX 76118
(817) 589-2666
Est.: 1962
Contact/ Instrcutor: Bill Yeatts
Students/yr: 25
Sessions: 3 days
Student Rounds Fired: 75
Shooting Taught: WS
Wingshooters: are they born or
made? Texan Bill Yeatts' technique
shows shooters are made–with
proper instruction.
See Our Ad Pg. 159

Broxton Bridge Plantation
Shooting School
PO Box 97, Hwy. 601
Ehrhardt, SC 29081
(800) 437-4868
Contact: Jerry Varn, Jr. (7am-9pm)
Instructor: Marty Fischer
School Location: 25 miles West I-
95 (Walterboro Exit); 60 miles
West of Charleston
Sessions: 1st Saturday of Every
Month
Loaner Guns Available
Brochure Available

Buz Fawcett's
Wingshooting Workshop
2090 S. Meridian Rd.
Meridian, ID 83642
(800) 788-3415
(208) 888-3415
Est.: 1986
Contact: Buz or Barbara Fawcett
Instructor: Buz Fawcett
Students/yr: 100+
School Location: The Shooting
Grounds, Boise, Idaho
Sessions: M/T/W; Th/ F/S/3 days
Group Size: 1 or 2 only
School side-by-sides only available
Student Rounds Fired: Case +\-
Method Taught: Buz Fawcett's
method of Instinctive shooting
Shooting Taught: SC, WS
Money Back Guarantee
Brochure Available
This past Associate Editor of Sports
Afield, Editor of Guns & Ammo
and military shooting instructor,
brings to you 50 years of side-by-
side experience, coupled with a
unique way to succeed in shotgun
shooting. What's more, it's guaran-
teed!
See Our Ad Left

Carlisle
Shotgun Sports
1747 Ridgecrest Ave.
Aiken, SC 29801
(803) 641-2228
Est.: 1978
Instructor: Dan Carlisle
School Location: Available by ap-
pointment to travel to your club
anywhere in ths U.S.
Sessions: By appt./1-4 hrs.
Group Size: 1-4
Loaner Guns Available
Method Taught: The Carlise
Method
Shooting Taught: SC,WS
See Our Ad Above Right

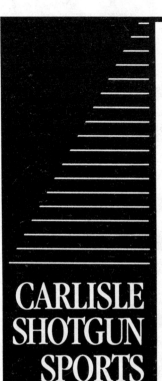

**Casa de Campo
Shooting Center**
PO Box 140
La Romana
Dominican Republic
(809) 523-3333
Est.: 1988
Shooting Director: Michael W. Rose
Instructors: Hermo Guennero,
Alfredo Herrera, Jesus Santana,
Antonio Peguero
Students/yr: 3,000
Sessions: Everyday/1-5 hrs
Group Size: 1 to 25
Loaner Guns Available

**Chesapeake Clays
Shooting School**
16090 Oakland Rd.
(Rt. 312, Bridgetown)
Henderson, MD 21640

(410) 758-1824
FAX: (410) 482-7189
Est.: 1990   Staff: 5
Contact: Bill Connors
Instructor: Gary Phillips & Staff
Students/yr: 200
Location: Chesapeake Hunt Club;
65 miles NE Washington, DC
Sessions: By appt.
Group Size: 1 to 6
Shooting Taught: SC, WS
Brochure Available

**Deborah Cleverdon
Shooting Clinic**
15306 Bonita Springs
Houston, TX 77083
(713) 530-3754
FAX: (713) 530-0851
Est.: 1995
Instructor: Deb Cleverdon

Students/Yr: 100
School Location: Available to travel
to your club by appt.
Sessions: Hourly, 1/2 day, full day
Group Size: 1-10
Loaner Guns Available
Method Taught: Instinctive
Shooting Taught: SC, WS
Handgun for personal protection
Brochure Available

**Clove Valley
Sports Corp.**
Hidden Brook Farm
RR1, Box 110 A
Salt Point, NY 12578
(914) 266-5954
Est.: 1980   Staff: 4
Instructor: Charles Conger
Students/yr: 200
School Location: Several
Sessions: Hourly
Group Size: Individual
Loaner Guns Available
Method Taught: C.P.S.A.
Shooting Taught: SC, WS
See Our Ad Pg. 159

**Deep River
Shooting School**
3420 Cletus Hall Rd.
Sanford, NC 27330
(919) 774-7080 (Phone/Fax)
Est.: 1991
Contact: Bill Kempffer
Instructors: 4 certified on staff
School Location: 35 minutes SW of
Raleigh, NC
Sessions: Hourly by app't., Pack-
ages available
Group Size: 1 to 5
Loaner Guns Available
Method Taught: All Methods
Shooting Taught: SC, WS
See Our Ad Left

Dowtin Gunworks
7815 W. Bridle Trail
Flagstaff, AZ 86001
(520) 779-1898
Contact: Bill Dowtin
Instructor: Bill Dowtin
School Location: Phoenix, AZ, ses-
sions can be arranged at other
locations
Sessions: By appt./3 days
Group Size: 1 to 4
Loaner Guns Available

Method Taught: Instinctive Wingshooting
Shooting Taught: WS
Brochure Available
If you shoot a side by side, my Instinctive Wingshooting Instruction is for you. I teach the correct shooting technique for the side by side double gun. Learning this technique will add confidence and pleasure to your days afield. Please call me...so I can put my 20 years of professional experience to use...making you the best shot you can be.

Andy Duffy
Shooting Clinics
RD1, Box 926
Middletown, NY 10940
(914) 343-1877
Contact: Andy Duffy
School Location: Available to travel to your club
Sessions: By Appt.
Method Taught: Swing through, pull away, sustained
Shooting Taught: SC, WS
Specializing in FITASC
'92 and '93 USSCA National Champion
'93 and '94 National FITASC Champion
'94 NSCA National Champion

Dunn's Shooting School
Rt. 3, Box 39D4
Holly Springs, MS 38635
(800) 564-1396
Est.: 1993
Contact: Stephen Pannell
School Location: Dunn's Shooting Grounds
Sessions: Call for schedule
Loaner Guns Available
Shooting Taught: SC, WS
Brochure Available
Our expert and personal instruction can sharpen the skill of an experienced gunner or provide a perfect start for novices. The three day course of instruction includes classroom, 10 station sporting clays course, and gun fitting. Among the nationally recognized coaches at the shooting school are Gil Ash, Jerry Meyer and many others. Shooting schools run Fall, Winter and Spring. [Cont'd>]

Nestled on 1,000 acres of beautiful, rolling countryside, Dunn's Shooting Grounds includes a 6,000 sq. ft. lodge and 8 bedroom motel. Airport pickup from nearby Memphis International Airport available. Call for information & latest schedule.

Federal Wing & Clay Shooting School
Operated by Federal Cartridge Co.
900 Ehlen Dr.
Anoka, MN 55303
(800) 888-WING (9464)
Contact: Steve Schultz
Instructors: All instructors are NSCA Level II or Level III
Chief Instructor: Steve Schultz, NSCA Level III
Students/yr: Non-restrictive

School Location: Travels Nationwide; Also at specific locations (call for current listing)
Group Size: 6 students/instructor
Sessions: 3 day comprehensive school; one day clinics nationwide
Loaner Guns & Accessories Available
Student Rounds Fired: 200+ per day
Method Taught: All
Shooting Taught: All
Brochure Available
Ammunition Provided
See Our Ad Across

Purveyor to the Wingshooter & Angler

FIELDSPORT Shooting School
2581 Hedwidge Dr.
Traverse City, MI 49684
(616) 933-0767
Est.: 1994
Contact: Bryan Bilinski
Instructor: Bryan Bilinski

School Location: Traverse City, MI
Sessions: 1/2 day to 2 days
Loaner Guns Available
Method Taught: Churchill/Instinctive
Shooting Taught: SC, WS
Brochure Available
Bryan is the founder of Sporting Clays in the U.S. while managing Orvis/Houston. Bryan is a qualified gunfitter and fitting agent for AYA and A.H. Fox shotguns.
See Our Ad Pg. 133

Griffin & Howe

Griffin & Howe
36 W. 44th St., Suite 1011
New York, NY 10036
(212) 921-0980
Contact: Richard Welch
or 33 Claremont Rd.,
Bernardsville, NJ 07924
(908) 766-2287
Contact: Joe Prather
Instructor: Rex Gage
School Location: 1 hour outside N.Y.C.
Students/yr: 450
Sessions: Spring/Fall (April-May; Sept-Oct) Hourly, 1/2 day, day
Individual Hourly Instruction
Method Taught: Instinctive
Loaner Guns Available
Shooting Taught: SC, WS
Brochure Available
For a quarter of a century discriminating shooters have been coming to the Griffin & Howe Shooting School to learn the "Instinctive" method, and to improve their shooting skills. Our school is the original "Instinctive" wingshooting school in this country. All lessons are given on an individual basis. Whether you are new to shooting, or an experienced shooter, give us a call to book your lessons (908) 766-2287.
See Our Ad Pg. 25

Shooting Taught Key:
SC: Sporting Clays
WS: Wingshooting
TR: Trap
SK: Skeet

BRING YOUR PUPILS TO OUR SCHOOL.

If you've got an eye on improving your shooting, look into the Federal® Wing & Clay Shooting School. We're a nation-wide, travelling school bringing top-level, NSCA certified instructors to shooters of every skill level. You'll receive three days of personalized instruction, with all ammunition and targets provided. And you'll come away a more confident hunter or shooter. For details just mail in the coupon below, or call our toll-free number: **1-800-888-WING.**

Grinders Switch Club
1608 Chickering Rd.
Nashville, TN 37215
(615) 729-9732
Instructor: Barry Claud
School Location: 50 miles West of Nashville
Sessions: Individual & Group
Group Size: 1-3
Loaner Guns Available
Shooting Taught: SC, WS & FITASC
Brochure Available
John Wooley, is one of the world's leading wingshooting and sporting clays instructors. John is available at Grinders Switch and also to host clinics at your facility.

Holland & Holland Sporting Clays Weeks
PO Drawer 2770, Avon, CO 81620
(800) 323-4386
FAX: (303) 845-7205
Est.: 1991
Contact: John Horan-Kates
Instructor: Ken Davies & others
Students/yr: 100
School Locations: (1) Vail Rod & Gun Club -Wolcott, CO in June; (2) Papaka Sporting Clays-Maui, HI in February
Sessions: Annually/3 Weeks
Group Size: 3 to 5
Loaner Guns Available
Student Rounds Fired: +\- 1,200
Method: Holland & Holland
Shooting Taught: SC, WS
Brochure, Guidebook Available
Top quality instruction in a first class location.
See Our Ad Above

The Homestead Shooting School
PO Box 2000
Hot Springs, VA 24445
(540) 839-7787
Contact: David Judah, Club Mgr.
Instructors: 5 Certified NSCA Instructors on staff
School Location: The Homestead, Hot Springs, VA
Sessions: Hourly, 1/2 day or full day clinics
Loaner Guns Available
Shooting Taught: SC, TR, SK
Shooting packages available (2 and 3 day) which include accommodations, shells, targets and **[cont'd>]**

Jon Kruger: World Champion Turns Shooting Instructor

The key to success is eliminating the "frustration factor"

"What sets Jon Kruger apart from the rest of the top sporting clays shooters," said one of his fiercest competitors on the tournament circuit, "is that he's so consistent. He never has a really bad day. And he *NEVER* seems to get frustrated!"

I spoke to Jon about it later. "It's not true that I don't have bad days," he said with a smile. "Everyone who shoots does. But it is true that I don't get frustrated. Frustration is self-defeating, and only feeds on itself to make things even more difficult. Beyond technique and visualization and everything else, it's the key point I try to teach to all of the shooters I instruct. Don't beat yourself by getting frustrated!"

Jon Kruger's name has become almost synonymous with sporting clays in America since he started in the game back in 1987. His list of titles would fill half this page. But, unbeknownst to many, equally important to him has been the success he's had instructing both new and experienced Sporting shooters.

KISS: Keep It Simple Shooter

"My objective," says Jon, "is to simplify the game of shooting. Everybody seems to make the game harder than it really is. My objective is to teach the student what to think about before attempting any target. When they understand both the physical AND mental mechanics of the process, it takes the frustration out of any target presentation."

Too many American shooters have an inherent disdain for instruction, and psychologists would have a field day ferreting out the reasons. But the fact of the matter is instruction makes common sense. Like any sport that requires physical dexterity (shooting a shotgun at a clay target is the classic example of hand/eye coordination; no other game requires that you coordi-

Photo: L. Ré

Kruger, left, helping a student "simplify the game".

nate three moving objects to be successful: target, gun, shot charge), it takes input from someone who's been through the long learning process to make logical and practical sense out of it. If you were to take up any other sport (golf, tennis, etc.) you'd go to an instructor or coach to help you get off the ground. Maybe not the minute you pick up the racket or club for the first time, but soon after you've lost a couple dozen golf balls, or have chased down a wheelbarrow full of tennis balls sprayed all over adjacent courts. Shooting should be no different because improvement, and satisfaction, accelerate when you learn the "right" things you're doing as well as the "wrong".

Asking the wrong question

"In most cases," says Jon, "shooters only want to know why they've missed a target, never why they've hit one. Until they understand the necessity of that part of the game, they can only progress so far. It's when you know why you've broken a clay that you begin to generate the memory, both physical and mental, that allows you to repeat the same thing over and over again."

Kruger's instruction process starts off on a patterning board or plate in order to determine gun fit. If necessary, minor adjustments to the gun can be made. (Major changes are another story, and he's wise enough to know you don't achieve anything but frustration--there's that word again--if the shooter's gun doesn't point where he looks.)

The next step is the actual shooting at

clays. If you're at his training center in Iowa, it'll initially be on the 5-Stand field equipped with American made traps from Parker-Boss, one of several of Jon's major industry sponsors. You'll start off with basic singles so Jon can get a feel for your ability and temperament. And so you can ease into the comfortable, relaxed atmosphere that his typically Midwest, laid-back personality generates. Being relaxed is important. Few people learn well if they're confronted with an instructor (in any sport except maybe aerobics), who's hyper or artificially over enthusiastic. And, generally, an instructor that isn't too full of his own ego can better analyze and deal differently with each personality depending on their wants and needs.

Personal attention

There's not enough space here to describe Jon's entire instructional process. Justice couldn't be done to it, because it's such a uniquely personal experience. Suffice it to say that it includes all manner of target presentations. (The Iowa facility can provide everything from floppy pairs in your face to long going-away or crossing birds off a 100 foot tower. At other gun clubs around the country where he does clinics, target presentations are carefully selected or specifically set-up to be equally suitable.) And the level of instruction and shooting method taught have been fine-tuned by experience to accommodate the rank novice all the way up to the advanced shooter looking for those few extra targets that mean the difference between High Overall and also-ran in tournament competition. For example, Jon focuses on his own, obviously successful method with novices. For the more advanced shooter, on the other hand, he offers alternative methods for any specific target; something you can keep in reserve if circumstances demand a change from your normal technique.

To illustrate the importance of that final point, California's Medardo Canales invested in a couple of days with Jon in 1990, and another in '93. One week later, Medardo shot the very first 100 straight registered Sporting Score in the United States.

There's more. . . . .

In addition to instruction, Jon has also built a national reputation for course design. Everywhere you go around the country, you'll see clubs unabashedly proclaim their successful layout as a "Jon Kruger Signature Course". He also performs exhibitions for charities and special events--something you almost never hear about in the black and white, "who won what" world of Sporting.

As Jon freely admits, much of what he continues to accomplish in sporting clays wouldn't be possible without the support of the best companies in the industry. *Krieghoff, Remington, Parker-Boss, Kolar, Ballistic Specialties, ESP and Lube Shot* (guns, cartridges, traps, small-gauge tubes, chokes, ear protection and lubricants, respectively) would be expected to support a winner. But they also support the person. And that alone says all you need to know about the "quality" on both sides of the equation.

"Jon helps you truly understand all the simple things one normally takes for granted," said Canales. "Focus and mindset for any type of competitor are the biggest hurdles they must overcome."

Eliminating the "frustration factor" is a major step in learning how to shoot sporting clays well. And who better to teach you the process than the most successful Sporting shooter in the U.S.? A full day of private instruction, which includes targets, costs $400. Group instruction (five shooters maximum so everyone gets ample personal attention) is $175 per person for a 4 1/2 hour session. Scheduling can be arranged at the Iowa training center, or at any number of clubs around the country. **[For more information, simply call Jon Kruger at 515-736-4893.]**

instruction. Packages can be arranged to suit individual preferences. Please call for details.

See Our Ads Pgs. 51 & 174

Hunter's Creek Club Shooting School
675 Sutton Rd.,
Metamora, MI 48455
(810) 664-4307
Contact: Charlie Mann
Instructor: Pat Lieske
Beginners to Advanced level.
Quarterly stock-fitting seminars.
Monthly group clinics & kid's clinics.

Instructional Shooting Associates, Ltd.
PO Box 764, Bethel Park, PA 15102
(412) 835-5749
Est.: 1989
Master Instructor: Connie L. Fournier (SCA & NSCA Certified)
Chief Instructor: John DeLallo, Jr.
15 Certified Staff Instructors
School Location: Facilities across U.S.
Group Size: 1-5
Sessions: By Appt.
Loaner Guns Available
Method Taught: English Sporting
Shooting Taught: SC, WS, TR, SK, Int'l. TR & SK, Personal Protection
Brochure Available

Kids' Shotgun Shooting Camp
Joshua Creek Ranch
PO Box 1946, Boerne, TX 78006
(210) 537-5090
Contact: Ann Kercheville
Instructor: John Higgins
School Location: Joshua Creek Ranch, 25 miles NW of San Antonio
Sessions: 3 days
Group Size: 10
Loaner Guns Available
Brochure Available
See Our Ad Pg. 182

Jon Kruger
Box 213. St. Ansgar, IA 50472
(515) 736-4893
Instructor: Jon Kruger
Students/yr: 200
School Location: Kruger's Clay World, St. Ansgar, Iowa; available to travel to your club or facility.
Sessions: Hourly; 1/2 day; full day
Group Size: 1 to 5
Loaner Guns Available
Student Rounds Fired: Varies
Shooting Taught: SC, WS, TR
See Our Ad Pgs. 163-64

Mad River Sportsman's Club Shooting School
1055 County Rd. 25
Bellefontaine, OH 43311
(513) 593-8245
FAX: (513) 592-5625
Est.: 1991
Contact: Tony Stratton, Mgr. (8-5)
Club Pro & Instructor: Jim Arnold, NSCA Level III
Students/yr: 300+
School Location: Mad River Sportsman's Club, Ohio
Sessions: 1, 2 & 3 Day Clinics
Loaner Guns Available

Shooting Taught: SC,WS,TR,SK
Brochure Available
See Our Ad Pg. 160

Middleditch Shooting School
1930 Wynfield Point Dr.
Buford, GA 30519
(404) 963-5414
Instructor: Steve Middleditch
School Location: Wolf Creek Sport Shooting, Atlanta, GA and available to travel to your club.
Sessions: Hourly, 1/2 , full, 3 day
Group Size: 1-4
Loaner Guns Available
Method Taught: The Natural Way
Shooting Taught: SC, WS, FITASC, TR, SK
Brochure Available
See Our Ad Below

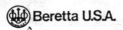

The Midwest Shooting School

950 Hwy. 33, Wrenshall, MN 55797
(218) 384-3670
Est.: 1988
Contact: Patrick LaBoone
Instructor: Patrick LaBoone
Students/yr: 200
School Location: 6.5 miles south of Duluth, MN at Clear Creek Outdoors, Inc. Also available to travel to your club or facility.
Sessions: Hrly./ 1/2, 1 & multi-day schools
Group Size: 1 to 6
Loaner Guns Available

Student Rounds Fired: Varies
Method Taught: English- Mitchell
Shooting Taught: SC, WS, TR, SK
Brochure Available
My instructional video "A Shotgunning Philosophy" will be available in Fall, '95. Sixteen months in the making, this video will be an excellent self help and reference tool for a lifetime of shooting.
See Our Ad Across

MillbrookShooting School & Preserve Ltd.

RR1, Box 193A, Millbrook, NY 12545
(914) 677-5756
Est.: 1993

Contact: Margaret Schneible
Instructors: Mark Elliot &Charles Schneible
Location: 70 mi. North of NYC
Sessions: Anytime by appt/ hourly, 1/2 day, 2 day schools
Group Size: 1 to 20
Loaner Guns Available
Student Rounds Fired: 75-100/hr
Method Taught: The best method for the target & student
Shooting Taught: SC, WS
Brochure Available
See Our Ad Below Left

Fred Missildine Shooting School

Sea Island Gun Club, Box 30296, Sea Island, GA 31561
(912) 638-3611
Est.: 1945   Contact: Fred Missildine
Oldest operating shooting school in the nation.

Dan Moseley Recreational Shooting Sports Service

16115 Alta Mesa Dr.
Houston, TX 77083
(713) 530-1620
(713) 628-6726
Est.: 1970
Instructors: Dan & Glynne Moseley
Location: Houston or your club
Group Size: 1 to 20
Loaner Guns Available
Method Taught: "Instinctive" Relaxed Method
Shooting Taught: SC, WS
Brochure Available
Level III & Level II Certifications held by USSCA, SCA, WSSF, FITASC & NRA. Gunfitting and custom gunsmithing on request.

Mt. Blanca Wingshooting & Sporting Clays Seminars

PO Box 236, Blanca, CO 81123
(719) 379-3825
FAX: (719) 379-3589
Contact: Bill Binnian
Instructors: Bill Binnian, John Meitzen, Dennis Rapp, John Rever
Students/yr: 150
School Location: Mt. Blanca Game Bird & Trout, Blanca-CO 150 mi. SW of Colorado
Sessions: Seminars in June-private & group available any other time
Group Size: Max. 4 per instructor
Loaner Guns Available
Rounds Fired: 50/100 per hour
Shooting Taught: SC, WS
Method Taught: Instinctive/maintained depending on target/ student
Brochure Available on Request
See Our Ad Pg. 157

Michael Murphy & Sons

6400 S.W. Hunter Rd.
Augusta, KS 67010
(800) 843-4513
(316) 775-2137
FAX: (316) 775-1635
Chief Instructor: Michael Murphy
Instructors: Daryl Banmister; Ed Scherer
Students/yr: 400
Location: 15 miles E. of Wichita
Sessions: Formal 3 day schools; 12x/year; 4 students max. per instructor. Private lessons by appt.
Summer classes at The Broadmoor, Colorado & The Homestead, VA; Winter classes at Palm Springs, CA & Orlando, FL
Loaner Guns Available

Method Taught: Swing through & pull away
Shooting Taught: SC, WS
Brochure Available
Stock Fitting Available
See Our Ads Pgs. 169-172

NSCA Instructors School
5931 Roft Rd.
San Antonio, TX 78253
(210) 688-3371 (Ext. 103)
FAX: (210) 688-3014
Est.: 1989
Chief Instructor: John Higgins
Students/yr: 150
School Location: All over the U.S. by appt. at your club. Call for application forms.
Group Size: 6
Sessions: 2-3 times per month at different locations

Shooting Taught: SC, SK
Flyer Available
NSCA Instructors School certifies 3 levels of instructors: Level I, II, III.

NSCA Shooting School
5931 Roft Rd.
San Antonio, TX 78253
(210) 688-3769
FAX: (210) 688-3769
Est.: 1992   Staff: 3
Manager: Peter Crabtree
Chief Instructor: John Higgins
Phone (210) 688-3371, Ext. 103
School Location: National Gun Club
Sessions: By appointment-Lessons, Clinics, Corporate
Method Taught: NSCA Shooting
Shooting Taught: SC
Flyer Available

School's Open.

Now, Remington® offers the very best in shotgun instruction on clays. The new Remington Shooting School features 2½-day sessions for beginners through experienced shooters—including special classes for trap, skeet, sporting clays, women and youths.

The Shooting School opens May 31 and runs through mid-October. It's located in New York's scenic Mohawk Valley at Ilion—historic home of Remington Arms.

To register or for more details, call (315) 895-3574 today.

SHOOTING SCHOOL

Remington®

OSP/Optimum Shotgun Performance Shooting School
15020 Cutten Rd.
Houston, TX 77070
(713) 897-0800
FAX: (713) 469-2450
Est.: 1994
Contact: Gil Ash
Instructor: Jerry Meyer, NSCA Level III
Instructor: Gil Ash, NSCA Level III
School Location: All major gun clubs throughout the U.S.
Sessions: 2 1/2 days
Group Size: 4-6
Loaner Guns Available
Method Taught: Instinctive
Shooting Taught: SC, WS, SK
Brochure Available
See Our Ad Pg. 173

On Target
19702 Larkridge
Yorba Linda, CA 92886
(714) 970-8072
Est.: 1986
Contact: Jay Braccini
Instructor: Jay Braccini
Students/yr: 100
School Location: Raahaughes Shooting Grounds, 5800 Bluff St., Corona, CA
Sessions: By hour/up to 2 days
Loaner Guns Available
Rounds Fired: 1 case/da
Method: "Dan Carlisle" Method
Shooting Taught: SC, WS, TR, SK
Flyer Available

Go to School With the Masters

by Ed Scherer

This past summer when the heat index climbed above 100°, this writer found a cool spot at the Broadmoor Hotel Shooting Grounds in Colorado Springs, CO, home of the 1990 and 1991 U.S.S.C.A. National Championships. The Broadmoor boasts 2 trap, 2 skeet and 2 sporting clays ranges. Master stock fitter Michael Murphy can be found there during the summer and he has some interesting things to say.

Michael Murphy—Master Shooting Coach

The key: proper gun fit

With the advent of sporting clays in the U.S.A, better American shooters are slowly accepting what English shooters have known for the better part of a century: The gun must fit the shooter if the target is to be hit consistently. No one knows this better than Murphy, who has done over 3,000 stock fittings in the past 12 years and is one of the most sought after stock fitters in the U.S.

If you want to shoot with better than average skill, your shotgun must be properly fitted. If the drop at heel is too low, but is correct for drop at comb and length of pull, the shooter will raise his head from time-to-time and get a different sight picture with each shot. Discomfort at the cheek or shoulder may be the result of mounting too far out on the shoulder--with the resulting shot going to the left for right handers. A stock that is too short in length can cause nose or cheek problems.

One size does not fit all

Murphy points out that most of the guns sold in this country are made to a "standard" dimension—1 1/2" drop at comb, 2 1/2" at heel, 14" pull, zero cast, 2" down pitch. This is fine for those fortunate few who are 5'9", 160 lbs., 32" sleeve and have a slender face with average cheek bones. In reality, less than 10% of all shooters fit this mold. Another 30% of the population are close enough to these dimensions so that they can shoot a "standard" gun reasonably well. But the remaining 60% of shooters aren't so

lucky, and it is this group that benefits most from a custom fitted gun.

Unfortunately, there's no "check your fit at home kit" available, so it is best to visit a "gun doctor"—a professional stock fitter. Ideally, he is one who also teaches shooting, so he can check your mount and shooting form. Murphy fits the bill on all counts. And that's why shooters who travel to Augusta, Kansas, to work with Murphy find the trip worthwhile.

Indeed, the ideal trip includes a first day stock-fit by Murphy followed by three days attending one of the Scherer-Murphy clinics. Only ten of these clinics are held each year at the Augusta site. There you will find Murphy's new shooting complex, his well equipped gun shop which includes many, many guns with different stock lengths, comb heights and casts. Murphy, by the way, is one of Beretta's largest gun dealers but he handles Browning and Krieghoff as well. Just above Murphy's shop you'll find Jim Greenwood, one of the best stock benders and stock makers in the world. To top it off, Murphy has a sporting clays range in his back yard where you can take a lesson after your shotgun is properly fit.

Your gun, not a "try gun"

Early on, Murphy learned that it's best to fit the gun you are actually going to purchase from him (or an existing gun you own) instead of using the "try gun" used for 125 years in England and favored by many gunfitters. Murphy points out that

Ed Scherer—The Teacher's Teacher

the fit from a "try gun" does not always transfer well to a different gun. That's why he prefers to fit the actual gun you will use, opting for the "try gun" only when you are building a new stock or gun from scratch. (Murphy emphasized that he has 2 "try guns"—SxS and O/U—and will use one effectively if needed.) To begin the fit, he will analyze your height, weight, sleeve length, measure your hand and check your eye dominancy. He knows also that a person must know good gun mounting techniques and possess good form to properly shoot at a pattern board. If a brand new shooter approaches Murphy, he may give that person a gun that fits close to proper dimensions, ask him or her to shoot it for a period of time and then return for a session on the pattern board. The final fit may include bending the stock up, down or sideways. He actually adjusts the comb like a windage on a rifle.

Murphy quotes various cases where identically dimensioned guns will not shoot the same on the pattern board. The reasons: concentricity of barrels is a factor, along with various width of combs and other phenomena he has run across in the 3,000 plus gun fittings he's done. Murphy says he once purchased a 28 gauge side-by-side that fit his dimensions perfectly, yet shot low due to non concentricity of bores. By bending the stock repeatedly with the hot oil method, Murphy finally

got the gun to center its pattern on a pattern board. Concentricity of bores is where the interior alignment of barrels or chokes doesn't match the exterior.

Be careful, Murphy says, when you purchase a gun without shooting it at a pattern board first. If the stock is too long, it will move out on the arm, and not fit neatly into the pocket of your shoulder. Too high a comb will result in a high shooting gun. If the comb is too low, the gun will shoot low, but worse yet, the cheek and head will have to be raised to see over the receiver of the gun. Contact with the comb is essential when firing for consistent shooting.

But back to the pattern board. If a gun shoots to the left, and mine did on the pattern board, the gun stock must actually be bent to the right. Now all my guns have a 5/16" cast to the right.

Though most people ignore it, the pitch of the butt stock is also a factor. A slender person, for example, requires a 1" or 1 1/2" down pitch, while a heavier person requires approximately a 2 1/2" down pitch. Full-figured women are best advised to have 3" to 3 1/2" down pitch. Pitch regulates what happens when the shotgun is fired. Too much pitch moves the stock up in firing and causes the barrels to go down. Not enough down pitch causes the gun to shoot high but hurts the lower chest as the gun slips down.

The blind mount test

The old wives tale method of laying the gun stock in the crook of your arm to measure stock length tells you one thing--the length of your arm. It, however, tells you nothing about gun fit.

If you wonder about the stock fit of your gun, try the blind mount test. Close your eyes and bring the stock to your cheek, making sure not to move your head in the process. Then, open your eyes and if you are looking right down the barrel, the gun is a close fit. If not, it's off to Murphy's in Augusta, Kansas 800-843-4513, FAX 316-775-1635 for a fit. Murphy cautions his customers about gun ribs that start high and then slant down toward the muzzle. These guns will always

shoot high and he can't fit you for sporting clays with this this type of rib.

The shooting clinics, with a maximum of eight participants between the two instructors, have grown so popular that Murphy and Scherer now hold ten clinics at Augusta, Kansas, plus a few at various locations nationwide each year, like the one recently held at Blackjack Sporting Clays in Orlando, FL.

With each student firing over 750 shells in the three day session, rapid progress is made in learning wingshooting skills. The teachers give one-on-one instruction throughout the three day clinics, watching every shot fired and giving helpful instruction on improving scores.

A master or dominant eye check is made and much attention is given to ballistics and reducing recoil. Footwork and gun mount are stressed and three methods of breaking a target (swing-through, constant lead and pull away) are demonstrated and taught. It's a very informative session for the novice or AA shooter.

Master Instruction...

With a Master's degree in education from East Texas University, Scherer has helped over 5,000 students to become better wingshots over the past 12 years. He has been given an honorary degree in the exclusive British Association of Clay Target Instructors (the first American member). Murphy has taught hundreds at his home base sporting clays range in Augusta, Kansas and fitted thousands. Phone Murphy or Scherer for details.

And call now for Ed Scherer's videos and books, 1-800-451-1253, or write to W30059 Woodcrest Drive, Waukesha, WI 53188-9430, Mastercard, Visa and American Express welcome.

For details of the stock fitting-wingshooting Scherer-Murphy clinics planned for this year and next, call: 800-843-4513 or FAX 316-775-1635 at Augusta, Kansas.

GUNFITTING MEASUREMENTS

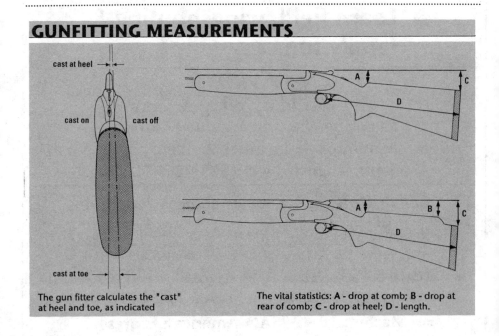

The gun fitter calculates the "cast" at heel and toe, as indicated

The vital statistics: A - drop at comb; B - drop at rear of comb; C - drop at heel; D - length.

Consistent Shotgunning
SHARPEN YOUR SKILLS WITH OSP.

OSP's Jerry Meyer and Gil Ash covered 15 states last year including Hawaii, with their unique talents — demonstrating and teaching the "Instinctive" Shooting Techniques that are so popular in England. Both instructors are NSCA and NSSA certified. In their intensive, two- and -a -half day school, they cover the essentials of:

- VISUAL SKILL DEVELOPMENT
- TARGET ANALYZATION
- GUN FIT
- SHOOTING STANCE
- GUN MOUNT
- CHOKE AND LOAD PERFORMANCE.

VIDEOS NOW AVAILABLE! (VHS-1-OPTIMUM SHOTGUN PERFORMANCE AND VHS-2-CHOKES & LOADS)
OSP offers 2 educational videos to help you improve your shooting skills and get the best performance out of your shotgun. Look at what students are saying after attending one OSP shooting school.

> **"The Choke & Load information is BRILLIANT!"**
> *Vail Rod & Gun Club*

> **"I had never fired a shotgun before this course. The excellence of the instructors allowed me to gain a skill level in excess of my most optimistic expectations!"**
> *Burge Plantation*

> **"After the first half day of your school, I was breaking targets with no thought of lead. The perception of shooting at the Leading Edge of the target is the simplest and most effective way of shooting targets."**
> *Indian River Sporting Clays*

> **"The instructors are what make this school as excellent as it was. Not only do they have an understanding of sporting clays technique, but also they have a superb ability to analyze what a student is doing and help them make any necessary changes."**
> *Dunns Shooting Grounds*

> **"The Instructors were superb in their knowledge, dedication and personal attention, they really care about results!"**
> *Hunters Ridge Hunt Club*

 ENDORSED BY NSCA

 **OPTIMUM SHOTGUN PERFORMANCE SHOOTING SCHOOL**

15020 CUTTEN ROAD, HOUSTON, TEXAS 77070

For More Information, Please Call: 713-897-0800

Sponsored By:

SOUNDSCOPES/E·A·R   Beretta U.S.A.   Jeep   BRILEY
Serving The Shooting Enthusiast Since 1976.

Orlando World Shooting Center Wingshooting School
PO Box 721412, Orlando, FL 32872
(407) 240-9444
General Mgr: Steven A. Smith
Chief Instructor: Andy Duffy
Touring Instructors: Tom Sebring, John Satterwhite, Bonnie McLaurin, Michael Murphy and Ed Scherer, Steve Middleditch, Marty Fischer, Dan Carlisle
Novice Instruction by: Steve Smith & Virgil Minshew
Students/yr: 500
School Location: Blackjack Sporting Clays, Orlando, FL
Sessions: By Appt.
Group Size: 1-6
Loaner Guns Available
Method Taught: Sustained Lead, Swing Through, Pull-Away, Positive Shooting Method
Special Services: Gunsmith & stock fit; Beretta loaner guns

See Ad Florida Clays Section

Orvis Shooting Schools
Historic Rt. 7A,
Manchester, VT 05254
(800) 235-9763
Est.: 1973
Contact: Rick Rishell
Director: Rick Rishell
Students/yr: 350-400
School Location & Sessions:
Manchester, VT–Mid- July through Mid-October; Mays Pond Plantation, Monticello, FL–Nov./Dec.
Group Size: 4 to 16
Loaner Guns Available
Student Rounds Fired: 500 Average
Method Taught: Instinctive
Shooting Taught: SC, WS
Brochure Available

See Our Ad Pg. 155

Outdoors Unlimited
PO Box 515, Eagle Lake, TX 77434
(409) 234-5750
FAX: (409) 234-7603
Contact: John Meitzen
Students/Yr: 200
School Location: Texas, New Mexico, Colorado, Oklahoma, Arkansas, Louisiana, Mississippi
Group Size: No more than 6
Sessions: Hourly, 1/2 day or full day
Loaner Guns Available

Method Taught: NSCA
Shooting Taught: SC, WS, SK
Brochure Available
Traveling instruction and shotgun shooting promotion is available.

Pawling Mountain Club Shooting School
PO Box 573, Pawling, NY 12564
(914) 855-3825
Contact/ Instructor: Keith Lupton
Students/yr: 1,000
School Location: Pawling, NY and other locations by request
Sessions: By appt., hourly, 1/2-1 day
Group Size: 1 to 5
Loaner Guns Available
Method Taught: English style
Shooting Taught: SC, WS
Brochure Available
Keith Lupton has 15 years experience teaching & coaching in the U.K. and the U.S.A., offering expert gunfitting with the use of "Try Guns" in both side by side and over and under.

See Our Ad Across

GUN FIT
A Sure Way To Improve Your Shooting

by Hans Boye Boyesen

*I*t is a simple analogy. When you prepare to drive a car, there are adjustments that enhance your ability to drive...the mirror, the seat, and the steering wheel must fit your personal needs. So is the case in shotgunning.

Keith Lupton, chief instructor of the Pawling Mountain Shooting School in Pawling, New York, is the country's foremost expert in the field of gun fitting.

"It is a proven fact, that proper gunfit definitely improves the ability of the shooter," states the British born Lupton. "Our system of assisting the shotgunner is a basic one." Keith begins by observing the person shooting. The next step takes place at the *Pattern Board*. This allows the shooter to see the shot pattern after mounting and shooting the gun at a stationery target. An evaluation of where the gun shoots (i.e., left and low) is then made.

Enter now, the "TRY GUN", a specially engineered shotgun which is fully adjustable to the shooters anatomy. Arm length, neck height and facial structure all come into play. Once the gun is adjusted to fit at the pattern board, the shooter will then graduate to the excersise of moving

targets thrown in a variety of angles and speeds replicating realistic shooting situations. Careful observation by Keith will then facilitate the *fine adjustments* which will result in a perfect match between the shooter and the shotgun.

Keith showing a client the left target depicting poor gun fit.(insufficient cast-off) Right target indicates corrected fit with the try gun.

The Pawling Mountain Shooting School offers expert gunsmithing services for correcting gunfit.

With the increasing popularity of shotgunning, more shooters are finding gunfit essential to improve both target and wingshooting skills.

The Pawling Mountain Shooting School welcomes both individuals and groups for gunfit and instruction. Keith is also available for corporate clinics and off-premises instruction.

For further information call **914 855-3825**

PAWLING MOUNTAIN CLUB
SHOOTING SCHOOL

P.O.Box 573 Pawling, NY 12564
Gary Hall- General Manager

Gary Phillips
Shooting Instruction
1210 Shallcross Ave.
Wilmington, DE 19806
(302) 655-7113
Est.: 1985
Instructor: Gary Phillips
Students/yr: 250+
School Location: Available to travel
to clubs across U.S.
Group Size: 1-5
Sessions: 2 hours, 1/2 day & full
days
Loaner Guns Available
Method Taught: All Methods Used
Shooting Taught: SC; WS; FITASC;
SK & TR available upon request
Brochure Available
Call now and reserve your copy of
"Hitting the Hard Shots", by Gary
Phillips for just $59.95 plus ship-
ping (1-800-862-6399) or call Gary
direct at (302) 655-7113.
See Our Ad Across

The Preserve and Shooting School
206 Front St., Milford, PA 18337
(717) 296-2354
FAX: (717) 296-8639
Instructor: Neil Chadwick
School Location: The Preserve, Rt.
209, 2 mi. south of Milford, PA
Sessions: Hourly rates, group ses-
sions, corporate days
Group Size 1-6
Loaner Guns Available
Shooting Taught: SC, WS, FITASC
See Our Ad Below

The Remington Shooting School
Remington Arms Company, Inc.
14 Hoefler Ave., Ilion, NY 13357
(315) 895-3574
FAX: (315) 895-3665
Director: Dale Christie
School Location: Ilion Fish & Game
Club
Sessions: 2 1/2 Days
Loaner Guns Available
Method Taught: Most
Shooting Taught: SC, WS, TR, SK
Brochure Available
See Our Ad Pg. 7

River Road Sporting Clays
PO Box 3016
Gonzales, CA 93926
(408) 675-2473
FAX: (408) 675-3495
Contact: Bruce Barsotti
Instructors: 8 Certified NSCA Level
I & II instructors on staff
Students/yr: 200+
School Location: River Road Sport-
ing Clays
Sessions: By appointment
Group Size: Individual or Group
Loaner Guns Available in all
gauges

Rounds Fired: Varies
Method Taught: All Methods
Shooting Taught: SC, WS, FITASC
Also available: Gunfitting, stock
bending, gunsmithing and custom
gun building by Dale Tate, formally
of James Purdey & Son, London,
England. We have a wide range of
shooting available: Sporting Clays
(40 stations), 5-Stand, Duck Tower
(10 stations), FITASC, Trap, &
Skeet (American & International).
Modern guest-rooms; fishing
ponds.

Royal Berkshire Shooting School at Timberdoodle
The Timberdoodle Shooting Club
One Webster Hwy.
Temple, NH 03084
(603) 654-9510
Est.: 1967
Contact: Randall Martin
Instructors: George Digweed/
Robert Cross
Location: U.S., 1 hr. N of Boston;
U.K., 3/4 hr. W of London Loaner
Guns Available
Method: Stanbury
Shooting Taught: SC, WS
See Our Ad Pg. 178

Shooting Taught Key:	
SC:	Sporting Clays
WS:	Wingshooting
TR:	Trap
SK:	Skeet

Gary Phillips - 1995 World English Sporting Clays HOA Turns Students into Champions

by Katy Skahill

He's a smooth operator

"Smooth" is the first thing most people think when they watch Gary Phillips shoot. "He hardly moves his gun", an onlooker will exclaim. This simple observation characterizes Gary's approach to shooting. The less gun movement, the less margin for error. Whether it's the long crossers his countrymen are famous for throwing, or the more "Americanized" targets featuring curl and speed rather than distance, Gary teaches his students to score more by doing less. Gary has won numerous titles during his twenty year shooting career, including the prestigious British Open in his native country. (Since his arrival in this country, he has been High Overall Gun at both NSCA and USSCA Nationals, the Portuguese Open, the Big Pig, and has earned a silver medal at the World FITASC Championships.)

Gary Phillips: Simplicity of style and years of experience.

Student champions

Though Gary's shooting accomplishments are amazing—some would say mind-boggling—great shooters are not always great teachers. But Gary is one of those rare top performers who is able to impart fundamentals to a rank beginner just as easily as he helps an intermediate player jump to the big time. Perhaps the greatest testament to his teaching ability are the accomplishments of his students: Gary has coached the 1993 US Open Champion, the 1994 US Open Sub-Junior Champion, and the 1995 World English Lady Champion, to name just a few. He can help students overcome eye dominance problems and provide valuable advice on gun fit. And he is one of the very few instructors in this country qualified to teach the demanding discipline of FITASC Sporting.

His secret

The secret to Gary's shooting and teaching success is the simplicity of his style. "Getting your gun position and feet position right is more than half the battle", he says. Gary demonstrates his method in an easy, relaxed manner and generally has his students hitting targets that they thought were unbreakable only moments before. In addition, students are able to continue learning even after the lesson is over, as they review the simple principles that Gary covered.

Years of experience

Watching him shoot today, it's hard to imagine that Gary was once a B Class shooter anxiously awaiting the weekend when he could explore the joys of breaking clays. Now, as a teacher, he is quick to share stories about both his successes and his failures, and notes how he has often learned more from losing than from winning. Whether beginner or advanced, Gary's students benefit immeasurably from his years of experience.

Personal instruction and clinics

Because Gary had to work so hard to achieve his current status in the sporting world, he is uniquely qualified to assist with the mental side of the game, as he understands all too well the inevitable disappointments that result from lofty expectations. Gary is available for private, semi-private and small group instruction at very reasonable rates. He can visit clubs anywhere in the U.S. Contact Gary at the number below for more information or to make arrangements. **Gary Phillips Shooting School, 1210 Shallcross Ave., Wilmington, DE 19806 (302) 655-7113**

SCA INSTRUCTORS Course
9 Mott Ave.
Norwalk, CT 06850
(203) 831-8483
Est.: 1986
Contact: Timothy Nichols or
Ben Baldridge
School Location: SCA Affiliated
ranges throughout the USA
Students/yr: 30-36
Sessions: 1 every 2 mos; 4 full days
Group Size: 4-8
Rounds Fired: 500-600
Method Taught: Sustained & pass-
through, also pull away
Shooting Taught: SC
Flyer Available
Level 1 course for would be instruc-
tors who are already experienced
shooters. Level 2 for those instruc-
tors who have already worked 50
hours. Prior knowledge of shotgun
mechanics and ballistics required.

Ed Scherer Shooting School
W30059 Woodcrest Dr.
Waukesha, WI 53188
(800) 451-1253
(414) 968-4788
FAX: (414) 968-3048
Est.: 1981
Contact: Ed Scherer

Instructor: Ed Scherer
Students/yr: 450
School Location: Nationwide, Can-
ada, Puerto Rico, England
Sessions: 30 Weekends/yr. &
wkdays/1 or 2 days
Group Size: 1 to 5
Method Taught: CPSA (Roger
Silcox) method of pull-away, swing-
through and maintained lead
Loaner Guns Available
Student Rounds Fired: 350-400 per
day
Shooting Taught: SC, WS, SK
Brochure, Video Available
See Ads Pgs 169-72 & 179

Tom Sebring
2039 N. Meridian Rd.
Tallahassee, FL 32303
(904) 386-2762

"Shoot Where You Look"
Exemplary Instruction
408 Fair St.
Livingston, TX 77351
(800) 201-5535
(713) 457-1250
FAX: (713) 457-1255
Contact: Leon Measures
Want to learn to shoot a shot-

gun...like an expert? Want to
teach your kid how to hit those fas-
cinating targets? Leon Measures
has designed a comprehenisve self-
help instructional program and kit,
complete with: An adult-size BB
gun (without sights), 1500 BB's,
"The Shoot Where You Look"
book, a one hr., 20 min. training
video, two pairs of safety glasses,
and a shoulder patch. For only
$165, we'll UPS ship these items in
a convenient shipping/carrying
case anywhere in the continental
U.S. This will be the best $165 you
ever spent...to teach or improve
your shotgunning skills! Call today!

Shooting Sports Unlimited
1500 Oliver Rd., #K
Suite 231, Fairfield, CA 94533
(800) 731-7277
FAX: (707) 255-5095
Est.: 1990
Contact: Dennis Rapp
Instructor: Dennis Rapp
Students/yr: 125
School Location: Northern Califor-
nia; Also available to travel to your
location.
Sessions: By appointment
Group Size: 1-4
Method Taught: Instinctive/
Wingshooting
Shooting Taught: SC, WS
For four years my mentor Jack
Mitchell, World Renowned Shoot-
ing Instructor has been teaching
me the finer points of shooting in-
struction. With this knowledge and
the NSCA Level I & II Certification
behind me, I can provide you with
the skills necessary to become a
better shooter.

SKAT Shooting School
PO Box 137,
New Ipswich,
NH 03071
(603) 878-1257
Est.: 1988
Contact: Cyn-
thia Winship
Instructors:
Tony Haigh and
Cynthia Winship
Students/Yr: 1,000
Group Size: 1-20
Sessions: By Appointment
Loaner Guns Available
Method Taught: Modified Churchill
Shooting Taught: SC, WS, TR, SK
Brochure Available

Opta Praestarae

Victory Shooting School
PO Box 7148
Columbia, MO 65205
(314) 442-9189
Est.: 1990
Contact: Mark Brownlee
Instructor: Mark Brownlee
School Location: Columbia, MO;
and other locations
Sessions: Hourly & 1-3 days by
appt./individualized
Group Size: 1-6
Method Taught: Instinctive, CPSA,
Maintained
Shooting Taught: SC, WS, SK
Brochure Available
Certified: USSCA/SCA Level II,
NSCA, NRA
Two time All American Team.
Master's degree Sport Psychol-
ogy/Human Performance
consultant providing the highest
professional expertise in physical, vi-
sual and psychological shooting
skills development. Victory Shoot-
ing School provides a truly unique

learning experience by offering a
total commitment to teaching excellence combined with knowledge
from eastern and western sport sci-
ences to maximize your success
and enjoyment.
- Instruction for beginning,
intermediate and advanced individuals.
- Ladies and youth schools.
- Complete coaching for the competitor.
- Advanced mental skills training
seminars.
Victory Shooting School is your
guide to a new enhanced level of
thought and performance. Choose
to excel and begin to realize your
infinite potential.

Westervelt Turkey School
PO Box 2362,
Tuscaloosa, AL 35403
(205) 556-3909
Est.: 1977
Instructor: Tom Kelly
Sessions: Once in Spring/3 days
Group Size: 1 to 20
Shooting Taught: WS
Brochure Available

**White Oak Farm
Turkey School**
2098 Hwy. 36 W.
Jackson, GA 30233

(800) 666-2619
(404) 775-2619
Est.: 1983
Contact: Bob Boan
Students/yr: 25
Sessions: Once a year/3 days
School Location: White Oak Farm,
Georgia
Group Size: 1 to 3
Loaner Guns Available
Shooting Taught: WS
Brochure Available

**White Oak Plantation
Shooting Schools**
5215 B County Road 10
Tuskegee, AL 36083
(334) 727-9258
FAX: (334) 727-3411
Contact: Robert Pitman
Chief Instructor: Steve
Schultz/Federal Wing & Clay School
School Location: White Oak Planta-
tion shooting grounds; 45 miles
east of Montgomery
Sessions: 4x/yr, Feb-May/Private &
group by appt.

Group Size: 6
Student Rounds Fired: +/- 750
Method Taught: All
Shooting Taught: SC, WS

Youth Shooting Schools and Camps at White Oak Plantation
(334) 727-9258
Contact: Matthew or Robert Pitman
Location: 45 miles east of Montgomery
Sessions: 3x/yr-1 week each/June & July
Group Size: 12
Ages: 10-14, Coed
Lodging: Overnight/2 per bedroom
Taught: Conservation, Shooting, Hunter Safety
See Our Ad Pg. 154

Wings & Clays Shooting School
at Bald Mountain Gun Range
2500 Kern Rd.,
Lake Orion, MI 48360
(810) 814-9193
Est.: 1993
Contact: Larry Woo
Instructor: Pat Lieske
Student/Yr: 100
School Location: Bald Mountain Gun Range
Group Size: Max. of 5

Sessions: 1/2 to full day
Loaner Guns Available
Shooting Taught: SC, WS, TR, SK
Brochure Available
Guest instructors throughout the year

Wise Wingshooting Academy
7829 Sandy Bottom Rd.
Chestertown, MD 21620
(410) 778-4950
Est.: 1989
Contact: Ben E. Wise
Instructor: Ben E. Wise
Students/yr: 40-50
School Location: J&P Sporting Clays, Chestertown, MD
Group Size: 1 to 10
Sessions: Feb-Oct (per day) week or weekends
Loaner Guns Available
Method Taught: Instinctive
Shooting Taught: SC, WS, TR, Flyer Shooting
Brochure Available

Shooting Taught Key:
SC: Sporting Clays
WS: Wingshooting
TR: Trap
SK: Skeet

- Shotgun Instruction by Experienced & Certified Coaches
- Certified B.A.S.C. (British Assn. of Shooting & Conservation) Coach
- 30 Years Teaching Experience in Both Shotgun & Handgun
- Instruction Tailored to Your Needs
- Ladies, Gentlemen & Children - Beginners or More Experienced Shooters Welcome
- All Instruction on a One to One Basis, or a Group of People Who Know Each Other.

Shooting Clubs by Special Arrangement

Woodcock Hill Inc.
THOMAS BLAND & SONS
RD #1, Box 147 • Benton, PA 17814
(717) 864-3242 FAX: (717) 864-3232
— Easy Access by Road or Air —
Located in Northeast PA

Woodcock Hill
Thomas Bland & Sons
Gunmakers, Ltd.
RD#1, Box 147, Benton, PA 17814
(717) 864-3242
FAX: (717) 864-3232
Est.: 1989
Contact: Christa Baker/Glenn Baker
Our, British Association of Shoot-
ing and Conservation, Certified
Coach (only one in the USA) will
teach you the "Method" of shoot-
ing which is equally effective in
clay or game shooting. We offer
complete on the premises try gun
fittings (7 to select from). Instruc-
tion can be tailored to your needs.
See Our Ad Pg.181

**Woods and Water
Shooting School**
Rt. 1, Box 319, Catoosa, OK 74015
(919) 266-5551
Contact: Doug Fuller
Instructor: Doug Fuller
Sessions: 1/2 to 2 day programs
Loaner Guns Available
Shooting Taught: SC, WS, TR, Flyers

Learn Wingshooting with a BB Gun!

- Great for youngsters, ladies or any age beginner.
- Major emphasis on safety.
- Lots of fun and new friends!
- Learn Shooting Fundamentals.
- Qualified instructors.
- Sponsored by NSSF, NSSA and NSCA.

BB Flyers, the new BB Gun Moving Target Program, is a fun and exciting way to learn how to handle a gun safely.
For more information contact Program Director Micheal Hampton, Jr., at 1/800-877-5338 or 210/688-3371 ext.124.

KIDS' Shotgun Shooting Camp at Joshua Creek Ranch

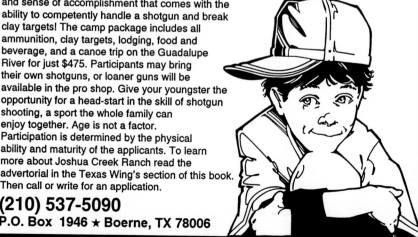

Each July Joshua Creek Ranch holds a Shotgun Shooting Camp just for kids. At the camp, an expert instructor guides a maximum of 10 youngsters through an exciting and challenging three day shooting itinerary. Each participant will experience the pride and sense of accomplishment that comes with the ability to competently handle a shotgun and break clay targets! The camp package includes all ammunition, clay targets, lodging, food and beverage, and a canoe trip on the Guadalupe River for just $475. Participants may bring their own shotguns, or loaner guns will be available in the pro shop. Give your youngster the opportunity for a head-start in the skill of shotgun shooting, a sport the whole family can enjoy together. Age is not a factor. Participation is determined by the physical ability and maturity of the applicants. To learn more about Joshua Creek Ranch read the advertorial in the Texas Wing's section of this book. Then call or write for an application.

(210) 537-5090
P.O. Box 1946 ★ Boerne, TX 78006

SHOTGUN TRADE NAMES & MANUFACTURERS

Know the gun or trade name but not the company that manufactures, imports or distributes it? The index below may help. Find the name in the *Gun* column and across from it you'll find the name of the company—or companies—that can provide you with the information you need. You'll find detailed listings on each of these companies organized alphabetically in the directory section that follows.

Gun	Manufacturer/ Importer	Gun	Manufacturer/ Importer
AYA	Armes de Chasse	Holland & Holland	Holland & Holland, Ltd.
Abbiatico & Salvinelli	Southwest Shooters Supply	IGA	Stoeger Industries
American Arms	American Arms, Inc.	Ithaca	Ithaca Acquisition Corp.
Armas "Azor"	Armes de Chasse	Kemen	USA Sporting, Inc.
Arrieta	Quality Arms, Inc.	Kolar	Kolar Arms
	New England Arms Co.	Krieghoff	Krieghoff International, Inc.
	Orvis	Charles Lancaster	Lewis Drake & Assoc.
	Jack. J. Jansma	Laurona	Intercontinental Trading Spec.
	Hi-Grade Imports	Ljutic	Ljutic Industries, Inc.
Asprey	The Asprey Gun Room	Bosis Luciano	Bosis Luciano
Baikal	K.B.I., Inc.	Marocchi	Precision Sales Int'l., Inc.
Benelli	Heckler & Koch, Inc.	Maverick by Mossberg	Maverick Arms, Inc.
Beretta	Beretta U.S.A.	McKay Brown	McKay Brown
Bernardelli	Armsport, Inc.	Merkel	G.S.I., Inc.
Bertuzzi	New England Arms Co.	Miroku	British Sporting Arms
Thomas Bland	Thomas Bland & Sons Gunmakers, Ltd.	Mossberg	O.F. Mossberg & Sons
		Parker Reproductions	Parker Reproductions
Boss	Boss & Co., Ltd.	Perazzi	Perazzi USA, Inc.
Brno Arms	Bohemia Arms	Piotti	William L. Moore & Co.
Browning	Browning	William Powell	William Powell & Son
CVC Classic Sporter	Connecticut Valley Classics, Inc.	Purdey	James Purdey & Sons, Ltd.
		Remington	Remington Arms Co., Inc.
Chapuis Armes	Chapuis Armes	B. Rizzini	William L. Moore & Co.
Churchill	E.J. Churchill Gunmakers		New England Arms Co.
		F. Ili Rizzini	William L. Moore & Co.
Colt Armsmear	Colt's Mfg. Co., Inc.		New England Arms Co.
Charles Daly	Outdoor Sports Headquarters, Inc.	John Rigby	John Rigby & Co.
		Rottweil Paragon	Dynamit-Nobel/RWS, Inc.
Desanzani	Armi Desanzani	Ruger	Sturm, Ruger & Co.
John Dickson	John Dickson & Son	J&L Rutten	Labanu, Inc.
William Evans	William Evans	SKB	SKB Shotguns
Fabarm	Ithaca Acquisition Corp.	Savage	Savage Arms, Inc.
Fabbri	Fabbri snc	Silma	Century Int'l. Arms, Inc.
Ferlib	New England Arms Co.	Sky Stalker	Sile Distributors, Inc.
A.H. Fox	Connecticut Shotgun Manufacturing Co.	Symes & Wright	Symes & Wright, Ltd.
		Tikka	Stoeger Industries
Franchi	American Arms, Inc.	Tristar	Tristar Sporting Arms, Ltd.
Francotte	Armes de Chasse	Ugartechea	Bill Hanus Birdguns
Daniel Fraser	Daniel Fraser & Co.	Weatherby	Weatherby
A. Galazan	Connecticut Shotgun Mfg. Co.	Westley Richards	Westley Richards & Co.
Renato Gamba	Gamba U.S.A.	Winchester	U.S. Repeating Arms Co.
Garbi	William L. Moore & Co.	Winchester Model 21	Connecticut Shotgun Mfg. Co.
Harrington & Richardson	H & R 1871, Inc.	Zoli	Antonio Zoli
Hatfield	Hatfield Gun Co., Inc.	Zanotti	New England Arms Co.

SHOTGUNS, MANUFACTURERS & IMPORTERS

American Arms, Inc.
"A Step Ahead"

American Arms, Inc.
715 Armour Rd.
N. Kansas City, MO 64116
(816) 474-3161
Est.: 1982   Staff: 23
Available: Retail
Manufactured in: Italy & Spain
Price Range: $499 to $2,798 & custom guns to $21,000 SxS - boxlock and side lock actions, entry level to custom grades. O/U - all gauges; hunting competition, specialty 10 & 12 ga. 3 1/2", entry level to pro-

fessional/competition grade. Luigi Franchi - shotguns.
See Our Ad Pg. 188

Armes de Chasse
Box 86
Hertford, NC 27944
(919) 426-2245
Est.: 1982   Staff: 3
Mktg. Mgr: Art Foley
Available: Retail & Direct
Price Range: $3,000 & Up
Auguste Francotte - Belgium;
Aguirre Y Aranzabal-Spain; Armas "Azor"-Spain
See Our Ad Below

Armsport, Inc.
3590 NW 49th St.
Miami, FL 33142
(305) 635-7850
FAX: (305) 633-2877
Est.: 1974   Staff: 8

Contact: Paul Bines
Available: Retail
Manufactured in: Italy
Importer of Bernardelli shotguns.
Side by side and over and under competition shotguns including sporting clays.

Arrieta, S.L.
5 Barrio Ursandi
E-20870 Elgoibar, Spain
FAX: 011-34-43-74-3154
Available: Retail
Manufactured in: Spain
Importers: Jack J. Jansma, Grand Rapids, MI (616) 455-7810; Hi-Grade Imports, Gilroy, CA (408) 842-9301; New England Arms Co., Kittery Point, ME (207) 439-0593; Quality Arms, Houston, TX (713) 870-8377.

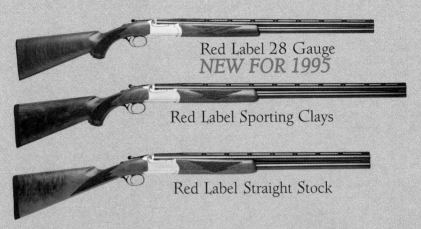
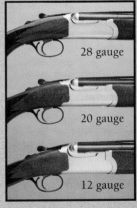

The Asprey Gun Room
23 Albemarle St.
London, W1X 3HA England
011-44-71-493-6767 Ext. 2302
FAX: 011-44-71-491-0384
Est: 1990
Mgr: Tony Pritchard
Available: Direct
Manufactured in: England
Side by Side; available in 12 gauge
to .410.

Beretta U.S.A.

17601 Beretta Dr.
Accokeek, MD 20607
(301) 283-2191
Est.: 1977　Staff: 520
Exec. VP: Robert Bonaventure
Mktg: Rafael Aguirre-Sacasa
Available: Retail

O/U and Semi-Automatic Competition Shotguns and Field Guns. Pistols, knives, gun cases, Beretta Sport clothing and accessories.
See Our Ad Pg. 19

Thomas Bland & Sons Gunmakers, Ltd.
RD#1, Box 147
Benton, PA 17814
(717) 864-3242
FAX: (717) 864-3232
Est.: 1840
Contact: Christa Baker or Glenn Baker
Available: Direct
English shotguns & rifles made to order in England by the English gun trade; all hand crafted by experts.

Bohemia Arms International
17101 Los Modelos
Fountain Valley, CA 92708
(714) 963-0809
FAX: (714) 963-0809
Available: Direct
Manufactured in: Czech Republic
Importer of the Brno Arms O/U and SxS Shotguns.

Boss & Co., Ltd.
13 Dover St.
London, W1X 3PH England
011-44-71-493-1127
Est.: 1812
Contact: Tim Robertson
Available: Direct
Manufactured in: England
Side by Side; available in 12, 20, 28 gauge and .410. Over and Under; available in 12, 20, 28 gauge and .410.

British Sporting Arms
RR1, Box 193A
Millbrook, NY 12545
(914) 677-8303
Est.: 1988
Contact: Charles Schneible
Available: Retail & Direct
Specializing in sporting clays guns; the European Spec. B325 Browning, the Belgium made B25 Browning, and the Miroku Sporters.

Browning
One Browning Place
Morgan, UT 84050
(800) 333-3288 (Customer)
(801) 876-2711 (General)
Est.: 1878　Staff: 350
Available: Retail
Firearms, gun safes, knives, gun accessories, gun cases, boots, clothing, archery equipment.
See Our Ad Pg. 17

Century International Arms, Inc.
PO Box 714
5 Lemnah Dr.
St. Albans, VT 05478
(802) 527-1258
FAX: (802) 524-4922
Est.: 1949　Staff: 180
Marketing: Steve Kehaya
Available: Retail
Importers of: Silma Shotgun (12 ga.)-Italy; Russian TOZ-34P (12 ga.)- Russia

DEMAND
"The Difference"®

THE

D

DIFFERENCE^{SM}

Lifetime
Replacement Coverage!

Ask your dealer for details!

"The Difference"® is not a manufacturer's warranty.

Chapuis Armes
Z.I. La Gravoux, B.P. 15
St. Bonnet-le-Chateau, 42380
France
011-33-77-500696
FAX: 011-33-77-501070
Contact: Rene Chapuis
Available: Direct
Price Range: Contact directly for price quote
High quality SxS and O/U shotguns. Manufactured on a limited basis.

E.J. Churchill Gunmakers, Ltd.
Ockley Rd., Beare Green, Dorking, Surrey RH5 4PU England
011-44-306-711435
Manufactured in: England
Side-by-side shotguns with custom features

Colt's Manufacturing Company, Inc.
4885 A McKnight Rd.
Pittsburgh, PA 15237
(800) 962-COLT
(412) 931-3512
FAX: (412) 931-1719
Shotgun Mgr: Rob Silinski
Contact: Eric Polkis
Colt Armsmear O/U 12 ga.

Connecticut Shotgun Manufacturing Co.
PO Box 1692
New Britain, CT 06051-1692
(203) 225-6581
FAX: (203) 832-8707
Contact: Dick Perrett
Available: Retail & Direct
Manufacturer of shotguns in the United States:
- A.H. Fox 20 gauge side by side shotgun in five grades, priced from $7,200.
- Winchester Model 21 built to order in conjunction with US Repeating Arms. Also, factory repair and parts.
- A. GALAZAN full sidelock over & under shotgun in any gauge (12, 16, 20, 28, .410), priced from $40,000.

Connecticut Valley Classics, Inc.
PO Box 2068
12 Taylor Lane
Westport, CT 06880
(203) 435-4600
FAX: (203) 256-1180
Est.: 1991   Staff: 10
Contact: Dean Jendsen

Available: Retail
Price Range: $2,995 and up
High quality US made double barreled shotguns. Sporting clays and field models. Gun line available to retailers and gun club pro-shops seeking to build franchise in high grade shotguns. Manufacturing being expanded to increase availability and offer various custom features. Call or write for catalog.
See Our Ad Across

Armi Desenzani
Via Oberdan, 20H
20125 Brescia, Italy
011-39-30-383-656

John Dickson & Son
21 Frederick Street
Edinburgh EH2 2NE Scotland
011-44-31-225-4218
Est.: 1820
Contact: Mr. Wight or Mr. Nelson
Available: Direct
Manufactured in: U.K.
Side by Side round action ejector; available in 12 and 20 gauge.

Lewis Drake & Associates
305 S. 8th St., Murray, KY 42071
(502) 436-5270
FAX: (502) 436-5257

The CVC Classic Sporter

Over thirty years ago the Model 101 Over/Under Shotgun was borne. The dependability, balance and pointability have proved second to none. The same is true today with its successor, the American made CVC Classic Sporter.

From the hand checkered, black walnut stock and fore end to the machined, stainless steel frame, the fit and finish are superb. The 28", 30" and 32" barrels feature lengthened forcing cones and overbored tubes with screw-in chokes. Shot after shot these new guns will deliver balanced, crushing shot patterns and a lifetime of "Classic Value".

For a brochure on the 12ga. "Classic Sporter" and "Classic Waterfowler", a price list and the name of your nearest dealer, please contact us.

Connecticut Valley Classics, Inc.

P.O. Box 2068-WC,   Westport, CT 06880   Tel: 203-435-4600

Contact: Lewis Drake
Available: Direct
Manufactured in: England
Price Range: $30,000-$50,000
Charles Lancaster "twelve-twenty"
is the lightest and strongest side
by side ever made.

Dynamit Nobel

Dynamit-Nobel/RWS, Inc.
81 Ruckman Rd.
PO Box 430
Closter, NJ 07624
(201) 767-1995
FAX: (201) 767-1589
Contact: Frank Turner
Available: Retail & Direct
Manufactured in: Germany
Importer of Rottweil Paragon
shotgun (Germany) and Rottweil
Brenneke slugs. Written inquiries
welcome.
See Our Ad Pg. 193

William Evans Ltd.
67 a St. James's Street
London SW1A 1PH England
011-44-71-493-0415
Est.: 1833

Mngg. Dir: M. Gates Fleming
Available: Direct
Manufactured in: England
Side by Side; available in 12, 16
and 20 gauge. Over and Under;
available in 12 and 20 gauge.

Fabbri snc
Via Dante Alighieri, 29
25062 Concesio (BS), Italy
011-39-30-275-2050

Daniel Fraser & Co.
Colony Wood, Cromarty
Ross-shire, Scotland
011-44-38-160-0294
Est.: 1878
Contact: Bernard Horton-Corcovan
Available: Direct
Manufactured in: Scotland
Side by Side; available in 12 gauge
to .410.

G.S.I. Incorporated
108 Morrow Ave.
PO Box 129
Trussville, AL 35173
(205) 655-8299
Est.: 1983
Sales Rep: Matt Bryant
Sales Rep: Ken Johnson

Sales Rep: Einar Hoff
Available: Retail
Manufactured in: Germany
US importer and service center
featuring Merkel side by side and
over and under shotguns, drillings
and combinations guns. Traditional
German quality, meticulous hand
craftsmanship, exceptional value.
See Our Ad Across

Gamba U.S.A.
The First National Gun
Banque Corp.
PO Box 60452
Colorado Springs, CO 80960
(719) 578-1145
FAX: (719) 444-0731
Est.: 1989   Staff: 4
President: Karl C. Lippard
Available: Retail
Exclusive importer of Renato
Gamba Firearm Line. O/U & SxS
sporting guns in standard to highly
engraved models. Factory warranty
service.

H&R 1871, Inc.
60 Industrial Rowe
Gardner, MA 01440
(508) 632-9393
FAX: (508) 632-2300
Est.: 1991   Staff: 270
VP/Sales & Mktg.: Robin Sharpless

Available: Retail
Manufactured in: USA
Price Range: $69 to $199
Single barrel single shot, shotguns
including special models for deer
(slug) hunting and turkey guns.
From .410 to 10 ga. as well as
eight distinct youth guns including
a 28 ga. We are the worlds largest
producer of single barrel shotguns.

Bill Hanus

Birdguns

Bill Hanus Birdguns
PO Box 533, Newport, OR 97365
Est.: 1988   Staff: 1
Sole distributor of Ugartechea
small gauge SxS shotguns, priced
under $1,500 with lifetime opera-
tional warranty. Send stamped,
self-addressed #10 envelope for
complete product information and
dealer list.

Hatfield Gun Co. , Inc.
224 North 4th St.
St. Joseph, MO 64501
(816) 279-8688
FAX: (816) 279-2716
Est.: 1981   Staff: 15
President: Ted Hatfield
C.F.O: Charles Roberts

Dir. of Mktg: Neil Oldridge
Available: Retail & Direct
Makers of Hatfield black powder rifles, uplander SxS shotguns and
fine over and under shotguns.

Heckler & Koch, Inc.
21480 Pacific Blvd.
Sterling, VA 20166
(703) 450-1900
Est.: 1976   Staff: 49
Dir. of Creative Svcs: Steven Gallo-
way
President: Steve Otway
VP: Jim Woods
Available: Retail
Benelli shotguns and Heckler &
Koch firearms

Holland & Holland, Ltd.
31-33 Bruton St.
London, W1X 8JS England
011-44-171-499-4411
FAX: 011-44-71-499-4544
Chairman: Alain Drach
Contact: Daryl Greatex
118 North Saint Asaph St.
Alexandria, VA 22314
(703) 549-5540
FAX: (703) 739-8967
Contact: J.G. Roosenburg
Est: 1835
Available: Direct
Manufactured in: England
"Royal" Side by Side; available in 12

gauge to .410. "Royal" Over and
Under; available in 12, 20, 28 or
.410 gauge. "Sporting" Over and
Under; available in 12 or 20 gauge.

**Intercontinental
Trading Specialists**
PO Box 4208
Chatsworth, CA 91313
(818) 772-7358
FAX: (818) 772-7301
Contact: Juan Capdet
Available: Direct
Manufactured in: Spain
Importer of Laurona shotguns;
O/U models for hunting & competi-
tion.

**Ithaca Acquisition
Corporation/Ithaca Gun**
891 Rt. 34B
PO Box 4
King Ferry, NY 13081
(315) 364-7171
(315) 364-7182 (Cust. Svc.)
FAX: (315) 364-5134
Est.: 1987   Staff: 29
Contact: Eric-Stephan Neill
President: Paul Guttenberg
Sales Support Desk: Kenn Van
Dieren
Service Mgr: Les Hovencamp
Product Mgr: Robert Nase
Available: Retail
Pump, O/U & SxS shotguns

K.B.I., Inc.
3405 N. 6th St., PO Box 5440
Harrisburg, PA 17110
(717) 540-8518
Est.: 1988   Staff: 7
VP/Sales: Steven M. Cohen
Available: Retail
Price Range: $110 to $20,000
Baikal, over/under, side by side
and single barrels (Russia), Sabatti
O/U's (Italy).

Kolar Arms
1925 Roosevelt Ave.
Racine, WI 53406
(414) 554-0800
Est.: 1968   Staff: 46
President: John Ramagli
Partner: Don Mainland
Available: Retail & Direct
Manufactured in: U.S.
Price Range: $6,900 & Up
New skeet, trap and sporting O/U

**Krieghoff
International, Inc.**
7528 Easton Rd.
PO Box 549, Ottsville, PA 18942
(610) 847-5173
FAX: (610) 847-8691
Est.: 1985   Staff: 14
Chairman: Dieter Krieghoff
President: Jim Hollingsworth
Available: Retail
Manufactured in: Germany
Price Range: $3,600 & Up
Krieghoff International imports, distributes and provides factory service for K-80, KS-5 competition shotguns for trap, skeet & sporting clays.
See Our Ad Pg. 11

Labanu, Inc.
2201 F Fifth Ave.
Ronkonkoma, NY 11779
(516) 467-6197
FAX: (516) 981-4112
Est.: 1991   Staff: 6
VP: Hafiz Rahman
Available: Direct
Manufactured in: Belgium
Price Range: $1,295-$1,495
Importers of J&L Rutten of Herstal, Belgium. Available in 12 gauge-offering 2 models.

Ljutic Industries, Inc.
732 N. 16th Ave., Suite 22
Yakima, WA 98902
(509) 248-0476
Est.: 1937   Staff: 25
Gen. Mgr.: Nadine Ljutic

Available: Retail
Manufactured in: USA
Price Range: $4,495 to $21,995
12 ga. single barrel target shotguns (only Ljutic designs) 12 ga.
O/U's for trap, skeet, live birds & international trap/skeet. The only totally custom shotguns produced in U.S.

Bosis Luciano
Via G. Marconi, 32
25039 Travaglioto (BS), Italy
011-39-30-660-413

**MagTech Recreational
Products, Inc.**
4737 College Park, Suite 101
San Antonio, TX 78249
(210) 493-4427
FAX: (210) 493-9534
Est.: 1990   Staff: 5
Contact: Dan Flaherty
Available: Retail
Importers of numerous shotguns, ammunition and rifles.

Maverick Arms, Inc.
7 Grasso Ave.
PO Box 497
North Haven, CT 06473
(203) 230-5300
Est.: 1988
Contact: Ron Fine
Available: Retail

Price Range: Under $200
Maverick by Mossberg pump
shotguns.

McKay Brown
32 Hamilton Road, Bothwell
Glasgow, G71 8NA Scotland
011-44-69-885-3727
Est.: 1967
Contact: David McKay Brown
Available: Direct
Manufactured in: Scotland
Side by Side; available in 12 gauge
to .410. Over and Under; available
in 12 gauge to .410.

**William Larkin
Moore & Co.**
31360 Via Colina
Westlake Village, CA 91361
(818) 889-4160
Contact: Bill Moore
8227 E. Via De Commercio
Suite A
Scottsdale, AZ 85258
(602) 951-8913
FAX: (602) 951-3677
Est: 1979
Available: Direct
Importer of: Piotti, F.lli Rizzini, B.
Rizzini, Garbi

O.F. Mossberg & Sons, Inc.
7 Grasso Ave.
PO Box 497
North Haven, CT 06473-9844
(203) 288-6491
FAX: (203) 288-2404
Est.: 1918   Staff: 400
Mktg. Mgr: Joe Koziel
Available: Retail
Model 500, 12 & 20 gauge pump
action; Model 835, pump action
12 gauge; Model 9200, 12 gauge
autoloader 3 1/2".
See Our Ad Pg. 13

New England Arms Co.
PO Box 278
Lawrence Lane
Kittery Point, ME 03905
(207) 439-0593
Est.: 1975   Staff: 6
Contact: Jim Austin or

Steve McCarthy
Available: Retail & Direct
Exclusive U.S. distributors for F.lli
BERTUZZI, Importers and dealers
for F.lli Rizzini, Tecni-Mec,
Armitalia, Cosmi, Fabbri, Ferlib,
Casartelli, Zanotti, Arrizabalaga,
Arrieta, H. Dumoulin, A.H. Fox Gun
Co.
Extensive inventory specializing in
high quality doubles. You will find
names like, Purdey, Boss, Holland
& Holland, Churchill, Westley Rich-
ards, Parker, A.H. Fox, Lefever,
Winchester, Francotte, Piotti, Ber-
etta, Perazzi, Merkel, Sauer,
Browning, and many more.
Complete gunsmithing services by
British gunsmith. Stock fitting and
bending. Complete restoration ser-
vices.

ORVIS®

Orvis
Historic Rt. 7A
Manchester, VT 05254
(802) 362-3622
Contact: Jack Dudley
Available: Retail & Direct
Only U.S. company offering cus-
tom stocked Berettas offered in all
configurations using the finest exhi-
bition grade walnut, completed in
six weeks.
- Importers of Arrieta side by side
shotguns.
- Professional gun fitting by
experienced fitters using our own
Beretta try guns.
- Custom stocking, alterations, and
complete gun repair.
- Complete line of used double
guns.
- Consignment gun sales.

**Outdoor Sports
Headquarters, Inc.**
967 Watertower Lane
Dayton, OH 45449-2463
(800) 444-6744
FAX: (800) 488-6744
VP: Roger Vignolo
Importer of Charles Daly: Three
models in current series: Charles
Daly Field O/U - 12 & 20 gauge;
Charles Daly Deluxe Field O/U - 12
& 20 gauge; Charles Daly Sporting
Clays O/U - 12 gauge

Parker Reproductions
124 River Rd., Middlesex, NJ 08846
(908) 469-0100
FAX: (908) 469-9692
Est.: 1984   Staff: 250
Available: Retail
Exact reproductions of the original
Parker in 12, 16/20, 20, & 28 bore.

Perazzi USA Inc.
1207 S. Shamrock Ave.
Monrovia, CA 91016
(818) 303-0068
FAX: (818) 303-2081
Est.: 1981   Staff: 6
Vice President: Lucio Sosta
Available: Through our Dealers
Manufactured in: Italy
We offer a full line of shotguns, in
all configurations for use in Sport-
ing Clays, American Trap & Skeet,
International Trap & Skeet and
Hunting. Perazzi shotguns are avail-
able from the Standard Grade
Models through Extra-Extra Gold
Grade. For a full color catalogue
and price list or the dealer nearest
you please call or write to us.
See Our Ad Pgs. 2-3

William Powell & Son
35-37 Carrs Lane
Birmingham, B4 7SX, England
011-44-21-643-0689
Est.: 1802
FAX: 011-44-21-631-3504
Contact: Peter Powell
Available: Direct
Manufactured in: England
Side by Side; available in 12, 16
and 20 gauge.

**Precision Sales
International, Inc.**
PO Box 1776
Westfield, MA 01086
(413) 562-5055
Est.: 1978   Staff: 5
Contact: Alan Johnson
Available: Retail

James Purdey & Sons, Ltd.
57-58 S. Audley St.
London, W1Y 6ED England
011-44-171-499-1801
FAX: 011-44-171-355-3297
Est: 1814
Contact: Nigel Beaumont or
Robin Nathan
Available: Direct

Manufactured in: England
Side by Side sidelock ejector;
available in 12, 16 and 20 gauge.
Over and Under sidelock ejector;
available in 12, 16, 20, 28 gauge
and .410.

Quality Arms, Inc.
PO Box 19477
Houston, TX 77224
(713) 870-8377
Est.: 1975   Staff: 3
Contact: John Boyd
Available: Retail & Direct
Importer of Arrieta
See Our Ad Right

Remington Arms Company, Inc.
Delle Donne Corporate Center
1011 Centre Road, Second Floor
Wilmington, DE 19805-1270
(800) 243-9700
(302) 993-8500 (Business Offices)
Est.: 1816
Available: Retail
Autoloading, pump, special purpose and break-action shotguns
for the hunter. Autoloading, pump
and break-action shotguns for the
trap, skeet and sporting clays
shooters. Also, ammunition; reloading components; clay targets;
traps; gun care and cleaning products; gun cases; and knives.
See Our Ad Pg. 15

John Rigby & Co.
66 Great Suffolk Street
Southwark, London SE1 0BU
England
011-44-171-734-7611
Contact: Paul Roberts
Available: Direct
Manufactured in: England
Side by Side sidelock ejector; available in 12 gauge to .410.

SKB Shotguns
PO Box 37669
Omaha, NE 68137
(402) 330-4492
Contact: Rob Johanson
Available: Retail

Manufactured in: Japan
Price Range : $1,000 and up.
Importer for the SKB shotgun line.
See Our Ad Pg. 4

Savage Arms, Inc.
100 Springdale Rd.
PO Box 1110
Westfield, MA 01085
(413) 568-7001
Est.: 1989   Staff: 190
Manufacturer of rifle/shotgun combination guns & centerfire high
power sporting rifles.

Sile Distributors, Inc.
998 N. Colony Rd.
Meriden, CT 06450
(800) 243-3404
(203) 238-4285
FAX: (203) 237-9324
VP: Dominick Derobertis
7 Centre Market Place
New York, NY 10013
(212) 925-4111
Est: 1958
Available: Direct
Manufactured in: Italy
Price Range: $359 to $389
Over and Under shotguns; Sky
Stalker I (fixed chokes) and Sky
Stalker II (changeable chokes);
available in 12, 20, 28 gauge and
.410.

Southwest Shooters Supply
Box 9987
Phoenix, AZ 85068
(602) 943-8595
FAX: (602) 943-1713
Est.: 1976   Staff: 3
Contact: Alan Peck or
Bruce Kinkner
Available: Direct
Manufactured in: Italy
Price Range: $8,000 to $83,000
Importers of the Abbiatico &
Salvinelli Shotgun.

Stoeger Industries
5 Mansard Court,
Wayne, NJ 07470
(201) 872-9500
FAX: (201) 872-2230
VP: David C. Perkins
Price Range: $120 to $689
Distribute IGA & TIKKA Shotguns
that include O/U, SxS, coach guns
and single barrel models including
a youth model.

Sturm, Ruger & Company
217 Lacey Place
Southport, CT 06490
(520) 778-6555
FAX: (520) 778-1217
Est.: 1949   Staff: 1700
Dir. of Mktg: Syl Wiley
Available: Retail
Price Range: $1,215 to $1,675
Ruger Red Label and (new in
1995) Woodside Shotguns are engineered with American firearms
know-how, based on contemporary American target and field
experience. Produced in 12, 20
and now 28 (Red Label only)
gauge, straight stock and pistol-grip, sporting clays (12 and 20
gauge only) and standard models,
there is a Ruger shotgun to fit
every over-and-under user.
*See Our Ad Pgs. 185
& Back Cover*

Symes & Wright, Ltd.
8 Monmouth Place
London W2 5SA England
011-44-71-792-9698
FAX: 011-44-71-221-1424

Contact: Peter Symes
Available: Direct
Manufactured in: England
Traditional side by side, exquisite over and under or double rifle crafted to owners specifications. 14 month delivery.

Tristar Sporting Arms, Ltd.
PO Box 7496
1814-16 Linn St.
N. Kansas City, MO 64116
(816) 421-1400
FAX: (816) 421-4182
Est.: 1994
President: George Woford
Vice President: Marty Fajen
Available: Wholesale & Retail
Manufactured in: Turkey
Price Range: $400-$750
TRISTAR SPORTING ARMS, LTD., a new sales & marketing company with 50 years of firearms industry experience. TRISTAR's product offering is made by the Uzumlu Factory, under the direction of the MINT Engineering Company, in the country of Turkey. Historically, their entire production has been sold to the Turkish market and bordering countries. (Turkey has the 2nd largest general hunting population in the world, after the U.S.). TRISTAR has been selected as the exclusive marketing agent, in the USA, for these fine firearms. Please see our ad for the models available. Dealer inquiries welcome.
See Our Ad Left

U.S. Repeating Arms Co.
275 Winchester Ave.
Morgan, UT 84050
(801) 876-3440
FAX: (801) 876-3737
Est.: 1866
Available: Retail
Manufactured in: USA & Japan
Price Range: $300 & Up
Turkey, deer and field guns in RealTree camouflage patterns.

USA Sporting, Inc.

1330 N. Glassell, Suite M
Orange, CA 92667
(800) 538-3109
(714) 538-3109
FAX: (714) 538-1334
Est.: 1957
Available: Direct
Manufactured in: Spain

Price Range: $6,200-$34,500
Kemen Custom Shotguns Representative for USA & Canada Custom made 12 gauge over and unders for trap, trap doubles, sporting clays, skeet, bunker, hunting and flyers, with many options.
See Our Ad Pg. 192

Weatherby
2781 Firestone Blvd.
South Gate, CA 92080
(800) 227-2016 (Cust.Service)
(213) 569-7186
Est.: 1946   Staff: 65
Available: Retail
Manufactured in: Japan
Price Range: $1,050 to $2,450
Orion Grade shotguns I, II & III;
Athena Grade shotguns IV, & V,
High Grade Over & Under Shotguns.

Westley Richards & Co., Ltd.
40 Grange Road, Bournbrook
Birmingham B29 6AR England
FAX: 011-44-21-472-1701
Est.: 1819
Contact: Simon Clode
Available: Direct
Manufactured in: England
Side by Side: William Bishop Sidelock Ejector; 12, 16, 20 and 28 gauge. Carlton Boxlock Ejector; 12, 20, 28 gauge and .410. Connaught Boxlock Ejector; 12, 20 and 28 gauge.

Antonio Zoli
Via Zanardelli 39
25063 Gardone Val Trompia,
Italy
011-39-30-891-21612
FAX: 011-39-30-891-1165
Manufactured in: Italy

SHOTGUNS/
NATIONAL DEALERS

Allem's Gun Craft
7937 Sigmund Rd.
Zionsville, PA 18092
(215) 679-9016
FAX: (215) 679-8016
Contact: Nancy Allem

G.M. Bartelmay Guns, Inc.
911 W. Jefferson
Morton, IL 61550
(309) 263-8032
Contact: George Bartelmay

Cape Outfitters, Inc.
Rt. 2 Box 437-C
Cape Girardeau, MO 63701
(314) 335-4103
FAX: (314) 335-1555

Colonial Gun Shop
143 Boone Square St.
Hillsborough, NC 27278
(919) 732-8396
(919) 732-5663
Staff: 10
President: Mark Stone
Contact: Johnny Clayton or
Stephen Young
Specializing in fine doubles & collectibles. Factory authorized
Krieghoff & Perazzi dealer–call for
all your shotgun needs.

David Condon, Inc.
Antique & Sporting Arms
109 E. Washington St.
Middleburg, VA 22117
(540) 687-5642
FAX: (540) 687-5649
President: David Condon
Manager: Britton Condon
Manager: Harriet Condon
Willing to buy or consign whole collections or individual items.

See Our Ad Above

Michael DeChevrieux
PO Box 1182
Haily, ID 83333
(208) 788-4628
FAX: (208) 788-7523

du Pont/Krieghoff Gun Company
PO Box 8007
Vero Beach, FL 32963-8007
(800) 73K-GUNS

Joel Etchen Guns
HC64, Box 109
Ligonier, PA 15658
(412) 238-0332
FAX: (412) 238-0334
Contact: Joel Etchen

FIELDSPORT
2581 Hedwidge Dr.
Traverse City, MI 49684
(616) 933-0767
Contact: Bryan Bilinski
FIELDSPORT specializes in sales of
fine American and European SxS
and O/U for game shooting and
sporting clays. Our inventory of
over 100 guns includes AYA, A.H.
Fox, Belgium Browning, English-
made Parker, Boss, Winchester
Model 21, Beretta and many more.
Call for current gun list. Trades welcome. Field Sport also appraises
and purchases fine gun collections.

See Our Ad Pg. 133

A.J. Frigon Guns
627 West Crawford
Clay Center, KS 67432
(913) 632-5607
Proprietor: A.J. Bloom

Gamaliel Shooting Supply, Inc.
1525 Fountain Run Rd.
Box 156
Gamaliel, KY 42140
(800) 356-6230 (Orders)
(502) 457-2825
FAX: (502) 457-3974
Contact: Garon Pare

"Willing to buy or consign
whole collections or
individual items."

David Condon
President

Britton Condon
Manager

Post Office Box 7
109 E. WashingtonStreet
Middleburg, VA 22117
(540) 687-5642
FAX: (540) 687-5649

Griffin
&
Howe

Griffin & Howe
36 W. 44th St., Suite 1011
New York, NY 10036
(212) 921-0980
33 Claremont Rd.
Bernardsville, NJ 07924
(908) 766-2287
Contact: Joe Prather
See Our Ad Pg. 25

The Gun Maker's Cabinet
PO Box 2696, Liverpool, NY 13089
(315) 652-9025
FAX: (315) 622-9629

Guns Unlimited
4325 S. 120th St.,Omaha, NE 68137
(402) 339-0771
FAX: (402) 330-8029
Contact: Bill Hickman

Hi-Grade Shooters Supply
Box 448, Jacktown, Irwin, PA 15642
(800) 245-6824
(412) 863-8200 (Alaska/Hawaii)

J&J Sporting Goods
868 Derby Farms Dr.
Severn, MD 21144
(410) 551-0488

Jaqua's Fine Guns, Inc.
900 E. Bigelow Ave.
Findlay, OH 45840
(419) 422-0912
FAX: (419) 422-3575
Contact: Camille Ranzau

John's Trap Guns, Inc.
334 Peterson Rd.
Libertyville, IL 60048
(800) 448-GUNS
(708) 549-6226
FAX: (708) 549-6230

**Mid-Maryland
Outfitters, Inc.**
3000 E. Ventrie Court
Myersville, MD 21773
(301) 694-7305
(301) 293-1936
FAX: (301) 293-3622
We stock a full line of Krieghoff
K80's and Browning guns, along
with Bob Allen clothes. Try *our
own* shooting gloves, gun sleeves,
& shell bags. We own and promote the "Big Pig Open". We help
promote and sponsor over 5 state
championships, National Ducks Unlimited, Quail Unlimited, National
Wild Turkey, Ladies Charity Classics, and The Louise Mandrell
Celebrity Shoot.

See Our Ad Below

Monsoor's Sports Shop
517 Copeland Ave.
LaCrosse, WI 54603
(608) 784-0482
FAX: (608) 784-0481

**Scott Moss Gun & Tackle
of Norwalk, Inc.**
4 New Canaan Ave.
Norwalk, CT 06850
(203) 847-4008, Ext. 300
FAX: (203) 847-8064
Contact: Scott Moss
See Our Ad Pg. 186

Michael Murphy
& Sons
6400 S.W. Hunter Rd.
Augusta, KS 67010
(316) 775-2137
FAX: (316) 775-1635
President: Michael Murphy
See Our Ads Pgs. 169-172

New England Arms Co.
PO Box 278
Lawrence Lane
Kittery Point, ME 03905
(207) 439-0593
Est.: 1975   Staff: 6
Contact: Jim Austin or
Steve McCarthy
Retail showroom with over 1000
shotguns and sporting rifles. Called
"The Best Gunshop in the World",
by FORBES F.Y.I. Magazine. Also
hailed "All That a Gun Store Should
Be", by Field & Stream. Extensive in-
ventory specializing in high quality
doubles. You will find names like,
Purdey, Boss, Holland & Holland,
Churchill, Westley Richards, Parker,
A.H. Fox, Lefever, Winchester,
Francotte, Piotti, Beretta, Perazzi,
Merkel, Sauer, Browning, and
many more. Complete gunsmi-
thing services by British gunsmiths.
Stock fitting and bending. Com-
plete restoration services.

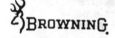

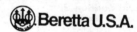

New England Outdoorsman, Inc.
217 South Main St.
Rutland, VT 05701
(802) 747-3355
Contact: Mike Pratico

Pachmayr.

Pachmayr Ltd.
831 N. Rosemead Blvd.
S. El Monte, CA 91733
(800) 350-7408
(818) 579-5201
FAX: (818) 358-7251
Contact: Arthur Bright
Visit our fully stocked PRO SHOP, located at the Pachmayr Shooting Sports Park, 831 N. Rosemead Blvd., S. El Monte, CA. Our PRO SHOP features Perazzi, Browning and Beretta shotguns, reloading supplies and accessories.
See Our Ad Pg.143

Paxton Arms
PO Box 150245, Dallas, TX 75226
(214) 651-9018
FAX: (214) 748-2999
Est.: 1978
Contact: Robert V. Paxton

Carl Poston
2009 Mowbray Pike
Daisy, TN 37379
(615) 875-4868 (Store)
(615) 332-1195 (Gun Club)
FAX: (615) 332-1972

Quality Arms, Inc.
PO Box 19477
Houston, TX 77224
(713) 870-8377
Est.: 1975   Staff: 3
Contact: John Boyd

Schroll Shooting Supplies
1320 San Bernardino Rd., #56
Upland, CA 91786
(909) 985-7147
FAX: (909) 981-0436
Contact: Wendell Schroll

Southwest Shooters Supply
PO Box 9987
Phoenix, AZ 85068
(602) 943-8595
FAX: (602) 943-1713

Sundog Firearms
HC82, Box 234
Kimberly, OR 97848
(503) 934-2117 (Phone/Fax)
Est.: 1985   Staff: 2
Contact: Jerry Russell
German Merkel shotguns; finest handcrafted quality. Best value in the world today.

SHOTGUN SHELLS

ACTIV Industries, Inc.
1000 Zigor Rd., PO Box 339
Kearneysville, WV 25430
(304) 725-0451
Pres: Luis A. Perez
VP: L. Andres Perez
Customer Service Mgr: Linda Barnhart
Plant Manager: Doug Dockeney

Bismuth Cartridge Company
3500 Maple Ave., Dallas, TX 75219
(800) 759-3333
(214) 521-5880
President: W.S. Montgomery
Contact: Skutch Mason/Elizabeth Stearns
The first real non-toxic alternative to lead. Exclusive to the Bismuth Cartridge Company in North America, these premium shotshells contain patented bismuth alloy shot, the only known non-toxic metal with the approximate density and hardness of lead. This shot's ballistic qualities are similar to those of shotshells loaded with a like amount of lead shot and powder. Offered in a variety of loads. Available from fine sporting goods stores or call us direct for your nearest dealer.
See Our Ad Below

Brownell
Silver Mountain Rd.
Rockerville, SD 57702
Staff: 2
Contact: Bob Brownell
Available: Direct
Licensed manufacturer of ammunition shotshells. Brownells Shells (formerly "Brownells" West) custom manufactured 2.75" Remington R&L - Winchester AA, once fired shotshells. Designed for upland, trap & skeet and various clays sports. 10 years experience in pattern performance; 35 years experience in competition shooting and upland. Only the finest quality components are utilized.

Clever Mirage
Gene Sears Supply Co.
2003 South Shepard Dr.
El Reno, OK 73036
(800) 654-4520
Contact: Gene Sears, Jr.

Cubic Shot Shell Company
98 Fatima Dr., Campbell, OH 44405
(216) 755-0349
Staff: 2
Contact: Marilyn Terlecki or Thomas E. Terlecki

Eley Ammunition
(Tomart, Inc.)
122 Lafayette Ave., PO Box 610
Laurel, MD 20725
(301) 953-3301
FAX: (301) 490-8904

Est.: 1984 Staff: 4
Contact: Art Cook

Eley Ltd.
PO Box 705, Witton
Birmingham B6 7UT England
011-44-21-356-8899
FAX: 011-44-21-331-4173
Contact: Alan Ward
.22 rimfire cartridge manufacturers; distributors of shotshell cartridges

Estate Cartridge Company
2778 FM 830
Willis, TX 77078
(409) 856-7277 (Plant)

Contact: Paul Butaud
(713) 980-4209: (Sales Office)
Contact: Rick Shoupe
Est.: 1980 Staff: 15
Available: Distributor, Dealer, & Consumer Direct
Sales are conducted through key retailers and distributors for commercial products and direct to the consumer on custom items. Commercial items include a complete line of hunting, target and promotional shotshells. Custom items include 2 1/2" English light loads, competition flyer and custom requests.
Estate Cartridge, Inc. manufactures the finest shotgun shells available today. These shells are especially designed to give maximum power, superior long range penetration, and extremely uniform patterns. All of our components are (ballisti-

cally) matched to give the highest possible performance. The most modern ballistic laboratory equipment is used to insure maximum quality control. We specialize in making ammunition to the customers specifications. We also have the unique capability of personalizing the shells by printing names, initials or corporate logos directly onto the hull. "IF QUALITY IS YOUR GOAL, ESTATE SHOULD BE YOUR CHOICE."
See Our Ad Across Right

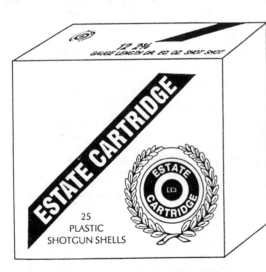

Kent Cartridge
CHAMPION

Shoot the Finest.
Shoot Kent.

Recognized as the finest shotshells manufactured in Europe, Kent Cartridges are now available in North America. Fast, consistent and hard-hitting, Kent Champions are the first choice of World Champion sporting clay shooter George Digweed. Call us at 800-759-3333 for a color brochure detailing our full line of Kent Cartridge products, including Champion, Biowad, Fibre and Topmark.

Dealer Inquiries Welcome.

KENT CARTRIDGE USA

Gamebore Cartridge Co., Inc.
New England Arms Co.
Box 278, Lawrence Lane
Kittery Point, ME 03905
(207) 439-0593
FAX: (207) 439-6726
Est.: 1975   Staff: 6
Contact: Jim Austin or Steve McCarthy
Available: Retail or Mail Order, No FFL required, UPS shipment
Gamebore Black Powder loads, 8 ga. 3 1/8", 10 ga. 2 7/8", 12, 16, & 20 ga. 2 1/2"
Nitro loads in 10, 12, 16, 20, 24, 28, & .410 (2") also 12 ga. 2". NEW this year-Paper Case 12 gauge loads.
Gamebore Steel shot, and Pattern Spreaders in 12 gauge
New England Arms offers the sportsman the widest variety of gauges and loadings, as well as over 1000 shotguns in stock. All shells manufactured in Great Britain to the highest quality standards. Your headquarters for specialty shotshells for older American, British and European shotguns. Brochure available upon request.

Hull Cartridge Company, Ltd.
Bontoft Ave., National Ave.
Hull HU5 4HZ England
011-44-482-42571
FAX: 011-44-482-46103
Director: Hugh Clark
Sales Mgr: David A. Allen

Imperial Ammunition
Shotco Ammunition Corp.
3821 Williamson Way
Bellingham, WA 98226
(360) 738-8888
Contact: James Del Vecchio

Kent Cartridge
USA

3500 Maple Ave., Dallas, TX 75219
(214) 521-5883
Est.: 1982
Contact: Skutch Mason
Available: Direct
Kent Shotshells are recognized as the finest manufactured in Europe. In fact, George Digweed earned three Sporting and FITASC simultaneous World Championships shooting off-the-shelf Kent Champions exclusively. And you can shoot them too! Kent Cartridge's outstanding line of shotshells–Champion, Biowad, Fibre & Topmark–are now available in North America. Shoot the finest. Shoot Kent. Call for a dealer near you. Dealer inquires welcome.
See Our Ad Above

Lyalvale
Express Shells
XRC, Inc.
10001 Meadowbrook Dr.
Suite 100
Dallas, TX 75229
(214) 373-4742
FAX: (214) 373-0761
Est.: 1993   Staff: 5
President: Jack Brumbelow
Sales Mgr: Rod Jaroch
Available: Retail & Direct
NOW AVAILABLE IN THE U.S.: Lyalvale Express Shells. Consistently rated one of the highest quality, best performing shells available anywhere! Lyalvale's outstanding engineering and high quality controls have produced a shell that one American shooting editor described by saying "there is nothing over here that compares." Call for information on prices and delivery: 214-373-4742.
See Our Ad Pg. 200

Olympia U.S.A.
1050 Crown Pointe Pkwy.
Suite 360, Atlanta, GA 30338
(404) 913-9977
FAX: (404) 913-9838
President: Jean Constantinides
See Our Ad Pgs. 44-45

Orvis "Shot"
Historic Rt. 7A, PO Box 798,
Manchester, VT 05254
(800) 548-9548

Polywad
Shotgun Shell
PO Box 7916, Macon, GA 31209
(912) 477-0669
Est.: 1986   Staff: 4
Contact: Jay Menefee
Excellent choice for upland gamebird hunters. Also NSCA approved. POLYWAD, whose "Spred-R" component for handloaders has been a hit for over 10 years, now has 2 versions of factory loaded "Spred-R" shotshells in 12 gauge. Availabe in 3 Dr. 1 1/8 oz. of #9, 8, 7 1/2 and 6 shot; and 2 3/4 Dr., 28 Gram (1 oz.) in #9, 8 1/2, 8 and 7 1/2 shot. These shells combine distinctive looks with high performance and overall superior quality. 12 gauge, 2 1/2" shells available soon–please inquire. For upland game and sporting clays, "Spred-Rs" take the worry out of being close!
See Our Ad Right

RST LTD.

RST, Ltd.
7 Weston Way
Ctr. Conway, NH 03813-0127
(603) 447-6769
(603) 447-6770
FAX: (603) 447-1856
Contact: George E. Olson
Designed by shooters, for shooters, RST Ltd. uses only the finest components from around the world and are assembled right here in the USA. Whether for game shooting or a specific target discipline, RST Cartridges will give you the best performance money can buy. Competition & game loads are available in 12, 16 & 20 gauge in both 2 3/4" (70mm) & 2/12" (65mm) cartridges. Custom logos may be ordered for your club or business. Specialty loads may also be available. Call for details.

Remington
C O U N T R Y

Remington Arms Company, Inc.
Delle Donne Corporate Center
1011 Centre Road, Second Floor
Wilmington, DE 19805-1270
(800) 243-9700 (Consumer)

(302) 993-8500 (Business Office)
Est.: 1816
Available: Retail
Remington manufactures shotshells for upland hunting and small game; turkey loads; steel shot waterfowl loads; rifled slugs, sabot slugs and buckshot loads for larger game; "duplex" layered shotshells for hunting and target shooting; lead and steel shot target loads for sporting clays, trap and skeet; reloading components; and a variety of special purpose loads.

See Our Ad Pgs. 28-29

Sellier & Bellot, USA

PO Box 5007
Kansas City, KS 66119
(913) 371-4930
FAX: (913) 371-1823
Contact: Ed Grasso
Available: Retail
Made in: Cech Republic; Shotgun shells–all gauges–target & hunting.
See Our Ad Below

Tru-Tracer

Kent Cartridge USA
3500 Maple Ave.
Dallas, TX 75219
(214) 521-5883
Contact: Skutch Mason
Available: Retail & Direct
Tru-Tracers are a revolutionary new tracer cartridge that for the first time give an accurate assessment of where the shot has gone. Based on an entirely new concept the trace is carried in a single projectile which stays in the centre of the pattern for over 50 yards. Clearly visible in daylight the cartridge gives the shooter immediate information on where the shot has gone. They are invaluable training aids for both teacher and shooter, beginner and expert alike. Tru-Tracers are finding major use in Police and Military training, and is non-phosphorus, safe and non-icendiary.

See Our Ad Pg. 206

CARTRIDGE COMPANY

Victory Cartridge Company

PO Box 1081
100 Victory Dr.
Milford, PA 18337
(717) 296-2354
FAX: (717) 296-8639
Contact: Neil Chadwick
Choose VICTORY shells for price and performance. Victory's new TRAP & SKEET cartridges are designed specifically for the U.S.-featuring low recoil and super patterning. See our ad for the distributor in your area.

See Our Ad Right

Winchester Ammunition

Olin Corporation
427 North Shamrock
East Alton, IL 62024
(618) 258-2000
See Our Ad Pg. 23

TARGETS

AmericanZZ, Inc.
(formerly Lee's Target Pigeon)
171 Spring Hill Rd.
Trumbull, CT 06611
(203) 261-1058
FAX: (203) 452-9359
Contact: Millo Bertini
Available: Direct
American "ZZ" Bird, AmericanZZ Trap line simulates box-bird live pigeon shooting. The targets are plastic discs fitted onto stamped-metal propellers. A "bird" is counted as "dead" when the shot separates the disc from the prop. Launchers include the Sport Wing, with a non-oscillating, or fixed head, designed for sporting clays ranges, where more consistent target presentation are often needed.

The Flush Bird is an oscillating unit that's capable of throwing pigeons in almost any direction. Five or nine of these units with a computer controller are all that is needed for a simulated box-bird ring. The targets are susceptible to wind currents and speed. The discs are reusable if they are not hit, and the props are good for about eight throws. "ZZ" targets are approved in the NSCA rule book.
See Our Ad Pg. 213

CCI International
Clark Clay Industries, Ltd.
Priors Haw Road, Corby
Northamptonshire, NN17, 5JG
England
011-44-1536-260933
FAX: 011-44-1536-401138
Est.: 1982   Staff: 40
Chairman: Jonathan Cridland
Full range of sporting clay pigeons and automatic traps

CHAMPION TARGET COMPANY

Champion Targets
232 Industrial Pkwy.
Richmond, IN 47374
(317) 966-7745
Est.: 1975
Contact: Kelvin Johnston
Available: Retail
The only USA target manufacturer

who produces the complete line of targets needed for trap, skeet, international and sporting clay shooting.
Champion's new Classic Trap and Skeet clay has been designed to be the target of the future. A new engineered shape and construction promotes strength for use with automatic traps and provide a very breakable surface area when hit. The new Classic is available only from Champion shooting supply distributors.

Kromson
Oviedo 5-7, 50007, Zaragoza Spain
011-34-76-379900
FAX: 011-34-76-271913
Contact: Carlos Alonso

LAPORTE AMERICA
One Trans-Border Drive
Champlain, NY 12919
(800) 335-TRAP
FAX: (514) 449-1431
LAPORTE is the largest manufacturer in Europe and offers a complete range of targets in a wide range of colors, for trap, skeet, sporting (midi, mini, battue & autorabbit), international as well as flash. Please contact us for further details and a color brochure of our range.
See Ads, Inside Front Cover, Pgs. 223 & 225

Lawry Shooting Sports, Inc.
27 Industrial Dr., Caledonia, Ontario, Canada N3W 2G6
(905) 765-3343
Est.: 1984   Staff: 10
Contact: Bob Lawry or Richard Lawry
Targets for trap /skeet shooting.

Midwest Target Co.
1103 S. State St.,Litchfield, IL 62056
(217) 324-4895
Est.: 1980   Staff: 15
Gen. Mgr: Jon Sutton
Available: Retail & Direct
Manufacturer of clay targets.

Northwest Targets
278 78th St., NE, Salem, OR 97302
(503) 399-7879
Est.: 1979   Staff: 3
Contact: Tim Elliott
Available: Retail & Direct
Maker of trap & skeet targets.

Quack Sporting Clays, Inc.
4 Ann & Hope Way
PO Box 98
Cumberland, RI 02864
(401) 723-8202
FAX: (401) 722-5910
Contact: Colleen Hamel
Available: Retail & Direct
Quack Sporting Clays, Inc., a multi-faceted manufacturer, also makes a series of tough almost unbreakable plastic targets that fly exactly like the real clays for fun and games. Plastic birds are available in standard, midi, mini and rabbit and can be used many times. Black, white and colors available – "Flash" target kits are also available. For more information contact us.
See Our Ads Pgs. 228-229

Remington Arms Company, Inc.
Delle Donne Corporate Center
1011 Centre Road, Second Floor
Wilmington, DE 19805-1207
(800) 243-9700
(302) 993-8500 (Business Offices)
Est.: 1816
Available: Retail

TARGETS

White Flyer Targets
124 River Rd.
Middlesex, NJ 08846
For the name of your nearest distributor please call:
East - 800/423-6077
Central - 800/647-2898
West - 800/872-7888
California - 909/823-0679
Manufacturing quality targets from three modern plants. The shooters choice for over one hundred years. Full and complete line of Trap, Skeet, International and Sporting Clays targets in the widest variety of colors. Knowledgeable distributors throughout the country.
See Our Ad Pg. 207

Black's
WING & CLAY

Wing & Clay has information on just about every product and service needed by an operator of a hunting preserve, sporting clays, trap or skeet location. In additon to the listings on this page, please refer to:

CLAY TARGETS

STANDARD
4 ¼ inches in diameter, 1 ⅛ inches thick; dome shaped; standard in trap and skeet.

BATTUE
4 ¼ inches in diameter; ⅜ inch thick; "flying razor blade," difficult to pick up edge-on; does rolls and wingovers.

ROCKET
4 ¼ inches in diameter; ⅝ inch thick; deceptive in flight; appears to float, but retains more velocity than the standard.

MIDI
3 ½ inches in diameter, ⅞ inch thick; smaller size make it appear farther away than it actually is; retains initial velocity longer than other targets.

RABBIT
4 ¼ inches in diameter; ½ inch thick; rolls and bounces on the ground; thick rim, density prevent shattering on impact with ground.

MINI
2 ⅜ inches in diameter, ⅝ inch thick; deceptive because small size makes it appear to be moving faster than it actually is; slows quickly because it's light.

TRAPS

Buying A Trap: What To Look For

Knowing what you want when you're buying a trap is easier said than done. And the problem compounds when you try to match your needs with the growing number of clay target throwers—made in the U.S. and abroad—now available on the market.

As always, knowledge is your best ally. So whether you are an individual shooter looking for a portable trap or a gun club manager putting in a tournament quality sporting clays course, here are some tips on getting the best value for your dollar.

First the basics: Clay target throwers fall into two broad categories: manual and automatic.

Manual Traps

Very basic, and less-expensive manual machines usually allow only minimal adjustment for the height or speed and distance the target travels. The durability of these models depends on design and construction, but, generally speaking, those made with solid metal frames are more durable than the light sheet metal variety.

Greater durability comes at greater cost, as does a variety of desirable features such as a double throwing arm (for launching two targets simultaneously); target height, angle and speed adjustment; teal clips (for throwing targets vertically); electric release; a semi-cocking device that makes it easier for the machine to be cocked; a feature that allows different size sporting targets to be thrown by the same machine (including rabbit targets that bounce along the ground); a seat attached to the base; and finally, extra safety features.

Automatic Traps

Automatic traps range in complexity from relatively simple, no nonsense designs to feats of engineering wizardry. But remember, the greater the automation, the higher the price. Before buying, consider the following: Was the machine you are considering designed for the use you have planned? Many machines do a fabulous job at skeet, for example, but don't perform as well when put out on a sporting clays course, and vice versa.

Key Concerns

Maintenance: If you're all thumbs around any thing mechanical, you'll want a machine that you can deal with easily and quickly in the event of breakdown. Key questions to ask when you are shopping: What are the machine's annual maintenance requirements and costs? Are replacement parts readily available? What

about service technicians, when you can't make the necessary repairs.

Durability And Dependability: How many targets will the trap throw before breaking down? How many in its lifetime? Also, experts agree that a good trap will usually break less than 3% of the targets it throws. How does the model you're considering compare to this standard?

Versatility: What else can this trap do? Certain shooting disciplines, American Trap (ATA) and Skeet, for example, do not require much versatility from a trap. They do require a high degree of target flight consistency, though. Models destined for use as a sporting clays thrower, on the other hand, should be more versitile. Additional features to look for include:

- Portability--light weight construction (to make it easier to move around the course)

- Adjustable elevation -- ideally to the teal position (the ultimate in height adjustment!)

- Fast recocking time (good for "following pairs")

- Battery power option (see Power Source)

- Tiltability-- can be the model be tilted over on its side to throw curving targets (increasingly popular with shooters).

Target Capacity: How many targets should a machine hold? The consensus among experts is that 300 to 400 is the most efficient number. Remember, the more targets the machine holds, the longer it takes to fill it--but you won't have to fill as often!

Power Source: Plug-in or battery power? The installation costs for plug-in power (110v AC) can be high. Power cables have to be buried and this generally confines the size and "changeability" of your layout. With battery power, you can install a machine practically anywhere, and move it as often as you want.

Release Sytems: Ask about the different ways targets can be released--manually, electrically, by radio, and even by voice. Also, ask about the back-up systems that can be used if the primary release system fails.

A Final Word

Finally, as with many products, trap prices are often more a measure of mechanical complexity than quality. The type of trap and the make you buy should be determined by the your needs and budget. To avoid being trapped with the wrong trap, do your homework. Contact as many of the manufacturers and distributors listed on the following pages as you can. Check references. Call gun club and clay target operators for personal recommendations, before you write that check.

[For information about the cost and acreage requirements of shotgun shooting games and disciplines, see following chart on page 212.]

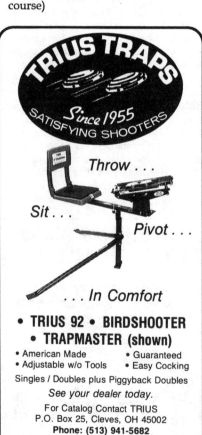

COST & ACREAGE REQUIREMENTS OF SHOTGUN SHOOTING DISCIPLINES & GAMES

	ACREAGE & COST ESTIMATES				THROUGHPUT OF SHOOTERS			
DISCIPLINE/ GAME	ACRES Construction	Fallout *	COST Machine Construction (in thousands of dollars)		CONSTRUCTION COMMENTS	SHOOTERS PER HOUR	TIME PER SHOOTER/ SQUAD	NO. OF TARGETS
TRAP ** (ATA, ABT, DT)	.25	52	7-9	2.5-8	Layout, trap pit, walkways, electr.,floodlights	18-25	13-16 min./ 5 shooters	
OLYMPIC TRAP	.38	52	42-65	12-28	Large pit for traps, walkways,electr., floodlights	18-24	15-18 min./ 6 man squad	
UNIVERSAL TRENCH	.32	52	14-22	8-16	5 trap pit, walkways, electr., floodlights	18-24	15-18 min./ 6 man squad	
ZZ BIRD	.38	52	.5-9	.2-1	Layout & small fence	6-12	6-8 min./ shooter	
SKEET (NSSA/UIT)	.34	58	8-9	8-12	Layout, buildings, walkways, elect., floodlights	10-12	25 min./ 5 shooters	
SPORTING ***	20-30	100/ 200	M: 12-16	4-23	Stands, trap mounts, gun racks, shelters, walkways	50	1 hr./5 man squad	50
			A: 73-92	12-45	As above + trap houses & electr.			
FITASC	15-30	100/ 200	M: 18-32	8-30	Stands, trap mounts,racks, shelters, walkways	20	2 hrs./5 man squad	200
			A: 90-150	18-68	As above + trap houses & electr.			
CRAZY QUAIL	1	58	M: 1 A: 5-9	1	Trap pit	12-15	5 min./ shooter	25
TWO-MAN FLUSH	.20	48	A: 5-9	1-1.8	Trap house/ shooting platform	60-80	34 sec./ 2 shooters	24
TRAP HOUSE	6	100	7	0	Trailer with 10-20 M traps	10-40	25-35 min./ 5 man squad	50
5-STAND SPORTING®	.80	58	A: 18-30	0	Skeet or empty field	10-15	20-25 min./ 5 man squad	25
QUAIL WALK	0.5-2	50-60	M: 3-9	1-4		4-10	15 min./ shooter	25
			A:18-40	3-15	Including electr.			
SUPERSPORT	10-30	150/ 200	A: 80-140	15-25	12-25 traps & electrics	4-10	15-25 min./ shooter	50
TOWER SHOOTING	.2	160	A: 7-10	2.5-15	Tower	10-20	6-10 min.	25
PRO- SPORTING	1	58	A: 15-18	1.5-5	5 traps	360	36-50 sec./ 6 man squad	25/ squad
SUB-TRAP	1	58	.6 - .8	.1-1.5		18-25	10-25 min./ 5 man squad	25
FLUSH AND FLURRIES	0.5-2	50/ 110	M: 1.2-2 A: 4.8-6.6	.1-1.5 .6-2		100-300	36 sec./ 4,5 or 6 man squad	25/ squad
STARSHOT	.34	58	48	3-25		15-30	3 min./shooter	25
DOUBLE RISE	.25	52	7.6-9.2	2.5-8		18-25	16-22 min./ 6 man squad	25

* No shot larger than 7 1/2.   ** For a Skeet/Trap overlay field, the combined construction costs would be $10,000-$17,000.
*** Quality of landscaping varies price.   M = Manual   A = Automatic   Source: The Shooting Academy

TRAP MANUFACTURERS & IMPORTERS

AmericanZZ, Inc.
(formerly Lee's Target Pigeon)
171 Spring Hill Rd.
Trumbull, CT 06611
(203) 261-1058
FAX: (203) 452-9359
Contact: Millo Bertini
Available: Retail & Direct
We can set-up America's version of the European "ZZ" Bird three different ways. AMERICANZZ provides an effective simulation of the zig-zagging, unpredictable flight of a live pigeon at reasonable cost. Five or nine computer controlled launching machines placed in a pigeon ring release targets at controllable speed from 25 to 40 mph. Birds randomly selected by computer. Machines oscillate 130-degrees. Adjustable launch angles, and an innovative head design provides unpredictable height variations when bird is released. FLUSHBIRD is a single launcher designed to provide wing shooters with a training target that simulates the erratic flight of wild game such as snipe, quail, dove, woodcock and pheasant. A perfect low-cost alternative for small clubs, hunting preserves and private installations. SPORT WING model for Sporting Clays applications. DEALER INQUIRIES WELCOME!
See Our Ad Below & Pg. 179

Auto-Arm Rabbit
Clay-Tech Industries, Inc.
1003 M-55 Ave., NE
Calgary, Alberta
Canada T2E 6W1
(800) 940-2529

FAX: (403) 295-2531
Contact: Harry Isaac
Manufactured in: Canada/USA
Available: Direct
A portable throwing arm style rabbit, featuring instant release. Battery powered or 115V AC. Adjustable to throw "Looper" Targets. Simple, quiet, reliable operation; the most affordable arm rabbit in its class.
See Our Ad Across

Auto-Rabbit

Clay-Tech Industries, Inc.
1003 M-55 Ave., NE
Calgary, Alberta
Canada T2E 6W1
(800) 940-2529
FAX: (403) 295-2531
Contact: Harry Isaac

Manufactured in: Canada/USA
Available: Direct
Auto-Rabbit has a wheel-type throwing system and is portable battery powered or AC/DC with unique programmable automatic shut-down battery saver. Throws straight ahead or right and left arcing rabbits. Target speeds electronically controlled. Exclusive shock absorbing launching ramp for consistency in thrown targets and gentle handling for fragile re-throws. Economy model Auto-Rabbit also available.
See Our Ad Across

Auto-Sporter

Clay-Tech Industries, Inc.
1003 M-55 Ave., NE
Calgary, Alberta
Canada T2E 6W1
(800) 940-2529
FAX: (403) 295-2531
Contact: Harry Isaac
Manufactured in: Canada/USA
Available: Direct
Automatic
Commercial duty, portable automatic sporting clay trap machine, battery powered or AC/DC. Over 4000 throws per charge. Fast recocking for following pairs, adjustable to springing teal position. Quick installation *midi* conversion kit. Solid state electrical control system. Extremely simple design for easy servicing. Available with oscillating base for ATA, "Crazy Quail" targets, or remote angle adjustment in towers. The "Wobble" version provides both vertical and horizontal unpredictable (interrupted) movement for an entire sporting clays course in one machine. The ideal 5-Stand machine.
See Our Ad Across

AutoClay Traps

Acorn Systems
2726 134th Ave.
Hopkins, MI 49328
(616) 793-7400
Contact: Jim Spray
Available: Direct
Manufactured in: England
Automatic
The AutoClay is a portable, reliable automatic trap with a 50 clay capacity hopper. It operates on a 12V battery and a full charge launches 3,500 targets 90-100 meters. Target presentation ranges from horizontal to 70 degrees. Optional extras include foot operated switch, 50 metre extension cable, electronic upgrade module, "Midi" size mechanism and auto angling base. Please see our ad for additional information, features and contact information.
See Our Ad Left

BEOMAT
500 SERIES MACHINES

Beomat of America, Inc.
300 Railway Ave.
Campbell, CA 95008
(408) 379-4829
Contact: Sten Nilsson
Manufactured in: Sweden
Automatic
The 500 Series machines will be available for all disciplines of clay target shooting: Skeet, Trap, Double Trap, Wobble Trap/Ball Trap, Olympic Trap, Sporting Clays, 110V AC or 12V DC. Any of the machines load 530 targets standard (except Olympic trap with 350 targets per machine– for a total of 5250 targets loaded in the bunker) 900 target magazine optional for all except the wobble trap. MJDT500 and the MTD500 throw single targets as well as American Trap doubles, utilizing any standard American target, and can with a simple magazine conversion throw 90 mm targets in both single and double mode. The machines are using any standard American trap or skeet target (108 mm) and all International (110 mm) trap or skeet targets without any changes. The weight of the trap machines has been reduced substantially as compared to our 400 series machines, and all trap machines are now equipped with adapter brackets to fit the existing (standard) trap house pier. Improved power distribution internally, includes so called motor saver device, or if you will, an electric power saving feature; i.e., the machine shuts itself down into a "sleep mode" after 5 minutes of no activity, and re-activates itself automatically. Any of the 500 series machines can be equipped with 12V DC motors. Simplified target loading, magazine release, allows all targets to be loaded from the most convenient position.
See Our Ad Across

Bowman
Clay-Sport International, Inc.
Box 663, Bragg Creek
Alberta, Canada T0L 0K0
(403) 949-3654
Contact: Raymond Foreman
Manufactured in: England
Manual
A versatile and sturdy range of manual throwers, with a model to meet every sporting clays needs. The best selling manual thrower in Great Britain.

CCI International
Clark Clay Industries, Ltd.
Priors Haw Road, Corby
Northants, NN17 5JG, England
011-44-1536-260933
FAX: 011-44-1536-401138
Est.: 1982
Chairman: Jonathan Cridland
Automatic

Cherokee Trap
McCammon Engineering
Rt. 5, Box 237, Sullivan, IN 47882
(812) 398-3040
Staff: 4
Contact: Brent McCammon
Available: Direct
Manufactured in: U.S.A.
Manual
The Cherokee Trap is a 3/4-cock manual clay target thrower built around a 450 ft.-lb. sprag clutch with oil flushing/changing capabilities for durable yet silent operation. Horizontal and vertical target directions are quickly adjustable, as is spring tension. The arms, either single or dual, are counterbalanced for smooth operation, and full-arm springing teal clips ensure positive target hold at any trap attitude. A solid-steel stand, seat, weather cover, and teal clips are all standard on this American-made machine. For all the details, please call (812) 398-3040.

Chucker Clay
Thrower Traps
R.L. Torresdal Co., Inc.
Hwy. 52 East, Ossian, IA 52161
(319) 532-9884
FAX: (319) 532-9387
Contact: Ray Torresdal
Manufactured in: Iowa, US
Manual
New from the R.L. Torresdal Co., in Ossian, Iowa, is a lever operated flush/flurry machine that throws birds as fast as the operator can pull the lever. Although designer Ray Torresdal said he has heard of this machine keeping 13 birds in the air at a time, he limits his claim to 10 birds in the air at once. Magazines hold 30 birds, and they are offered for standard, midi and mini clay birds. Magazines are interchangeable and can be changed in minutes. It's also a safe machine; with the magazine setting the birds and a lever launching them, a trapper's hands stay clear of moving parts. For sporting applications, the unit easily throws following pairs, report pairs and flurries. Also in the Chucker Clay Thrower Line is a manual trap and a rabbit trap. Available for each is a stand with

removable legs for easy portability and transportation, a bolt down base, and a swivel base which may be truck mounted. The machines are three-quarter cock with double arms, making them commercial- grade units. New for '95-'96 is a Crazy Quail stand which allows 360 degrees of rotation. The stand can be used with either the 3/4 cock chucker or the covey chucker.
See Our Ad Below

Clay-Sport Sporting Traps
Unit II, Whitehall Ind. Estate
Walkern Rd., Watton-at-Stone, Hartford
ordshire SG1 43RP England
011-44-92-083-0070
FAX: 011-44-92-830-989
Manufactured in: England
Manual & Automatic

Clubmaster Traps
Rota-Trap
537 A Mt. Pleasant Rd.
Toronto Canada M4S 2M5
(416) 487-9133
Est.: 1985 Staff: 5
Contact: Jeff Beallor
Available: Retail & Direct
Manufactured in: New Zealand
Manual

Due/Matic Traps
Golden West Industries
750 Arroyo Ave.
San Fernando, CA 91340
(800) 548-5444
(818) 365-3946
FAX: (818) 365-8725
Contact: Chuck Elton

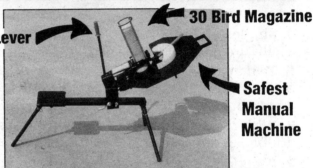

Manufactured in: Denmark
Automatic & Manual
In automatic versions, these Danish machines are available in skeet, ISU, ATA, bunker and sporting configurations. All feature easy access to changes of elevation and target direction. 200-target magazine capacity (expandable to 400 on skeet and sporting models) one-way bearing on throwing arm to ensure limited vibration, safety guards on throwing arm, and claims of "problem-free target feeding with all brands of targets." Additionally the sporting model features interchangeable magazines for 110mm and 90mm targets. A Due/Matic manual version is available with throwing arms for mini, midi, standard, battue or rabbit targets.

G.M.V. Super-Star Traps

G.H. Enterprises
Box 939, Okotoks
Alberta, Canada T0L 1T0
(403) 938-6070
FAX: (403) 938-3206
Contact: Gert Holmqvist
Manufactured in: Sweden
Automatic
This full range of automatic traps features a special elevator that lower targets gently onto the throwing table, thus reducing target breakage. The large throwing table and long throwing arm puts a fast spin on the target for a consistent flypath. The lineup of these Swedish-built traps include G.M.V. 285T which throws DOUBLES and SINGLE targets. The G.M.V. 274T singles trap, G.M.V. 296T Wobble trap all with a 400 target capacity. The G.M.V. 455S Skeet and G.M.V. 466S Sporting trap feature a vertical angle adjustment up to 60 degrees on accessory spring for throwing targets up to 90 yards. The sporting comes with a 24-volt release and the skeet with Winchester compatibility or 24-volt release. The G.M.V. 477S are 12 Volt machines with a target capacity ranging from 250 to 700. New to the lineup of excellent machines are the G.M.V. 800ST Teal with horizontal and vertical adjustments and hold 250 targets. The G.M.V. 840R Rabbit is a wheel operated rabbit with a 400 target magazine. The target speed and distance is easily changed with a five speed selector lever. The machine has two carrying handles for easy handling. The G.M.V. 380T Olympic Trench is also available. Accessories includes: acoustic releases, remote releases and magazine inserts that makes these machines versatile for even midi and mini targets.
See Our Ad Below

TO ATTAIN PEAK PERFORMANCE, SMOOTH HANDLING AND A QUIET RIDE ... YOU NEED THE RIGHT VEHICLE.

And now the choice is even easier. Whether you're shooting for fun or in competition, Lincoln has a model to suit your demands. Constructed to be reliably consistent, whisper quiet, and weather resistant, Lincoln's design and style combine all of these features to offer easy cocking and superb control. Protected by a unbeatable warranty and built in America with pride. Optional accessories and equipment are available. Call your Lincoln dealer for details and *Discover the Difference* the right vehicle can make.

LINCOLN

1009 South Lincoln Avenue
Lebanon, PA 17042-7166
717-274-8676

HOPPE'S ⑨™
A DIVISION OF PENGUIN INDUSTRIES, INC.

Hoppe's—Penguin Industries, Inc.
Airport Industrial Mall
Coatesville, PA 19320
(610) 384-6000
FAX: (610) 857-5980
Contact: Patricia Lucas
Available: Retail
Manual
Hoppe's Sta-Put Clay Target Thrower has a modified throwing arm with "dimples" which keeps birds from sliding during the release. Portable and lightweight, Hoppe's target thrower is the best built launcher in its class.
See Our Ad Pg. 209

IBIS Traps - IBIS Clay Target Products
Div. of Show Me Sports Corp.
8267 N. Revere, Kansas City, MO 64151
(816) 587-9540
FAX: (816) 587-3906
Est.: 1978
Contact: Andy Perkins
Manufactured in: USA & Australia
Automatic & Manual
Traps for Trap, Skeet, Sporting Clays & private use.
IBIS Target Products manufactures clay target traps which are ideally suited to all possible requirements. The traps are affordable enough for small and private ranges, yet they are of World Class standard, suitable for the largest sporting events. The IBIS Hand Traps and Autos have set the standards for quality in the shooting industry. Call for free quote before making your purchase. Hand Traps starting @ $350; Autos starting @ $2750. References available upon request. IBIS Traps are rated #1 by top course designers among all major brands for overall customer satisfaction.
See Our Ad Pg. 211

Kromson Traps

ACTIV Industries, Inc.
1000 Zigor Rd., PO Box 339
Kearneysville, WV 25430
(304) 725-0451
FAX: (304) 725-2080

President: Luis A. Perez
VP: L. Andres Perez
Manufactured in: Spain
Automatic & Manual
Kromson offers four unique models: (1) Supermini–portable, 7 lbs., hand held trap that throws midis and minis 60 & 80 yards. (2) Supercoto 2000–manual trap with tripod and seat, with 10 position trajectory locator. (3) Supercaza–manual trap with folding tripod and seat. Two launcher arms for bird and rabbit combination station. It also launches doubles and it's multi-directional. (4) Kromson Model SP-650– fully automatic for sporting clays. It throws regular and mini targets. Magazine for 360 or 650. Launching up to 100 meters with special base to be placed on the ground without need to be permanently affixed. Available in 24 v. batteries. Plug-in control box and hand control included. Option radio-control. With safety-ring included. Available also in A/C. Based on our popular Model A-350. Very easy maintenance.

WINCHESTER® by
LAPORTE®

LAPORTE AMERICA
One Trans-Border Drive
Champlain, NY 12919
(800) 335-TRAP
FAX: (514) 449-1431
Est.: 1927
Available: Retail
Manufactured in: France
Semi-Automatic, Automatic & Manual
Established since 1927, the LAPORTE strength and success lies in it's commitment to service and quality. The company prides itself on producing machines that are reliable and always at the forefront of the market in their technological developments and revolutionary ideas: This quality is recognized worldwide.
All Winchester by LAPORTE traps are of a simple design and virtually maintenance free. The LAPORTE Skeet machine is endorsed by the NSSA and is the most accurate machine on the market, with its uncomplicated design and user friendly adjustment mechanisms. The LAPORTE range of Sporting automatic traps is available in both 12V & 110V and of a technical excellence that is recognized worldwide. Whilst our automatic trap range for American & International style shooting, including the new revolutionary 285 LAPORTE TWIN LAP is the finest and most technically advanced available on the market.

WINCHESTER® by LAPORTE®

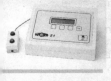

When you purchase a WINCHESTER BY LAPORTE trap you can rest assured that the service and technical support you receive will live up to the highest standards of the American sportsman.

*See Our Ads Pgs. 223, 225 &
Inside Front Cover*

LINCOLN

Lincoln Traps
1009 S. Lincoln Ave.
Lebanon, PA 17042
(717) 274-8676
FAX: (717) 274-8672
Manufactured in: Pennsylvania, USA
Manual
Discover the Difference a Lincoln Trap can make. All Lincoln Traps are whisper quiet and feature an UNBEATABLE WARRANTY. We offer a full line of manual traps to accommodate shooters from beginner to expert. The Falcon, our new 3/4 cock trap, designed for personal use, offers affordability for the serious shooter who demands consistency. The JR-93 is a manual cock trap that along with the SC-90E and The Falcon, will throw singles or doubles, standards, midis, minis, and battues. The RBT-92 rabbit trap throws singles or doubles and is capable of throwing fast and slow rabbits simultaneously, with no wire clips. All Lincoln

Traps feature a durable aluminum cast design for years of sporting excitement. Lincoln also offers a wide range of trap accessories to meet all your sporting clay needs.
See Our Ad Pg. 33

MIDAS GOLD

The Midas Gold - Rhodeside, Inc.,
1704 Commerce Dr., Piqua, OH 45356
(513) 773-5781   Est.: 1991
Pres: Jim Printz
Available: Direct
Manufactured in: U.S.   Type: Manual
The Midas Gold is a 3/4 cocking manual trap. Heavy duty zinc plated steel construction for years of dependable service. Easily recocked, very quiet release, and all traps have a two year warranty. One mainspring adjusts to throw any size or quantity of targets the desired distance. The two piece extruded aluminum carrier arms can be unbolted to use only one carrier arm, thereby throwing the target(s) a greater distance. All carrier arms throw singles or doubles, standards, minis, midis, & battues. Heavy duty bearings are installed on mainshaft and roller release. Trap base easily mounts to any flat surface or trap stand. Trap base has slots to adjust elevation and windage. Trap weighs less than 30 pounds for UPS shipments. All this for less than $400.
See Our Ad Below

Outers Traps

Blount, Inc., Sporting Equipment Division
PO Box 856,
2299 Snake River Ave.
Lewiston, ID 83501
(800) 627-3640
Contact: Dick Stawarz
Manufactured in: U.S.A.
Manual
American Sporter, Flightmaster, Flightmaster Jr.
& Birdmaster

Parker Traps International, Inc.

624 W. McNair St.,
Chandler, AZ 85224
(602) 345-2911
FAX: (602) 345-2772
Contact: John Lockwood
Automatic
Parker Traps from England has now added new
features that have improved an already great
trap. Built to last and virtually maintenance free.
Together with the longest Warranty in the industry.
Machines are available for every discipline. All
machines (except the Battue) will throw multiple target sizes (Standard, Midi, etc). Even our
Arm Rabbit machine is designed to throw Rabbit and Standard targets. All Sporting traps will
throw Teal presentations. Skeet layouts are con-
figured to American Skeet. However, they are
supplied standard with an ISU loom. A special
adapter allows a quick change from a Skeet
trap to a Sporting trap (for limited area sporting
games). Our Wobble trap is another machine
that has benefited from a special high lift
adapter. That allows you to throw and extra
high target while oscillating. Accessories include
inserts and radio release systems (also, available
for multiple trap release with counter). All machines are available in 12 volt DC and 110 volt
AC.
See Our Ad Across

Parker/Boss

118 Ira Court
PO Box 309
Andover, KS 67002
(316) 733-2876
FAX: (316) 733-1240
Contact: Larry Leatherman

Manufactured in: USA
Automatic & Manual
This line of automatic traps is now
manufactured in Wichita, Kansas. The automatic traps originated in England, but were
redesigned for the American market by Graham
Parker, so that they are capable of throwing any
make of target. All traps have sealed-for-life
heavy duty gearboxes and oilite bushes. Maintenance is low and the machines are warranted
for two years parts and labor (extended warranty available) the main bearing has a five year
warranty. The automatic product line includes:
Skeet traps - 110 volt or 12 volt DC with or without ISU timer. 400 or 500 magazine capacity;
ATA traps - double or single 110 volt with timer.
400 or 500 magazine capacity. Wobble - double
or single 110 volt with timer. 400 or 500 magazine capacity; Sporting - double or single 110
volt or 12 volt. 400 or 500 magazine capacity.
All sporting traps can be fitted with midi and
mini inserts. A quick adjustment converts the
sporting trap to a springing teal. The single
sporter can be adapted to throw single or double battues. Sporting Rabbit - 110 volt only. 400
or 500 magazine capacity. Double Arm Rabbit -
110 volt or 12 volt 400 or 500 magazine capacity. This machine is not only capable of
throwing double rabbits, but can throw double
chandelle or a mix chandelle and rabbit at the
same time. The manual product line includes:
3/4 cock machines in sporting, rabbit and teal.
A special teal stand is available as is a rabbit
adapter for the basic stand. A new bearing
(same as the automatic traps) has been fitted
to the manual traps and carries a FIVE YEAR
warranty.
See Our Ad Pg. 219

Pat-Trap

Henniker Pallet Co. Inc.
16 Colby Hill Rd.
Henniker, NH 03242
(603) 428-3396
Contact: Amy Patenaude
Manufactured in: U.S.A.
Automatic
The automatic PAT-TRAP throws doubles and single targets too! The patented PAT-TRAP
Automatic Doubles machine is American made
and with its no nonsense design is simple to operate and easy to load. It holds four full cases of
clay targets with a side-loader magazine available. The PAT-TRAP fits ATA regulation trap
houses and is able to throw doubles while oscillating for Sporting Clays. The vibration-free
PAT-TRAP features commercial grade heavy
duty steel construction, sealed ball and roller

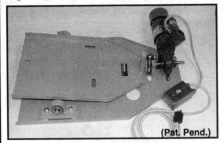

bearings and oilite bushings. It is fully adjustable for windage and elevation. The hydraulic mode of operation means no gear boxes. With today's ever increasing array of State and insurance regulations, the PAT-TRAP will pay for itself in no time. No personnel in the trap house means safety and savings. The PAT-TRAP can be equipped for voice release eliminating the need for pullers. Double scores can increase due to the ease and convenience of changing from singles to doubles in seconds allowing more practice time. The PAT-TRAP will make shooting more enjoyable and save money too.

See Our Ad Below

Promatic
Chain Distributing
6213 Grissom Rd., #604
San Antonio, TX 78238
(210) 520-6518
Contact: John Van Ess
Made in U.K.

Pat-Trap™ Automatic "Doubles"

And Singles Too!!
- **Automatic Doubles**
No personnel in trap house
- **Fully Automatic**
Changes from doubles to singles in seconds & vice versa
- **No Gear Boxes - All Hydraulic**
- **Holds 4 Full Cases of Targets**

All Sealed Bearings • Powered by 110 V. AC
Fully Adjustable • Vibration Free • Simple to Operate • Uses Winchester Pull Cord • Easy Loading • American Made • Sideloading Magazines Available • Fits ATA Regulation Traphouse • Throws Doubles While Oscillating

FOR MORE INFORMATION CALL OR WRITE:
Stuart W. Patenaude • Henniker Pallet Co. Inc.
16 Colby Hill Rd. • Henniker, NH 03242

603-428-3396

Quack Traps
Quack Sporting Clays, Inc. & Decoy Corp.
4 Ann & Hope Way
PO Box 98
Cumberland, RI 02864
(401) 723-8202
FAX: (401) 722-5910
Est.: 1987
Pres/CEO: Kenneth Gagnon, Sr.
Available: Retail & Direct
Manufactured in: Rhode Island, USA
Manual
Quack 3/4 cock traps are the safest, fastest, easiest to operate and set-up, most universal, quietest, most durable (all weather), most dependable (lifetime warranty on clutch), and most reasonably priced machine made in the United States today. Throws ALL birds, springing teal and rabbit, 110, 90, 60, battue, rocket-available in portable or permanent set-up. Manufactured in Rhode Island, USA since 1987. For more information contact us. New for 1995 – LEFT handed 3/4 cock machine with up to 4 throwing arms & 3 assorted spring tensions: Light (30-40 yds); Medium (70-80 yds); Heavy (100 yds+).

See Our Ads Pgs. 228-229

Quality Model '92
Quality Replacement Parts
1015 North 195 Ave.
Buckeye, AZ 85326
(800) 742-0425
(602) 278-9556
Est.: 1982
Contact: Roger Coveleskie
Available: Retail & Direct
Electric handset trap.

Quikfire Traps

Hunters Pointe Mfg. Corp.
Rt. 1, Box 166, Augusta, KS 67010
(316) 778-1122
FAX: (316) 778-1115
Est.: 1983
Contact: Larry Cero
Available: Direct
Manufactured in: Kansas, USA
Automatic & Manual
Superior performance – proven design, Quikfire II-60; Price $1,595. Full automatic operation 12-volt portable one-man operate. Shoot capability 60-target magazine. The most versatile automatic trap made. Other automatic traps from $645 complete. Manual rabbits complete from $100. Hunters Pointe has been making reliable, quality traps at affordable prices for over 12 years! We are the only company in the industry that designs and manufactures our own oil-filled, sprague clutch. Call us today to find out more about our reliable products.
See Our Ad Below

Remington Arms Company, Inc.

Delle Donne Corporate Center
1011 Centre Road, Second Floor
Wilmington, DE 19805-1207
(800) 243-9700
(302) 993-8500 (Business Offices)
Est.: 1816
Available: Retail
Remington provides both manual and automatic traps.

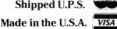

Serena Fabbrica Lanciapiatelli
Northwest Ohio International
mailing: 2923 Plumbrook
Maumee, OH 43547
(419) 867-8884
FAX: (419) 867-8884
Contact: Joseph Rusin
Manufactured in: Brescia, Italy
Automatic & Manual
Trap machines for: sporting clays (manual & automatic, including specialty traps) for rabbit, teal sparrow (mini), pheasant (chandelle); Automatic ATA singles and double; continental or wobble trap machines; complete line of Int'l. Bunker in manual and automatic; International & American skeet machines; specialty machines can be set up for 12V, 115, 220, 240 or 360V. Also available is a full line of electric selectors and phono-pull (voice release) systems.

Sportrap
Sportrap Clay Target Products
PO Box 708
Millville, NJ 08332
(609) 327-2030
FAX: (609) 327-2030
Est.: 1989Staff: 2
Contact: Brian Keen
Available: Retail & Direct
Manual
3/4 cocking, counter balanced, quiet operation fast and easy recocking for on-report or following pairs. Trap with dual arms and choice of launch spring–$395. 3 leg portable stand with swivel trap mount–$135.
With our specialty launch arms you can throw many different target presentations such as:
1. Hi-Low Arm–throws vertically split pairs
2. Fur and Feather Arm–throws rabbit and chandelle
3. Rabbit Arm-throws one or two rabbits, just drop in to load
4. Following Pair Arm–throws one slow one fast target

5. Jersey Devil Arm–throws rising targets
6. Battue Arm– throws one or two battue targets
7. 3 or 4 Bird Flush Arms–throws multiple targets
Quantity discounts, call for further information and brochure price list. UPS Delivery. Visa-Mastercard Accepted.

Trius Traps

Trius Products, Inc.
221 S. Miami Ave.
PO Box 25
Cleves, OH 45002
(513) 941-5682
FAX: (513) 941-7970
Est.: 1955Staff: 10
Contact: Hart Luebkeman
Manufactured in: Ohio, U.S.A.
Manual
TRIUS, manufacturing clay target traps since 1955 has progressed from its first trap Model E56 to 8 models in 1993. These models consist of 3 traps for the recreational shooter and 5 models for Hunter Clays/Sporting Clays. The 3 recreational models, TRIUS TRAP, BIRDSHOO-TER AND TRAPMASTER, are available through

finer retailers and catalog mail order firms nationwide. Prices range from $59 to $299. TRIUS for 38 years has been known for the quality of the thrown target and minimum of maintenance. For brochure or dealer information, please call today.
See Our Ad Pg. 210

Western Traps

by H-S Precision, Inc.
1301 Turbine Dr.
Rapid City, SD 57701
(605) 341-3006
FAX: (605) 342-8964
Manufactured in: South Dakota, USA
Automatic & Manual
For regulation, international and skeet shooting, Western Traps have long been the machine of choice by trap shooting enthusiasts the world over. During the past several decades, Western Trap machines have been the only equipment used at the Grand American Trap Shoot. For more information on Western Traps, parts or our network of distributors, contact H-S Precision, Inc.
See Our Ad Below

SHOTGUNNER'S SOURCE

Whiteside's Mfg. Co., Inc.

45408 160th St. West
Lancaster, CA 93536
(805) 724-1974
FAX: (805) 724-1905
Contact: David Whiteside
Automatic
The Whiteside Model 300 is an automatic 12-Volt sporting clay thrower that is known for three things:
* Simplicity in design
* Reliability
* Heavy-duty construction
Mike Raahauge. . .a range operator from southern California said,"It's a good, simple, reliable machine that's priced right. From day one, it has worked flawlessly."
See Our Ad Left

WINCHESTER® by LAPORTE®

LAPORTE AMERICA
One Trans-Border Drive, Champlain, NY 12919
(800) 335-TRAP   FAX: (514) 449-1431
Est.: 1927   Available: Retail
Manufactured in: France
Semi-Automatic, Automatic & Manual
Established since 1927, the LAPORTE strength and success lies in it's commitment to service and quality. The company prides itself on producing machines that are reliable and always at the forefront of the market in their technological developments and revolutionary ideas: This quality is recognized worldwide. All Winchester by LAPORTE traps are of a simple design and virtually maintenance free. The LAPORTE Skeet machine is endorsed by the NSSA and is the most accurate machine on the market, with its uncomplicated design and user friendly adjustment mechanisms. The LAPORTE range of Sporting automatic traps is available in both 12V & 110V and of a technical excellence that is recognized worldwide. Whilst our automatic trap range for American & International style shooting, including the new revolutionary 285 LAPORTE TWIN LAP is the finest and most technically advanced available on the market.
When you purchase a WINCHESTER BY LAPORTE trap you can rest assured that the service and technical support you receive will live up to the highest standards of the American sportsman.
See Our Ads Pgs. 223, 225
& Inside Front Cover

TRAP ACCESSORIES

Auto-Counter
Clay-Tech Industries, Inc.
1003 M-55 Ave., NE
Calgary, Alberta
Canada T2E 6W1
(800) 940-2529
FAX: (403) 295-2531
Contact: Harry Isaac
Hand held automatic counter ideal for unsupervised sporting clays courses. Simply plug into trap release cable and the Auto-Counter records all targets fired for easy tabulation at the clubhouse. Entirely self-contained, nothing left out in the field. Affordably priced.

Auto Pilot
11551 Douglas Rd.
Rancho Cordova, CA 95742
(916) 351-0538
Est.: 1994   Staff: 3
Contact: Pat Glaze
Programmable microprocessor controls up to 25 custom launch sequences.

the *BIRDBRAIN.* system

Bird Brain
Clay-Sport International, Inc.
Box 663, Bragg Creek
Alberta, Canada T0L 0K0
(403) 949-3654
Contact: Raymond Foreman
An innovative trap control system, featuring our own invention - 5-Stand Sporting - includes other original games designed to attract hunters and competitors. Automatic "hands free" function.

See Our Ad Pg. 215

Claymaster ATA & OLY Voice Release Systems
Clay Target Enterprises
300 Railway Ave.
Campbell, CA 95008
(408) 379-4829
Contact: Sten Nilsson
Imported from Norway, the Claymaster Voice Release System is available for ATA & Olympic Trap.

Claymate Voice Activated Trap Release
Claymate, Inc.
PO Box 903, Concord, NH 03302

(800) 603-2286
Contact: Bill Anzaldi
Radio Controlled voice release system with many applications including trap, sporting clays & games.

Coastal Industries Products
4082 N. South Bank, Suite C
Oxnard, CA 93030
(805) 988-5845
FAX: (805) 988-5847
Contact: Ron Whitney
Coastal Industries manufactures 4 different trap accessories: (1) Limited Area Sporting Clays which is an electronic controller and the base unit costs $1,100. (2) A Voice Release System which costs $750. (3) A Radio Release System for eight traps which costs $2,400. (4) A Trap Counter which costs $220/station & $125 for the carrying unit.

Course Control Bird Counter
The Shooting Academy
8130 E. LaJunta Rd.
Scottsdale, AZ 85255
(602) 585-0882
Contact: Mike Davey
System that allows a shooter or group of shooters to go around a course or shooting field on their

own, pulling as many targets as they wish. This system allows to keep check on targets released and eliminates trapper help.

Crazy Quail Base
Whiteside's Mfg. Co., Inc.
45408 160th St. West
Lancaster, CA 93536
(805) 724-1974
Contact: David Whiteside
A flat platform that can rotate 360 degrees. The user can mount any standard skeet type of machine on it. Can be used in continuous or positional mode.

InteliTrap
DNK, Inc., 5809 S.W. 5th St.
Oklahoma City, OK 73128
(800) 730-6656
(405) 947-6656
FAX: (405) 947-7014
Est.: 1994   Staff: 6
Contact: David Park
Available: Retail

LASERSPORT
Intermark of Virginia, Ltd.
Box 925, Cedar Crest, NM 87008
(800) 386-4861
(505) 281-2971
Est.: 1989
President: Alan Haley
Available: Retail & Direct
Real but deactivated shotguns fire harmless Infra Red Beams at regular sized plastic clay targets. With full sound simulation, shot pattern spread, & a large scoreboard showing player progress, LASERSPORT is guaranteed to keep profits rolling at gun clubs, hunt preserves, shooting tournaments.
See Our Ad Pg. 235

Long Range Systems
10840 Switzer, #110
Dallas, TX 75238
(800) 987-6749
FAX: (214) 349-6027
Contact: Ken Lovegreen
Wireless release systems for 5-Stand & skeet. Also manufacture a target counter.
See Our Ad Below

Tail Gunner
Throw-Rite Inc.
913 Baltimore,
Kansas City, MO 64105
(800) 624-9083
Contact: Laurence R. (Brud) Jones, III
Available: Retail & Direct
Tail Gunner - portable trap platform. Mounts on any vehicle using a 1 7/8" ball.

Trapper's Buddy
Clay-Tech Industries, Inc.
1003 M-55 Ave., NE
Calgary, Alberta, Canada T2E 6W1
(800) 940-2529
FAX: (403) 295-2531
Contact: Harry Isaac
Budget priced manually operated eight (8) trap controller. Fires up to 8 traps simultaneously or individually. Great for training purposes, creating your own games or back-up for your electronic controller. Optional remote release. Ideal as teaching aid. Fully portable, self-contained and requires no external power source.

The Ventriloquist
The Computer Learning Works, Inc.
Rt. 4, Box 866, Starkville, MS 39759
(800) 445-3038
(601) 323-3542
FAX: (601) 324-1189
Vice President: Gary N. Brunner
The Computer Learning Works, Inc. has applied the skills and technology developed over 10 years as a national educational software manufacturer to "The Ventriloquist" line of products. The Ventriloquist - Dealer uses the power and flexibility of the personal computer to design and throw 5-Stand and other sporting clay games with up to 8 machines. The Ventriloquist Voice Release uses internal microprocessors to throw voice released targets for trap and skeet. Call for a free 12 minute video tape of these products.

Voice Pull
124 Country Club Dr.
Heath, TX 75087
(214) 772-3111
Contact: Don Rackley

Voice Release Self Pull
The Shooting Academy
8130 E. Lajunta
Scottsdale, AZ 85255
(602) 585-0882
Contact: Mike Davey
Used for firing any automatic trap(s) by recognition of a voice activated command, i.e., shooter calls "Pull" and the unit fires the trap. Unit operates by radio remote control with a range of up to 800 yds.

TRAP DISTRIBUTORS

Clay Games, Inc.
55 Lane 240 Big Otter Lake
Fremont, IN 46737
(219) 833-6645
FAX: (219) 833-6649
Est.: 1993
President: Joel Werner
Available: Direct
Exclusive manufacturer of "Upland Clays" and distributors of NRA-Clays, Lincoln Traps and Target Pigeon.
See Our Ad Pg. 240

Clay-Sport International, Inc.
Box 663, Bragg Creek
Alberta, Canada T0L 0K0
(403) 949-3654
Contact: Raymond Forman
Distributor of Auto-Sporter, Bowman, IBIS, G.M.V. Super Star and Cock Pheasant Traps.

Clove Valley Sports Corp.
Hidden Brook Farm
RR1, Box 110 A
Salt Point, NY 12578
(914) 266-5954
Est.: 1980   Staff: 4
Contact: Charles Conger
Dealers and course designers welcome. Distributor of IBIS target products.

Deep River Sporting Clays and Shooting School
3420 Cletus Hall Rd
Sanford, NC 27330
(919) 774-7080
FAX: (919) 774-7080
Contact: Bill Kempffer
LAPORTE AMERICA Distributor

Marty Fischer
SportShooting Consultants, Inc.
PO Box 207
Rincon, GA 31326
(912) 826-0072
Est.: 1992
Contact: Marty Fischer
Available: Direct
Lincoln and IBIS automatic traps

Doug Fuller
c/o Woods & Water
Rt. 1, Box 319
Catoosa, OK 74105
(918) 266-5551
Parker/Boss Distributor

G.H. Enterprises
Box 939, Okotoks, Alberta
Canada T0L 1T0
(403) 938-6070
FAX: (403) 938-3206
Contact: Gert Holmqvist

Golden West Industries
750 Arroyo Ave.
San Fernando, CA 91340
(818) 365-3946
Contact: Chuck Elton
Due/Matic Traps Importer

J&S Wholesale, Inc.
PO Box 638
13200 Jackson Gate Rd.
Jackson, CA 95642
(800) 445-4867, Ext. 231
In CA: **(800) 441-8484**
Pres: Jerry Jones
Available: Retail
LAPORTE AMERICA Distributor.
Wholesaler of ammunition, targets, reloading supplies, gun cases, gun safes, chokes and accessories.
See Our Ad Pg. 232

Jon Kruger
Box 213,. St. Ansgar, IA 50472
(515) 736-4893
Parker/Boss Distributor

Monterey Sporting Clays
2726 134th St., Hopkins, MI 49328
(616) 793-7400
Est.: 1992   Staff: 1
Contact: Jim Spray

Michael Murphy & Sons
6400 S.W. Hunter Rd.
Augusta, KS 67010
(316) 775-2137
Est.: 1976   Staff: 2
Pres: Michael Murphy
Distributor of Kromson, Lincoln and Quikfire Traps

Outdoors Unlimited
PO Box 515, 107 Stevenson St.
Eagle Lake, TX 77434
(409) 234-5750
(210) 683-3165 (Parts & Service)
FAX: (409) 234-7603
Contact: Johnny Meitzen
LAPORTE AMERICA Distributor

Gordon C. Philip
1701 Northwest Cookingham
Kansas City, MO 64155
(816) 734-4044

Rhodeside, Inc.
1704 Commerce Dr.
Piqua, OH 45356
(513) 773-5781
FAX: (513) 778-9056
Contact: Jim Printz
LAPORTE AMERICA Distributor

Shooters Network
450 Briscoe Blvd.
Lawrenceville, GA 32045
(404) 338-1405
FAX: (404) 338-0732
Contact: Steve Middleditch
LAPORTE AMERICA Distributor

SHOW-ME SPORTS

Show-Me Sports Corp.
Headquarters for IBIS Clay Target Products
8267 N. Revere
Kansas City, MO 64151
(816) 587-9540
FAX: (816) 587-3906
Est.: 1978
Contact: Andy Perkins
Headquarters for IBIS Clay Target Products & Distributor for major quality brands of traps and trap accessories for all shooting disciplines. Call for competitive quotes before making your purchase. Extended warranty and service contracts available.
See Our Ad Pg. 211

SHYDA'S SERVICES, INC.

Shyda's Services, Inc.
Home of Lincoln Traps
1009 S. Lincoln Ave.
Lebanon, PA 17042
(717) 274-8676
FAX: (717) 274-8672
LAPORTE AMERICA Distributor
Trap sales, parts, service and repairs. Distributor for most major brands of automatic traps as well as manual Lincoln Traps. Serving the clay target industry since 1985.
See Our Ad Pg. 37

R.L. Torresdal Co., Inc.
Hwy. 52 East
Ossian, IA 52161
(319) 532-9884
FAX: (315) 532-9387
Contact: Ray Torresdal

Trap Services Company
333 West 6160 South
Murray, UT 84107
(801) 288-9056
FAX: (801) 261-4149
Contact: Bruce Tofft
LAPORTE AMERICA Distributor

Tyler Trap Repair Center
4839 Justin Dr.
Dryden, MI 48428
(810) 796-2625
FAX: (810) 796-2625
Contact: Tyler Stewart
LAPORTE AMERICA Distributor

Robert W. Zeller
45 W 660 Plank Rd.
Hampshire, IL 60140
(708) 683-2039
Chucker Clay Thrower Trap
Distributor

HAND TRAPS

Clark ProThrow
C. Richard Co., Inc.
2218 Taggert St.
Erie, PA 16510
(814) 899-7533
Est.: 1993   Staff: 3
Contact: Dick Clark
Contact: Andrew Clark
Available: Direct
Hand held clay target thrower,
made of high quality wood &
metal. Comes in a reusable plastic
bag. Throws every time without
breakage.

Crazie Covie
2929 West Seventh St.
Fort Worth, TX 76107
(817) 332-7332

FAX: (817) 332-3666
Est.: 1986
Contact: Christopher K. Ryan
Crazie Covie is the only TrueHand*
Trap that has the capability of
throwing up to four targets at a
time. Using a whipping type throwing motion, will give you limitless
bird & target presentation with
never having to make any adjustments to the throwers. Made in
the USA of 100% colored anodized aluminum to prevent rust or
corrosion. Crazie Covie is very lightweight and has a unique storage
capability that allows you to store
all four throwers in area smaller
than a shotgun. Crazie Covie
comes in four sizes: Standard,
Midi, Mini or Battue. Order individually or save and order the complete
set. Dealers Welcome!
See Our Ad Below

EZ-Throw Hand Throwers
and Stick Bird Thrower
MTM Case-Gard
PO Box 14117
Dayton, OH 45413
(513) 890-7461
FAX: (513) 890-1747
Contact: Al Minneman
Available: Retail
EZ-Double-Throw; EZ-Throw-II; EZ-
Throw-MR hand held throwers.

The Hurler
PO Box 702861
Tulsa, OK 74170
(918) 631-1264
Contact: Bill Herring
Throws doubles or singles.

TRAPS FOR HIRE & MOBILE UNITS

Clay Games, Inc.
55 Lane 240 Big Otter Lake
Fremont, IN 46737
(219) 833-6645
FAX: (219) 833-6649
Est.: 1993
President: Joel Werner
Portable unit with compact design
fits on a single trap or skeet field.
Throws standard trap & skeet,
midis, minis, rabbits, battues, &
AmericanZZ. Please call for more in-
formation.
See Our Ad Pg. 241

MID-CAL
Trap Sales & Service
7728 West McKinley
Fresno, CA 93722
(209) 275-1775
Contact: Al Milla or Ron Doris
Completely mobile and automatic
sporting clays and 5-station unit.
Target Pigeon/ZZ also available.
Set-ups at your club events or pri-
vate property.
See Our Ad Pg. 240

John Meitzen
Outdoors Unlimited
Box 515, Eagle Lake, TX 77434
(409) 234-5750
Contact: John Meitzen
Our mobile unit specializes in specialty targets. All equipment is
battery (12V) operated. Certified instruction available.

NSCA 5-Stand Sporting
5931 Roft Rd.
San Antonio, TX 78253
(210) 688-3371 (Ext. 109)
FAX: (210) 688-3014
5-Stand Scheduler: Don Snyder
Thanks to the sponsorships of
Ducks Unlimited, Winchester and
The Texas Parks & Wildlife Department, the NSCA has 3 single game
5-Stand units available.

Quack Mobile Tour
Quack Sporting Clays, Inc.
4 Ann & Hope Way, PO Box 98
Cumberland, RI 02864
(401) 723-8202
FAX: (401) 722-5910
Pres/CEO: Kenneth Gagnon, Sr.
Now equipped with a demo portable "Modern Skeet & Clay" field,
we are available for instructional
clinics. For more information, call
us at (401) 723-8202.
See Our Ad PgS. 228-229

R & R Sales & Service
Your complete clay target company!

R&R Sales and Service
9903 Geronimo Oaks
San Antonio, TX 78254
(210) 688-3165
FAX: (210) 688-9048
Contact: F.M. "Butch" Roberson, III
We sell and service Lincoln, Super
Star, Winchester by Laporte, Parker
Boss and Hunters Pointe machines.
We offer a traveling mobile 5-
Stand, as well as design and install
5-Stand, Sporting Clays, Skeet and
Trap fields. Quint Roberson is our
Level I Skeet and Sporting Clays in-
structor. Bobby Head is our chief
technician. My Place or Yours!

Retriever Sporting Clays/Targets to Go
2929 West Seventh St.
Fort Worth, TX 76107
(817) 332-7332
FAX: (817) 332-3666
Contact: Christopher K. Ryan
Our mobile demonstration unit can
provide: full sporting clays, flush 5-
stand sporting clays, crazy quail,
trap or skeet. We cover the Southwest region including: TX, NM,
CO, OK, KS, AR, LA MS and Mexico. We bring our fun to you.

SHOW-ME SPORTS
Show Me Clays
8267 N. Revere,
Kansas City, MO 64151
(816) 587-9540
FAX: (816) 587-3906
Est.: 1978
Contact: Andy Perkins
Centrally located in Kansas City.
Specializing in major shoot sup-
port. Tournaments, fund raisers,
company outings, private parties,
organizations and club events. Cus-
tom design to suit your needs for
trap, skeet, wobble, 5-Stand,
FITASC and sporting. We can assist
in making your event a success.
Call: Andy (816) 587-9540.
See Our Ad Across

South Jersey Sporting Clays
404 S. White Horse Pike
Berlin, NJ 08009 (609) 768-8149
Contact: Bill Barrett

Trap-House
Sporting Clays
Next Generation, Inc. 1927 Halls
Mill Rd., Unionville, TN 37180
(800) 671-8121
Contact: Mickey Moore
A self-contained transportable unit
holding 15 traps to present all the
angles, shots and target capabilities seen on a "traditional" sporting
clays course. 13 shooting stations,
separated by safety screens are positioned around the periphery of
the unit. This game can be set up
in the woods, in an open field or
on a skeet field. Trap-House Sporting Clays has representatives in
CO, IN, FL, MI, MN, NY, OH, OR,
PA, TN, TX, and WI, and should be
throughout the U.S. by 1995. Reps
will bring in sufficient trailers to accommodate fun shoots, tournaments, fund raisers, company picnics, private parties and other
organizations/clubs. Call 1-800-671-
8121 to schedule your shoot.
See Our Ad Pg. 239

Top Gun
Shooting Sports
800 3rd Ave., Waseca MN 56093
(507) 835-8245
Contact: Ed Prechel/Brian Beck
See Ad Across

WINGSHOOTING TRAVEL ADVENTURES

Let An Expert Show You The Way

Today there are wonderful opportunities to shoot abroad—-whitewinged dove in Mexico, driven grouse in Scotland, waterfowl in Argentina, and others. The problem, of course, is taking advantage of them.

Even when expense is not an issue, the myriad arrangements necessary to make a wingshooting trip abroad can seem daunting to the average sportsman. Each country has its own laws concerning the movement of firearms; game licenses; shotgun and firearm certificates; carrying and purchasing ammunition (Mexico, for example, allows only 100 cartridges to be brought in by each person entering the country).

Why not have your fun the easy way? Let an expert show you the way. For want

of a better designation, we'll call them wingshooting travel agents. In point of fact, many also serve big game hunters, fishing fanatics, and photo enthusiasts. Most of them are top-flight, highly experienced sportsmen themselves. Very often, the names of the companies they run are suggestive of the services offered. Some specialists restrict their services to North America. Others can place you or a group—fully escorted—-virtually anyplace in the world.

Services are extensive, customized to fit your time, schedule and budget, and designed to assure a carefree experience. Beginning with the basics, like a list of gear to bring, they include travel arrangements, reservations at lodges or resorts, professional guides, and more.

Additionally, these well traveled entrepreneurs handle all the details involved in reaching foreign destinations. And their knowledge of local customs and requirements—from Austria to Argentina, from New Zealand to Nairobi—makes shooting, not coping, the most memorable part of your trip.

TRAVEL AGENTS

Joe Abbott Tours
4420 Stanford Ave.
Dallas, TX 75225
(800) 233-8211
FAX: (214) 739-3330
Est.: 1986
Contact: Joe Abbott
Destinations: Argentina
Birds Hunted: Dove, Duck, Geese &
Perdiz over dogs

Addieville Adventures
200 Pheasant Dr.
Mapleville, RI 02839
(401) 568-3185
FAX: (401) 568-3009
Est.: 1979   Staff: 8
Contact: Geoff Gaebe
Destinations: Argentina, England &
Nova Scotia
Birds Hunted: Dove, Pigeon, Geese
Partridge, Driven Pheasant, Woodcock
Packages/Comments: Not your typical booking agent - personal

attention before, during and after trips; booking from 1-8.
● Nova Scotia - the ultimate rod and gun combination of Atlantic Salmon and grouse and woodcock - two (2) weeks a year only for the combination of the Salmon run and grouse and woodcock. We are now offering pheasant hunting trips in Nova Scotia.
● Classic English Driven Pheasant while residing on centuries old estates and accompanied by world renowned shooting coach JACK MITCHELL.
● Argentina - doves like you never imagined, perdiz and duck; staying in a hotel but near the action on a beautiful ranch with ALEX SANTOS who has guided on four (4) continents and will be with you from arrival to departure.

Adventures in the Americas
7575 San Felipe, #150
Houston, TX 77063
(800) 428-4868
(713) 266-4868
FAX: (713) 977-0590
Est.: 1992

Contact: David M. Ballard or
Destinations: Alaska to Argentina,
New Zealand, Great Britain, Africa
Birds: Hunted: Doves (Multiple
Species), Quail, Chukar, Pheasant
(Walk Up and Driven), Waterfowl,
Prairie Chicken, Sharptail Grouse,
Guineafowl, Sandgrouse, Francolin
and Perdiz.

American Adventure Travel
680 N. Germantown Pkwy., #42
Cordova, TN 38018
(800) 288-4868
FAX: (901) 755-8514
Est.: 1989   Staff: 8
Contact: Dave Harwood
Destinations: Worldwide
Birds Hunted: Quail, Ducks, Geese,
Dove & legal exotics
Dedicated to providing our clients

with the finest hunting & fishing opportunities around the world. Guaranteed lowest domestic & International airfares. Catalog available upon request.

Argentina Wings

207 Temelec Dr.
Sonoma, CA 95476
(800) 946-4486
FAX: (707) 938-0937
Est.: 1980
Contact: Carlos A. Brouard
Wingshooting and fishing with first class lodging at exclusively private country estates (Estancias). Excellent options for non-shooting guests.

With many years of experience in the European market, Argentina Wings is now offering their services to hunters in the United States. We inaugurated our newest lodge located on 20,000 acres over looking the Parana' River (5th largest in the world). Our programs are custom tailored to meet each individual group's preferences. Discover the amazing wonders of Argentina's wildlife. Please call for our brochure and more information.

See Our Ad Right

Dave Bennett's Great Outdoor Expeditions
11904 Hidden Hills Dr.
Jacksonville, FL 32225
(904) 646-9722
FAX: (904) 641-5285
Est.: 1952 Staff: 3
Contact: Dave Bennett
Destinations: Argentina, Nicaragua
Birds Hunted: Dove, Quail, Duck and Partridge

Border South Consultants
PO Box 674, Wimberley, TX 78676
(512) 392-8748
Contact: Jerry Kilpatrick
Mexico–Guided hunts/season leases; deer, quail, dove, fishing

Carolina Outdoor Consultants
PO Box 481
Bethune, SC 29009
(803) 334-6620
Est.: 1985
Contact: John Boulware
Destinations: Alaska, Mexico, Costa Rica (Worldwide)
Birds Hunted: Ducks, Geese, Quail, Dove

The Detail Co., Inc.
3220 Audley, Houston, TX 77098
(800) 292-2213
(713) 524-7235
FAX: (713) 524-7244
Est.: 1980
Contact: Jeri Booth or Shawna Von Ness
Destinations: Mexico, Central America, South America, U.S., Scotland, S. Africa, Spain
Birds Hunted: Dove, Duck, Goose Perdiz, Pheasant, Quail, Partridge
Fishing: Bass, Marlin Tarpon,

Peacock, Snook, Salmon, Sail, Trout Packages: The Detail Company specializes in individual or groups and will personally oversee the planning of your itinerary. Let us worry about all the details. Just enjoy the hunt of a lifetime. Call today.
See Our Ad Pg. 244

Dunn's Adventure Travel
One Madison Ave.
Grand Junction, TN 38039
(800) 228-3006
FAX: (901) 764-2658
Est.: 1950 Staff: 75
Mgr./Hunter Svcs: Jeff Sellers
Destinations: Worldwide
Birds Hunted: Upland, Waterfowl

Escorted Adventures for Disabled Adults
PO Box 87, R.R. 25A
Orford, NH 03777
(603) 353-9826
Contact: Frank Lepore
Destinations: Worldwide, individually-tailored, one-on-one, hunting, fishing and sporting trips.

Esplanade Tours
581 Boylston St., Boston, MA 02116
(800) 628-4893
FAX: (617) 262-9829
Contact: Bill Keith

Fishing International
PO Box 2132
Santa Rosa, CA 95405
(800) 950-4242
FAX: (707) 539-3366
Contact: Bob Nauheim or Pat Pendergast
Destinations: Argentina, Mexico
Birds Hunted: Duck, Dove

Frontiers International Travel
PO Box 959, Wexford, PA 15090
(800) 245-1950
FAX: (412) 935-5388
Est.: 1969   Staff: 44
Contact: Mike Fitzgerald, Jr.

Destinations: Worldwide, Including Mexico, Argentina, Africa & Europe

Gage Outdoor and Adventure Travel
10000 Highway 55
Minneapolis, MN 55441-6365
(800) 888-1601
FAX: (612) 595-5981
Contact: Chuck Ross

Global Sporting Syndicate
PO Box 5870
Glendale, CA 91221
(818) 790-5717
FAX: (818) 790-5728
Contact: Dick Kennerknecht
Destinations: Mexico, California, Oregon, Colorado; Soon: Australia & New Zealand
Birds Hunted: Fliers (Mexico); All type of Pacific flyway Dove, Ducks & Geese

Griffin & Howe

Griffin & Howe
36 W. 44th St., New York, NY 10036
(212) 921-0980 or
33 Claremont Rd.
Bernardsville, NJ 07924
(908) 766- 2287
Est.: 1923Staff: 15
Contact: Joe Prather
Destinations: African & North American big game and wingshooting. England, Scotland & Europe for wingshooting.
See Our Ad Pg. 25

Hendry, Ramsay & Wilcox
415 Madison Ave., 20th Fl.
New York, NY 10017
(212) 768-3272
FAX: (212) 832-1040
President: Guy A. Bignell

High Adventure Company
2941 Little River Rd.
Madison, GA 30650
(800) 847-0834
Contact: Steve Spears
Destinations: South America, Africa, North America
Birds Hunted: Dove, Ducks, Geese, Perdiz, Francolin, also Big Game

and Big Game Fishing Packages/Comments: We have been in the hunting and fishing business 23 years, and have personally hunted and fished each location, let us put that experience to work for you. Your custom trip will be to the right place, at the right time, for the right price. URUGUAY: High volume Dove, Pigeon & Perdiz shoot, four - eight guns, we can help put your party together. Beautiful estancia, great food, and wine, four days of shooting. Hunts start at $2640 includes air from Atlanta, New York or Miami. SOUTH AFRICA: Great Duck & Goose hunting, along with fantastic upland birds. it takes less time to reach SA than it does to go to Argentina. Included is a Big Game Photo Safari, superb food and accommodations, 8 days; $3890 includes everything but shells. Let the HIGH ADVENTURE CO. take you there, so you can say "Been There - Done That!"

Holland & Holland, Ltd.
32 Bruton Street
London W1X 8JS England
011-44-171-499-4411
Est.: 1835
Chairman: Alain Drach
Contact: Piers Vaux
Driven partridge and pheasant at our own Devon estate.

The Hollek Company, Ltd.
117 East Louisa St., Box 144
Seattle, WA 98102
(206) 621-0846
FAX: (206) 621-0756
Est.: 1993
Owner: Harvey Hollek
Destinations: Russia, New Guinea, Brazil, Argentina
Birds Hunted: Ducks, Pygmy Geese, Pheasants, Dove, Partridge

Sheila Horne Associates
PO Box 474, Salem, SC 29676
(803) 944-0300 (Phone/Fax)
Contact: Johanna Reader
Luxury hunting & fishing holidays/tours in the British Isles. Travel Agents welcome. Tailormade packages for any requirements including non-participation available.

J/B Adventures & Safaris
2275 E. Arapahoe Rd., #109
Littleton, CO 80122
(303) 794-4485
FAX: (303) 794-4486
Contact: Beverley Wunderlich
Destinations: Worldwide, Africa,

North America, Pacific Rim, South America, Mexico & Argentina
Birds Hunted: Dove, Duck, Partridge, Geese

Laguna Vista International
PO Box 44, Combes, TX 78535
(800) 274-4401
FAX: (210) 421-4402
Contact: Roger Gerdes
Destinations: Northern Mexico, Tampico, Vera Cruz
Birds Hunted: Whitewing Dove, Wild Quail, Duck, Geese, Sandhill Crane

LandsEnd Expeditions
5878 Springwood Dr.
Mentor, OH 44060
(216) 257-9403
FAX: (216) 257-9403
Est.: 1988　Staff: 3
Contact: Larry King

Destinations: Canada, Alaska, South America, Europe, Russia
Birds Hunted: Geese, Ducks, Sea Ducks, Pheasant, Grouse, Dove
Packages/Comments: We offer packages for groups of 2 to 20. Our wingshooting packages offer the client the best shooting available anywhere.

Jim McCarthy Adventures
4906 Creek Dr.
Harrisburg, PA 17112
(717) 652-4374
FAX: (717) 652-5888
Est.: 1979　Staff: 11
Contact: Jim McCarthy
Destinations: Africa, Texas, Mexico, Argentina, Canada
Birds Hunted: Dove, Geese, Ducks, Francolin, Sand Grouse

MexHunt Bookings
3302 Josie Ave.
Long Beach, CA 90808
(310) 421-6215
Est.: 1990
Contact: Jim Cauley
Destinations: Mexico
Birds Hunted: Dove, Duck, Quail,
Pheasant

Outdoor Adventures, Inc.
PO Box 608, McAllen, TX 78505
(800) 375-4868
FAX: (210) 618-1037
Est.: 1987   Staff: 7
Contact: Don Turner
Destinations: Mexico, Costa Rica,
Canada, Alaska, Argentina, Africa
Birds Hunted: Whitewing Dove,
Quail, Duck, Geese
- Outdoor Adventures is a professional travel company with a FULL TIME dedication to consistently providing our clients with the finest adventure travel.
- Outdoor Adventures' staff personally previews each destination to assure our standards are maintained. "Follow-up" trips are regularly scheduled.
- Outdoor Adventures provides an important service to our outfitters-CLIENTS! As a result, our clients often receive preferential treatment and preferred dates.
- Outdoor Adventures services are provided AT NO COST to our clients. All fees are incurred by the outfitter at the same cost as if you would have booked direct.
See Our Ad Pg. 251

Outdoor Travel, Inc.
PO Box 131687
Houston, TX 77219
(800) 533-7299
FAX: (713) 526-4302
Est.: 1984
Contact: J. David Settles
Destinations: Hacienda San Juan in Northern Mexico
Birds Hunted: Whitewing Dove, Quail, Geese

Rod & Gun Resources, Inc.
Rt. 3, Box 465, Killeen, TX 76542
(512) 556-8237
FAX: (512) 556-2367
Est.: 1980   Staff: 8

Contact: David Gregory
Destinations: Mexico, Argentina, Uruguay, Alaska, Texas, Idaho
Birds Hunted: Dove, Wild Quail, Pheasant, Perdiz & Duck

Safari de Colombia Hunting & Fishing
420 Lincoln Rd., Suite 323
Miami Beach, FL 33139
(305) 674-9887
FAX: (305) 674-3227
Contact: Julio Hernandez
Destination: Cauca Valley, Colombia
Birds Hunted: Dove
Dove hunting Feb-May & Aug-Nov.

Scots Style Safaris
39 Fuller St., #2
Chicopee, MA 01020
(413) 594-5359 (Weekdays)
(617) 335-8076 (Weekends)
Contact: Ken Schworm
Destinations: Scotland
Birds Hunted: Driven and walk-up shooting for birds. Also wildfowling.

Sporting Adventures
20211 Patio Dr., Suite 240
Castro Valley, CA 94546
(510) 886-5544
FAX: (510) 886-2250
Est.: 1987
Owner: Lee Bohner
Destinations: Western Mexico, Alberta, Colombia, Argentina, Botswana
Birds Hunted: Ducks, Dove, Geese, Partridge, Goulds Turkey

Sporting Charters
PO Box 160818, Austin, TX 78716
(512) 458-8900
FAX: (512) 458-6935
Est.: 1988   Staff: 3
Contact: Tosh Brown
Destinations: U.S., Mexico
Birds Hunted: Quail, Geese, Pheasant, Dove, Partridge, Ducks

Sporting Holidays International
1701 Northwest Cookingham
Kansas City, MO 64155
(816) 734-4044
FAX: (816) 734-9650
Est.: 1977   Staff: 25
Contact: Gordon Philip
Destinations: Scotland, England
Birds Hunted: Black Game, Red Leg & Gray Partridge, Pheasant, Woodcock, Duck
Packages/Comments: 8 guns per party, completely guided; luxurious accomodations. No extra charge for non-shooting guests.
Alaska fishing trips: June, July, Aug., Sept. All arrangements-

guides, accommodations, transportation, one full week of the greatest fishing in the world.

Sporting International
13201 Northwest Frwy., #800
Houston, TX 77040
(800) 231-6352
Est.: 1967   Staff: 30
Contact: Tommy Morrison
Destinations: Mexico, Scotland, Botswana, Tanzania, Argentina, Colombia, Western U.S.
Birds Hunted: Whitewing Dove, Quail, Geese, Pheasant, Grouse, Duck, Francolin, Guinea Fowl, Sand Grouse.

Sportsmen's Travel Service, Inc.
119 E. Palatine Rd.,
Palatine, IL 60067
(708) 359-0149
Est.: 1969
Contact: Jerry Samuels
Destinations: Worldwide
Birds Hunted: Waterfowl & Upland

Stafford & Stafford, Inc.
PO Box 11196
Jacksonville, FL 32239-1196
(800) 383-0245
FAX: (904) 725-2588
Est.: 1991   Staff: 4
Contact: Ron Stafford
Destinations: Argentina, Colombia
Birds Hunted: Duck, Geese, Whitewing & Mourning Dove, Quail, Perdiz
Packages/Comments: Stafford & Stafford is a service-oriented company, specializing in exclusive & private hunting trips, generally for 6-8 hunters, but groups of 4 welcome. A complete line of Central & South American fishing trips is also available.
See Our Ad Above Right

Sunbelt Hunting & Fishing
3554 Boca Chica Blvd.
Brownsville, TX 78521
(800) 876-4868
FAX: (210) 544-4731
Est.: 1972   Staff: 6
Contact: Barry Batsell
Destinations: Mexico
Birds Hunted: Dove, Quail, Geese

The TBJ Group, Inc.
17326 W. Bluff Rd.,
Lemont, IL 60439
(708) 972-1060
Est.: 1993   Staff: 3
Pres: Tom Jagielski
Destinations: Arg., Guinea Bissau
Birds Hunted: Dove, Pigeon, Duck,
Geese, Partridge, Guinea Fowl

Tex Mex Hunts, Inc.
Box 701189, Houston, TX 77270
(800) 284-1286
Est.: 1987   Staff: 4
Contact: Bob Hallette
Destinations: Argent., Mexico, Tex.
Birds Hunted: Whitewing Dove,
Ducks, Geese, Quail

The Timberdoodle Club
One Webster Hwy.,
Temple, NH 03084
(603) 654-9510
FAX: (603) 654-5964
Est.: 1967   Staff: 4
Contact: Randall Martin
Destinations: United Kingdom, Africa, Central America
Packages/Comments: Small private groups, custom itineraries.

Trek International Safaris
Box 19065, Jacksonville, FL 32245
(800) 654-9915
Est.: 1973   Staff: 14
Contact: Mike Cloaninger
Destinations: South America, Central America, Europe, Canada, Alaska, Africa Birds Hunted: Duck, Geese, Dove, Quail, Partridge, Grouse, Francolin, Guinea Fowl

Venture West
PO Box 7543, Missoula, MT 59807
(406) 825-6200
Est.: 1984
Contact: Cathy Ream, PhD
Destinations: Montana, Idaho, North Dakota, Wyoming & Oregon
Birds Hunted: For a consultation fee of $10, we will set up hunts for the following birds: Pheasants, Huns, Blue Grouse, Ruffed Grouse, Francolin, Chukar, Turkey, Sharptail Grouse, Sage, Waterfowl.

Whitehair Hunting & Fishing Travel
1604 South Rolling Rd.
Relay, MD 21227
(410) 242-3916
Est.: 1989   Staff: 5
President: G. Michael Whitehair
Destinations: Argentina, Can., U.S.
Birds Hunted: Ducks, Geese, Quail, Pheasant, Prairie Chicken, Grouse

Wilderness Expeditions, Inc.
1080 Goffle Rd.,
Hawthorne, NJ 07506
(201) 427-8600
Est.: 1979   Staff: 3
Contact: Nancy Alward/Phil Alward
Destinations: North America
We arrange trips for hunting, fishing & birds all over N.A. and some areas in So. America.

Wilderness Pursuits Int'l., Ltd.
PO Box 1258,
Center Harbor, NH 03226
(800) 231-1650
FAX: (603) 253-3043
Est.: 1989   Staff: 3
Pres.: Rick Davis
Destinations: Canada & West. U.S.
Birds Hunted: Grouse, Woodcock, Wilson Snipe, Canada Geese, Black and Sea Ducks, Ptarmigan.

Wing Shooting Adventures
4320 Kalamazoo Ave., SE
Grand Rapids, MI 49508
(616) 455-7810
FAX: (616) 455-5212
Est.: 1982   Staff: 4
Contact: Jack J. Jansma
Destinations: Hungary & Spain
Birds Hunted: Driven Pheasant & Driven Partridge

Wings, Inc.
403 Greene St., PO Box 743

Camden, SC 29020-0743
(803) 425-7260
FAX: (803) 425-7270
Est.: 1987   Staff: 3
Contact: Don Terrell
Destinations: Argentina, Canada, Mexico & Venezuala
Birds Hunted: Ducks, Geese, Dove, Partridge, Pigeon, Quail

World Hunts, Inc.
PO Box 777, Latrobe, PA 15650
(412) 537-7668
FAX: (412) 537-5301
Est.: 1986
Contact: Peter C. Theron
Destinations: Africa, Mexico, South Pacific & Europe
Birds Hunted: Egyptian Geese, Guinea Fowl, Rock Pigeon, Red-Eye Dove, Cape Turtle Dove, Rameron Pigeon, Yellow Bill Duck, Red Bill Teal, Cape Teal, African Shelduck, Cape Shovelier, Pheasant, Francolin & Partridge (grey wing).

Worldwide Hunting Adventures, Inc.
Box 93687, Las Vegas, NV 89193
(702) 791-2079
FAX: (702) 798-0530
Est.: 1988   Staff: 3
Contact: Dick Krafve
Destinations: Worldwide
Birds Hunted: All types of birds with special emphasis on collectors and waterfowl.

High Volume Wingshooting—Closer Than You Think

Tamaulipas, Mexico

Think you have to travel halfway around the world and spend upwards of $6,000 for some high-volume wingshooting? Not so. Just south of the Texas border in the Mexican state of Tamaulipas you can find wild-bird shooting (whitewing and mourning dove; bobwhite quail; ducks, geese and sandhill cranes) the equal of which hasn't been available--or legal--in this country for years.

How far is "just south" of the border? Well, most of the shooting lodges catering to the U.S. market, some for 25 years, lie within a two hour drive--or 30 minute charter—flight from two border towns McAllen and Harlingen, Texas. American and Continental Airlines have several flights a day from Dallas and Houston, respectively, so it is easy to reach Harlingen. From Harlingen booking agents transport hunters to the various lodges, by van or charter flight, depending upon clients preferences and whether the lodge has a landing strip.

Most of lodges in Tamaulipas are American owned or operated--a fact most foreign-travel leery U.S. shooters find comforting. The quality of the local water supply is good and there is little worry about the intestinal afflictions common in other parts of Mexico. Nonetheless it is a good idea to pack an over-the-counter anti-diarrheal, just in case, and a strong sunblock to avoid the biggest health hazard you'll encounter on trip to Tamaulipas: sunburn.

The question of limits

Inevitably, the quest for high-volume shooting leads to the question of bag limits. And in Tamaulipas the answer to the question falls, as so many things in Mexican life do, into that gray area where what is very often far from what's supposed to be. [For a knowledgeable answer to the question of limits see Stuart William's comments in box, pg. 250.].

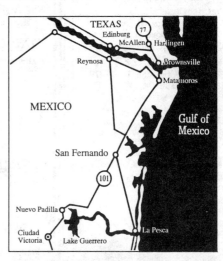

The best advice for anyone planning a trip to Tamaulipas is to let a booking agent cut through the red tape and make the arrangements for you. A good agent will provide detailed information, book accommodations, handle the complex paperwork required to get hunting licenses and import guns into Mexico, and meet you at the border to get you through customs and then transport you to and from your shooting lodge. And remember, you don't pay the agent directly for services; he's compensated by the shooting lodges he's associated with. [See the following listing section for information on contacting agents.

The only big negative about a trip to Tamaulipas is the cost of a gun permit-- $250-$300 depending on who makes the arrangements and how many species you wish to shoot. The permit allows you to import two guns for 10 days, with two boxes of shells for each gun. (Additional shells are available at all lodges at prices somewhat higher than in the U.S.) Generally speaking, the process of securing the needed permits takes anywhere from 1-6 weeks to complete. The permit form will ask for:

- Detailed information about your guns (make, gauge and so on)

- A "letter of good conduct" from your local sheriff or chief of police.
- Proof of citizenship (passport, birth certificate, Voter Registration card).
- Six passport size, color photos.

The birds

Dove - Virtually all of the lodges in Tamaulipas offer whitewing dove shooting, long a specialty of area. The quality of the shooting varies from year to year and is highly dependent on rainfall. Copious rain in March through July is a blessing that results in abundant yields of sunflowers, corn and sorghum, and large swarms of birds. Heavy rainfall during the dove season itself is a curse, making most fields totally inaccessible.

The quality of a dove shoot is gauged not by the numbers of birds killed, but by the numbers of boxes fired. A poor shoot is a 0-2 box shoot; a fair shoot, 3-4 boxes; a good shoot, 5-6 boxes; and an excellent shoot, over 6 boxes. This is for a half-day shoot.

Quail - Rain likewise determines quail populations. Heavy spring and summer rains will mean explosive quail populations. Some lodges hunt quail primarily by "pushin' bush," i.e., driving the birds out of the bush by beating it with long sticks, throwing stones and shouting. Other lodges import top American dog handlers with lots of dogs. Believe it or not, "pushin' bush" is usually more productive. A complete quail hunt should include some of both. In a good area in a good year, a hunter should see 25-40 covey rises per day. There is no quail shooting anywhere else that even comes close.

Goose - Hunted out of pits over vast spreads or rags, windsocks and shell decoys. When it is good--as it usually is--the goose hunting is second only to Argentina, and some days it's better. Primary species are snows, specklebellies, and lesser Canadas, in descending order of abundance. Note: because of very slight hunting pressure, geese are noticeably less wary in Mexico than in the U.S.

The Ideal Trip

If you're thinking about your first trip to Tamaulipas, plan on spending 5 days away—2 days for travel and 3 days for hunting. Then start planning ahead. Though you can book a hunt with as little as 2 months lead time— the permit paperwork alone takes a month— you'd be smart to start the process at least 6 months in advance. This is especially true if you're interested in early season whitewing shooting.

Planning well in advance will also allow you ample time to review the brochures provided by the lodges and their agents. And to check references. Tip: Have the booking agent provide you with the names and numbers of at least six people who have recently hunted at the lodges he represents. Then spend some time and money calling them. It could save you a bundle in the long run.

Key Questions for Your Agent

- Ask your agent about his affiliation to the lodge you are staying at. Is he an exclusive agent? An independent agent? How long has he been associated with the lodge?

- Will the agent personally meet you at the border and transport you to the lodge? If not, who will?

- How much rain has fallen near the lodge in recent months? (rainfall determines bird numbers more than any other factor)

- Will you be shooting in fields exclusive to your lodge, or will you be competing with shooters from other lodges?

- How long is the drive from the lodge to the shooting area? (One hour maximum is advisable)

- How big are the shooting parties? (no more than two for quail or four for geese is best)

- Cost of shotshells? (expect to pay more than in the states, but beware of truly exorbitant prices)

Birds & Hunting Seasons in Tamaulipas, Mexico*	
Whitewing and Mourning Dove	Mid August through October
Quail	November 1 through mid-February
Ducks	November 1 through mid-February
Geese	November 1 through mid-February
Sandhill Cranes	November 1 through mid February

* Seasons change annually. Check with your booking agent for the latest information.

Duck - Duck shooting--which is practiced along the Gulf of Mexico--is done entirely by decoying. One of the big attractions is the opportunity to shoot species that one seldom gets to shoot in the States such as redheads, canvasback and mottled ducks. The biggest attraction is the excellent pintail shooting.

The agents

Picking the right agent to handle your trip to Tamaulipas is important. As you look through listings that follow , you'll see that most of the booking agents are based in the U.S., close to the Texas-Mexico border, where they can personally handle paperwork and greet incoming

A Word On Limits

Officially, shooters in Tamaulipas are limited to 5 geese, 10 quail, 15 ducks and 25 doves per day. In my estimation, these fairly modest limits are the result of pressure from environmental groups in and outside of Mexico. But Mexican wildlife officials know that strict enforcement of the "official" limits will stem the lucrative flow of shooters to the area, so they are observed more in the breach than the adherence. Whether you observe them or not is largely a matter of your own conscience. Speaking personally, I find it hard to limit myself to just five geese a day when in neighboring Texas the limit is twelve and wildlife authorities are practically begging hunters to kill more snow geese to avoid the problems of overpopulation—Stuart Williams [Mr. Williams, a former shooting editor of Field & Stream, has hunted in Tamaulipas over 25 times in the last 22 years].

hunters. And though many of the lodges are represented by more than one booking agent, experienced hunters recommend working with the lodge's in-house or primary independent agent whenever possible.

The lodges

All of the lodges that appear in the listing section that follows are clean and comfortable. Most have swimming pools. The quality of the service and amenities they provided ranges from basic to deluxe. But the mix of appetizing American and Mexican dishes they serve will satisfy all but the pickiest of gourmets. (Gratuities, by the way, are expected: ask your lodge owner or operator for guidelines about proper amounts.) Finally, as with most things, price is often—but not always— a fairly good index of quality.

TAMAULIPAS, MEXICO

Arnoldo's Hunting Services
745 West Elizabeth, Brownsville, TX 78520
(210) 542-3571; in Mexico 011-52-131-67452
Contact Arnoldo Rodriquez
Birds Dove, Quail, Duck

Club Exclusive & Big Bass Tours
(800) 531-7500 Contact Rick Schroeder
Location 60 mi. S of San Fernando on Lake Guerrero
Birds Dove, Quail **U.S. Gateway** Car/van from border **Airstrip** Yes **Agent** Bob Hallette
(713) 266–5515

Classic Adventure Group (Lodge #1)
PO Box 2186, Harlingen, TX 78557
(800) 447-6420   Dial Dunkin
Location 65 mi. S of San Fernando in Jimenez, Mex.
Est 1994 **Staff** 6-8 **Capacity** 8
Birds Dove **U.S. Gateway** Car/van from Harlingen
Airstrip Yes
Classic Adventure Group (Lodge #2)
PO Box 2186, Harlingen, TX 78557

(800) 447-6420   Dial Dunkin
Location 80 mi. N of San Fernando
Capacity Small **Birds** Duck, Geese, Quail
U.S. Gateway Car/van from Harlingen

Classic Adventure Group (Lodge #3)
PO Box 2186, Harlingen, TX 78557
(800) 447-6420   Dial Dunkin
Location 80 mi. SE of San Fernando on Lake Lorenzo
Capacity Medium **Birds** Duck, Geese, Quail
U.S. Gateway Car/van from Harlingen **Airstrip** No

Finca La Herradura Lodge
011-52-88-440944   Ruben Caballero
Location In San Fernando
Est 1989   **Staff** 20+   **Capacity** 12- 30
Birds Quail, Doves, Duck, Geese **U.S. Gateway**
Car/van from Harlingen or McAllen **Airstrip** Yes
Agent Outdoor Sports Consultants; 800-992-5767;
Contact: Chuck Stankey; Bob Hallette (713) 266–5515

Gerald Glasco Kennels and Guide Service
RR7, Box 302, Marion, IL 62959
(618) 997-6583   Gerry Glasco
Birds Quail

Hacienda San Juan
c/o Outdoor Travel
1973 W. Gray, #9, Houston, TX 77019
(800) 533-7299   **David Settles**
Location 100 mi. S of San Fernando
Capacity 6-62 **Birds** Quail, Dove **U.S. Gateway**
Car/van from Harlingen **Airstrip** Yes

Laguna Vista Lodge
PO Box 44, Combes, TX 78535
(800) 274-4401   Roger Gerdes
Location 30 mi. E of San Fernando on Gulf Coast
Est 1989 **Staff** 10-12 **Capacity** 2-30
Birds Duck, Dove, Quail **U.S. Gateway** Car/van
from Harlingen or Brownsville **Airstrip** Yes

La Loma Lodge
c/o Sunbelt Hunting and Fishing
PO Box 3009, Brownsville, TX 78520
(800) 876-4868   Barry Batsell
Location Approx. 50 mi. W of San Fernando
Est 1993 **Staff** 12-14 **Capacity** 2-52
Birds Dove, Quail **U.S. Gateway** Car/van from
Brownsville or Harlingen **Airstrip** No
Agent Rod & Gun Resources, Sporting Charters

La Marina del Rio
PO Box 720071, McAllen, TX 78504
011-52-132-70460, ext. 199 Cavi del Rio
Location 120 mi. SE of San Fernando on the Gulf
Coast at La Pesca
Est 1988 **Staff** 12-16 **Capacity** 2-24
Birds Duck, Geese, Quail, Dove, Turkey
U.S. Gateway Car/van from harlingen or McAllen
Airstrip Yes **Agent** Tex-Mex Hunting & Fishing;
(800) 284-1286; contact Bob Hallette

Loma Colorado Lodge
Box 202, Linn, TX 78563
(210) 380-2303   Philip Veale
Location 5 mi. E of San Fernando
Est 1986 **Staff** 12 **Capacity** 16

SHOTGUNNER'S SOURCE

Birds Quail, Duck, Geese, Dove **U.S. Gateway**
Car/van from Harlingen or McAllen **Airstrip** Yes

Los Patos
PO Box 608, McAllen, TX 78505
(800) 375-4868 Fax: (210) 618-1037 Don Turner
Location 30 mi. E San Fernando
Est 1992 **Staff** 12 **Capacity** 12
Birds Duck, Geese
Car/van from McAllen, TX **Airstrip** Yes
Agent: Outdoor Adventures (owner/operator)
See Our Ad Pg. 251

Mescalero Outfitters Lodge
c/o Outdoor Mexico
PO Box 8520, Brownsville, TX 78520
(800) 635-1594   Danny Putegnat or Hector Sanchez
Location 60 mi S. of San Fernando
Est 1980 **Staff** 14-16 **Capacity** 22
Birds Dove, Quail, Geese **U.S. Gateway** Car/van
from Brownsville or Harlingen **Airstrip** Yes

Gene Naquin's
Fin and Feathered Safaris

Gene Naquin's Fin & Feathered Safaris
P.O. Box 1734
Laredo, TX 78044
(210) 724-4648 Gene Naquin
Location: Miquel Aleman
Est 1980
Birds Quail, Duck, Geese, Dove **U.S. Gateway**
Car/van from Laredo or McAllen **Airstrip** No
Hunting for over 25 years in Mexico, I have developed
a keen sense of what my guests are looking for in a
quality hunt—and I give it to them. We pride ourselves
in well-organized and enjoyable hunts. Short driving
distances between lodging and hunting areas are our
specialty. I am not a booking agent. I do not send you
to Mexico; I take you. Call me today for more
information.

No Le Hace Lodge
c/o Sports Resorts International
730 N. Post Oak Blvd., Suite 302, Houston, TX 77024
(713) 956-1628; 957-4396 Lloyd Fite
Location 20 mi E of San Fernando
Est 1968 **Staff** 14 **Capacity** 26
Birds Quail, Duck, Geese **U.S. Gateway** Car/van
from Harlingen **Airstrip** Yes **Agent** Detail Co.,
(800) 292-2213, contact Jeri Booth; LandsEnd
Expeditions, Inc., (216) 257-9403

No Le Hace Hacienda
c/o Sports Resorts International
730 N. Post Oak Blvd., Suite 302, Houston, TX 77024
011-52-131-71773 Lloyd Fite/Doug Johnson

Location 90 mi. SW of San Fernando on Lake Guerrero
Est 1977 **Staff** 12-14   18
Birds Quail, Dove **Airstrip** Yes **Agent** Detail
Co. & LandsEnd Expeditions

Operacion Las Palomas
PO Box 608, McAllen, TX 78505
(800) 375-4868 Fax: (210) 618-1037 Don Turner
Location San Fernando, 85 mi. S of McAllen, TX
Est 1987 **Staff** 30 **Capacity** 4-45
Birds Dove, Quail, Duck, Geese
Car/van from McAllen, TX **Airstrip** Yes
Agent: Outdoor Adventures (owner/operator)
See Our Ad Pg. 251

Rio Corona Lodge
Location 80 mi. S of San Fernando on Rio Corona
Est 1990 **Staff** 5 **Capacity** 10
Birds Quail **U.S. Gateway** Car/van from
Harlingen or McAllen **Airstrip** Yes **Agent** Detail
Co., (800) 292-2213, contact Jeri Booth

El Sargento Lodge
c/o Sunbelt Hunting & Fishing
PO Box 3009, Brownsville, TX 78520
(800) 876-4868   Eduarddo Lalo Maraboto
Location Approx. 60 mi. S of San Fernando
Est 1975 **Staff** 8-10 **Capacity** 2-12
Birds Quail **U.S. Gateway** Car/van from
Harlingen or Brownsville Airstirp No **Agent** Rod
& Gun Resources

South Padre Island Rod & Gun Club
Los Ebanos Island, Mexico
(800) 77-LODGE Nat B. Nofsinger or K.G. Wiles
Birds Dove, Quail, Duck, Geese

El Tejon Lodge
c/o Sunbelt Hunting & Fishing
PO Box 3009, Brownsville, TX 78520
(800) 876-4868   Barry Batsell
Location 18 mi. N of San Fernando
Est 1972 **Staff** 20-25 **Capacity** 2-24
Birds Quail, Geese **U.S. Gateway** Car/van from
Brownsville or Harlingen **Airstrip** No
Agent Rod & Gun Resources; Sporting Charters

El Tesoro Lodge
c/o BT Hunting
17319 Methil, Spring, TX 77379
(713) 251-3244   Bruno Taino
Location 2 mi. N of San Fernando
Est 1980 **Staff** 12-16 **Capacity** 2-26
Birds Quail, Dove, Duck **U.S. Gateway** Car/van
from Harlingen or Brownsville **Airstrip** Yes
Agent Bob Hallette (713) 266-5515

TROPHIES, AWARDS & PROMOTIONS

Champion Awards

Champion Awards
3116 E. Shea Blvd., #153
Phoenix, AZ 85028
(602) 493-3064
FAX: (602) 956-7763
Est.: 1979   Staff: 2
Owner: D.W. "Nick" Nichols
Owner: Joyce M. Nichols
Available: Direct
Gun Club award specialists. Distinctive awards of the highest quality. Custom designed for your needs and budget. Specializing in buckles, money clips, bracelets, pendants, custom logos. Extensive line of awards: Wildlife Collectibles, Stained Glass, Framed Wildlife Scenes, Etched Glass, Clocks, Steins, Decanters, Collectors Plates, Sports Glassware. Call for quote.

Crown Trophy
1 Odell Plaza, Yonkers, NY 10701
(914) 963-0005
FAX: (914) 963-0181
Customer Svc. Mgr: Anne Birde
Custom event medals; trophies and plaques.

KK Awards
PO Box 5870, Glendale, CA 91221
(818) 790-5717
FAX: (818) 790-5728
Contact: Dick Kennerknecht

Specializing in custom medals, pins, coins, plaques & belt buckles.

Kapan-Kent Co., Inc.
701 E. 60th St.
Los Angeles, CA 90001
(800) 845-1097 (Factory)
(213) 233-6162
FAX: (213) 233-6635
Est.: 1958
Contact: Kipp K. Anders
Custom glass & ceramic decorating-
-promotional, events & gift items.

Linden Awards
6201 Miller Rd., Suite C
Swartz Creek, MI 48473
(800) 253-9579
FAX: (810) 635-9112
Contact: Ron Alle or Dennis Milem
Suppliers of Trophies for trap and skeet clubs nationwide. Suppliers for all Michigan Trap Association events.

Mains Enterprises, Inc.
1770 B Industrial
Las Vegas, NV 89102-2620
(702) 474-9200
FAX: (702) 474-9897
CEO: Brandon T. Blackwell
Extensive line of trophy buckles, money clips, jewelry items and pins. Gun accessories - bird scene and monogram grip caps, gold bird scene & initial trigger guards, and custom side plates. Please call today for our free brochure.

See Our Ad Below

Murray's Gun Shop
14720 NE Sandy Blvd.

Portland, OR 97230
(800) 459-3503
(503) 254-0303
FAX: (503) 254-8191
Est.: 1969   Staff: 3
Contact: Randy Murray
Custom carved awards from hard-woods–incorporating shotgun shells, clay pigeons and logos.

Nordik of America, Ltd.
3739 Douglas Ave.
Racine, WI 53402
(800) 972-5905
Contact: Robert Lovdahl

O.C. Monogram Co.
Box 250, Ocean City, MD 21842
(410) 213-7707
(800) 845-8306
Contact: Cathy Ritchie
Custom embroidery & garments. Hats, jackets, ties, sportshirts, towels & more.

Quack Sporting Clays, Inc.
K.G. Mfg. Co.
4 Ann & Hope Way
PO Box 98, Cumberland, RI 02864
(401) 723-8202
FAX: (401) 722-5910
Contact: Colleen Hamel
Available: Retail & Direct
Quack Sporting Clays sister company K.G. Mfg. Co. has been manufacturing skeet, trap and sporting clays (shotgun) awards and prizes since 1968. Our partici-

pant and merit pins are worn by shotgun shooters worldwide. We can accomodate small (100 pcs) or larger orders. Many items in stock for resale, pins, buckles, silver bowls, decorative decoys, etc. Custom in house engraving, quality products and workmanship, quick delivery, affordable prices, are the reasons why we have celebrated over 25 years in business. For more information call (401) 723-8202. *See Our Ads Pgs. 228-229*

Shamrock Leathers, Inc.
9722 320th St., St. Joe, MN 56374
(800) 728-5184
(612) 363-7441
President: Edward Brophy
Available: Direct

Shooting Awards
PO Box 138, Miquon, PA 19452
(215) 828-0885
President: Terry O'Donnell
Exact replica of the AA White Flyer in bronze and aluminum.

Silver State Silver
1469 Greg St., Sparks, NV 89431
(702) 358-1320
Contact: Jack or Karlin Elkins
We manufacture trophy belt buckles, gold and silver items, awards including bronze statues, prints, decoys, clocks and more.

Tilden & Bonser, Inc.
1175 Spring Centre S.
Altamonte Springs, FL 32714
(800) 682-2646
FAX: (407) 682-1967
Contact: Jim Beasley
Available: Direct
Tilden & Bosner specializes in trophies of real & lasting value for the

shooting sports. Complete line of rare coin & precious metal trophies, belt buckles, money clips & jewelry items. Call for information. *See Our Ad Above*

The Wildlife Den
6401 Schantz, Allentown, PA 18104
(610) 395-0140
FAX: (610) 395-0140
Est.: 1985   Staff: 3
Contact: Freeman or Barbara Kline
Nationwide suppliers of fine quality prizes, trophies and awards for Trap, Skeet and Sporting Clays clubs and associations. Extensive line of wildlife-themed sculptures,

bronze statues, afgans, decoys, pewter steins and plates, custommade buckles, engravings, art, limited edition prints, leather items, keepsake boxes, wall clocks, lamps, marble pictures and coasters, weather stations watches, jewelry and scrimshaw. Engraving available on all orders. In business ten years. Supplier of prizes to numerous State and Zone Shoots, smaller shoots, & leagues. Large inventory for last minute orders. Request our 24-pg. catalogue and check out our affordable prices. *See Our Ad Below*

HUNTING PRESERVES

Hunting Preserves: Fantastic

If you've ever hunted a well run preserve, you know there's just one word for it: Fantastic!

Preserves offer longer seasons, larger bag limits and more consistent results. They're not overcrowded and are extremely safe.

More importantly, they're fun. There's no better place to train a new hunter--your spouse, son, daughter, or friend--than a hunting preserve. No better, more convenient place to enjoy a day afield.

Where else but a preserve can you begin the day with a big cup of coffee in front of the clubhouse pot-belly stove followed by shooting 25 rounds at the wobble trap to sharpen the eye and get the heart pounding.

Then you're off on a half-day hunt for any one of a variety of flighty birds, led by an experienced guide and a well trained dog. Just at the moment your stomach lets you know it's lunchtime, it's back to the clubhouse for a bite.

What's next? Perhaps a round of sporting clays or an afternoon dove hunt, while the staff processes the morning's take.

It's hard for today's time-pressured hunter to find a more convenient and flexible way to pursue his beloved pastime. In short, preserves offer something for everyone and surely as much hunting as you want.

It all depends on where you are, what you're looking for, and, of course, what you can afford. Whatever the case, Wing & Clay can help you find it-- near home or while you're traveling on business or vacation.

What To Expect

Hunting preserves are state licensed hunting areas that offer extended season or year-round hunting for ring-necked pheasants, bobwhite quail, chukar, Hungarian partridge, mallard ducks, wild turkey, and other birds, depending on locale. They are open to the public on a daily-fee or an annual membership basis or both.

What should you expect when you hunt a preserve? For starters, a warm welcome. Preserve hunters are valued customers, not tolerated intruders, and your host should do everything he can to provide a safe, enjoyable hunt.

Once afield, expect the preserve grounds to look like good hunting country with a rich blend of natural and planted cover. Properly reared, the game birds will be mature, full-plumed, strong flyers-- the same color and conformation as their wild counterparts.

Almost all preserves provide experienced guides and trained hunting dogs; many preserves will allow you to hunt with your own dog, if you prefer.

At some preserves, the hunt is only half the story. Roomy, well-appointed clubhouses, quality meals, comfortable, private accommodations and a variety of services

WINGS

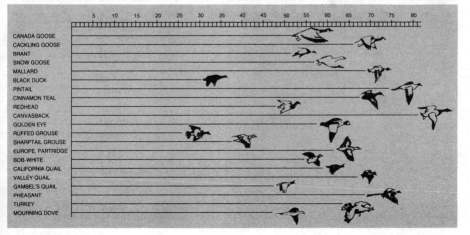

FLIGHT SPEED OF GAMEBIRDS IN MPH

CANADA GOOSE
CACKLING GOOSE
BRANT
SNOW GOOSE
MALLARD
BLACK DUCK
PINTAIL
CINNAMON TEAL
REDHEAD
CANVASBACK
GOLDEN EYE
RUFFED GROUSE
SHARPTAIL GROUSE
EUROPE, PARTRIDGE
BOB-WHITE
CALIFORNIA QUAIL
VALLEY QUAIL
GAMBEL'S QUAIL
PHEASANT
TURKEY
MOURNING DOVE

and amenities--ranging from airport pickup and shooting instruction to dog kenneling and sporting clays--await you. At other preserves, the services and amenities are more modest, or unavailable.

But one type is not necessarily better than the other. It all depends on you. Whether you're a new or seasoned hunter looking for a red-letter day of good dog work and flighty birds or a corporate executive looking for a place to entertain clients, there's a preserve out there to meet your needs and tastes. But remember, you may have to shop around.

Costs

How about cost? Well, again, it depends on how much hunting you want and the kind of "extras" you're looking for. Some hunting preserves charge a set-up fee for game birds released; others charge for a half- or full-day hunt (some offer longer hunt packages). All charge a minimum fee per hunter or hunting party. Some charge for dressing game birds; others do not.

In any case, fees vary. But a day on a hunting preserve doesn't have to cost more than a so-called "free hunt", and will certainly

take up far less of your time and probably prove more consistent and satisfying results.

Wherever you live in the U.S., there is likely to be a good hunting preserve within easy driving distance. And, if you're a typical hunter without landowner contacts, that preserve may be the most practical (and in the long run, the cheapest) way to spend a day afield with dog, gun and game birds.

Who To Contact

Inside Wing & Clay you'll find information on over 1,100 U.S. preserves open to the public on a daily-fee or a membership basis: Preserve names, addresses, and telephone numbers; the name of the person to call to ask questions or make a reservation; even information about the best time to call, not to mention details on the size and scope of the operation, the types of shoots offered, birds hunted, membership details and more. [See sample listing in the How To Use Wing & Clay section on the following page for a complete rundown on what you learn about a preserve from a Wing & Clay listing.]

Calling Checklist

Once you know what you're looking for, Wing & Clay's listings will help you identify those preserves likely to fit the bill. But it's a pretty good idea to put together a checklist of questions to ask, before you make a call. A quick question on the phone could save you a disappointing day in the field. For example: Does the preserve...

☐ Provide needed licenses?
☐ Provide airport pickup?
☐ Kennel bird dogs?
☐ Process game birds?
☐ Have a sporting clays course?
☐ Have deer hunting?
☐ Provide shooting instruction?
☐ Serve quality meals?
☐ Have special hunting jeeps?
☐ Train bird dogs?
☐ Have private bedrooms?
☐ Provide loaner guns?
☐ Sell factory ammo?
☐ Have a quality clubhouse?
☐ Offer other recreational activities?

Wing & Clay can help you explore the wide and exciting world of hunting adventures that awaits you. Enjoy. Safe hunting!

JUDGING RANGE

40yd

30yd

50yd

60yd

20yd

TO HELP JUDGE RANGE

Prop up this page or lay it open on the floor. Select one of the birds in the chart and place the muzzle of your gun directly below it on the page itself. Look along the barrel. The bird will look the same size that it would appear at the selected distance.

How to Use Wing & Clay's Hunting Preserve Directory

Your Prime Source Of Information

Finding a place to hunt takes time—especially when you are in parts of the country you don't know very well. Fortunately, you now have a copy of Wing & Clay to make the job easier.

The heart of the Hunting Preserve or Wings section of this book is its list of wingshooting preserves—the most comprehensive published.

An individual listing in Wing & Clay contains all the information you need to locate and contact a hunting operation that offers the kind of experience you're looking for. [See explanation of a Typical Listing found on page 260]. The advertisements that appear in the Wings section provide even more information about an operation. In short, they are an operator's way of telling you he or she is eager for your business, of saying, "Shotgunner's Welcome—stop by for a visit!"

A Note On Calling Or Writing

Contacting a hunting preserve by phone can be tricky, owing mostly to the seasonal nature of the business and that many operators work full time jobs in addition to running their hunting operations. Don't be put off if you have trouble making contact by phone. Many of the listings in the Wings section contain information on the best time to call. Look for times immediately following the contact name and call again. Or write and ask for a flyer, brochure or, when available, a video.

Say You Saw It In Wing & Clay

The publication of Wing & Clay would be impossible without the advertising support of hundreds of companies in the shotgun industry trying to reach and influence you efficiently and effectively. So whenever you contact one of these companies, tell them that you have benefitted from seeing their ad or listing. And don't forget to say that you "saw it in Wing & Clay."

HUNTING PRESERVE STATE/PAGE INDEX

Southeastern Illinois College: The Only School in the U.S. Training Preserve Managers

by Raymond Goydon

There was a time in this country when the words "commercial hunting property" described a farmer looking to squeeze an extra dollar or two from his land by making it available to hunters. Times have changed. Who says so? Bruce Hering, for one. Hering is the founder and director of an innovative program at Southeastern Illinois College designed to train the industry's first generation of professional hunting preserve managers.

"There's a growing number of hunting operations out there that exist as discrete business operations—not just agricultural sidelines," he says. And these operations make entirely different "management demands" on their operators.

Hering points out that the operator of yesteryear needed only to understand the use and care of hunting dogs, a bit about hand reared game birds, and at least a rudimentary idea of how to organize and run a hunt. "Some basic social skills never hurt either," Hering adds.

Southeastern's Shooting Preserve Commercial Wildlife Management program—the only one of its kind in the country—confers on its graduates an Associate Degree and a solid footing in disciplines ranging from game bird propagation and wildlife management to human relations and the principles of marketing.

Program participants spend three semesters in class and the field and a fourth, year-long semester interning on a working hunting preserve for what Hering describes as a "ground level view of how the industry works."

Students range from 18 to 35 years of age and come to the program from diverse backgrounds. (A recent class included an ex-coal miner, a former computer science major, and a tele-communications technician.) All have high school diplomas, and some have bachelor or graduate degrees.

"The program gives you the big picture," says a current participant just beginning his year-long internship at a prestigious southeastern plantation. "I had worked in the industry for three years before enrolling, but it wasn't until I started the program that I realized how complex a business this really is," he adds.

Hering's own research shows that the majority of successful commercial hunting operations have implemented a "professional" management plan dealing with all facets of the business. While no two plans are exactly alike, most include fairly sophisticated marketing and advertising programs, designated work assignments, and a clear sense of the importance of quality customer relations.

That last area—dealing with the public—is one of Hering's and the program's primary concerns: "When it comes right down to it, the student has to learn to make the customer comfortable or else we've failed. Knowing how to raise birds, tend cover and run hunts just isn't enough."

If industry response is any indication, Hering is clearly on the right track. The program's files are filled with glowing letters of praise for interns and graduates who have only just started to have an impact on the day-to-day operations of the industry.

"Like all businesses, commercial hunting operations will have to grow and evolve, or face the consequences," Hering says. "With a little bit of luck and a lot of hard work, our graduates will help lead the way."

INTERESTED IN LEARNING MORE?
Each year the Shooting Preserve Commercial Wildlife Management program enrolls up to 16 students and places an additional 16 in intern programs across the U.S.

Operators and students interested in learning more about the program, its interns and graduates should write Bruce Hering at Southeastern Illinois College, P.O. Box 200, Vienna, IL 62995; or call (618) 658-2211.

TYPICAL LISTING

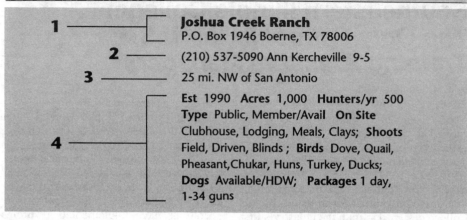

1 — **Joshua Creek Ranch**
P.O. Box 1946 Boerne, TX 78006

2 — (210) 537-5090 Ann Kercheville 9-5

3 — 25 mi. NW of San Antonio

4 —
Est 1990 Acres 1,000 Hunters/yr 500
Type Public, Member/Avail On Site
Clubhouse, Lodging, Meals, Clays; Shoots
Field, Driven, Blinds ; Birds Dove, Quail,
Pheasant,Chukar, Huns, Turkey, Ducks;
Dogs Available/HDW; Packages 1 day,
1-34 guns

How The Directory Is Organized

Listings in Wing & Clay's Hunting Preserve Directory are organized alphabetically by state—Alabama through Wyoming—and within each state alphabetically by preserve name.

1 Preserve Name & Address Obviously helpful in finding a hunting operation's location, the address can help you gather detailed information when you are planning a hunting excursion. Write and ask for a descriptive flyer or brochure, most preserves have them.

2 Telephone Number, Contact name(s) & Best Time to Call The number and name of the person to call when you're looking for information or making a reservation. In many listings information about the best time to call follows the contact name.

3 Nearest Major Town/City Distance in miles and direction from a large city or town; intended to give you a better general idea of where the hunting operation is located.

4 Particulars Whenever possible, Wing & Clay offers detailed information—provided by the operator— about each hunting location. The categories are described below.

Est The year the preserve began operation.

Acres Number of acres owned or leased.

Hunters/yr The approximate number of hunters using the facility annually.

Type Specifically, type of membership. That is, whether the operation is open to all hunters (Public) or to members only–individual (Member/Avail or Member/Ltd) or corporate (Corp). Many membership clubs are also open to the public. Membership usually means an annual fee (ranging from $15.00 to more than $15,000) is required.

Member/Ltd. (or Limited) implies that the club's membership roster was filled at the time Wing & Clay went to press. **Member/Avail** means the club is private but new members are welcome. If you are interested in a club membership, Wing & Clay strongly urges you to write or call for information. Preserves typically respond quickly and courteously even when memberhip is currently filled.

On Site Services and amenities available at the preserve. Clubhouse, Lodging, Meals and Clays (some form of clay target shooting, not necessarily a sporting clays course). Note: Hunting preserve Lodging runs the gamut from barebones bunkhouses to luxurious private suites; similarly, meals might mean a hot dog and iced tea or a candle lit gourmet event.

Shoots Type of hunts or shoots offered at the preserve, including Field Hunts, Tower Releases, Driven Shoots, and Blinds and Boats.

Birds Type of birds hunted at the preserve. Wing & Clay currently tracks the following birds: Dove, Quail, Pheasant, Ruffed Grouse, Woodcock, Chukar, Huns (Hungarian Partridge), Wild Turkey, Prairie Chicken, Sage Grouse, Snipe, Sharp-Tail Grouse, Ducks and Geese.

Dogs Avail indicates that the preserve provides dogs and guides. /HDW means "hunter's dogs welcome" and you may hunt with your own dog if you wish.

Packages Indicates the shortest hunt package available, usually 1/2- or 1-day. The number of guns is the range of hunters the preserve will accommodate from the smallest to largest number. (Example: a preserve that will allow a single hunter to hunt, but can handle up to 4 guns per party on each of 4 separate hunting fields would include **1-16 guns** in its listing.)

Alan Kelly's Eagle Recreational Consultants Help Hunting Lodges Achieve...

Uncompromising Quality

If there's anything Alan Kelly knows, it's how to deliver a quality wingshooting and fishing experience to today's demanding sportsman. But that's not very surprising when you consider that much of what Kelly has done in his private and professional life has prepared him for his role as expert in the field.

Expert in the making

Early experiences with bird hunting and fly fishing led Kelly to a career in wildlife management, first as a U.S. government biologist on the famous Big Horn River in Montana. In 1981 Kelly set out on his own as a consultant, advising clients around the country in fish and wildlife management. Later Kelly developed Eagle Outfitters and Eagle Nest Lodge to serve the growing hunting and fly fishing public drawn to his beloved Big Horn River.

Within a short time, Eagle Nest established itself as the premiere fishing and wingshooting lodge on the Big Horn, a reputation capped by a coveted endorsement from Orvis, Inc.

Today, the lodge's tradition of excellence continues under Kelly's direction and, he's quick to point out, with the help of his wife Wanda and sons, Keith and Matthew. (Orvis, Inc., was so impressed with the uncompromising quality of Eagle Nest that it selected Kelly to direct and manage its endorsed wingshooting lodge program. See sidebar for more.)

Consultant will travel

In addition to his work at the lodge and with Orvis, Eagle Recreational Consultants continues to advise many established and developing wingshooting and fly fishing lodges, both public and private.

Says Kelly: "I tell each of my clients that the lodge business is one of the most challenging, frustrating, educational and, ultimately, rewarding ventures an entrepreneur can undertake."

Kelly's consulting clients can tap his vast store of knowledge and experience in subjects as wide ranging as habitat development and management and customer service to lodge design and marketing strategies. Operators interested in learning more about Eagle Recreational and the Orvis Endorsement Programs should write Kelly at P.O. Box 926, Lincoln, MT 59639; or call (406) 362-4270.

ORVIS ENDORSED WINGSHOOTING LODGES

Launched in 1989, the Orvis Endorsed Wingshooting Program has one clear purpose: to identify the best bird hunting experiences available in the U.S. Of the hundreds of top-notch lodges currently in operation only 15, at the time of this writing, have earned the coveted endorsement.

To qualify, a lodge must convince program director Alan Kelly that it meets or exceeds Orvis's exacting standards. Kelly evaluates each lodge nominated for the program personally. In addition to what Orvis calls a"complete and totally uncompromising bird hunting experience", the lodge must provide professional guides and well-trained bird dogs. Equal in importance to the quality of the hunt is the lodge itself: first rate accommodations, prompt courteous service, memorable dining, and after-hunt amenities are a must.

"When you choose an Orvis Endorsed Lodge, you can be sure you're in for one of the finest hunting experiences available anywhere," says Kelly. For more information about the program contact: Alan Kelly, P.O. Box 926, Lincoln MT 59639; (406) 362-4270.

Ten Reasons Why Sportsmen Enjoy Hunting Preserves

Good birds. Good dogs. Good guides. Good cover. And More.
They're yours -- every time -- at a well run preserve.

1 You're Always Welcome
Youngster, oldster or "inbetweenster", new to the sport or an "old hand",at any hunting preserve you're always a welcome guest. . .a hunter among hunters, not a barely tolerated intruder.

2 An Ideal Environment
Managed by experts, the preserve is a natural environment that tests your skills, and those of your fellow sportsmen, under safe, controlled conditions. You hunt huntable land that's a well planned combination of natural and planted cover. And there are often special provisions for beginners and the handicapped.

3 Plenty of High Quality Birds
In addition to its natural population of wild birds, the preserve is restocked regularly with carefully bred top quality game birds to guarantee you shooting opportunities. Go for ring-necked pheasants, bobwhite quail, chukar, Huns, mallards, doves--even wild turkey-- depending on locale.

4 Well Trained Dogs
Most preserves provide thoroughlytrained dogs that add to the satisfaction--and success--of the hunt. Many preserves allow you to shoot over your own dog, if you prefer, and offer first rate dog boarding facilities.

5 Longer Seasons/No Limits
Hunt at your convenience. For a half day, a weekend, or more. Preserves offer longer seasons. (In some states you can hunt all year!) With no bag limits on many species.

6 All Types of Hunting
Why be confined to field hunting only? Many preserves offer a variety of hunts, from pass shooting from blinds to European style driven shoots and even the excitement of a 1,200 bird tower release.

7 An Ideal Training Site
If you set out to design a perfect place to train hunters, you'd end up with a preserve: near ideal setting, guaranteed birds, expert guides and quality dogs. What better place to introduce a beginner--spouse, child, friend or business associate--to shotgun safety and good hunting techniques? Great place to work your dog, too!

8 Shotgunning (And lots of it!)
More than half of the nation's hunting preserves offer practice clays. Many have sporting clays. Warm up or end your visit with a skill-sharpening round.

9 Services and Amenities
Preserves pamper their clients with top notch guides and various combinations of services, which often include food, lodging, airport pick-up, licenses, ammo, loaner guns and much, much more.

10 Convenient & Established.
Every state has them. And with well over one thousand preseves operating in the U.S., there's one out there to fit every taste and budget. Most are open to the public. Many offer reasonably priced memberships. Call one today!

A Message Promoting America's Hunting Preserves.

From the Publishers of Black's Wing & Clay "The Shotgunner's Annual Guide To Wing & Clay Shooting"
Black's Wing & Clay ■ PO Box 2029 ■ 43 West Front Street ■ Red Bank, New Jersey 07701 ■ (908) 224-8700

ALABAMA

Aldar Hunting Lodge
PO Box 806, Greenville, AL 36037
(334) 382-9660 Alan or Lorie Gentry
Type Public; **On Site** Clubhouse, Lodging, Meals;
Shoots Field; **Birds** Turkey; **Dogs** Avail/HDW

Arrowhead Lodge
PO Box 711, Butler, AL 36904
(205) 459-2604 David L. Ezell 8:30am-8pm
26 mi. SW of Meridian, MS
Est 1985; **Acres** 8,500; **Hunters/yr** 150; **Type**
Public; **On Site** Clubhouse, Lodging, Meals; **Shoots**
Field; **Birds** Turkey; **Dogs** Avail; **Packages** 2 Days,
1-16 guns

Bent Creek Lodge
PO Box 4267, Jachin, AL 36910
(205) 398-3437 Leo Allen
35 mi. E of Meridian **Est** 1983; **Acres** 30,000;
Type Public; **On Site** Clubhouse, Lodging, Meals;
Shoots Field; **Birds** Quail, Turkey; **Dogs**
Avail/HDW; **Packages** 1/2 Day, 4-12 guns

Bubber Cameron's Shooting Preserve
Rt. 1, Box 144, Aliceville, AL 35442
(205) 455-2420 Bubber Cameron/Rush Cameron
60 mi. SW of Tuscaloosa

Est 1974; **Acres** 2,300; **Type** Public, Corp.; **On**
Site Clubhouse, Lodging, Meals; **Shoots** Field;
Birds Dove, Quail, Snipe; **Dogs** Avail/HDW;
Packages 1 Day, 1-15 guns O NAGA/See Pg. 72

Cedar Ridge Hunting Lodge
1137 Co. Rd. 258, Five Points, AL 36855
(334) 864-0404 Frazier Rudd/David Lowe
Type Public; **On Site** Lodging; **Shoots** Field; **Birds**
Quail, Chukar O NAGA/See Pg. 72

Dixieland Plantation
PO Box 168, Hatchechubbee, AL 36858
(334) 667-7876 Donald Dixon 8 am to 9 pm
25 mi. SW of Columbus, GA
Acres 5,000; **Type** Public; **On Site** Clubhouse,
Lodging, Meals, Clays; **Shoots** Field; **Birds** Dove,
Quail, Turkey; **Dogs** Avail/HDW; **Packages** 1/2
Day, up to 8 guns

Enon Plantation
Rt. 2, Box 275, Midway, AL 36053
(800) 950-1892 Diane & John Rex Gates 9-5
60 mi. SE of Montgomery
Est 1991; **Acres** 10,000; **Type** Public; **On Site**
Clubhouse, Lodging, Meals, Clays; **Shoots** Field;
Birds Quail; **Dogs** Avail; **Packages** 1 Day, 4-6 guns

Greenfield Hunting Preserve
Hwy. 4 West, PO Box 174, Pittsview, AL 36867
(334) 855-9118 Rick Cunningham

25 mi. S of Columbus, GA
Est 1987; **Acres** 2,200; **Type** Public; **On Site** Clubhouse, Lodging, Meals, Clays; **Shoots** Field; **Birds** Quail; **Dogs** Avail/HDW; **Packages** 1/2 Day, 2-12 guns

Gunsmoke Kennels

Rt. 2, Box 15, Union Springs, AL 36089
(334) 738-4642 Herb Holmes anytime
40 mi. SE of Montgomery
Est 1987; **Acres** 2,000; **Hunters/yr** 150; **Type** Public; **On Site** Clubhouse, Lodging, Meals; **Shoots** Field; **Birds** Quail, Pheasant, Chukar; **Dogs** Avail/HDW; **Packages** 1/2 Day, 2-6 guns
O NAGA/See Pg. 72
O Brochure Available   O Puppies & Started Dogs
O Trained Gun Dogs   O Professional Training
O Stud Service to Great Hunting Dogs

Limestone Hunting Preserve
Box 227A, Ardmore, AL 35739
(205) 423-6029 Wayne Mitchell after 6pm
12 mi. N of Huntsville
Est 1990; **Acres** 500; **Type** Public; **On Site** Clubhouse; **Shoots** Field; **Birds** Dove, Quail, Pheasant, Chukar, Ducks; **Packages** 1/2 Day, 1-9 guns

Master Rack Lodge
Rt. 1, Box 95-A, Union Springs, AL 36089
(334) 738-4000 Tony/Becky Gibson 8-5
50 mi. SE of Montgomery
Est 1986; **Acres** 10,000; **Hunters/yr** 200; **Type** Public; **On Site** Clubhouse, Lodging, Meals; **Shoots** Field; **Birds** Quail, Turkey; **Dogs** Avail; **Packages** 3 Days, 5-20 guns

Parches Cove Hunting Preserve
4415 Parches Cove Rd., Union Grove, AL 35175
(205) 498-2447 Houston Lindsay After 6pm
20 mi. SE of Huntsville
Est 1988; **Acres** 3,000; **Type** Public; **On Site** Clubhouse, Lodging, Meals, Clays; **Shoots** Field, Blinds; **Birds** Dove, Quail, Pheasant; **Dogs** Avail/HDW; **Packages** 1/2 Day, 1-12 guns

Portland Landing Hunting Reserve
3201 International Dr., Selma, AL 36703
(334) 875-2414 Phil Blake 7am-3:30pm, CT
40 mi. W of Montgomery
Est 1987; **Acres** 14,000; **Type** Public; **On Site** Clubhouse, Lodging, Meals; **Shoots** Field; **Birds** Turkey; **Packages** 3 Days, 1-8 guns

Rhodes Quail Hunting Preserve
105 N. Dobson Ave., Bay Minette, AL 36507
(334) 937-7580 Virgil V. Rhodes, Jr. Noon & 5-9pm
30 mi. NE of Mobile

Est 1984; **Acres** 140; **Hunters/yr** 150; **Type** Public; **Shoots** Field; **Birds** Quail; **Dogs** Avail/HDW; **Packages** 1/2 Day, 1-6 guns
O NAGA/See Pg. 72

Rockfence Station
4388 Chmbrs. Cty Rd. 160, Lafayette, AL 36862
(800) 627-2606 Branch McClendon Su-S, 8am-5pm
95 mi. SW of Atlanta
Est 1986; **Acres** 7,000; **Hunters/yr** 1,000; **Type** Public; **On Site** Clubhouse, Lodging, Meals, Clays; **Shoots** Field, Tower; **Birds** Dove, Quail, Pheasant, Chukar, Turkey; **Dogs** Avail/HDW; **Packages** 1/2 Day, 2-16 guns O NAGA/See Pg. 72

Selwood Hunting Preserve
706 Selwood Rd., Alpine, AL 35014
(800) 522-0403 O.V. Hill 8-5
35 mi. E of Birmingham
Est 1984; **Acres** 1,000; **Type** Public, Member/Avail, Corp.; **On Site** Clubhouse, Meals, Clays; **Shoots** Field; **Birds** Quail; **Dogs** Avail; **Packages** 1/2 Day, 2-10 guns O NAGA/See Pg. 72

Westervelt Hunting Lodge

PO Box 2362, Tuscaloosa, AL 35403
(205) 556-3909 John C. Roboski
50 mi. SW of Tuscaloosa
Acres 14,000; **Type** Public; **On Site** Clubhouse, Lodging, Meals, Clays; **Shoots** Field; **Birds** Dove, Quail, Turkey; **Dogs** Avail; **Packages** 1/2 Day, 1-12 guns

See Our Ads Pgs. 261 & Across

Wheeler Station Hunting Preserve
PO Box 594, Courtland, AL 35618
(205) 637-8770 A.G. Simmons Nights
35 mi. W of Huntsville
Est 1989; **Acres** 13,000; **Type** Public; **On Site** Clubhouse, Lodging, Meals, Clays; **Shoots** Field; **Birds** Dove, Quail, Pheasant; **Dogs** Avail/HDW; **Packages** 1/2 Day, 2-25 guns

White Oak Plantation

5215 B County Road 10, Tuskegee, AL 36083
(334) 727-9258 Robert Pitman Anytime
45 mi. E of Montgomery
Est 1983; **Acres** 16,000; **Hunters/yr** 500; **Type** Public; **On Site** Clubhouse, Lodging, Meals, Clays; **Shoots** Field; **Birds** Quail, Turkey, Ducks; **Dogs** Avail/HDW; **Packages** 1/2 Day, 2-16 guns

Shooting Instruction Available - See Pg. 154

Wood's Gamebird Farm
18247 US Hwy. 231, Titus, AL 36080

Alabama's Westervelt Lodge: Where Business Is A Pleasure

Entertaining clients and attending meetings are facts of business life, endured or enjoyed according to circumstance. But few meetings, conferences or seminars are likely to be as memorable—or as productive—as those held at Westervelt Lodge in Alabama.

A Favored Destination

Indeed, Westervelt, with its elegant lodge, sumptuous meals and abundance of unsurpassed hunting and fishing, is a favorite among those who plan meetings, and those who attend them.

The reasons for this popularity are quickly apparent. Sprawling across 22 square miles of lush pine ridges and hardwood bottomlands, pristine lakes and fields of corn and millet, Westervelt offers all the amenities a businessperson treasures, all the excitement an avid sportsman craves.

As a meeting site/conference center, the Lodge specializes in accommodating groups of 26 or fewer overnight. But larger groups can be pampered here, too, at day meetings conducted in hotel-like comfort; or overnight with a combination of on-site and off-site lodging. Westervelt offers all the modern conveniences and equipment—including audio/visual—that contribute to a successful business gathering and its "away from it all" environment adds sharp focus to a meeting.

True Southern Style Quail Hunting

It's the lure of a wide variety of outdoor sports, however, that makes Westervelt a unique experience. But it's quail hunting, according to John Roboski, Westervelt's sales manager, that is favored by many of Westervelt's corporate guests. "Especially those eager to impress an important client or prospect," he quickly adds.

With hard-flying birds, good honest dog work, and a guide who puts you where the opportunities are, a Westervelt quail hunt begins with a plantation-style breakfast, continues in quiet, comfortable mule-drawn wagons that convey you to the action, and ends in a flurry of native wild quail and peak-quality, flight conditioned birds released throughout the year.

Westervelt's main lodge—the perfect place for mixing business and pleasure .

Wild turkeys thrive at Westervelt, too, and the Lodge's spring turkey hunts are world renowned. Accompanied by your personal guide—a certified master turkey hunter—you'll hunt the wily tom in your own assigned 1,000-acre area. The Lodge is also noted for our three-day school for turkey hunters, a concentrated course that sharpens your skills at calling, camouflage and shooting.

Westervelt is prime habitat for trophy whitetail deer, which modern wildlife management techniques maintain at ideal population levels. So when guests apply their skills to this demanding sport—each in his own exclusive hunting area—the chances of success are high.

Other Attractions?

Westervelt abounds in activities and services. Among them: Bowhunting and bowhunting schools. Dove shoots. A rifle range. A professionally designed sporting clays course. The finest bass fishing in Alabama. Equipment rentals, licensing and game processing. And food so good it lends new fame to Southern cooking.

For business...for sport...for the happy combination of both...you're sure to be thrilled when you visit Alabama's pride, Westervelt Lodge. To find out how you can take advantage of the South's pre-eminent sporting/business entertainment location write John Roboski at PO Box 2362, Tuscaloosa, AL 35403; or call him at (205) 556-3909.

(334) 567-7711 Thomas E. Wood 7 to 10 pm
20 mi. N of Montgomery
Est 1982; **Acres** 400; **Hunters/yr** 250; **Type**
Public; **Shoots** Field; **Birds** Quail, Pheasant; **Dogs**
Avail/HDW; **Packages** 1/2 Day, 4-5 guns
○ NAGA/See Pg. 72

ALASKA

Afognak Wilderness Lodge
, Seal Bay, AK 99697
(800) 478-6442 Roy & Shannon Randall
Est 1973; **Type** Public; **On Site** Clubhouse,
Lodging, Meals; **Birds** Ducks

Alaska Trophy Hunting & Fishing
PO Box 220247, Anchorage, AK 99522
(907) 344-8589 Mel Gillis After 3pm
550 mi. SW of Anchorage
Est 1983; **Acres** 500,000; **Hunters/yr** 45; **Type**
Public; **On Site** Clubhouse, Lodging, Meals; **Shoots**
Field;   ; **Dogs** Avail/HDW; **Packages** 6 Days, 2-10
guns

Eagles' Ridge Ranch
HC62, Box 5780, Delta Junction, AK 99737
(907) 895-4329 Mike Crouch
100 mi. S of Fairbanks
Est 1994; **Acres** 2,800; **Hunters/yr** 100; **Type**
Public; **On Site** Clubhouse, Meals, Clays; **Shoots**
Field, Blinds; **Birds** Quail, Ruffed Grouse, Pheasant,
Chukar, Turkey, Sharp Tail Grouse, Ducks, Geese;
Dogs Avail/HDW; **Packages** 1/2 Day, 1-10 guns
○ NAGA/See Pg. 72
Fish for salmon and wingshoot–all on the same
trip? Yep, can fish kings, reds & silvers one day,
hunt pheasant, quail, grouse and chukar the next.
Alaska's unusual April 1- October 31 wingshooting
season makes it possible. Add Geese & Cranes to
the quarry beginning September 1. Interested?
Just give us a call at Eagles' Ridge Ranch and we'll
put together a complete package specifically designed for you and your party. (Sporting Clays
shooters see our listing in the Alaska Clays section.)
Call today!

ARIZONA

Arizona Hunt Club
PO Box 1021, Mayer, AZ 86333
(520) 632-7709 Kent Henry 8am-5pm
65 mi. N of Phoenix
Est 1986; **Acres** 730; **Type** Public, Member/Avail,
Corp.; **On Site** Clubhouse, Clays; **Shoots** Field,
Driven; **Birds** Dove, Quail, Pheasant, Chukar; **Dogs**
Avail/HDW; **Packages** 1/2 Day, 1-4 guns
○ NAGA/See Pg. 72

Long Meadow Preserve
HC30, Box 1030, Prescott, AZ 86301
(602) 778-9563 Jim Puntenney 8-6 daily

20 mi. NW of Prescott
Est 1982; **Acres** 6,000; **Type** Public, Member/Avail,
Corp.; **On Site** Clubhouse, Lodging, Clays; **Shoots**
Field, Blinds; **Birds** Dove, Quail, Pheasant, Chukar,
Snipe, Ducks, Geese; **Dogs** Avail/HDW; **Packages**
1/2 Day, 1-16 guns ○ NAGA/See Pg. 72

River's Edge Sporting Retreat
HC1, Box 742, Benson, AZ 85602
(520) 212-4868 Norm Crawford Anytime
70 mi. SE of Tucson
Est 1989; **Acres** 700; **Type** Public, Member/Avail,
Corp.; **On Site** Clubhouse, Lodging, Meals, Clays;
Shoots Field; **Birds** Dove, Quail, Pheasant, Chukar;
Dogs Avail/HDW; **Packages** 1/2 Day
○ NAGA/See Pg. 72

Wingshooters Lodge
1305 N. Grand Ave., Suite 20-122, Nogales, AZ 85621
Ruben Del Castillo 011-52-641-49934 (Mexico)
from Obregon, Mexico
Est 1972; **Hunters/yr** 300; **Type** Public; **On Site**
Clubhouse, Lodging, Meals; **Shoots** Field, Blinds,
Boat; **Birds** Dove, Quail, Turkey, Ducks; **Packages** 2
Days, 2-12 guns

ARKANSAS

Black Dog Hunting Club
4232 US Hwy. 165E, England, AR 72046
(501) 275-3733 Todd/Gwen Brittain before 8pm
15 mi. S of Stuttgart
Type Public; **On Site** Clubhouse, Lodging, Meals;
Shoots Field, Blinds, Boat; **Birds** Dove, Ducks, Geese;
Dogs Avail/HDW

Casscoe Quail
Hunting Club
PO Box 215, Stuttgart, AR 72160
(501) 673-7283 Carroll Evans Daytime
17 mi. E of Stuttgart
Est 1993; **Acres** 140; **Hunters/yr** 50; **Type**
Public; **On Site** Clubhouse, Lodging; **Shoots** Field;
Birds Quail; **Dogs** Avail/HDW; **Packages** 1/2 Day,
2-8 guns

Cordell Game Birds, Inc.
Rt. 2, Box 334-1, Malvern, AR 72104
(501) 332-3215 John Fowler
50 mi. SW of Little Rock
Acres 750; **Type** Public, Member/Avail, Corp.; **On
Site** Clubhouse, Meals, Clays; **Shoots** Field; **Birds**
Quail, Pheasant; **Dogs** Avail/HDW; **Packages** 1/2
Day, 1-40 guns

Drake's Landing
Rt. 1, Box 177, Tichnor, AR 72166
(800) 548-4389 Tommy or Chris Turner
45 mi. SE of Stuttgart
Type Public; **On Site** Clubhouse, Lodging, Meals,
Clays; **Shoots** Blinds; **Birds** Ducks; **Dogs** HDW
○ NAGA/See Pg. 72

Ducks and Ducks, Inc.

Rt. 1, Box 169-C, Lake City, AR 72437
(800) 822-3825 Dutch Noe Anytime
3.5 mi. S of Jonesboro
Acres 1,100; **Hunters/yr** 400; **Type** Public; **On Site** Clubhouse, Lodging, Meals; **Shoots** Field, Blinds, Boat; **Birds** Pheasant, Turkey, Ducks; **Dogs** Avail/HDW; **Packages** 2 Days, 2-24 guns
O NAGA/See Pg. 72

Farelly Lake Duck Club

PO Box 629, DeWitt, AR 72042
(501) 946-3853 Lester McKinley
6 mi. S of DeWitt
Acres 10; **Hunters/yr** 300; **Type** Public; **Shoots** Blinds; **Birds** Ducks; **Dogs** Avail

Foothills Quail Farm & Hunting Preserve

265 Water Valley Rd., Imboden, AR 72434
(501) 892-8906 Tim or Pam Miller Anytime
155 mi. NE of Little Rock
Est 1983; **Acres** 280; **Type** Public, Member/Avail, Corp.; **On Site** Clubhouse, Lodging, Meals; **Shoots** Field; **Birds** Quail; **Dogs** Avail/HDW; **Packages** 1/2 Day, 1-12 guns

Grandview Plantation

PO Box 201, Columbus, AR 71831
(501) 983-2526 Charles Butler
120 mi. SW of Little Rock
Acres 5,160; **Type** Public, Member/Avail, Corp.; **On Site** Clubhouse, Lodging, Meals, Clays; **Shoots** Field; **Birds** Dove, Quail, Pheasant, Chukar, Ducks; **Dogs** Avail/HDW; **Packages** 1/2 Day

Great Guns

20492 Raceway Rd., Harrisburg, AR 72432
(501) 578-9700 Steve Skillern
60 mi. NW of Memphis, TN
Est 1993; **Acres** 200; **Type** Public; **On Site** Lodging, Meals, Clays; **Shoots** Field, Blinds, Boat; **Birds** Quail, Ducks, Geese; **Dogs** Avail/HDW; **Packages** 1/2 Day, 1-4 guns
O Premier Arkansas Duck Hunting
O Quail Hunting w/Dog & Guide Oct.- Mar.
O In Season Combination Packages: Ducks, Quail, Clays, Food & Lodging
O 60 miles NW of Memphis–Just 1/2 hour from I-55

Greenhead Hunting Club

PO Box 306, Gillett, AR 72055
(501) 548-2365 Danny or Sara Sloate 8am-8pm
90 mi. SE of Little Rock
Est 1986; **Acres** 2,000; **Type** Public; **On Site** Clubhouse, Lodging, Meals; **Shoots** Field, Blinds; **Birds** Ducks; **Dogs** Avail/HDW

Hawk's Range Hunting Club

PO Box 589, Foreman, AR 71836
(501) 542-7350 Paul Hawkins, Jr.
30 mi. W of Texarkana
Est 1990; **Acres** 4,000; **Type** Public; **On Site** Clubhouse, Clays; **Shoots** Field, Blinds, Boat; **Birds** Ducks; **Dogs** Avail/HDW; **Packages** 1 Day, 2-6 guns

Hunting Sports Plus

710 Main St., Ste. E, Blue Springs, MO, Hunting in 7 States inclu, AR
(800) 729-1924 Dan Gasser
Est 1989; **Acres** 200,000; **Type** Public, Member/Avail; **On Site** Clubhouse, Lodging, Meals, Clays; **Shoots** Field, Blinds, Boat; **Birds** Quail, Pheasant, Turkey, Prairie Chicken, Ducks, Geese; **Dogs** Avail/HDW; **Packages** 1 Day, 1-24 guns

Quality Hunting on over 200,000 acres of private farm land in 7 Midwest States–AR, IA, IL, KS, MO, NE, OK. Hunt quail, pheasant, turkey, deer, prairie chicken, ducks and geese. Affordable Midwestern hospitality. Large selection of low cost memberships, daily plans or hunting vacation package hunts. Call today for more information.

Nevada Gamebirds

Rt. 1, Box 171, Buckner, AR 71827
(501) 899-2902 Karl Salb
100 mi. S of Little Rock
Est 1982; **Acres** 1,500; **Hunters/yr** 600; **Type** Public, Corp.; **On Site** Clubhouse, Lodging, Meals, Clays; **Shoots** Field, Tower; **Birds** Quail, Pheasant, Chukar; **Dogs** Avail/HDW; **Packages** 1/2 Day, 1-36 guns

Point Remove WMA, Inc.

PO Box 133, Hattieville, AR 72063
(501) 354-0136 Scott Kaufman 8-4 weekdays
60 mi. NW of Little Rock
Est 1982; **Acres** 3,500; **Type** Member/Avail, Corp.; **On Site** Clubhouse, Lodging, Meals, Clays; **Shoots** Field, Blinds, Boat; **Birds** Dove, Quail, Pheasant, Turkey, Ducks; **Dogs** Avail/HDW

Quail Busters, Inc.

9432 Batesville Rd., Jacksonville, AR 72076
(501) 988-5302 Charles Venus
25 mi. NE of Little Rock
Est 1990; **Acres** 800; **Type** Public; **On Site** Clubhouse, Lodging, Meals; **Shoots** Field; **Birds** Dove, Quail; **Dogs** Avail/HDW; **Packages** 1/2 Day, up to 15 guns O NAGA/See Pg. 72

Quail Mountain Enterprises

811 Hymes, Van Buren, AR 72956
(501) 474-9294 Jerry Friddle
25 mi. N of Ft. Smith
Est 1990; **Acres** 500; **Type** Public; **On Site** Clubhouse, Lodging, Meals, Clays; **Shoots** Field; **Birds** Quail, Pheasant, Chukar; **Dogs** Avail/HDW; **Packages** 1/2 Day, 2-4 guns O NAGA/See Pg. 72

WINGS

Dennis Seidenschwarz
PO Box 151, Ulm, AR 72170
(501) 241-3855 Dennis Seidenschwarz After 6pm
6 mi. NE of Stuttgart
Est 1978; **Acres** 800; **Hunters/yr** 150; **Shoots**
Field, Blinds; **Birds** Ducks; **Dogs** Avail; **Packages**
1/2 Day, 1-7 guns

Trotter Shooting Preserve
PO Box 162, Roe, AR 72134
(501) 241-3318 Wiley L. Lawson After 6pm
60 mi. SE of Little Rock
Est 1987; **Acres** 400; **Hunters/yr** 120; **Type**
Public, Member/Avail; **Shoots** Field; **Birds** Quail;
Dogs Avail/HDW; **Packages** 1/2 Day, 2-6 guns

Waterfowl Flyway, Inc.
PO Box 323, Wynne, AR 72396
(800) 545-5944 Cecil "Shorty" Owens 7am-9pm
65 mi. W of Memphis, TN
Est 1989; **Acres** 8,000; **Type** Public, Corp.; **On**
Site Clubhouse, Lodging, Meals; **Shoots** Field,
Driven, Blinds; **Birds** Ducks, Geese; **Dogs**
Avail/HDW; **Packages** 1 Day, 1-26 guns

White Front Hunting Lodge
Rt. 2, Box 75, Stuttgart, AR 72160
(501) 673-6543 Jerry Maier after 8pm
5 mi. NE of Stuttgart
Est 1984; **Acres** 15,000; **Hunters/yr** 120; **Type**
Public; **On Site** Clubhouse, Lodging, Meals; **Shoots**
Field, Blinds, Boat; **Birds** Ducks, Geese; **Dogs**
Avail/HDW; **Packages** 1/2 Day, 2-16 guns

CALIFORNIA

Antelope Valley
45408 160th St., W., Lancaster, CA 93536
(805) 724-1291 Dave Whiteside
60 mi. N of Los Angeles
Acres 3,500; **Type** Public, Member/Avail, Corp.;
On Site Clubhouse, Meals, Clays; **Shoots** Field,
Tower, Driven, Blinds; **Birds** Dove, Quail, Pheasant,
Turkey, Geese; **Dogs** Avail/HDW; **Packages** 1 Day,
2-35 guns
O Sporting Clays   O Fishing
O Western Style Barbecues O Camping & RV Area
O Special Hunts: Dove & Pheasant Openers

Birds Landing Hunting Preserve
PO Box 5, Birds Landing, CA 94512
(707) 374-5092 Dan Cirillo
60 mi. NE of San Francisco
Est 1987; **Acres** 1,200; **Hunters/yr** 6,000; **Type**
Public, Member/Avail; **On Site** Clubhouse, Meals,
Clays; **Shoots** Field; **Birds** Pheasant, Chukar; **Dogs**
Avail/HDW; **Packages** 1/2 Day, 1-120 guns

Birds of a Feather
Box 3645-Parkfield, San Miguel, CA 93451
(805) 463-2335 Mel or Ruth Taylor 8pm-9:30pm
115 mi. NW of Los Angeles
Est 1990; **Acres** 320; **Type** Public, Member/Avail;
On Site Clays; **Shoots** Field; **Birds** Pheasant,
Chukar; **Dogs** Avail/HDW; **Packages** 1/2 Day, 1-8
guns O NAGA/See Pg. 72

Black Point Game Bird Club
7711 Lakeville Hwy., Petaluma, CA 94954
(707) 763-0076 Mike Sutsos
25 mi. N of San Francisco
Est 1964; **Acres** 1,000; **Type** Member/Avail; **On
Site** Clubhouse, Meals, Clays; **Shoots** Field; **Birds**
Pheasant, Chukar; **Dogs** Avail/HDW

C&L Pheasant Club
1831 Road R, Willows, CA 95988
(916) 934-8805 Lisa Heuschkel
10 mi. SW of Maxwell
Acres 500; **Hunters/yr** 30; **Type** Member/Avail;
Shoots Field; **Birds** Pheasant O NAGA/See Pg. 72

C.C.F. Hunting Club
2005 Alice Ave., Palermo, CA 95968
(916) 894-5555 Peter Rouse
125 mi. N of San Francisco
Est 1952; **Acres** 800; **Type** Member/Avail, Corp.;
On Site Clubhouse; **Shoots** Field; **Birds** Pheasant;
Dogs HDW O NAGA/See Pg. 72

Cahoon Pheasant Club
31249 E. Combs Rd., Escalon, CA 95320
(209) 838-6085 Dave & Patti Cahoon
3 mi. N of Escalon
Est 1990; **Acres** 430; **Hunters/yr** 3,000; **Type**
Public, Member/Avail; **On Site** Clubhouse, Meals;
Shoots Field; **Birds** Pheasant, Chukar, Turkey;
Dogs Avail/HDW; **Packages** 1 Day, 20-50 guns
O NAGA/See Pg. 72

Camanche Hills Hunting Preserve
2951 Curran Rd., Ione, CA 95640
(209) 763-5270 Larry J. Skinner
80 mi. E of San Francisco
Est 1981; **Acres** 1,500; **Type** Public, Member/Avail;
On Site Clubhouse, Lodging, Meals, Clays; **Shoots**
Field, Driven; **Birds** Pheasant, Chukar, Ducks; **Dogs**
Avail/HDW; **Packages** 1 Day

Cameron Outing, Inc.
10411 Old Placerville, #220, Sacramento, CA 95827
(916) 366-0486 Thomas Neutzling
1 mi. SE of Riooco
Acres 1,600; **Hunters/yr** 40; **Type** Member/Avail;
On Site Clubhouse; **Shoots** Blinds; **Birds** Dove,
Pheasant, Ducks, Geese

Camp 5
1230 Arbor Rd., Paso Robles, CA 93446
(805) 237-1201 Craig W. Rossier
Type Public, Member/Avail; **Shoots** Field; **Birds**
Pheasant O NAGA/See Pg. 72

Circle HH
Hunting Preserve
HCR#1, Box 512, Nipton, CA 92364
(702) 642-9405 Fred Hymes/Jessie Hymes 5pm-10pm
84 mi. S of Las Vegas, NV
Est 1988; **Acres** 200; **Hunters/yr** 72; **Type**
Public, Member/Avail, Corp.; **On Site** Clubhouse,
Meals, Clays; **Shoots** Field; **Birds** Dove, Quail,
Pheasant, Chukar, Turkey; **Dogs** Avail/HDW;
Packages 1/2 Day, 1-6 guns O NAGA/See Pg. 72
Circle HH Hunting Preserve is located in unspoiled
country, surrounded by California's East Mojave
Natural Preserve Area just 85 miles south of Las
Vegas, 50 miles west of Laughlin, with interstate
access off I-15 and I-40. We have committed ourselves to provide excellent hunting of pheasant,
chukar and quail on a preserve that incorporates
habitat improvement. An altitude of nearly 5,000
feet presents changing temperatures throughout
the day. The Preserve is set up to accommodate six
(6) hunters per 1/2 day reservation hunt.

Clear Creek Sports Club
3971 Keefer Rd., Chico, CA 95926
(916) 343-9263 Bob or Janet Henman
45 mi. N of Sacramento
Est 1986; **Acres** 1,000; **Type** Public, Member/Avail,
Corp.; **On Site** Clays; **Shoots** Field; **Birds**
Pheasant, Chukar; **Dogs** Avail/HDW; **Packages** 1
Day, 4-60 guns O NAGA/See Pg. 72

Creekside Pheasant Club
Box 3640, Parkfield Rt., San Miguel, CA 93451
(805) 463-2349 Larry Hamilton
115 mi. NW of Los Angeles
Est 1985; **Acres** 800; **Type** Member/Avail; **On
Site** Lodging, Clays; **Shoots** Field, Blinds; **Birds**
Dove, Quail, Pheasant, Chukar, Ducks; **Dogs**
Avail/HDW O NAGA/See Pg. 72

Cummings Valley Hunting Club
25400 Banducci Rd., Tehachapi, CA 93561
(800) 322-4263 Kim Cummings/Christy Ward
125 mi. N of Los Angeles
Est 1854; **Acres** 8,000; **Hunters/yr** 1,000; **Type**
Public, Member/Avail, Corp.; **On Site** Clubhouse,
Lodging, Meals, Clays; **Shoots** Field; **Birds** Dove,
Quail, Pheasant, Chukar, Turkey, Ducks, Geese; **Dogs**
Avail/HDW; **Packages** 1/2 Day, 1-60 guns

Diamond "H"
840 Hinckley Rd., Suite 250, Burlingame, CA 94010
(415) 697-6010 Joe Piazza 10-5
180 mi. NE of San Francisco
Est 1989; **Acres** 30,000; **Type** Public; **On Site**
Clubhouse, Lodging, Meals, Clays; **Shoots** Field;
Birds Quail, Pheasant, Chukar, Huns; **Dogs**
Avail/HDW; **Packages** 1/2 Day, 2-8 guns
See Our Ad Across

The Duck Club
PO Box 323, Richvale, CA 95974
(916) 534-8401 Jack Smith
85 mi. NW of Sacramento
Acres 725; **Type** Public; **On Site** Lodging, Meals;
Shoots Field, Blinds; **Birds** Pheasant, Ducks, Geese;
Dogs Avail; **Packages** 1 Day, 1-24 guns

Duck's Home
3133 Morgan Territory Rd., Clayton, CA 94517
(510) 672-7220 Bob Griffiths
8 mi. SE of Los Banos
Acres 260; **Hunters/yr** 22; **Type** Member/Avail;
Shoots Blinds; **Birds** Ducks, Geese

Fairlee Ranch
1740 Colusa Way, Gridley, CA 95948
(916) 392-7260 Jean Davis
115 mi. NE of San Francisco
Acres 400; **Type** Public; **Shoots** Blinds; **Birds**
Ducks, Geese; **Dogs** Avail; **Packages** 1/2 Day

First in the Field Guide Service
1003 West 2nd St., Alturas, CA 96101
(916) 233-5755 Paul Siegel 5-8pm
10 mi. SE of Altunas
Est 1983; **Acres** 10,000; **Type** Public; **Shoots**
Field, Blinds; **Birds** Ducks, Geese; **Dogs** Avail/HDW;
Packages 1 Day, 4-8 guns

Four Winds Pheasant Club
2806 May Ave., Redondo Beach, CA 90278
(310) 370-2238 Sam Elder
Type Public; **Shoots** Field; **Birds** Quail, Pheasant,
Chukar O NAGA/See Pg. 72

G&G Pheasant Shoot
PO Box 116, Gazelle, CA 96034
(916) 435-2309 John or Dot Giorgi
250 mi. N of Sacramento
Est 1980; **Acres** 750; **Type** Public; **On Site**
Clubhouse; **Shoots** Field; **Birds** Pheasant, Chukar;
Dogs Avail; **Packages** 1/2 Day, 1-20 guns
O NAGA/See Pg. 72

Gabilan Valley
Sportsmans Club
PO Box 1207, Gilroy, CA 95021
(800) 632-HUNT J. Harvey/E. Weis 8-4
35 mi. S of San Jose
Est 1987; **Acres** 360; **Hunters/yr** 3,500; **Type**
Public, Member/Avail, Corp.; **On Site** Clubhouse;
Shoots Field, Blinds; **Birds** Quail, Pheasant, Chukar,
Huns, Ducks; **Dogs** Avail/HDW; **Packages** 1/2 Day,
up to 50 guns O NAGA/See Pg. 72

Gaines Afton Ranch
PO Box 132, Durham, CA 95938
(916) 345-1206 Fred Gaines
35 mi. SW of Chico
Acres 300; **Hunters/yr** 30; **Type** Public,
Member/Avail; **Shoots** Field, Blinds; **Birds** Dove,
Pheasant, Ducks, Geese; **Dogs** Avail

Golden Ram Sportsman Club
840 Hinckley Rd., #250, Burlingame, CA 94010
(415) 692-6670 Nick Tacito/Lou Federico 10-5, M-F
10 mi. NW of Sacramento
Est 1970; **Acres** 3,000; **Hunters/yr** 700; **Type**
Public, Member/Avail, Corp.; **On Site** Clubhouse,
Meals; **Shoots** Field; **Birds** Quail, Pheasant, Chukar,
Huns, Ducks, Geese; **Dogs** Avail/HDW; **Packages**
1/2 Day, 25-50 guns

Guns & Roosters Hunting Preserve
31661 Rd. 160, Visalia, CA 93292
(209) 798-1966 Dave Hamilton After 5pm
45 mi. S of Fresno
Est 1991; **Acres** 1,200; **Hunters/yr** 500; **Type**
Public, Member/Avail, Corp.; **Shoots** Field; **Birds**
Quail, Pheasant, Chukar; **Dogs** Avail/HDW;
Packages 1/2 Day, 2-35 guns ○ NAGA/See Pg. 72

H&H Gun Club
3971 Keefer Rd., Chico, CA 95926
(916) 343-9263 Bob Henman
10 mi. S of Chico
Acres 1,100; **Hunters/yr** 90; **Type** Member/Avail;
On Site Clubhouse; **Shoots** Field; **Birds** Pheasant,
Chukar; **Dogs** Avail

Hastings Island Hunting Preserve
7758 Hastings Island Rd., Rio Vista, CA 94571
(916) 678-3325 Mike & Bonnie Mitchell 8am-4pm
50 mi. E of San Francisco
Est 1969; **Acres** 4,700; **Type** Member/Avail, Corp.;
On Site Clubhouse, Meals, Clays; **Birds** Pheasant;
Dogs Avail/HDW ○ NAGA/See Pg. 72

Hayes Hunting Club
PO Box 1373, Colusa, CA 95932
(916) 473-2952 Sheila or Bob Hayes W-Su, 8am-3pm
60 mi. NW of Sacramento
Est 1986; **Acres** 1,500; **Hunters/yr** 1,000; **Type**
Public, Member/Avail; **Shoots** Field, Blinds; **Birds**
Quail, Pheasant, Chukar, Ducks, Geese; **Dogs** HDW
○ NAGA/See Pg. 72

Knowles Ranch Sporting Clays
PO Box 982, Willows, CA 95988
(916) 934-5595 Clark Knowles 8am-5pm
75 mi. N of Sacramento
Est 1950; **Acres** 1,100; **Hunters/yr** 200; **Type**
Public; **On Site** Clubhouse, Clays; **Shoots** Field,
Blinds; **Birds** Pheasant, Chukar, Ducks, Geese; **Dogs**
Avail/HDW; **Packages** 1 Day, 2-16 guns

Lakeview Farms, Inc.
5490 Riosa Rd. West, Lincoln, CA 95648
(916) 633-9112 Donald Norris
20 mi. NE of Sacramento
Acres 1,000; **Hunters/yr** 350; **Type** Public,
Member/Avail; **On Site** Clubhouse, Lodging;
Shoots Field, Blinds; **Birds** Dove, Quail, Pheasant,
Chukar, Ducks, Geese; **Dogs** Avail ○ NAGA/See Pg. 72

Lone Pine Pheasant Club
430 N. Main St., Lone Pine, CA 93545
(619) 876-4595 Bruce Ivey 8am-3pm
200 mi. N of Los Angeles
Est 1988; **Acres** 1,000; **Hunters/yr** 500; **Type**
Public, Member/Avail; **On Site** Clubhouse, Meals;
Shoots Field; **Birds** Quail, Pheasant, Chukar; **Dogs**
Avail/HDW; **Packages** 1 Day, 1-12 guns
○ NAGA/See Pg. 72

Moffatt Road Gun Club
700 Vine St., Menlo Park, CA 94025
(415) 281-2180 Giulio Accornero
60 mi. SE of San Jose
Acres 426; **Hunters/yr** 22; **Type** Member/Avail;
On Site Clubhouse, Lodging, Meals; **Shoots** Field,
Blinds; **Birds** Pheasant, Ducks, Geese

WINGS

Napa Shooting Preserve
3195 Wooden Valley Rd., Napa, CA 94558
(707) 255-5095 Dennis Rapp
Type Member/Avail; **On Site** Clays; **Shoots** Field;
Birds Quail, Pheasant, Chukar, Ducks
O NAGA/See Pg. 72

Oak Creek Ranch
PO Box 808, Jamul, CA 91935
(619) 468-3857 Ken Davis/Don Cooper
35 mi. SE of San Diego
Acres 80; **Hunters/yr** 300; **Type** Public,
Member/Avail; **On Site** Clubhouse, Lodging, Clays;
Shoots Field; **Birds** Quail, Pheasant, Chukar; **Dogs** Avail

Pheasant Flats
Box 311, Dayton, CA 82836
(307) 655-9638 Robert Mock
60 mi. S of Medford, OR
Est 1993; **Type** Member/Avail; **Shoots** Field;
Birds Pheasant   O NAGA/See Pg. 72

Potter Valley Sportsmen's Club
6950 Hwy. 20, Ukiah, CA 95482
(707) 485-5188 Jim Guntly Morning or evening
50 mi. N of Santa Rosa
Est 1991; **Acres** 5,500; **Type** Public, Member/Avail;
On Site Clays; **Shoots** Field; **Birds** Dove, Quail,
Pheasant, Chukar, Turkey; **Dogs** Avail/HDW
O NAGA/See Pg. 72

Mike Raahauge
Shooting Enterprises
5800 Bluff St., Norco, CA 91760
(909) 735-2361 Mike Raahauge
35 mi. E of Los Angeles
Acres 2,000; **Hunters/yr** 400; **Type** Public,
Member/Avail, Corp.; **On Site** Clubhouse, Clays;
Shoots Field, Blinds; **Birds** Pheasant, Chukar, Ducks;
Dogs Avail/HDW; **Packages** 1 Day, 1-50 guns
O NAGA/See Pg. 72
See Our Ad Below

Red Bank Ale & Quail Gamebird Club
PO Box 627, Red Bluff, CA 96080
(916) 527-6199 Jim or Melodi Byrne 8am-5pm
170 mi. N of San Francisco
Est 1976; **Acres** 5,000; **Hunters/yr** 1,500; **Type**
Public; **On Site** Clubhouse, Lodging, Meals, Clays;
Shoots Field, Blinds; **Birds** Dove, Quail, Pheasant,
Turkey, Ducks, Geese; **Dogs** Avail/HDW; **Packages**
1/2 Day, up to 22 guns O NAGA/See Pg. 72

Reibar Hunt Club
7480 Domingos Rd., Lompoc, CA 93436
(805) 736-5309 Glady Istre
6 mi. W of Boellton
Acres 150; **Hunters/yr** 65; **Type** Public,
Member/Avail; **On Site** Clubhouse, Meals; **Shoots**
Field; **Birds** Dove, Pheasant, Chukar; **Dogs** Avail

Rock Springs Ranch

11000 Old Hernandez Rd., Paicines, CA 95043
(800) 209-5175 Ken Range
75 mi. S of San Jose
Est 1994; Acres 16,000; Type Public; On Site Lodging, Meals, Clays; Shoots Field, Driven; Birds Dove, Quail, Pheasant, Chukar, Huns, Turkey; Dogs Avail/HDW; Packages 1/2 Day, 1-24 guns ○ NAGA/See Pg. 72

See Our Ad Pg. 267

Romero Ranch

PO Box 517, Likely, CA 96116
(916) 233-4938 Chris or Rich Hamel 10-5
125 mi. N of Reno, NV   .
Est 1989; Acres 1,680; Hunters/yr 300; Type Public; On Site Clubhouse, Lodging, Meals, Clays; Shoots Field, Tower, Blinds; Birds Pheasant, Chukar, Ducks, Geese; Dogs Avail/HDW; Packages 1/2 Day, 1-16 guns ○ NAGA/See Pg. 72

Silverado Hunt Club

50 Hegenberger Loop, Oakland, CA 94621
(510) 568-4831 Greg Lyons
Type Public; Shoots Field; Birds Quail, Pheasant, Huns ○ NAGA/See Pg. 72

Stillwater Sportsmen's Club

PO Box 49, Palo Cedro, CA 96073
(916) 365-6845 Doyle & Laurel Besecker
160 mi. N of Sacramento
Acres 1,500; Type Member/Avail, Corp.; Shoots Field, Blinds; Birds Dove, Quail, Pheasant, Chukar, Huns, Turkey, Ducks; Dogs Avail/HDW

Suisun Marsh Hunting Preserve

PO Box 698, Fairfield, CA 94533
(707) 425-4158 Barney Bryan
40 mi. NW of San Francisco
Est 1972; Acres 1,200; Type Member/Avail; On Site Clubhouse; Shoots Field; Birds Pheasant; Dogs Avail/HDW

Timbuctoo Sporting Estate

PO Box 357, Smartville, CA 95977
(916) 639-2200 Sam Craig
50 mi. NW of Sacramento
Est 1988; Acres 6,000; Hunters/yr 500; Type Public; On Site Clubhouse, Meals, Clays; Shoots Field, Driven, Blinds, Boat; Birds Quail, Chukar, Huns, Turkey, Ducks; Dogs Avail/HDW ○ NAGA/See Pg. 72

Valley Quail Hunting Club

PO Box 942, Lathrop, CA 95330
(209) 239-2576 John & Robin Herrera
5 mi. from Lathrop
Acres 2,000; Type Member/Avail; On Site Lodging, Meals; Shoots Field; Birds Dove, Quail, Pheasant, Chukar, Ducks; Dogs Avail

West Valley Sportsmen Club

PO Box 257, Gustine, CA 95322
(209) 634-1547 Robert Kloepfer 8-5
80 mi. SE of San Francisco

Est 1987; Acres 1,875; Type Public, Member/Avail, Corp.; On Site Clubhouse, Meals, Clays; Shoots Field; Birds Quail, Pheasant, Chukar; Dogs Avail/HDW ○ NAGA/See Pg. 72

Wild Wings Preserve

PO Box 572, Sutter, CA 95982
(916) 755-0524
160 mi. N of San Francisco
Acres 4,000; Type Public, Member/Avail; On Site Clubhouse; Shoots Field; Birds Quail, Pheasant, Chukar, Huns, Turkey; Dogs Avail/HDW; Packages 1 Day ○ NAGA/See Pg. 72

Wilderness Unlimited

20954 Corsair Blvd., Hayward, CA 94545
(510) 785-4868 Rick Copeland Anytime
from 30+ Calif. Hunting Facilities
Acres 125,000; Hunters/yr 1,000; Type Member/Avail, Corp.; On Site Clubhouse; Shoots Field, Blinds; Birds Dove, Quail, Pheasant, Ducks, Geese; Dogs HDW

Wildlife Game Birds

2787 Pleasant Grove Rd., Pleasant Grove, CA 95668
(916) 656-2544 George Zents 8am-4pm
25 mi. NE of Sacramento
Est 1984; Acres 700; Hunters/yr 1,500; Type Public, Member/Avail, Corp.; On Site Clubhouse, Meals; Shoots Field; Birds Pheasant, Chukar; Dogs Avail/HDW; Packages 1/2 Day, 1-40 guns

Willow Run Hunting Preserve

Rt. 1, Box 530, Glenn, CA 95943
(916) 934-3407 Chris Beane/Gary Alves
Type Public, Member/Avail; Shoots Field; Birds Quail, Pheasant ○ NAGA/See Pg. 72

COLORADO

A J Gamebirds

1251 Paddock, Elizabeth, CO 80107
(303) 646-0229 Jerry William
On Site Clays; Shoots Field; Birds Quail, Pheasant, Chukar ○ NAGA/See Pg. 72

Bang-A-Away Gun Club & Kennels

17629 Weld County Rd. 5, Berthoud, CO 80513
(303) 535-4538 Bill Voigt 8am-4pm
40 mi. N of Denver
Est 1972; Acres 300; Type Member/Ltd, Corp.; On Site Clubhouse, Clays; Shoots Field; Birds Pheasant, Chukar; Dogs Avail/HDW; Packages 1/2 Day, 1-4 guns ○ NAGA/See Pg. 72

Chipeta Guest Ranch

1938 Hwy. 133, Paonia, CO 81428
(800) 521-4055 Larry Mantz
70 mi. W of Aspen
Est 1991; Acres 4,000; Hunters/yr 50; Type Public; On Site Clubhouse, Lodging, Meals, Clays; Shoots Driven; Birds Pheasant, Turkey, Sage Grouse, Ducks, Geese; Dogs HDW

WINGS

Colorado Pheasant Association
RD53, Kiowa, CO 80117
(303) 693-1065 Clay Blyth 9-4pm
35 mi. SE of Denver
Est 1989; Acres 840; Hunters/yr 500; Type
Public, Member/Avail; On Site Clubhouse, Meals,
Clays; Shoots Field, Blinds; Birds Dove, Quail,
Pheasant, Chukar, Ducks; Dogs Avail/HDW;
Packages 1/2 Day, 3-15 guns

Four Directions
Upland Game Club
2690 O Rd., Hotchkiss, CO 81419
(303) 835-3658 Charlie & Marilee Gilman
60 mi. SW of Aspen
Est 1982; Acres 2,000; Hunters/yr 400; Type
Public, Member/Avail; On Site Clubhouse, Lodging,
Meals; Shoots Field; Birds Quail, Pheasant, Chukar;
Dogs Avail/HDW; Packages 1 Day, 2-6 guns
○ NAGA/See Pg. 72

Fox II
6085 S. Iola Way, Englewood, CO 80111
(303) 290-6236 Ron Wilson
35 mi. N of Denver Est 1990; Acres 330; Type
Member/Avail; On Site Clubhouse; Shoots Field,
Blinds; Birds Quail, Pheasant, Chukar, Ducks, Geese;
Dogs HDW; Packages 1/2 Day, up to 30 guns

Go-Fer Broke Gun Club
19995 Myers Rd., Colorado Springs, CO 80928
(719) 683-3807 Jerry Shatley
Est 1985; Acres 200; Type Public; Shoots Field;
Birds Quail, Pheasant, Chukar; Packages 1/2 Day,
2-10 guns ○ NAGA/See Pg. 72

High Country Game Birds
33300 County Rd. 25, Elizabeth, CO 80107
(303) 646-3315 Todd Pederson 7 am - 7 pm

35 mi. SE of Denver Est 1985; Acres 200;
Hunters/yr 1,150; Type Public, Member/Avail,
Corp.; On Site Clubhouse, Lodging, Meals, Clays;
Shoots Field; Birds Dove, Quail, Pheasant, Chukar,
Huns, Ducks, Geese; Dogs Avail/HDW; Packages
1/2 Day, 2-5 guns ○ NAGA/See Pg. 72

Indian Bend Ranch
1619 N. Greenwood St., Pueblo, CO 81003
(719) 544-7115 Charles Bedard
28 mi. E of Pueblo
Acres 402; Hunters/yr 50; Type Public,
Member/Avail; On Site Clubhouse; Shoots Field,
Blinds; Birds Dove, Quail, Pheasant, Ducks, Geese;
Dogs Avail ○ NAGA/See Pg. 72

Jalmor Sportsmen's Club
47939 Elbert Co. Rd. 22, Ramah, CO 80832
(719) 541-2854 Al & Jane Morse
100 mi. SE of Denver
Est 1980; Acres 300; Type Public, Member/Avail,
Corp.; On Site Clubhouse, Clays; Shoots Field;
Birds Dove, Pheasant, Chukar, Ducks; Dogs
Avail/HDW ○ NAGA/See Pg. 72

Mt. Blanca
Game Bird & Trout
PO Box 236, Blanca, CO 81123
(719) 379-3825 Bill Binnian 7am - 7pm
150 mi. SW of Colorado Springs
Est 1987; Acres 6,000; Hunters/yr 1,000; Type
Public, Member/Avail, Corp.; On Site Clubhouse,
Lodging, Meals, Clays; Shoots Field, Driven, Blinds;
Birds Dove, Quail, Pheasant, Chukar, Ducks, Geese;
Dogs Avail/HDW; Packages 1/2 Day, 1-16 guns
○ NAGA/See Pg. 72
Shooting Instruction Available - See Pg. 157
See Our Ads Below & Across

Mt. Blanca *GAME BIRD & TROUT, INC.* : One of the Best
by Stuart Williams

Wild encounters
One of the best shooting preserves in the Southwest is Mt.
Blanca Game Bird & Trout near Blanca, Colorado. Here you can hunt gamebirds on
some 6,000 acres of the shaggiest cover I've
ever seen on a private facility. What you get
is the kind of hunting that you typically encounter in the wild—big gaudy rooster
pheasants exploding from dense patches of
willows and coveys of quail and chukar
bursting from scrubby tangles and weedy
stream banks.
Manager Bill Binnian and his crew raise
and release birds throughout the year. They
also entertain guests on Mt. Blanca's own

championship sporting
clays course and guide them to quality fly-
fishing on local waters.

Favorite packages
One of Binnian's favorite packages is $500
for two shooters, which includes a day of
hunting, sporting clays, meals and one
night's stay in Mt. Blanca's handsome 6,300-
square-foot lodge. Contact Binnian at
719-379-3825; Fax: (719) 379-3589.
[A longer version of this article first appeared
in *Sporting Classics* magazine.]

Picketwire Pheasant & Quail
30835 RD 13 - PO Box 88, Las Animas, CO 81054
(719) 456-0813 Rudy Estrada Evenings
125 mi. SE of Colorado Springs
Est 1989; Acres 1,500; Hunters/yr 200; Type
Public, Member/Avail, Corp.; On Site Lodging;
Shoots Field, Blinds; Birds Dove, Quail, Pheasant,
Chukar, Huns, Ducks, Geese; Dogs HDW; Packages
1/2 Day, 1-30 guns

Quail Run Hunting Preserve
PO Box 693, Nucla, CO 81424
(303) 864-7985 Byron or Tandie Morgan Evenings
100 mi. S of Grand Junction
Est 1992; Acres 840; Type Public; Shoots Field;
Birds Quail, Pheasant, Chukar; Dogs Avail/HDW;
Packages 1/2 Day, 2-10 guns   O NAGA/See Pg. 72

R&T Gun Club
9912 Downing, Thornton, CO 80229
(303) 452-4777 Dave Redell 8-5
100 mi. NE of Denver
Est 1974; Acres 15,000; Type Public,
Member/Avail, Corp.; On Site Clubhouse, Lodging,
Meals, Clays; Shoots Field, Driven, Blinds; Birds
Dove, Quail, Pheasant, Chukar, Turkey, Ducks, Geese;
Dogs Avail/HDW; Packages 1/2 Day, up to 30 guns

Renegade Gun Club, Inc.
3570 Weld County Road #23, Fort Lupton, CO 80621
(303) 857-6000 Dick Chikuma
30 mi. N of Denver
Est 1974; Acres 400; Type Member/Avail; On
Site Clubhouse, Meals, Clays; Shoots Field, Blinds;
Birds Dove, Quail, Pheasant, Chukar, Turkey, Ducks,
Geese; Dogs Avail/HDW; Packages 1/2 Day

Robinson Game Brids L.L.C.
217 E. 37th St., Durango, CO 81301
(303) 259-4673 Rob Robinson
Shoots Field; Birds Quail, Pheasant, Chukar
O NAGA/See Pg. 72

Rocky Mountain Roosters
PO Box 10164, Colorado Springs, CO 80932
(719) 635-3257 Brett M. Axton 9-6
35 mi. E of Colorado Springs
Est 1985; Acres 8,000; Hunters/yr 2,000; Type
Public, Member/Avail, Corp.; On Site Clubhouse,
Meals, Clays; Shoots Field, Blinds; Birds Dove,
Quail, Pheasant, Chukar, Turkey, Ducks, Geese; Dogs
Avail/HDW; Packages 1/2 Day, 1-60 guns
O NAGA/See Pg. 72
See Our Ad Below

Rocky Mountain Training Kennel
18519 WCR3, Berthoud, CO 80513
(303) 535-4600 Bobbie Christensen Evenings
30 mi. N of Denver
Est 1960; **Acres** 160; **Type** Public; **Shoots** Field;
Birds Quail, Pheasant, Chukar; **Dogs** Avail/HDW;
Packages 1/2 Day

Rocky Ridge Hunting Club
633 Gait Circle, Ft. Collins, CO 80524
(303) 221-4868 Michael Q. Moreng 7 am - 9 pm
55 mi. N of Denver
Est 1984; **Acres** 700; **Hunters/yr** 300; **Type**
Public, Member/Avail, Corp.; **On Site** Clubhouse,
Clays; **Shoots** Field, Tower, Driven, Blinds; **Birds**
Quail, Pheasant, Chukar, Ducks, Geese; **Dogs**
Avail/HDW; **Packages** 1/2 Day, 1-12 guns
○ NAGA/See Pg. 72

Rogers Country
32259 Road 13, Lamar, CO 81052
(719) 336-2124 Jim Rogers
100 mi. E of Pueblo
Acres 3,000; **Type** Public, Member/Avail; **Shoots**
Field; **Birds** Dove, Quail, Pheasant, Chukar, Ducks;
Dogs HDW; **Packages** 1 Day, up to 1 guns

SPORTHAVEN, LTD.
50500 E. 72nd Ave., Bennett, CO 80102
(303) 644-3030 David A. Lincoln, Jr. 8am-5pm
20 mi. NE of Denver
Est 1993; **Acres** 400; **Type** Public, Member/Avail;
On Site Clubhouse, Clays; **Shoots** Field, Tower;
Birds Dove, Quail, Pheasant, Chukar; **Dogs**
Avail/HDW; **Packages** 1/2 Day, 1-8 guns

Stillwater Gun Club
& Upland Game Preserve
16588 Telluride St., Brighton, CO 80601
(303) 659-8665 Mark Beam After 6pm, MST
15 mi. N of Denver
Est 1983; **Acres** 10,000; **Type** Public,
Member/Avail; **Shoots** Field, Blinds; **Birds** Quail,
Pheasant, Ducks, Geese; **Dogs** Avail/HDW;
Packages 1/2 Day
Colorado is one of the hottest goose and duck
hunting areas in North America. Thousands upon
thousands of waterfowl winter here along
Colorado's front range. I invite you to join us for
some of the finest decoy gunning for waterfowl
one can experience. We're Colorado's only licensed
outfitter specializing in waterfowl hunting.

Valhalla-Bijou Inc.
450 Co. Rd. 133, Bennett, CO 80102
(303) 644-4300 Steve Barnhardt
20 mi. E of Denver
Est 1989; **Acres** 2,000; **Hunters/yr** 900; **Type**
Member/Avail; **On Site** Clubhouse, Meals, Clays;
Shoots Field; **Birds** Dove, Pheasant, Chukar; **Dogs**
Avail/HDW; **Packages** 1/2 Day, 1-20 guns
○ NAGA/See Pg. 72

Western
Wildlife Adventure
6255 WCR 74, Windsor, CO 80550
(303) 686-5210 Tim Brough Mornings or T/Th pm
50 mi. N of Denver
Est 1985; **Acres** 1,000; **Hunters/yr** 500; **Type**
Public, Member/Avail, Corp.; **On Site** Clubhouse,
Clays; **Shoots** Field; **Birds** Dove, Quail, Pheasant,
Chukar, Huns; **Dogs** Avail/HDW; **Packages** 1/2
Day, 1-25 guns ○ NAGA/See Pg. 72

CONNECTICUT

Connecticut
Woods & Water
6 Larson St., Waterford, CT 06385
(203) 442-6343 Capt. Dan Wood
100 mi. NE of New York
Est 1982; **Acres** 5,000; **Hunters/yr** 300; **Type**
Public; **Shoots** Blinds, Boat; **Birds** Ducks, Geese;
Dogs Avail/HDW; **Packages** 1/2 Day, 1-12 guns
○ Hunting License   ○ Bird Processing
○ Kennel Bird Dogs   ○ Brochure Available✷
○ Gunsmith Service   ○ Fishing
○ Factory Ammunition

Markover Game Farm & Hunting Preserve
719 Cook Hill Rd., Danielson, CT 06239
(203) 774-4116 Norman Olsen
75 mi. SW of Boston, MA
Est 1917; **Acres** 300; **Type** Public; **On Site**
Clubhouse, Meals, Clays; **Shoots** Field; **Birds**
Pheasant, Chukar, Ducks; **Dogs** Avail/HDW;
Packages 1/2 Day ○ NAGA/See Pg. 72

Millstream Preserve
130 Lake Rd., Columbia, CT 06237
(203) 228-1657 Jay Lembo
25 mi. E of Hartford
Acres 300; **Type** Public; **Shoots** Field; **Birds**
Pheasant; **Dogs** Avail/HDW; **Packages** 1/2 Day

Venwood Lake Hunting Preserve
541 Rt. 148, Killingworth, CT 06419
(203) 663-2655 Donald or Diane Venuti Anytime
20 mi. E of New Haven   **Est** 1994; **Acres** 350;
Type Public; **Shoots** Field; **Birds** Quail, Pheasant;
Dogs Avail/HDW ○ NAGA/See Pg. 72

DELAWARE

Owens Station Sporting Clays
RD1, Box 101-C, Greenwood, DE 19950
(302) 349-4478 Bill Wolter/Ernie Bennett
75 mi. E of Washington, DC
Est 1979; **Acres** 600; **Type** Public, Member/Avail,
Corp.; **On Site** Clubhouse, Lodging, Meals, Clays;
Shoots Field, Tower, Blinds, Boat; **Birds** Dove, Quail,
Pheasant, Chukar, Huns, Ducks, Geese; **Dogs**
Avail/HDW; **Packages** 1/2 Day, 1-4 guns

WINGS

FLORIDA

Bienville Plantation
White Springs, FL
(912) 755-0705 Steve Barras
60 mi. W of Jacksonville, FL
Est 1994; **Acres** 3,500; **Type** Public, Member/Avail,
Corp.; **On Site** Clubhouse; **Shoots** Field, Blinds;
Birds Dove, Quail, Ducks; **Dogs** Avail/HDW;
Packages 1/2 Day
See Our Ad Left

Big D Plantation
Rt. 2, Box 294-C, Lake City, FL 32055
(904) 752-0594 Charlie Parnell
30 mi. N of Gainesville
Est 1988; **Acres** 1,400; **Hunters/yr** 750; **Type**
Public, Member/Avail; **On Site** Clubhouse, Meals,
Clays; **Shoots** Field; **Birds** Dove, Quail, Pheasant,
Chukar; **Dogs** Avail/HDW; **Packages** 1/2 Day, up
to 16 guns O NAGA/See Pg. 72
See Our Ad Across Right

Bonnette Hunting
& Fishing Club
5309 Hood Rd., Palm Beach Gardens, FL 33418
(407) 626-5180 Alix Bonnette
10 mi. N of West Palm Beach
Est 1961; **Acres** 3,200; **Hunters/yr** 500; **Type**
Member/Avail; **On Site** Clubhouse, Lodging, Meals,
Clays; **Shoots** Field; **Birds** Quail, Pheasant, Chukar;
Dogs Avail/HDW; **Packages** 1/2 Day, up to 20 guns
O Kennel Bird Dogs   O Sporting Clays
O Gourmet Meals   O Brochure Available
O Quality Clubhouse   O Rifle & Pistol Range

Richard Davis, Jr. Hunting Preserve
2114 NW 15th Ave., Gainesville, FL 32605
(800) 541-1015 R.B. Davis
7 mi. S of Jasper
Acres 300; **Hunters/yr** 30; **Type** Public; **Shoots**
Field; **Birds** Quail; **Dogs** Avail

Dixie Wildlife Safaris
5001 Hwy. 630 East, Frostproof, FL 33843
(813) 696-3300 Mike Acreman
48 mi. S of Orlando
Est 1980; **Acres** 5,000; **Type** Public; **On Site**
Clubhouse, Meals; **Shoots** Field; **Birds** Quail;
Dogs Avail/HDW; **Packages** 1/2 Day

Donna Plantation
Rt. 6, Box 61, Quincy, FL 32351
(904) 875-1615 Al Hartman
1 mi. NE of Quincy
Type Public; **On Site** Lodging; **Shoots** Field, Blinds;
Birds Turkey, Ducks

Double WW Hunting Preserve

1200 Cassat Ave., Jacksonville, FL 32205
(904) 783-2626 Wayne Scarborough, Jr.
12 mi. SW of Jacksonville
Est 1988; **Acres** 700; **Hunters/yr** 400; **Type**
Public; **On Site** Clubhouse, Meals, Clays; **Shoots**
Field; **Birds** Dove, Quail; **Dogs** Avail/HDW;
Packages 1/2 Day, 1-8 guns
○ Airport Pickup   ○ Brochure Available
○ Family Run Business   ○ 2 Sporting Clays Courses
○ NSCA Certified Instructor
○ Corporate Hunts Our Specialty
○ Southern Home Cooking   ○No License Required

El Rancho Hunting Preserve

Rt. 2, Box 25, Chipley, FL 32428
(904) 638-1353 Rex T. Yates
65 mi. W of Tallahassee
Est 1956; Acres 320; Hunters/yr 400; Type Public;
On Site Clubhouse, Lodging, Meals; Shoots Blinds,
Boat; Birds Ducks; Dogs Avail/HDW; Packages 1
Day, up to 20 guns

Everglades Adventures

3280 4th Ave., NE, Naples, FL 33964
(813) 455-5910 Mark Clemons 8am-9pm
20 mi. E of Naples
Est 1989; Acres 4,000; Hunters/yr 300; Type
Public, Member/Avail, Corp.; On Site Meals; Shoots
Field, Tower; Birds Dove, Quail, Turkey, Snipe, Ducks;
Dogs Avail/HDW; Packages 1/2 Day, 2-6 guns
○ NAGA/See Pg. 72
○ Brochure Available
○ Custom Vehicles
EVERGLADES ADVENTURES–Featuring bountiful
and beautiful wild Osceola turkeys native only to
Florida. Your hunt day begins at pre-dawn with
you traveling with your guide to the selected site
where he has roosted gobblers located.
At first light we call the gobbler in using various
combinations of calls. We shoot only in range customer selected trophy toms. This hunt lasts from
daylight until 1 pm and is available during the
spring season only–$300 per day, per person or
$750 for a three day hunt. You may enjoy a full
day in the field at your option, by joining the guide
the evening before to assist in stalking **[cont'd>]**

gobblers to the roost for the next day hunt. Our quail hunts consists of riding on custom vehicles while watching the bird dogs working. Once they go on point we get off the vehicle and in position to shoot. 1/2 day hunts, including drinks, guides, vehicles and dogs–$375 for two guns, $550 for three. Our dove shoots are over large prepared fields planted with millet and cover-shot once per week on Sunday afternoon for 3-4 hours–we can handle 50 or more hunters at $65 per gun.

Fin and Feather Guide Service
6551 12th Ave., NW, Naples, FL 33999
(813) 597-6020 Steve Ambrose 5 to 9 pm
30 mi. SW of Okeechobee
Est 1981; **Acres** 23,000; Hunters/yr 300; Type Public, Member/Avail, Corp.; On Site Clubhouse, Lodging, Meals; Shoots Field; Birds Dove, Quail, Turkey, Snipe, Ducks; Dogs Avail/HDW; Packages 1/2 Day, 1-25 guns
○ Brochure Available
○ Southwest Florida's Best Dove & Quail Hunts
○ Wild Boar, Deer & Turkey
○ Bass Fishing   ○ Excellent Guides & Dogs

Fisheating Creek Hunting Preserve
PO Box 117, Palmdale, FL 33944
(813) 675-4117 David Austin 9 to 5 pm
100 mi. S of Orlando
Est 1988; **Acres** 25,000; Hunters/yr 150; Type Public; On Site Clubhouse, Lodging; Shoots Field; Birds Quail, Turkey; Dogs Avail/HDW; Packages 2 Days, 1-9 guns

Fox Creek Plantation
PO Box 39, Monticello, FL 32344
(904) 997-8063 Jimmy Thurman 8am-5pm
32 mi. NE of Tallahassee
Est 1987; **Acres** 600; Hunters/yr 200; Type Public; On Site Clubhouse, Lodging, Meals, Clays; Shoots Field; Birds Quail, Pheasant; Dogs Avail/HDW; Packages 1/2 Day, 1-6 guns

Golden Leaf Plantation
Rt. 2, Box 160, Greenville, FL 32331
(904) 948-7891 Joe Reams, Jr.
42 mi. E of Tallahassee
Est 1988; **Acres** 1,000; On Site Clubhouse, Lodging, Meals, Clays; Shoots Field; Birds Dove, Quail; Dogs Avail/HDW; Packages 1/2 Day, 1-8 guns

Golden Pheasant
Hunting Preserve
15701 Co. Rd. 675, Parrish, FL 34219
(813) 776-3114 Jim Allen, Mgr. Anytime
25 mi. N of Sarasota
Est 1992; **Acres** 629; Type Public, Member/Avail, Corp.; On Site Clubhouse, Clays; Shoots Field, Blinds; Birds Quail, Pheasant, Chukar, Turkey, Ducks; Dogs Avail/HDW; Packages 1 Day, 1-12 guns
○ NAGA/See Pg. 72
○ Bird Processing   ○ Sporting Clays
○ Shooting Instruction   ○ Hunting Jeeps
○ Train Bird Dogs   ○ Loaner Guns
○ Brochure Available   ○ Factory Ammunition

Hardy Bradford Shooting Preserve
2114 NW 15th Ave., Gainesville, FL 32601
(800) 541-1015 R.B. Davis 9 to 5
85 mi. W of Jacksonville Est 1992; **Acres** 300; Type Public, Member/Avail; Shoots Field; Birds Dove, Quail; Dogs Avail/HDW; Packages 1/2 Day, 1-6 guns

Iron-Wood Preserve
PO Box 1949, Lake City, FL 32056
(904) 963-3508 Nickey Jackson
60 mi. W of Jacksonville
Est 1985; **Acres** 2,000; Hunters/yr 80; Type Public, Member/Avail; On Site Clubhouse, Lodging, Meals, Clays; Birds Quail; Dogs Avail/HDW; Packages 1/2 Day, up to 5 guns

J&R Hunting Preserve
8400 S.W. Fox Brown Rd., Indiantown, FL 34956
(407) 597-4757 Joe or Liz O'Bannon 7am-9pm
30 mi. W of West Palm Beach
Est 1984; **Acres** 5,000; Hunters/yr 300; Type Public, Member/Avail, Corp.; On Site Clubhouse, Lodging, Meals, Clays; Shoots Field, Tower; Birds Dove, Quail, Pheasant, Chukar, Turkey, Sage Grouse, Snipe; Dogs Avail/HDW; Packages 1/2 Day, 1-8 guns ○ NAGA/See Pg. 72
○ Sporting Clays   ○ Brochure Available
○ 30 Miles NW of West Palm Beach
○ Axis Deer Hunting & Exotics ○ Processing Available

Jennings Bluff
Hunting Preserve

Rt. 2, Box 4250, Jennings, FL 32053
(904) 938-5555 Troy Tolbert 9 to 5
65 mi. NE of Tallahassee
Est 1989; **Acres** 1,800; Hunters/yr 504; Type Public, Member/Avail; On Site Clubhouse, Lodging, Meals, Clays; Shoots Field, Tower; Birds Quail, Pheasant; Dogs Avail/HDW; Packages 1/2 Day, 3-16 guns ○ NAGA/See Pg. 72
○ Hunting License   ○ Airport Pickup
○ Brochure Available   ○ Quality Clubhouse
○ Family Run Business

Niblack Farms
PO Box 206, Fort White, FL 32038
(904) 497-1577 Joel Niblack
Shoots Field; **Birds** Quail, Pheasant, Chukar
○ NAGA/See Pg. 72

Plantation Outfitters
14 N. Cone St., Quincy, FL 32351
(904) 575-1260 David A. Avant, III Evenings
35 mi. NW of Tallahassee
Est 1823; **Acres** 3,000; **Hunters/yr** 300; **Type**
Public, Member/Avail; **On Site** Clubhouse, Lodging,
Meals, Clays; **Shoots** Field, Driven, Blinds; **Birds**
Dove, Quail, Pheas., Chukar, Turkey, Snipe, Ducks;
Dogs Avail/HDW; **Packages** 1/2 Day ○ NAGA/SPg. 72

R.C.M. Farms
Rt. 3, Box 418C, Havana, FL 32333
(904) 539-4535 Tuck Munroe
On Site Lodging, Clays; **Shoots** Field; **Birds** Quail,
Pheasant, Chukar, Turkey ○ NAGA/See Pg. 72

H.D. Ryals Preserve
PO Box 1867, Punta Gorda, FL 33950
(813) 639-3656 Jim Kelly 6pm-9pm
25 mi. N of Ft. Myers
Est 1952; **Acres** 12,000; **Hunters/yr** 400; **Type**
Public, Member/Avail; **On Site** Meals; **Shoots** Field;
Birds Dove, Quail, Snipe, Ducks; **Dogs** Avail;
Packages 1 Day, 2-4 guns

Sid's Hunting Preserve
Rt. 7, Box 600, Chipley, FL 32428
(904) 638-0781 Sid Snell 9 to 5
138 mi. W of Tallahassee
Est 1990; **Acres** 400; **Type** Public; **On Site**
Clubhouse, Lodging, Meals, Clays; **Shoots** Field;
Birds Quail; **Dogs** Avail/HDW; **Packages** 1/2 Day

Two Rivers Ranch
40 Ranch Rd., Thonotosassa, FL 33592
(813) 986-5788 Janet Turkovics 9-5
10 mi. NE of Tampa
Acres 17,000; **Type** Public; **On Site** Clubhouse,
Lodging; **Shoots** Field; **Birds** Dove, Turkey; **Dogs** Avail

Wingshooters
PO Box 980, LaBelle, FL 33935
(813) 693-2549 Don Teston
30 mi. E of Ft. Myers
Acres 4,000; **Type** Public, Member/Avail; **On Site**
Clubhouse, Lodging, Meals; **Birds** Quail, Turkey,
Snipe; **Dogs** Avail

GEORGIA

Ashburn Hill
Hunting Preserve, Inc.
PO Box 128, Moultrie, GA 31776
(912) 985-1507 F.R. Pidcock, III 8:30am-4:30pm
60 mi. NE of Tallahassee
Est 1968; **Acres** 5,000; **Hunters/yr** 400; **Type**
Public; **On Site** Clubhouse, Lodging, Meals, Clays;
Shoots Field; **Birds** Quail; **Dogs** Avail/HDW;
Packages 1 Day, 1-24 guns

Barksdale
Bobwhite
Plantation
Cochran, GA

Barksdale
Bobwhite Plantation
Rt.4, Longstreet Rd., P.O. Box 851, Cochran, GA
31014
(912) 934-6916 Ronnie Wright FAX: (912) 934-0877
35 mi. S of Macon
Est 1991; **Acres** 2,200; **Type** Public; **On Site**
Clubhouse, Meals, Clays; **Shoots** Field; **Birds** Quail,
Pheasant, Chukar; **Dogs** Avail/HDW; **Packages** 1/2
Day, 2-24 guns ○ NAGA/See Pg. 72
○ Sporting Clays, Skeet, 5-Stand
  Shooting Instruction Available
○ Res/Non-Resident Hunting License Provided
  Gun Rental & Ammunition Available
○ Corporate Packages
  Field Transportation & Trained Dogs
○ Birds Cleaned - No Charge
○ Deer Hunting   ○ Lodging
○ Brochure/Video Available
See Our Ad Pg. 280

Bevy Burst Hunting Preserve
Rt. 2, Box 245, Edison, GA 31746
(800) 447-9389 Kathy Gray 9am-5pm
40 mi. SW of Albany
Est 1991; **Acres** 2,500; **Type** Public; **On Site**
Clubhouse, Lodging, Meals, Clays; **Shoots** Field;
Birds Dove, Quail; **Dogs** Avail/HDW; **Packages** 1/2
Day, 1-10 guns

WINGS

Bienville Plantation

1158 Oakcliff Road, Macon, GA 32211
(912) 755-0705 Steve Barras
60 mi. W of Jacksonville, FL
Est 1994; **Acres** 19,000; **Type** Public,
Member/Avail, Corp.; **On Site** Clubhouse, Lodging,
Meals, Clays; **Shoots** Field, Blinds, Boat; **Birds**
Dove, Quail, Ducks; **Dogs** Avail/HDW; **Packages**
1/2 Day, 1-20 guns
See Our Ad Pg. 276

Big Red Oak Plantation

PO Box 247, Gay, GA 30218
(706) 538-6870 Arthur Estes 8am-10pm
50 mi. S of Atlanta
Est 1976; **Acres** 3,500; **Hunters/yr** 2,000; **Type**
Public, Member/Avail, Corp.; **On Site** Clubhouse,
Lodging, Meals, Clays; **Shoots** Field; **Birds** Dove,
Quail, Pheasant, Chukar, Turkey; **Dogs** Avail/HDW;
Packages 1/2 Day, 2-12 guns

○ Family Run Business   ○ Great Home Cooking
○ Fish for Bass & Bream   ○ Professionally Trained Dogs
○ 45 min./Atlanta Airport

Boggy Pond Plantation

1084 Lanier Rd., Moultrie, GA 31768
(912) 985-5395 Mackie Dekle 9-7
55 mi. NE of Tallahassee, FL
Est 1983; **Acres** 3,000; **Hunters/yr** 250; **Type**
Public; **On Site** Clubhouse, Lodging, Meals, Clays;
Shoots Field; **Birds** Dove, Quail, Pheasant, Chukar;
Dogs Avail/HDW; **Packages** 1/2 Day, 2-14 guns

Boll Weevil Plantation
4264 Thompson Bridge Rd., Waynesboro, GA 30830
(706) 554-6227 Al McClain M-F, 9-5
35 mi. S of Augusta
Est 1987; **Acres** 6,191; **Type** Public; **On Site**
Clubhouse, Lodging, Meals, Clays; **Shoots** Field;
Birds Dove, Quail, Turkey; **Dogs** Avail; **Packages**
1/2 Day, 1-27 guns ○ NAGA/See Pg. 72

Burge Plantation
Rt. 1, Morehouse Rd., Mansfield, GA 30255
(706) 787-5152 A.G. Morehouse
45 mi. SE of Atlanta
Est 1982; **Acres** 1,000; **Type** Member/Ltd; **On**
Site Clubhouse, Lodging, Meals, Clays; **Shoots** Field,
Driven; **Birds** Dove, Quail, Pheasant, Turkey, Ducks;
Dogs Avail/HDW; **Packages** 1/2 Day
○ NAGA/See Pg. 72

Burnt Pine Plantation

2941 Little River Rd., Madison, GA 30650
(706) 342-7202 Steve Spears
60 mi. E of Atlanta
Est 1973; **Acres** 7,000; **Hunters/yr** 2,000; **Type**
Public, Member/Avail; **On Site** Clubhouse, Lodging,
Meals, Clays; **Shoots** Field, Tower, Driven; **Birds**
Dove, Quail, Pheasant, Chukar, Turkey, Ducks; **Dogs**
Avail/HDW; **Packages** 1/2 Day, 1-25 guns
○ NAGA/See Pg. 72
See Our Ad Across

Chokee Hunting Preserve
186 Philema Rd., Leesburg, GA 31763
(912) 759-9303 Calvin Watson
Birds Quail, Pheasant, Turkey, Ducks

Come Away Plantation
3739 N. Elam Church Rd., NW, Norwood, GA 30821
(706) 465-3292 Jodie McWhorter 8am-6pm
100 mi. E of Atlanta
Est 1985; **Acres** 4,000; **Hunters/yr** 200; **Type**
Public; **On Site** Clubhouse, Lodging, Meals, Clays;
Shoots Field; **Birds** Quail, Turkey; **Dogs**
Avail/HDW; **Packages** 1/2 Day, 3-12 guns
○ NAGA/See Pg. 72

Copperhead Kennels
1202 Old Adgateville Rd., Hillsboro, GA 31038
(706) 468-8368 David Bentley
Shoots Field; **Birds** Quail, Pheasant ○ NAGA/See Pg. 72

BURNT PINE PLANTATION...
New, Different, Diverse—Better!
by Aaron Pass

Burnt Pine Plantation, near historic Madison, Georgia, is now operating under new management, but that's not all that is new and different. Burnt Pine has been well known as the South's premier trophy whitetail hunting plantation for 20 years, but new programs have developed the bird-hunting/wing-shooting potential to that same high level. The game resource base has been deepened and the quality, quantity and variety of shooting have been greatly expanded.

In other words, there is more to shoot, more to do and more traditional sporting fun to be had at the "new" Burnt Pine than ever before.

Enhanced quail shooting in a natural and "classic" quail hunting setting.

Choose the challenge

Quail management activities and shooting areas have been increased and enlarged. Quail habitat is carefully managed, burned and planted in quail food crops, including grain and native wild food plants, to provide enhanced quail shooting in a natural and "classic" quail hunting setting. The various quail courses are classed by "difficulty factor" so that the individual bird hunter can choose just how challenging and sporty he wants his quail shooting to be. Natural production in natural cover is augmented by birds stocked early in the season to provide well-acclimated, strong-flying game birds until season's end. The plantation kennel is stocked with stylish, well-trained bird dogs assuring the high-class dog work associated with quality quail hunting. Every effort is made by the Burnt Pine staff to preserve and provide the traditional style and amenities of Old South quail hunting.

Pheasant and chukar partridge shooting also are available. When hunted over pointing dogs, these two strong-flying species provide a different and very exciting bird hunting challenge.

Continental shoots

The Continental Shoot is a new and very special wing shooting experience now offered at Burnt Pine Plantation. The "Continental" affords the unique experience and social esthetics of European driven game shooting at a fraction of the cost of trans-Atlantic air fare. Duplicating the driven pheasant shoots of Britain and the red-legged partridge shooting of Spain, gunners take high incomers from a series of shooting butts just as upper-class European sportsmen have done for decades. Ideally suited for group entertainment, the Continental Shoot is a fast-paced adventure in world-class wing shooting.

Waterfowling is Burnt Pine's newest and most ambitious venture. The focus is on decoyed ducks shot from a blind in the classic manner. Well-set decoy spreads, expert callers and trained retrievers provide high-quality waterfowling in the grand manner of old-time duck hunting with limits to match.

Of course, the Burnt Pine deer hunting program remains first rate. Two decades of trophy management have resulted in a quality deer herd significantly superior to that commonly found on over-shot public land. Private land and controlled access provide an un-crowded and safe deer hunting experience. This is fair-chase, fair-chance hunting for wild whitetails with a better than average chance for a real trophy buck.

Clays and fishing

More shotgun shooting opportunity is provided by expanded clay target facilities. The existing trap range has been aug-

The lodge is comfortable and spacious. And no, you don't have to "dress" for dinner.

mented by a unique Crazy Quail range and a 20-bird Quail Walk that no one has yet run straight on their first (or second) attempt. Great recreational shooting in themselves, the clay birds also offer "Top Gun" tie-breakers for hunting buddies who have scored equally well in the game fields.

With this much shooting potential, it is possible that a Burnt Pine guest might become temporarily burned out on burned powder. Should that occur, bass fishing offers a first-rate angling option. Eleven ponds are well stocked with big largemouth bass, feisty bluegills and tasty catfish and you have to really work at not filling your stringer. Fly fisherman take notice -- these classic shallow-water farm ponds offer the ideal environment for serious topwater bass bugging.

The Burnt Pine lodge and guest cabins have been completely renovated and expanded to luxurious standards. The main lodge now provides 5,000 square feet and includes a fully equipped game room and well-stocked bar for after-hunt relaxation. Burnt Pine's longstanding reputation for great food remains unchanged except that the traditional hearty home cooking now shares the gastronomic spotlight with gourmet dining and fine wines.

Obviously, with such a diverse resource base and variety of facilities, Burnt Pine Plantation has a lot to offer. Whether one wants to focus on one species or try a bit of everything, customized agendas are easily arranged. Special events, such as the Continental Shoot, are fast-paced and exciting. A mixed program including a morning duck shoot and an afternoon quail hunt (with a hearty lunch and maybe a siesta in

the middle) are more leisurely. The emphasis is on individual service and attention to detail. The atmosphere is low-key and relaxed. The shooting is good, the food is good and the beds are soft. Bagging a good time is the goal and rat racing is not allowed. A genteel "sporting weekend in the country" is the Burnt Pine product line.

From complimentary morning coffee served with your wake-up call to after dinner drinks and a good cigar, Burnt Pine Plantation is dedicated to providing a quality shooting, excellent food, comfortable facilities and relaxed "good old days" hunting experience to modern sportsmen.

Burnt Pine Plantation Shooting Programs

BIRD SHOOTING — Season, Oct. 1-Mar. Preserve License provided by Burnt Pine Plantation.

QUAIL — Full day (16 Birds) $339; half day (8 birds) $199. Additional birds $6.95 each.

PHEASANT/CHUKAR (w/dogs) — Half days (8 pheasant/10 chukar) $210. Additional birds, pheasant $14.99/chukar $9.75.

CONTINENTAL/DRIVEN PHEASANT SHOOT — 15 birds released per gun. Shooting from butts, European style. Including lunch and apres hunt refreshments, $235 per gun. Six public hunts per season; private parties accommodated.

DUCK — Two guns per blind, limit 10 ducks. (shooters must have a valid Federal Migratory Bird Stamp) $250 per gun.

DEER — Georgia seasons and licensing requirements apply. Numerous options and hunting packages, including archery and either sex hunting from mid-September through 1 January. High-success parent/child deer hunts are a specialty. Write for details. Also spring wild turkey and feral hog hunting, write for details.

Except as noted, prices do not include lodging/meals. Ammunition and rental firearms are available. Located just over one hour east of Atlanta, GA, limo service to Atlanta airport is available.

CONTACT:
BURNT PINE PLANTATION, 2941 Little River Road, Madison, GA 30650. Phone: (706) 342-7202. FAX (706) 342-2170.

Covey Rise Plantation, Inc.
Rt. 1, Box 30, Camilla, GA 31730
(912) 336-5413 Robin Singletary
60 mi. N of Tallahassee
Acres 3,500; **Type** Public; **On Site** Clubhouse,
Lodging, Meals; **Shoots** Field; **Birds** Dove, Quail;
Dogs Avail/HDW; **Packages** 1 Day, 2-6 guns

Dogwood Hunting Preserve
376 Grainey Rd., Cairo, GA 31728
(912) 872-3508 Sidney Gainey 7am-11pm
25 mi. N of Tallahassee
Est 1987; **Acres** 1,500; **Hunters/yr** 350; **Type**
Public, Member/Avail; **On Site** Clubhouse, Lodging,
Meals, Clays; **Shoots** Field, Tower, Driven; **Birds**
Dove, Quail, Pheasant, Chukar, Turkey; **Dogs**
Avail/HDW; **Packages** 1/2 Day, 2-9 guns

DOGWOOD PLANTATION

Hunting Preserve, Inc.

1409 Hwy. 42 South, McDonough, GA 30253
(404) 957-7005 Bill Pullin (404) 229-8284 9-5
28 mi. S of Atlanta
Est 1989; **Acres** 1,000; **Type** Public; **On Site**
Clubhouse, Lodging, Meals; **Shoots** Field, Tower;
Birds Quail, Pheasant; **Dogs** Avail/HDW; **Packages**
1/2 Day, 2-10 guns   O NAGA/See Pg. 72
O Airport Pickup   O Loaner Guns
O Family Run Business   O Brochure & Video Available
O Tower Shoots Available for up to 25 Guns

Flint River Hunting, Inc.
385 Killian Rd., Suite A, Lilburn, GA 30247
(404) 564-4826 J.M. Tierney
45 mi. SW of Macon
Est 1990; **Acres** 1,500; **Type** Public, Member/Avail,
Corp.; **On Site** Lodging, Meals; **Shoots** Field;
Birds Dove, Quail, Pheasant, Chukar, Turkey; **Dogs**
Avail/HDW; **Packages** 1/2 Day

Good Hope Plantation

Rt. 1, Box 1175, Naylor, GA 31641
(912) 482-2240 Margie Young
12 mi. E of Valdosta
Est 1994; **Acres** 2,000; **Type** Public; **On Site**
Clubhouse, Lodging, Meals, Clays; **Shoots** Field;
Birds Quail; **Dogs** Avail/HDW

See Our Ad Below

Hog Liver
Quail Shooting Preserve
2863 Hog Liver Rd., Carrollton, GA 30117
(404) 834-6296 Harold Hendrix 8am-9pm
40 mi. W of Atlanta
Est 1987; **Acres** 475; **Type** Public; **On Site**
Clubhouse, Lodging, Meals, Clays; **Shoots** Field;
Birds Quail, Pheasant; **Dogs** Avail/HDW; **Packages**
1/2 Day, 2-16 guns   O NAGA/See Pg. 72
O Airport Pickup   O Bird Processing
O Loaner Guns   O 45 Minutes from Atlanta
O Umbrella Hunting License: In-state & Out-of-state

WINGS

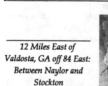

Live Oak Plantation
Rt. 2, Box 308, Adel, GA 31620
(800) 682-4868 Cecil S. Harrell 9am-5pm, M-F
45 mi. SE of Valdosta
Est 1987; **Acres** 2,000; **Hunters/yr** 800; **Type**
Public; **On Site** Clubhouse, Lodging, Meals, Clays;
Shoots Field; **Birds** Quail, Pheasant; **Dogs**
Avail/HDW; **Packages** 1/2 Day, 2-16 guns
See Our Ads Below & Pg. 9

Marsh Hunting Preserve
3079 Metts Rd., Statesboro, GA 30458
(912) 587-6211 Windel Marsh 9 am to 12 pm
50 mi. NW of Savannah
Est 1960; **Acres** 600; **Hunters/yr** 1,000; **Type**
Member/Avail, Corp.; **On Site** Clubhouse, Lodging,
Meals, Clays; **Shoots** Field; **Birds** Dove, Quail;
Dogs Avail/HDW; **Packages** 1/2 Day, up to 12 guns

Llewellin's Point
Hunting Preserve & Kennel
4897 Salem Rd., Pine Mountain, GA 31822
(800) 636-9819 Floyd Clements
70 mi. S of Atlanta
Est 1952; **Acres** 1,100; **Type** Public, Member/Avail;
On Site Clubhouse, Lodging, Meals, Clays; **Shoots**
Field; **Birds** Quail, Pheasant, Chukar; **Dogs**
Avail/HDW; **Packages** 1/2 Day, 1-35 guns
○ NAGA/See Pg. 72
See Our Ad Across & In Georgia CLAYS

Millcreek Hunting Preserve, Inc.
PO Box 131, Rincon, GA 31326
(912) 826-4968 William Exley/Jesse 9-5
15 mi. N of Savannah
Est 1992; **Acres** 8,000; **Type** Public, Member/Avail,
Corp.; **On Site** Clubhouse, Lodging, Meals, Clays;
Shoots Field; **Birds** Dove, Quail, Turkey; **Dogs**
Avail/HDW; **Packages** 1/2 Day, 1-20 guns

Mountain Creek Quail
Farm Hunting Preserve
121 Barker Rd., Molena, GA 30258
(706) 495-5894 Tony Benefield
55 mi. S of Atlanta
Est 1986; **Acres** 1,000; **Hunters/yr** 500; **Type**
Public, Member/Avail, Corp.; **On Site** Clubhouse,
Lodging, Meals; **Shoots** Field; **Birds** Dove, Quail,
Woodcock, Pheasant, Chukar, Turkey, Snipe, Ducks;
Dogs Avail/HDW; **Packages** 1/2 Day, 1-12 guns
Tired of paying outrageous prices for mediocre
hunting? Come to Mountain Creek, where the
hunting's twice as good but the price is half that of
nearby "prestige" locations. Our experienced
guides and well-trained Brittanys will show you
what Quail hunting in Georgia is supposed to be
like. Guided hunts for parties of 2 or more are our
specialty. Dog training, too! Call for info and reservations. LESS THAN 1 HOUR FROM ATLANTA!

Myrtlewood Hunting/Sporting Clays
PO Box 199, Thomasville, GA 31799
(912) 228-0987 Bob or John
35 mi. NE of Tallahassee
Est 1988; **Acres** 3,300; **Type** Public; **On Site**
Clubhouse, Lodging, Meals, Clays; **Shoots** Field;
Birds Quail; **Dogs** Avail
On site clubhouse, 3 lodges, meals available, 1/2
day and full day quail hunts with trained dogs and
guides, Sporting Clays. Specializing in corporate

groups. Brochure available upon request. Myrtlewood offers field Quail hunting on 1000 acres of
beautiful South Georgia high pine country, you'll
hunt with trained dogs, professional guides and
rigs. Myrtlewood also offers one of the areas most
challenging Sporting Clays courses. Trophy deer
hunting and premier bass fishing are also available.
Myrtlewood's spacious course and large clubhouse
is especially convenient to accommodate corporate
groups up to 80. Run by great ol' southern boys,
Myrtlewood is a place for every sportsman.

Camilla, GA
(904) 561-1230 Tanya Gibbens 8:30am-5:00pm
60 mi. N of Tallahassee in Southwest Georgia
Est 1989; **Acres** 1,600; **Hunters/yr** 500; **Type**
Public; **On Site** Clubhouse, Lodging, Meals; **Shoots**
Field; **Birds** Dove, Quail, Pheasant, Chukar; **Dogs**
Avail/HDW; **Packages** 1/2 Day, 2-8 guns
○ Hunting License   ○ Airport Pickup
○ Bird Processing   ○ Kennel Bird Dogs
○ Deer Hunting   ○ Gourmet Meals
○ Hunting Jeeps   ○ Loaner Guns
○ Fishing   ○ Factory Ammunition
○ Private Bedrooms   ○ Beautiful Lodge

Ochlocknee Plantation
PO Box 423, Sylvester, GA 31791
(912) 776-1122 Todd Ford
20 mi. SE of Albany
Acres 2,500; **Hunters/yr** 700; **Type** Public,
Member/Avail; **On Site** Clubhouse, Lodging, Meals,
Clays; **Shoots** Field; **Birds** Dove, Quail; **Dogs** Avail

Quail Hunting in the traditional manner for the Serious Sportsman in the Heart of the Georgia Quail Belt

Exclusive Hunting Privileges
Peak Season November 15 - March 1

255 Kimbrel Road • Colquitt GA, 31737 • 912-758-6602 • Fax 912-758-6608

Partridge Point Hunt Club
PO Box 15241, Savannah, GA 31416
(912) 354-2020 Tony Calandra After 6pm
55 mi. from Savannah
Est 1987; **Acres** 944; **Hunters/yr** 700; **Type**
Public, Member/Avail, Corp.; **Shoots** Field; **Birds**
Dove, Quail, Pheasant; **Dogs** Avail/HDW; **Packages**
1/2 Day, 2-8 guns

Pear Tree Farm
6730 Seven Island Rd., Madison, GA 30650
(706) 342-3017 James Patrick 9-5
60 mi. E of Atlanta **Est** 1994; **Acres** 500; **Type**
Public; **On Site** Clubhouse, Lodging, Meals; **Shoots**
Field; **Birds** Quail; **Dogs** Avail

Pine Hill Plantation
255 Kimbrel Rd., Colquitt, GA 31737
(912) 758-6602 G.J. Kimbrel, III
60 mi. NW of Tallahassee
Acres 5,000; **Type** Public, Corp.; **On Site**
Clubhouse, Lodging, Meals, Clays; **Shoots** Field;
Birds Quail; **Dogs** Avail/HDW; **Packages** 1 Day, 3-6
guns O NAGA/See Pg. 72
See Our Ad Pg. 286

Pinefields Plantation
Rt. 2, Box 215, Moultrie, GA 31768
(912) 985-2086 Charlie Cannon, III 8 to 8
12 mi. E of Moultrie
Est 1912; **Acres** 5,000; **Hunters/yr** 600; **Type**
Public; **On Site** Clubhouse, Lodging, Meals, Clays;
Shoots Field; **Birds** Dove, Quail; **Dogs** Avail/HDW;
Packages 1 Day, up to 8 guns

Pineknot
Hunting Preserve
PO Box 556, Metter, GA 30439
(912) 685-5555 Tommy Bland or Bill Adams 8am-5pm
50 mi. W of Savannah
Est 1985; **Acres** 700; **Hunters/yr** 300; **Type**
Public, Member/Avail, Corp.; **Shoots** Field, Blinds;
Birds Dove, Quail, Turkey, Ducks; **Dogs** Avail/HDW;
Packages 1/2 Day, 1-12 guns
ENJOY THE EXCITEMENT–Good Bird Dog Work,
Hard Flying Quail and a Steady Point. Hunting in
comfort...from an A.T.V. Wagon being with the
dogs only a few steps away to covey rise...THAT'S
LIVING! Starlight Kennel Championship Line English
Setters; Puppies and Trained Dogs Available for Sale.

Pretoria Station
Hunting Preserve
4601 Leary Rd., Albany, GA 31707
(912) 439-4132 Bob Hayes
80 mi. N of Tallahassee
Est 1989; **Acres** 1,800; **Type** Public, Member/Avail,
Corp.; **On Site** Clubhouse, Lodging, Meals, Clays;
Shoots Field; **Birds** Dove, Quail, Turkey; **Dogs**
Avail/HDW; **Packages** 1/2 Day, 2-12 guns
See Our Ad Above Right

Quail Country Lodge
Rt. 1, Box 690, Arlington, GA 31713
(912) 725-4645 Joy and Tom Newberry
30 mi. W of Albany
Est 1972; **Acres** 5,000; **Hunters/yr** 500; **Type**
Public, Member/Avail, Corp.; **On Site** Clubhouse,
Lodging, Meals, Clays; **Shoots** Field; **Birds** Quail;
Dogs Avail/HDW; **Packages** 1/2 Day, 2-16 guns

Quail Creek
PO Box 2846, Valdosta, GA 31604
(912) 244-6558 Chuck May
80 mi. NE of Tallahassee
Type Member/Ltd; **On Site** Lodging, Meals, Clays;
Shoots Field; **Birds** Quail, Pheasant, Chukar
O NAGA/See Pg. 72

Quail Ridge Preserve
Rt. 3, Box 387-C, Douglas, GA 31533
(912) 384-0025 Francis Fountain
140 mi. NE of Tallahassee
Est 1990; **Acres** 900; **Type** Public; **On Site**
Clubhouse, Meals; **Shoots** Field, Blinds; **Birds** Dove,
Quail; **Dogs** Avail/HDW; **Packages** 1/2 Day, 2-10
guns O NAGA/See Pg. 72

Quailridge Plantation
PO Box 155, Norman Park, GA 31771
(912) 985-5011 Edwin Norman 8 to 5
35 mi. E of Albany
Est 1969; **Acres** 4,000; **Hunters/yr** 750; **Type**
Public; **On Site** Clubhouse, Lodging, Meals, Clays;
Shoots Field; **Birds** Quail; **Dogs** Avail/HDW;
Packages 1 Day, 2-12 guns

Redhawk Plantation
PO Box 882, Unadilla, GA 31091
(912) 783-1991 Mitch Slay
40 mi. S of Macon
Acres 8,000; **Type** Public, Member/Avail; **On Site**
Clubhouse, Lodging, Meals; **Shoots** Field; **Birds**
Dove, Quail, Turkey, Ducks; **Dogs** Avail; **Packages**
1/2 Day, 1-10 guns

Riverview Plantation
Rt. 2, Box 515, Camilla, GA 31730
(912) 294-4904 Cader B. Cox, III 9-5
30 mi. SW of Albany
Est 1957; **Acres** 12,000; **Type** Public,
Member/Avail; **On Site** Clubhouse, Lodging, Meals,
Clays; **Shoots** Field; **Birds** Quail; **Dogs** Avail;
Packages 1 Day, 2-30 guns ○ NAGA/See Pg. 72

Rosin Pine Quail Hunts
PO Box 36, Barwick, GA 31720
(912) 735-2095 Bill & Ruby Turner 9-5
60 mi. NW of Tallahassee
Est 1975; **Acres** 5,000; **Hunters/yr** 200; **Type**
Public, Member/Avail, Corp.; **On Site** Clubhouse,
Lodging, Meals, Clays; **Shoots** Field; **Birds** Dove,
Quail, Ducks; **Dogs** Avail/HDW; **Packages** 1 Day,
2-16 guns
Rosin Pine quail hunting special rates; first class
hunting in beautiful pines. Big discount to parties
of 8 or more, call 1-800-785-2095.

Samara Plantation
PO Box 356, Norman Park, GA 31771
(912) 769-3065 Harold Ivey during noon hour
80 mi. NE of Tallahassee
Acres 5,100; **Hunters/yr** 1,100; **Type** Public; **On
Site** Clubhouse, Lodging, Meals, Clays; **Shoots** Field;
Birds Quail; **Dogs** Avail; **Packages** 1/2 Day, 1-24 guns

Senalf Plantation
279 Philema Rd., Leesburg, GA 31763
(912) 436-1796 Ronnie or Kathy Beane
Acres 10,000; **Shoots** Field; **Birds** Quail

Shirahland Plantation
Rt. 1, Box 340, Camilla, GA 31730
(800) 538-8559 Krista Boerrigter
25 mi. S of Albany
Acres 9,000; **Type** Public; **On Site** Clubhouse,
Lodging, Meals, Clays; **Shoots** Field; **Birds** Quail;
Dogs Avail/HDW; **Packages** 1 Day, 2-6 guns

Southpoint Plantation
PO Box 4309, Albany, GA 31706
(912) 888-6598 Darryl E. Pinkston 8 to 5, M-F
20 mi. NW of Albany
Est 1990; **Acres** 3,400; **Hunters/yr** 300; **Type**
Public; **On Site** Clubhouse, Meals, Clays; **Shoots**
Field; **Birds** Quail; **Dogs** Avail/HDW; **Packages**
1/2 Day, up to 4 guns
See Our Ad Left

Spring Creek Lodge
PO Box 38, Brooklet, GA 30415
(912) 842-2197 W.M. Sheppard
40 mi. NW of Savannah
Type Public, Member/Avail, Corp.; **On Site**
Clubhouse, Lodging, Meals; **Shoots** Field; **Birds**
Turkey; **Dogs** Avail; **Packages** 1/2 Day

Starrsville Plantation
283 Bo Jones Rd., Covington, GA 30209
(404) 787-1366 Nathan V. Hendriks, III
30 mi. E of Atlanta
Acres 700; **Type** Public; **On Site** Clubhouse,
Lodging, Meals, Clays; **Shoots** Field; **Birds** Dove,
Quail; **Dogs** Avail; **Packages** 1/2 Day

Tannenwood-A Hunting & Shooting
PO Box 130, Davidsboro, GA 31018
(912) 348-4931 Chad Tanner
60 mi. SW of Augusta
Est 1995; **Type** Public; **On Site** Meals, Clays;
Shoots Field, Blinds; **Birds** Dove, Quail, Turkey,
Ducks; **Dogs** Avail/HDW; **Packages** 1/2 Day, 2-6
guns

Three Creeks Farm
Rt. 5, Box 765, Bainbridge, GA 31717
(912) 246-2266 John M. Simmons
38 mi. NW of Tallahassee
Est 1985; **Acres** 2,000; **Type** Member/Ltd; **On
Site** Clubhouse, Lodging, Meals, Clays; **Shoots** Field;
Birds Quail; **Dogs** Avail/HDW; **Packages** 1 Day, 2-6 guns

White Oak Farm
2098 Hwy. 36 W., Jackson, GA 30233
(404) 775-2619 Bob Boan Anytime
50 mi. S of Atlanta
Est 1984; **Acres** 5,000; **Type** Public; **Shoots** Field;
Birds Dove, Turkey; **Packages** 1 Day, 1-30 guns

Wise Olde Pine Plantation
Rt. 2, Box 39, 3 Bridges Rd., Americus, GA 31709
(912) 846-5491 Jean Wise, Jr. After 6:30 pm
30 mi. N of Albany
Acres 4,000; **Hunters/yr** 200; **Type** Public; **On Site** Clubhouse, Lodging, Meals, Clays; **Shoots** Field;
Birds Quail, Woodcock, Pheasant, Turkey; **Dogs** Avail/HDW; **Packages** 1/2 Day, up to 6 guns

Woodland Farms/Brier Creek
1100 Woodland Academy Rd., Matthews, GA 30818
(706) 547-3712 Mary Barnes After 6pm
25 mi. S of Augusta
Est 1977; **Acres** 365; **Type** Public; **Shoots** Field;
Birds Dove, Quail, Pheasant, Chukar; **Dogs** Avail/HDW; **Packages** 1/2 Day, 1-3 guns

Wynfield Plantation
2413 Tarva Rd., Albany, GA 31707
(912) 883-2210 Larry L. Ruis
180 mi. S of Atlanta
Est 1988; **Acres** 1,500; **Type** Public; **On Site** Clubhouse, Lodging, Meals, Clays; **Shoots** Field;
Birds Quail; **Dogs** Avail/HDW; **Packages** 1 Day, 2-9 guns
O Hunting License   O Airport Pickup
O Bird Processing   O Loaner Guns
O Fishing

HAWAII

Ulupalakua Hunting Club
191 Mano Dr., Kula, HI 96790
(808) 878-6632 Patrick Fisher Evenings
25 mi. SE of Kahului
Est 1992; **Acres** 1,600; **Hunters/yr** 300; **Type** Public, Member/Avail; **On Site** Lodging, Meals, Clays;
Shoots Field, Driven; **Birds** Dove, Quail, Pheasant, Chukar; **Dogs** Avail/HDW; **Packages** 1/2 Day, 1-8 guns O NAGA/See Pg. 72

Waialua Hunt Club
PO Box 922, Waialua, HI 96791
(808) 637-9441 Steve Gelakoski
On Site Clays; **Shoots** Field; **Birds** Pheasant
O NAGA/See Pg. 72

WINGS

Buying a new shotgun?

That's great! But with over 68 companies manufacturing and importing shotguns for the U.S. market, how do you go about finding the right gun for you? Easy! The perfect place to start the buying process is in **Wing & Clay**. Turn to the following sections to begin:

SHOTGUN MANUFACTURERS & IMPORTERS   Page 184

You'll find detailed information on the 68 different shotgun companies and importers serving the U.S. market. Company and individual contact names, addresses, telephone and fax numbers. Brand names, models, price ranges and the country in which the shotguns are manufactured. And cross-references to a score of informative advertisements.

SHOTGUNS/NATIONAL DEALERS   Page 197

31 of the best shotgun dealers in the country—stocking thousands of shotguns—are just a phone call away with this valuable section. Use it to check prices and availability. Locate "hard to find" items. Order by mail or phone.

SHOTGUN TRADE NAME & MANUFACTURERS CHART   Page 183

Know the shotgun name but not the maker? This chart will help you find the manufacturer, importer or distributor of almost every gun available in the U.S.

HIGH DESERT RANCH

Experience high volume guided hunts with top-rated pointing dogs for 10 species of upland birds, plus waterfowl, in the famous Snake River Valley. This immense private ranch combines the largest variety of wing-shooting in North America with first class accommodations.

The unique 9,000 square foot cedar lodge includes 14 spacious bedrooms with spectacular views, 3 rooms for entertaining, plus a sauna and spa. The state of the art kitchen offers a select menu which caters to guest tastes and dietary needs.

No livestock inhabit the ranch and thousands of acres are developed for cover and habitat yearly. 5-stand sporting clays, custom shooting rigs, horseback hunts and convenient air arrival available.

For Information & Reservations Write or Call:

P.O. Box 470 • Idaho 83672

1-800-284-2843

IDAHO

Caribou Bird Preserve
128 River Rd., Grace, ID 83241
(208) 247-6643 Kimball Evans
120 mi. N of Salt Lake City
Est 1993; **Acres** 1,600; **Type** Public, Member/Avail, Corp.; **On Site** Clubhouse, Lodging, Meals, Clays; **Shoots** Field, Blinds; **Birds** Pheasant, Huns, Ducks, Geese; **Dogs** Avail/HDW; **Packages** 1/2 Day, 1-10 guns   O NAGA/See Pg. 72

Flying B Ranch
Rt. 2, Box 12C, Kamiah, ID 83536
(208) 935-0755 Steve Evans 9-5, M-F
65 mi. SE of Lewiston, ID
Est 1986; **Acres** 5,000; **Hunters/yr** 150; **Type** Public; **On Site** Clubhouse, Lodging, Meals; **Shoots** Field; **Birds** Quail, Ruffed Grouse, Pheasant, Chukar, Huns, Sage Grouse, Ducks; **Dogs** Avail/HDW; **Packages** 2 Days, 1-14 guns   O NAGA/See Pg. 72
See Our Ad Across Right

High Desert Ranch
P.O. Box 470, Weiser, ID 83672
(800) 284-2843
65 mi. NW of Boise   Est 1994; **Type** Public; **On Site** Clubhouse, Lodging, Meals; **Shoots** Field; **Birds** Quail, Ruffed Grouse, Pheasant, Chukar, Huns, Sage Grouse, Sharp Tail Grouse, Ducks, Geese; **Dogs** Avail/HDW; **Packages** 1 Day, 2-24 guns
See Our Ad Left

Rt. 2, Box 14A, Homedale, ID 83628
(208) 337-4443 George & Dolly Hyer
40 mi. W of Boise
Est 1988; **Type** Public, Member/Avail, Corp.; **On Site** Clubhouse, Clays; **Shoots** Field; **Birds** Quail, Pheasant, Chukar; **Dogs** Avail/HDW; **Packages** 1/2 Day
O NAGA/See Pg. 72
O Airport Pickup   O Kennel Bird Dogs
O Sporting Clays   O Train Bird Dogs
O On-Site Pro Shop   O Family Run Business

Teton Ridge Guest Ranch
200 Valley View Rd., Tetonia, ID 83452
(208) 456-2650 Albert Tilt
40 mi. W of Jackson Hole, WY **Est** 1985; **Acres** 4,000; **Type** Member/Avail; **On Site** Clubhouse, Lodging, Meals, Clays; **Shoots** Field; [cont'd>]

The Flying B, Idaho's Hunting Utopia

The road in to the 6,000 acre Flying B Ranch parallels a trout stream that demands your attention. The canyon walls on both sides of the stream climb toward the sky and, on certain days, disappear into the mists. Follow the canyon floor road until you see the first of the Flying B's outbuildings and you'll soon realize that this is no ordinary ranch. More hunting dogs than horses, for instance. And no cows.

Enjoying Idaho's hunting utopia!

Focus on top quality

But no surprise, here, since The Flying B is a year-round outfitter that focuses hard on providing top quality services to a discriminating clientele and has done so since 1986.

The Flying B can pretty much replicate any kind of bird hunt you desire. A typical day of wingshooting begins with a hearty breakfast and warm greeting from one of the Ranch's experienced guides. Most hunts are a mixed bag affair, the kind that never allow you to relax with one flying speed. The birds range from quail to pheasants and you're never quite sure what the splendidly trained dogs are pointing.

Five species of big game

As an aside, the Flying B has excellent big-game hunting for five species of big game including elk, cougar, bear, whitetail and mule deer. Big game hunters enjoy all the comforts of home at the Ranch's lodge or in well situated back country camps.

Built entirely of native logs, the Lodge captures the essence of Northwestern friendliness and warmth and is easily as impressive as the hunting. Fifteen spacious guest rooms, elegant dining, a huge main trophy room, conference room, game and relaxation areas, gun room, sauna, and Jacuzzi are among the splendid features of this centerpiece of the Flying B experience.

In addition, the Flying B offers sporting clays, 3-D archery, pistol and rifle ranges. For more information about this spectacular facility set in some of the last pristine frontier in the U.S., call or write, Mike Gould, Ranch Manager, The Flying B, Rt. 2, Box 12C, Kamiah, ID 83536; or call: 208-935-0755].

The new, 14-bedroom lodge at the Flying B Ranch

Birds Quail, Pheasant, Chukar, Huns, Sharp Tail Grouse; **Dogs** Avail/HDW; **Packages** 1 Day

Tews Ranches
745 N. 550 W., Shoshone, ID 83352
(208) 886-2100 Rusty or Carla Tews 8pm mst
50 mi. S of Sun Valley, ID
Est 1989; **Acres** 600; **Hunters/yr** 1,000; **Type** Public, Member/Avail, Corp.; **On Site** Clubhouse, Meals, Clays; **Shoots** Field; **Birds** Pheasant, Chukar; **Dogs** Avail/HDW; **Packages** 1/2 Day, 1-20 guns

ILLINOIS

Ambraw Valley Outdoors
RR4, Box 202, Newton, IL 62448
(618) 783-3160 Wade Eaton/Doug Hartke Anytime
120 mi. E of St. Louis, MO
Est 1993; **Acres** 400; **Type** Public, Member/Avail, Corp.; **On Site** Clubhouse, Meals, Clays; **Shoots** Field, Driven; **Birds** Dove, Quail, Pheasant, Chukar; **Dogs** Avail/HDW; Packages 1/2 Day, 1-20 guns
o NAGA/See Pg. 72

Autumn Flight Game Fields
PO Box 135, Toluca, IL 61369
(815) 452-2004 Gilbert R. Holz 10pm
80 mi. SW of Chicago
Est 1960; **Acres** 350; **Hunters/yr** 50; **Type** Public; **Shoots** Field; **Birds** Pheasant, Turkey, Ducks; **Dogs** Avail/HDW; Packages 1/2 Day, 1-2 guns

HUNTING PRESERVE
Rt. 4, Box 31, Warsaw, IL 62379
(217) 647-3355 John or Sue Caldwell After 6pm
100 mi. NW of Springfield
Est 1988; Acres 740; Hunters/yr 450; On Site Clubhouse, Lodging, Meals, Clays; Shoots Field, Blinds; Birds Quail, Pheasant, Turkey, Ducks, Geese; Dogs Avail/HDW m NAGA/See Pg. 72

Love to hunt? Then The Break is for you! Enjoy guided pheasant, chukar and quail hunting on 700+ acres along the Mississippi in west central Illinois. Duck, turkey and deer hunting are also available. Fishing, too! Our A-frame lodge has all the modern conveniences you'd expect to find at an exclusive sportsmen's club. Home cooked meals and comfortable overnight accommodations. You deserve a break...at The Break! Call today for information.

Briar Knoll
Hunting & Fishing
1502 Briar Knoll Rd., Amboy, IL 61310
(815) 857-2320 Ivan Trauernicht
90 mi. W of Chicago
Acres 500; Type Member/Avail; On Site Clubhouse, Lodging, Meals, Clays; Shoots Field; Birds Dove, Quail, Pheasant, Chukar; Dogs HDW; Packages 1/2 Day o NAGA/See Pg. 72
o Sporting Clays   o Shooting Instruction
o Train Bird Dogs   o Factory Ammunition
o Quality Clubhouse

Bull Valley Hunt Club
916 N. Cold Spring Rd., Woodstock, IL 60098
(815) 338-4240 George Wold, Jr. 8am-5pm
50 mi. NW of Chicago
Est 1959; **Acres** 1,475; **Hunters/yr** 2,200; **Type** Member/Avail, Corp.; **On Site** Clubhouse, Lodging, Meals; **Shoots** Field, Driven, Blinds, Boat; **Birds** Dove, Quail, Pheasant, Chukar, Ducks, Geese; **Dogs** Avail/HDW; **Packages** 1/2 Day, 1-40 guns

Covey Ridge I & II
Rt. 1, Box 256A, Geff, IL 62842
(618) 854-2269 Charles R. Hazel
110 mi. E of St. Louis
Est 1988; **Acres** 896; **Type** Public; **Shoots** Field; **Birds** Dove, Quail, Pheasant, Chukar; **Dogs** Avail/HDW; **Packages** 1/2 Day, 1-20 guns

Cranfill Shooting Preserve
RR2, Hillsboro, IL 62049
(217) 532-2797 Don Cranfill
50 mi. SE of Springfield
Est 1954; **Acres** 372; **Hunters/yr** 250; **Type** Public, Member/Avail, Corp.; **On Site** Clubhouse, Meals, Clays; **Shoots** Field; **Birds** Quail, Pheasant, Chukar; **Dogs** Avail/HDW; **Packages** 1/2 Day, 1-12 guns

Custer Park Pheasant Club
1540 Mannkeim Rd., Stone Park, IL 60165
(708) 865-1310 Paul W. Bartels
from Chicago
Acres 600; **Type** Member/Avail; **Shoots** Field; **Birds** Pheasant

D&M Hunting Club
Rt. 5, Box 71, Marion, IL 62959
(618) 993-8914 Doc & Mark Schaede 7-10pm
SW of Marion
Est 1980; **Acres** 80; **Hunters/yr** 900; **Type** Public; **On Site** Clubhouse; **Shoots** Blinds; **Birds** Geese; **Dogs** Avail; **Packages** 1/2 Day, 8-39 guns

Dewey's Hunting Club
601 E. Cole, Heyworth, IL 61745
(309) 473-3114 Bob Dewey After 5pm
125 mi. SW of Chicago
Est 1986; **Acres** 240; **Hunters/yr** 150; **Type** Public; **On Site** Clubhouse; **Shoots** Field; **Birds** Quail, Pheasant, Chukar; **Dogs** Avail/HDW;
Packages 1/2 Day, 2-8 guns

Doctorman's Cache Core Hunting
Rt. 1, Box 69, Ulin, IL 62992
(618) 845-3367 Dean Doctorman
150 mi. SE of St. Louis
Type Public; **Shoots** Field; **Birds** Quail, Pheasant; **Dogs** Avail/HDW

East Grove Game Farm, Inc.
841 Todd Rd., Ohio, IL 61349
(815) 376-4901 James Schulte anytime
120 mi. W of Chicago
Est 1990; **Acres** 400; **Type** Member/Avail; **On Site** Clubhouse; **Shoots** Field; **Birds** Quail, Pheasant, Chukar, Turkey; **Dogs** Avail/HDW; **Packages** 1/2 Day

El-J World Class Shooting Preserve
RR1, Box 448, Johnston City, IL 62951
(618) 983-8758 James R. Moore
80 mi. SE of St. Louis
Est 1988; **Acres** 228; **Hunters/yr** 100; **Type** Public, Member/Avail; **On Site** Clubhouse, Lodging, Meals; **Shoots** Field; **Birds** Quail, Pheasant; **Dogs** Avail/HDW; **Packages** 1/2 Day, up to 2 guns

Elliot Acres Hunting Club
PO Box 783, Huntley, IL 60142
(708) 669-5564 Steve Berggreiter
Shoots Field; **Birds** Pheasant ○ NAGA/See Pg. 72

Elm River Shooting Preserve
RR#2, Box 188, Cisne, IL 62823
(618) 673-2372 Donald Lewis
120 mi. E of St. Louis
Est 1988; **Acres** 250; **Type** Public; **On Site** Clubhouse; **Shoots** Field; **Birds** Quail; **Dogs** Avail/HDW; **Packages** 1/2 Day, 2-6 guns

Frisco Game Preserve
RR1, Ewing, IL 62836
(618) 629-2527 M. Norris Webb 6-7am
15 mi. from Benton
Est 1985; **Acres** 915; **Hunters/yr** 2,000; **Type** Public, Member/Avail, Corp.; **On Site** Clubhouse, Meals; **Shoots** Field, Tower; **Birds** Dove, Quail, Pheasant, Chukar, Turkey; **Dogs** Avail/HDW; **Packages** 1/2 Day, 2-8 guns ○ NAGA/See Pg. 72
New! Continental Hunt in the Round. Fast action. Frisco Game Preserve offers 900+ acres of prime southern Illinois hunting land. Varied wildlife habitat with an abundance of native quail, deer and rabbit. Hunting to suit almost anyone's liking. You won't be disappointed. Call today for details.

Garden Plain Hunt Club
7737 Long Rd., Fulton, IL 61252
(309) 887-4439 Curt Ebersohl Anytime
Est 1991; **Acres** 1,000; **Hunters/yr** 800; **Type** Public, Member/Avail, Corp.; **On Site** Clubhouse, Lodging, Meals, Clays; **Shoots** Field; **Birds** Dove, Quail, Pheasant, Chukar, Huns, Turkey; **Dogs** Avail/HDW; **Packages** 1/2 Day, 2-50 guns

Giant Goose Ranch
25369 N. Goose Ranch Rd., Canton, IL 61520
(309) 647-5108 George Connett
20 mi. SW of Peoria **Shoots** Field, Blinds; **Birds** Quail, Pheasant, Ducks, Geese

Grassy Lake Hunting Club
RR2, Jonesboro, IL 62952
(618) 883-7890 Collin Cain
Acres 300; **Type** Public; **On Site** Clubhouse, Meals; **Shoots** Blinds; **Birds** Geese; **Dogs** Avail/HDW; **Packages** 1 Day

Green Acres
Sportsman's Club, Inc.
1458 N 1700 E Rd., Roberts, IL 60962
(217) 395-2588 Randy Sellek
80 mi. SW of Chicago
Acres 700; **Type** Public, Member/Avail; **On Site** Clubhouse, Clays; **Shoots** Field; **Birds** Dove, Quail, Pheasant, Chukar, Ducks; **Dogs** Avail/HDW; **Packages** 1/2 Day, 1-50 guns ○ NAGA/See Pg. 72
○ Bird Processing   ○ Family Recreation
○ Shooting Instruction   ○ Train Bird Dogs
○ Fishing

Green River Roger Conservation Area, Inc.
727 Maytown Rd., Ohio, IL 61349
(815) 379-2702 Roy or Roxie Rogers
Acres 2,300; **Type** Public; **Shoots** Field; **Birds** Pheasant; **Dogs** Avail/HDW

Grizzle's Gamebirds
RR#2, Brighton, IL 62012
(618) 372-8672 Terry Grizzle
30 mi. NE of St. Louis, MO
Est 1986; **Acres** 260; **Type** Public; **On Site** Clubhouse, Clays; **Shoots** Field; **Birds** Quail, Pheasant; **Dogs** Avail/HDW; **Packages** 1/2 Day, 2-6 guns

Hickory Grove Hunting Club
RR1, Wyanet, IL 61379
(815) 699-2603 Leroy Wirth
Acres 1,100; **Type** Member/Avail; **Shoots** Field; **Birds** Dove, Quail, Pheasant, Chukar, Turkey, Ducks; **Dogs** Avail/HDW; **Packages** 1/2 Day

Hillendale Club, Inc.
PO Box 398, 9417 N. Solon Rd., Richmond, IL 60071
(815) 678-4392 Arnold N. May after 5pm
50 mi. NW of Chicago
Est 1958; **Acres** 700; **Type** Member/Avail; **On Site** Clubhouse, Clays; **Shoots** Field; **Birds** Dove, Quail, Pheasant, Chukar, Turkey; **Dogs** HDW

Hopewell Views Hunting Club
Rt. 2, Rockport, IL 62370
(217) 734-9234 Rick Wombles
85 mi. NW of St. Louis, MO
Acres 1,900; **Type** Public, Member/Avail, Corp.; **On Site** Clubhouse, Lodging, Meals, Clays; **Shoots** Field; **Birds** Dove, Quail, Pheasant, Chukar, Turkey, Ducks, Geese; **Dogs** Avail/HDW; **Packages** 1/2 Day ○ NAGA/See Pg. 72

WINGS

The Hunt Club
Rt. 1, Box 204, Percy, IL 62272
(618) 497-2526 Ron Doering 8-5
50 mi. SE of St. Louis, MO
Est 1988; **Acres** 10,300; **Hunters/yr** 350; **Type**
Member/Avail, Corp.; **On Site** Clubhouse, Lodging,
Meals; **Shoots** Field, Driven, Blinds, Boat; **Birds**
Dove, Quail, Pheasant, Chukar, Turkey, Ducks, Geese;
Dogs Avail/HDW; **Packages** 1/2 Day, 2-24 guns

Hunting Sports Plus
710 Main St., Ste. E, Blue Springs, MO,
Hunting in 7 States including, Illinois
(800) 729-1924 Dan Gasser
Est 1989; **Acres** 200,000; **Type** Public,
Member/Avail; **On Site** Clubhouse, Lodging, Meals,
Clays; **Shoots** Field, Blinds, Boat; **Birds** Quail,
Pheasant, Turkey, Prairie Chicken, Ducks, Geese;
Dogs Avail/HDW; **Packages** 1 Day, 1-24 guns
Quality hunting on over 200,000 acres of private
farm land in 7 Midwest States–AR, IA, IL, KS, MO,
NE, OK. Hunt quail, pheasant, turkey, deer, prairie
chicken, ducks and geese. Affordable Midwestern
hospitality. Large selection of low cost member-
ships, daily plans or hunting vacation package
hunts. Call today for more information.

RR4, Box 98, Mt. Sterling, IL 62353
(217) 289-3366 Larry Hanold 9-5
110 mi. N of St. Louis, MO
Est 1986; **Acres** 3,500; **Type** Public, Member/Avail,
Corp.; **On Site** Clubhouse, Lodging, Meals, Clays;
Shoots Field, Blinds; **Birds** Dove, Quail, Pheasant,
Chukar, Turkey, Ducks; **Dogs** Avail/HDW; **Packages**
1/2 Day, 2-16 guns
What do we offer? A challenging 20 position sporting clays field, trap, lodging for 36, home-cooked,
gourmet meals, beautiful wooded hills interspersed
with hunting fields, guided upland bird hunting for
pheasants, quail and chukar. We have world class
trophy bucks and wild turkey. Hunt in the finest
habitat Mother Nature can provide. "Hunting the
way it used to be," since 1986. Brochure available.

Keck's Marsh
RR2, Box 190, Vandalia, IL 62471
(618) 425-3740 Fred Keck
65 mi. NE of St. Louis
Est 1984; **Acres** 3,000; **Type** Public; **Shoots** Field;
Birds Quail, Pheasant, Chukar, Ducks, Geese;
Packages 1/2 Day

Kline's Sunup to Sundown Hunt Club
10N910 Belmont, Elgin, IL 60123
(708) 695-1221 Anne Kline After 8 pm
50 mi. NW of Chicago

Type Member/Avail, Corp.; **Shoots** Field; **Birds**
Dove, Quail, Pheasant, Chukar, Turkey, Ducks; **Dogs**
Avail/HDW

Knights Prairie Hunt Club/MacKenzie Kennels
Rt. 1, Box 142, McLeansboro, IL 62859
(618) 736-2690 Gerry MacKenzie after 5pm
90 mi. SE of St. Louis
Est 1988; **Acres** 1,200; **Type** Public, Member/Avail,
Corp.; **On Site** Clubhouse, Meals, Clays; **Shoots**
Field; **Birds** Dove, Quail, Pheasant; **Dogs**
Avail/HDW; **Packages** 1/2 Day, 2-10 guns
○ Kennel Bird Dogs   ○ Deer Hunting
○ Hunting Jeeps   ○ Train Bird Dogs
○ Brochure Available

Koberlein's Hunting Preserve
274 County Rd., 1400 E., Tolono, IL 61880
(217) 867-2310 Debbi Koberlein
25 mi. S of Champaign
Acres 440; **Hunters/yr** 365; **Type** Public,
Member/Avail; **On Site** Clubhouse, Lodging, Meals,
Clays; **Shoots** Field; **Birds** Dove, Quail, Pheasant,
Chukar, Ducks; **Dogs** Avail ○ NAGA/See Pg. 72

Little Wabash Shooting Preserve
610 E. 5th St., Neoga, IL 62447
(217) 895-2677 Gary Hartke 8-5
100 mi. NE of St. Louis
Est 1986; **Acres** 320; **Type** Public; **Shoots** Field;
Birds Quail, Pheasant, Chukar; **Dogs** Avail/HDW;
Packages 1/2 Day, 1-18 guns ○ NAGA/See Pg. 72

McCullom Lake Hunt Club
10603 Okeson Rd., PO Box 303, Hebron, IL 60034
(815) 648-2775 Skip Hauri 8-5
40 mi. E of Rockford
Est 1956; **Acres** 400; **Type** Member/Avail; **On
Site** Clubhouse, Meals, Clays; **Shoots** Field, Tower;
Birds Dove, Quail, Pheasant, Chukar; **Dogs**
Avail/HDW ○ NAGA/See Pg. 72

Middlefork Valley Shooting Sports
PO Box 8, Paxton, IL 60957
(217) 379-4828 Joe Eaves
110 mi. S of Chicago
Type Member/Avail; **On Site** Clubhouse, Lodging;
Shoots Field; **Birds** Dove, Quail, Pheasant, Chukar,
Ducks, Geese

Millbrook Hunting Club
7519 Finnie Rd., Newark, IL 60541
(708) 232-3004 David W. Withall M-F, 9-4
60 mi. SW of Chicago
Est 1949; **Acres** 400; **Hunters/yr** 400; **Type**
Member/Avail; **On Site** Clubhouse, Meals, Clays;
Shoots Field, Blinds; **Birds** Dove, Quail, Pheasant,
Chukar, Ducks; **Dogs** Avail/HDW; **Packages** 1/2
Day, 1-8 guns ○ NAGA/See Pg. 72
○ Bird Processing   ○ Deer Hunting
○ Gourmet Meals   ○ Brochure Available
○ Fishing

Nilo
7900 Highway 67-111, Brighton, IL 62012
(618) 466-0613 Roger C. Jones, Mgr.
35 mi. NE of St. Louis, MO
Est 1953; **Acres** 640; **Hunters/yr** 900; **Type** Member/Avail; **On Site** Clubhouse, Meals, Clays; **Shoots** Field, Blinds; **Birds** Quail, Pheasant, Chukar, Ducks; **Dogs** Avail; **Packages** 1 Day, 8-16 guns ○ NAGA/See Pg. 72

Nishkawee Preserve
21887 Pigeon Rd., Morrison, IL 61270
(815) 772-3394 Norman F. Spencer
140 mi. W of Chicago
Est 1994; **Acres** 240; **Type** Public, Member/Avail; **On Site** Lodging, Clays; **Shoots** Field; **Birds** Quail, Pheasant, Huns; **Dogs** Avail/HDW; **Packages** 1/2 Day, 1-30 guns ○ NAGA/See Pg. 72

Oakmount Game Club
30808 N. Darrell Rd., McHenry, IL 60050
(815) 385-2144 Peter Reiland, Jr.
45 mi. NW of Chicago
Est 1982; **Acres** 1,200; **Type** Member/Avail, Corp.; **On Site** Clubhouse, Meals, Clays; **Shoots** Field; **Birds** Quail, Pheasant, Chukar, Turkey; **Dogs** Avail/HDW; **Packages** 1/2 Day, 1-4 guns ○ NAGA/See Pg. 72

Otter Creek Hunting Club
Rt. 3, Box 125G, Jerseyville, IL 62052
(618) 376-7601 Mike Runge
40 mi. N of St. Louis, MO
Est 1990; **Acres** 3,000; **Type** Public, Member/Avail, Corp.; **On Site** Clubhouse, Lodging, Meals, Clays; **Shoots** Field; **Birds** Dove, Quail, Pheasant, Turkey; **Dogs** Avail/HDW; **Packages** 1/2 Day, 2-30 guns ○ NAGA/See Pg. 72
Trophy whitetail Archery-Gun hunting; factory stands placed for hunters. 3-5-7 day hunts available. Some ground archery with a 120 pope & young minimum only. Waterfowl hunting packages available! Waterfowl in the a.m.; pheasant, chukar, quail in the p.m. Turkey hunts available, too–with and without guides. We can fly hunters in from other areas in a private plane. Call today for more information.

Pheasant Valley Hunt Club
R#1, Box 360, Bunker Hill, IL 62014
(618) 585-3956 Sharon Wilkinson
30 mi. NE of St. Louis, MO
Est 1970; **Acres** 200; **Hunters/yr** 100; **Type** Public, Member/Avail; **On Site** Clubhouse, Clays; **Shoots** Field; **Birds** Dove, Quail, Pheasant, Chukar; **Dogs** Avail/HDW; **Packages** 1/2 Day, 1-16 guns

Pinewood Hunt Club
RR#1, Box 36, Beaverville, IL 60912
(815) 435-2314 Wayne DeYoung 6am-7pm
55 mi. S of Chicago
Est 1975; **Acres** 875; **Hunters/yr** 500; **Type** Member/Avail, Corp.; **On Site** Clubhouse, Lodging, Meals, Clays; **Shoots** Field; **Birds** Dove, Quail, Pheasant, Chukar, Huns; **Dogs** Avail/HDW; **Packages** 1/2 Day, 2-16 guns

Prairie Lakes Hunt Club
PO Box 410, 2550 N. 32nd Rd., Marseilles, IL 61341
(815) 795-5107 Jack Knoebel/Brian Carlson
55 mi. SW of Chicago
Est 1952; **Acres** 1,250; **Hunters/yr** 450; **Type** Member/Avail; **On Site** Clubhouse, Lodging, Meals, Clays; **Shoots** Field, Blinds; **Birds** Quail, Pheasant, Chukar, Turkey, Ducks, Geese; **Dogs** Avail/HDW; **Packages** 1/2 Day, 1-5 guns ○ NAGA/See Pg. 72
○ Bird Processing ○ Gourmet Meals
○ On-Site Pro Shop ○ Fishing
○ Quality Clubhouse ○ Family Recreation Activities
○ Private Bedrooms ○ Sporting Clays Course
○ 2 Miles N. of I-80

Richmond Hunting Club
Hwy. 173, Rt. 12, Richmond, IL 60071
(815) 678-3271 Chuck Wonderlic
50 mi. NW of Chicago
Acres 800; **Hunters/yr** 1,000; **Type** Public, Member/Avail, Corp.; **On Site** Clubhouse, Meals, Clays; **Shoots** Field; **Birds** Quail, Pheasant, Chukar, Huns, Turkey, Ducks; **Dogs** Avail/HDW; **Packages** 1/2 Day

Riverwood Game Preserve, Ltd.
RR1, Box 68, Tennessee, IL 62374
(309) 776-4368 Sam Biswell
110 mi. N of St. Louis
Est 1990; **Acres** 1,000; **Hunters/yr** 500; **Type** Public; **On Site** Lodging, Clays; **Shoots** Field; **Birds** Quail, Pheasant, Chukar; **Dogs** Avail/HDW ○ NAGA/See Pg. 72

WINGS

Roy Rogers
Hunting Club, Inc.
727 Maytown Rd., Ohio, IL 61349
(815) 379-2427 Roy or Roxie Rogers 6-8pm
100 mi. W of Chicago
Est 1957; **Acres** 1,300; **Hunters/yr** 1,500; **Type**
Public, Member/Avail, Corp.; **On Site** Clubhouse,
Meals, Clays; **Shoots** Field, Tower, Blinds; **Birds**
Dove, Quail, Pheasant, Chukar, Huns, Turkey, Ducks;
Dogs Avail/HDW; **Packages** 1/2 Day, 1-36 guns
O NAGA/See Pg. 72

O Hunting License   O Airport Pickup
O Bird Processing   O Quality Clubhouse
O Family Run Business

Sand Prairie Farms
185 Rogers Rd., Ohio, IL 61349
(815) 376-6641 Tom Yucus 7-9am; 8-10pm
90 mi. W of Chicago
Est 1990; **Acres** 680; **Type** Member/Avail, Corp.;
On Site Clubhouse, Lodging, Meals, Clays; **Shoots**
Field, Blinds; **Birds** Dove, Quail, Pheasant, Chukar,
Huns, Turkey, Ducks, Geese; **Dogs** Avail/HDW;
Packages 1/2 Day, 1-4 guns   O NAGA/See Pg. 72

Sandy Creek Ranch
RR# 2, Box 244, Winchester, IL 62694
(217) 927-4223 Clubhouse
60 mi. N of St. Louis
Est 1994; **Acres** 1,000; **Type** Public, Member/Avail;
On Site Clubhouse, Lodging, Meals, Clays; **Shoots**
Field; **Birds** Dove, Quail, Pheasant, Chukar, Turkey;
Dogs Avail/HDW; **Packages** 1/2 Day, 1-20 guns
O Alt. Phone: (217) 886-2540; Steve Wheeler
The Ranch consists of 1,000 contiguous acres of up-
land terrain in West Central Illinois. Located 60
miles from Springfield, St. Louis and Quincy, it lies
just two miles off the Illinois River in Green and
Scott counties. We offer "sporting clays", big game
bow hunting, upland game hunting, dog training,
kennels, a shooting lodge and campsite.

Seneca Hunt Club
PO Box 824, Seneca, IL 61360
(815) 357-8080 Larry Higdon 8am-4:30pm
60 mi. SW of Chicago
Est 1982; **Acres** 715; **Hunters/yr** 2,500; **Type**
Public, Member/Avail, Corp.; **On Site** Clubhouse,
Lodging, Meals, Clays; **Shoots** Field, Tower, Blinds;
Birds Dove, Quail, Pheasant, Chukar, Huns, Turkey,
Ducks, Geese; **Dogs** Avail/HDW; **Packages** 1/2
Day, up to 6 guns O NAGA/See Pg. 72

Smokin' Gun Hunt Club
Box 392, RR1, Hamilton, IL 62341
(217) 847-2227 Darrin Miller
100 mi. NW of Springfield
Est 1991; **Acres** 320; **Type** Public, Member/Avail,
Corp.; **On Site** Clubhouse, Meals, Clays; **Shoots**
Field; **Birds** Dove, Quail, Pheasant, Chukar, Turkey;
Dogs Avail/HDW; **Packages** 1/2 Day, 1-16 guns

Tamarack Farm Hunt Club
7210 Keystone Rd., Richmond, IL 60071
(815) 678-4989 Dick Hendricksen 8am-2pm
40 mi. NW of Chicago
Est 1986; **Acres** 1,100; **Type** Member/Ltd; **On
Site** Clubhouse, Lodging, Meals, Clays; **Shoots** Field,
Tower; **Birds** Pheasant; **Dogs** Avail; **Packages** 1
Day, 10-32 guns

Top Gun Hunt Club
3100 N. Leaf River Rd., Mt. Morris, IL 61054
(815) 734-4891 John Carbaugh
80 mi. W of Chicago
Type Public, Member/Avail, Corp.; **Shoots** Field;
Birds Pheasant, Chukar, Huns

Trail of Tears Sports Resort
Rt. 1, Old Cape Rd., Jonesboro, IL 62952
(618) 833-8697 Ron & Deb Charles
15 mi. NE of Cape Girardeau
Est 1988; **Type** Public, Member/Avail, Corp.; **On
Site** Clubhouse, Lodging, Meals, Clays; **Shoots** Field;
Birds Dove, Quail, Pheasant, Chukar, Turkey, Ducks,
Geese; **Dogs** Avail/HDW; **Packages** 1/2 Day

Tri-R Hunting Preserve
408 W. Arch, Jerseyville, IL 62052
(618) 498-4666 Robert Swearingin
40 mi. N of St. Louis
Est 1988; **Acres** 380; **Type** Public, Member/Avail;
On Site Clubhouse; **Shoots** Field; **Birds** Dove,
Quail, Pheasant, Chukar; **Dogs** Avail; **Packages** 1/2
Day, 1-12 guns

Upland Bay Rod & Gun Club
PO Box 337, Spring Grove, IL 60081
(815) 678-4411 Bob Robinson
45 mi. NW of Chicago
Est 1982; **Acres** 500; **Type** Public, Member/Avail,
Corp.; **On Site** Clubhouse, Lodging, Meals, Clays;
Shoots Field, Blinds; **Birds** Dove, Quail, Woodcock,
Pheasant, Chukar, Huns, Turkey, Snipe, Ducks, Geese;
Dogs Avail/HDW; **Packages** 1/2 Day, 1-4 guns
O NAGA/See Pg. 72

Upland Hunt Club
14755 Edson Rd., Davis Junction, IL 61020
(815) 874-7444 Mike McInerney, Mgr. 8am-10pm
55 mi. W of Chicago
Est 1987; **Acres** 250; **Hunters/yr** 1,000; **Type**
Public, Member/Avail, Corp.; **On Site** Clubhouse,
Meals, Clays; **Shoots** Field; **Birds** Dove, Quail,
Pheasant, Chukar, Turkey; **Dogs** Avail/HDW;
Packages 1/2 Day, 1-25 guns

White Oak Reserve
RR1, Box 153, Barry, IL 62312
(217) 335-2921 George Metcalf
Type Public, Member/Avail; **Shoots** Field; **Birds**
Quail, Pheasant, Chukar O NAGA/See Pg. 72

Wild Acres Quail Preserve
1002 S. Odel, W. Frankfort, IL 62896
(618) 937-1509 Bob Gentry
Type Public; **Birds** Quail

Wild Cat Run
961 Hawns Rd., RR1, Box 46, Keithsburg, IL 61442
(800) 484-9611 David McCaw Anytime
30 mi. S of Moline
Est 1993; **Acres** 2,000; **Type** Public, Member/Avail,
Corp.; **On Site** Clubhouse, Meals, Clays; **Shoots**
Field, Blinds; **Birds** Dove, Quail, Pheasant, Chukar,
Huns, Turkey, Ducks, Geese; **Dogs** Avail/HDW;
Packages 1/2 Day, 1-20 guns

Woodstock
Hunt Club, Inc.
2505 Deep Cut Rd., PO Box 879, Woodstock, IL 60098
(815) 338-1385 E. Johnson/B. Robinson/J. Ingram
60 mi. N of Chicago
Est 1988; **Acres** 730; **Type** Member/Avail, Corp.;
On Site Clubhouse, Lodging, Meals, Clays; **Shoots**
Field, Blinds; **Birds** Quail, Pheasant, Chukar, Turkey,
Ducks, Geese; **Dogs** Avail/HDW; **Packages** 1/2
Day, 2-30 guns ○ NAGA/See Pg. 72

- ○ Hunting License
- ○ Kennel Bird Dogs
- ○ Family Recreation
- ○ Gourmet Meals
- ○ Train Bird Dogs
- ○ Brochure Available
- ○ Factory Ammunition
- ○ Private Bedrooms
- ○ Bird Processing
- ○ Sporting Clays
- ○ Shooting Instruction
- ○ Hunting Jeeps
- ○ Loaner Guns
- ○ Fishing
- ○ Quality Clubhouse

Fred K. Wright
Rt. 1, Box 195, Bridgeport, IL 62417
(618) 945-7409 Fred Wright After 7:30 pm
125 mi. E of St. Louis
Est 1980; **Acres** 300; **Type** Public; **Shoots** Field;
Birds Quail; **Dogs** HDW; **Packages** 1/2 Day, 1-5 guns

*Say you "Saw it in Wing & Clay" whenever
you contact a company listed in these pages
about a product or service.*

INDIANA

Barnes Hunting Farm
9014 N. Spearsville Rd., Morgantown, IN 46160
(812) 597-4995 Maurice & Catherine Barnes
Est 1989; **Acres** 120; **Type** Public; **On Site**
Clubhouse, Meals, Clays; **Shoots** Field; **Birds** Quail,
Pheasant, Chukar, Huns; **Dogs** Avail/HDW;
Packages 1/2 Day, 1-4 guns ○ NAGA/See Pg. 72

Blue Creek Game Preserve
28498 Blue Creek Rd., Sunman, IN 47041
(812) 623-3742 Earl Stenger
30 mi. W of Cincinnati
Acres 240; **Hunters/yr** 200; **Type** Public,
Member/Avail; **On Site** Clubhouse; **Shoots** Field;
Birds Quail, Pheasant, Chukar; **Dogs** Avail/HDW;
Packages 1/2 Day, 1-5 guns

Buck Run Shooting Preserve
24 Webster St., Chesterfield, IN 46017
(317) 378-6341 Berg Bert
6 mi. NW of Anderson
Acres 244; **Type** Public; **On Site** Clubhouse,
Lodging, Meals; **Shoots** Field, Blinds; **Birds** Quail,
Pheasant, Ducks, Geese; **Dogs** Avail

C/R USA, Inc.
PO Box 35, Griffith, IN 46319
(219) 365-3696 Richard Reed
60 mi. E of Indianapolis
Acres 1,500; **Type** Public, Member/Avail; **Shoots**
Field; **Birds** Dove, Quail, Pheasant, Chukar; **Dogs** Avail

County Line Hunt Club
855 N. 1200 E., Plymouth, IN 46563
(219) 935-4526 Mark Hedges
40 mi. S of South Bend
Est 1991; **Acres** 155; **Hunters/yr** 50; **Type**
Public; **On Site** Clubhouse, Lodging; **Shoots** Field;
Birds Quail, Pheasant, Chukar, Huns; **Dogs**
Avail/HDW; **Packages** 1/2 Day, 2-5 guns
○ NAGA/See Pg. 72

WINGS

DAWN TO DUSK HUNT CLUB

901 N. 264 W., Valparaiso, IN 46383
(219) 763-3362 David W. Griffith
35 mi. SE of Chicago
Acres 300; **Type** Public, Member/Avail, Corp.; **On Site** Clubhouse; **Shoots** Field, Blinds; **Birds** Dove, Quail, Pheasant, Chukar, Geese; **Dogs** Avail/HDW; **Packages** 1/2 Day, 2-6 guns O NAGA/See Pg. 72
O Airport Pickup   O Bird Processing
O Loaner Guns   O Quality Clubhouse
O Professional Guides Handling Experienced Dogs
O Featuring the Reeves Pheasant-Trophy Bird of Long Tailed Pheasants

Flatrock
Hunting Preserve
5188 W SR 244, Milroy, IN 46156
(317) 629-2354 Merrill Carrigan 6-8am, 7-10pm
40 mi. SE of Indianapolis
Est 1991; **Acres** 104; **Type** Public; **On Site** Clubhouse; **Shoots** Field; **Birds** Quail, Pheasant, Chukar; **Dogs** Avail/HDW; **Packages** 1/2 Day, 1-4 guns O NAGA/See Pg. 72

THE HOLLOW
HUNTING PRESERVE

4611 Morningside Dr., Bloomington, IN 47408
(317) 795-3999 Jim Burhans, Owner/Operator
40 mi. SW of Indianapolis
Est 1989; **Acres** 400; **Hunters/yr** 1,000; **Type** Public; **On Site** Clubhouse, Meals, Clays; **Shoots** Field; **Birds** Dove, Quail, Pheasant, Chukar; **Dogs** Avail/HDW; **Packages** 1/2 Day O NAGA/See Pg. 72
O Chosen One of the Top 25 Courses in the U.S. by Esquire Sportsman Magazine
O Preserve Hunting Season: Sept. 1 - April 30. Shooting & hunting instruction.
O Licenses available. Young hunters welcome. Handicapped accessible.
O On site pro shop, rental guns, & equipment available. See our listing in the IN Clays section.
O Located in Cloverdale, IN, 40 mi. SW of Indianapolis off I-70
See Our Ad Pg. 297

Horrall Hunting Preserve
PO Box 131, Petersburg, IN 47567
(812) 354-6129 Mike Horrall After 8pm
45 mi. NE of Evansville
Acres 400; **Type** Public; **Shoots** Field; **Birds** Quail, Pheasant, Chukar; **Dogs** Avail/HDW; **Packages** 1/2 Day, 2-20 guns O NAGA/See Pg. 72

J.E.M.P.
711 South 21st St., Chesterton, IN 46304
(219) 926-1023 Ed Lewandowski 4-9pm
40 mi. E of Chicago
Est 1988; **Acres** 100; **Hunters/yr** 30; **Type** Public, Member/Avail; **On Site** Clays; **Shoots** Field, Blinds, Boat; **Birds** Dove, Quail, Woodcock, Pheasant, Chukar, Ducks, Geese; **Dogs** Avail/HDW; **Packages** 1/2 Day, 1-4 guns O NAGA/See Pg. 72

King Farms
Rt. 1, Box 12, Parker, IN 47368
(317) 468-6706 Eldred King
50 mi. NE of Indianapolis
Est 1970; **Type** Public, Corp.; **On Site** Clubhouse, Meals; **Shoots** Field; **Birds** Dove, Quail, Pheasant, Chukar; **Dogs** HDW; **Packages** 1/2 Day

Lost River Game Farm
PO Box 82, Orleans, IN 47452
(812) 865-3021 Bob or Laura Hudelson
75 mi. S of Indianapolis
Est 1985; **Acres** 1,000; **Hunters/yr** 250; **Type** Public, Member/Avail; **On Site** Clubhouse, Meals, Clays; **Shoots** Field; **Birds** Dove, Quail, Pheasant, Chukar, Huns, Turkey; **Dogs** Avail/HDW; **Packages** 1/2 Day, 3-5 guns
See Our Ad Left

Lyon's Shooting Preserve
RR1, Portland, IN 47371
(219) 726-9194 John B. Lyons
80 mi. NE of Indianapolis
Type Public; Shoots Field; Birds Quail, Pheasant,
Chukar; Dogs Avail/HDW ○ NAGA/See Pg. 72

Maier Pheasant Farm & Hunting Area
65450 Fir Rd., Bremen, IN 46506
(219) 633-4654 Marvin Maier
80 mi. E of Chicago
Est 1955; Type Public; Shoots Field; Birds Quail,
Pheasant; Packages 1/2 Day, up to 3 guns
○ NAGA/See Pg. 72

Muddy Fork Hunting Preserve
5666 E. 1000 N., Seymour, IN 47274
(812) 522-2684 Donn O. Schlehuser
4 mi. NW of Seymour
Acres 320; Hunters/yr 350; Type Public,
Member/Avail; On Site Clubhouse, Clays; Shoots
Field; Birds Dove, Quail, Pheasant, Chukar; Dogs
Avail

P.D.Q. Hunting Preserve
64500 Elm, Bremen, IN 46506
(219) 633-4044 Jim Haines After 5pm
60 mi. E of Chicago
Est 1988; Acres 200; Hunters/yr 800; Type
Public; On Site Clubhouse; Shoots Field; Birds
Quail, Pheasant; Dogs Avail/HDW; Packages 1/2
Day, 2-6 guns ○ NAGA/See Pg. 72

Pleasant Valley Hunting Preserve
RR1, Box 140A, Carbon, IN 47837
(317) 548-2449 Rod Mace
52 mi. SW of Indianapolis
Acres 609; Type Public; On Site Meals; Shoots
Field; Birds Quail, Pheasant, Chukar; Dogs
Avail/HDW; Packages 1/2 Day ○ NAGA/See Pg. 72

Quail Ridge
Sportsman's Club
PO Box 515, Aurora, IN 47001
(812) 926-4999 Brian E. Lane 8-5
45 mi. W of Cincinnati
Est 1990; Acres 850; Hunters/yr 1,000; Type
Member/Avail, Corp.; On Site Clubhouse, Lodging,
Meals, Clays; Shoots Field, Tower, Driven; Birds
Dove, Quail, Pheasant, Chukar, Huns, Turkey; Dogs
Avail/HDW; Packages 1/2 Day, up to 30 guns
○ NAGA/See Pg. 72

Springer Run Hunting Farm
PO Box 816, New Albany, IN 47151
(812) 739-4848 Tony Thomas
3 mi. N of Levenworth
Est 1992; Acres 700; Type Public; On Site
Clubhouse, Clays; Shoots Field; Birds Quail,
Pheasant, Chukar; Dogs Avail/HDW; Packages 1/2
Day, 1-20 guns

Sugar Creek Hunting
& Sporting Clays
RR2, Box 413, Mitchell, IN 47446
(812) 849-2296 Dale Waldbieser or (812) 849-5020
40 mi. S of Bloomington
Est 1992; Acres 500; Type Public; On Site
Clubhouse, Meals, Clays; Shoots Field; Birds Quail,
Pheasant, Chukar; Dogs Avail/HDW; Packages 1/2
Day, 1-6 guns ○ NAGA/See Pg. 72
○ Bird Processing   ○ Sporting Clays
○ Loaner Guns   ○ Brochure Available
○ Factory Ammunition   ○ Family Run Business
○ Less than 1 hour from Lousiville, KY
○ Just 35 minutes off I-65

West Creek Shooting Preserve
15547 W. 169th Ave., Cedar Lake, IN 46303
(219) 696-6101 Patty Lukasik 9am-8pm
50 mi. SE of Chicago
Est 1975; Acres 340; Hunters/yr 400; Type
Public; On Site Clubhouse, Meals, Clays; Shoots
Field; Birds Dove, Pheasant, Chukar; Dogs
Avail/HDW; Packages 1/2 Day, 2-10 guns
○ NAGA/See Pg. 72

IOWA

Arrowhead Hunting Club
3529 170th St., Goose Lake, IA 52750
(319) 577-2267 Gloria or Dan Mullin 8-5
40 mi. N of Davenport
Est 1952; Acres 1,173; Hunters/yr 800; Type
Public, Member/Avail, Corp.; On Site Clubhouse,
Meals, Clays; Shoots Field; Birds Quail, Pheasant,
Chukar; Dogs Avail/HDW; Packages 1/2 Day, 1-20
guns ○ NAGA/See Pg. 72

Beckridge Hunting Preserve
944 613th Ave., Sabula, IA 52070
(319) 687-2935 Jim Beck Early am or after evening
45 mi. N of Davenport
Est 1992; Acres 450; Type Public, Member/Avail;
On Site Clubhouse, Meals, Clays; Shoots Field;
Birds Quail, Pheasant; Dogs Avail/HDW; Packages
1/2 Day, 1-12 guns ○ NAGA/See Pg. 72

Cedar Valley Pheasants
30332 Goose Hill Rd., Cascade, IA 52033
(319) 852-3933 Ron & Donna Miller
30 mi. SW of Dubuque
Est 1987; Acres 1,000; Type Public; Shoots Field;
Birds Quail, Pheasant; Dogs Avail/HDW; Packages
1/2 Day ○ NAGA/See Pg. 72

WINGS

Doc's Dog Kennel
& Hunt Club
2933 Prospect Circle, Adel, IA 50003
(515) 993-3711 Pat or Harold Adams 8-6, M-S
20 mi. W of Des Moines
Est 1980; **Acres** 600; **Hunters/yr** 1,000; **Type**
Public, Member/Avail, Corp.; **On Site** Clubhouse,
Meals, Clays; **Shoots** Field; **Birds** Quail, Pheasant,
Chukar; **Dogs** Avail/HDW; **Packages** 1/2 Day, 2-25
guns ○ NAGA/See Pg. 72

Flood Creek Hunting Preserve
1760 Cameo Rd., Rockford, IA 50468
(515) 756-2327 Todd A. Peterson
120 mi. N of Des Moines
Est 1989; **Acres** 640; **Type** Public, Member/Avail;
On Site Clubhouse, Meals; **Shoots** Field; **Birds**
Quail, Pheasant; **Dogs** Avail/HDW; **Packages** 1 Day

Hunting Sports Plus
710 Main St., Ste. E, Blue Springs, MO, Hunting in 7
States inclu, IA
(800) 729-1924 Dan Gasser
Est 1989; **Acres** 200,000; **Type** Public,
Member/Avail; **On Site** Clubhouse, Lodging, Meals,
Clays; **Shoots** Field, Blinds, Boat; **Birds** Quail,
Pheasant, Turkey, Ducks, Geese; **Dogs** Avail/HDW;
Packages 1 Day, 1-24 guns

Iowa Sure Shot Guide Service
838 N. 21st St., Ft. Dodge, IA 50501
(515) 573-4076 Randy Risetter
Type Public; **Shoots** Field; **Birds** Quail, Pheasant,
Chukar, Ducks, Geese; **Dogs** Avai

TRIPLE H RANCH
HUNTING PRESERVE & SPORTING CLAYS
Individual Hunts & Corporate Entertaining Plans
PHEASANT • QUAIL • CHUKAR
MALLARDS • TURKEY
Super Hunting: hard flying birds,
great guides, stylish dogs
Sporting Clays: super course...
the perfect hunter tuneup!
Call Or Write For Our Free Brand New Video!
319-985-2253
16365 70th Avenue • Burlington, IA 52601

K-Bar-C Hunting Preserve
Box 118, Davis City, IA 50065
(515) 876-2473 Arnold W. Thompson 7-10pm
80 mi. S of Des Moines
Est 1989; **Acres** 960; **Hunters/yr** 100; **Type**
Public, Member/Avail, Corp.; **On Site** Clubhouse,
Lodging, Meals, Clays; **Shoots** Field; **Birds** Quail,
Pheasant, Chukar, Turkey; **Dogs** Avail/HDW;
Packages 1/2 Day, 2-6 guns

Bill Kuntz's Oakwood
Sporting Resort
RR#2, Box 69, Sigourney, IA 52591
(800) 432-3290 Bill Kuntz 7am or pm
40 mi. SW of Iowa City
Est 1990; **Acres** 2,000; **Hunters/yr** 125; **Type**
Public, Member/Avail, Corp.; **On Site** Clubhouse,
Lodging, Meals, Clays; **Shoots** Field; **Birds** Quail,
Pheasant, Chukar; **Dogs** Avail/HDW; **Packages** 1/2
Day, 2-12 guns ○ NAGA/See Pg. 72

Lampe Shooting Preserve
1056 122nd St., Hillsboro, IA 52630
(319) 253-5421 Larry Lampe
40 mi. E of Burlington
Acres 750; **Type** Public; **On Site** Clubhouse,
Lodging, Meals; **Shoots** Field; **Birds** Quail,
Pheasant, Chukar, Turkey; **Dogs** HDW; **Packages**
1/2 Day, up to 6 guns

Lazy H Hunting Club
RR#2, Woodbine, IA 51579
(712) 647-2877 Murray Hubbard 9-5
45 mi. NE of Omaha/Co. Bluffs
Est 1988; **Acres** 360; **Hunters/yr** 350; **Type**
Public, Member/Avail, Corp.; **On Site** Clubhouse,
Lodging, Meals, Clays; **Shoots** Field, Driven; **Birds**
Quail, Pheasant, Chukar; **Dogs** Avail/HDW;
Packages 1/2 Day, 1-20 guns

Oak View Hunting Club
RR2, Prairie City, IA 50228
(515) 994-2094 Ronald De Bruin Evening
Est 1963; **Acres** 1,280; **Type** Public, Member/Avail,
Corp.; **On Site** Clubhouse, Meals, Clays; **Shoots**
Field; **Birds** Quail, Pheasant, Chukar, Ducks; **Dogs**
Avail/HDW; **Packages** 1/2 Day, 1-20 guns
○ NAGA/See Pg. 72

Outdoorsman Hunting Club
RR1, Box 32, Webb, IA 51366
(712) 838-4890 Larry Buettner
90 mi. NE of Sioux City
Est 1968; **Acres** 1,000; **Type** Public, Member/Avail;
On Site Clubhouse, Lodging; **Shoots** Field; **Birds**
Quail, Pheasant, Chukar, Turkey, Ducks, Geese; **Dogs**
Avail/HDW

Pheasants Galore
Box 83, Corning, IA 50841
(515) 322-3749 Darwin Linn 8-5
125 mi. SW of Des Moines
Est 1986; **Acres** 300,000; **Hunters/yr** 1,000;
Type Public; **Shoots** Field; **Birds** Quail, Pheasant,

Huns, Ducks, Geese;   **Dogs** Avail/HDW;   **Packages** 2 Days, 1-12 guns

SAFARI IOWA
—HUNTING FARMS—

Safari Iowa Hunting Farms
3018 "O" Ave., Parnell, IA 52325
(319) 664-3472 Larry or Jan Statler 7am-6pm
40 mi. SW of Cedar Rapids
Est 1988;   **Acres** 2,700;   **Type** Public, Member/Avail, Corp.;   **On Site** Clubhouse, Lodging, Meals, Clays;   **Shoots** Field;   **Birds** Quail, Pheasant, Chukar, Turkey, Ducks, Geese;   **Dogs** Avail/HDW;   **Packages** 1/2 Day
O NAGA/See Pg. 72   O Family Run Business
O Call About Our Special Sportsman's Plan
O Native Bird & Stocked
O Open Range-Double Your Limit
O 100 Miles E of Des Moines

Timber Ridge Hunting Preserve
RR1, Box 203A, Castana, IA 51010
(712) 353-6517 Richard Bumann
90 mi. N of Omaha, NE
Est 1990;   **Acres** 1,200;   **Type** Public, Member/Avail;   **On Site** Clubhouse, Lodging, Meals, Clays;   **Shoots** Field;   **Birds** Quail, Pheasant;   **Dogs** Avail/HDW;   **Packages** 1/2 Day, 1-20 guns

Triple H Ranch
Hunting Preserve
16365 70th Avenue, Burlington, IA 52601
(319) 985-2253 Keith A. Hoelzen 7am-8pm
140 mi. SE of Des Moines
Est 1986;   **Acres** 950;   **Hunters/yr** 300;   **Type** Public;   **On Site** Clubhouse, Meals, Clays;   **Shoots** Field, Tower, Driven, Blinds, Boat;   **Birds** Quail, Woodcock, Pheasant, Chukar, Turkey, Ducks, Geese;   **Dogs** Avail/HDW;   **Packages** 1/2 Day, 1-25 guns
O NAGA/See Pg. 72
See Our Ad Across Left

Wingshoot Iowa
RR1, Box 35C, Vinton, IA 52349
(319) 472-4484 Dave Wessling 8pm-10pm
25 mi. from Cedar Rapids
Est 1991;   **Acres** 1,000;   **Hunters/yr** 40;   **Type** Public;   **On Site** Clubhouse, Lodging, Meals;   **Shoots** Field;   **Birds** Quail, Pheasant, Huns, Ducks, Geese;   **Dogs** Avail/HDW;   **Packages** 2 Days, 4-12 guns

Winterset Hunt Club and Lodge
RR1, Box 100, Lorimor, IA 50419
(515) 763-2505 Curt Sandahl 7-7
47 mi. SW of Des Moines
Est 1981;   **Acres** 911;   **Hunters/yr** 300;   **Type** Public, Member/Avail;   **On Site** Clubhouse, Lodging, Meals, Clays;   **Shoots** Field;   **Birds** Quail, Pheasant, Chukar, Turkey;   **Dogs** Avail/HDW;   **Packages** 1 Day, 1-20 guns   O NAGA/See Pg. 72

KANSAS

B&R Guide
Box 128, Montezuma, KS 67867
(800) 340-2202 Tom Brown/David Robertson 9-5
30 mi. NE of Dodge City
Est 1983;   **Type** Public;   **On Site** Clubhouse, Lodging, Meals;   **Shoots** Field;   **Birds** Dove, Quail, Pheasant, Chukar, Huns, Turkey;   **Dogs** Avail/HDW;   **Packages** 1 Day, 4-12 guns

Blue Line Club
Rt. 1, Box 139A, Solomon, KS 67480
(913) 488-3785 Bernie Janssen After 8pm
25 mi. NE of Salina   **Est** 1969;   **Acres** 640;   **Hunters/yr** 200;   **Type** Public;   **Shoots** Field, Driven;   **Birds** Dove, Quail, Pheasant, Chukar, Turkey, Prairie Chicken;   **Dogs** Avail/HDW;   **Packages** 1/2 Day, 1-30 guns   O NAGA/See Pg. 72

Broken Bar 7 Hunting Safari
HC1, Box 19, St. Francis, KS 67756
(913) 332-2416 Dean/Kaye O'Brien
160 mi. E of Denver, CO
Est 1989;   **Acres** 1,280;   **Type** Public;   **On Site** Clubhouse, Lodging, Meals, Clays;   **Shoots** Field;   **Birds** Quail, Pheasant, Huns;   **Dogs** Avail/HDW;   **Packages** 1 Day, 1-10 guns

Classic Upland Pheasant Hunting
RR1, Box 209, Liberal, KS 67901
(316) 624-2245 Stan Boles
6 mi. W of Liberal   **Acres** 2,200;   **Hunters/yr** 200;   **Type** Public;   **On Site** Clubhouse, Meals;   **Shoots** Field;   **Birds** Quail, Pheasant;   **Dogs** Avail

Claythorne Lodge
Rt. 1, Box 13, Hallowell, KS 66725
(316) 597-2568 Sam or Frieda Lancaster
150 mi. S of Kansas City   **Type** Public, Member/Avail;   **On Site** Clubhouse, Lodging, Meals, Clays;   **Shoots** Field;   **Birds** Quail, Pheasant, Chukar;   **Dogs** Avail/HDW;   **Packages** 1/2 Day, 1-10 guns

WINGS

Cokeley Farms

RR1, Box 149, Delia, KS 66418
(913) 771-3817 Will Cokeley
22 mi. NW of Topeka
Est 1988; **Acres** 2,000; **Type** Public, Member/Avail,
Corp.; **On Site** Clubhouse, Lodging, Meals, Clays;
Shoots Field, Driven, Blinds; **Birds** Quail, Pheasant,
Chukar, Huns, Turkey, Prairie Chicken, Ducks, Geese;
Dogs Avail/HDW; **Packages** 1/2 Day, 1-20 guns
See Our Ad Below

The Farm

HC1, Box 61, Clayton, KS 67629
(913) 567-4646 Raymond Scheetz
100 mi. NW of Hays
Est 1989; **Acres** 3,000; **Type** Public, Member/Avail,
Corp.; **On Site** Lodging, Meals, Clays; **Shoots** Field;
Birds Dove, Quail, Pheasant, Chukar; **Dogs**
Avail/HDW; **Packages** 2 Days, 2-6 guns
O NAGA/See Pg. 72

Five Double Bar Farms

RR1, Box 55, Selden, KS 67757
(913) 687-3785 Tom Beckman 7-10pm
270 mi. E of Denver
Est 1989; **Acres** 34,000; **Hunters/yr** 70; **Type**
Public; **On Site** Meals; **Shoots** Field; **Birds** Quail,
Pheasant, Turkey; **Dogs** Avail/HDW; **Packages** 1
Day, 1-6 guns

Flint Hills

PO Box 33, Atlanta, KS 67008
(316) 394-2345 Brent Flemming
45 mi. SE of Witchita
Est 1991; **Type** Public; **On Site** Clubhouse,
Lodging, Meals, Clays; **Shoots** Field; **Birds** Dove,
Quail, Prairie Chicken; **Dogs** Avail/HDW; **Packages**
1/2 Day, 2-10 guns

Flint Oak

Rt. 1, Box 262, Fall River, KS 67047
(316) 658-4401 Pete Laughlin 8:30am-5pm
75 mi. E of Wichita
Est 1979; **Acres** 2,800; **Type** Public, Member/Avail,
Corp.; **On Site** Clubhouse, Lodging, Meals, Clays;
Shoots Field, Driven; **Birds** Dove, Quail, Pheasant,
Chukar, Turkey; **Dogs** Avail/HDW; **Packages** 1/2
Day, 1-78 guns   O NAGA/See Pg. 72

Flying W Pheasant Ranch

6199 4 Rd., Plains, KS 67869
(316) 563-7679 Leon Winfrey
50 mi. SW of Dodge City
Est 1990; **Acres** 2,500; **Hunters/yr** 200; **Type**
Public; **On Site** Clubhouse, Lodging, Meals; **Shoots**
Field; **Birds** Pheasant, Chukar; **Dogs** Avail/HDW;
Packages 1/2 Day, 2-15 guns

Gunsmoke Hunting

PO Box 128, Hanston, KS 67849
(800) 476-6827 Walt/Gwen Salmans
35 mi. NE of Dodge City
Est 1982; **Acres** 4,000; **Hunters/yr** 200; **Type**

Public, Member/Avail;   **On Site** Lodging, Meals;
Shoots Field;   **Birds** Dove, Quail, Pheasant, Chukar;
Dogs Avail/HDW;   **Packages** 1 Day, 2-14 guns

Gunthunder
RR3, Great Bend, KS 67530
(316) 793-3738 John R. Miorandi Anytime
80 mi. NW of Wichita
Est 1974;   **Acres** 60,000;   **Hunters/yr** 65;   **Type**
Public;   **On Site** Clubhouse, Lodging, Meals, Clays;
Shoots Field, Blinds;   **Birds** Dove, Quail, Pheasant,
Prairie Chicken, Snipe, Sharp Tail Grouse, Ducks, Geese;
Dogs Avail/HDW;   **Packages** 2 Days, 1-5 guns

Horseshoe Bend

PO Box 121, Hoxie, KS 67740
(913) 675-2150 Delmar Foster 8pm-10pm
200 mi. E of Denver
Est 1989;   **Acres** 4,000;   **Hunters/yr** 65;   **Type**
Public, Member/Avail;   **On Site** Clubhouse, Lodging,
Clays;   **Shoots** Field;   **Birds** Dove, Quail, Pheasant,
Turkey, Prairie Chicken;   **Dogs** HDW;   **Packages** 2
Days, 1-6 guns

○ Hunting License	○ Bird Processing
○ Factory Ammunition	○ Quality Clubhouse
○ Family Run Business	○ Private Bedrooms
○ 16 RV Hook Ups	
○ White-Tail & Mule Deer Hunting Available	

The Hunnewell
Hunting Club, Inc.

RR#1, Box 9, South Haven, KS 67140
(316) 892-5821 Allan Helsel 9-3 Wkdays
50 mi. S of Wichita
Est 1991;   **Acres** 3,000;   **Hunters/yr** 50;   **Type**
Public;   **On Site** Clubhouse, Lodging, Meals, Clays;
Shoots Field;   **Birds** Quail, Pheasant, Huns;   **Dogs**
Avail/HDW;   **Packages** 1/2 Day, 1-12 guns

If you're looking for the kind of wingshooting experience that Kansas is justly famous for, look no
further than The Hunnewell Hunting Club. Our
packages include meals and the use of a roomy,
comfortable lodge. We provide you with the best
Kansas wild and released pheasant and released
Hungarian partridge hunting experience imaginable. Wild quail hunting, too! Small groups are our
specialty and personal attention is a Hunnewell Hallmark. Call today for more information and
reservations.

See Our Ad Below

Lil' Toledo Lodge

In Beautiful Southeast Kansas

1,000 Acres on the Neosho River
PHEASANT • CHUKAR • QUAIL
MALLARD DUCKS AVAILABLE

- Excellent Guides & Dogs
- Overnight Lodging Available
- Corporate & Private Meetings
- Sporting Clays & Five Stand
- Airport & Airport Limo Available

Call for information and reservations:

316-244-5668 or 316-763-2494
Rt. #4, Box 117, Chanute KS 66720

Hunting Sports Plus
710 Main St., Ste. E, Blue Springs, MO,
Hunting in 7 states including, Kansas
(800) 729-1924 Dan Gasser
Est 1989; Acres 200,000; Type Public,
Member/Avail; On Site Clubhouse, Lodging, Meals,
Clays; Shoots Field, Blinds, Boat; Birds Quail,
Pheasant, Turkey, Prairie Chicken, Ducks, Geese;
Dogs Avail/HDW; Packages 1 Day, 1-24 guns
See Our Ad Pg. 301

Jayhawk Outfitting
PO Box 117, Hill City, KS 67642
(913) 674-2284 Steve Lewis
180 mi. NW of Wichita
Est 1989; Acres 18,000; Hunters/yr 150; Type
Public; On Site Clubhouse, Lodging, Meals; Shoots
Field; Birds Quail, Pheasant; Dogs Avail/HDW;
Packages 1 Day, 1-15 guns

Lazy J Hunting Service
PO Box 832, Sublette, KS 67877
(316) 675-2338 Dave Holloway
50 mi. W of Dodge City
Est 1980; Acres 10,000; Hunters/yr 400; Type
Public; On Site Clubhouse, Meals; Shoots Field;
Birds Pheasant, Chukar; Dogs Avail; Packages 1/2
Day, 1-40 guns

Lil' Toledo Lodge
Rt. 4, Box 117, Chanute, KS 66720
(316) 244-5668 Ron King 8-5
100 mi. SW of Kansas City
Est 1991; Acres 2,000; Type Public, Member/Avail;
On Site Clubhouse, Lodging, Meals, Clays; Shoots
Field; Birds Quail, Pheasant, Chukar, Huns, Turkey,
Sage Grouse; Dogs Avail/HDW; Packages 1/2 Day,
1-5 guns
See Our Ad Above

Lone Pine Shooting Preserve
RR#1, Box 79, Toronto, KS 66777
(316) 637-2967 Mike Hammon
75 mi. E of Wichita
Acres 550; Type Public; Shoots Field; Birds Quail,
Pheasant, Chukar; Dogs Avail/HDW O NAGA/See Pg. 72

Mid America Adventure
11565 E. Plymell Rd., Pierceville, KS 67860
(316) 335-5522 Earl & Crystal Reist
Type Public; Shoots Field; Birds Pheasant, Chukar
O NAGA/See Pg. 72

Mill Creek Hunting Preserve
RR2, Box 78, Washington, KS 66968
(913) 325-2529 Charles Penning
100 mi. NW of Topeka
Est 1994; Acres 680; Type Public; On Site Clays;
Shoots Field; Birds Quail, Pheasant

Ole Olson's Wild Bird Hunts
225 S. Main, Lindsborg, KS 67456
(913) 227-2528 Jeffrey D. Olson After 6pm
from Salina
Est 1982; Acres 15,000; Type Member/Avail;
Shoots Field; Birds Dove, Quail, Pheasant, Prairie
Chicken; Dogs Avail/HDW; Packages 1 Day

Pheasant Creek
Box 209, Lakin, KS 67860
(316) 355-7118 J.R. Dienst 8am-12noon
210 mi. W of Wichita
Est 1988; Acres 15,000; Hunters/yr 200; Type
Public; On Site Clubhouse, Lodging, Meals; Shoots
Field; Birds Quail, Pheasant, Chukar, Turkey, Prairie
Chicken; Dogs Avail; Packages 1 Day, 1-30 guns
O NAGA/See Pg. 72

Pheasant
Hunters
Paradise

Pheasant Hunters Paradise
RR#1, Box 96, Kismet, KS 67859
(316) 563-7544 C.J. Wettstein
180 mi. W of Wichita
Est 1990; Acres 880; Hunters/yr 250; Type
Public, Member/Avail, Corp.; On Site Clubhouse,
Lodging, Meals, Clays; Shoots Field; Birds Quail,
Pheasant; Dogs Avail/HDW; Packages 1 Day, 1-25
guns
O Hunting License   O Airport Pickup
O Bird Processing   O Kennel Bird Dogs
O Quality Clubhouse

Pheasants Galore
HCR1, Box 5, Sublette, KS 67877
(316) 675-8418 Jill or Vern Hibbard
150 mi. W of Wichita
Est 1981; Acres 5,000; Hunters/yr 300; Type
Public; On Site Clubhouse, Lodging, Meals; Shoots
Field; Birds Pheasant, Chukar; Dogs Avail/HDW

Prairie Land Wildlife, Inc.
2009 South Sylvia Rd., Sylvia, KS 67581
(316) 486-2496 Rodney or Marilyn Hurst
80 mi. NW of Witchita
Est 1995; **Acres** 3,500; **Type** Public; **On Site**
Clubhouse; **Shoots** Field, Blinds; **Birds** Dove, Quail,
Pheasant, Turkey, Ducks, Geese; **Dogs** Avail/HDW;
Packages 1 Day, 1-5 guns

Prairie Winds Guide Service
1611 K-157 Hwy., Junction City, KS 67441
(913) 257-3234 Thomas D. Slick After 9pm
120 mi. W of Kansas City
Est 1988; **Acres** 4,000; **Hunters/yr** 40; **Type**
Public; **On Site** Lodging, Meals; **Shoots** Field;
Birds Dove, Quail, Pheasant, Turkey, Prairie Chicken;
Dogs Avail/HDW; **Packages** 1/2 Day, 1-6 guns

Quail Valley
Sporting Clays & Hunt Club
16501 NW 72nd; RR1, Box 134,
Moundridge, KS 67107
(316) 345-8367 Mike & Greg Stucky 8-10 evenings
35 mi. NW of Wichita
Est 1992; **Acres** 320; **Type** Public; **On Site**
Clubhouse, Lodging, Meals, Clays; **Shoots** Field;
Birds Quail, Pheasant, Chukar; **Dogs** Avail/HDW;
Packages 1/2 Day, 1-10 guns O NAGA/See Pg. 72

RMF Guide Service
PO Box 1924, Manhattan, KS 66502
(913) 537-4682 Ronald M. Ford 5-6am; 7-10pm
58 mi. W of Topeka
Est 1991; **Acres** 100,000; **Hunters/yr** 200; **Type**
Public; **On Site** Lodging, Meals; **Shoots** Field;
Birds Dove, Quail, Pheasant, Turkey, Prairie Chicken,
Ducks, Geese; **Dogs** Avail/HDW; **Packages** 1 Day,
2-12 guns

Ravenwood Hunting
Preserve & Sporting Clays
10147 SW 61 St., Topeka, KS 66610
(913) 256-6444 Ken Corbet
50 mi. W of Kansas City
Est 1985; **Acres** 1,500; **Type** Public, Member/Avail,
Corp.; **On Site** Clubhouse, Meals, Clays; **Shoots**
Field; **Birds** Dove, Quail, Pheasant, Chukar, Turkey,
Prairie Chicken, Ducks, Geese; **Dogs** Avail/HDW;
Packages 1/2 Day, 1-20 guns O NAGA/See Pg. 72
See Our Ad Below

Red Rock Game Farm
10855 Broderick, Wamago, KS 66547
(913) 456-7664 Lynn Pugh
10 mi. N of Wamego   **Acres** 320; **Type** Public;
On Site Clays; **Shoots** Field; **Birds** Quail, Pheasant,
Chukar; **Dogs** Avail/HDW

Ringneck Ranch Inc.

HC61, Box 7, Tipton, KS 67485
(913) 373-4835 Keith or Debra Houghton Day or
evening
75 mi. NW of Salina
Est 1983; **Acres** 10,000; **Hunters/yr** 900; **Type**
Public; **On Site** Clubhouse, Lodging, Meals, Clays;
Shoots Field, Blinds; **Birds** Dove, Quail, Pheasant,
Turkey, Prairie Chicken, Ducks, Geese; **Dogs**
Avail/HDW; **Packages** 1 Day, 1-30 guns
○ NAGA/See Pg. 72
See Our Ad Below

Show-Me Bird Hunting Resort

Rt. 1, Box 134, Baxter Springs, KS 66713
(316) 674-8863 Kim Shira
Type Public; **On Site** Lodging; **Shoots** Field; **Birds**
Pheasant, Chukar ○ NAGA/See Pg. 72

Solomon Valley Farm

1894 W. 70th Dr., Alton, KS 67623
(913) 346-2570 Bob Saylor
6 mi. N of Osborne
Acres 1,100; **Hunters/yr** 200; **Type** Public; **On
Site** Lodging, Meals, Clays; **Shoots** Field; **Birds**
Quail, Pheasant, Turkey, Prairie Chicken; **Dogs** Avail

Spillman Creek Lodge

RD1, Box 40, Sylvan Grove, KS 67481
(913) 277-3424 Merrill Nielsen
55 mi. NW of Salina
Est 1987; **Acres** 1,200; **Type** Public; **On Site**
Clubhouse, Lodging, Meals; **Shoots** Field; **Birds**
Quail, Pheasant; **Dogs** Avail/HDW; **Packages** 1/2
Day, 1-16 guns ○ NAGA/See Pg. 72
See Our Ad Across Right

Sporting Chance Shooting

PO Box 112, Downs, KS 67437
(913) 454-6233 Bill Myers
90 mi. W of Salina
Acres 2,000; **Type** Public; **On Site** Lodging, Meals;
Shoots Field; **Birds** Quail, Pheasant; **Dogs** Avail;
Packages 1/2 Day

Sullivan Sand and Sage

3019 North Road G, Ulysses, KS 67880
(316) 356-3924 Shane/Mary Sullivan
200 mi. W of Wichita
Est 1988; **Acres** 1,500; **Hunters/yr** 50; **Type**
Public, Corp.; **On Site** Lodging, Meals, Clays;
Shoots Field; **Birds** Quail, Pheasant, Chukar, Huns;
Dogs Avail/HDW; **Packages** 1 Day, 2-15 guns
○ NAGA/See Pg. 72

Tinkle Creek Game Farm

Rt. 1, Box 56, Marquette, KS 67464
(913) 546-2387 Rhonda Lindstedt
75 mi. NW of Wichita
Acres 1,840; **Hunters/yr** 75; **Shoots** Field; **Birds**
Quail, Pheasant, Turkey, Prairie Chicken; **Dogs** Avail

Eldon R. Trost

RR#2, Box 70, Belleville, KS 66935
(913) 243-3934 Eldon R. Trost Before 7:30am, After
6pm
60 mi. N of Salina
Est 1986; **Acres** 6,000; **Hunters/yr** 200; **Type**
Public; **On Site** Lodging; **Shoots** Field; **Birds** Dove,
Quail, Pheasant, Turkey, Prairie Chicken, Snipe, Ducks,
Geese; **Dogs** Avail/HDW; **Packages** 1/2 Day, 1-15
guns
○ Bird Processing   ○ Deer Hunting
○ Loaner Guns   ○ Fishing
○ Family Run Business

Twin Mounds Lodge

RR2, Box 14B, Plainville, KS 67663
(913) 434-2488 Phil Hinger 6-8pm
30 mi. N of Hays
Est 1988; **Acres** 3,000; **Hunters/yr** 100; **Type**
Public; **On Site** Clubhouse, Lodging, Meals; **Shoots**

Field; **Birds** Dove, Quail, Pheasant, Prairie Chicken;
Dogs Avail/HDW; **Packages** 1 Day, 1-10 guns

Uhlik Hunting Grounds
RR1, Box 51, Washington, KS 66968
(913) 325-2747 Mark Uhlik After 7 pm
150 mi. NW of Kansas City
Est 1987; **Acres** 12,000; **Type** Public; **Shoots**
Field; **Birds** Quail, Pheasant, Turkey, Prairie Chicken;
Dogs Avail/HDW; **Packages** 1 Day, 2-18 guns

Walnut Ridge
Hunting Preserve
RR1, Box 35A, Walnut, KS 66780
(316) 354-6713 Mike or Barb Duling
120 mi. S of Kansas City
Est 1988; **Acres** 760; **Type** Public; **On Site**
Clubhouse, Clays; **Shoots** Field; **Birds** Quail,
Pheasant, Chukar; **Dogs** Avail/HDW; **Packages** 1/2
Day O NAGA/See Pg. 72
O Bird Processing   O Sporting Clays
O Brochure Available   O Quality Clubhouse
O Family Run Business

Walnut Valley Guide Service
Rt. 2, Box 250, Arkansas City, KS 67005
(316) 442-6442 Steve Shirley Anytime
40 mi. SE of Wichita
Est 1989; **Type** Public; **On Site** Clubhouse,
Lodging, Clays; **Shoots** Field; **Birds** Dove, Quail,
Pheasant, Chukar, Turkey, Prairie Chicken, Ducks,
Geese; **Dogs** Avail/HDW; **Packages** 2 Days,

*Whenever you contact one of the
companies listed or advertising in Wing &
Clay, please remember to tell them that you
benefitted from the information you found
here. And don't forget to say : "I saw it in
Wing & Clay."*

KENTUCKY

Cane Spring Hunting Preserve
4156 Deatsville Rd., Shepherdsville, KY 40165
(502) 543-6327 Gussy Allen
Type Public; **On Site** Lodging; **Birds** Quail,
Pheasant, Chukar O NAGA/See Pg. 72

The Cooper Field Hunting Club
641 Colvin Lk. Rd., Kevil, KY 42053
(502) 224-2668 Ed Allcock
120 mi. N of Nashville, TN
Est 1983; **Acres** 3,000; **Hunters/yr** 700; **Type**
Public; **On Site** Clubhouse, Lodging, Meals, Clays;
Shoots Field, Blinds; **Birds** Quail, Pheasant, Chukar,
Ducks, Geese; **Dogs** Avail/HDW; **Packages** 2 Days

Deer Creek Outfitters
P.O. Box 39, Sebree, KY 42455
(502) 835-2424 Tim Stull
140 mi. SW of Louisville
Est 1984; **Acres** 5,000; **Type** Public, Member/Avail;
On Site Clubhouse, Lodging, Meals, Clays; **Shoots**
Field, Blinds; **Birds** Dove, Quail, Pheasant, Chukar,
Turkey, Ducks, Geese; **Dogs** Avail/HDW; **Packages**
1/2 Day, 1-12 guns
See Our Ad Pg. 308

Gary & Jerry Shooting Preserve
3415 Ashbyburg Rd., Slaughters, KY 42456
(502) 884-7760 Jerry Morehead After 4 pm
50 mi. S of Evansville, IN
Est 1994; **Acres** 183; **Type** Public; **Shoots** Field;

Birds Quail, Woodcock, Pheasant, Chukar, Huns; **Dogs** Avail/HDW; **Packages** 1/2 Day, 1-8 guns

Grassy Lake Lodge
PO Box 319, Wickliffe, KY 42087
(502) 462-3595 Greg Joles
32 mi. SW of Paducah   **Est** 1985; **Acres** 4,000; **Type** Public, Member/Avail; **On Site** Clubhouse, Lodging, Meals, Clays; **Shoots** Field, Blinds; **Birds** Dove, Ducks, Geese; **Dogs** Avail/HDW; **Packages** 3 Days, 4-12 guns

Happy Ridge Quail Farm & Preserve
111 Shucks Rd., Pleasureville, KY 40057
(502) 878-4903 Eddie Shuck 6-10pm
45 mi. NE of Louisville
Est 1988; **Acres** 122; **Hunters/yr** 40; **Type** Public; **On Site** Clubhouse; **Shoots** Field; **Birds** Quail, Chukar; **Dogs** Avail/HDW; **Packages** 1/2 Day, 2-3 guns ○ NAGA/See Pg. 72

Kentucky Wonderland
Shooting Preserve
14301 Castle Hwy., Pleasureville, KY 40057
(502) 878-4412 Murray Armstrong Afternoons
50 mi. E of Louisville
Est 1973; **Acres** 350; **Type** Public, Member/Avail; **Shoots** Field; **Birds** Quail, Pheasant, Chukar, Turkey; **Dogs** Avail/HDW; **Packages** 1/2 Day, 1-20 guns
Want some exciting hunting this fall? Get in on the action at the Kentucky Wonderland Shooting Preserve. For the first time, controlled Turkey Hunts. Early morning hunts only. Turkey can be taken with muzzle loaders, bow, rifles or shotguns. Also available: Pheasant, Quail and Chukar. Give us a call!

Kentucky-Tennessee Quail Plantation
4785 Huffman Mill Rd., Hopkinsville, KY 42240
(502) 885-8877 Donnie or Goebel Adams After 4 pm
75 mi. NW of Nashville
Est 1988; **Acres** 550; **Type** Public; **On Site** Clubhouse, Lodging, Meals, Clays; **Shoots** Field; **Birds** Dove, Quail, Pheasant, Chukar; **Dogs** Avail/HDW; **Packages** 1/2 Day, 2-6 guns

Knotty Pine Hunting Preserve
2511 Coldwater Rd., Murray, KY 42071
(502) 753-5261 Paul Butterworth, Jr. Evenings
50 mi. S of Paducah, KY
Est 1989; **Acres** 300; **Hunters/yr** 100; **Type** Public; **On Site** Clubhouse; **Shoots** Field; **Birds** Quail, Pheasant, Chukar; **Dogs** Avail/HDW; **Packages** 1/2 Day, 1-4 guns ○ NAGA/See Pg. 72

Little Southfork Quail Preserve
1205 Hickory Ridge Rd., Waddy, KY 40076
(502) 223-2935 James S. Miller
7 mi. SW of Frankfort   **Acres** 130; **Type** Public, Member/Avail; **On Site** Lodging, Meals; **Shoots** Field; **Birds** Quail, Pheasant; **Dogs** Avail/HDW; **Packages** 1/2 Day ○ NAGA/See Pg. 72

Quail Run Hunting Preserve
Box 164, Walton, KY 41094
(606) 463-0912 Kelly Hance

45 mi. SW of Cincinnati, OH
Acres 250; **Hunters/yr** 350; **Type** Public; **On Site**
Clubhouse; **Shoots** Field; **Birds** Dove, Quail,
Pheasant, Turkey; **Dogs** Avail

Shoot Fire Sportsman's Farm
290 Koostra Rd., Bowling Green, KY 42101
(502) 781-9545 Kent Koostra
60 mi. N of Nashville
Est 1991; **Acres** 1,000; **Type** Public; **On Site**
Clubhouse, Meals, Clays; **Shoots** Field; **Birds** Quail,
Pheasant, Chukar, Turkey; **Dogs** Avail/HDW;
Packages 1/2 Day, 3-15 guns ○ NAGA/See Pg. 72

Sugar Creek Hunting
& Sporting Clays
RR2, Box 413, Mitchell, KY 47446
(812) 849-2296 Dale Waldbieser or (812) 849-5020
54 mi. NE of Lousiville
Est 1992; **Acres** 500; **Type** Public; **On Site**
Clubhouse, Meals, Clays; **Shoots** Field; **Birds** Quail,
Pheasant, Chukar; **Dogs** Avail/HDW; **Packages** 1/2
Day, 1-6 guns ○ NAGA/See Pg. 72

Turkey Creek Hunting Preserve
2145 Turkey Town Rd., Crab Orchard, KY 40419
(606) 355-7301 John Blanton 6-8 pm
40 mi. W of Lexington **Est** 1992; **Acres** 255;
Type Public; **Shoots** Field, Tower, Driven; **Birds**
Quail, Pheasant, Chukar; **Dogs** Avail/HDW

LOUISIANA

Ace Hunting Club
Rt. 1, Box 1465, Abbeville, LA 70510
(318) 643-2910 Gerald Patin
40 mi. from Lafayette
Acres 12,000; **Hunters/yr** 400; **Type** Public,
Member/Avail; **On Site** Clubhouse, Meals; **Shoots**
Tower, Blinds; **Birds** Ducks, Geese; **Dogs** Avail

C&C Game Birds Hunting Preserve
612 W. Main St., Broussard, LA 70518
(318) 837-6782 Charles E. Langlinais Anytime
150 mi. W of New Orleans
Est 1980; **Acres** 1,000; **Type** Public; **Shoots** Field;
Birds Chukar; **Dogs** Avail/HDW; **Packages** 1/2
Day, 1-4 guns ○ NAGA/See Pg. 72

Doug's Hunting Lodge
Rt. 1, Box 143, Gueydan, LA 70542
(800) 888-0960 Doug Sonnier Anytime
40 mi. SW of Lafayette
Est 1991; **Acres** 200; **Type** Public, Corp.; **On Site**
Clubhouse, Lodging, Meals, Clays; **Shoots** Field,
Tower, Blinds, Boat; **Birds** Dove, Quail, Pheasant,
Chukar, Snipe, Ducks, Geese; **Dogs** Avail/HDW;
Packages 1/2 Day, 1-54 guns

Dry Creek Ranch
Rt. 2, Box 510A, Ragley, LA 70657
(318) 666-2657 Josh & Rane Sills 6:30-5
30 mi. NE of Lake Charles
Acres 2,000; **Hunters/yr** 1,000; **Type** Public; **On
Site** Clubhouse, Lodging, Meals, Clays; **Shoots** Field,

WINGS

HILL COUNTRY PLANTATION INC.
HUNTING & SHOOTING ADVENTURES
• *Less Than One Hour From New Orleans* •

1500 acres of prime hunting land professionally managed to offer
the finest hunting and shooting entertainment available!

• Guided Duck, Quail, Pheasant & Dove Hunts •
• Newest and Largest 3-D Archery Range in 2 States •

GREAT CORPORATE ENTERTAINMENT & CONFERENCE CENTER

First Class Sporting Clays • Hunt Foot or Jeep • NSCA Level 2 Instruction • Quality Clubhouse

Contact: Owen Brennan at 800-986-4868
272 Dunleith Drive • Destrehan, LA 70047

Tower, Blinds;   **Birds** Dove, Quail, Pheasant, Chukar, Ducks;   **Dogs** Avail/HDW;   **Packages** 1/2 Day, 2-20 guns ○ NAGA/See Pg. 72

JM Futch, Inc.
PO Box 364, Arcadia, LA 71001
(318) 263-2850 John M. Futch
16 mi. SE of Arcadia
Acres 100;   **Hunters/yr** 6;   **Type** Member/Avail;
Shoots Field;   **Birds** Quail;   **Dogs** Avail

Hill Country Plantation
272 Dunleith Plantation, Destrehan, LA 70047
(800) 986-4868 Owen Brennan
50 mi. NE of New Orleans
Est 1994;   **Acres** 1,500;   **Type** Public;   **On Site**
Clubhouse, Lodging, Meals, Clays;   **Shoots** Field,
Tower, Driven, Blinds;   **Birds** Dove, Quail, Pheasant,
Chukar, Turkey, Ducks;   **Dogs** Avail/HDW;   **Packages**
1/2 Day, 1-50 guns
See Our Ad Pg. 309

Hilltop Quail Farm & Preserve
287 Hwy. 135, Winnsboro, LA 71295
(318) 435-6318 Sherman Phillips 9am-12pm; 1-9pm
50 mi. SE of Monroe, LA
Est 1985;   **Acres** 150;   **Type** Public;   **Shoots** Field;
Birds Quail;   **Dogs** Avail/HDW;   **Packages** 1/2 Day,
1-4 guns ○ NAGA/See Pg. 72

Land of Lakes
Rt. 3, Box 93, Ville Platte, LA 70586
(318) 363-6310 Woodson Harvey
Type Public;   **On Site** Clubhouse, Lodging, Meals;
Shoots Field;   **Birds** Dove, Pheasant, Chukar;   **Dogs**
Avail;   **Packages** 1/2 Day

Ace Cullum's
PIN OAK MALLARDS
711 Hwy. 15, Rayville, LA 71269
(800) 259-3827 Ace Cullum (318) 248-3549
15 mi. E of Monroe
Acres 1,000;   **Type** Public, Member/Avail;   **On Site**
Clubhouse, Lodging, Meals, Clays;   **Shoots** Field;
Birds Quail, Ducks;   **Dogs** Avail/HDW
PIN OAK MALLARDS "Best Damn Duck Club in Louisiana(R) with modern rustic lodge overlooking duck reservoir. 3 Meals; Experienced guides, excellent callers; Loaner Guns; Bird Processing; Crappie fishing; Brochure available; Flooded timber hunting; Boat to heated blinds or wade hunts; $200 per gun per day; airport pickup; clay shoots. Call Ace Cullum (318) 248-3549.

Plum Ridge Shooting Preserve
PO Box 364, Arcadia, LA 71001
(318) 263-2850 John M. Futch
50 mi. E of Shreveport
Type Public, Member/Avail;   **Shoots** Field;   **Birds**
Quail;   **Dogs** Avail/HDW;   **Packages** 1/2 Day, up to
3 guns

Wild Wings Hunting Preserve
Rt. 2, Box 26, Downsville, LA 71234
(318) 982-7777 Steve Bryan
75 mi. NE of Shreveport
Est 1979;   **Acres** 2,000;   **Type** Public, Member/Avail,
Corp.;   **On Site** Clubhouse, Lodging, Meals, Clays;
Shoots Field;   **Birds** Dove, Quail, Pheasant, Chukar,
Turkey, Ducks;   **Dogs** Avail/HDW

MAINE

Bosebuck Mtn. Camps
Rt. 16, Box 330, Wilsons Mills, ME 03579
(207) 243-2945 Tom Rideout 8 am to 10 pm
90 mi. N of Portland
Est 1907;   **Acres** 200,000;   **Hunters/yr** 150;   **Type**
Public;   **On Site** Clubhouse, Lodging, Meals;   **Shoots**
Field;   **Birds** Ruffed Grouse, Woodcock;   **Dogs**
Avail/HDW;   **Packages** 1 Day, 1-20 guns

The Bradford Camps
PO Box 499, Patten, ME 04765
(207) 746-7777 Dave or Nancy Youland
75 mi. W of Presque Isle
Est 1890;   **Acres** 1,000,000;   **Type** Public;   **On Site**
Clubhouse, Lodging, Meals, Clays;   **Shoots** Field;
Birds Ruffed Grouse, Woodcock;   **Dogs** Avail/HDW;
Packages 3 Days, up to 10 guns

Coastal Maine Outfitters
RFD#1, Box 2380, Brooks, ME 04921
(207) 722-3218 Joe Lucey
40 mi. SE of Bangor
Est 1980;   **Acres** 5,000;   **Hunters/yr** 200;   **Type**
Public;   **On Site** Clubhouse, Lodging, Meals, Clays;
Shoots Field, Boat;   **Birds** Ruffed Grouse, Woodcock,
Ducks;   **Dogs** Avail/HDW;   **Packages** 3 Days, 2-8 guns

Freehold Lodge Club, Inc.
RFD1, Box 141, Perry, ME 04667
(207) 726-5093 George W. Fennell
100 mi. E of Bangor
Est 1992;   **Acres** 500;   **Type** Public;   **On Site**
Clubhouse, Lodging, Meals;   **Shoots** Field;   **Birds**
Ruffed Grouse, Woodcock, Ducks, Geese;   **Dogs**
HDW;   **Packages** 1 Day, up to 1 guns

Georges River Outfitters
1364 Atlantic Hwy., Warren, ME 04864
(207) 273-3818 Jeff Bellmore
Est 1986;   **Type** Public;   **On Site** Clubhouse,
Lodging, Meals;   **Shoots** Field, Blinds, Boat;   **Birds**
Ruffed Grouse, Woodcock, Ducks;   **Dogs** Avail/HDW;
Packages 1 Day, 2-6 guns

King & Bartlett Fish & Game Club
PO Box 500, New Gloucester, ME 04260
(207) 926-4147 Matthew Thurston 8-4, M-F

120 mi. NW of Bangor
Est 1894; **Acres** 24,000; **Type** Public,
Member/Avail; **On Site** Clubhouse, Lodging, Meals,
Clays; **Shoots** Field, Blinds, Boat; **Birds** Ruffed
Grouse, Woodcock, Ducks, Geese; **Dogs** Avail/HDW;
Packages 1 Day, 1-12 guns

Long Lake Camps
PO Box 807, West St., Princeton, ME 04668
(800) 435-0212 Ed & Kyle Staples
110 mi. NE of Bangor
Est 1945; **Acres** 65; **Hunters/yr** 60; **Type** Public;
On Site Clubhouse, Lodging, Meals, Clays; **Shoots**
Field, Blinds, Boat; **Birds** Ruffed Grouse, Woodcock,
Ducks, Geese; **Dogs** Avail/HDW; **Packages** 1 Day,
1-35 guns

Maine Game Bird Guides
RR#2, Box 468, Belfast, ME 04915
(207) 722-3664 Jo-Ann Moody Evenings
40 mi. S of Bangor
Est 1987; **Hunters/yr** 50; **Type** Public; **On Site**
Lodging, Meals; **Shoots** Driven; **Birds** Ruffed
Grouse, Woodcock, Pheasant; **Dogs** Avail/HDW;
Packages 1 Day, 1-8 guns

Medawisla on Second Roach Pond
RR 76, Box 592, Greenville, ME 04441
(207) 695-2690 Larry LeRoy Daytime
70 mi. NW of Bangor
Acres 10,000; **Type** Public; **On Site** Lodging, Clays;
Shoots Field; **Birds** Ruffed Grouse, Woodcock;
Dogs HDW

Northern Outdoors
Rt. 201, PO Box 100, The Forks, ME 04985
(800) 765-7238 Wayne Hockmeyer
100 mi. NW of Bangor
Type Public; **On Site** Clubhouse, Lodging, Meals;
Shoots Field; **Birds** Ruffed Grouse, Woodcock;
Dogs Avail

Pathfinder Guide Service
RR1, Box 4173, Camden, ME 04843
(207) 236-0832 Bob Foshay 8am-8pm
50 mi. S of Bangor
Est 1989; **Type** Public; **On Site** Meals; **Shoots**
Field, Driven; **Birds** Ruffed Grouse, Woodcock;
Dogs Avail/HDW; **Packages** 1 Day, 1-3 guns

Red River Camps
PO Box 320, Portage, ME 04765
(207) 435-6000 Mike Brophy
135 mi. N of Bangor
Est 1900; **Acres** 1,000; **Hunters/yr** 50; **Type**
Public; **On Site** Clubhouse, Lodging, Meals; **Shoots**
Field; **Birds** Ruffed Grouse; **Dogs** HDW; **Packages**
2 Days, 4-12 guns

Ridge Runner Guide Service
RFD1, Box 645, Monroe, ME 04951
(207) 525-3588 Les Thompson
24 mi. SW of Bangor
Est 1988; **Type** Public; **On Site** Clubhouse,
Lodging; **Shoots** Field; **Birds** Ruffed Grouse,
Woodcock; **Dogs** Avail/HDW; **Packages** 1 Day, 1-3
guns

River View Hunting Preserve
PO Box 278, Anson, ME 04911
(207) 696-3076 Chet Flanagin 9-4, M-S
10 mi. N of Madison
Est 1990; **Acres** 200; **Hunters/yr** 150; **Type**
Public; **Shoots** Field; **Birds** Quail, Pheasant; **Dogs**
Avail/HDW; **Packages** 1/2 Day, 1-4 guns

The Village Camps
Box 101-W, Forest City, ME 04413
(207) 448-7726 Lance Wheaton
110 mi. NE of Bangor **Est** 1989; **Type** Public; **On
Site** Lodging; **Shoots** Field; **Birds** Ruffed Grouse,
Woodcock, Ducks, Geese; **Dogs** Avail/HDW

MARYLAND

B&J Goose Hunting
31106 Chesterville Bridge Rd., Millington, MD 21651
(410) 928-5260 Joe Kuhn **Est** 1973; **Type** Public;
Shoots Field, Blinds, Boat; **Birds** Ducks, Geese;
Dogs Avail; **Packages** 1 Day, 1-5 guns

Bourbon Brook Hunting Preserve
141 Seney Rd., Church Hill, MD 21623
(410) 556-6177 Wayne or Donnie McFarland Evenings
40 mi. E of Annapolis **Est** 1989; **Acres** 400;
Hunters/yr 250; **Type** Public; **Shoots** Field, Blinds;
Birds Quail, Pheasant, Chukar, Huns, Turkey, Geese;
Dogs Avail/HDW; **Packages** 1/2 Day, 1-10 guns

Steve Campbell
Box 256, Galesville, MD 20765 ·
(410) 867-7144 Steve Campbell
Type Public, Member/Avail; **Shoots** Field; **Birds**
Quail, Pheasant, Chukar O NAGA/See Pg. 72

Caroline County
Shooting Preserve
8785 New Bridge Rd., Denton, MD 21629
(410) 479-2364 Tom/Don/Steve Swann 6 to 10 pm
60 mi. E of Washington, DC
Est 1963; **Acres** 400; **Hunters/yr** 1,200; **Type**
Public; **On Site** Clubhouse; **Shoots** Field, Blinds;
Birds Dove, Quail, Pheasant, Chukar, Huns, Ducks;
Dogs Avail/HDW; **Packages** 1/2 Day, 1-10 guns
O Hunting License   O Airport Pickup
O Bird Processing   O Brochure Available
O Family Run Business
In 1963, the Swann family began operating one of
the first and possibly the best hunting and shooting paradises in the Mid-Shore area. The grounds
are located conveniently 4 miles west of Denton
and 12 miles east of Easton on Route 328. The
Swann family knows what makes a good hunt and
personally sees that your expectations are met – so
they can count on you returning for many more enjoyable experiences.
HUNT PACKAGES: $10 per gunner on all bird hunts-
-includes dog and guide-gratuity not included. Pheasant $15; Quail $5; Chukar $10; Hungarian Par-
tridge $12; Mallard Ducks $14–all are per bird
released.

Chesapeake Hunt
16090 Oakland Rd. (Rt. 312, Bridgetown)
Henderson, MD 21640
(410) 758-1824 Bill Connors Su-S, 9am-6pm
65 mi. NE of Washington, DC
Est 1990; **Acres** 419; **Hunters/yr** 150; **Type**
Public, Member/Avail; **On Site** Clubhouse, Lodging,
Meals, Clays; **Shoots** Field, Tower, Driven, Blinds;
Birds Dove, Quail, Pheasant, Chukar, Turkey, Ducks,
Geese; **Dogs** Avail/HDW

Bill Clark's Goose Hunting
23141 Schooner Rd., Chestertown, MD 21620
(410) 778-5854 Bill Clark
50 mi. E of Baltimore
Acres 2,000; **Type** Public, Member/Avail, Corp.;
On Site Lodging; **Shoots** Blinds, Boat; **Birds** Ducks,
Geese; **Dogs** Avail/HDW

Jeffrey Barnett Clark, Sr.
405 Spider Web Rd., Centreville, MD 21617
(410) 758-2763 Jeff Clark
W of Centreville
Acres 1,000; **Hunters/yr** 400; **Type** Public;
Shoots Field, Blinds; **Birds** Dove, Quail, Pheasant,
Chukar, Ducks, Geese; **Dogs** Avail

Fair Winds Gun Club
5886 Quaker Neck Rd., Chestertown, MD 21620
(410) 778-5363 Clint Evans 9-5
from Chestertown
Est 1980; **Acres** 2,500; **Hunters/yr** 750; **Type**
Public, Corp.; **On Site** Lodging, Meals; **Shoots**
Field, Blinds, Boat; **Birds** Dove, Ducks, Geese; **Dogs**
HDW; **Packages** 1 Day
○ Hunting License　　　　○ Airport Pickup
○ Bird Processing　　　　○ Gourmet Meals
○ Brochure Available　　○ Seasonal Packages Available
Fair Winds Gun Club manages over 2,200 acres in
and around Chestertown on Maryland's Eastern
Shore. We have day hunts with fully trained, experi-
enced professionals. Through its habitat
management program, the September Dove shoot-
ing is superb. Diverse hunting grounds provide for
widest variety of waterfowl shooting – including
Canada & Snow Geese, puddle, diving & Sea Ducks.
Early reservations are urged. We will arrange for accommodations & meals per your request.

Fairs Regulated Shooting Area
1605 Old Virginia Rd., Pocomoke City, MD 21851
(410) 957-1749 Ray Fair
30 mi. S of Salisbury
Acres 270; **Type** Public; **On Site** Clubhouse, Clays;
Shoots Field; **Birds** Quail, Pheasant, Chukar, Huns;
Dogs Avail/HDW ○ NAGA/See Pg. 72

Fly-By-Island, Inc.
3052 Crosiadore Lane, Trappe, MD 21673
(410) 476-3843 Bo Kennedy Evenings
17 mi. from Easton
Est 1975; **Acres** 1,500; **Type** Public; **On Site**
Meals, Clays; **Shoots** Field, Blinds; **Birds** Ducks,
Geese; **Packages** 1 Day

Goose Valley Farming & Outfitting
12504 Augustine Herman Hwy., Kennedyville, MD
21645
(410) 778-5300 Floyd-Tom-Kay 10 to 5
35 mi. E of Baltimore
Est 1956; **Acres** 5,000; **Hunters/yr** 561; **Type**
Public, Member/Avail, Corp.; **On Site** Lodging,
Meals; **Shoots** Field, Tower, Blinds; **Birds** Dove,
Pheasant, Chukar, Ducks, Geese; **Dogs** Avail/HDW;
Packages 1 Day, up to 150 guns

Green Rest Hunting Preserve
Star Rt. 2, Box 2, Valley Lee, MD 20692
(301) 994-2104 Ronnie Carter Evenings
60 mi. SE of Washington, DC
Est 1990; **Acres** 450; **Type** Public; **On Site**
Clubhouse; **Shoots** Field, Tower; **Birds** Dove, Quail,
Pheasant, Chukar, Huns; **Dogs** Avail/HDW;
Packages 1/2 Day, 2-8 guns

Greensboro Regulated Hunting Preserve
PO Box 159, Greensboro, MD 21639
(410) 482-6873 A.W. Spiering, Jr.
60 mi. E of Washington, DC
Est 1980; **Acres** 500; **Type** Public, Member/Avail,
Corp.; **On Site** Clubhouse, Lodging, Clays; **Shoots**
Field, Blinds; **Birds** Dove, Quail, Pheasant, Chukar,
Huns, Ducks, Geese; **Dogs** Avail/HDW; **Packages**
1/2 Day, 2-10 guns

Gunpowder Game Farm
17904 Gunpowder Rd., Hampstead, MD 21074
(410) 374-1434 David or Wendy Tracey
30 mi. N of Baltimore
Est 1991; **Acres** 300; **Type** Public; **Shoots** Field;
Birds Quail, Pheasant; **Dogs** Avail/HDW; **Packages**
1/2 Day, 1-4 guns ○ NAGA/See Pg. 72
○ Brochure Available　　○ Family Run Business
○ Entertain Clients　　　○ Hard Flying Birds
○ Wide Variety of Hunts

Hopkins Game Farm
PO Box 218, Kennedyville, MD 21645
(410) 348-5287 George or Patti 9 to 9
35 mi. E of Baltimore
Est 1983; **Acres** 600; **Type** Public; **On Site**
Clubhouse, Lodging, Meals, Clays; **Shoots** Field,
Tower, Blinds; **Birds** Dove, Quail, Pheasant, Chukar,
Huns, Ducks; **Dogs** Avail/HDW; **Packages** 1/2 Day
○ NAGA/See Pg. 72

Masons Branch Hunting Preserve
22 Mason Branch, Queen Anne, MD 21657
(410) 758-0162 Donald Lee Dean, Jr. After 6 pm
50 mi. E of Washington, DC
Est 1989; **Acres** 300; **Hunters/yr** 150; **Type**
Public, Member/Avail; **On Site** Meals; **Shoots** Field,
Blinds; **Birds** Dove, Quail, Pheasant, Chukar, Huns,
Turkey, Ducks, Geese; **Dogs** Avail/HDW; **Packages**
1/2 Day, 1-10 guns

Pintail Point Farm

511 Pintail Point Farm Lane, Queenstown, MD 21658
(410) 827-7029 Carol Johnson or Bob Burris
Eastern Shore, 20 mi. E of Bay Bridge
Est 1993; **Acres** 1,250; **Type** Public, Member/Avail;
On Site Clubhouse, Lodging, Meals, Clays; **Shoots**
Field, Blinds, Boat; **Birds** Dove, Quail, Pheasant,
Chukar, Huns, Ducks, Geese; **Dogs** Avail/HDW;
Packages 1/2 Day, 1-16 guns ○ NAGA/See Pg. 72
○ Hunting License   ○ Airport Pickup
○ Loaner Guns   ○ Sporting ClayS, 5-Stand Ranges
○ Arrange accommodations locally
See Our Ad Below

Quaker Neck Gun Club, Inc.

PO Box 2600, Chestertown, MD 21620
(410) 778-6965 F. Tyler Johnson 8-4
3 mi. SE of Chestertown
Est 1981; **Acres** 3,500; **Type** Public, Member/Avail,
Corp.; **On Site** Clubhouse, Lodging, Clays; **Shoots**
Blinds, Boat; **Birds** Dove, Turkey, Ducks, Geese;
Dogs Avail/HDW; **Packages** 1 Day, 1-20 guns

Schrader's Hunting

900 Red Lion Branch Rd., Millington, MD 21651
(410) 778-1895 Ken, Owner/Operator
50 mi. E of Washington, DC
Est 1982; **Acres** 10,000; **Type** Public,
Member/Avail; **Shoots** Field, Blinds, Boat; **Birds**
Dove, Quail, Pheasant, Chukar, Huns, Ducks, Geese;
Dogs Avail/HDW; **Packages** 1/2 Day, 1-16 guns
○ NAGA/See Pg. 72
○ Hunting License   ○ Deer Hunting
○ Train Bird Dogs   ○ Brochure Available
○ Fishing

Sheaffer's Hunting Preserve

PO Box 28, Pioneer Point, Centreville, MD 21617
(410) 778-0185 John Whaley 7-10 pm
Est 1985; **Acres** 350; **Type** Public; **Shoots** Field,
Tower; **Birds** Quail, Pheasant, Chukar; **Dogs**
Avail/HDW; **Packages** 1/2 Day, up to 4 guns

Southern Maryland Gun Club

PO Box 332, West River, MD 20778
(410) 823-4399 Kevin Colheck
20 mi. S of Annapolis
Est 1993; **Acres** 1,400; **Type** Public, Corp.; **On
Site** Meals; **Shoots** Field; **Birds** Dove, Quail; **Dogs**
Avail/HDW; **Packages** 1/2 Day, 1-25 guns

Windy Hill Shooting Preserve

8145 Shire Dr., Berlin, MD 21811
(410) 641-4553 Randall M. Hastings after 6 pm
120 mi. S of Philadelphia

Est 1988; **Acres** 300; **Hunters/yr** 100; **Type** Public; **Shoots** Field, Blinds; **Birds** Dove, Quail, Pheasant, Chukar, Ducks; **Dogs** HDW; **Packages** 1/2 Day, 1-4 guns

MASSACHUSETTS

Fullflight Game Farm & Preserve
4 Brattleboro Rd., Bernardston, MA 01337
(413) 648-9580 Edwin Gray
Type Public, Member/Avail; **Shoots** Field; **Birds** Quail, Pheasant, Chukar, Huns ○ NAGA/See Pg. 72

Hedgerow Kennel & Hunt Club
Rt. 32, RFD2, Athol, MA 01331
(508) 249-7115 Patrick Perry
70 mi. W of Boston
Est 1986; **Acres** 108; **Hunters/yr** 300; **Type** Public, Member/Avail, Corp.; **On Site** Clubhouse; **Shoots** Field, Tower; **Birds** Quail, Pheasant, Chukar; **Dogs** Avail/HDW; **Packages** 1/2 Day, 1-3 guns

Lissivigeen
221 Adams Rd., Oakham, MA 01068
(508) 882-3404 Kevin J. Coakley After 8pm
55 mi. W of Boston
Est 1988; **Acres** 240; **Hunters/yr** 250; **Type** Public, Member/Avail, Corp.; **On Site** Clubhouse, Meals, Clays; **Shoots** Field, Tower; **Birds** Quail, Ruffed Grouse, Woodcock, Pheasant, Chukar, Ducks, Geese; **Dogs** Avail/HDW; **Packages** 1/2 Day, up to 4 guns ○ NAGA/See Pg. 72

Royal Hunt Club, Inc.
98 Old Plain St., E. Middleboro, MA 02346
(508) 947-8141 Joseph L. Di Santis 7am to 9pm
50 mi. from Boston
Est 1967; **Acres** 2,000; **Type** Member/Avail, Corp.; **On Site** Clubhouse, Lodging, Meals, Clays; **Shoots** Field, Driven, Blinds, Boat; **Birds** Dove, Quail, Ruffed Grouse, Woodcock, Pheasant, Chukar, Huns, Snipe, Ducks, Geese; **Dogs** Avail/HDW; **Packages** 1 Day, 1-24 guns

MICHIGAN

Andy's Acres
Shooting Preserve
14902 A Dr. N., Marshall, MI 49068
(616) 781-8676 Jack H. Anderson 8am-10pm
30 mi. S of Lansing or Ft. Wayne, IN
Est 1977; **Acres** 118; **Type** Public, Member/Avail, Corp.; **On Site** Clubhouse; **Shoots** Field; **Birds** Quail, Pheasant, Chukar, Ducks, Geese; **Dogs** Avail/HDW; **Packages** 1/2 Day, 1-8 guns

○ Airport Pickup   ○ Family Recreation
○ Shooting Instruction   ○ Train Bird Dogs
○ Loaner Guns   ○ Quality Clubhouse
○ Family Run Business

Big Creek Shooting Preserve
PO Box 369, 269 Zimowske Rd., Mio, MI 48647
(517) 826-3606 Steven A. Basl 8am-5pm

130 mi. NE of Grand Rapids
Est 1991; **Acres** 365; **Hunters/yr** 500; **Type** Public, Member/Avail, Corp.; **On Site** Clubhouse, Clays; **Shoots** Field, Tower, Blinds; **Birds** Ruffed Grouse, Woodcock, Pheasant, Chukar, Turkey, Ducks, Geese; **Dogs** Avail/HDW; **Packages** 1/2 Day, 1-32 guns ○ NAGA/See Pg. 72

Blendon Pines
8455 88th Ave., Zeeland, MI 49464
(616) 875-7000 Arvin Boersema
20 mi. SW of Grand Rapids
Est 1990; **Acres** 200; **Type** Public, Member/Avail; **On Site** Clubhouse, Meals, Clays; **Shoots** Field; **Birds** Quail, Chukar, Huns; **Dogs** Avail/HDW; **Packages** 1/2 Day, 1-15 guns ○ NAGA/See Pg. 72

Ciavola Ranch
77377 McKay, Romeo, MI 48065
(810) 752-2133 Howard Ciavola
Type Member/Avail; **Shoots** Field; **Birds** Pheasant ○ NAGA/See Pg. 72

Deer Creek Hunt Club
18000 Basswood Rd., Three Oaks, MI 49128
(616) 756-6600 George W. Daniels
50 mi. SE of Chicago
Est 1993; **Acres** 500; **Type** Member/Avail; **On Site** Clubhouse, Meals, Clays; **Shoots** Field, Tower; **Birds** Quail, Pheasant, Chukar, Huns; **Dogs** Avail/HDW; **Packages** 1/2 Day ○ NAGA/See Pg. 72

Farmland
Pheasant Hunters
7104 Gosline Rd., Brown City, MI 48416
(810) 346-3672 Preston H. Mann 7am-9pm
45 mi. NE of Flint
Est 1987; **Acres** 4,000; **Type** Member/Avail; **Shoots** Field; **Birds** Quail, Ruffed Grouse, Woodcock, Pheasant; **Dogs** HDW; **Packages** 1 Day, 1-120 guns

Fowler Farms Shooting Preserve
RR2, Box 298, S. Haven, MI 49090
(616) 637-4381 Carter Fowler
50 mi. SW of Grand Rapids
Est 1980; **Acres** 640; **Type** Public; **On Site** Clubhouse, Lodging; **Shoots** Field; **Birds** Quail, Pheasant, Geese; **Dogs** Avail/HDW; **Packages** 1/2 Day, 1-30 guns ○ NAGA/See Pg. 72

Hunter's Creek Club
675 Sutton Rd., Metamora, MI 48455
(810) 664-4307 Charlie Mann
30 mi. N of Detroit
Est 1957; **Acres** 860; **Type** Member/Avail, Corp.; **On Site** Clubhouse, Meals, Clays; **Shoots** Field, Driven; **Birds** Quail, Pheasant, Chukar, Huns, Ducks; **Dogs** Avail/HDW; **Packages** 1/2 Day, 1-100 guns ○ NAGA/See Pg. 72

See Our Ad Across

"Doing things right" at Michigan's Hunters Creek Club

Metamora, MI — If you've been running a bird hunting preserve for nearly 40 years ... and if, in the process, you've become one of the best known and most popular establishments in the state ... you must be doing something right! And doing it right they are at Hunters Creek Club in southeastern Michigan, about an hour's drive from Detroit.

Hunters Creek encompasses 1,000 acres of woods, meadows, and fields of sorghum, timothy and brome grass, and boasts an impressive array of attractions and activities designed to appeal to a broad segment of sportsmen. Bird hunters, clay shooters, fishermen, and even gourmets, express constant enthusiasm for Hunters Creek.

Founded by Preston Mann in 1958, when hunting preserves in the United States were few and far between, Hunters Creek is a private club that is renowned for its attention to member needs. Certain Club services, however, are available to non-members, notably dog training and professional shooting instruction.

Shooting School...The More You Know

Headed by Sporting Clays All American Pat Lieske, the shooting school offers intensive individual instruction by appointment on all aspects of gun safety, shooting etiquette and proper technique. The school is open to all levels, beginner to advanced. Quarterly stock fitting seminars, monthly group and kids' shooting clinics are also part of the program.

"Hunting and clay shooting are like any other human activity," Charlie Mann says. "The more you know about something, the better you'll become at it. And the better you become, the more you'll enjoy yourself."

Dogs to Savvy Hunting Companions

With on-site kennels that can accommodate 60 dogs, Hunters Creek's widely acclaimed dog-training program converts untutored animals into obedient—and savvy—hunting companions. Charlie Mann, club owner, puts retrievers through their paces, while club manager Dale Jarvis handles pointers. Hunters Creek also sells pedigreed pups, including Brittany Spaniels and Labs.

Founder Preston Mann and members of the Class of '97.

To ensure that dog and hunter are never disappointed, the club, under the guidance of Charlie Mann—who also serves as president of the North American Gamebird Association—stocks thousands upon thousands of gamebirds. Hunters Creek Club provides a cornucopia of benefits for its members. A spacious clubhouse, for example, includes private lockers so time-pressured business people can leave the office, drive to the site, and change quickly into field gear. And a Pro Shop is generously stocked with accessories and equipment, including footwear, shooting vests, foul weather gear, optical products and luggage.

Catering To Clay Shooters

Clay shooters are catered to at Hunters Creek, with trap and skeet fields and a sporting clays course that entice novices and challenge old-timers. "We're never entirely satisfied with the ranges," Charlie Mann says. "Like everything else at Hunters Creek, there's not a year goes by that we don't try to improve them."

Hunters Creek also satisfies the appetite. It is a favorite location for group picnics. And folks are more than willing to drive from the city to feast on home cooked pheasant, duck in orange sauce, pan fried trout or New York strip steak.

For more information on membership, dog training and shooting instruction at Hunters Creek, where "doing things right" is a way of life, write **Charlie Mann at the club, 675 Sutton Road, Metamora, MI 48455, or phone (810) 664-4307.**

Lucky Feather Game Farm
2040 N. Pittsford Rd., Hillsdale, MI 49242
(517) 523-2050 Hal/Karen Bennett
80 mi. SW of Detroit

Hunter's Ridge Hunt Club
3921 Barber, Oxford, MI 48371
(810) 628-4868 Dave Fischer 9-5, T-Su
25 mi. N of Detroit
Est 1981; Acres 650; Hunters/yr 5,000; Type
Member/Avail, Corp.; On Site Clubhouse, Lodging,
Meals, Clays; Shoots Field, Tower; Birds Quail,
Pheasant, Chukar, Huns; Dogs Avail/HDW;
Packages 1/2 Day, 4-25 guns

Est 1988; Acres 856; Hunters/yr 600; Type
Public, Member/Avail, Corp.; On Site Clubhouse,
Meals, Clays; Shoots Field, Blinds; Birds Quail,
Pheasant, Chukar, Huns, Ducks, Geese; Dogs
Avail/HDW; Packages 1/2 Day, 1-40 guns
O NAGA/See Pg. 72
O Hunting License   O Airport Pickup
O Bird Processing   O Kennel Bird Dogs
O Sporting Clays

Lucky Feather is a family-run business specializing
in flighty birds and fine dogwork in a wilderness
setting. In addition to upland bird hunting, we've
got Sporting Comfortable clubhouse and local accommodations. Ask about our Family
Memberships. Call today!

Hunters Quest Game Ranch
Box 158, Onondaga, MI 49264
(810) 254-4746 Ted Fitzgerald Anytime
20 mi. S of Lansing
Est 1990; Acres 315; Type Public; On Site
Clubhouse, Lodging, Meals; Shoots Field, Tower;
Birds Pheasant, Turkey; Dogs Avail/HDW;
Packages 1 Day, 4-16 guns

M L Shooting Preserve
7169 W4 Rd., Mesick, MI 49668
(616) 269-3137 Mike Luther
Type Public, Member/Avail; On Site Clays; Shoots
Field; Birds Quail, Pheasant, Chukar O NAGA/ Pg. 72

The Huntsman Hunt Club Inc.
3166 Havens Rd., Dryden, MI 48428
(810) 796-3962 Craig Novotney
40 mi. N of Detroit
Est 1979; Acres 850; Type Member/Avail, Corp.;
On Site Clubhouse, Meals, Clays; Shoots Field,
Tower, Driven, Blinds; Birds Quail, Pheasant, Chukar,
Ducks; Dogs Avail/HDW; Packages 1/2 Day, 2-30
guns

Michigan Sportsmen's Hunt Club
4242 Oak Rd., Vassar, MI 48768
(517) 823-2157 Lawrence S. Joseph
40 mi. NE of Flint
Est 1969; Acres 600; Type Member/Avail, Corp.;
On Site Clubhouse, Meals, Clays; Shoots Field,
Tower; Birds Quail, Ruffed Grouse, Woodcock,
Pheasant, Chukar, Huns; Dogs Avail/HDW

I-69 Shooting Preserve
10081 Moser Dr., Bronson, MI 49028
(517) 369-9288 John Welch Evening
65 mi. S of Lansing
Est 1971; Acres 468; Type Member/Ltd; Shoots
Field; Birds Quail, Pheasant; Dogs HDW;
Packages 1/2 Day, up to 9 guns

Midland Michigan -Mel Su Jac
140 Camelot, Apt. I-11, Saginaw, MI 48603
(517) 793-0712 John W. Manning
30 mi. NW of Flint
Est 1967; Acres 275; Hunters/yr 40; Type
Public, Member/Avail; Shoots Field; Birds Ruffed
Grouse, Pheasant, Turkey; Dogs HDW; Packages
1/2 Day, 1-20 guns

In Seasons Adventures Inc.
PO Box 308, Mesick, MI 49668
(616) 885-1481 Carl Salling
100 mi. N of Grand Rapids
Acres 600; Type Public, Member/Avail; On Site
Clubhouse, Lodging, Meals, Clays; Shoots Field,
Tower; Birds Pheasant, Chukar; Dogs Avail/HDW

Mitchell Farms Hunt Club
10542 McWain Rd., Grand Blanc, MI 48439
(810) 694-2281 Bill Teer 9-5
10 mi. S of Flint
Est 1985; Acres 500; Type Member/Avail, Corp.;
On Site Clubhouse; Shoots Field; Birds Pheasant,
Chukar; Dogs Avail/HDW O NAGA/See Pg. 72

Lost Arrow Hunting Preserve
1749 Bomanville Rd., Gladwin, MI 48624
(517) 345-7774 Avery Sterling 9-5
15 mi. NE of West Branch
Est 1994; Acres 160; Type Public; On Site
Clubhouse, Lodging, Meals, Clays; Shoots Field,
Tower; Birds Pheasant, Chukar, Huns; Dogs
Avail/HDW; Packages 1/2 Day, 1-24 guns
O NAGA/See Pg. 72

Mitchell Hill Pheasant Hunting Preserve
Rt. 1, Box 130B, Ellsworth, MI 49729
(616) 588-6063 James Ruster After 5pm
160 mi. N of Grand Rapids
Est 1988; Acres 18; Hunters/yr 75; Type Public;
On Site Meals; Shoots Field; Birds Pheasant;
Dogs Avail/HDW; Packages 1/2 Day, 1-5 guns

Whisky River...*A Hunt Here Can Be "Intoxicating"*

Maybe it's the name. Or just something that happens to a hunter when the setting is picture perfect, the dog work superb, and the birds as abundant, wily and wicked-on-wing as they come. Whatever the reason, the discriminating sportsman will find a visit to Whisky River Hunt Club, well... *"intoxicating."*

Whisky River, by the way, is not really a river at all, but a series of ponds, small lakes and channels on 500 acres of land less than an hour and a half from Detroit. The Club takes the concept of a shooting preserve one-step beyond thanks to the hard work and vision of owner Mike Damman and consultant Marty Fischer. It's a refuge for busy sportsmen, and an ideal place for corporate execs to entertain clients.

A beautiful setting to begin and end a hunt.

Outstanding pheasant hunting

The hunting fields at Whisky River vary from switchgrass to marsh and woodlot edges where briars and brambles offer excellent cover. If you turn the right way and gaze across the hillocks of brome grass and plots of grain sorghum, you'll swear you've been transported to South Dakota. The plentiful pheasant--naturally present and stocked by Damman and his staff--have apparently noted the resemblance. Whisky River's birds fly like they took lessons from their legendary S.D. cousins. Fortunately, Damman's expert guides and peerless pointers are up to the challenge and almost every day in the field at Whisky River is the stuff of which a wingshooter's dreams are made.

Anglers may also take advantage of the Club's thirty acres of ponds, streams and channels, stocked with bass--on a good day up to 50 can be caught and released--bluegills, trout and walleyes.

Sporting clays and more

"What I've tried to do," says Damman, "is put together a club that I'd want to be a member of. A place that offers the best hunting and shooting opportunities around." To reach his goal, Damman has concentrated on more than just hunting.

He's built an automatic skeet range, plus 2, 10-station sporting clays courses--50 and 100 shots--that take full advantage of his property's varied terrain. The clays courses offer hunting guests a chance to warm-up before or cool-down after a hunt or serve simply as a challenging diversion all by themselves.

Shotgunner's interested in improving their shooting skills need only ask about Whisky River's individual instruction from Bruce Shultz an NSCA certified instructor, shooting schools and excellent gun-fitting program.

Log lodge

A building contractor by trade, Damman hasn't skimped on the Hunt Club's physical plant. The setting for its new log hunting lodge is reminiscent of New England, set as it is in a hollow surrounded by oaks, maples, and other hardwoods. The lodge offers a comfortable venue to discuss the day's activities, and a pool table and a 5' screen television with satellite dish to provide relaxing diversions. A brand new building that will house a recreation room and additional sleeping quarters is nearing completion.

Outdoor writer Tom Huggler summed it all up in a letter written to Damman after a recent visit: "It looks to me like you're doing everything right. Class and quality along with good flying, mature birds." Simply, *intoxicating.*

For information about Whisky River Hunt Club, write, 4555 Cambria Road, Hillsdale, MI 49242; or call Mike Damman at 517-357-4424.

Orchard Hill Sporting Clays Inc.
PO Box 463, Escanaba, MI 49829
(906) 466-2887 Mike Gierke
4 mi. NW of Bark River
Est 1993; **Type** Public; **On Site** Clubhouse,
Lodging, Clays; **Shoots** Field; **Birds** Ruffed Grouse,
Woodcock, Pheasant, Turkey, Geese; **Dogs** HDW

Paradise Shooting Preserve
1300 State St., Carsonville, MI 48419
(810) 622-9800 Don Mackley
80 mi. N of Detroit
Acres 180; **Type** Public, Member/Avail, Corp.; **On
Site** Clubhouse, Meals; **Shoots** Field, Tower; **Birds**
Quail, Pheasant, Chukar; **Dogs** Avail/HDW
○ NAGA/See Pg. 72

Wycamp Lake Club

*Upland Bird & Waterfowl Hunting in
Michigan's Most Scenic Cover*

ANNUAL FALL EUROPEAN STYLE PHEASANT DRIVES

Fall 1995 Schedule

Date	Release	Cost *
Sat., Sept. 30th	300 pheasant	$275/gun
Sat., Oct. 7th	300 pheasant	$275/gun
Sat., Oct. 14th	300 pheasant	$275/gun
Sat., Oct. 21st	300 pheasant	$275/gun
Sat., Oct. 28th	300 pheasant	$275/gun
Sat., Nov. 4th	250 pheasant	$225/gun
Fri., Nov. 24th	300 pheasant	$275/gun
Sat., Nov. 25th	300 pheasant	$275/gun
Sat., Dec. 2nd	250 pheasant	$225/gun
Thur., Dec. 28th	300 pheasant	$275/gun
Fri., Dec. 29th	300 pheasant	$275/gun
Sat., Dec. 30th	400 pheasant	$375/gun

* Non-member cost

For information and reservations, call

(616) 537-4830 or 526-6651

5484 Pleasantview Rd., Harbor Springs, MI 49740

PINE HILL

Kennels & Sportsmen's Club
8347 10 Mile Rd. NE, Rockford, MI 49341
(616) 874-8459 Jim or Sue
15 mi. NE of Grand Rapids
Est 1980; **Acres** 190; **Type** Public; **On Site**
Clubhouse, Clays; **Shoots** Field; **Birds** Quail,
Pheasant, Chukar, Huns; **Dogs** Avail/HDW;
Packages 1/2 Day, 1-5 guns

Pleasant Lake Farm
PO Box 465, Delton, MI 49046
(616) 623-5853 James Alden 5-11pm
20 mi. NE of Kalamazoo
Est 1988; **Acres** 410; **Type** Member/Avail; **On
Site** Clubhouse, Lodging, Meals, Clays; **Shoots** Field,
Blinds, Boat; **Birds** Quail, Pheasant; **Dogs**
Avail/HDW; **Packages** 1/2 Day, 1-32 guns
○ NAGA/See Pg. 72
○ Airport Pickup   ○ Bird Processing
○ Kennel Bird Dogs   ○ Deer Hunting
○ Family Run Business

Rips Pheasant & Chukar Farm
5997 Burtch Rd., Jeddo, MI 48032
(810) 327-2035 Rip/Maureen Burch
Type Public, Member/Avail; **Shoots** Field; **Birds**
Pheasant, Chukar ○ NAGA/See Pg. 72

Rolling Hills Shooting Preserve
17025 McKenzie St., Marcellus, MI 49067
(616) 646-9164 Curt Johnson Evenings
60 mi. SW of Grand Rapids
Est 1982; **Acres** 275; **Hunters/yr** 500; **Type**
Public; **On Site** Clubhouse, Clays; **Shoots** Field;
Birds Quail, Pheasant, Chukar; **Dogs** Avail/HDW;
Packages 1/2 Day, 1-15 guns ○ NAGA/See Pg. 72

ROOSTER RANCH
HUNT CLUB, INC.

7480 Germania, Ubly, MI 48475
(517) 658-2332 R. Kim Anthony Days
90 mi. N of Detroit
Est 1987; **Acres** 600; **Hunters/yr** 800; **Type**
Public, Member/Avail, Corp.; **On Site** Clubhouse,
Lodging, Meals; **Shoots** Field; **Birds** Quail,
Pheasant, Chukar; **Dogs** Avail/HDW; **Packages** 1/2
Day, 1-40 guns

Woodmoor: A Michigan Delight
... Now Orvis Endorsed

Here's a recipe for sportsmen that never fails to please. Mix wingshooting, sporting clays, fishing, hiking, boating, horseback riding and a championship golf course. Add luxurious accommodations and gourmet dining. The result is Woodmoor on Drummond Island, a resort masterpiece in northern Michigan that more than satisfies the appetite for outdoor adventure.

Striking architecture and plenty of room to relax at Woodmoor.

Among the Elite

The Woodmoor experience—and no other term describes a visit as well—is unique.And the quality of its wingshooting program is such that the resort has been designated an Orvis endorsed wingshooting lodge, one of only 15 in the world (at the time of this writing).

Encompassing 2,000 acres, and situated on Drummond Island in the state's Upper Peninsula, Woodmoor is a sporting enthusiast's dream come true. Among its attractions are professionally guided hunts over well-trained pointers and retrievers. Pheasants and Hungarian partridge abound on the preserve, and 50,000 nearby acres of state and federally-managed land offer the challenges of ruffed grouse, woodcock, ducks and geese.

Woodmoor also offers world-class sporting clays with targets released in a blur of angles and speeds from covers of every description and shooting instruction provided by Orvis-trained personnel.

Fishing Hemingway Admired

The salmon fishing at Woodmoor will test the mettle of the most avid sportsman. Established near the island's shores, these pugnacious beauties feed only on flies, and roam the waters at depths of ten feet or less. Additional thrills are available at the rapids at Sault Ste. Marie, where fly fishing reaches a zenith that Ernest Hemingway admired.

Is it golf you crave? Woodmoor brings you The Rock, named one of Michigan's top ten courses by *Michigan Golfer Magazine*. A visual treat, this championship-caliber course de-mands skill, patience and perseverance of duffer and pro alike.

Scenic Splendor

And, when you're not shooting, casting or golfing, you're sure to enjoy the scenic wonders of Woodmoor's many hiking trails, the invigorating pleasure of horseback riding, or the pure fun of boating on Lake Huron.

Not the least of Woodmoor's attractions, however, are those that invite relaxation. Supervised by General Manager Dan Serrine, Woodmoor includes a 40-room log lodge with conference facilities for ten to 150, and the Bayside dining room that overlooks nearby islands. Quiet times are also the promise of eight large private cabins in wooded settings, five of traditional log construction and three in the architectural style of Frank Lloyd Wright.

Woodmoor, on Drummond Island is accessible by car ferry or plane (a 4,000 foot runway, ADF/NDB rated, with hangar facilities, is available). Out of the way, to be sure. But the Woodmoor experience is one you'll never forget. And one, we are certain, that you'll want to repeat again and again!

For further information, or to make reservations, please contact **John Cook, Director of Orvis Services, at (906) 493-1039 or Fax at (906) 493-5576; write: 26 Maxton Road, Drummond Island, MI 49726.**

Smith Creek Hunt Club

8669 Lashbrook, Goodlles, MI 48027
(810) 325-1135 Joe Musu Anytime
40 mi. E of Detroit
Est 1985; **Acres** 200; **Type** Public, Member/Avail;
On Site Clubhouse, Meals, Clays; **Shoots** Field,
Tower; **Birds** Quail, Pheasant, Chukar, Ducks; **Dogs**
Avail/HDW; **Packages** 1/2 Day, 1-20 guns

Thundering Aspens
4421 N. 5 1/2 Rd., Mesick, MI 49668
(616) 885-2420 Greg Wright
110 mi. N of Grand Rapids
Est 1989; **Acres** 400; **Hunters/yr** 500; **Type**
Public, Member/Avail, Corp.; **On Site** Clays; **Shoots**
Field; **Birds** Quail, Ruffed Grouse, Woodcock,
Pheasant, Chukar, Huns, Turkey, Geese; **Dogs**
Avail/HDW; **Packages** 1/2 Day, 1-4 guns
○ NAGA/See Pg. 72

Top Gun Hunt Club
1937 68th St., Fennville, MI 49408
(616) 543-3351 George Vuillemot Evenings
35 mi. SW of Grand Rapids
Est 1990; **Acres** 250; **Hunters/yr** 200; **Type**
Public, Corp.; **On Site** Clubhouse, Meals, Clays;
Shoots Field, Driven; **Birds** Quail, Pheasant, Chukar,
Huns; **Dogs** Avail/HDW; **Packages** 1/2 Day, 2-4
guns

Trapper Jim's Hunt Club
4300 E. Sanilac Rd., Kingston, MI 48741
(517) 683-2620 Jim Pruett 8am-5pm
40 mi. NE of Flint
Est 1967; **Acres** 500; **Hunters/yr** 1,200; **Type**
Member/Avail, Corp.; **On Site** Clubhouse, Meals,
Clays; **Shoots** Field, Tower; **Birds** Quail, Ruffed
Grouse, Woodcock, Pheasant, Chukar, Huns; **Dogs**
Avail/HDW; **Packages** 1/2 Day, 1-80 guns

Whisky River Hunt Club
4555 Cambria Rd., Hillsdale, MI 49242
(517) 357-4424 Mike Damman 8am
80 mi. SW of Detroit
Est 1989; **Acres** 800; **Hunters/yr** 500; **Type**
Public, Member/Avail; **On Site** Clubhouse, Lodging,
Clays; **Shoots** Field, Blinds; **Birds** Quail, Pheasant,
Ducks; **Dogs** Avail/HDW; **Packages** 1/2 Day
○ NAGA/See Pg. 72
See Our Ad Pg. 317

Wild Wings Game Farm
PO Box 1232, Gaylord, MI 49735
(616) 584-3350 James W. Avery 8am-5:30pm
160 mi. N of Lansing
Type Public; **On Site** Clays; **Shoots** Field; **Birds**
Pheasant, Chukar, Huns; **Dogs** Avail/HDW
○ NAGA/See Pg. 72

Willow Lake Sportsmen's Club
51704 U.S. 131, Three Rivers, MI 49093
(616) 279-7124 Woodrow R. Thompson
65 mi. S of Grand Rapids
Est 1976; **Acres** 250; **Hunters/yr** 1,000; **Type**
Member/Avail, Corp.; **On Site** Clubhouse, Lodging,
Meals, Clays; **Shoots** Field, Tower; **Birds** Quail,
Pheasant, Chukar, Huns, Turkey; **Dogs** Avail/HDW;
Packages 1/2 Day, 1-35 guns ○ NAGA/See Pg. 72

DRUMMOND ISLAND

26 Maxton Rd., Drummond Isl., MI 49726
(906) 493-1039 John Cook 9-5,M-F
40 mi. SE of Sault Ste. Marie
Est 1986; **Acres** 2,000; **Type** Public; **On Site**
Clubhouse, Lodging, Meals, Clays; **Shoots** Field,
Blinds, Boat; **Birds** Ruffed Grouse, Woodcock,
Pheasant, Huns, Ducks, Geese; **Dogs** Avail/HDW
See Our Ad Pg. 319

Wycamp Lake Club, Inc.
5484 Pleasantview Rd., Harbor Springs, MI 49740
(616) 526-6651 Dirk Shorter 8am-8pm
180 mi. N of Grand Rapids
Est 1983; **Acres** 900; **Type** Public, Member/Avail,
Corp.; **On Site** Clubhouse, Lodging, Meals, Clays;
Shoots Field, Driven, Blinds, Boat; **Birds** Quail,
Ruffed Grouse, Woodcock, Pheasant, Chukar, Ducks,
Geese; **Dogs** Avail/HDW; **Packages** 1/2 Day, 2-24
guns ○ NAGA/See Pg. 72
See Our Ad Pg. 318

MINNESOTA

A Wild Acres
Hunting Club
HC83, Box 108, Pequot Lakes, MN 56472
(218) 568-5024 Mary Ebnet 7am-7pm
150 mi. N of Minneapolis
Est 1970; **Acres** 400; **Hunters/yr** 600; **Type**
Public, Member/Avail, Corp.; **On Site** Clubhouse,
Lodging, Meals, Clays; **Shoots** Field, Tower, Blinds;
Birds Quail, Pheasant, Chukar, Turkey, Ducks; **Dogs**
Avail/HDW; **Packages** 1/2 Day, 2-20 guns
○ NAGA/See Pg. 72

American Heritage Hunting Club
Rt. 2, Box 131, Eagle Bend, MN 56446
(218) 738-5143 Don/Sue Ellwanger 8am-10pm
140 mi. NW of Minneapolis
Est 1986; **Acres** 558; **Hunters/yr** 300; **Type**
Public, Member/Avail, Corp.; **On Site** Clubhouse,
Lodging, Meals, Clays; **Shoots** Field, Blinds, Boat;

Birds Quail, Pheasant, Chukar, Turkey, Ducks, Geese;
Dogs Avail/HDW;   **Packages** 1/2 Day, 1-25 guns

Bader's Pheasant Run
Box 270, Federal Dam, MN 56641
(218) 654-5097 Wade or Deb Huotari
110 mi. W of Duluth, WI
Type Public;   **On Site** Clubhouse, Lodging, Meals;
Shoots Field;   **Birds** Quail, Pheasant;   **Dogs**
Avail/HDW o NAGA/See Pg. 72

Bullseye Hunting Preserve & Game Farm
R2, Box 140A, Aitkin, MN 56431
(218) 678-2910 Dan Schmidt
100 mi. NW of Minneapolis
Est 1988;   **Acres** 300;   **Type** Public, Member/Avail,
Corp.;   **On Site** Clubhouse, Clays;   **Shoots** Field,
Blinds, Boat;   **Birds** Pheasant, Chukar, Turkey, Ducks;
Dogs Avail/HDW;   **Packages** 1/2 Day, 1-10 guns

Caribou Gun Club
Shooting Preserve
Rt. 1, Box 26, Le Sueur, MN 56058
(612) 665-3796 Randy Voss anytime
60 mi. SW of Minneapolis-St. Paul
Est 1953;   **Acres** 600;   **Hunters/yr** 2,500;   **Type**
Public, Member/Avail, Corp.;   **On Site** Clubhouse,
Lodging, Meals, Clays;   **Shoots** Field, Tower;   **Birds**
Quail, Pheasant, Chukar;   **Dogs** Avail/HDW;
Packages 1/2 Day, 1-50 guns o NAGA/See Pg. 72

Cedar Hill
Box 485, Northome, MN 56661
(218) 897-5659 Jim Stone Evenings
135 mi. NW of Duluth
Acres 300,000;   **Type** Public;   **On Site** Lodging,
Meals;   **Shoots** Field;   **Birds** Ruffed Grouse,
Woodcock;   **Dogs** Avail/HDW

Charlie's Hunting Club
RR1, Box 173, Danvers, MN 56231
(612) 567-2276 Jim Langan
115 mi. W of Minneapolis
Acres 2,000;   **Type** Public;   **On Site** Clubhouse,
Lodging, Meals, Clays;   **Shoots** Field;   **Birds**
Pheasant, Geese;   **Dogs** Avail/HDW
o NAGA/See Pg. 72
Charlie's is committed to quality hunting. Two thousand acres of prime habitat supports a large native
pheasant population. Goose hunting is available at
near-by Lac Qui Parle goose refuge. Finish the day
at Charlie's. The farm, homesteaded in the early
1900s, has a renovated dairy barn that serves as
the clubhouse. Call today!

Clear Creek Outdoors
950 Hwy. 23, Wrenshall, MN 55797
(218) 384-3670 Patrick LaBoone 8-8
6 mi. SW of Duluth
Est 1983;   **Acres** 300;   **Type** Member/Avail, Corp.;
On Site Clubhouse, Meals, Clays;   **Shoots** Field,
Driven;   **Birds** Quail, Ruffed Grouse, Woodcock,
Pheasant, Chukar, Huns, Turkey;   **Dogs** Avail/HDW;
Packages 1/2 Day, up to 25 guns
o NAGA/See Pg. 72
Shooting Instruction Available - See Pg. 167

Dead Horse Creek Shooting Preserve
RR 2, Box 103, Frazee, MN 56544
(218) 334-4868 Chris or Ben Wacker All Day
180 mi. NW of Minneapolis
Est 1993;   **Acres** 1,000;   **Type** Public, Member/Avail;
On Site Clubhouse, Lodging, Clays;   **Shoots** Field;
Birds Pheasant, Chukar;   **Dogs** Avail/HDW;
Packages 1/2 Day, 1-70 guns o NAGA/See Pg. 72

Deer Ridge Hunting
5050 470th St., Harris, MN 55032
(612) 288-0020 Henry J. Gregoire, Jr.'
Type Public, Member/Avail;   **On Site** Clays;   **Shoots**
Field;   **Birds** Quail, Pheasant, Chukar, Ducks
o NAGA/See Pg. 72

Double Arrow Hunting Preserve
6524 145th St. N., Hugo, MN 55038
(612) 429-6645 Jim Bramstedt 9-9
18 mi. from St. Paul
Est 1963;   **Acres** 200;   **Type** Public;   **Shoots** Field;
Birds Quail, Pheasant;   **Dogs** Avail/HDW;   **Packages**
1/2 Day, up to 10 guns o NAGA/See Pg. 72

Elsing Prairies & Wildlife
107 Johnson Dr., Box 58, Rushmore, MN 56168
(507) 478-4482 Willie Elsing Evening
50 mi. E of Sioux Falls, SD
Est 1986;   **Acres** 320;   **Type** Public, Member/Avail,
Corp.;   **On Site** Clubhouse, Lodging;   **Shoots** Field,
Driven, Blinds;   **Birds** Quail, Pheasant, Chukar, Huns,
Ducks, Geese;   **Dogs** Avail/HDW;   **Packages** 1/2
Day, 1-8 guns o NAGA/See Pg. 72

Fischer's Kennels & Hunt Club
29512 223rd Ave., Albany, MN 56307
(612) 597-2729 Pete Fischer
85 mi. NW of Minneapolis
Acres 320;   **Hunters/yr** 1,000;   **Type**
Member/Avail, Corp.;   **On Site** Clubhouse, Meals,
Clays;   **Shoots** Field;   **Birds** Pheasant;   **Dogs**
Avail/HDW;   **Packages** 1/2 Day, 1-40 guns

Gold Meadows Hunting Preserve
18506 260th St., Richmond, MN 56368
(612) 597-2747 Joe Doubek
90 mi. NW of Minneapolis
Est 1968;   **Acres** 800;   **Type** Public;   **On Site**
Clubhouse;   **Shoots** Field;   **Birds** Quail, Pheasant,
Chukar, Turkey; **Dogs** Avail/HDW o NAGA/See Pg. 72

WINGS

Golden Valley Pheasant Run
HCR4, Box 116A, Roseau, MN 56751
(218) 425-7401 Rod Wulff/Steve Johnson 8am-10pm
120 mi. NE of Grand Forks, ND
Est 1988; **Acres** 550; **Hunters/yr** 200; **Type**
Public; **On Site** Clubhouse, Lodging, Meals, Clays;
Shoots Field; **Birds** Quail, Pheasant, Chukar, Turkey;
Dogs Avail/HDW

H&R Shooting Preserve
34934 140th Ave., Avon, MN 56310
(612) 356-7427 David J. Raab
75 mi. NW of Minneapolis
Est 1986; **Acres** 240; **Type** Public; **On Site**
Clubhouse, Clays; **Shoots** Field; **Birds** Quail,
Pheasant, Chukar; **Dogs** Avail/HDW; **Packages** 1/2
Day, 1-40 guns   O NAGA/See Pg. 72

Hidden Valley Game Birds, Inc.
RR1, Box 323, Pine Island, MN 55963
(507) 356-8887 Butch Owens 8am-Sundown
55 mi. SE of Minneapolis
Est 1989; **Acres** 850; **Hunters/yr** 200; **Type**
Public, Member/Avail, Corp.; **On Site** Clubhouse,
Clays; **Shoots** Field, Driven; **Birds** Quail, Pheasant,
Chukar, Huns; **Dogs** Avail/HDW; **Packages** 1/2
Day, up to 12 guns   O NAGA/See Pg. 72

Lac Qui Parle Hunting Camp
RR5, Box 67A, Montevideo, MN 56265
(612) 269-9769 Steve or Stan Baldwin 8am-10pm
110 mi. W of Minneapolis
Est 1987; **Acres** 1,500; **Hunters/yr** 2,500; **Type**
Public; **On Site** Clubhouse, Lodging, Meals, Clays;
Shoots Field, Blinds; **Birds** Quail, Pheasant, Chukar,
Ducks, Geese; **Dogs** Avail/HDW; **Packages** 1/2
Day, 1-100 guns

Langhei Hills
Rt. 1, Box 29, Hancock, MN 56244
(612) 392-5808 Ken Reese
155 mi. W of Minneapolis
Acres 1,000; **Type** Public, Member/Avail, Corp.;
On Site Clubhouse, Lodging, Meals, Clays; **Shoots**
Field; **Birds** Pheasant; **Dogs** Avail/HDW
O NAGA/See Pg. 72

Don Le Blanc Hunting Preserve
Rt. 5, Box 228, Little Falls, MN 56345
(612) 745-2522 Don or Marge Le Blanc dawn-noon,
after dark
85 mi. NW of Minneapolis
Est 1959; **Acres** 2,000; **Hunters/yr** 1,050; **Type**
Public, Member/Avail, Corp.; **On Site** Clubhouse,
Meals, Clays; **Shoots** Field, Driven, Blinds; **Birds**
Quail, Pheasant, Chukar, Turkey, Ducks; **Dogs**
Avail/HDW; **Packages** 1/2 Day, 1-35 guns
O NAGA/See Pg. 72

LeBlanc Rice Creek Hunting
Rt. 5, Box 213, Little Falls, MN 56345
(612) 745-2451 Gregg LeBlanc 8am-12 Noon
85 mi. N of Minneapolis
Est 1982; **Acres** 1,500; **Type** Public, Member/Avail,
Corp.; **On Site** Clubhouse, Lodging, Meals, Clays;
Shoots Field, Blinds; **Birds** Quail, Pheasant, Chukar,
Turkey, Ducks; **Dogs** Avail/HDW; **Packages** 1/2
Day, 1-50 guns   O NAGA/See Pg. 72

Leech Lake Hunting Area
Box 310, Federal Dam, MN 56641
(218) 654-3998 Robert A. Wake Anytime
110 mi. W of Duluth
Est 1962; **Acres** 1,000; **Type** Public; **Shoots** Field;
Birds Pheasant; **Dogs** Avail/HDW

Little Moran Hunting Club
Rt. 1, Pheasant Valley Rd., Staples, MN 56479
(218) 894-3852 Steve & Gayle Grossman
130 mi. NW of Minneapolis
Est 1984; **Acres** 320; **Type** Public, Member/Avail,
Corp.; **On Site** Clubhouse, Lodging, Meals, Clays;
Shoots Field; **Birds** Ruffed Grouse, Woodcock,
Pheasant, Chukar, Turkey, Ducks, Geese; **Dogs**
Avail/HDW   O NAGA/See Pg. 72

Major Ave. Hunt Club
11721 Major Ave., Glencoe, MN 55336
(612) 864-6025 Gerald G. Martin Daylight Hours
45 mi. W of Minneapolis
Est 1988; **Acres** 360; **Type** Public, Member/Avail,
Corp.; **On Site** Clubhouse, Lodging, Meals, Clays;
Shoots Field, Tower; **Birds** Quail, Pheasant, Chukar,
Ducks, Geese; **Dogs** Avail/HDW; **Packages** 1/2
Day, 2-50 guns   O NAGA/See Pg. 72

Maple Island Hunt Club, Inc.
425 Hamm Bldg., St. Paul, MN 55102
(612) 439-2405 Maurice Grogan
25 mi. NE of St. Paul
Est 1965; **Acres** 1,000; **Type** Member/Avail, Corp.;
On Site Clubhouse, Meals, Clays; **Shoots** Field,
Tower, Boat; **Birds** Quail, Pheasant, Chukar, Ducks,
Geese; **Dogs** Avail/HDW

Maple Landing Preserve
RR3, Box 113, Erksine, MN 56535
(218) 687-2175 Mike Kolden
110 mi. NE of Fargo, ND
Acres 340; **Type** Public; **On Site** Clubhouse, Meals;
Shoots Field; **Birds** Pheasant, Chukar, Turkey;
Dogs Avail/HDW

McCollum's Hunting Preserve
Rt. 1, Box 9, Bejou, MN 56516
(218) 935-2468 Terry/Theresa McCollum 7am-10pm
165 mi. NW of Duluth
Est 1989; **Acres** 350; **Type** Public; **On Site**
Clubhouse, Lodging, Meals, Clays; **Shoots** Field,
Driven; **Birds** Quail, Pheasant, Chukar; **Dogs**
Avail/HDW; **Packages** 1/2 Day, 1-30 guns

Mille Lacs Hunting Lodge
RR2, Box 273, Onamia, MN 56359

(612) 532-3384 John or Dave Barsody
90 mi. N of Minneapolis
Est 1993; **Type** Public, Member/Avail; **On Site**
Clubhouse, Lodging, Meals, Clays; **Shoots** Field,
Blinds; **Birds** Pheasant, Chukar, Huns; **Dogs**
Avail/HDW ○ NAGA/See Pg. 72

Minnesota Horse & Hunt Club
2920 220th St., Prior Lake, MN 55372
(612) 447-2272 Terry Correll 8am-5pm, M-Su
25 mi. SW of Minneapolis
Est 1969; **Acres** 750; **Hunters/yr** 5,000; **Type**
Member/Avail; **On Site** Clubhouse, Lodging, Meals,
Clays; **Shoots** Field, Driven, Blinds; **Birds** Quail,
Pheasant, Chukar, Huns, Turkey, Ducks; **Dogs**
Avail/HDW; **Packages** 1/2 Day, up to 60 guns
○ NAGA/See Pg. 72

Misty Meadows Shooting Preserve
HC9, Box 439, Detroit Lakes, MN 56501
(218) 847-4680 Steve Laine After 6pm
16 mi. E of Detroit Lakes
Est 1988; **Acres** 300; **Hunters/yr** 500; **Type**
Public, Member/Avail, Corp.; **On Site** Clubhouse,
Meals, Clays; **Shoots** Field, Tower, Driven; **Birds**
Quail, Pheasant, Chukar, Turkey, Ducks; **Dogs**
Avail/HDW; **Packages** 1/2 Day ○ NAGA/See Pg. 72

North Star Hunting Preserve
Rt. 1, Box 190, Ft. Ripley, MN 56449
(218) 829-1042 Randy Tomberlin Evenings
125 mi. N of Minneapolis-St. Paul
Est 1985; **Acres** 520; **Hunters/yr** 200; **Type**
Public; **On Site** Clubhouse; **Shoots** Field; **Birds**
Pheasant, Chukar, Turkey; **Dogs** Avail/HDW;
Packages 1/2 Day, 1-6 guns

Oak Point Shooting Preserve
RR3, Box 44-A, Wadena, MN 56482
(218) 631-4467 Don Dykhoff
Type Public; **On Site** Lodging, Clays; **Shoots** Field;
Birds Quail, Pheasant, Chukar ○ NAGA/See Pg. 72

Oakdale Ridge Hunting Preserve
8900 Union Hill Blvd., Belle Plaine, MN 56011
(612) 873-6423 Dale Stender
45 mi. SW of Minneapolis
Acres 1,000; **Type** Member/Avail, Corp.; **On Site**
Clubhouse, Meals, Clays; **Shoots** Field; **Birds** Quail,
Pheasant, Chukar, Turkey; **Dogs** Avail/HDW

Pheasant Dreams
15033 70th St., Elk River, MN 55330
(612) 441-7204 Greg Lefebvre 9-10am, After 7pm
35 mi. NW of Minneapolis
Est 1987; **Acres** 200; **Hunters/yr** 500; **Type**
Public, Member/Avail, Corp.; **On Site** Clubhouse;
Shoots Field; **Birds** Quail, Pheasant, Chukar, Turkey;
Dogs Avail/HDW; **Packages** 1/2 Day, 1-10 guns
○ NAGA/See Pg. 72

Pleasant Acres
RR3, Box 144, New Ulm, MN 56073
(507) 359-5770 Lester Zwach 8-5
70 mi. SW of Minneapolis
Est 1981; **Acres** 1,000; **Hunters/yr** 1,100; **Type**
Public, Member/Avail; **On Site** Clubhouse, Lodging,

Meals, Clays; **Shoots** Field, Driven; **Birds** Quail,
Pheasant, Chukar; **Dogs** Avail/HDW; **Packages** 1/2
Day, 1-60 guns ○ NAGA/See Pg. 72

Ringneck Ranch
RR2, Box 137, Wheaton, MN 56296
(612) 563-4705 Peter & Miki Bertram
165 mi. W of Minneapolis
Est 1985; **Acres** 850; **Type** Public, Member/Avail;
On Site Clubhouse, Lodging, Meals; **Shoots** Field;
Birds Quail, Pheasant, Chukar; **Dogs** Avail/HDW;
Packages 1/2 Day, 1-16 guns

Ringneck Ranch Hunting Preserve
Rt. 2, Box 373, Aitkin, MN 56431
(218) 678-2169 Clark Holcomb 6-8am
100 mi. N of St. Paul
Est 1987; **Acres** 400; **Type** Public, Member/Avail,
Corp.; **On Site** Clubhouse; **Shoots** Field; **Birds**
Quail, Pheasant, Ducks; **Dogs** Avail/HDW;
Packages 1/2 Day, 1-10 guns

Ringneck Ridge Shooting Preserve
Rt. 1, Box 319, Motley, MN 56466
(218) 575-2913 John & Carol Jacklitch Anytime
100 mi. N of Minneapolis
Est 1993; **Type** Public; **On Site** Clubhouse, Clays;
Shoots Field, Blinds; **Birds** Pheasant, Chukar, Ducks,
Geese; **Dogs** Avail/HDW; **Packages** 1/2 Day, 1-20
guns

Rooster Ridge Hunting Club
PO Box 7, Browerville, MN 56438
(612) 594-6031 Russ Noland/Ev Sykora
120 mi. NW of Minneapolis
Est 1989; **Acres** 465; **Hunters/yr** 480; **Type**
Member/Avail, Corp.; **On Site** Clubhouse, Meals;
Shoots Field, Tower; **Birds** Pheasant, Chukar,
Turkey; **Dogs** Avail/HDW; **Packages** 1/2 Day, 1-30
guns

Rudquist's Shooting Preserve
HC76, Box 105, Backus, MN 56435
(218) 947-3044 George Rudquist
150 mi. N of Minneapolis
Est 1991; **Acres** 900; **Hunters/yr** 400; **Type**
Public; **Shoots** Field; **Birds** Quail, Pheasant, Chukar;
Dogs Avail/HDW; **Packages** 1/2 Day, 1-36 guns

Rum River Pheasant Club
30925 CR 5 NW, Princeton, MN 55371
(612) 389-2316 Rick Johnson
45 mi. N of Minneapolis
Type Public, Member/Avail, Corp.; **On Site**
Clubhouse, Meals, Clays; **Shoots** Field; **Birds**
Pheasant, Chukar, Ducks; **Dogs** Avail/HDW

Sedan Hunting Club
Rt. 1, Box 1, Sedan, MN 56380
(800) 930-3367 Luther & Eyvonne Hoese
8 mi. E of Glenwood
Acres 740; **Type** Public; **On Site** Clubhouse;
Shoots Field; **Birds** Pheasant, Chukar; **Dogs**
Avail/HDW ○ NAGA/See Pg. 72

Shamrock Shooting Preserve
59563 300th St., RR3, Litchfield, MN 55355

WINGS

(612) 693-8725 Mark/Jon/Pat Finnegan 7am-10pm
70 mi. W of Minneapolis
Est 1988; **Acres** 400; **Hunters/yr** 500; **Type**
Public, Member/Avail, Corp.; **On Site** Clubhouse,
Clays; **Shoots** Field, Blinds, Boat; **Birds** Quail,
Pheasant, Chukar, Turkey, Ducks, Geese; **Dogs**
Avail/HDW; **Packages** 1/2 Day, 1-10 guns

Spunk River Hunting Club
15718 390th St., Avon, MN 56310
(612) 746-2442 Tom Dickhausen
75 mi. NW of Minneapolis **Acres** 500; **Type** Public;
On Site Clubhouse, Lodging, Meals, Clays; **Shoots**
Field, Blinds; **Birds** Quail, Pheasant, Ducks; **Dogs**
Avail/HDW
○ NAGA/See Pg. 72

Stoney Flats Hunting Preserve
Rt. 3, Box 102A, Milaca, MN 56353
(612) 447-1780 Jack Wenz
65 mi. N of Minneapolis
Acres 270; **Type** Public, Member/Avail, Corp.; **On**
Site Clubhouse, Clays; **Shoots** Field; **Birds** Quail,
Pheasant, Chukar; **Dogs** Avail/HDW; **Packages** 1/2 Day

Ten Mile Creek Hunting Preserve
Rt. 1, Box 85, Dunnell, MN 56127
(507) 695-2544 Michael Honnette Evenings
140 mi. SW of Minneapolis
Acres 200; **Type** Public; **On Site** Meals; **Shoots**
Field; **Birds** Pheasant; **Dogs** Avail/HDW

Thompson Hunting Preserve
Rt. 2, Box 162, Barnesville, MN 56514
(218) 493-4222 Eldon Thompson 7am-10pm
30 mi. SE of Fargo, ND
Est 1987; **Acres** 240; **Hunters/yr** 400; **Type**
Public; **On Site** Clubhouse, Lodging, Meals, Clays;
Shoots Field; **Birds** Pheasant, Chukar; **Dogs**
Avail/HDW; **Packages** 1/2 Day, 1-30 guns

Traxler's Hunting Preserve
R2, LeCenter, MN 56057
(612) 357-6940 Jeff Traxler 7am-6pm
50 mi. SW of Minneapolis
Est 1985; **Acres** 600; **Hunters/yr** 1,000; **Type**
Public, Member/Avail, Corp.; **On Site** Clubhouse,
Meals, Clays; **Shoots** Field, Tower, Driven, Blinds;
Birds Quail, Pheasant, Chukar, Ducks; **Dogs**
Avail/HDW; **Packages** 1/2 Day, 1-40 guns

Udovich Guide Service
12503 Sethers Rd., Gheen, MN 55771
(218) 787-2237 Dennis Udovich
225 mi. N of Minneapolis
Est 1991; **Acres** 700; **Hunters/yr** 600; **Type**
Public, Member/Avail, Corp.; **On Site** Clubhouse,
Lodging, Meals, Clays; **Shoots** Field, Tower; **Birds**
Quail, Pheasant; **Dogs** Avail/HDW; **Packages** 1/2
Day, 1-20 guns ○ NAGA/See Pg. 72

Valhalla Hunt Club
RR1, Albert Lea, MN 56007
(507) 377-7225 Gary Pestorious
85 mi. S of Minneapolis **Est** 1986; **Acres** 500;
Hunters/yr 500; **Type** Public, Member/Avail, Corp.;

On Site Clubhouse, Meals, Clays; **Shoots** Field,
Tower; **Birds** Pheasant; **Dogs** Avail/HDW

Viking Valley Hunt Club
Rt. 1, Box 198, Ashby, MN 56309
(218) 747-2121 Les Bensch 8-6
140 mi. NW of Minneapolis
Est 1988; **Acres** 1,800; **Hunters/yr** 250; **Type**
Public, Member/Avail, Corp.; **On Site** Clubhouse,
Lodging, Meals, Clays; **Shoots** Field, Blinds, **Birds**
Woodcock, Pheasant, Chukar, Huns, Ducks, Geese;
Dogs Avail/HDW; **Packages** 1/2 Day, 2-12 guns

Voyager Sportsmans Paradise
PO Box 1236, International Falls, MN 55649
(218) 283-2701 Kenneth Bahr
Type Public; **Shoots** Field; **Birds** Pheasant
○ NAGA/See Pg. 72

Western Wild Wings
13766 55th St., NW, Annandale, MN 55302
(612) 274-3513 Doug Streu
Type Public, Member/Avail; **Shoots** Field; **Birds**
Pheasant ○ NAGA/See Pg. 72

Wild Wings of Oneka
9491 152nd St., N., Hugo, MN 55038
(612) 439-4287 Jeff Hughes/Gary Schulte Anytime
15 mi. NE of Minneapolis
Est 1956; **Acres** 500; **Hunters/yr** 9,000; **Type**
Member/Avail; **On Site** Clubhouse, Meals, Clays;
Shoots Field, Driven, Blinds; **Birds** Quail, Pheasant,
Chukar, Huns, Turkey, Ducks; **Dogs** Avail/HDW;
Packages 1/2 Day, 4-50 guns ○ NAGA/See Pg. 72

MISSISSIPPI

Clear Creek Quail Farm
156 Oilfield Rd., Lumberton, MS 39455
(601) 796-5063 Herman B. Morgan
35 mi. S of Hattiesburg
Acres 300; **Hunters/yr** 45; **Type** Public; **Shoots**
Field; **Birds** Quail; **Dogs** Avail/HDW; **Packages**
1/2 Day ○ NAGA/See Pg. 72

Dunn's Shooting Grounds
Rt. 3, Box 39D4, Holly Springs, MS 38635
(601) 564-1111 Stephen Pannell 8-5, M-S
35 mi. SE of Memphis
Est 1993; **Acres** 1,000; **Hunters/yr** 100; **Type**
Public; **On Site** Clubhouse, Lodging, Meals, Clays;
Shoots Field; **Birds** Quail; **Dogs** Avail/HDW;
Packages 1/2 Day, 2-12 guns
○ Airport Pickup   ○ Bird Processing
○ Kennel Bird Dogs   ○ Sporting Clays
○ Hunting Jeeps   ○ Brochure Available
○ Factory Ammunition   ○ Quality Clubhouse
○ Private Bedrooms

Get Away Place
8176 Hwy. 84 E., Waynesboro, MS 39367
(601) 735-5764 Dan Young
125 mi. SE of Jackson
Acres 275; Type Public, Member/Avail; On Site
Clubhouse, Lodging, Meals, Clays; Shoots Field;
Birds Quail, Pheasant, Turkey; Dogs Avail

Hill Country Plantation
1488 Bowie Rd., Carriere, MS 39426
(800) 986-4868 Owen Brennan
50 mi. NE of New Orleans
Est 1994; Acres 1,500; Type Public, Member/Avail;
On Site Clubhouse, Lodging, Meals, Clays; Shoots
Field, Tower, Driven, Blinds; Birds Dove, Quail,
Pheasant, Chukar, Turkey, Ducks; Dogs Avail/HDW;
Packages 1/2 Day, 1-50 guns
See Our Ad Pg. 309

Kearney Park
Shooting Preserve
151 Ergon Rd., Flora, MS 39071
(601) 879-3249 Chuck Boyer/T.W. Tolleson
6:30am-4pm
10 mi. N of Jackson
Est 1980; Acres 600; Hunters/yr 342; Type Public;
On Site Clubhouse, Lodging, Meals, Clays; Shoots
Field; Birds Quail; Dogs Avail/HDW; Packages 1/2
Day, 1-16 guns

Longleaf Plantation
PO Box 511, Lumberton, MS 39455
(601) 794-6001 George Alexander M-F, 8 to 4:30
90 mi. N of New Orleans
Est 1970; Acres 3,200; Type Public; On Site
Clubhouse, Lodging, Meals, Clays; Shoots Field;
Birds Quail; Dogs Avail/HDW; Packages 1/2 Day,
6-24 guns

Prairie Shooting Preserve
20645 Old Magnolia Hwy., Prairie, MS 39756
(601) 369-9291 Harold Loftin 5:30 to 7:30 pm
35 mi. S of Tupelo
Est 1987; Acres 1,200; Hunters/yr 45; Type Public;
On Site Clubhouse, Lodging, Meals; Shoots Field;
Birds Quail; **Dogs** Avail/HDW; **Packages** 1/2 Day,
2-12 guns

Prospect Farms Shooting Preserve
30353 Hwy. 41, Nettleton, MS 38858
(601) 256-8227 Bud & Patsy Stevens
20 mi. S of Tupelo
Est 1987; **Acres** 800; **Type** Public, Member/Avail;
On Site Clubhouse, Lodging, Meals, Clays; **Shoots**
Field; **Birds** Quail, Pheasant; **Dogs** Avail/HDW;
Packages 1/2 Day, 2-20 guns ○ NAGA/See Pg. 72

Savage Quail Hunting Preserve
Rt. 1, Box 840, Coldwater, MS 38618
(601) 562-4083 Bobby or Eddie Savage
43 mi. S of Memphis, TN
Acres 400; **Hunters/yr** 100; **Type** Public; **Shoots**
Field; **Birds** Quail; **Dogs** Avail

Thornhill Shooting Preserve
Rt. 3, Box 68, Jayess, MS 39641
(601) 876-5633 Conn Thornhill
Type Public; **Shoots** Field; **Birds** Quail ○ NAGA

Wildwood Hunt Club
Box 7, Wildwood Rd., Benton, MS 39039
(601) 673-9717 Thomas E. Johnson Anytime
45 mi. N of Jackson
Est 1989; **Acres** 2,500; **Hunters/yr** 500; **Type**
Public, Member/Avail, Corp.; **On Site** Clubhouse,
Lodging, Meals, Clays; **Shoots** Field; **Birds** Quail,
Ducks; **Dogs** Avail/HDW; **Packages** 1/2 Day, 2-10
guns ○ NAGA/See Pg. 72

MISSOURI

B&L Hunting
RR1, Box 28, Monticello, MO 63457
(314) 767-5367 Bruce Hinton Evenings
125 mi. NW of St. Louis
Acres 500; **Type** Public; **On Site** Lodging, Meals;
Shoots Field; **Birds** Quail, Pheasant **Dogs** HDW

Baier Den Kennels
& Hunting Preserve
, Peculiar, MO 64078
(816) 758-5234 Bud Baier 9-6
25 mi. S of Kansas City
Est 1951; Acres 4,000; Type Public, Member/Avail;
On Site Clubhouse, Lodging, Meals; Shoots Field;
Birds Quail, Pheasant, Chukar, Turkey; Dogs
Avail/HDW; Packages 1/2 Day, 2-4 guns
○ NAGA/See Pg. 72

○ Hunting License	○ Bird Processing
○ Kennel Bird Dogs	○ Deer Hunting
○ Shooting Instruction	○ Brochure Available
○ On-Site Pro Shop	○ Factory Ammunition
○ Quality Clubhouse	○ Family Run Business
○ Train Bird Dogs-No Electric Collars	

Bird Dogs & Retrievers Trained The Old Fashioned
Proven Way. Patience and hard work on quail, partridge or pheasants (ducks for retrievers) with
plenty of birds...actual field conditions. Special attention paid to developing staunchness on point,
retrieving and hunting dead. All dogs broke to whis-
tle. Monthly report with pictures on dog's
progress. Clean, modern cement kennels in the
heart of Missouri quail country. Write or phone for
free folder. Come visit our kennels and hunt our
preserve!

Rich Baumgartner
610 Camborne, St. Louis, MO 63125
(314) 452-3511
33 mi. SW of St. Louis
Acres 300; **Type** Public, Member/Avail; **On Site**
Clubhouse, Clays; **Shoots** Field; **Birds** Dove, Quail,
Ruffed Grouse, Pheasant, Chukar, Turkey; **Dogs** Avail

Big River Hunting Club & Kennels
PO Box 30, Fletcher, MO 63030
(314) 452-3511 Evenings
33 mi. SW of St. Louis
Est 1993; **Acres** 300; **Type** Member/Avail, Corp.;
On Site Clubhouse, Lodging, Clays; **Shoots** Field;
Birds Dove, Quail, Pheasant, Chukar; **Dogs**
Avail/HDW; **Packages** 1/2 Day, 2-4 guns

Blackhawk Valley
Hunting Preserve
Rt. 1, Box 118, Old Monroe, MO 63369
(314) 665-5459 Mickey Palmer After 6pm
40 mi. NW of St. Louis
Est 1968; **Acres** 600; **Hunters/yr** 75; **Type**
Member/Avail, Corp.; **On Site** Clubhouse, Meals,
Clays; **Shoots** Field; **Birds** Dove, Quail, Pheasant,
Chukar, Ducks; **Dogs** Avail/HDW; **Packages** 1/2
Day, 1-12 guns O NAGA/See Pg. 72

BrownFeather Shooting & Hunting Club
3460 St. Hwy. N, Clever, MO 65631
(417) 743-2527 Dan Dover
15 mi. SW of Springfield
Est 1992; **Acres** 600; **Type** Public, Member/Avail,
Corp.; **On Site** Clubhouse, Lodging, Meals, Clays;
Shoots Field; **Birds** Dove, Quail, Pheasant, Chukar;
Dogs Avail/HDW; **Packages** 1/2 Day, 1-3 guns
O NAGA/See Pg. 72

Brush Creek
RR#1, Box 41, Mayview, MO 64071
(816) 237-4218 Todd Hulver
40 mi. E of Kansas City
Acres 240; **Type** Member/Avail; **On Site**
Clubhouse, Meals; **Shoots** Field; **Birds** Quail,
Pheasant, Chukar; **Dogs** Avail

J.L. Burditt Hunting
916 N. Main St., Monroe City, MO 63456
(314) 735-2608
21 mi. S of Hannibal
Acres 320; **Shoots** Field; **Birds** Pheasant; **Dogs** Avail

Clear Fork Hunting Preserve
321 SE 671, Warrensburg, MO 64093
(816) 747-2588 Ruth or Ron Dillingham
50 mi. SE of Kansas City
Est 1993; **Acres** 600; **Type** Public; **On Site**
Clubhouse; **Shoots** Field; **Birds** Quail, Pheasant,

Chukar; **Dogs** Avail/HDW; **Packages** 1/2 Day, 1-20
guns O NAGA/See Pg. 72

The Fraley Ranch
16300 County Road 7250, Newburg, MO 65550
(314) 364-3017 Tom or Barb Fraley Anytime
110 mi. SW of St. Louis
Est 1986; **Acres** 1,000; **Type** Public; **On Site**
Clubhouse, Lodging, Meals; **Shoots** Field; **Birds**
Turkey; **Packages** 2 Days

Heartland Wildlife Ranches
PO Box 264, Bucklin, MO 64631
(816) 486-3344 Bart Slaugh
Type Public; **Shoots** Field; **Birds** Quail, Pheasant,
Turkey, Ducks O NAGA/See Pg. 72

Hereforedale Ranch
Rt. 1, Queen City, MO 63561
(800) 835-1302 Curtis Sidwell
Acres 5,000; **Type** Public; **On Site** Clubhouse;
Shoots Field; **Birds** Turkey

Hi Point Hunting Club
R1, Box 28, Breckenridge, MO 64625
(816) 644-5708 Brian Guffey
65 mi. NE of Kansas City
Est 1968; **Acres** 1,200; **Hunters/yr** 900; **Type**
Public, Member/Avail, Corp.; **On Site** Clubhouse,
Meals, Clays; **Shoots** Field; **Birds** Quail, Pheasant,
Chukar, Huns, Turkey; **Dogs** Avail/HDW; **Packages**
1/2 Day, 2-30 guns O NAGA/See Pg. 72

"Not a country club, just a club in the country."
That's Hi Point, located in beautiful Northwest Missouri with good motels & restaurants nearby. Our
business is built by return customers. We can handle any type of hunting, from one man working a
young dog to a corporate outing. Visit us for a challenging and sporty hunt you'll long remember. Call
today!

High Adventure Ranch
20 Worthington Access Dr., Maryland Hts., MO 63043
(314) 434-0506 Charles J. Puff 12-5pm
125 mi. SW of St. Louis
Est 1984; **Acres** 1,000; **Type** Public; **On Site**
Clubhouse, Lodging, Meals; **Shoots** Field; **Birds**
Quail, Pheasant, Chukar, Turkey; **Dogs** Avail/HDW;
Packages 1/2 Day, up to 10 guns

High Meadow Hunt Club
828 Wild Horse Valley, Chesterfield, MO 63005
(314) 458-3550 John O'Shaugnessy
10 mi. NW of Chesterfield
Acres 256; **Type** Member/Avail; **On Site** Clays;
Shoots Field; **Birds** Quail, Pheasant, Turkey; **Dogs**
Avail

Hunting Farms Management
RR1, Box 244, Browning, MO 69630
(816) 946-4153 Jim Dwiggins 8-9pm
100 mi. NE of Kansas City
Est 1990; **Acres** 360; **Type** Public; **On Site**
Clubhouse, Lodging, Meals; **Shoots** Field; **Birds**

Dove, Quail, Pheasant, Turkey, Ducks, Geese; **Dogs** Avail/HDW; **Packages** 2 Days, 3-9 guns

Hunting Sports Plus
710 Main St., Suite E, Blue Springs, MO 64015
(800) 729-1924 Dan Gasser
Locations in 7 Midwest States
Est 1989; **Acres** 200,000; **Type** Public,
Member/Avail; **On Site** Clubhouse, Lodging, Meals,
Clays; **Shoots** Field, Blinds, Boat; **Birds** Quail,
Pheasant, Turkey, Prairie Chicken, Ducks, Geese;
Dogs Avail/HDW; **Packages** 1 Day, 1-24 guns
Quality hunting on over 200,000 acres of private
farm land in 7 Midwest States–AR, IA, IL, KS, MO,
NE, OK. Hunt quail, pheasant, turkey, deer, prairie
chicken, ducks and geese. Affordable Midwestern
hospitality. Large seclection of low cost member-
ships, daily plans or hunting vacation package
hunts. Call today for more information.

Kena Shooting Preserve
RR1, Emden, MO 63439
(314) 439-5075 Ken Rowden
110 mi. NW of St. Louis
Est 1990; **Acres** 480; **Type** Public; **Shoots** Field;
Birds Quail, Pheasant, Chukar; **Dogs** Avail;
Packages 1/2 Day

Lake of the Ozarks Hunting Preserve
Rt. 70, Box 964, Camdenton, MO 65020
(314) 873-3566 Gloria Beattie 9-5, Th-Su
9 mi. N of Camdenton
Est 1994; **Acres** 480; **Type** Public, Member/Avail,
Corp.; **On Site** Clubhouse, Clays; **Shoots** Field;
Birds Quail, Pheasant, Chukar; **Dogs** Avail/HDW;
Packages 1/2 Day, up to 3 guns

Malinmor Sporting Estate, Inc.
RR4, Box 108, Eolia, MO 63344
(314) 324-3366 Rick Merritt 8-4
65 mi. NW of St. Louis
Est 1987; **Acres** 2,100; **Type** Member/Avail, Corp.;
On Site Clubhouse, Lodging, Meals, Clays; **Shoots**
Field, Blinds; **Birds** Dove, Quail, Woodcock, Pheasant,
Chukar, Turkey, Ducks; **Dogs** Avail/HDW; **Packages**
1/2 Day, 2-12 guns ○ NAGA/See Pg. 72

McCutchan Ent. Inc. Shooting Division
R2, Box 35, Monticello, MO 63457
(314) 767-5359 Dennis McCutchan
35 mi. from Quincy, IL
Acres 311; **Type** Public; **On Site** Clays; **Shoots**
Field; **Birds** Quail, Pheasant, Turkey; **Dogs** Avail

Midway Farms, Inc.
700 County Rd. 404, Fayette, MO 65248
(816) 248-3838 Lee Myers 8-5:30
125 mi. E of Kansas City
Est 1991; **Acres** 1,250; **Hunters/yr** 500; **Type**
Public, Member/Avail; **On Site** Clubhouse, Meals,
Clays; **Shoots** Field; **Birds** Pheasant, Chukar; **Dogs**
Avail/HDW; **Packages** 1/2 Day, 4-24 guns
○ NAGA/See Pg. 72

Miller's Kennel & Hunting Preserve
Rt. 2, Box 172, Miller, MO 65707
(417) 246-5389 Gary Keel
120 mi. S of Kansas City
Est 1988; **Acres** 160; **Hunters/yr** 100; **Type**
Public; **On Site** Clubhouse, Meals; **Shoots** Field;
Birds Quail, Pheasant, Chukar, Turkey; **Dogs**
Avail/HDW; **Packages** 1/2 Day, 1-4 guns

Moser's Pheasant Creek
502 County Rd. 327, Franklin, MO 65250
(816) 848-2621 Bonnie & Mike Moser
100 mi. E of Kansas City
Est 1985; **Acres** 480; **Type** Public; **On Site** Meals;
Shoots Field; **Birds** Pheasant; **Dogs** Avail/HDW ○
NAGA/See Pg. 72

New London Hunting Club
Rt. 1, Box 269a, New London, MO 63459
(314) 985-7477 Steve & Pam Swon anytime
88 mi. N of St. Louis
Est 1988; **Acres** 1,500; **Hunters/yr** 1,200; **Type**
Public, Member/Avail, Corp.; **On Site** Clubhouse,
Lodging, Meals, Clays; **Shoots** Field; **Birds** Dove,
Quail, Woodcock, Pheasant, Chukar, Turkey; **Dogs**
Avail/HDW; **Packages** 1/2 Day, 1-40 guns

Newcastle Hunt Club
3100 Broadway, #711, Kansas City, MO 64111
(816) 931-9551 Larry Carter 8-6
75 mi. NE of Kansas City
Est 1989; **Acres** 582; **Type** Public, Member/Avail,
Corp.; **On Site** Meals, Clays; **Shoots** Field; **Birds**
Quail, Pheasant, Chukar; **Dogs** Avail/HDW;
Packages 1/2 Day, 4-20 guns

Pond Fort Hunt Club & Kennels
8860 Hwy. N., O'Fallon, MO 63366
(314) 332-9084 Kerry Mische
23 mi. W of St. Louis
Acres 400; **Type** Member/Avail, Corp.; **Shoots**
Field, Tower; **Birds** Quail, Pheasant, Chukar, Turkey;
Dogs Avail/HDW ○ NAGA/See Pg. 72

Range Line Hunt Club
Rt. 1, Box 31, Osborn, MO 64474
(816) 449-2670 Leslie Kerns
50 mi. N of Kansas City
Est 1989; **Acres** 350; **Hunters/yr** 100; **Type**
Public; **On Site** Clubhouse, Meals, Clays; **Shoots**
Field, Blinds; **Birds** Dove, Quail, Pheasant, Chukar,
Turkey, Ducks, Geese; **Dogs** Avail/HDW; **Packages**
1/2 Day, up to 10 guns

Salt Creek Game Farm & Hunting Preserve
Rt. 1, Box 62, Farber, MO 63345
(314) 249-5048 Dave or Lori Sutton After 5pm
100 mi. W of St. Louis
Est 1992; **Acres** 172; **Type** Public; **On Site**
Clubhouse, Lodging; **Shoots** Field; **Birds** Quail,
Pheasant; **Dogs** Avail/HDW; **Packages** 1/2 Day, 2-8
guns ○ NAGA/See Pg. 72

Show-Me Safaris
PO Box 108, Summersville, MO 65571
(417) 932-4423 Mark Hampton Evenings

WINGS

30 mi. S of Rolla
Est 1992;   **Acres** 1,350;   **Hunters/yr** 100;   **Type**
Member/Avail;   **On Site** Clubhouse, Lodging, Clays;
Shoots Field;   **Birds** Turkey;   **Dogs** Avail;   **Packages**
2 Days, 1-6 guns

Snow White Hunting Preserve
Rt. 1, Box 40, Carrollton, MO 64633
(816) 542-3037 Carol L. Atherton
50 mi. E of Kansas City
Type Public;   **Shoots** Field;   **Birds** Quail, Pheasant,
Chukar;   **Dogs** Avail/HDW;   **Packages** 1/2 Day   o
NAGA/See Pg. 72

Sorenson's S.C.
& Preserve Hunting
1703 Hwy. DD, Defiance, MO 63341
(314) 828-5149 Tom & Kay Sorenson 8am-6pm
19 mi. W of St. Louis
Est 1963;   **Acres** 250;   **Type** Public;   **On Site**
Clubhouse, Meals, Clays;   **Shoots** Field, Tower;
Birds Quail, Pheasant, Chukar;   **Dogs** Avail/HDW;
Packages 1/2 Day, 2-4 guns

Stillwater Kennel & Game Farm
Rt. 2, Box 239, Silex, MO 63377
(314) 384-6290 Ron & Monica Garringer
60 mi. NW of St. Louis
Est 1989;   **Acres** 180;   **Type** Public;   **On Site**
Clubhouse;   **Shoots** Field;   **Birds** Quail, Pheasant,
Chukar;   **Dogs** Avail/HDW

Sumgoose Club, Inc.
30 Sumgoose Rd., Box 30A, Sumner, MO 64681
(816) 856-3348 Roy McCallum
Type Public, Member/Avail;   **On Site** Lodging, Clays;
Shoots Field;   **Birds** Quail, Pheasant, Chukar, Turkey,
Ducks   o NAGA/See Pg. 72

Tall Oaks Club
295 Tall Oaks Rd., Warrenton, MO 63383
(314) 456-8265 Jeff Brand
Type Public, Member/Avail;   **On Site** Lodging;
Shoots Field;   **Birds** Quail, Pheasant, Chukar, Huns,
Ducks   o NAGA/See Pg. 72

Turkey Creek Hunting Preserve
RR1, Box 117A, LaClede, MO 64651
(816) 963-2538 Jim Tollerton
85 mi. NE of Kansas City
Type Public, Member/Avail;   **Shoots** Field;   **Birds**
Quail, Pheasant, Chukar, Turkey   o NAGA/See Pg. 72

Twin Lakes Sporting Club
Rt. 1, Box 203, Mexico, MO 65265
(314) 581-1877 Wally Feutz 7am-9pm
110 mi. NW of St. Louis
Est 1991;   **Acres** 1,280;   **Hunters/yr** 200;   **Type**
Public, Member/Avail;   **On Site** Clubhouse, Meals,
Clays;   **Shoots** Field, Blinds;   **Birds** Dove, Quail,
Pheasant, Chukar, Turkey, Ducks, Geese;   **Dogs**
Avail/HDW;   **Packages** 1/2 Day, 1-15 guns
o NAGA/See Pg. 72

White Oak Ranch
RR1, Box 169, Edina, MO 63537
(816) 397-2451 Bill Ingalls 8am-8pm
200 mi. NW of St. Louis
Est 1994;   **Acres** 2,500;   **Type** Public;   **On Site**
Clubhouse, Lodging, Meals, Clays;   **Shoots** Field;
Birds Quail, Pheasant, Chukar;   **Dogs** Avail/HDW;
Packages 1/2 Day, 1-30 guns

Wildwood Hunting & Sporting Clays
RR1, Box 143, Houstonia, MO 65333
(816) 879-4451 Bill Wall After 5pm
100 mi. SE of Kansas City
Est 1986;   **Acres** 1,100;   **Type** Public, Member/Avail;
On Site Clubhouse, Lodging, Meals, Clays;   **Shoots**
Field;   **Birds** Dove, Quail, Woodcock, Pheasant,
Chukar, Turkey;   **Dogs** Avail/HDW;   **Packages** 1/2
Day, 1-35 guns

Wilson Creek Hunts
Rt. 1, Box 74, Eldorado Springs, MO 64744
(417) 465-2240 Kent Ablee
Type Public, Member/Avail;   **On Site** Lodging;
Shoots Field;   **Birds** Quail, Pheasant, Chukar   o
NAGA/See Pg. 72

Wings - St. Albans Properties, L.L.C.
PO Box 49, St. Albans, MO 63073
(314) 458-6523 Gale Oertli 8-5
35 mi. W of St. Louis
Est 1963;   **Acres** 320;   **Type** Member/Avail, Corp.;
On Site Clubhouse, Lodging, Meals, Clays;   **Shoots**
Field, Blinds;   **Birds** Quail, Pheasant, Chukar, Ducks;
Dogs Avail/HDW;   **Packages** 1/2 Day, 2-9 guns   o
NAGA/See Pg. 72

MONTANA

Big Island Shooting Preserve
HC53, Box 31C, Columbus, MT 59019
(406) 322-5339 John Sherwood
32 mi. W of Billings
Acres 122;   **Hunters/yr** 50;   **Type** Public;   **On Site**
Clubhouse, Clays;   **Shoots** Field;   **Birds** Quail,
Pheasant;   **Dogs** Avail/HDW;   **Packages** 1/2 Day

Big Sky Hunting Preserve
& Sporting Clays
PO Box 10, Polson, MT 59860
(406) 883-2000 Dick Mandeville
4 mi. NW of Polson
Est 1993;   **On Site** Clubhouse, Lodging, Meals, Clays;
Shoots Field, Blinds
See Our Ad Across

Birds of Plenty
PO Box 427, Broadus, MT 59317
(406) 436-2433 Dennis Schaffer
Type Public, Member/Avail;   **Shoots** Field;   **Birds**
Quail, Pheasant, Chukar, Huns, Turkey
o NAGA/See Pg. 72

Diamond J Guest Ranch
PO Box 577W, Ennis, MT 59729
(406) 682-4867 Tim Combs M-F, 8-5pm mst
60 mi. SW of Bozeman
Est 1930; **Acres** 25,000; **Type** Public; **On Site**
Clubhouse, Lodging, Meals, Clays; **Shoots** Field,
Blinds, Boat; **Birds** Ruffed Grouse, Pheasant, Chukar,
Huns, Ducks, Geese; **Dogs** Avail/HDW; **Packages** 3
Days, 2-12 guns
See Our Ad Pg. 330

Eagle Nest Lodge
PO Box 470, Hardin, MT 59034
(406) 665-3799 Nick & Francine Forrester
45 mi. S of Billings
Est 1981; **Acres** 50,000; **Hunters/yr** 20; **Type**
Public; **On Site** Clubhouse, Lodging, Meals, Clays;
Shoots Field; **Birds** Pheasant, Chukar, Huns, Turkey,
Sharp Tail Grouse, Ducks, Geese; **Dogs** Avail/HDW;
Packages 2 Days, 2-6 guns

Fetch Inn Hunting Preserve
PO Drawer 1429, Hamilton, MT 59840
(800) 854-6732 Tom Fox 8-6
40 mi. S of Missoula
Est 1973; **Acres** 1,000; **Hunters/yr** 100; **Type**
Public, Member/Avail, Corp.; **On Site** Clubhouse,
Lodging, Meals, Clays; **Shoots** Field, Blinds; **Birds**

Quail, Pheasant, Chukar, Huns, Turkey, Ducks, Geese;
Dogs Avail/HDW; **Packages** 1/2 Day, 1-8 guns

Mike/Elaine Krueger
4155 W. Kootenai Rd., Rexford, MT 59930
(406) 889-3297 Mike Krueger
100 mi. NW of Kalispell
Acres 250; **Hunters/yr** 30; **Type** Public; **On Site**
Lodging, Meals; **Shoots** Field; **Birds** Pheasant, Chukar

Montana Bird Hunts
Box 5031, Bozeman, MT 59717
(406) 587-5923 Dennis Kavanagh 7am-9pm
100 mi. E of Great Falls
Est 1982; **Acres** 50,000; **Hunters/yr** 80; **Type**
Public; **On Site** Clubhouse, Lodging, Meals; **Shoots**
Field; **Birds** Ruffed Grouse, Pheasant, Huns, Sage
Grouse, Snipe, Sharp Tail Grouse, Ducks; **Dogs**
Avail/HDW; **Packages** 3 Days, 2-9 guns

Montana Outdoor Expeditions
76370 Gallatin Rd., Gallatin Gateway, MT 59730
(406) 763-4749 Bob Griffith
10 mi. SW of Bozeman
Type Public; **On Site** Clubhouse, Lodging, Meals;
Shoots Field; **Birds** Quail, Pheasant, Chukar, Huns,
Turkey, Sharp Tail Grouse; **Dogs** Avail/HDW;
Packages 1 Day

Powder River Outfitters
Box 678, Broadus, MT 59317
(406) 436-2538 Ken Greslin
160 mi. E of Billings
Acres 600,000; **Type** Public; **On Site** Lodging,
Meals; **Shoots** Field; **Birds** Pheasant, Turkey

WINGS

The Diamond J: A Little Montana Magic

In 1959, Peter and Jinny Combs were on their way to Alaska, looking to move from the ever-increasing development of southern California. They stopped at the Diamond J Ranch, and the rest is history-- and a little Montana Magic.

Located in the Madison River Valley just outside Ennis, the Diamond J, nestled in a separate canyon at 5,800 feet with Jack Creek running along side, is a sportsman's delight: trap, skeet, sporting clays, wingshooting, fly-fishing and a whole lot more.

Your hosts, Jinny and Pete Combs

Today Pete, Jinny and their son, Tim, manage the ranch. Together they see to it that all thirty-six guests are well looked after.

Bird Hunting

The Diamond J offers exceptional private upland bird-hunting on a 30,000 acre ranch located on the east side of the famous Madison River. So exceptional is the hunting, that the Diamond J is one of a handful of Lodges across the U.S. endorsed by the Orvis Wingshooting Program.

An abundance of Hungarian & Chukar Partridge, Ring-necked Pheasant, Blue & Ruffed Grouse (and ducks and geese in season) can be hunted September through December on terrain consisting of river bottom, hay meadows, willows and natural grass cover. Expert guides and dogs are provided by the Diamond J at no additional cost says Tim Combs, but guests are welcome to hunt with their own dogs and "we have excellent facilities to shelter and care for the dogs while they are here." A typical hunt starts with a morning round of sporting clays, a mid-day break for a delicious home-cooked lunch from the ranch kitchen, and an afternoon afield. (No need to panic if you've forgotten your bird-hunting equipment or need additional clothing, ammunition or a gun. The Diamond J's gift shop is fully stocked with Orvis hunting and fishing equipment.)

Great Fishing

Whether you're a seasoned veteran of fly fishing or an eager beginner, fishing at the Diamond J is an experience you will long remember (The Diamond J is an Orvis endorsed fishing lodge, too!). From June through October the fishing includes any-thing from wet to dry flies. From the outlet of Quake Lake and running along 52 miles downstream to Ennis Lake, the famous and swift upper Madison River offers some of the most consistent fishing for Rainbow and Brown Trout you will ever find--anywhere. (The adventuresome fisherman can opt for an all-day to three-day pack trip by horseback to fish mountain lakes.)

Welcome Pardner

The Diamond J's appeal doesn't end with fine fishing and hunting. A fully operational dude ranch, the Diamond J offers a range of activities tailored to individual, family or corporate needs: horseback riding, hiking, square dancing, camp fire sing-a-longs, a pool, and, even, an excellent library. Ten log cabins, each with its own rock fireplace and full bath, but no telephones or television, accommodate up to 36 guests. Meals--hearty and delicious-- are served family style three times a day in the Main Lodge.

Getting to the Diamond J in Ennis is very easy. A commercial airport, Gallatin Field in Belgrade, is a little more than an hour's drive from the ranch, and is served by Delta, Northwest and Frontier Airlines. Ennis has a 4,800 foot paved runway that can accommodate private planes and corporate jets.

Finally, a word of caution: One trip to the Diamond J--alone, with friends, or family-- may start an annual tradition. And the Combses wouldn't have it any other way! **Call (406) 682-4867 or write Diamond J Ranch, Box 577W, Ennis, Montana 59729 for more information, a beautiful color brochure or reservations.**

South Fork Lodge
Rural Rt. 10, Utica, MT 59452
(406) 374-2356 Ben Steel 8am-11pm
100 mi. SE of Great Falls
Est 1967; Acres 200,000; Hunters/yr 75; Type
Public; On Site Clubhouse, Lodging, Meals; Shoots
Field, Blinds; Birds Ruffed Grouse, Pheasant, Huns,
Turkey, Sage Grouse, Sharp Tail Grouse, Ducks; Dogs
Avail/HDW; Packages 3 Days, 3-8 guns

Stillwater Shooting Preserve
1141 Church Dr., Kalispell, MT 59901
(406) 755-1959 Brian Tutvedt
10 mi. NW of Kalispell
Acres 500; Type Public; On Site Clays; Shoots
Field, Blinds; Birds Quail, Pheasant, Chukar, Ducks,
Geese; Dogs Avail

Tamarack Lodge
32855 South Fork Rd., Troy, MT 59935
(406) 295-4880 Bill & Judy McAfee
Type Public; On Site Clubhouse, Lodging; Shoots
Field; Birds Ruffed Grouse

Troilus Kennels & Guide Service
RR 1, Box 1213, Bridger, MT 59014
(406) 662-3576
Est 1994; Acres 2,000,000; Type Public; Shoots
Field; Birds Pheasant, Huns, Sage Grouse, Sharp Tail
Grouse; Packages 5 Days, 4-100 guns

Two Leggins Outfitters
Box 2120, Star Rt., Hardin, MT 59034
(406) 665-2825 David Schaff
49 mi. SE of Billings
Acres 80,000; Hunters/yr 40; Type Public; On
Site Lodging, Meals; Shoots Field, Blinds; Birds
Pheasant, Chukar, Turkey, Sharp Tail Grouse, Ducks,
Geese; Dogs Avail

Whitcomb Lodge
Box 1173, Malta, MT 59538
(406) 654-2089 Roy Ereaux Anytime
200 mi. N of Billings
Est 1985; Acres 30,000; Hunters/yr 50; Type
Public; On Site Clubhouse, Lodging, Meals, Clays;
Shoots Field, Driven, Blinds; Birds Pheasant, Chukar,
Huns, Sage Grouse, Sharp Tail Grouse, Geese;
Dogs Avail/HDW; Packages 3 Days, 1-14 guns

Wolf Creek Shooting Preserve
HC76, Box 45, Denton, MT 59435
(406) 567-2436 Floyd Blair
40 mi. N of Lewistown
Acres 1,280; Type Public; Birds Pheasant, Chukar,
Huns, Ducks, Geese

Yaak River Lodge
27744 Yaak River Rd., Troy, MT 59935
(406) 295-5463 Gloria Racine/Donald Belcher
On Site Clubhouse, Lodging, Meals; Birds Ruffed
Grouse; Dogs Avail

NEBRASKA

Boardman Springs
HC32, Box 31, Valentine, NE 69201
(402) 376-1498 Bill Weller
110 mi. N of North Platte
Acres 20,000; Type Public; On Site Lodging,
Meals; Shoots Field; Birds Dove, Pheasant, Sharp
Tail Grouse, Ducks, Geese; Dogs Avail/HDW;
Packages 2 Days, 3-12 guns

Calamus Safari
HC79, Box 2-1, Burwell, NE 68823
(308) 346-5330 Mick Phillipps
Type Public; Shoots Field; Birds Quail, Pheasant
O NAGA/See Pg. 72

Can-Hunt
Rt. 1, Seward, NE 68434
(402) 588-2448 Todd Halle After 8pm
60 mi. SW of Omaha
Est 1988; Acres 440; Hunters/yr 150; Type
Public, Member/Avail, Corp.; On Site Clubhouse,
Clays; Shoots Field; Birds Dove, Quail, Pheasant,
Chukar; Dogs Avail/HDW; Packages 1/2 Day, 1-15
guns O NAGA/See Pg. 72

Frenchman River Hunting
HC65, Box 113, Wauneta, NE 69045
(308) 394-5511 Pat Kitt
65 mi. S of North Platte
Est 1989; Acres 3,000; Hunters/yr 100; Type
Public; On Site Lodging, Meals, Clays; Shoots Field,
Blinds; Birds Dove, Quail, Pheasant, Chukar, Ducks,
Geese; Dogs Avail/HDW; Packages 1/2 Day, 1-7
guns

H&H
PO Box 334, Cozad, NE 69130
(308) 784-2410 Dean Herrington
Acres 160; Type Public; Shoots Field; Birds Quail,
Pheasant O NAGA/See Pg. 72

Honore Hilltop Shooting Preserve
1605 North E Rd., Phillips, NE 68865
(402) 886-2215 Nina & John Honore 6am-10pm
130 mi. W of Omaha
Est 1985; Acres 1,000; Type Public; On Site
Clubhouse, Meals, Clays; Shoots Field, Tower;
Birds Quail, Pheasant, Chukar, Huns, Turkey; Dogs
Avail/HDW; Packages 1/2 Day, 1-30 guns
O NAGA/See Pg. 72

Hunt Nebraska, Inc.
PO Box 328, Arapahoe, NE 68922
(800) 486-8632 Johnny Hemelstrand
180 mi. W of Lincoln
Est 1986; Acres 10,000; Hunters/yr 300; Type
Public; On Site Clubhouse, Lodging, Meals, Clays;
Shoots Field, Blinds; Birds Dove, Quail, Pheasant,
Chukar, Turkey, Sharp Tail Grouse, Ducks, Geese;
Dogs Avail/HDW; Packages 1 Day, 1-20 guns

WINGS

Hunting Sports Plus
710 Main St., Ste. E, Blue Springs, MO,
Hunting in 7 States including Nebraska
(800) 729-1924 Dan Gasser
Est 1989; **Acres** 200,000; **Type** Public,
Member/Avail; **On Site** Clubhouse, Lodging, Meals,
Clays; **Shoots** Field, Blinds, Boat; **Birds** Quail,
Pheasant, Turkey, Prairie Chicken, Ducks, Geese;
Dogs Avail/HDW; **Packages** 1 Day, 1-24 guns

K-D Hunting Acres
RR1, Box 182A, Tekamah, NE 68061
(402) 374-1428 Kim or Dee Snow Anytime
40 mi. N of Omaha
Est 1992; **Acres** 1,000; **Hunters/yr** 700; **Type**
Public, Member/Avail, Corp.; **On Site** Clubhouse,
Lodging, Meals, Clays; **Shoots** Field; **Birds** Quail,
Pheasant, Chukar; **Dogs** Avail/HDW; **Packages** 1/2
Day, 1-15 guns ○ NAGA/See Pg. 72

L and P Ranch
RR2, Box 80A, Orchard, NE 68764
(402) 655-2244 Linda or Paul Hayes 9am-5pm
75 mi. NW of Norfolk
Est 1993; **Acres** 680; **Hunters/yr** 100; **Type**
Public; **On Site** Clubhouse, Lodging, Meals, Clays;
Shoots Field; **Birds** Pheasant; **Dogs** Avail/HDW;
Packages 1/2 Day, 1-6 guns ○ NAGA/See Pg. 72

Pheasant Haven Hunting Acres
PO Box 650, Elkhorn, NE 68022
(402) 779-2608 Scott Bruhn 7am
15 mi. NW of Omaha
Est 1987; **Acres** 1,000; **Hunters/yr** 500; **Type**
Public, Member/Avail, Corp.; **On Site** Clubhouse,
Lodging, Meals; **Shoots** Field; **Birds** Quail,
Pheasant, Chukar; **Dogs** Avail/HDW; **Packages** 1/2
Day, up to 4 guns ○ NAGA/See Pg. 72

Prairie Hills Hunting Club
1104 W. Division, Grand Island, NE 68801
(308) 226-2540 John & Kathleen McElroy 8-5
13 mi. NW of Grand Island

Est 1985; **Acres** 1,200; **Hunters/yr** 600; **Type**
Public, Member/Avail, Corp.; **On Site** Clubhouse,
Lodging, Meals, Clays; **Shoots** Field; **Birds** Dove,
Quail, Pheasant, Chukar, Prairie Chicken; **Dogs**
Avail/HDW; **Packages** 1/2 Day, 4-20 guns
○ NAGA/See Pg. 72

Rooster Ranch
RR1, Box 51, Ruskin, NE 68974
(402) 279-2035 Rocky Renz 8-5
130 mi. SW of Omaha
Est 1989; **Acres** 120; **Hunters/yr** 20; **Type**
Public; **On Site** Clubhouse, Lodging, Meals; **Birds**
Dove, Quail, Pheasant, Chukar; **Dogs** Avail/HDW;
Packages 1 Day, 3-6 guns

Sand Prairie Preserve
Box 94, Alliance, NE 69301
(308) 762-2735 William or Bev Lore Evenings
6 mi. SE of Alliance
Est 1992; **Acres** 360; **Type** Public; **On Site**
Clubhouse, Lodging, Meals, Clays; **Shoots** Field;
Birds Quail, Pheasant, Chukar, Turkey; **Dogs**
Avail/HDW; **Packages** 1/2 Day, 4-20 guns
○ NAGA/See Pg. 72

Sandhills Adventures
HC63, Box 28, Brewster, NE 68821
(308) 547-2450 Scott Cozart
125 mi. NW of Grand Island
Est 1989; **Acres** 16,000; **Type** Public, Corp.; **On
Site** Clubhouse, Lodging, Meals, Clays; **Shoots** Field,
Driven, Blinds; **Birds** Dove, Pheasant, Chukar, Huns,
Turkey, Prairie Chicken, Ducks, Geese; **Dogs**
Avail/HDW; **Packages** 1 Day, 1-24 guns
See Our Ad Below

Sappa Creek Hunt Preserve
PO Box 357, Orleans, NE 68966
(308) 473-3308 Tim Rief
165 mi. SW of Lincoln

Est 1993; **Acres** 76,000; **Type** Public; **On Site** Clubhouse, Lodging, Meals, Clays; **Shoots** Field, Driven; **Birds** Quail, Pheasant, Chukar; **Dogs** Avail/HDW; **Packages** 1 Day, 2-12 guns

Swanson Hunting Acres, Inc.
PO Box 99, Niobrara, NE 68760
(402) 857-3514 Janet Swanson
85 mi. W of Sioux City, IA
Est 1983; **Acres** 2,200; **Type** Public; **On Site** Clubhouse, Lodging, Meals, Clays; **Shoots** Field; **Birds** Quail, Pheasant, Chukar; **Dogs** Avail/HDW
○ NAGA/See Pg. 72

Table Top Hunting Preserve
1011 Table Rd., Chadron, NE 69337
(308) 432-5828 Melvin Bruns
23.5 mi. SW of Chadron
Acres 1,000; **Type** Public; **On Site** Meals; **Shoots** Field; **Birds** Quail, Pheasant, Chukar; **Dogs** Avail
○ NAGA/See Pg. 72

Trapper's Creek Outdoors
RR1, Box 64, Burwell, NE 68823
(308) 346-5024 Gary & Mary Hughes
90 mi. NE of Grand Island
Acres 251; **Type** Public; **On Site** Lodging, Meals; **Shoots** Field; **Birds** Dove, Quail, Pheasant, Prairie Chicken; **Dogs** Avail ○ NAGA/See Pg. 72

Turtle Creek Hunting Preserve
Rt. 1, Box 89, Hoskins, NE 68740
(402) 565-4581 Randy Wagner After 6pm
50 mi. SW of Sioux City, IA
Est 1991; **Acres** 1,500; **Hunters/yr** 50; **Type** Public; **On Site** Clubhouse, Lodging, Meals, Clays; **Shoots** Field; **Birds** Dove, Quail, Pheasant; **Dogs** Avail/HDW; **Packages** 1 Day, 2-16 guns

Upland Hunts
PO Box 58, Broken Bow, NE 68822
(308) 872-2998 Keith "Cas" McCaslin
70 mi. NE of North Platte
Est 1985; **Acres** 15,000; **Hunters/yr** 150; **Type** Public, Corp.; **On Site** Clubhouse, Lodging, Meals; **Shoots** Field; **Birds** Quail, Pheasant, Huns, Turkey, Prairie Chicken, Sharp Tail Grouse; **Dogs** Avail/HDW; **Packages** 1 Day, 2-12 guns ○ NAGA/See Pg. 72

NEVADA

Canyon Pheasant Club
HC62, Box 300, Wells, NV 89835
(702) 752-3065 Sterling Nixon
60 mi. NE of Elko
Acres 13,000; **Hunters/yr** 100; **Type** Public, Member/Avail; **On Site** Lodging, Meals, Clays; **Shoots** Field; **Birds** Dove, Pheasant, Chukar, Prairie Chicken, Ducks, Geese; **Dogs** Avail

Casino West/LM Ranches
11 N. Main St., Yerington, NV 89447
(702) 463-2481 L. Bryan Masini Wkdys, 8-5
90 mi. SE of Reno
Est 1979; **Acres** 3,000; **Hunters/yr** 500; **Type**

Public; **On Site** Clubhouse, Meals; **Shoots** Field, Blinds; **Birds** Dove, Quail, Pheasant, Chukar, Geese; **Dogs** Avail/HDW; **Packages** 1 Day, 10-100 guns

Honey Lake Ranch
PO Box 7575, Reno, NV 89510
Louis Capurro
7 mi. from Janesville, CA **Acres** 1,200; **Hunters/yr** 100; **Type** Member/Avail; **On Site** Clubhouse; **Shoots** Blinds; **Birds** Dove, Quail, Pheasant, Chukar, Huns, Ducks, Geese

The Humboldt Hunting Club
PO Box 70341, Reno, NV 89570
(702) 356-6080
72 mi. N of Winnemucca
Acres 17,000; **Type** Member/Avail; **On Site** Clubhouse; **Shoots** Field; **Birds** Dove, Quail, Pheasant, Chukar; **Dogs** HDW

Red Hills Hunting Preserve
PO Box 493, Gardnerville, NV 89410
(702) 266-3856 George Asay
60 mi. S of Reno
Acres 10,000; **Type** Public, Member/Avail; **On Site** Clubhouse, Meals, Clays; **Shoots** Field; **Birds** Quail, Pheasant, Chukar, Ducks, Geese; **Dogs** Avail/HDW
○ NAGA/See Pg. 72

Sage Hill Clay Sports & Game Hunting
11500 Mira Loma Rd., Reno, NV 89511
(702) 851-1123 Rich & Darlene Bullard
12 mi. SE of Reno
Est 1991; **Acres** 1,900; **Type** Public, Member/Avail, Corp.; **On Site** Clubhouse, Meals, Clays; **Shoots** Field; **Birds** Quail, Pheasant, Chukar; **Dogs** Avail/HDW; **Packages** 1 Day, 1-10 guns

NEW HAMPSHIRE

Chase Farm
Rt. 31, PO Box 245, Washington, NH 03280
(603) 495-3729 Brian or Pamela Vaillancourt
8am-9pm
25 mi. W of Concord
Est 1989; **Acres** 150; **Hunters/yr** 200; **Type** Public, Member/Avail; **On Site** Clubhouse, Lodging, Meals; **Shoots** Field, Tower; **Birds** Quail, Pheasant, Chukar; **Dogs** Avail/HDW; **Packages** 1/2 Day, 1-12 guns

Green Boughs
& Tail Feathers
Center Hill Rd., Epsom, NH 03234
(617) 665-5011 John Baldi/Mike Hickey after 5
72 mi. N of Boston
Est 1990; **Acres** 400; **Type** Public, Member/Avail; **On Site** Clubhouse; **Shoots** Field, Driven; **Birds** Quail, Pheasant, Chukar; **Dogs** Avail/HDW; **Packages** 1/2 Day, up to 4 guns

Green Mountain Kennels Hunting Preserve
RR1, Box 438F, Center Ossipee, NH 03814
(603) 539-2106 David Bardzik 8-5
50 mi. NE of Concord

WINGS

Est 1995;   Acres 400;   Type Public;   On Site Clays;
Shoots Field, Tower;   Birds Quail, Pheasant, Chukar;
Dogs Avail/HDW

Hidden Meadow Farm
PO Box 64, Webster Rd., Temple, NH 03084
(603) 924-6030   Martin T. Connolly
50 mi. NW of Boston
Est 1986;   Acres 1,200;   Type Member/Avail, Corp.;
On Site Clubhouse;   Shoots Field;   Birds Quail,
Pheasant, Chukar, Huns, Ducks;   Dogs Avail/HDW

High Point Upland Game, Inc.
RR1, Box 241-A1, Alton, NH 03809
(603) 875-3552   Jonathan Caley
Type Public, Member/Avail;   Shoots Field;   Birds
Quail, Pheasant, Chukar   O NAGA/See Pg. 72

SKAT
PO Box 137, New Ipswich, NH 03071
(603) 878-1257   Tony Haigh
50 mi. NW of Boston
Est 1952;   Acres 350;   Hunters/yr 1,000;   Type
Public, Member/Avail, Corp.;   On Site Clubhouse,
Lodging, Meals, Clays;   Birds Pheasant, Chukar, Huns,
Ducks;   Dogs Avail/HDW;   Packages 1/2 Day, 2-30
guns

Sportsmen's Hill Hunting Preserve
Old Leonard Farm Rd., West Swanzey, NH 03469
(603) 357-0386   Gary or Joan Polishan
6 mi. S of Keene
Est 1986;   Acres 125;   Type Public;   On Site
Clubhouse, Clays;   Shoots Field;   Birds Pheasant,
Chukar;   Dogs Avail/HDW;   Packages 1/2 Day, 1-4
guns

Tall Timber Lodge
231 Beach Rd., Pittsburg, NH 03592
(800) 835-6343   Cindy Sullivan
180 mi. N of Manchester
Est 1946;   Acres 200,000;   Type Public;   On Site
Clubhouse, Lodging, Meals;   Shoots Field;   Birds
Ruffed Grouse, Woodcock, Pheasant;   Dogs HDW;
Packages 1 Day

The Timberdoodle Club
One Webster Hwy., Temple, NH 03084
(603) 654-9510   Randall Martin
55 mi. NW of Boston
Est 1967;   Acres 1,000;   Type Member/Ltd, Corp.;
On Site Clubhouse, Lodging, Meals, Clays;   Shoots
Field, Tower, Driven;   Birds Quail, Pheasant, Chukar,
Huns;   Dogs Avail/HDW

O Airport Pickup   O Bird Processing
O Sporting Clays   O Family Recreation
O On-Site Pro Shop   O Quality Clubhouse

Shooting Instruction Available - See Pg. 178

NEW JERSEY

Amwell Valley Conservancy
117 Bowne Station Rd., Stockton, NJ 08559
(609) 397-3113   Ron Dombrowski
25 mi. N of Philadelphia   Type Member/Avail;

B&B Pheasantry
78 Whitehall Rd., Pittstown, NJ 08867
(908) 735-6501   Ben Beckage   Nights
50 mi. SW of New York City
Est 1979;   Acres 1,000;   Hunters/yr 5,000;   Type
Public, Member/Avail;   Shoots Field, Tower, Blinds;
Birds Quail, Pheasant, Chukar, Huns, Geese;   Dogs
Avail/HDW;   Packages 1/2 Day, up to 20 guns
O Hunting License   O Bird Processing
O Loaner Guns   O Factory Ammunition
O German Shorthairs   O NAGA/See Pg. 72

Belleplain Farms
Shooting Preserve
346 Handsmill Rd., Belleplain, NJ 08270
(609) 861-2345   Nick Germanio   8 to 6
50 mi. SE of Philadelphia
Est 1983;   Acres 1,200;   Hunters/yr 1,500;   Type
Public, Member/Avail, Corp.;   On Site Clubhouse,
Lodging, Clays;   Shoots Field, Tower;   Birds Quail,
Ruffed Grouse, Woodcock, Pheasant, Chukar;   Dogs
Avail/HDW;   Packages 1 Day, 1-40 guns
O NAGA/See Pg. 72
O Family Run Business
O Great Deer Hunting
We offer both daily hunts and memberships. Daily
hunts are a full day hunt at $95 per person and in-
clude 4 pheasants or 6 chukars or 10 quail per
person (2 person minimum). A full season $1,350
membership will entitle you to hunt 7 days a week
if you wish with 3 of your guests and includes release of 45 pheasants or 60 chukars or 120 quail.
Members may use on-site rifle & pistol range and
receive a discount on sporting clays and shooting
supplies. At our on-site gun center (BELLEPLAIN
SUPPLY) we stock a full line of top quality firearms
and sporting goods, such as: Browning, Remington, Weatherby, Benelli, Carhartt, LaCrosse and
many more. Come shoot & handle Browning sporting clay guns before you buy. Shoot sporting clays
on a 50 target multi-station range for $12 per
round (2 person minimum). Shoot Crazy Quail or 5-
stand, 25 targets for $6. Call for more information
on this multi-activity shooting preserve located on
prime upland farmland.

Big Spring Game Farm
RD#3, Box 591, Sussex, NJ 07461
(201) 875-3373   Bob Hogg   8am-4pm

50 mi. NW of New York City
Est 1967; **Acres** 180; **Hunters/yr** 150; **Type**

Bradway's Hunting
149 Jericho Rd., RD2, Salem, NJ 08079
(609) 935-5696 Joan/John/Mike Bradway 6 to 9 pm
30 mi. SW of Philadelphia
Est 1970; **Acres** 315; **Hunters/yr** 300; **Type**
Public; **On Site** Clubhouse, Lodging, Meals; **Shoots**
Field, Blinds; **Birds** Quail, Pheasant, Chukar, Turkey,
Ducks; **Dogs** Avail/HDW; **Packages** 1/2 Day, up to
16 guns

Buttonwood
Game Preserve
810 Harmony Station Rd., Phillipsburg, NJ 08865
(908) 454-8377 Gail & Frank Vargo
60 mi. W of New York
Est 1994; **Acres** 150; **Type** Public, Member/Avail;
On Site Clays; **Shoots** Field, Tower; **Birds** Quail,
Pheasant, Chukar, Huns; **Dogs** Avail/HDW;
Packages 1/2 Day, 1-8 guns O NAGA/See Pg. 72
See Our Ad Below Right

RR#2, Box 195, Woodstown, NJ 08098
(609) 769-0035 John or Cheryl DiGregorio 7am-8pm
20 mi. SE of Philadelphia
Est 1983; **Acres** 450; **Type** Public, Member/Avail,
Corp.; **On Site** Clubhouse, Lodging, Meals; **Shoots**
Field, Tower, Driven; **Birds** Quail, Pheasant, Chukar,
Geese; **Dogs** Avail/HDW; **Packages** 1/2 Day, 1-4
guns O NAGA/See Pg. 72
O Family Run Business
O Excellent Trainings Site for Dogs-Special in Oct.
O Secluded Acres-Just You, Your Party, Your Dog
O Comfortable (New) Clubhouse
O Excellent Cover-Natural & Managed
O 20 Minutes from Philadelphia & Wilmington & 2 hrs.
  New York City

Gibersons Game Farm
& Hunting Preserve
317 Sooys Landing Rd., Port Republic, NJ 08241
(609) 652-1939 Clem or Lois Giberson Evenings
15 mi. NW of Atlantic City
Est 1994; **Acres** 500; **Type** Public, Member/Avail,
Corp.; **On Site** Clubhouse, Meals, Clays; **Shoots**
Field, Tower, Blinds, Boat; **Birds** Quail, Woodcock,
Pheasant, Chukar, Turkey, Ducks, Geese; **Dogs**
Avail/HDW; **Packages** 1/2 Day, 1-12 guns
O NAGA/See Pg. 72
O Bird Processing   O Kennel Bird Dogs
O Sporting Clays   O Family Recreation
O Fishing   O Family Run Business
O RV Campsite Available
O Alternate Phone: (609) 748-1948
See Our Ad Pg. 337

M&M Hunting Preserve

Hook & Winslow Rds., Pennsville, NJ 08070
(609) 935-1230 Anthony Matarese 9-3
25 mi. SW of Philadelphia
Est 1980; **Acres** 1,500; **Hunters/yr** 8,000; **Type**
Public, Member/Avail; **On Site** Clubhouse, Meals,
Clays; **Shoots** Field, Tower, Blinds, Boat; **Birds**
Pheasant, Chukar, Ducks, Geese; **Dogs** Avail/HDW;
Packages 1/2 Day, 1-48 guns ○ NAGA/See Pg. 72
See Our Ad Pg. 335

Meadows Grove Sportsmen

58 West Chrystal St., Dover, NJ 07801
(201) 366-3687 Frank G. Hulsman, Pres. After 6 pm
50 mi. W of New York City
Est 1981; **Acres** 800; **Type** Member/Avail; **On
Site** Clubhouse; **Shoots** Field; **Birds** Quail,
Woodcock, Pheasant, Chukar, Geese; **Dogs** Avail/HDW

Meadowview Sporting
Dog Club & Preserve

P.O. Box 486, Hancock's Bridge, NJ 08038
(609) 935-8077 Steven Veltman

15 mi. SE of Wilmington
Est 1993; **Acres** 1,400; **Type** Public, Member/Avail,
Corp.; **On Site** Clubhouse, Lodging, Meals, Clays;
Shoots Field, Tower, Blinds, Boat; **Birds** Quail,
Pheasant, Chukar, Huns, Ducks; **Dogs** Avail/HDW;
Packages 1/2 Day, 1-24 guns
See Our Ad Below

Oak Lane Farms

Dutch Mill Rd., Piney Hollow, NJ 08344
(609) 697-2196 John Scavelli day or evening
30 mi. N of Atlantic City
Est 1974; **Acres** 200; **Type** Public; **On Site**
Clubhouse, Lodging, Meals, Clays; **Shoots** Field,
Tower, Blinds; **Birds** Quail, Pheasant, Ducks; **Dogs**
Avail/HDW; **Packages** 1/2 Day, 1-4 guns
○ NAGA/See Pg. 72

Oak Ridge
Sportsman Club

261 Garrison Rd., Phillipsburg, NJ 08865
(908) 859-1615 William MacQueen
50 mi. W of New York
Est 1975; **Acres** 425; **Type** Public, Member/Avail;
On Site Clubhouse, Clays; **Shoots** Field; **Birds** >

Quail, Pheasant, Chukar, Huns; **Dogs** Avail/HDW;
Packages 1/2 Day, 1-10 guns ○ NAGA/See Pg. 72
○ Family Run Business
○ Less than 1 Hr. from NYC
○ Day Hunts Available
○ Season Memberships: $600-$800
○ Target Shooting: Pistol, Rifle, Bow

One Flew Over the Hedgerow
748 Coles Mill Rd., Franklinvolle, NJ 08322
(609) 728-6454 Mike Moffa
25 mi. SE of Philadelphia
Acres 200; **Type** Public; **Shoots** Field; **Birds** Quail,
Pheasant, Ducks; **Dogs** Avail/HDW; **Packages** 1/2
Day, 1-6 guns ○ NAGA/See Pg. 72

Shallow Brook Sportsmen
982 Fairview Lake Rd., Newton, NJ 07821
(201) 579-9443 Lindsey Dwyer
60 mi. W of New York City
Type Public, Member/Avail; **Shoots** Field; **Birds**
Pheasant; **Dogs** Avail; **Packages** 1/2 Day
○ NAGA/See Pg. 72

West Creek Gunning Club
433 Stipson Island Rd., Eldora, NJ 08270
(609) 861-2760 Donna or George Campbell, Jr. 8 -9
45 mi. from Philadelphia
Est 1959; **Acres** 900; **Hunters/yr** 50; **Type**
Member/Avail; **On Site** Clubhouse, Meals, Clays;
Shoots Field, Tower, Blinds, Boat; **Birds** Quail,
Woodcock, Pheasant, Chukar, Ducks, Geese; **Dogs**
Avail/HDW
○ Bird Processing   ○ Sporting Clays
○ Shooting Instruction   ○ Brochure Available
○ Factory Ammunition   ○ Quality Clubhouse
○ Family Run Business

Wing & Shot
64 Fern St., Browns Mills, NJ 08015
(609) 893-6266 Keith 4 to 9 pm
25 mi. E of Philadelphia
Est 1985; **Acres** 1,100; **Type** Public, Member/Avail;
Shoots Field; **Birds** Quail, Pheasant, Chukar, Turkey,
Ducks; **Dogs** Avail/HDW; **Packages** 1/2 Day, 2-4
guns

NEW MEXICO

Cotton Wood Gun Club
2311 W. Grand, PO Box 1086, Artesia, NM 88211
(505) 746-9777 Jesse McGary
35 mi. S of Roswell
Type Member/Ltd;

Stanley Hunting

PO Box 614, Stanley, NM 87056
(505) 832-6356 Bob Stitt Evenings
35 mi. NE of Albuquerque
Est 1988; **Acres** 6,800; **Hunters/yr** 300; **Type**
Public, Member/Avail, Corp.; **Shoots** Field; **Birds**
Dove, Quail, Pheasant; **Dogs** Avail/HDW; **Packages**
1/2 Day, 1-4 guns O NAGA/See Pg. 72
Less than an hour's drive from Santa Fe and Albuquerque! We're a "low key", "no fancy stuff"
operation, but if you want to stretch your legs,
huntin' quail, pheasant or chukars on our 6800
acres can't be beat. Hunt with your dog or one of
our LOS CASADORES PUDLEPOINTERS. Puppies,
started dogs and trained dogs sometimes available.
Call today. Thanks.

Tinnin Hunt Club

20 First Plaza NW, Suite 518, Albuquerque, NM 87103
(505) 242-2871 Tom Tinnin
45 mi. S of Albuquerque
Est 1992; **Acres** 500; **Type** Public; **On Site**
Clubhouse, Meals, Clays; **Shoots** Field, Blinds; **Birds**
Dove, Quail, Pheasant, Chukar, Ducks, Geese; **Dogs**
Avail/HDW; **Packages** 1/2 Day, 3-50 guns
O NAGA/See Pg. 72
O Kennel Bird Dogs   O Sporting Clays
O Brochure Available   O Fishing
O Factory Ammunition   O Family Run Business

*Flying within the United States on a
commercial airliner with your unloaded
shotgun is legal and easy. All airlines
require a hard-shell, crush proof gun case.
And just to be safe, you should allow an
additional 15 minutes at check-in.*

*For a step-by-step guide that'll help you
breeze through the process and leave you
wondering why you ever left your shotgun
at home, see the "Traveling With Your
Shotgun" article on page 75 of the Gun
Case section.*

NEW YORK

Austerlitz Club
634 Dogway Rd., Chatham, NY 12037
(518) 392-9879 Terry Cozzolino 7am-9pm
Est 1928; **Acres** 500; **Type** Public, Member/Avail;
On Site Clubhouse, Meals; **Shoots** Field, Tower;
Birds Pheasant, Chukar; **Dogs** Avail/HDW;
Packages 1/2 Day, 1-30 guns O NAGA/See Pg. 72

Back-Bay Outfitters, Inc.
1250 76th St., Brooklyn, NY 11228
(718) 833-6930 Tom Cornicell
40 mi. from New York City
Type Public; **Shoots** Field, Blinds, Boat; **Birds**
Ducks, Geese; **Packages** 1/2 Day, 1-4 guns

Bill's Hunting
RD2, Box 288A, Mohawk, NY 13407
(315) 823-1708 John or Linda Bills
Type Member/Avail; **Shoots** Field; **Birds** Pheasant
O NAGA/See Pg. 72

Catskill Pheasantry
& Sporting Clays
PO Box 42, Long Eddy, NY 12760
(914) 887-4487 Alex Papp 8am-8pm
100 mi. NW of New York City
Est 1981; **Acres** 400; **Type** Public, Member/Avail,
Corp.; **On Site** Clubhouse, Lodging, Meals, Clays;
Shoots Field; **Birds** Quail, Pheasant, Chukar; **Dogs**
Avail/HDW; **Packages** 1/2 Day, 1-4 guns
O NAGA/See Pg. 72

Chemung
Shooting Preserve
115 Lilac Dr., Horseheads, NY 14845
(607) 739-9238 Pat Colligan Anytime
70 mi. S of Syracuse
Est 1995; **Acres** 300; **Type** Public, Member/Avail;
On Site Clubhouse, Meals, Clays; **Shoots** Field;
Birds Quail, Pheasant, Chukar; **Dogs** Avail/HDW;
Packages 1/2 Day, 1-15 guns
Chemung Preserve is fifty minutes from
Binghampton, NY and just minutes from the Seneca Lake Winery Trail. Enjoy skeet, sporting clays
and bird hunting in the morning then follow our
maps to some of the best winery tours in the North-
east or combine your fall archery hunting with a
guided pheasant hunt since we are close to the
Pennsylvania border.

Chenango Valley Kennels
PO Box 502, Greene, NY 13778
(607) 656-7257 Vincent & Irene Guglielmo Nights
15 mi. N of Binghampton
Est 1987; **Acres** 110; **On Site** Clays; **Shoots** Field;
Birds Quail, Pheasant, Chukar; **Dogs** Avail/HDW;
Packages 1/2 Day, 1-4 guns

East Mountain Shooting Preserve

150 McCarthy Rd., Dover Plains, NY 12522
(914) 877-6274 Victor D'Avanzo 6am-9pm
80 mi. N of New York City
Acres 500; **Type** Public; **On Site** Clubhouse, Clays;
Shoots Field, Tower; **Birds** Quail, Pheasant, Chukar,
Ducks; **Dogs** Avail/HDW; **Packages** 1/2 Day, 1-12
guns

○ Kennel Bird Dog   ○ Sporting Clays
○ Factory Ammunition   ○ Quality Clubhouse
○ Family Run Business

Eldred Preserve

1040 Rt. 55, Eldred, NY 12732
(914) 557-8316 Bonnie Robertson 8-4pm
16 mi. from Monticello
Est 1967; **Acres** 600; **Type** Public, Member/Avail;
On Site Clubhouse, Lodging, Meals, Clays; **Shoots**
Field; **Birds** Turkey; **Packages** 1 Day, up to 25 guns

Empire Game Farm

3720 Rt. 41, Solon, NY 13040
(607) 836-6620 W. Douglas Whittaker
30 mi. S of Syracuse
Est 1987; **Acres** 275; **Hunters/yr** 60; **Type**
Public; **Shoots** Field; **Birds** Quail, Pheasant; **Dogs**
Avail/HDW; **Packages** 1/2 Day, 1-4 guns

Forrestal Farm Hunting Preserve

4660 Water Works Rd., Medina, NY 14103
(716) 798-0222 Bill Keppler
30 mi. NE of Buffalo
Est 1975; **Acres** 680; **Hunters/yr** 500; **Type**
Public, Member/Avail; **On Site** Clubhouse, Lodging,
Meals; **Shoots** Field, Tower, Blinds; **Birds** Pheasant,

Ducks, Geese; **Dogs** Avail/HDW; **Packages** 1/2
Day, up to 16 guns ○ NAGA/See Pg. 72

Four Winds Hunting Club

525 Maple Dr., PO Box 133, East Chatham, NY 12060
(518) 399-2559 Peter Giakoumis Weekdays
100 mi. N of New York City
Est 1982; **Acres** 205; **Hunters/yr** 180; **Type**
Public, Member/Avail; **On Site** Clubhouse, Meals,
Clays; **Shoots** Field, Tower; **Birds** Quail, Pheasant,
Chukar, Turkey; **Dogs** Avail/HDW; **Packages** 1 Day,
2-8 guns

Golden Blew Acres Shooting Preserve

1835 Lewiston Rd., Basom, NY 14013
(716) 948-5690 Terry Blew Anytime
25 mi. W of Buffalo **Est** 1970; **Acres** 300;
Hunters/yr 125; **Type** Public, Member/Avail;
Shoots Field; **Birds** Pheasant; **Dogs** Avail/HDW;
Packages 1/2 Day, 1-12 guns

Gray's Farms

2839 Lockport Rd., Oakfield, NY 14125
(716) 948-9269 David Gray 9-5
30 mi. E of Buffalo
Est 1947; **Acres** 600; **Hunters/yr** 800; **Type**
Public; **On Site** Clubhouse; **Shoots** Field; **Birds**
Pheasant; **Dogs** Avail/HDW; **Packages** 1/2 Day,
1-20 guns ○ NAGA/See Pg. 72

Green Mountain Shooting Preserve

PO Box 12, Denver, NY 12421
(914) 586-4831 Craig Massell
5 mi. N of Margaretville
Acres 158; **Type** Public; **On Site** Lodging, Meals,
Clays; **Shoots** Field; **Birds** Ruffed Grouse, Pheasant,
Turkey; **Dogs** Avail/HDW; **Packages** 1/2 Day

WINGS

Highland Farm
Pheasant Preserve
Box 193, Highland Rd., Old Chatham, NY 12136
(518) 784-2614 Joe Nastke 9-9
25 mi. SE of Albany
Est 1985; **Acres** 500; **Type** Public; **On Site**
Clubhouse, Lodging, Meals; **Shoots** Field, Tower;
Birds Quail, Ruffed Grouse, Pheasant, Chukar, Turkey;
Dogs Avail/HDW; **Packages** 1/2 Day, 1-16 guns
Located only 25 miles southeast of Albany and just
2 1/2 hours from Downtown Manhattan, Highland
Farm Pheasant Club is a sportsman's paradise. At
highland you'll hunt on over 500 acres of some of
the best pheasant cover in the northeast. Joe
Nastke, Highland's Coordinator of Events will personally see that your visit will be eventful and
rewarding. Overnight accommodations are available in large peaceful rooms with private baths. In
addition to walk-up pheasant hunts, English-style
pheasant tower releases, guided grouse and spring-
time turkey hunts are offered. Call today for
information and don't forget to ask about our special Youth and Ladies programs.

Horton Brook
Shooting Preserve
846 Horton Brook Rd., Roscoe (Horton), NY 12776
(607) 498-5852 Joe or Joann Bracco Evening/Early
Morning
8 mi. W of Roscoe
Est 1994; **Acres** 500; **Type** Public, Corp.; **On Site**
Lodging, Meals, Clays; **Shoots** Field, Tower; **Birds**
Quail, Pheasant, Chukar, Turkey; **Dogs** Avail/HDW;
Packages 1/2 Day, 1-8 guns
Horton Brook Shooting Preserve & Sporting Clays–
Here at Horton Brook we only buy top quality flight
conditioned birds from the most experienced breed-
ers. We pride ourselves on our personalized
attention. So if it's quail, pheasant or sporting clays
you want to shoot, call Joe or Joann at (607) 498-
5852. Free lessons for first time shooters.

Hull-O-Farms Game Preserve
Box 48, Cochrane Rd., Durham, NY 12422
(518) 239-6950 Frank Hull
Type Public; **On Site** Lodging; **Shoots** Field; **Birds**
Pheasant, Chukar, Turkey, Ducks   ○ NAGA/See Pg. 72

Indian Mountain Lodge
PO Box 774, Pine Plains, NY 12567
(518) 789-6801 Joseph L. Blank 8am-5pm
100 mi. N of Manhattan
Est 1994; **Acres** 532; **Type** Public, Member/Avail,
Corp.; **On Site** Clubhouse, Meals, Clays; **Shoots**
Field, Tower, Driven, Blinds, Boat; **Birds** Quail,
Pheasant, Chukar, Huns, Turkey, Ducks, Geese; **Dogs**
Avail/HDW; **Packages** 1/2 Day, 1-24 guns
○ NAGA/See Pg. 72
See Our Ad Pg. 339

Kidney Creek Farms & Preserve
PO Box 27, Schaghticoke, NY 12154
(518) 753-0309 Gary Breski
Type Public, Member/Avail; **Shoots** Field; **Birds**
Quail, Pheasant, Chukar, Turkey ○ NAGA/See Pg. 72

Brian Klug Hunting Preserve
184 Old Country Rd., Speonk, NY 11972
(516) 325-1180
W of West Hampton
Acres 150; **Type** Member/Avail; **On Site**
Clubhouse; **Shoots** Field; **Birds** Quail, Pheasant,
Chukar; **Dogs** Avail

Lido's Game Farm
68 Berkshire Rd., Box 277, Hillsdale, NY 12529
(518) 329-1551 Lido or Francine 12-3pm
45 mi. S of Albany
Acres 6,000; **Hunters/yr** 2,000; **Type** Public,
Member/Avail; **On Site** Clubhouse, Meals; **Shoots**
Field, Tower; **Birds** Quail, Pheasant, Chukar; **Dogs**
Avail; **Packages** 1/2 Day, 1-10 guns ○ NAGA/See Pg. 72

LoPinto Farms Lodge
355 Sheldon Rd., Freeville, NY 13068
(800) 551-5806 Joe LoPinto
10 mi. N of Ithaca
Est 1993; **Acres** 320; **Type** Public, Member/Avail,
Corp.; **On Site** Clubhouse, Lodging, Meals; **Shoots**
Field; **Birds** Quail, Pheasant, Turkey; **Dogs**
Avail/HDW; **Packages** 1/2 Day, up to 9 guns
○ NAGA/See Pg. 72

○ Airport Pickup	○ Bird Processing
○ Deer Hunting	○ Family Recreation
○ Shooting Instruction	○ Gourmet Meals
○ Brochure Available	○ Fishing
○ Quality Clubhouse	○ Family Run Business
○ Private Bedrooms	

Mountain View Shooting Preserve
1123 Albany Post Rd., Gardiner, NY 12525
(914) 255-5398 John/Pat Leavitt Evening
85 mi. N of New York City
Est 1981; **Acres** 125; **Hunters/yr** 700; **Type**
Public, Member/Avail, Corp.; **On Site** Clubhouse;
Shoots Field, Tower, Blinds; **Birds** Quail, Woodcock,
Pheasant, Chukar, Ducks; **Dogs** Avail/HDW;
Packages 1/2 Day, 2-5 guns

Nine Partners Pheasant Farm
RR#3, Box 47, Millbrook, NY 12545
(914) 677-3114 Jonathan L. Wicker
80 mi. N of New York City
Est 1982; **Type** Public, Member/Avail; **On Site**
Clubhouse, Clays; **Shoots** Field, Tower; **Birds** Quail,
Pheasant, Chukar, Huns, Ducks; **Dogs** Avail/HDW;
Packages 1/2 Day, 1-24 guns ○ NAGA/See Pg. 72

North Fork Preserve, Inc.

5330 Sound Ave. (Mail to:349 Penny's Rd),
Riverhead, NY 11901
(516) 369-1728 Brett Jayne or Robert H. Krudop 8-4
70 mi. E of New York
Est 1984; **Acres** 400; **Type** Member/Avail; **On
Site** Clubhouse, Meals, Clays; **Shoots** Field, Tower;
Birds Quail, Woodcock, Pheasant, Chukar, Ducks,
Geese; **Dogs** Avail/HDW; **Packages** 1/2 Day, 1-3 guns
Exclusive Sportsman's Club on Eastern Long Island -
has limited owner/memberships available. Facilities
include sporting clays, FITASC, skeet, excellent upland game and cover, deer, bass ponds, clubhouse
and tennis courts. Non-member, private and corpo-
rate shoots and functions may be arranged. Call:
North Fork Preserve: (516) 369-1728 (days); (516)
722-3152 (evenings).
See Our Ad Pg. 343

Pawling Mountain Club

PO Box 573, Pawling, NY 12564
(914) 855-3825 Gary Hall
80 mi. N of New York City
Est 1987; **Acres** 900; **Type** Member/Ltd, Corp.;
On Site Clubhouse, Lodging, Meals, Clays; **Shoots**
Field, Tower; **Birds** Quail, Pheasant, Chukar, Turkey,
Ducks; **Dogs** Avail/HDW   O NAGA/See Pg. 72

Shooting Instruction Available - See Pg. 175

Petan Farms Shooting Preserve
South Quaker Hill Rd., Pawling, NY 12564

(914) 878-3183 John O'Hara 5:30-8:30 pm
50 mi. N of New York City
Est 1980; **Acres** 150; **Hunters/yr** 75; **Type**
Public; **On Site** Clubhouse; **Shoots** Field; **Birds**
Quail, Pheasant, Chukar; **Dogs** Avail/HDW;
Packages 1/2 Day, 2-6 guns

Pheasant Ridge at Saratoga
Rt. 40 North, Greenwich, NY 12834
(518) 692-9464 V.A. Mallon
13 mi. E of Saratoga
Est 1989; **Acres** 102; **Type** Public, Corp.; **On Site**
Clubhouse, Meals; **Shoots** Field, Tower; **Birds**
Pheasant; **Dogs** Avail; **Packages** 1/2 Day, 1-24
guns   O NAGA/See Pg. 72
Set in the foothills of the Adirondacks, just 13
miles from Saratoga Springs, Pheasant Ridge offers
hunters 100 acres of prime pheasant habitat. On
Saturdays during the hunting season, novice and
veteran shooters alike can experience the un-
matched thrill of a traditional English Style
Continental Pheasant Shoot. Nearby inns and the
Little Colfax Executive Retreat provide charming
and comfortable accommodations. Shooting lessons are available. The splendid foliage makes a
visit to Pheasant Ridge a special treat in Autumn.
Call today for information.

Pond Hollow Hunting Preserve
676 North Sanford Rd., Deposit, NY 13754
(607) 467-4165 Kevin J. McGibney
150 mi. NW of New York City
Est 1986; **Type** Public, Member/Avail; **On Site**
Clubhouse, Lodging; **Shoots** Field; **Birds** Quail,
Pheasant, Chukar; **Dogs** Avail/HDW; **Packages** 1/2
Day, 1-8 guns O NAGA/See Pg. 72

Port of Missing Men
, Township of Southampton, NY
(516) 354-3442 Robert Penn 9-5
120 mi. E of New York City
Acres 2,000; **Type** Public; **Shoots** Field, Tower,
Driven, Blinds; **Birds** Pheasant, Ducks; **Packages** 1
Day, 2-12 guns
See Our Ad Pg. 341

Quigg Hollow Hunting Preserve
3130 Quigg Hollow Rd., Andover, NY 14806
(607) 478-5222 Rod & Phyllis Walker
90 mi. S of Rochester
Est 1965; **Acres** 225; **Hunters/yr** 320; **Type**
Public, Member/Avail, Corp.; **On Site** Clubhouse,
Meals, Clays; **Shoots** Field, Blinds; **Birds** Quail,
Pheasant, Chukar, Ducks; **Dogs** Avail/HDW;
Packages 1/2 Day, 1-20 guns O NAGA/See Pg. 72

Ringneck
Hunting Preserve
2407 Broadway, Darien Center, NY 14040
(716) 547-3749 Eugene Bontrager after 5pm
28 mi. E of Buffalo
Est 1988; **Acres** 120; **Hunters/yr** 130; **Type**
Public; **On Site** Clubhouse, Lodging; **Shoots** Field;
Birds Quail, Pheasant, Chukar; **Dogs** Avail/HDW;
Packages 1/2 Day, 1-4 guns

H. Rottmoss & Sons
508 Col. Cty. Rt. 3, Anciandale, NY 12503
(518) 329-1369 Henry Rottmoss
Acres 700; **Type** Public; **On Site** Clays; **Shoots**
Field; **Birds** Pheasant, Turkey, Ducks, Geese

Seneca River Hunting Preserve
11915 Rt. 176, Cato, NY 13033
(315) 626-2834 Virgil Perry
Type Public, Member/Avail; **Shoots** Field; **Birds**
Quail, Pheasant, Chukar, Huns O NAGA/See Pg. 72

Serendipity Farms
12201 Rt. 62, Lawtons, NY 14091
(716) 337-9828 Vincent E. Lorenz
25 mi. S of Buffalo
Est 1991; **Acres** 200; **Type** Public, Member/Avail;
On Site Clubhouse, Clays; **Shoots** Field; **Birds**
Quail, Pheasant, Chukar; **Dogs** Avail/HDW;
Packages 1/2 Day, 1-16 guns O NAGA/See Pg. 72
O Bird Processing   O Sporting Clays
O Family Run Business   O Train Your Dog Here

Sherburne Shooting Preserve
RR#1, Box 148-J, Skinner Hill Rd., Sherburne, NY 13460
(607) 674-4707 Joe Regan Morning or Evening
45 mi. SE of Syracuse
Est 1985; **Acres** 300; **Type** Public; **Shoots** Field;
Birds Quail, Pheasant, Chukar; **Dogs** Avail/HDW;
Packages 1/2 Day, 1-4 guns

Sno-Fun
Hunting Preserve
26809 Beckwith Rd., Evans Mills, NY 13637
(315) 629-4801 Richard Farr 6-9
6 mi. N of Watertown
Est 1985; **Acres** 500; **Hunters/yr** 300; **Type**
Public; **On Site** Clubhouse, Lodging, Meals, Clays;
Shoots Field; **Birds** Quail, Pheasant, Chukar; **Dogs**
Avail/HDW; **Packages** 1/2 Day, 1-12 guns

The Sportsman's Shooting Preserve
19 Auburn St., Wolcott, NY 14590
(315) 594-2527 Danny Valentine
45 mi. E of Rochester
Acres 220; **Hunters/yr** 100; **Type** Public,
Member/Avail; **On Site** Clubhouse; **Shoots** Field;
Birds Quail, Pheasant, Chukar; **Dogs** Avail;
Packages 1/2 Day

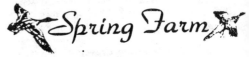

PO Box 301, Sag Harbor, NY 11963
(516) 725-0038 Dave Schellinger
100 mi. E of New York City
Est 1940; **Acres** 150; **Type** Public; **On Site**
Clubhouse; **Shoots** Field, Tower, Blinds; **Birds**
Pheasant, Chukar, Huns, Ducks; **Dogs** Avail/HDW;
Packages 1/2 Day, 1-8 guns O NAGA/See Pg. 72
O Bird Processing
O Loaner Guns
O Family Run Business

Stonegate Hunting Preserve
262 A Beattie Rd., Rock Tavern, NY 12575
(914) 496-9811 James Filardi 9am-6pm, M-Su
55 mi. N of New York City
Est 1979; **Acres** 400; **Hunters/yr** 1,000; **Type**
Public, Member/Avail, Corp.; **On Site** Clubhouse,
Lodging, Meals, Clays; **Shoots** Field, Tower, Blinds;
Birds Quail, Ruffed Grouse, Woodcock, Pheasant,
Chukar, Huns, Turkey, Ducks; **Dogs** Avail/HDW;
Packages 1/2 Day, 1-20 guns

Stoney Lane Pheasant Farm
2967 Quaker Rd., Gasport, NY 14067
(716) 772-2744 Martin L. Richardson
50 mi. W of Rochester
Est 1990; **Acres** 200; **Type** Public; **On Site** Clays;
Shoots Field; **Birds** Pheasant, Ducks; **Dogs**
Avail/HDW; **Packages** 1/2 Day, 1-4 guns

T-M-T
Hunting Preserve, Inc.
RR1, Box 297, School House Rd., Staatsburg, NY 12580
(914) 266-5108 Thomas F. Mackin Anytime
55 mi. N of New York City
Est 1966; Acres 209; Hunters/yr 1,500; Type
Public; On Site Clubhouse, Clays; Shoots Field,
Blinds; Birds Pheasant, Chukar, Ducks; Dogs
Avail/HDW; Packages 1/2 Day, 1-16 guns
○ NAGA/See Pg. 72

○ Bird Processing   ○ Sporting Clays
○ Hunting Jeeps   ○ Quality Clubhouse
○ Family Run Business

Tailfeathers Game Farm
Rt. 2, Box 23C, Geer Rd., Chaffee, NY 14030
(716) 496-5162 Bill Howell 9-5
30 mi. S of Buffalo
Est 1991; Acres 410; Hunters/yr 100; Type
Public; Shoots Field; Birds Quail, Ruffed Grouse,
Woodcock, Pheasant, Chukar, Huns; Dogs
Avail/HDW; Packages 1/2 Day, 1-20 guns

Tamarack Preserve Ltd.
RR#1, Box 111B, Millbrook, NY 12545
(914) 373-7084 Bob Vanecek
65 mi. N of New York
Est 1991; Acres 2,400; Hunters/yr 150; Type
Member/Avail, Corp.; On Site Clubhouse, Lodging,
Meals, Clays; Shoots Field, Driven, Blinds; Birds
Quail, Pheasant, Chukar, Huns, Turkey, Ducks, Geese;
Dogs Avail/HDW; Packages 1/2 Day, 1-40 guns
○ NAGA/See Pg. 72

Chuck Tiranno Kennels & Game Farm
5409 Salt Works Rd., Middleport, NY 14105
(716) 798-1522 Chuck or Carolyn Tiranno 7 pm
38 mi. NE of Buffalo
Est 1975; Acres 2,400; Type Public, Member/Avail,
Corp.; On Site Clays; Shoots Field, Blinds; Birds
Pheasant, Turkey, Ducks, Geese; Dogs Avail/HDW;
Packages 1/2 Day

Tompkins Hunting Club
Box 682, Hancock, NY 13783
(607) 637-4574 Art Tompkins
Type Public, Member/Avail; Birds Turkey, Ducks
○ NAGA/See Pg. 72

Turkey Trot Acres
Tubbs Hill Rd., Candor, NY 13743
(607) 659-7849 Peter M. Clare Days & Evenings
20 mi. S of Ithaca   Est 1987; Acres 15,000;
Hunters/yr 175; Type Public; On Site Clubhouse,
Meals; Shoots Field; Birds Turkey; Dogs
Avail/HDW; Packages 3 Days, 1-8 guns

Ed Viola-Waterfowl Guide
87 Job's Lane, Southampton, NY 11968
(516) 287-1181 Ed Viola
90 mi. E of New York City
Est 1979; Acres 200; Type Public; Shoots Blinds;
Birds Ducks, Geese; Dogs HDW; Packages 1/2
Day, 2-4 guns

Whale Back Farms
Shooting Preserve & Sporting Clay
PO Box 301, Canandaigua, NY 14424
(800) 923-4868 R. Bruce Lindsay
40 mi. SE of Rochester
Est 1974; Acres 600; Type Member/Avail, Corp.;
On Site Clubhouse, Meals, Clays; Shoots Field,
Tower, Driven; Birds Quail, Ruffed Grouse,
Woodcock, Pheasant, Chukar, Turkey; Dogs
Avail/HDW; Packages 1 Day, 2-20 guns
Whale Back Farms owns 600 acres adjacent to
10,000 acres of state game management land. Excellent white-tail deer, wild turkey and grouse
hunting. Stocked game includes pheasants and
quail. Excellent bird dogs and guides available. Brochure on request. Fishing & sporting clays
available. Call 800-923-4868, Mon-Fri; or R. Bruce
Lindsay, 800-861-6208 all other times.

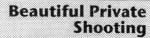

Whispering Pines
Hideaway
548 Townline Rd., Lyons, NY 14489
(315) 946-6170 Charlie & Jane Buisch
30 mi. E of Rochester
Est 1985; **Acres** 2,700; **Type** Public, Member/Avail,
Corp.; **On Site** Clubhouse, Lodging, Meals, Clays;
Shoots Field; **Birds** Quail, Pheasant, Chukar, Huns;
Dogs Avail/HDW; **Packages** 1/2 Day, 1-28 guns
O NAGA/See Pg. 72
We offer 2,600 acres of scenic Finger Lakes coun-
tryside for your hunting pleasure. Natural and
farmed cover. Hunt with our dogs or your own.
Morning, afternoon or all day hunts. No hunting li-
cense required. Bird processing available.
Season-long hunting passes, too! Special prices for
Husband/ Wife, Father/Daughter and Father/Son
hunts. Call for information.

NORTH CAROLINA

Adams Creek
Gunning Lodge
6240 Adams Creek Rd., Havelock, NC 28532
(919) 447-6808 Rusty or June Bryan (919) 447-7688
125 mi. SE of Raleigh near Morehead City
Type Public, Member/Avail, Corp.; **On Site**
Clubhouse, Lodging, Meals, Clays; **Shoots** Field,
Tower, Blinds; **Birds** Dove, Quail, Pheasant, Chukar,
Turkey, Ducks; **Dogs** Avail/HDW O NAGA/See Pg. 72

BUSICK QUAIL FARMS
HUNTING PRESERVE

11933 NC Hwy. 119 South, Burlington, NC 27217
(910) 421-5758 Roger D. Busick Anytime
20 mi. NE of Burlington
Est 1987; **Acres** 1,600; **Hunters/yr** 400; **Type**
Public, Member/Avail; **On Site** Clubhouse, Lodging,
Meals; **Shoots** Field, Driven; **Birds** Dove, Quail,
Pheasant, Chukar; **Dogs** Avail/HDW; **Packages** 1/2
Day, 1-20 guns O NAGA/See Pg. 72

Can't Miss Shooting Preserve
Rt. 1, Box 530, Aurora, NC 27806
(919) 322-5227 Earl Bonner/O.C. Bennett 6 am -10 pm
40 mi. E of Greenville
Est 1987; **Acres** 600; **Hunters/yr** 250; **Type**
Public; **Shoots** Field; **Birds** Quail, Pheasant; **Dogs**
Avail/HDW; **Packages** 1/2 Day, 1-10 guns

Chestnut Hunting Lodge
Rt. 2, Box 236, Taylorsville, NC 28681
(704) 632-3916 Jerry Rushing
50 mi. NW of Charlotte
Acres 700; **Type** Public; **On Site** Lodging; **Shoots**
Field; **Birds** Turkey; **Dogs** Avail/HDW

Contentnea Creek
Hunting Preserve - Kennel- Clays
Rt. 5, Box 60, Snow Hill, NC 28530
(919) 747-2020 S.M. Gray/Bob Steed
60 mi. SE of Raleigh
Est 1986; **Acres** 2,000; **Hunters/yr** 1,000; **Type**
Public, Member/Avail, Corp.; **On Site** Clubhouse,
Lodging, Meals, Clays; **Shoots** Field, Tower, Blinds,
Boat; **Birds** Dove, Quail, Pheasant, Chukar, Ducks;
Dogs Avail/HDW; **Packages** 1/2 Day, 2-30 guns

Crow Hill Farm, Inc.
758 Crow Hill Rd., Beaufort, NC 28516
(919) 728-7233 Charles Roffey
Type Member/Ltd; **Shoots** Field; **Birds** Quail,
Ducks O NAGA/See Pg. 72

Davis Farms Preserve
314 Joan Court, Beaufort, NC 28516
(919) 728-4080 Warren J. Davis 8-8
Est 1991; **Acres** 200; **Type** Public, Member/Avail;
On Site Clays; **Shoots** Field, Blinds; **Birds** Dove,
Quail, Woodcock, Snipe, Ducks; **Dogs** Avail/HDW;
Packages 1/2 Day, 1-2 guns O NAGA/See Pg. 72

Fairview
Hunting Preserve
8004 Concord Hwy., Monroe, NC 28110
(704) 753-4004 E.L. Connor
10 mi. N of Monroe
Acres 250; **Hunters/yr** 100; **Type** Public; **On Site**
Clubhouse, Clays; **Birds** Dove, Quail; **Dogs**
Avail/HDW; **Packages** 1/2 Day, up to 3 guns

Flint Ridge Shooting Preserve, Inc.
Rt. 2, Box 118, Polkton, NC 28135
(704) 826-8107 Keith Edwards
45 mi. SE of Charlotte
Est 1987; **Type** Public; **On Site** Clubhouse,
Lodging, Meals; **Shoots** Field; **Birds** Quail,
Pheasant, Chukar; **Dogs** Avail/HDW; **Packages** 1/2 Day

Gold Mine Hunting Preserve
6464 Smith Rd., Stanfield, NC 28163
(704) 786-0619 G.M. Almond Evenings
18 mi. E of Charlotte
Est 1979; **Type** Public; **On Site** Clubhouse,
Lodging, Meals; **Shoots** Field; **Birds** Turkey; **Dogs**
Avail/HDW; **Packages** 1 Day, up to 1 guns

Griffin Hill
Hunting Preserve
Rt. 3, Box 222, Wadesboro, NC 28170
(704) 694-5086 Al or Phyllis Griffin After 6 pm
50 mi. E of Charlotte
Est 1977; **Acres** 550; **Type** Public, Corp.; **On Site**
Clubhouse, Lodging, Meals, Clays; **Shoots** Field;
Birds Quail; **Dogs** Avail/HDW; **Packages** 1/2 Day,
1-12 guns ○ NAGA/See Pg. 72
See Our Ad Below

Gunners Point Plantation
PO Box 221, Harrells, NC 28444
(919) 532-4520 Gordon Dixon
85 mi. S of Raleigh
Est 1991; **Acres** 600; **Type** Public, Member/Avail;
Shoots Field; **Birds** Dove, Quail; **Dogs** Avail/HDW;
Packages 1/2 Day, 1-3 guns

Haddock's Shooting Preserve
Rt. 1, Box 467-10, Winterville, NC 28590
(919) 355-6539 David Haddock 7 am to 7 pm
65 mi. SE of Raleigh
Est 1985; **Acres** 5,000; **Hunters/yr** 500; **Type**
Public; **On Site** Clubhouse, Lodging; **Shoots** Field,
Driven, Blinds, Boat; **Birds** Dove, Quail, Pheasant,
Ducks, Geese; **Dogs** Avail/HDW; **Packages** 1/2
Day, 1-8 guns

Hunting Creek Quail & Pheasant Hunting
Rt. 2, Box 394, Hamptonville, NC 27020
(910) 468-4591 Bill Hudson After 5 pm
25 mi. W of Winston-Salem

Our Place Is Your Place!
At Griffin Hill, hunting parties of four or more enjoy
exclusive use of our sporting facilities.

At Griffin Hill our No. 1 priority is to
provide sportsmen with plenty of sporty
shots at flighty quail on our 50-bird per
half-day hunt. Use your dogs or ours—at
no extra charge. All hunts are guided.

Best of all, parties of four or more have
exclusive use of the preserve and our other
outstanding facilities. We're committed to
making your stay with us a memorable
experience afield. Call us today!

*Have a successful day of hunting.
This wish with you we share. Start every day in the
trust of God and end it with a prayer.*

Quail Hunting • Deer Hunting • Combination Hunts
Dogs and Handlers • All Weather Safe Stands • Game Processing
Excellent Accommodations • Home Cooked Meals

Al & Phyllis Griffin Invite You to Hunt Their Family Owned & Operated:

GRIFFIN HILL HUNTING PRESERVE
(704) 694-5086
RT. 3, Box 222 · Wadesboro, NC 28170
Preserve Operators: Our quality, hard flying quail are available for sale.

Shoots Field;   **Birds** Quail, Pheasant;   **Dogs**
Avail/HDW;   **Packages** 1/2 Day, 1-8 guns
O NAGA/See Pg. 72

Jones Island Hunt Club
PO Box 8365, Hobucken, NC 28537
(919) 745-7877   Fred Hampton
Type Member/Avail;   **On Site** Lodging;   **Shoots**
Field; **Birds** Quail, Pheasant, Ducks O NAGA/See Pg. 72

Kennis Creek Hunting Preserve
Rt. 2, Box 55A, Fuquay-Varina, NC 27526
(919) 552-9156   Frank Howard 8-11 pm
20 mi. S of Raleigh
Est 1991;   **Acres** 600;   **Hunters/yr** 200;   **Type**
Public;   **On Site** Lodging, Meals, Clays;   **Shoots** Field;
Birds Quail;   **Dogs** Avail/HDW;   **Packages** 1/2 Day,
1-10 guns

Louisburg Shooting Preserve
947 N. Main St., Louisburg, NC 27549
(919) 496-5076   Johnny King After 8 pm
25 mi. NE of Raleigh
Est 1992;   **Acres** 175;   **Hunters/yr** 250;   **Type**
Public;   **On Site** Clubhouse;   **Shoots** Field;   **Birds**
Quail, Pheasant, Chukar;   **Dogs** Avail;   **Packages** 1/2
Day, 2-6 guns

Lowes Shooting Preserve
108 Lowe St., Lawndale, NC 28090
(704) 538-7254   J.D. Lowe 8 to 11 pm
40 mi. W of Charlotte
Est 1983;   **Acres** 175;   **Hunters/yr** 250;   **Type**
Public;   **On Site** Clubhouse, Clays;   **Shoots** Field;
Birds Quail, Pheasant;   **Dogs** Avail/HDW;   **Packages**
1/2 Day, 3-10 guns

Mauney Hunting Preserve
548 Mauney Lane, Gastonia, NC 28052
(704) 861-8735   Roger Mauney
Type Public, Member/Avail;   **Shoots** Field;   **Birds**
Quail O NAGA/See Pg. 72

Maxwell Creek Plantation
707 Blind Bridge Rd., Magnolia, NC 28453
(910) 289-2171   Wendell Evans, Jr.
70 mi. E of Raleigh
Est 1979;   **Acres** 1,000;   **Type** Public;   **On Site**
Clubhouse, Lodging, Meals, Clays;   **Shoots** Field,
Blinds;   **Birds** Dove, Quail, Ducks;   **Dogs** Avail/HDW;
Packages 1/2 Day, 1-8 guns

Moree's Sportsman Preserve
14925 Hook Rd., Matthews, NC 28105
(704) 847-3094   Buddy Taylor 8 to 10:30 pm
10 mi. E of Charlotte
Acres 1,000;   **Type** Public;   **On Site** Clubhouse;
Shoots Field;   **Birds** Quail, Pheasant;   **Dogs**
Avail/HDW;   **Packages** 1/2 Day, 1-20 guns

Occoneechee Shooting Preserve
Rt. 1, Box 435, Jackson, NC 27845
(919) 583-1799   Gill Cutchin
90 mi. NE of Raleigh
Acres 5,000;   **Type** Public;   **On Site** Clubhouse,
Lodging, Meals, Clays;   **Shoots** Field;   **Birds** Turkey;
Dogs Avail/HDW

Old Homeplace
Shooting Preserve
5000 Holly Ridge Farm Rd., Raleigh, NC 27604
(919) 878-9183   Don Jones 8am-9pm
45 mi. S of Raleigh
Est 1992;   **Acres** 500;   **Hunters/yr** 150;   **Type**
Public;   **On Site** Clubhouse, Meals;   **Shoots** Field;
Birds Quail, Pheasant, Chukar, Huns;   **Dogs**
Avail/HDW;   **Packages** 1/2 Day, 1-12 guns
At the "Old Homeplace" you'll hunt the best flying
quail available in natural fields of oak and pine
ridges. Pheasant and chukar are available, too.
(Ask about our combination hunt packages.) All
hunts include a guide and a dog. Overnight accommodations for up to 6 people–including an old
fashioned country breakfast–are available in our recently renovated lodge that has a big porch,
tongue and groove floors and ceilings, and a fireplace in each room. The quality and low-price of
our no-limit hunts cannot be beat. Call today!

Paul's Place Hunting Preserve
11725 Hwy. 117 S., Rocky Point, NC 28457
(910) 675-2345   Dave Paul Anytime
12 mi. N of Wilmington
Est 1991;   **Acres** 250;   **Hunters/yr** 100;   **Type**
Member/Avail, Corp.;   **On Site** Lodging, Meals, Clays;
Shoots Field, Blinds;   **Birds** Quail, Pheasant, Chukar,
Ducks;   **Dogs** Avail/HDW

C. Pierce Farms Shooting Preserve
Rt. 2, Box 38, Ahoskie, NC 27910
(919) 332-5360   Cedric Pierce
6 mi. NE of Ahoskie
Acres 1,000;   **Hunters/yr** 500;   **Type** Public;   **On
Site** Clubhouse, Lodging, Meals, Clays;   **Shoots** Field,
Tower, Blinds;   **Birds** Quail, Pheasant, Chukar, Ducks;
Dogs Avail

Pine Lake Plantation
Beulah Hill Church Rd., West End, NC 27376
(910) 947-1696   J. Clayton Myrick
70 mi. S of Raleigh
Acres 4,000;   **Type** Public;   **Shoots** Field;   **Birds**
Quail;   **Dogs** Avail

Pungo Acres Hunting Retreat
PO Box 55, Pantego, NC 24860
(919) 935-5415   Edwin "Booger" Harris
115 mi. E of Raleigh
Est 1985;   **Acres** 12,000;   **Hunters/yr** 600;   **Type**
Public, Member/Avail, Corp.;   **On Site** Clubhouse,
Lodging, Meals, Clays;   **Shoots** Field, Blinds;   **Birds**
Dove, Quail, Pheasant, Ducks, Geese;   **Dogs**
Avail/HDW;   **Packages** 1/2 Day, 2-15 guns

Quail Creek Hunting Preserve
3461 Macon Farm Rd., Ramseur, NC 27316
(919) 879-4187 Stephen A. Grubb
8 mi. E of Asheboro
Acres 500; **Hunters/yr** 100; **Type** Public; **On Site** Clubhouse, Lodging, Meals, Clays; **Shoots** Field; **Birds** Dove, Quail; **Dogs** Avail

Quail Hatchery Shooting Preserve
1618 Friendship, Statesville, NC 28677
(704) 592-2935 Paul Harmon or Alma before 10 pm
40 mi. N of Charlotte
Est 1970; **Acres** 300; **Type** Public; **On Site** Lodging; **Shoots** Field; **Birds** Quail; **Dogs** HDW; **Packages** 1/2 Day, up to 1 guns

Quail Ridge Shooting Preserve
Rt. 1, Box 165, Hookerton, NC 28538
(919) 747-5210 R.E. Carraway
75 mi. SE of Raleigh
Est 1991; **Acres** 1,000; **Hunters/yr** 500; **Type** Public, Member/Avail, Corp.; **On Site** Clubhouse, Lodging, Meals, Clays; **Shoots** Field; **Birds** Quail, Pheasant; **Dogs** Avail/HDW; **Packages** 1/2 Day, 1-15 guns

Ray Ingold's Shooting Preserve
PO Box 381, Mt. Gilead, NC 27306
(910) 439-6318 Ray Ingold
50 mi. E of Charlotte **Type** Public; **Shoots** Field; **Birds** Quail; **Dogs** Avail/HDW

Salem Kennels & Shooting Preserve
Rt. 2, Box 107, Whitakers, NC 27891
(919) 443-5660 Craig Reid
45 mi. NE of Raleigh
Est 1983; **Acres** 300; **Type** Public; **Shoots** Field; **Birds** Quail, Pheasant; **Dogs** Avail/HDW; **Packages** 1/2 Day, 1-6 guns

Shady Knoll Preserve
3642 Shady Knoll Dr., Asheboro, NC 27203
(919) 879-3663 John W. Maness After 6 pm
8 mi. E of Asheboro
Est 1987; **Acres** 150; **Type** Public, Member/Avail, Corp.; **On Site** Meals; **Shoots** Field, Blinds; **Birds** Quail, Pheasant, Chukar, Ducks; **Dogs** Avail/HDW; **Packages** 1/2 Day, up to 6 guns ○ NAGA/See Pg. 72

Shelter Creek Plantation & Hunting
1523 N. Kerr Ave., Wilmington, NC 28405
(910) 791-7778 Jerry Simmons
22 mi. from Wilmington
Acres 1,500; **Hunters/yr** 124; **Type** Public, Member/Avail; **On Site** Clubhouse, Lodging, Meals, Clays; **Shoots** Field; **Birds** Quail, Pheasant, Ducks; **Dogs** Avail

Six Runs Plantation
Rt. 1, Box 179, Rose Hill, NC 28458
(910) 532-4810 Rebecca Todd-Edwards 6-9 pm
75 mi. SE of Raleigh
Est 1979; **Acres** 2,000; **Hunters/yr** 200; **Type** Public; **On Site** Clubhouse, Lodging, Meals, Clays; **Shoots** Field, Blinds, Boat; **Birds** Dove, Quail,

Chukar, Turkey, Ducks; **Dogs** Avail/HDW; **Packages** 1 Day, 2-12 guns

Stadler's Quail Farm
3412 NC 87, Reidsville, NC 27320
(910) 349-5531 Miles Stadler
25 mi. N of Greensboro
Acres 300; **Type** Public, Member/Avail, Corp.; **Shoots** Field; **Birds** Quail, Pheasant; **Dogs** Avail/HDW; **Packages** 1/2 Day ○ NAGA/See Pg. 72

Sun Valley Shooting Preserve
104 Griffin Circle, Monroe, NC 28110
(704) 289-3501 Jack Haney After 6 pm
15 mi. E of Charlotte **Acres** 100; **Type** Public; **Shoots** Field; **Birds** Quail; **Dogs** Avail/HDW

Tall Cotton Plantation
Rt. 1, Box 260-B, Murfreesboro, NC 27855
(919) 398-3491 E.R. Evans
6 mi. E of Murfreesboro
Type Public, Member/Avail; **On Site** Clubhouse; **Shoots** Field, Blinds; **Birds** Quail, Pheasant, Chukar, Ducks; **Dogs** Avail

Tobacco Stick Shooting Preserve
PO Box 310, Candor, NC 27229
(910) 974-7197 C.J. Reynolds
50 mi. S of Greensboro
Acres 500; **Hunters/yr** 100; **Type** Public; **On Site** Clubhouse, Lodging; **Shoots** Field, Blinds; **Birds** Quail, Pheasant, Chukar, Ducks; **Dogs** Avail

Voncannon's Shooting Preserve
2382 Old Humble Rd., Asheboro, NC 27203
(910) 629-9253 Nolan K. Voncannon
25 mi. S of Greensboro
Acres 340; **Type** Public, Member/Avail; **On Site** Clubhouse; **Shoots** Field; **Birds** Quail, Pheasant, Chukar; **Dogs** Avail/HDW; **Packages** 1/2 Day, 1-9 guns

Wintergreen Hunting Preserve
PO Box 981, Bladenboro, NC 28320
(910) 648-6171 Boyce White 7 am to 6 pm
85 mi. S of Raleigh
Est 1988; **Acres** 500; **Hunters/yr** 800; **Type** Public; **On Site** Clubhouse, Clays; **Shoots** Field; **Birds** Quail, Pheasant, Chukar; **Dogs** Avail/HDW; **Packages** 1/2 Day, 2-12 guns ○ NAGA/See Pg. 72

Yadkin Point Hunt & Sporting Clays
PO Box 313, Advance, NC 27006
(910) 998-9518 Howell W. Woltz
10 mi. W of Winston-Salem
Est 1991; **Acres** 300; **Type** Public, Member/Avail, Corp.; **On Site** Clubhouse, Lodging, Meals, Clays; **Shoots** Field; **Birds** Dove, Quail; **Dogs** Avail/HDW; **Packages** 1/2 Day, 1-15 guns

WINGS

NORTH DAKOTA

Bois de Sioux Game Farm
18270 95 R St. SE, Fairmount, ND 58030
(701) 474-5879 Arlen Spear   65 mi. S of Fargo
Type Public; **Shoots** Field; **Birds** Quail, Pheasant,
Chukar, Ducks; **Dogs** Avail/HDW

Dakota Hunting Club & Kennels
PO Box 13623, Grand Forks, ND 58208
(701) 775-2074 George Newton 8-5
12 mi. SW of Grand Forks
Est 1969; **Acres** 900; **Hunters/yr** 500; **Type**
Public, Member/Avail, Corp.; **On Site** Clubhouse,
Clays; **Shoots** Field; **Birds** Quail, Pheasant, Chukar,
Huns, Turkey, Ducks; **Dogs** Avail/HDW; **Packages**
1/2 Day, 3-12 guns ○ NAGA/See Pg. 72

Dakota Hunting Farms
RR1, Box 100, Ludden, ND 58447
(800) 356-5281 Tim or Julie Mertz
50 mi. S of Valley City   **Est** 1985; **Acres** 20,000;
Hunters/yr 200; **Type** Public; **On Site** Clubhouse,
Lodging, Meals, Clays; **Shoots** Field, Driven, Blinds;
Birds Dove, Pheasant, Turkey, Ducks, Geese; **Dogs**
Avail/HDW; **Packages** 1 Day, 1-40 guns

Hillview Hunting Acres, Inc.
RR4, Box 171A, Minot, ND 58701
(800) 838-1057 Bob Saunders
4.5 mi. SE of Minot   **Acres** 250; **Hunters/yr** 60;
Type Public; **Shoots** Field; **Birds** Pheasant; **Dogs**
Avail/HDW; **Packages** 1/2 Day, 1-6 guns ○ NAGA

Pride of the Prairie Hunts
HCR01, Box 75, Regent, ND 58650
(701) 563-4526 Brad & Cheryl Nasset
110 mi. SW of Bismarck
Acres 20,000; **Type** Public; **On Site** Lodging,
Meals; **Shoots** Field; **Birds** Pheasant, Huns, S. Tail
Grouse; **Dogs** Avail/HDW; **Packages** 1 Day, 2-8 guns

Ringnecks Unlimited, Inc.
Rt. 1, Box 12, Flasher, ND 58535
(701) 597-3032 Steve Craine
45 mi. SW of Bismarck   **Acres** 640; **Type** Public;
On Site Clubhouse, Lodging, Meals, Clays; **Shoots**
Field; **Birds** Quail, Pheasant, Chukar, Turkey; **Dogs**
Avail/HDW; **Packages** 1/2 Day ○ NAGA/See Pg. 72

Sheyenne Valley Lodge
RR1, Box 27, Goodrich, ND 58444
(701) 884-2432 Ted or Orlan Mertz
80 mi. NE of Bismarck
Acres 50,000; **Type** Public; **On Site** Clubhouse,
Lodging, Meals, Clays; **Shoots** Field; **Birds** Dove,
Pheasant, Huns, Sharp Tail Grouse, Ducks, Geese;
Dogs Avail/HDW; **Packages** 1 Day, 1-8 guns

Windmill Pheasant Farm
7504 130th Ave., SE, Lisbon, ND 58054
(701) 678-2652 Gene or Kandyce Sandstrom
75 mi. SW of Fargo   **Est** 1987; **Acres** 320; **Type**
Public; **On Site** Meals; **Shoots** Field; **Birds**
Pheasant; **Dogs** Avail/HDW; **Packages** 1 Day

OHIO

Brier Oak Hunt Club
5316 Sandhill Rd., Bellevue, OH 44811
(419) 483-4953 Kevin or Denise Schaeffer 9-5
65 mi. W of Cleveland
Est 1989; **Acres** 400; **Hunters/yr** 100; **Type**
Public, Member/Avail, Corp.; **On Site** Clubhouse,
Clays; **Shoots** Field; **Birds** Quail, Pheasant, Chukar;
Dogs Avail/HDW; **Packages** 1/2 Day, 1-32 guns
○ NAGA/See Pg. 72

Buckeye Pheasants Hunting Preserve
1608 S. Clayton Rd., New Lebanon, OH 45345
(513) 687-2523 Terry/Robert Parks Anytime
10 mi. W of Dayton
Est 1989; **Acres** 90; **Type** Public; **On Site**
Clubhouse, Meals; **Shoots** Field; **Birds** Quail,
Pheasant, Chukar, Huns; **Dogs** Avail/HDW;
Packages 1/2 Day, 1-6 guns ○ NAGA/See Pg. 72

Cherrybend
Pheasant Farm
2326 Cherrybend Rd., Wilmington, OH 45177
(513) 584-4269 Mary Hollister 8am-6pm
40 mi. NE of Cincinnati
Est 1956; **Acres** 368; **Type** Public, Member/Avail;
On Site Clubhouse, Meals, Clays; **Shoots** Field;
Birds Quail, Pheasant, Chukar; **Dogs** Avail/HDW;
Packages 1/2 Day, 1-20 guns ○ NAGA/See Pg. 72

Conneaut Creek Club
2265 Harcourt Dr., Cleveland, OH 44106
(216) 368-1565 H.F. Biggar, III 6-9pm
70 mi. NE of Cleveland
Est 1988; **Acres** 240; **Hunters/yr** 50; **Type**
Member/Avail, Corp.; **On Site** Clubhouse, Lodging,
Clays; **Shoots** Field; **Birds** Quail, Pheasant, Chukar;
Dogs Avail/HDW; **Packages** 1/2 Day, 1-5 guns

Elkhorn Hunt Club
4146 Klopfenstein Rd., Bucyrus, OH 44820
(419) 562-6131 Samuel A. Ballou Evenings
55 mi. N of Columbus
Est 1962; **Acres** 300; **Hunters/yr** 1,500; **Type**
Public, Member/Avail, Corp.; **On Site** Clubhouse,
Clays; **Shoots** Field; **Birds** Quail, Pheasant, Chukar,
Huns; **Dogs** Avail/HDW; **Packages** 1/2 Day, 1-24
guns ○ NAGA/See Pg. 72
○ Bird Processing   ○ Sporting Clays
○ Brochure Available   ○ Quality Clubhouse
○ Hold State Pheasant Championship

Federal Valley Pheasant Farm
16171 E. Kasler Creek Rd., Amesville, OH 45711
(614) 448-6747 Gene/Roseanna Hines
85 mi. SE of Columbus
Acres 200; **Type** Public, Member/Avail; **Shoots**
Field; **Birds** Quail, Pheasant; **Dogs** Avail/HDW;
Packages 1/2 Day ○ NAGA/See Pg. 72

Grand Valley Ranch

10198 Penniman Rd., Orwell, OH 44076
(216) 437-6440 Scott Adams T-Su, 9-4
40 mi. E of Cleveland
Est 1991; **Acres** 1,000; **Type** Public, Corp.; **On Site** Clubhouse, Clays; **Shoots** Field; **Birds** Quail, Pheasant, Chukar; **Dogs** Avail/HDW; **Packages** 1/2 Day, 1-12 guns

Hidden Haven
Shooting Preserve

9257 Buckeye Rd., Sugar Grove, OH 43155
(614) 746-8568 Ronald Blosser Anytime
50 mi. SE of Columbus
Est 1969; **Acres** 93; **Hunters/yr** 184; **Type** Public, Member/Avail; **On Site** Clubhouse, Lodging, Meals, Clays; **Shoots** Field; **Birds** Quail, Pheasant, Chukar; **Dogs** Avail/HDW; **Packages** 1/2 Day, 2-20 guns ○ NAGA/See Pg. 72

○ Hunting License   ○ Airport Pickup
○ Shooting Instruction   ○ Loaner Guns
○ Factory Ammunition   ○ Quality Clubhouse
○ 5-Stand Sporting & FITASC
○ Sporting Clays-10 Courses

Hill 'N Dale Club

3605 Poe Rd., Medina, OH 44256
(216) 725-2097 Terry L. Eicher 8-5
50 mi. S of Cleveland
Est 1952; **Acres** 300; **Hunters/yr** 400; **Type** Member/Avail; **On Site** Clubhouse, Lodging, Meals, Clays; **Shoots** Field, Tower, Driven; **Birds** Quail, Pheasant, Chukar, Huns; **Dogs** Avail/HDW; **Packages** 1/2 Day, 1-4 guns

Lone Oak Farm

3318 Panhandle Rd., Delaware, OH 43015
(614) 363-7219 Bill Oman
Type Public; **Shoots** Field; **Birds** Quail, Pheasant, Chukar ○ NAGA/See Pg. 72

Mad River
Sportsman's Club

1055 County Rd. 25, Bellefontaine, OH 43311
(513) 593-8245 Tony Stratton, Mgr. 8am-5pm
45 mi. NW of Columbus
Est 1991; **Acres** 300; **Hunters/yr** 1,200; **Type** Member/Avail, Corp.; **On Site** Clubhouse, Lodging, Meals, Clays; **Shoots** Field; **Birds** Quail, Pheasant, Chukar, Huns; **Dogs** Avail/HDW; **Packages** 1/2 Day, 1-4 guns ○ NAGA/See Pg. 72

○ Hunting License   ○ Bird Processing
○ Kennel Bird Dogs   ○ Sporting Clays
○ Shooting Instruction   ○ Gourmet Meals
○ Hunting Jeeps   ○ Brochure Available
○ On-Site Pro Shop   ○ Factory Ammunition
○ Quality Clubhouse

Shooting Instruction Available - See Pg. 160

Pheasant Recreation Inc.

18376 London Rd., Circleville, OH 43113

(614) 477-1587 Jack E. Carpenter
25 mi. S of Columbus
Acres 550; **Type** Public, Member/Avail, Corp.; **On Site** Clubhouse, Lodging, Meals, Clays; **Shoots** Field; **Birds** Dove, Quail, Pheasant, Chukar, Ducks; **Dogs** Avail/HDW; **Packages** 1/2 Day

Pheasant View Farm

11625 Beloit-Snodes Rd., Beloit, OH 44609
(216) 584-6828 Bob Anderson & Brian Galbraith 9-9
55 mi. SE of Cleveland
Est 1987; **Acres** 300; **Hunters/yr** 2,000; **Type** Public, Member/Avail, Corp.; **On Site** Clubhouse, Lodging, Meals, Clays; **Shoots** Field, Blinds, Boat; **Birds** Quail, Woodcock, Pheasant, Chukar, Huns, Ducks, Geese; **Dogs** Avail/HDW; **Packages** 1/2 Day, 1-18 guns ○ NAGA/See Pg. 72

Ringneck Ridge Sporting Club

1818 County Rd. 74, Gibsonburg, OH 43431
(419) 637-2332 Pete Ochs 8-5
85 mi. W of Cleveland
Est 1986; **Acres** 360; **Type** Member/Avail; **On Site** Clubhouse, Lodging, Meals, Clays; **Shoots** Field; **Birds** Quail, Pheasant, Chukar; **Dogs** Avail/HDW; **Packages** 1/2 Day, 1-16 guns ○ NAGA/See Pg. 72

Scioto River Hunting Club

17226 St. Rt. 235, Waynesfield, OH 45896
(513) 464-6560 Mary Zirkle 8am-5pm
60 mi. NW of Columbus
Est 1991; **Acres** 300; **Hunters/yr** 500; **Type** Public, Member/Avail; **On Site** Clubhouse, Lodging, Meals, Clays; **Shoots** Field; **Birds** Quail, Pheasant, Chukar; **Dogs** Avail/HDW ○ NAGA/See Pg. 72

Stinson Farms Hunting Preserve

5920 Good Hope Rd., Frankfort, OH 45628
(614) 998-4977 Manly Stinson 9pm
5 mi. SW of Frankfort
Est 1990; **Acres** 400; **Hunters/yr** 125; **Type** Public; **On Site** Clubhouse; **Shoots** Field; **Birds** Quail, Pheasant; **Dogs** Avail/HDW; **Packages** 1/2 Day, 2-10 guns ○ NAGA/See Pg. 72

Stull Hunting Preserve

10738 Ellen Dr., New Carlisle, OH 45344
(513) 845-3901 Dale Stull Eve.
17 mi. N of Dayton
Est 1991; **Acres** 165; **Type** Public; **Shoots** Field; **Birds** Pheasant, Chukar; **Dogs** Avail/HDW ○ NAGA/See Pg. 72

Tallmadge Pheasant
Farm & Hunting Preserve

16 County Rd. 1950, Jeromesville, OH 44840
(419) 368-3457 Jack or Nancy Tallmadge
50 mi. SW of Cleveland
Est 1922; **Acres** 300; **Type** Public; **On Site** Clubhouse, Clays; **Shoots** Field; **Birds** Pheasant; **Dogs** Avail/HDW; **Packages** 1/2 Day, 2-12 guns ○ NAGA/See Pg. 72

WR Hunt Club

5690 CR237, Clyde, OH 43410
(419) 547-8550 Betty or Robert Wright 7am-12noon
50 mi. W of Cleveland
Est 1986; **Acres** 300; **Hunters/yr** 400; **Type**
Public, Member/Avail, Corp.; **On Site** Clubhouse,
Lodging, Meals, Clays; **Shoots** Field; **Birds** Quail,
Pheasant, Chukar; **Dogs** Avail/HDW; **Packages** 1/2
Day, 1-5 guns ○ NAGA/See Pg. 72

Wooster Duck & Pheasant Hunting

470 Carter Dr., Wooster, OH 44691
(216) 262-1671 Louie Carter
Acres 585; **Hunters/yr** 1,200; **Type** Public,
Member/Avail, Corp.; **On Site** Clubhouse; **Shoots**
Field; **Birds** Pheasant; **Dogs** Avail/HDW; **Packages**
1/2 Day, 1-32 guns ○ NAGA/See Pg. 72

Wrestle Creek Game Club

23605 Fairmont - CR180, Waynesfield, OH 45896
(419) 568-2867 Jim Hardin 9am-6pm
12 mi. SE of Lima
Est 1990; **Acres** 160; **Hunters/yr** 400; **Type**
Public; **On Site** Clubhouse, Clays; **Shoots** Field;
Birds Quail, Pheasant, Chukar; **Dogs** Avail/HDW;
Packages 1/2 Day, 1-15 guns

○ Hunting License	○ Bird Processing
○ Sporting Clays	○ Family Recreation
○ Shooting Instruction	○ Train Bird Dogs
○ Loaner Guns	○ Brochure Available
○ Gunsmith Service	○ Factory Ammunition
○ Family Run Business	

OKLAHOMA

3H Hunting Ranch
608 Cedar Lane, Frederick, OK 73542
(800) 239-7676 Joe Horton
13 mi. NW of Frederick
Est 1995; **Acres** 6,000; **Type** Public; **On Site**
Clubhouse, Lodging, Meals, Clays; **Shoots** Field;
Birds Dove, Quail, Pheasant, Chukar, Turkey, Ducks,
Geese; **Dogs** Avail

Anderson Commercial
Rt. 1, Box 1, Sweetwater, OK 73666
(405) 534-2305 James Anderson
30 mi. W of Sweetwater
Acres 1,280; **Hunters/yr** 100; **Type** Public;
Shoots Field; **Birds** Quail, Pheasant; **Dogs** Avail

Bar B Commercial Hunting Area

Rt. 2, Box 130, Pawhuska, OK 74056
(918) 349-2231 Robert A. Boulanger
45 mi. NW of Tulsa
Est 1986; **Acres** 2,200; **Hunters/yr** 300; **Type**
Public; **On Site** Clubhouse, Meals; **Shoots** Field,
Tower; **Birds** Quail, Pheasant, Chukar, Turkey;
Dogs Avail/HDW; **Packages** 1/2 Day, 1-40 guns

Bird Haven
Rt. 1, Box 146D, Duncan, OK 73533
(405) 252-1393 John Johnson
65 mi. S of Oklahoma City
Est 1980; **Acres** 6,000; **Hunters/yr** 40; **Type**
Public, Member/Avail; **Shoots** Field; **Birds** Dove,
Quail, Ducks, Geese; **Dogs** HDW

Boxcar Hunting Club
3201 N.W. 13th, Oklahoma City, OK 73107
(405) 947-7525 Glen Decker 8am-10am
160 mi. SW of Oklahoma City
Est 1991; **Acres** 700; **Hunters/yr** 65; **Type**
Public; **On Site** Clubhouse, Lodging, Meals, Clays;
Shoots Field; **Birds** Dove, Quail, Turkey, Ducks;
Dogs Avail/HDW; **Packages** 1 Day, 4-6 guns

Canadian River Recreational Club
HC62, Box 146, Eufaula, OK 74432
(918) 689-5085 David/Patty Fisher 8-10am, 5-10pm
68 mi. S of Tulsa
Est 1990; **Acres** 26,000; **Type** Public,
Member/Avail; **On Site** Clubhouse, Lodging, Meals,
Clays; **Shoots** Field, Blinds; **Birds** Dove, Quail,
Pheasant, Turkey, Ducks, Geese; **Dogs** Avail/HDW;
Packages 1/2 Day, 2-3 guns

The Covey Connection
Rt. 2, Box 251, Macomb, OK 74852
(405) 333-2324 Marty S. Swinney
50 mi. E of Oklahoma City
Est 1992; **Acres** 80; **Type** Public; **Shoots** Field;
Birds Quail, Pheasant, Chukar; **Packages** 1/2 Day,
1-12 guns ○ NAGA/See Pg. 72

Deer Creek Outfitters
Rt. 2, Box 315A, Guthrie, OK 73044
(405) 348-8723 Steve Humphrey Evenings
60 mi. NW of Oklahoma City
Est 1987; **Acres** 9,000; **Hunters/yr** 200; **Type**
Public; **On Site** Clubhouse, Lodging, Meals; **Shoots**
Field; **Birds** Quail, Turkey; **Dogs** Avail/HDW;
Packages 1 Day, 3-5 guns

Deer Run Lodge
PO Box 1396, Durant, OK 74702
(405) 367-2687 Mike Clancy
100 mi. NE of Dallas
Est 1991; **Acres** 6,000; **Type** Public, Member/Avail,
Corp.; **On Site** Clubhouse, Lodging, Meals, Clays;
Shoots Field, Blinds, Boat; **Birds** Dove, Quail,
Pheasant, Chukar, Turkey, Ducks; **Dogs** Avail/HDW;
Packages 1/2 Day, 1-50 guns ○ NAGA/See Pg. 72
See Our Ad Across Left

Easy Point Hunting & Fishing Preserve
Rt. 1, Box 57, Gate, OK 73844
(405) 934-2210 Stephen & Peggy Henry After 5pm
180 mi. NW of Oklahoma City
Est 1989; **Acres** 7,000; **Hunters/yr** 200; **Type**
Public; **On Site** Clubhouse, Lodging, Meals; **Shoots**
Field; **Birds** Dove, Quail, Pheasant, Chukar, Turkey;
Dogs Avail/HDW; **Packages** 1 Day, 2-10 guns

Five Cedars Ranch
PO Box 14801, Oklahoma City, OK 73113
(918) 368-2331 Donna Duffy
45 mi. NE of Oklahoma City
Est 1987; **Acres** 2,000; **Type** Public; **On Site**
Clubhouse, Meals, Clays; **Shoots** Field; **Birds** Quail,
Pheasant, Chukar; **Dogs** Avail/HDW; **Packages** 1/2
Day, 2-8 guns ○ NAGA/See Pg. 72

Hunting Sports Plus
710 Main St., Ste. E, Blue Springs, MO,
Hunting in 7 States incluing Oklahoma
(800) 729-1924 Dan Gasser

Est 1989; **Acres** 200,000; **Type** Public,
Member/Avail; **On Site** Clubhouse, Lodging, Meals,
Clays; **Shoots** Field, Blinds, Boat; **Birds** Quail,
Pheasant, Turkey, Prairie Chicken, Ducks, Geese;
Dogs Avail/HDW; **Packages** 1 Day, 1-24 guns

J.W. Hunting Preserve
PO Box 1236, Henryetta, OK 74437
(918) 466-3299 John W. Willhite 10-10
80 mi. E of Oklahoma City
Est 1985; **Acres** 500; **Hunters/yr** 750; **Type**
Public; **On Site** Lodging, Clays; **Shoots** Field,
Tower; **Birds** Quail, Pheasant, Chukar, Turkey, Ducks;
Dogs Avail/HDW; **Packages** 1/2 Day, 2-12 guns

Melot's
8900 W. Memorial, Oklahoma City, OK 73142
(405) 721-4394 Mike Melot
10 mi. NW of Oklahoma City
Acres 160; **Type** Public, Member/Avail; **On Site**
Clays; **Shoots** Field; **Birds** Dove, Quail

Moorland Sportsman's Country Club
Box 454, Moorland, OK 73852
(405) 994-2755 C.M. Crawford Between 9-12
10 mi. E of Woodward
Est 1994; **Type** Member/Avail; **On Site** Clubhouse;
Shoots Field, Blinds; **Birds** Quail, Turkey, Ducks,
Geese; **Dogs** Avail/HDW ○ NAGA/See Pg. 72

Northwest Hunts
Rt. 1, Box 179, Woodward, OK 73801
(405) 256-8076 Milton Rose
Acres 35,000; **Type** Public; **On Site** Meals;
Shoots Field; **Birds** Quail, Turkey; **Dogs** Avail/HDW

Panhandle Pheasant & Chukar Hunts
Rt. 2, Box 16, Beaver, OK 73932
(405) 625-4809 Melvin Chaloupek
180 mi. NW of Oklahoma City
Est 1989; **Acres** 2,500; **Hunters/yr** 200; **Type**
Public; **On Site** Clubhouse, Meals, Clays; **Shoots**
Field; **Birds** Quail, Pheasant, Chukar; **Dogs**
Avail/HDW; **Packages** 1 Day, 2-10 guns
○ NAGA/See Pg. 72

Red Rock Ranch
Rt. 1, Box 64-M, Marland, OK 74644
(405) 268-9663 Bill Spires 8am-6pm
25 mi. SE of Ponca City
Est 1985; **Acres** 5,400; **Type** Public, Member/Avail;
On Site Clubhouse, Lodging, Meals, Clays; **Shoots**
Field; **Birds** Quail, Pheasant, Chukar, Turkey; **Dogs**
Avail/HDW; **Packages** 1 Day, 6-10 guns
○ NAGA/See Pg. 72

Rock Creek Commercial Hunting Area
Rt. 2, Box 130, Pawhuska, OK 74056
(918) 349-2231 Robert Boulanger
13 mi. W of Bartlesville
Acres 4,000; **Type** Public; **On Site** Lodging, Meals;
Shoots Field, Tower; **Birds** Quail, Pheasant, Chukar,
Turkey; **Dogs** Avail

Southern Ranch Hunting Club
Rt. 2, Box 75, Chandler, OK 74834
Dean/Terri Caton (405) 258-0000, 9-5

45 mi. NE of Oklahoma City
Est 1987; **Acres** 1,500; **Hunters/yr** 350; **Type**
Public, Member/Avail, Corp.; **On Site** Clubhouse,
Lodging, Meals, Clays; **Shoots** Field, Tower; **Birds**
Quail, Pheasant, Chukar, Turkey; **Dogs** Avail/HDW;
Packages 1/2 Day, 2-24 guns ○ NAGA/See Pg. 72

Thunder Ridge
924 North Imo Rd., Enid, OK 73703
(405) 242-7550 Keith Rasmussen
18 mi. E of Enid
Acres 320; **Hunters/yr** 100; **Type** Public; **Shoots**
Field; **Birds** Quail, Pheasant; **Dogs** Avail

West-Ok Outfitters
Rt. 1, Box 60, Gage, OK 73843
(405) 885-7745 Bob England
145 mi. NW of Oklahoma City
Est 1992; **Acres** 10,000; **Hunters/yr** 100; **Type**
Public; **On Site** Lodging, Meals; **Shoots** Field,
Blinds; **Birds** Dove, Quail, Turkey, Ducks, Geese;
Dogs Avail; **Packages** 1 Day, 2-6 guns

Woods and Water, inc.
Rt. 1, Box 319, Catoosa, OK 74015
(918) 266-5551 Doug Fuller M-F, 9-5
6.5 mi. E of Tulsa
Est 1994; **Acres** 4,000; **Type** Public, Member/Avail;
On Site Clubhouse, Lodging, Meals, Clays; **Shoots**
Field, Tower, Driven, Blinds, Boat; **Birds** Dove, Quail,
Pheasant, Chukar, Turkey, Ducks, Geese; **Dogs**
Avail/HDW; **Packages** 1/2 Day, 2-12 guns
See Our Ad Pg. 351

OREGON

Bear Creek Shooting Preserve
827519 Crooked River Hwy., Prineville, OR 97754
(503) 576-2096 Dan Greenfield
26 mi. SE of Primeville
Acres 640; **Hunters/yr** 200; **Type** Public; **Shoots**
Field; **Birds** Pheasant; **Dogs** Avail

Fish & Wildlife Resources
5014 Rosewood St., Lake Oswego, OR 97035
(503) 636-6744 Barry Morinaka
Type Public; **Shoots** Field; **Birds** Quail, Pheasant,
Chukar ○ NAGA/See Pg. 72

Great Basin Game Birds
PO Box 575, Burns, OR 97720
(800) 646-0058 Lance Okeson
95 mi. SE of Portland
Est 1994; **Type** Public, Member/Avail; **On Site**
Clays; **Shoots** Field; **Birds** Pheasant, Chukar, Huns;
Dogs Avail/HDW; **Packages** 1/2 Day, 1-8 guns

Great Expectations
Hunting Preserve

Oregon's Newest & Finest Upland Gamebird Hideaway

At Great Expectations you'll hunt pheasant, chukar and quail in a
  secluded canyon of swales, thickets and fields awash with color...
  or along rugged slopes that rise from the canyon floor through
  Juniper and Ponderosa pine.

This is where a sportsman's greatest expectations are met and
  exceeded. Where, in addition to world-class upland hunting,
  you'll experience the challenge of one of the most remote sporting
  clays courses in the world. And enjoy the best small mouth bass
  fishing in the West.

After each exciting day in the field you'll return to the comfort and
  seclusion of our fully furnished four bedroom lodge. Its well
  equipped kitchen allows you the flexibility of preparing your own
  meals or enjoying those prepared by an experienced local cook.

Quite simply the perfect destination for hunters who want to *"get
  away from it all"*, Great Expectations is located in remote Eastern
  Oregon—on the sunny side of the state—120 miles south of
  Pendleton and 70 miles northwest of John Day.

Great Expectations emphasizes personal attention and specializes in
  "Fly-ins", small groups and corporate entertaining. Airport
  transportation from Monument and Redmond, Oregon available.

Call or write Jerry & Kitty Russell today for an informative brochure:

503-934-2117

Star Rt. 2 • Kimberly, OR 97848

Great Expectations

Hunting Preserve
HC82, Box 234, Kimberly, OR 97848
(503) 934-2117 Jerry Russell
70 mi. NW of John Day
Est 1994; **Acres** 556; **Hunters/yr** 250; **Type** Public, Member/Avail; **On Site** Clubhouse, Lodging, Meals, Clays; **Shoots** Field; **Birds** Quail, Pheasant, Chukar, Huns; **Dogs** Avail/HDW; **Packages** 1/2 Day, 2-8 guns ○ NAGA/See Pg. 72
See Our Ad Pg. 353

Helms Canyon Hunt Club
200 West 9th St., The Dalles, OR 97058
(503) 296-9535 Doug Reid Evenings
115 mi. E of Portland
Est 1993; **Acres** 2,500; **Hunters/yr** 350; **Type** Public, Member/Avail, Corp.; **On Site** Clubhouse, Lodging, Meals; **Shoots** Field; **Birds** Dove, Quail, Pheasant, Chukar, Huns, Geese; **Dogs** Avail/HDW; **Packages** 1 Day, 2-4 guns ○ NAGA/See Pg. 72

Hulse Pheasant & Sporting Clay Ranch
60277 Tygh Ridge Rd., Dufur, OR 97021
(503) 467-2513 Mike & Debbie Hulse
100 mi. E of Portland
Est 1988; **Acres** 3,000; **Type** Public, Corp.; **On Site** Clubhouse, Meals, Clays; **Shoots** Field; **Birds** Dove, Quail, Pheasant, Chukar, Huns; **Dogs** Avail/HDW

Lonsford Pheasants
851 NE Yamhill, Sheridan, OR 97378
(503) 843-2684 Charles Lonsford 7pm-10pm
25 mi. NW of Salem
Est 1990; **Acres** 120; **Type** Public, Member/Avail; **On Site** Meals, Clays; **Shoots** Field; **Birds** Quail, Pheasant; **Dogs** Avail/HDW; **Packages** 1/2 Day, 1-4 guns

Muddy Creek
Sporting Club
29499 Buchanan Rd., Corvallis, OR 97333
(503) 753-9679 Don Hamblin
22 mi. N of Eugene
Est 1989; **Acres** 115; **Type** Public; **On Site** Clubhouse, Clays; **Shoots** Blinds; **Birds** Ducks; **Dogs** Avail/HDW
○ Sporting Clays   ○ Factory Ammunition
○ Quality Clubhouse   ○ Family Run Business
○ Corporate Shoots   ○ Day Hunts

Noble Sporting Adventures
Rt. 2, Box 185-X, Milton-Freewater, OR 97862
(800) 437-3966 Don Noble Evenings
235 mi. E of Portland

Est 1989; **Acres** 465; **Type** Public; **On Site** Clubhouse, Lodging, Meals, Clays; **Shoots** Field; **Birds** Quail, Pheasant, Chukar, Turkey; **Dogs** Avail/HDW; **Packages** 1/2 Day, 2-8 guns ○ NAGA/See Pg. 72

Oregon Blacktails Guide Service
PO Box 1737, Jacksonville, OR 97530
(503) 772-1010 Perry Allen 6-9
230 mi. S of Portland   **Est** 1989; **Acres** 2,000; **Type** Public; **On Site** Lodging, Meals; **Shoots** Field; **Birds** Quail, Ruffed Grouse, Turkey; **Dogs** Avail/HDW; **Packages** 2 Days, 1-2 guns

Pheasant Ridge, Inc.
80420 Ross Rd., Tygh Valley, OR 97063
(503) 544-2183 Steve Tessmer
115 mi. E of Portland
Est 1987; **Acres** 2,500; **Type** Public, Member/Avail; **On Site** Clubhouse, Lodging, Meals, Clays; **Shoots** Field; **Birds** Dove, Quail, Pheasant, Chukar, Ducks, Geese; **Dogs** Avail/HDW ○ NAGA/See Pg. 72

Ringneck Ranch
PO Box 316, Christmas Village, OR 97641
(503) 576-2532 Wayne Stutzman
Type Public; **On Site** Lodging; **Shoots** Field; **Birds** Quail, Pheasant, Chukar ○ NAGA/See Pg. 72

Round Barn Pheasant Farm
93614 Swamp Creek Rd., Blachly, OR 97412
(503) 927-3767 Chris Mooney
115 mi. SW of Portland
Type Public; **Shoots** Field; **Birds** Pheasant

Summer Ridge Shooting Preserve
3759 Reed Rd., Vale, OR 97918
(503) 473-3355 Tim McGuffin
65 mi. NW of Boise, ID
Acres 390; **Type** Public; **On Site** Lodging, Meals; **Shoots** Field; **Birds** Quail, Pheasant, Ducks, Geese; **Dogs** Avail

TREO Ranches
Rt. 1, Box 3171, Heppner, OR 97836
(503) 676-5840 Phil Carlson Anytime
180 mi. E of Portland
Est 1987; **Acres** 4,200; **Type** Public; **On Site** Clubhouse, Lodging, Meals, Clays; **Shoots** Field; **Birds** Pheasant, Chukar, Huns; **Dogs** Avail/HDW; **Packages** 1 Day, 2-10 guns
See Our Ad Across

Upland Meadows Hunting
1903 SW Jackson, Portland, OR 97201
(503) 640-5757 Charles Lilley
25 mi. W of Portland
Acres 300; **Type** Public, Member/Avail; **On Site** Clays; **Shoots** Field; **Birds** Quail, Pheasant, Chukar; **Dogs** HDW ○ NAGA/See Pg. 72
○ Hunting License   ○ Airport Pickup
○ Sporting Clays   ○ Brochure Available
○ Family Run Business

Oregon's TREO...
The Real Thing

by Virgil Rupp

"The real thing" -- that's the easiest, most accurate way to describe upland bird hunting at TREO.

Step out of your car -- or your plane or helicopter -- and a few minutes later, gun in hand, you're stepping lively behind some of the best bird dogs in the West.

The German wire-haired pointers move fast but never miss a scent trail. There! Gilda is on a bird. The dog freezes into a classic point.

Gilda helped.

You move in, the shotgun ready, your heart beating rapidly.

The rooster cackles. Wings whir--bird going up! Your gun settles naturally into your shoulder, allow a little lead, boom! And the big Chinese/Mongolian pheasant folds. Wipe the sweat from your brow. Reload. A dog brings you the 3 1/2 lb. pheasant. Slip it into your vest.

That's how it goes at TREO, where bird hunting is natural, the real thing.

Take chukars. TREO organizes hunts for big, wild chukars in Dry Fork Canyon. It's classic chukar habitat, rimrocks soaring above in intermittent water course. Lots of shooting is the rule in a TREO chukar hunt.

Relaxation minded

TREO is organized with your relaxation in mind. You will take a break during your hunt, time out for a cold drink, to chat with the other hunters, enjoy the antics of the lively dogs.

At noon, lunch will include build-your-own sandwiches with thick slices of ham, cups of steaming, flavorful pheasant soup, perhaps a juicy sausage.

At the end of your day afield, slip into the hot tub at TREO's guest house, and relive the great moments of the day.

Gourmet dining offers cognac pheasant, chukar with wild rice, prime rib of country beef, leg of spring lamb, or the latest addition to the menu, boneless breast of pheasant with filet mignon.

Sleep like a baby in TREO's comfortable beds, enjoy a trencherman's breakfast, and look ahead to another day of bird hunting, sporting clays, exploring the countryside on a mountain bike, trout fishing in a picturesque mountain lake.

Your guides in the hunt will be Phil and Clint Carlson. Phil handles the dogs. You may never have seen such dogs. Bundles of wiry energy, they hunt every day, flushing thousands of pheasants and chukars every season.

When one of these German wirehairs signals "bird!" you'd best pay attention and get close. Phil said. He's lean, blond and trim. He's good at coaching novice hunters.

Clint is somewhat quieter but it's worth your while to get him to open up with tales of classic hunts in TREO country.

The UNIQUE sporting clays course at TREO can sharpen your shooting eye as well as provide an opportunity to burn more gunpowder. The way to succeed at sporting clays is to relax, enjoy the challenge, let your instincts do the work.

For trout fishing, try Bull Prairie Lake first. It's especially rewarding for fly fishermen. But bait plunkers and lure users can expect to catch rainbows and brookies, too.

Bring your float tube or canoe. Sheltered Bull Prairie is perfect for such craft, for no motors are allowed. Often anglers will see deer or even Rocky Mountain elk along the water's edge at Bull Prairie.

Near the community of Heppner, anglers can try Willow Creek Lake and expect to catch bass as well as big trout.

Your mountain bike can carry you along miles of scenic rural roads winding through fields of wheat and grasslands. The main road past TREO's guest house runs along the crest of a major ridge -- scenery on every hand as you pedal your cares and tension away.

The real thing. At TREO.

[For more information and reservations call or write: Phil Carlson, TREO, Rt. 1, Box 3171, Heppner, OR 97836; (503) 676-5840.]

PENNSYLVANIA

Allegheny Bird Dog Club
RD 5, Box 213, Somerset, PA 15501
(814) 443-3326 Mark Holliday 9-9
60 mi. SE of Pittsburgh
Est 1990; **Acres** 250; **Type** Public, Member/Avail;
On Site Clubhouse, Lodging, Meals; **Shoots** Field;
Birds Quail, Pheasant, Chukar; **Dogs** Avail/HDW;
Packages 1/2 Day, 1-8 guns

Angus Conservation & Hunting Farms
RD#1, Box 260, Latrobe, PA 15650
(412) 423-4022 Jay Angus 9-5
35 mi. E of Pittsburgh
Est 1980; **Acres** 600; **Type** Public, Member/Avail;
On Site Lodging, Meals, Clays; **Shoots** Field, Tower,
Driven; **Birds** Quail, Pheasant, Chukar; **Dogs**
Avail/HDW; **Packages** 1/2 Day, 1-25 guns
○ NAGA/See Pg. 72

Big Pine Hunting Club
PO Box 45, Prompton, PA 18456
(908) 362-9008 George Rabtzow
20 mi. NE of Scranton
Est 1960; **Acres** 175; **Hunters/yr** 15; **Type**
Public, Member/Avail, Corp.; **On Site** Clubhouse,
Lodging, Clays; **Shoots** Field; **Birds** Dove, Quail,
Woodcock, Pheasant, Chukar, Turkey, Ducks; **Dogs**
HDW; **Packages** 1 Day, 3-15 guns

Blacklick Shooting Preserve
PO Box 191, Blairsville, PA 15717
(412) 459-8869 Daryl Thomas
40 mi. E of Pittsburgh
Acres 300; **Hunters/yr** 200; **Type** Public,
Member/Avail; **On Site** Clubhouse, Lodging, Meals;
Shoots Field, Tower; **Birds** Quail, Pheasant, Chukar;
Dogs Avail

Mr. Britt's Game Farm
PO Box 925, RD2, Homer City, PA 15748
(412) 479-9813 John A. Boris After 5
45 mi. E of Pittsburgh
Est 1980; **Acres** 2,300; **Hunters/yr** 700; **Type**
Public, Member/Avail, Corp.; **On Site** Clubhouse,
Meals, Clays; **Shoots** Field, Tower; **Birds** Dove,
Quail, Ruffed Grouse, Pheasant, Chukar, Turkey;
Dogs Avail/HDW; **Packages** 1 Day, 1-60 guns
○ Sporting Clays

Clover Hollow Hunting Preserve
6951 Lime Kiln Rd., Slatington, PA 18080
(610) 767-3319 Wilmer H. Dise
15 mi. N of Allentown
Acres 400; **Type** Public, Member/Avail, Corp.; **On
Site** Clubhouse; **Shoots** Field; **Birds** Quail,
Pheasant, Chukar; **Dogs** Avail/HDW; **Packages** 1/2
Day, 1-6 guns

Dancing Fields Outfitters
HCR11, Box 190, Meadville, PA 16335
(814) 789-3276 Joseph Tinko

Type Public, Member/Avail; **Shoots** Field; **Birds**
Quail, Pheasant, Chukar ○ NAGA/See Pg. 72

Four Seasons Game Bird Farm
115 List Hill, Valencia, PA 16059
(412) 898-2316 John L. Kennedy
26 mi. N of Pittsburgh
Est 1994; **Acres** 385; **Hunters/yr** 350; **Type**
Public, Corp.; **On Site** Clubhouse, Lodging, Meals;
Shoots Field, Driven; **Birds** Quail, Pheasant, Chukar;
Dogs Avail; **Packages** 1/2 Day, 1-20 guns

Gaybird Farms
6063 Sawmill Rd., Box 1, Carversville, PA 18913
(215) 297-5553 Barney Berlinger 8 am or noon
10 mi. N of Philadelphia
Type Member/Avail; **Shoots** Field; **Birds** Pheasant;
Dogs Avail/HDW; **Packages** 1/2 Day

Greater Pittsburgh Gun Club
RD1, Bulger, PA 15019
(412) 796-9111 Tex Freund Anytime
18 mi. W of Pittsburgh
Est 1968; **Acres** 700; **Type** Public, Member/Avail;
On Site Clubhouse, Meals, Clays; **Shoots** Field;
Birds Pheasant, Turkey, Ducks, Geese; **Dogs** HDW;
Packages 1/2 Day, up to 1 guns

Hay's Pheasant Hunt, Inc.
625 Meadowbrook Ln., Gettysburg, PA 17325
(717) 334-1588 Robert Hay
55 mi. N of Baltimore
Est 1988; **Acres** 200; **Hunters/yr** 300; **Type**
Public; **On Site** Clubhouse; **Shoots** Field; **Birds**
Pheasant; **Dogs** Avail/HDW; **Packages** 1/2 Day,
1-12 guns

Hemlock Acres Hunting Club
RR3, Box 87-1-A, Benton, PA 17814
(717) 458-5930 Jim LeVan
6 mi. from Benton
Acres 250; **Type** Public, Member/Avail; **On Site**
Lodging, Meals; **Shoots** Field; **Birds** Quail,
Pheasant, Chukar; **Dogs** Avail/HDW

Hemlock Hill Preserve
39 Odell Rd., Mandfield, PA 16933
(717) 662-3927 David Russell
5 mi. E of Mansfield
Acres 197; **Hunters/yr** 50; **Type** Public; **Shoots**
Field; **Birds** Quail, Pheasant; **Dogs** Avail

Hillendale Hunt Club
RD#1, Box 390, Tyrone, PA 16686
(814) 684-5015 Tom Crawford 7-8pm
90 mi. E of Pittsburg
Est 1977; **Acres** 475; **Hunters/yr** 600; **Type**
Public; **On Site** Clubhouse, Lodging, Meals; **Shoots**
Field, Driven; **Birds** Pheasant, Chukar; **Dogs**
Avail/HDW; **Packages** 1/2 Day, 2-12 guns
○ NAGA/See Pg. 72

Hillside Hunting Preserve
PO Box 56, Berlin, PA 15530
(814) 267-4484 James Scurfield 9-5
60 mi. SE of Pittsburgh

Sporting Clays available year around.

THE WARRINGTON CLUB

- Comfortable facilities with a gracious atmosphere.
- Complete pro shop.
- Located two hour drive from Philadelphia and Washington D.C.

Discover

The

GAME BIRD HUNTING

- Quail, Pheasant, Chukars and Huns.
- 365 acres of varied terrain, including 140 specialty planted acres.
- Dogs and guides available.

For information please complete the coupon below or call (717) 432-0643 or (717) 741-7214.

Please send me information on:
☐ Warrington Hunt Club
☐ Warrington Sporting Clays Course
☐ Both of the above

Name: _____
Address:_____
City/Town:_____State_____Zip _____
Tel:_____ Best time to call _____

Please return to: the Warrington Club, 400 Yeager Road, Wellsville, PA 17365

GAP VIEW HUNTING PRESERVE INC.
R.R. 1, Box 85, Dalmatia, PA 17017
LOCATED JUST 45 MINUTES NORTH OF HARRISBURG, PENNSYLVANIA
1300 ACRE PHEASANT HUNTING GROUNDS OPEN SEPTEMBER THROUGH MARCH

- **Season Memberships & Daily Hunts**
- **Special Arrangements For Large Groups, Corporations or Clubs**
- **Sporting Clays**

CALL: **800-326-8442**
Monday through Saturday-- 8:00 a.m. to 5:00 p.m.
By Reservation Only
Also Top Quality Ringneck Pheasant, Chukar & Hungarian Partridge for Sale

---

Est 1983; **Acres** 300; **Hunters/yr** 600; **Type** Public, Member/Avail, Corp.; **On Site** Clubhouse, Lodging, Meals, Clays; **Shoots** Field, Tower, Driven; **Birds** Quail, Pheasant, Chukar; **Dogs** Avail/HDW; **Packages** 1 Day, up to 10 guns ○ NAGA/See Pg. 72

Hopewell Pheasantry, Inc.
RD3, Box 680, Felton, PA 17322
(800) 847-8881 Bill or Gail Rinas
20 mi. S of York
Est 1987; **Acres** 300; **Type** Public, Member/Avail, Corp.; **Shoots** Field, Blinds; **Birds** Quail, Pheasant, Chukar, Geese; **Dogs** Avail/HDW; **Packages** 1/2 Day, 1-20 guns

Indian Run Country
Rt. 2, Centerville, PA 16404
(814) 967-2635 Dave & Nancy Stutzman
85 mi. N of Pittsburg
Est 1986; **Acres** 380; **Type** Public, Member/Avail; **On Site** Clubhouse, Meals, Clays; **Shoots** Field, Tower; **Birds** Quail, Pheasant, Chukar; **Dogs** Avail/HDW; **Packages** 1/2 Day, 1-24 guns ○ NAGA/See Pg. 72

JDZ Game Farm
RD#2, Box 75, Watsontown, PA 17777
(717) 649-5881 John Zaktansky Evenings
70 mi. SW of Scranton
Est 1988; **Acres** 80; **Type** Public, Member/Avail; **On Site** Clays; **Shoots** Field; **Birds** Quail, Pheasant, Chukar; **Dogs** Avail/HDW; **Packages** 1/2 Day, 1-4 guns

Kettle Creek Lodge
HCR62, Box 14B, Cross Fork, PA 17729
(814) 435-1019 Steve Benna
Acres 282,000; **Type** Public; **Shoots** Field; **Birds** Turkey; **Dogs** Avail/HDW

Kimble's Regulated Hunting Grounds
321 Newport Rd., Duncannon, PA 17020
(717) 834-5122 Dan Kimble
15 mi. NW of Harrisburg

Acres 226; **Type** Public, Member/Avail; **On Site** Clubhouse, Meals; **Shoots** Field; **Birds** Quail, Pheasant, Chukar; **Dogs** Avail; **Packages** 1/2 Day ○ NAGA/See Pg. 72

La-Da-Jo Pines
RD2, Box 67, New Ringgold, PA 17960
(717) 943-2213 Larry Delp 7am-9pm
65 mi. NW of Philadelphia
Est 1960; **Acres** 600; **Type** Public, Member/Avail, Corp.; **On Site** Clubhouse, Meals, Clays; **Shoots** Field, Tower, Driven; **Birds** Dove, Quail, Ruffed Grouse, Woodcock, Pheasant, Chukar, Huns, Turkey; **Dogs** Avail/HDW; **Packages** 1/2 Day, 3-15 guns ○ NAGA/See Pg. 72

Laurel Spring Hunt-Fishing Club
RD#2, Box 162, Rockwood, PA 15557
(814) 352-8803 Richard Sager
60 mi. SE of Pittsburgh
Est 1995; **Acres** 350; **Type** Public, Member/Avail, Corp.; **On Site** Clubhouse, Lodging, Meals, Clays; **Shoots** Field, Tower, Driven; **Birds** Quail, Pheasant, Chukar; **Dogs** Avail/HDW; **Packages** 1/2 Day, 1-10 guns

Lazy E Hunting Grounds
RD#4, Box 304, Tyrone, PA 16686
(814) 632-5291 Gary Eyer
90 mi. E of Pittsburg
Est 1990; **Acres** 200; **Type** Public, Member/Avail; **On Site** Lodging, Meals; **Shoots** Field; **Birds** Quail, Pheasant, Chukar; **Dogs** Avail/HDW; **Packages** 1/2 Day, 1-4 guns

Martz's Gap View Hunting Preserve
RR#1, Box 85, Dalmatia, PA 17017
(800) 326-8442 Don Martz 8am-5pm
38 mi. N of Harrisburg
Est 1955; **Acres** 1,300; **Hunters/yr** 5,000; **Type** Public, Member/Avail; **On Site** Clubhouse, Lodging, Meals, Clays; **Shoots** Field, Tower; **Birds** Pheasant, Chukar, Huns; **Dogs** Avail/HDW; **Packages** 1/2 Day, 1-15 guns ○ NAGA/See Pg. 72
See Our Ad Left

Mascari Shooting Grounds
RD#1, Levis Rd., Knox, PA 16232
(412) 366-7163 Don Mascari
65 mi. N of Pittsburgh
Acres 257; **Hunters/yr** 30; **Type** Public, Member/Avail; **On Site** Clubhouse, Meals, Clays; **Shoots** Field, Tower; **Birds** Pheasant

Mason Dixon Hunting Farm
RD3, Box 233, Glen Rock, PA 17327
(717) 235-2308 Jerry & Michele Walker
20 mi. S of York
Est 1990; **Acres** 190; **Hunters/yr** 100; **Type** Public; **Shoots** Field; **Birds** Quail, Pheasant, Chukar; **Dogs** Avail/HDW; **Packages** 1/2 Day, 1-6 guns

Medhia Shooting Preserve
Box 64, E. Waterford, PA 17021

(717) 734-3965 Donald Singer 6-10 pm
60 mi. NW of Harrisburg
Est 1988; **Acres** 611; **Hunters/yr** 800; **Type**
Public, Member/Avail, Corp.; **Shoots** Field; **Birds**
Pheasant, Chukar; **Dogs** Avail/HDW; **Packages** 1
Day, up to 16 guns ○ NAGA/See Pg. 72

Peter Meleason
850 Walnut Bottom Rd., Carlisle, PA 17013
(717) 243-5616
8 mi. W of Carlisle
Acres 180; **Type** Member/Avail; **On Site**
Clubhouse; **Shoots** Field; **Birds** Quail, Pheasant

Nightingale Shooting Preserve
RD#7, Box 485, Muncy, PA 17756
(717) 584-2274 Raymond P. Sones
60 mi. N of Harrisburg   **Type** Public; **On Site**
Lodging; **Shoots** Field; **Birds** Pheasant, Chukar;
Dogs Avail/HDW; **Packages** 1/2 Day, 1-36 guns

Pheasant Hill Farms
RD#6, Box 331, Wellsboro, PA 16901
(717) 724-3274 George S. Myers 8 am - 10 pm
110 mi. NW of Harrisburg
Acres 375; **Hunters/yr** 150; **Type** Public,
Member/Avail; **On Site** Lodging, Meals, Clays;
Shoots Field; **Birds** Quail, Pheasant; **Dogs**
Avail/HDW; **Packages** 1/2 Day, up to 5 guns
○ NAGA/See Pg. 72

The Preserve &
Shooting School
Rt. 209 S. (Box 1325), Milford, PA 18337
(717) 828-2544 Michael Adsit 8am-9pm
75 mi. NW of New York City
Est 1993; **Acres** 200; **Hunters/yr** 400; **Type**
Public, Member/Avail, Corp.; **On Site** Clays; **Shoots**
Field, Driven; **Birds** Quail, Pheasant, Chukar; **Dogs**
Avail/HDW; **Packages** 1/2 Day, 1-50 guns
Shooting Instruction Available - See Pg. 176

Quemahoning Trap & Field Club
RR7, Box 178-A, Somerset, PA 15501
(814) 443-4460 Kent Landefeld
15 mi. S of Johnstown   **Acres** 1,001; **Type**
Member/Avail; **On Site** Clubhouse; **Shoots** Field;
Birds Quail, Ruffed Grouse, Pheasant

Reading Reg.
Hunting Area, Inc.
RD1, Box 220A, Birdsboro, PA 19508
(610) 856-7671 Margaret Wisner After 4pm
42 mi. NW of Philadelphia
Est 1941; **Acres** 220; **Hunters/yr** 600; **Type**
Public, Member/Avail, Corp.; **On Site** Clubhouse,
Meals, Clays; **Shoots** Field; **Birds** Dove, Pheasant;
Dogs Avail/HDW; **Packages** 1/2 Day, 1-20 guns
○ Bird Processing   ○ Kennel Bird Dogs
○ Sporting Clays   ○ Brochure Available
○ Factory Ammunition   ○ Family Run Business
○ Family owned & operated 45 years

Rock Ridge Hunting Preserve
RD#3, Box 77M, Pine Grove, PA 17963
(717) 345-8900 Gregory Fedechko
50 mi. NE of Harrisburg
Acres 1,300; **Type** Public; **On Site** Clubhouse,
Meals, Clays; **Shoots** Field, Tower, Driven, Blinds;
Birds Quail, Pheasant, Chukar, Turkey, Ducks; **Dogs**
Avail/HDW; **Packages** 1/2 Day, 1-8 guns ○
NAGA/See Pg. 72

Sagulla Hunting Ground
826 Millbrook Rd., Jackson Center, PA 16133
(814) 786-7368 Joe or Pauline Sagulla Evening
60 mi. N of Pittsburgh
Est 1953; **Acres** 650; **Hunters/yr** 600; **Type**
Public; **On Site** Clubhouse; **Shoots** Field, Blinds;
Birds Pheasant, Chukar, Ducks; **Dogs** Avail/HDW;
Packages 1/2 Day

Smith Game Farm
206 Kepple Rd., Sarver, PA 16055
(412) 353-1107 Larry Smith
20 mi. NE of Pittsburgh
Est 1991; **Acres** 150; **Hunters/yr** 300; **Type**

Public; **On Site** Clubhouse, Meals; **Shoots** Field;
Birds Quail, Pheasant, Chukar; **Dogs** Avail/HDW;
Packages 1/2 Day, 1-6 guns

Spruce Hollow Hunting Farms, Ltd.
RD#2, Box 353, Kunkletown, PA 18058
(610) 381-3406 Junie & Cindy Kuehner Anytime
20 mi. N of Allentown
Est 1985; **Acres** 1,200; **Type** Public, Member/Avail,
Corp.; **On Site** Clubhouse, Lodging, Meals, Clays;
Shoots Field, Tower; **Birds** Quail, Pheasant, Chukar;
Dogs Avail/HDW; **Packages** 1/2 Day ○ NAGA/See Pg. 72

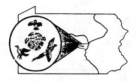

Susquehanna Valley
Game Farm
Box 8, RD2, McClure, PA 17841
(800) 338-7389 Todd Musser 9-4
20 mi. S of Lewistown off US Rt. 522
Est 1990; **Acres** 800; **Hunters/yr** 400; **Type**
Public, Member/Avail, Corp.; **On Site** Clubhouse,
Meals, Clays; **Shoots** Field; **Birds** Quail, Pheasant,
Chukar, Huns; **Dogs** Avail/HDW; **Packages** 1/2
Day, 2-4 guns   ○ NAGA/See Pg. 72
○ 3-D Archery Video Archery System
○ Archery Pro-Shop

Sutersville Sportsman's Club
PO Box 41, Sutersville, PA 15083
(412) 872-0910 John Vezzani Mon. 6-9
20 mi. SE of Pittsburgh   **Est** 1940; **Acres** 10; **Type**
Public, Member/Avail; **On Site** Clubhouse, Clays;
Shoots Field; **Birds** Dove, Ruffed Grouse, Pheasant,
Turkey; **Dogs** Avail/HDW

TNT Shooting Grounds
PO Box 236, Waltersburg, PA 15488
(412) 677-2609 Thomas Stewart 8-5
48 mi. S of Pittsburgh
Est 1980; **Acres** 300; **Hunters/yr** 1,800; **Type**
Public, Member/Avail, Corp.; **On Site** Clubhouse,
Meals, Clays; **Shoots** Field, Tower; **Birds** Quail,
Pheasant, Chukar, Ducks; **Dogs** Avail/HDW;
Packages 1/2 Day, 1-15 guns   ○ NAGA/See Pg. 72

Timberdoodle Farms
832 Cardinal Rd., St. Marys, PA 15857
(814) 781-7256 Robert Friedl
24 mi. E of Bradford
Acres 125; **Hunters/yr** 50; **Type** Public; **On Site**
Clubhouse, Lodging; **Shoots** Field; **Birds** Quail,
Ruffed Grouse, Woodcock, Pheasant, Chukar, Turkey;
Dogs Avail

Valley View Hunting
RR5, Box 5190, Spring Grove, PA 17362
(717) 225-3441 Alan Stubbs
75 mi. W of Philadelphia   **Acres** 350; **Hunters/yr**
30; **Shoots** Field; **Birds** Pheasant

W.C.J. Ranch
305 Jefferson St., Meadville, PA 16335
(814) 724-1930 Charles E. Schmitz
10 mi. NE of Meadville
Acres 200; **Type** Public; **On Site** Clubhouse, Clays;
Shoots Field; **Birds** Pheasant; **Dogs** Avail

400 Yeager Rd., Wellsville, PA 17365
(717) 741-7214 Reservations
15 mi. S of Harrisburg
Est 1991; **Acres** 365; **Type** Member/Avail, Corp.;
On Site Clubhouse, Lodging, Clays; **Shoots** Field;
Birds Quail, Pheasant, Chukar, Huns; **Dogs**
Avail/HDW; **Packages** 1/2 Day, 1-2 guns
See Our Ad Pg. 357

Shooting Preserve
RR1, Box 464, Warriors Mark, PA 16877
(814) 632-6680 Eric Gilliland
18 mi. SW of State College
Est 1994; **Acres** 1,000; **Type** Public, Member/Avail;
On Site Clubhouse, Meals, Clays; **Shoots** Field,
Tower; **Birds** Dove, Quail, Pheasant, Chukar, Turkey;
Dogs Avail/HDW; **Packages** 1/2 Day, 1-30 guns
○ Bird Processing   ○ Sporting Clays
○ Train Bird Dogs   ○ Loaner Guns
○ On-Site Pro Shop

Whitetail Enterprises
PO Box 1233, Conyngham, PA 18219
(717) 384-2314 Fran Curran
10 mi. NW of Hazleton
Acres 700; **Type** Public, Member/Avail; **On Site**
Clubhouse, Meals; **Shoots** Field, Tower; **Birds**
Quail, Pheasant, Chukar; **Dogs** Avail/HDW
○ NAGA/See Pg. 72

Windy Ridge
Game Farm & Kennels
RD#1, Box 59C, Tioga, PA 16946
(717) 835-5427 Robert Stewart/Tom Bower 7am-9pm
25 mi. S of Corning, NY
Est 1987; **Acres** 1,400; **Hunters/yr** 300; **Type**
Public, Member/Avail, Corp.; **On Site** Clubhouse,
Lodging, Meals, Clays; **Shoots** Field; **Birds** Quail,
Ruffed Grouse, Pheasant, Chukar, Turkey; **Dogs** >

Avail/HDW; **Packages** 1/2 Day, 1-20 guns
O NAGA/See Pg. 72
Return to the "Good Old Days!" We have the finest
near natural upland bird hunting in Northern Pennsylvania. Releasing pheasants, chukars and quail
9/15 through 4/15. Use your dog or ours. Moderate rates. Modern lodge available year round.
Deer, turkey and grouse hunting in PA season.
Skeet by reservation. Contact (717) 835-5427.

Wing & Shot Hunting Preserve
465 Camp Hebron Rd., Halifax, PA 17032
(717) 896-9077 Kirk Hartlaub 9-9
15 mi. NE of Harrisburg
Est 1990; **Acres** 240; **Hunters/yr** 400; **Type**
Member/Avail, Corp.; **Shoots** Field; **Birds** Quail,
Pheasant, Chukar; **Dogs** HDW O NAGA/See Pg. 72

RHODE ISLAND

Addieville East Farm
200 Pheasant Dr., Mapleville, RI 02839
(401) 568-3185 Geoff Gaebe 7am-8pm
20 mi. N of Providence
Est 1979; **Acres** 600; **Hunters/yr** 2,000; **Type**
Public, Member/Avail, Corp.; **On Site** Clubhouse,
Lodging, Meals, Clays; **Shoots** Field, Driven; **Birds**
Quail, Pheasant, Chukar, Huns; **Dogs** HDW
O NAGA/See Pg. 72

Peace Dale Shooting Preserve
441 Rose Hill Rd., Peace Dale, RI 02879
(401) 789-3730 Richie Frisella 8am-5pm
20 mi. S of Providence
Est 1950; **Acres** 200; **Type** Public; **On Site**
Clubhouse, Clays; **Shoots** Field, Tower; **Birds** Quail,
Pheasant, Chukar; **Dogs** Avail/HDW

SOUTH CAROLINA

4671 Timrod Rd., Bethune, SC 29009
(803) 475-4408 Grady Roscoe 7am-10pm
53 mi. NE of Columbia
Est 1995; **Acres** 1,100; **Type** Public, Member/Avail,
Corp.; **On Site** Clubhouse, Meals, Clays; **Shoots**
Field, Tower, Blinds; **Birds** Dove, Quail, Pheasant,
Chukar, Turkey, Ducks; **Dogs** Avail/HDW; **Packages**
1/2 Day, 1-12 guns

hunt Trophy Deer from tree stands over corn and
sunflower fields. Our three comfortable guest
lodges can accommodate up to 18 hunters. Sporting clays, too! Enjoy great hunting and Good Ol'
Southern Hospitality at Back Woods. Call today!

Bostick Plantation
Hunting Club
PO Box 728, Estill, SC 29918
(803) 625-4512 Joe Bostick 9-5
50 mi. NW of Savannah, GA
Est 1977; **Acres** 9,000; **Hunters/yr** 450; **Type**
Public; **On Site** Clubhouse, Lodging, Meals, Clays;
Shoots Field; **Birds** Quail, Turkey; **Dogs**
Avail/HDW; **Packages** 1/2 Day, 2-12 guns
See Our Ad Pg. 362

BACK WOODS
QUAIL CLUB

Rt. 3, Box 253F, Georgetown, SC 29440
(803) 546-1466 Rick Hemingway 7am-5pm
65 mi. N of Charleston
Est 1987; **Acres** 14,000; **Hunters/yr** 600; **Type**
Public, Member/Ltd, Corp.; **On Site** Clubhouse,
Lodging, Meals, Clays; **Shoots** Field; **Birds** Dove,
Quail, Turkey; **Dogs** Avail/HDW; **Packages** 1/2
Day, 2-18 guns O NAGA/See Pg. 72
Set on nearly 15,000 acres of open fields, timber
lands, and wooded areas, Back Woods offers sport-
ing variety few hunting operations can match. At
Back Woods you can hunt with us for days and
never work the same field twice—our five separate
hunting areas make that possible. You can also

Brays Island Plantation
PO Box 30, Sheldon, SC 29941
(803) 846-3100 Owner Services M-F, 9-5
50 mi. SW of Charleston
Est 1988; **Acres** 5,000; **Hunters/yr** 700; **Type**
Member/Avail; **On Site** Clubhouse, Lodging, Meals,
Clays; **Shoots** Field, Blinds; **Birds** Dove, Quail,
Chukar, Ducks; **Dogs** Avail/HDW; **Packages** 1/2
Day, 1-6 guns ○ NAGA/See Pg. 72

Broxton Bridge
Plantation
PO Box 97, Hwy. 601, Ehrhardt, SC 29081
(800) 437-4868 Jerry Varn, Jr. 7 am to 9 pm
60 mi. W of Charleston
Est 1965; **Acres** 7,000; **Hunters/yr** 600; **Type**
Public, Member/Avail; **On Site** Clubhouse, Lodging,
Meals, Clays; **Shoots** Field, Tower, Blinds; **Birds**
Dove, Quail, Pheasant, Turkey, Ducks; **Dogs**
Avail/HDW; **Packages** 1/2 Day, 2-12 guns
○ NAGA/See Pg. 72

See Our Ad Across

Buck Ridge Plantation
PO Box 2785, Orangeburg, SC 29116
(803) 531-8408 Michael C. Tourvilte
Type Member/Avail; **On Site** Lodging, Clays;
Shoots Field; **Birds** Pheasant, Chukar, Turkey
○ NAGA/See Pg. 72

Canvasback Kennel & Hunt Club
872 Gary Rd., Camden, SC 29020
(803) 432-4451 Felix Mock 8-6
35 mi. NE of Columbia
Est 1993; **Acres** 300; **Type** Public; **On Site** Meals;
Shoots Tower, Blinds; **Birds** Pheasant, Ducks; **Dogs**
Avail/HDW; **Packages** 1/2 Day, up to 8 guns
○ NAGA/See Pg. 72

Carter Shooting Preserve
2480 Hwy. 521 South, Sumter, SC 29153
(803) 481-2732 David C. Carter 8am-11pm
50 mi. E of Columbia
Est 1984; **Acres** 150; **Type** Public; **Shoots** Field;
Birds Quail; **Dogs** Avail/HDW; **Packages** 1/2 Day,
1-3 guns

Chelsea Plantation
Rt. 1, Box 310, Ridgeland, SC 29936
(803) 726-6887 Bill Apps 8am-5pm
35 mi. NE of Savannah, GA
Est 1872; **Acres** 5,300; **Hunters/yr** 200; **Type**
Public, Member/Avail; **On Site** Clubhouse, Lodging,
Meals, Clays; **Shoots** Field, Blinds; **Birds** Dove,
Quail, Ducks; **Dogs** Avail/HDW; **Packages** 1 Day,
4-8 guns ○ NAGA/See Pg. 72

Eleven Oaks Farm
Rt. 2, Box 318, Hartsville, SC 29550
(803) 332-9191 Stephen Beasley after 5pm
Near Columbia   **Est** 1995; **Acres** 600; **Type** Public;
On Site Clubhouse, Lodging; **Shoots** Field; **Birds**
Quail, Pheasant, Chukar; **Dogs** Avail/HDW;
Packages 1/2 Day, 1-8 guns ○ NAGA/See Pg. 72

Broxton Bridge Plantation

By: Peggy Boehmer

We recently had the pleasure of meeting G.D. "Jerry" Varn, who, along with his family, operates Broxton Bridge Plantation in Ehrhardt, South Carolina.

Towering almost seven feet tall, Jerry is easy to spot in a crowd. A charismatic guy with a heart as overwhelming as his stature, Jerry can quote chapter and verse from the bible or the constitution with equal eloquence. He is a true southern gentleman, and a shrewd businessman.

Broxton Bridge offers 7,000 acres of hunting land, and, according to its brochure, "Lasting memories for the serious sportsman." It even have a grass air strip. (Jerry, by the way, is a licensed pilot.)

Hunts

Broxton Bridge Plantation offers a wide variety of hunting opportunities—deer hunting, duck hunting over decoys, in addition to pheasants, chukar and, of course, quail.

Deer season opens August 15th, ends January 1st; bird hunting is available October 1st through March 31st. The deer hunting "package" includes meals and lodging and costs $225 per day. For groups of three or more the rate drops to $175 per day. There is a three day minimum.

The duck hunt—minimum four to a group, maximum, 20 (an individual can "join in" if he doesn't have enough guests)—is conducted from a blind using hand calls. The cost for a half-day (morning or after lunch) is $245, lunch included. Hunters have the opportunity to bag 8 mallards (the group divides the total bag evenly).

For safety's sake, only two hunters are allowed "on the ground" at one time during quail hunts. A half-day quail hunt (includes guide, dogs, 12 quail and bird cleaning) is priced at $160. An all day quail hunt includes all of that plus lunch and features 18 quail. The cost is $275. Broxton also offers an "ALL DAY SPECIAL" for $495. Guests hunt five different types of birds. The day begins with a duck hunt, then a trip through the sporting clays course. After lunch hunters have the opportunity to bag 2 pheasant, 3 chukar, and 6 quail. All game is cleaned and packaged.

Rooms to suit

Jerry offers his customers a wide variety of services and experiences. Guests can even choose accomodations to suit their style. There is a hunting lodge that I believe can accomodate 15-20 guests. The "hundred year old" lodge is comfortable (right down to the air conditioning) and rustic . Accomodations start at $30.

Hunting guests who prefer luxury can stay at "Ehrhardt Hall" (a restored mansion next to Jerry's house in town, about 5 miles from the plantation.), offering "Bed & Breakfast" style accomodations in spacious rooms with private bath, fireplaces, remote television and VCR's. The rate is $55 per night or $80 for two people in one room. (Continental breakfast is included.) Broxton also offers a "Victorian Cottage" across the street for $35 single, $65 double.

Sporting clays

At Broxton you can shoot one of four sporting clays ranges (25 shots each, for $10) or all four courses (100 shots for $35). (One course is named the "Dan Carlisle". after the champion shooter who designed it.) Broxton also has a 65 foot tower that offers a variety of shots, including one that simulates mallards "settling in" around decoys and another shot very similar to dove shooting.

Jerry requires a 50% deposit (non-refundable, but it may be transferred or rescheduled with 3 weeks prior notice). Broxton accepts Visa, Mastercard, and American Express. Jerry and his fine family offer quite a unique and extremely attractive hunting/outdoor experience. Call (1-800-437-HUNT) for information and reservations.

Graham & Carroll Shooting Preserve
PO Box 37, Smoaks, SC 29481
(803) 562-2574 John Graham
50 mi. NW of Charleston
Acres 400; **Hunters/yr** 150; **Type** Member/Avail;
On Site Clubhouse, Lodging, Meals, Clays; **Shoots**
Field; **Birds** Dove, Quail, Turkey; **Dogs** Avail/HDW;
Packages 1/2 Day, 1-3 guns ○ NAGA/See Pg. 72

Groton Plantation
Rt. 1, Box 98, Luray, SC 29932
(803) 625-4160 Robert Winthrop, II 8am-6pm
10 mi. W of Estill
Est 1975; **Acres** 23,000; **Hunters/yr** 200; **Type**
Member/Avail; **On Site** Clubhouse, Lodging, Meals;
Shoots Field; **Birds** Quail; **Dogs** Avail

Jack Island Gun Club
2602 Mullet Hall Rd., John's Island, SC 29455
(803) 729-3541 Sidi Limehouse
25 mi. S of Charleston
Acres 3,500; **On Site** Clubhouse, Lodging, Meals;
Shoots Field; **Birds** Dove, Quail, Ducks; **Dogs**
Avail/HDW; **Packages** 1/2 Day, 1-20 guns
See Our Ad Pg. 361

Little River Plantation
PO Box 1129, Abbeville, SC 29620
(803) 391-2300 Jim & John Edens 8am-9pm
54 mi. N of Augusta
Est 1980; **Acres** 4,200; **Hunters/yr** 400; **Type**
Public, Member/Avail, Corp.; **On Site** Clubhouse,
Lodging, Meals, Clays; **Shoots** Field; **Birds** Dove,
Quail, Pheasant, Chukar, Turkey, Ducks; **Dogs**
Avail/HDW; **Packages** 1/2 Day, 1-20 guns
DESIGN YOUR OWN HUNT! At Little River Planta-
tion flexibility is the key: You tell us what
gamebirds you want to hunt and how many—our
top-notch guides and well-trained dogs will do the
rest. Wild and liberated bird shooting available on
several thousand acres of prime wildlife habitat.
Spacious lodge and home-cooked meals. Sporting
clays course. Deer and turkey hunting, too.
Call today!
See Our Ad Pg. 365

Moree's Sportsman's Preserve
PO Box 118, Society Hill, SC 29593
(803) 378-4831 Gus Tucker 8:30 am to 5 pm
40 mi. SW of Columbia
Acres 1,000; **Type** Public; **On Site** Clubhouse;
Shoots Field, Blinds; **Birds** Quail, Pheasant, Chukar,
Ducks; **Dogs** Avail/HDW; **Packages** 1/2 Day, up to
4 guns ○ NAGA/See Pg. 72

Norfolk Southern Railroad
PO Box 27, Dorchester, SC 29437
(803) 563-5720 J.I. Chapman
Type Member/Avail; **Shoots** Field; **Birds** Quail,
Chukar, Turkey, Ducks ○ NAGA/See Pg. 72

Oak Ridge Hunting Preserve
1002 Hatchaway Bridge Rd., Aiken, SC 29803

(803) 648-3489 Clarence Chapman
25 mi. E of Augusta
Est 1966; **Acres** 5,000; **Type** Public; **On Site**
Clubhouse, Meals; **Shoots** Field; **Birds** Dove, Quail,
Turkey; **Dogs** Avail/HDW; **Packages** 1/2 Day, up
to 12 guns ○ NAGA/See Pg. 72

The Oaks Gun Club, Ltd.
Rt. 2, Box 196A, Georgetown, SC 29440
(803) 527-1861 Heyward Talley Anytime
48 mi. N of Charleston
Est 1987; **Acres** 2,000; **Type** Member/Avail, Corp.;
On Site Clubhouse, Clays; **Shoots** Field, Blinds;
Birds Quail, Pheasant, Ducks; **Dogs** Avail
○ NAGA/See Pg. 72

Quail Trough
Hunting Preserve
2032 Edgefield Hwy., Aiken, SC 29801
(803) 648-5483 Dennis Willing
50 mi. W of Colombia
Est 1994; **Acres** 450; **Type** Public, Member/Avail;
On Site Lodging; **Shoots** Field; **Birds** Dove, Quail,
Chukar, Turkey; **Dogs** Avail/HDW; **Packages** 1/2
Day, 1-12 guns
See Our Ad Pg. 366

River Bend
Sportsman's Resort
PO Box 279, Fingerville, SC 29338
(803) 592-1348 Ralph N. Brendle 8am-5pm
15 mi. NW of Spartanburg
Est 1985; **Acres** 535; **Hunters/yr** 3,000; **Type**
Public, Member/Avail, Corp.; **On Site** Clubhouse,
Lodging, Meals, Clays; **Shoots** Field, Tower; **Birds**
Quail, Pheasant, Chukar; **Dogs** Avail/HDW;
Packages 1/2 Day, 1-36 guns ○ NAGA/See Pg. 72
○ Hunting License   ○ Airport Pickup
○ Bird Processing   ○ Kennel Bird Dogs
○ Sporting Clays   ○ Shooting Instruction
○ Loaner Guns   ○ Brochure Available

Round O Kennel & Quail
Rt. 1, Box 296, Round O, SC 29474
(803) 835-5532 John Agee
Type Public, Member/Avail; **Shoots** Field; **Birds**
Quail ○ NAGA/See Pg. 72

Sandhill Sportsman's Club
421 Tap Harley Rd., Swansea, SC 29160
(803) 568-3126 Gene Jeffcoat
21 mi. S of Columbia
Acres 4,200; **Hunters/yr** 82; **Type** Public,
Member/Avail; **On Site** Clubhouse, Lodging, Meals,
Clays; **Shoots** Field; **Birds** Dove, Quail, Turkey;
Dogs Avail; **Packages** 1/2 Day, 2-3 guns

Sardis Shooting Preserve
4142 Sardis Hwy., Timmonsville, SC 29161
(803) 346-2497 J.D. Matthews
Type Member/Avail; **Birds** Chukar ○ NAGA/See Pg. 72

Sassafras Farm, Inc.
PO Box 8044, Greenville, SC 29604

(803) 232-1050 J.B. Gowan
Type Member/Avail;   **Shoots** Field;   **Birds** Quail
○ NAGA/See Pg. 72

Singletree Hunting Plantation
Rt. 1, Box 564, Clinton, SC 29325
(803) 833-5477 C.C. May
55 mi. NW of Columbia
Est 1982;   **Acres** 1,700;   **Type** Public, Member/Avail;
On Site Clubhouse, Lodging, Meals, Clays;   **Shoots**
Field, Tower;   **Birds** Dove, Quail, Pheasant, Chukar,
Turkey, Ducks, Geese;   **Dogs** Avail/HDW;   **Packages**
1/2 Day, 2-15 guns ○ NAGA/See Pg. 72

South Carolina
Outdoor Shooting
371 Cedar Branch Road, Windsor, SC 29856
(803) 648-5132 Richard Sherman 9 to 5
17 mi. E of Augusta, GA
Acres 400;   **Type** Public, Member/Avail;   **On Site**
Clubhouse, Meals, Clays;   **Shoots** Field, Tower;
Birds Dove, Pheasant, Chukar;   **Dogs** Avail/HDW;
Packages 1/2 Day, 2-12 guns
See Our Ad Pg. 365

Springrove
Shooting Preserve
PO Box 397, St. Stephen, SC 29479
(803) 567-3830 David Shealy
40 mi. N of Charleston
Est 1971;   **Acres** 1,500;   **Hunters/yr** 1,200;   **Type**
Public;   **On Site** Clubhouse, Lodging, Meals, Clays;
Shoots Field;   **Birds** Quail, Pheasant, Chukar;   **Dogs**
Avail/HDW;   **Packages** 1/2 Day, 1-16 guns

Tinker Creek
Shooting Preserve
Rt. 2, Box 76, Williston, SC 29853
(803) 266-4840 Gregg or Roger Bates 7pm-10pm
40 mi. E of Augusta, GA
Est 1990;   **Acres** 1,500;   **Hunters/yr** 300;   **Type**
Public, Member/Avail, Corp.;   **On Site** Clubhouse,
Lodging, Meals, Clays;   **Shoots** Field;   **Birds** Dove,
Quail, Chukar, Turkey;   **Dogs** Avail/HDW;   **Packages**
1/2 Day, 1-8 guns
See Our Ad Pg. 365

Tri-State Hunting Club
PO Box 101, Estill, SC 29918
(803) 625-4009 Tommy Rhodes
60 mi. N of Savannah
Type Public, Member/Avail;   **Birds** Turkey

"Say you saw it in Wing & Clay!"

The publication of Wing & Clay wouldn't be
possible without the support of hundreds of
shotgun industry companies listed and
advertising in this edition.

Whenever you contact one of these
companies, please remember to tell them
that you benefitted from the information
you found here. And don't forget to say:
"I saw it in Wing & Clay."

SOUTH DAKOTA

ALP Hunting
Rt. 2, Box 311, Elkton, SD 57026
(605) 542-5461 Adolph/LaVonne Peterson
Est 1990; **Acres** 640; **Hunters/yr** 300; **Type**
Public; **On Site** Clubhouse, Lodging, Meals, Clays;
Shoots Field; **Birds** Pheasant; **Dogs** Avail/HDW;
Packages 1 Day, 1-35 guns

Michael & Nola Ambur
HC80, Box 14, Presho, SD 57568
(605) 895-2281 Michael Ambur Before 8am, After 10
50 mi. S of Pierre
Est 1985; **Acres** 4,500; **Type** Public; **On Site**
Clubhouse; **Shoots** Field; **Birds** Pheasant, Prairie
Chicken, Sharp Tail Grouse; **Dogs** Avail/HDW;
Packages 2 Days, 1-10 guns

Audiss Hunting Service
RR2, Box 61, Dallas, SD 57529
(605) 835-9439 Cecil Audiss
105 mi. W of Gregory
Acres 2,000; **Type** Public; **On Site** Clubhouse,
Lodging, Meals; **Shoots** Field; **Birds** Dove,
Pheasant, Sharp Tail Grouse; **Dogs** Avail; **Packages**
1 Day

B&B Guide Service
1803 Flag Mountain Dr., Pierre, SD 57501
(605) 224-4381 Bruce Baker Evening
from Pierre
Est 1989; **Acres** 10,000; **Type** Public; **On Site**
Lodging, Meals; **Shoots** Field, Blinds, Boat; **Birds**
Pheasant, Ducks, Geese; **Dogs** Avail/HDW

Bass Pheasant Hunting
R-2, Box 15, Kimball, SD 57355
(605) 778-6842 Jim & Patsy Bass
120 mi. W of Sioux Falls
Est 1989; **Acres** 640; **Hunters/yr** 750; **Type**
Public; **On Site** Clubhouse, Lodging; **Shoots** Field;
Birds Pheasant; **Dogs** HDW; **Packages** 1/2 Day,
1-20 guns

Big Bend Ranch
1301 N. 4th St., Aberdeen, SD 57401
(605) 229-3035 Alex Falk
28 mi. SE of Pierre
Est 1955; **Acres** 10,000; **Type** Public,
Member/Avail, Corp.; **On Site** Clubhouse, Lodging,
Meals, Clays; **Shoots** Field, Blinds; **Birds** Pheasant,
Huns, Prairie Chicken, Sharp Tail Grouse, Ducks,
Geese; **Dogs** Avail/HDW; **Packages** 2 Days, 1-16
guns   O NAGA/See Pg. 72
O Orvis Endorsed Lodge
See Our Ads Below & Pg. 371

Biggins Hunting Service

Box 1, RR3, Gregory, SD 57533
(605) 835-8518 Gregg Biggins Anytime
145 mi. SW of Sioux Falls
Est 1980; **Acres** 12,000; **Hunters/yr** 100; **Type**
Public, Member/Avail, Corp.; **On Site** Clubhouse,
Lodging, Meals; **Shoots** Field; **Birds** Dove, Ruffed
Grouse, Pheasant, Chukar, Turkey, Prairie Chicken,
Sharp Tail Grouse, Geese; **Dogs** Avail/HDW;
Packages 2 Days, 1-40 guns
See Our Ad Across

Bush's Goose Camp

18279 283 Ave., Pierre, SD 57501
(605) 264-5496 Jeff Bush 8-10pm
25 mi. NW of Pierre
Est 1930; **Acres** 7,000; **Hunters/yr** 200; **Type**
Public, Member/Avail, Corp.; **On Site** Clubhouse,
Lodging, Meals, Clays; **Shoots** Field, Driven, Blinds,
Boat; **Birds** Pheasant, Huns, Ducks, Geese; **Dogs**
Avail/HDW; **Packages** 1/2 Day, 3-20 guns
See Our Ad Below

Circle CE Ranch

RR5, Box 98, Dixon, SD 57533
(605) 835-8281 Dick & Sally Shaffer Anytime
145 mi. W of Sioux Falls
Est 1988; **Acres** 3,000; **Type** Public; **On Site**
Clubhouse, Lodging, Meals; **Shoots** Field; **Birds**
Pheasant; **Dogs** Avail/HDW; **Packages** 3 Days, up
to 8 guns ○ NAGA/See Pg. 72

Circle H Ranch

PO Box 88038, Sioux Falls, SD 57105
(605) 336-2111 Peter Hegg 8-6
8 mi. S of Gregory
Est 1990; **Acres** 3,000; **Type** Public; **On Site**
Clubhouse, Lodging, Meals, Clays; **Shoots** Field;
Birds Dove, Pheasant; **Dogs** Avail/HDW; **Packages**
2 Days, 3-20 guns

Cocks Unlimited

RR2, Box 29, Gregory, SD 57533
(605) 835-8479 Bruce/Alice Shaffer
180 mi. SW of Sioux Falls
Est 1981; **Acres** 6,000; **Hunters/yr** 125; **Type**
Public; **On Site** Clubhouse, Lodging, Meals; **Shoots**
Field; **Birds** Dove, Pheasant, Prairie Chicken, Sharp
Tail Grouse, Ducks, Geese; **Dogs** Avail/HDW;
Packages 1 Day, 5-20 guns

Connie Farms Inc.

HCR57, Box 38, Ideal, SD 57541
(605) 842-2904 Wayne L. Lapsley
55 mi. SE of Pierre
Est 1980; **Acres** 3,000; **Hunters/yr** 200; **Type**
Public; **On Site** Clubhouse, Lodging, Meals; **Shoots**
Field; **Birds** Pheasant; **Dogs** Avail/HDW; **Packages**
1 Day, 1-20 guns ○ NAGA/See Pg. 72

Dakota Dream Hunts, Inc.

Rt. 2, Box 17, Arlington, SD 57212
(605) 983-5033 Doug/Richard Converse Anytime
65 mi. NW of Sioux Falls
Est 1979; **Acres** 1,140; **Type** Public, Member/Avail;
On Site Clubhouse, Lodging, Meals, Clays; **Shoots**
Field, Blinds; **Birds** Dove, Pheasant, Huns, Snipe,
Ducks, Geese; **Dogs** Avail/HDW; **Packages** 1 Day,
1-30 guns ○ NAGA/See Pg. 72

Dakota Expeditions

HC64, Box 109, Miller, SD 57362
(605) 853-2545 Clint Smith After 6pm
63 mi. E of Pierre
Est 1980; **Acres** 600; **Hunters/yr** 300; **Type**
Public, Member/Avail, Corp.; **On Site** Clubhouse,
Lodging, Meals, Clays; **Shoots** Field; **Birds** Dove,
Pheasant, Chukar, Huns, Turkey, Prairie Chicken, Sharp
Tail Grouse, Ducks, Geese; **Dogs** Avail/HDW;
Packages 1 Day ○ NAGA/See Pg. 72

ENJOY THE HUNT
OF THE RINGNECK

Come to South Dakota and enjoy a full service hunt!

Pheasant · Hungarian
Deer · Chukar
Turkey · Ducks

- Professional guides & hunting dogs
- Shells, targets & hunting licenses
- Lodging with meals & all beverages
- Professional bird processing
- Transportation to/from airport and field

Overlooking the Cheyenne River, our spacious lodge offers first-class accommodations and scenic views of the Black Hills. Visit us soon and enjoy some of the finest wingshooting imaginable.

· Orvis Endorsed ·

Call or write Tom Lauing:

1-800-622-3603

HC 56, Box 90, Oral, SD 57766

Dakota Hills Private
Shooting Preserve
HC56, Box 90, Oral, SD 57766
(800) 622-3603 Tom Lauing
60 mi. S of Rapid City Airport
Est 1988; **Acres** 6,000; **Hunters/yr** 150; **Type** Public; **On Site** Clubhouse, Lodging, Meals, Clays; **Shoots** Field, Driven, Blinds; **Birds** Dove, Pheasant, Chukar, Huns, Turkey, Sharp Tail Grouse, Ducks; **Dogs** Avail/HDW; **Packages** 1 Day, 1-14 guns
See Our Ad Left

Dakota Hunting Farms
RR1, Box 100, Hecla, SD 57446
(800) 356-5281 Tim or Julie Mertz
40 mi. NE of Aberdeen
Est 1985; **Acres** 20,000; **Hunters/yr** 200; **Type** Public; **On Site** Clubhouse, Lodging, Meals, Clays; **Shoots** Field, Driven, Blinds; **Birds** Dove, Pheasant, Turkey, Ducks, Geese; **Dogs** Avail/HDW; **Packages** 1 Day, 1-40 guns

Dakota Pheasant Hunt
Box 108, Warner, SD 57479
(605) 226-3474 Larry Braun
Acres 1,100; **Hunters/yr** 30; **On Site** Meals; **Shoots** Field; **Birds** Pheasant, Ducks, Geese; **Dogs** Avail

Dakota Ridge
RR2, Box 67, Altamont, SD 57226
(605) 874-2813 Charles Shomaker noon & 8pm
95 mi. N of Sioux Falls
Est 1988; **Acres** 2,500; **Hunters/yr** 200; **Type** Public; **On Site** Clubhouse, Lodging, Meals, Clays; **Shoots** Field, Blinds; **Birds** Pheasant, Chukar, Huns, Ducks, Geese; **Dogs** Avail/HDW; **Packages** 1/2 Day, 1-20 guns O NAGA/See Pg. 72

Etzkorn's Goose Camp
HCR531, Box 39, Pierre, SD 57501
(605) 875-3338 Terry Etzkorn
Type Public; **On Site** Meals; **Birds** Pheasant, Ducks, Geese

Folan Ranch
RR1, Box 128, Plankinton, SD 57368
(605) 942-7228 Bill Folan
90 mi. W of Sioux Falls
Acres 2,000; **Type** Public; **On Site** Clubhouse, Lodging; **Shoots** Field; **Birds** Pheasant, Ducks; **Dogs** Avail/HDW; **Packages** 1 Day, 1-8 guns

Forester Ranches
PO Box 102, Oacoma, SD 57365
(800) 982-6841 John Forester
125 mi. W of Sioux Falls
Est 1967; **Acres** 70,000; **Type** Public; **On Site** Lodging, Meals; **Shoots** Field; **Birds** Dove, Quail, Pheasant, Huns, Turkey, Prairie Chicken, Sharp Tail Grouse, Ducks, Geese; **Dogs** Avail/HDW; **Packages** 3 Days, up to 6 guns O NAGA/See Pg. 72

Orvis Discovers A Star: *South Dakota's Big Bend Ranch*

Pierre, SD - The world's best hotels rate 5 Stars from Mobil...the best restaurants, 3 Stars from Michelin...and the very best hunting lodges an endorsement from The Orvis Company. So it came as no surprise when an operation as rich in hunting tradition as Big Bend Ranch won a role in Orvis's star-studded cast of Endorsed Wingshooting Lodges.

Hunting the wily South Dakota Ringneck.

Orvis Endorsed

Orvis, America's oldest mail order company, created its Wingshooting Lodge Program to help clients find the best bird-shooting experiences in the country. "To qualify for the program, you have to meet stringent criteria established by Orvis," says Big Bend Ranch owner-operator Alex Falk. "First and foremost, you have to offer a complete and totally uncompromising bird hunting experience. But just as important," he adds, "is the quality of the lodging, dining and service."

Big Bend, a sprawling hunting paradise along the scenic Missouri River near Pierre, South Dakota, has clearly mastered both sides of the Orvis equation. Here, world class wingshooting—upland game and waterfowl—is the rule rather than the exception. In fact, the Ranch has been cited by knowledgeable hunters as the #1 Canada Goose hunting location in the world and has hosted the Annual South Dakota Governor's Pheasant Hunt for the past several years.

Spectacular hunting & shooting

Falk traces much of his success to aggressive habitat management. The Ranch's varied terrain includes farm fields, CRP, shelterbelts and river breaks where Ringneck Pheasant and Hungarian Partridge predominate, but coveys of Prairie Chicken and Sharptail Grouse are also encountered.

Big Bend Ranch is renowned for spectacular waterfowl pass and field shooting. Canada Geese are the primary waterfowl species but large flights of Northern mallards, White Front, Snow and Blue Geese are also seen frequently.

Throughout the hunting season guests begin the day with a big country style breakfast and then, in September and October, set off in pursuit of upland game—Hungarian Partridge, Sharptail Grouse or Prairie Chicken. Or, if they prefer, they can enjoy decoying Northern Mallards into one of Big Bend Ranch's many ponds. In November and December, early morning hunters can experience the finest Canada Goose hunting imaginable.

Morning hunts are followed by a break for a hearty home cooked lunch and then a trip afield to hunt the wily South Dakota Ringneck Pheasant. After a challenging but invariably successful pheasant hunt, many sportsman opt to return to the duck or goose blinds, while some head for the Ranch's private trout pond.

World class service

Big Bend's comfortable lodge is the perfect spot to reflect on a great day in the field and to anticipate a fine evening meal. Personal attention, service and hospitality are a hallmark at Big Bend. The Ranch staff is experienced, professional and attentive to their guests' every need.

Expert guides and professionally trained dogs earn their share of accolades from hunters at Big Bend. "We specialize in small groups," says Falk, "and we're always happy to customize a hunt to our guests' needs."

Big Bend is located 28 miles southeast of Pierre, South Dakota's capital. The Pierre airport has a 6800 foot airstrip with full service FBO. If you're interested in adding Big Bend's spectacular outdoor experience and hospitality to your memories, contact **Alex or Annie Falk, Big Bend Ranch 1301 N. 4th St., Aberdeen, SD 57401; Hunting Season:(605) 875-3445 or (605) 229-3035.**

Fort Randall
PO Box 459, Lake Andes, SD 57356
(605) 337-2301 J.A. Tonelli
115 mi. SW of Sioux Falls
Est 1965; **Acres** 1,300; **Hunters/yr** 60; **Type**
Public; **On Site** Clubhouse, Lodging, Meals; **Shoots**
Field, Blinds; **Birds** Dove, Pheasant, Prairie Chicken,
Sharp Tail Grouse, Ducks, Geese; **Dogs** Avail/HDW;
Packages 2 Days, 3-7 guns ○ NAGA/See Pg. 72

Funkrest Hunting Preserve
RR3, Box 167, Madison, SD 57042
(800) 351-1477 Don or Bonnie Funk 9-dusk
50 mi. NW of Sioux Falls
Est 1985; **Acres** 800; **Hunters/yr** 300; **Type**
Public, Member/Avail, Corp.; **On Site** Clubhouse,
Lodging, Meals, Clays; **Shoots** Field; **Birds**
Pheasant, Chukar, Turkey; **Dogs** Avail/HDW
○ NAGA/See Pg. 72

Great Plains Hunting
RR#2, Box 33, Wessington, SD 57381
(605) 883-4526 Clyde L. Zepp Evenings
22 mi. W of Huron
Est 1990; **Acres** 5,000; **Type** Public, Member/Avail;
On Site Clubhouse, Lodging, Meals; **Shoots** Field;
Birds Dove, Pheasant, Huns, Prairie Chicken, Sharp Tail
Grouse, Ducks; **Dogs** Avail/HDW; **Packages** 1 Day,
1-10 guns

Haines Hunting Service
RR1, Box 18, Gregory, SD 57533
(605) 835-9280 Edward Haines
90 mi. SE of Pierre
Acres 7,500; **Type** Public; **On Site** Clubhouse,
Lodging, Meals; **Shoots** Field; **Birds** Pheasant,
Prairie Chicken, Sharp Tail Grouse, Ducks, Geese;
Dogs HDW; **Packages** 2 Days, 1-10 guns

Hidden Valley Hunting Club
HC56, Box 51, Oral, SD 57766
(605) 424-2895 Bob Anderson Daytime
50 mi. S of Rapid City

Est 1985; **Acres** 640; **Type** Public, Corp.; **On Site**
Meals, Clays; **Shoots** Field; **Birds** Dove, Pheasant,
Ducks; **Dogs** Avail/HDW; **Packages** 1 Day, 1-6 guns

High Brass, Inc.
RR1, Box 4X, Chamberlain, SD 57325
(605) 734-6047 Tom Koehn Early morning/evening
120 mi. W of Sioux Falls
Est 1980; **Acres** 50,000; **Hunters/yr** 300; **Type**
Public; **On Site** Meals; **Shoots** Field; **Birds**
Pheasant, Prairie Chicken, Sharp Tail Grouse, Geese;
Dogs Avail/HDW; **Packages** 3 Days, 1-20 guns
○ NAGA/See Pg. 72

High Plains Game Ranch
HCR76, Box 192, Nisland, SD 57762
(605) 257-2365 Randy Vallery 7am-8pm
55 mi. N of Rapid City
Est 1986; **Acres** 1,280; **Hunters/yr** 200; **Type**
Public; **On Site** Clubhouse, Lodging, Meals, Clays;
Shoots Field; **Birds** Pheasant, Chukar, Turkey;
Dogs Avail/HDW; **Packages** 1/2 Day, 1-15 guns
○ NAGA/See Pg. 72

Horseshoe K Ranch
RR1, Box 94, Kimball, SD 57355
(605) 778-6714 8pm
110 mi. W of Sioux Falls
Est 1982; **Acres** 2,400; **Hunters/yr** 30; **Type**
Public, Member/Avail; **On Site** Clubhouse, Lodging,
Meals; **Shoots** Field; **Birds** Dove, Ruffed Grouse,
Pheasant, Huns, Sharp Tail Grouse; **Dogs** Avail/HDW

Hunter's Haven
RR1, Box 25, New Underwood, SD 57761
(605) 754-6986 Noreen Gibson 8am-10pm
25 mi. E of Rapid City
Est 1989; **Acres** 2,550; **Type** Public; **On Site**
Lodging, Meals, Clays; **Shoots** Field, Driven; **Birds**
Pheasant, Turkey; **Dogs** Avail/HDW; **Packages** 1/2
Day, 1-10 guns

Ingall's Prairie Wildfowl Hunts
RR1, Box 111, Bryant, SD 57221
(605) 628-2327 Jim/Joyce Ingalls
100 mi. NW of Sioux Falls
Est 1980; **Acres** 2,500; **Hunters/yr** 250; **On Site**
Clubhouse, Lodging, Meals; **Shoots** Field, Blinds;
Birds Pheasant, Ducks, Geese; **Dogs** Avail/HDW;
Packages 1 Day, 1-15 guns ○ NAGA/See Pg. 72

James Valley Hunting Resort, Inc.
Rt. 1, Box 39, Utica, SD 57067
(605) 364-7468 Harold or Jan Klimisch Evenings
55 mi. SW of Sioux Falls
Est 1985; **Acres** 1,200; **Hunters/yr** 500; **Type**
Public, Member/Avail, Corp.; **On Site** Clubhouse,
Lodging, Meals, Clays; **Shoots** Field; **Birds** Quail,
Pheasant, Chukar, Turkey; **Dogs** Avail/HDW;
Packages 1/2 Day, 1-40 guns ○ NAGA/See Pg. 72

K&M Hunting
Rt. 3, Box 15, Plankinton, SD 57368
(605) 942-7516 Michael & Kathye Miller
85 mi. W of Sioux Falls
Est 1982; **Acres** 1,200; **Type** Public; **On Site**
Clubhouse, Lodging, Meals; **Shoots** Field; **Birds**
Pheasant, Chukar; **Dogs** Avail/HDW; **Packages** 1
Day, 1-12 guns

Lake's Byron Lodge
109 Bluebell Dr., Pierre, SD 57501
(605) 224-0569 Doug Lake
17 mi. NE of Huron
Acres 2,000; **Hunters/yr** 70; **Type** Public; **On
Site** Lodging, Meals; **Shoots** Field, Blinds; **Birds**
Pheasant, Huns, Sharp Tail Grouse, Ducks, Geese;
Dogs Avail

Lubber's Farms Hunting Service
Rt. 1, Box 119, Gregory, SD 57533
(605) 835-9134 Jim Lubbers
120 mi. SE of Pierre
Est 1987; **Type** Public; **On Site** Clubhouse,
Lodging, Meals; **Shoots** Field; **Birds** Quail,
Pheasant, Chukar, Turkey, Prairie Chicken, Sharp Tail
Grouse; **Dogs** Avail

Medicine Creek Pheasant Ranch, Inc.
PO Box 63, Vivian, SD 57576
(605) 683-6411 Mike Authier
30 mi. S of Pierre
Est 1986; **Acres** 4,000; **Type** Public; **On Site**
Clubhouse, Lodging, Meals, Clays; **Shoots** Field,
Blinds; **Birds** Pheasant, Prairie Chicken, Sharp Tail
Grouse, Ducks, Geese; **Dogs** Avail/HDW; **Packages**
2 Days, 1-8 guns

Morris Game Farm
Box 126, Artesian, SD 57314
(605) 527-2424 Thomas Morris
Type Public, Member/Avail; **On Site** Lodging;
Shoots Field; **Birds** Pheasant, Chukar
○ NAGA/See Pg. 72

Paul Nelson Farm
119 Hilltop Dr., PO Box 183, Gettysburg, SD 57442
(605) 765-2469 Paul Nelson
65 mi. NE of Pierre
Acres 8,000; **Type** Public; **On Site** Clubhouse,
Lodging, Meals, Clays; **Shoots** Field; **Birds**
Pheasant; **Dogs** Avail/HDW; **Packages** 3 Days, 1-20
guns
See Our Ad Pg. 375

• Wild Flush, Inc. •
Wild Flush offers some of the
finest upland game bird hunting left in North
America! From the cultivated row crops &
CRP fields of Eastern South Dakota to the
last great unbroken virgin prairie grasslands
of Central South Dakota, you'll enjoy hunting
for the wily ringneck pheasant, the ever
elusive sharptail grouse to the explosive hard-
flying Hungarian partridge. For the
waterfowl enthusiast, you'll be treated to
some of the best duck and goose hunting
imaginable within the heart of the prairie
pothole region and close proximity of the
mighty Missouri River.

At Wild Flush you will be treated
to the finest in western hospitality, with
professional guides dedicated to your
successful hunt, be it hunting with friends &
family or entertaining business guests. To
book a spectacular fall hunt or to get more
information, call or write, Terry Frederick.

*Wild Flush,Inc.,RR2, Box 75, Waubay, SD
57273 (800)599-2393*

P&R Hunting Lodge
Rt. 5, Box 117, Dallas, SD 57529
(605) 835-8050 Paul Taggart 8am-10pm
110 mi. SE of Pierre
Est 1964; **Acres** 20,000; **Hunters/yr** 300; **Type**
Public; **On Site** Clubhouse, Lodging, Meals, Clays;
Shoots Field; **Birds** Pheasant, Sharp Tail Grouse,
Geese; **Dogs** Avail/HDW; **Packages** 1/2 Day, 1-85
guns

Pearson's Hunting
Adventures, Inc.
HC74, 256, Forestburg, SD 57314
(800) 286-2514 Marvin R. Pearson
16 mi. SE of Huron
Est 1946; **Acres** 2,000; **Type** Public, Corp.; **On
Site** Clubhouse, Lodging, Meals, Clays; **Shoots** Field,
Driven, Blinds; **Birds** Dove, Quail, Pheasant, Huns,
Turkey, Sharp Tail Grouse, Ducks, Geese; **Dogs**
Avail/HDW; **Packages** 2 Days, 1-20 guns
○ NAGA/See Pg. 72

See Our Ad Pg. 372

Pheasant Haven Farms
Box 373, Wagner, SD 57380
(605) 384-3296 Dennis Kuhlman
120 mi. SW of Sioux Falls
Est 1986; **Acres** 2,500; **Hunters/yr** 50; **Type**
Public; **On Site** Lodging, Meals, Clays; **Shoots** Field;
Birds Pheasant, Chukar, Geese; **Dogs** Avail/HDW;
Packages 1 Day, 3-20 guns

Prairie Bird Paradise
1212 Rice St., Gregory, SD 57533
(605) 835-9522 Tom Falencik
30 mi. SW of Pierre
Acres 17,000; **Hunters/yr** 100; **Shoots** Field;
Birds Dove, Pheasant, Turkey, Prairie Chicken, Sharp
Tail Grouse, Ducks, Geese; **Dogs** Avail

Prairie Paradise Hunts
325 Crow, Pierre, SD 57501
(605) 224-5573 Verne Olson
30 mi. W of Pierre
Hunters/yr 200; **Type** Public; **On Site** Lodging,
Meals; **Shoots** Field; **Birds** Dove, Pheasant, Prairie
Chicken, Sharp Tail Grouse, Geese; **Dogs** Avail

Bob Priebe Pheasant Hunting Country
HC69, Box 36, Chamberlain, SD 57325
(605) 734-6153 Bob Priebe
140 mi. W of Sioux Falls
Est 1986; **Acres** 1,000; **Hunters/yr** 130; **Type**
Public; **On Site** Lodging, Meals; **Shoots** Field;
Birds Dove, Pheasant; **Dogs** Avail/HDW; **Packages**
1/2 Day, 1-20 guns

Ralph Erickson Hunting Preserve
RR1, Box 50, Humboldt, SD 57035
(605) 297-3561 Ralph Erickson Late evenings
15 mi. W of Sioux Falls
Est 1990; **Acres** 1,000; **Hunters/yr** 100; **Type**
Public; **On Site** Meals; **Shoots** Field; **Birds**
Pheasant; **Dogs** Avail/HDW; **Packages** 1/2 Day, up
to 12 guns

Don Reeves
Pheasant Ranch
Rt. 2, Box 30, White Lake, SD 57383
(605) 249-2693 Genevieve Reeves 7am-10pm
100 mi. W of Sioux Falls
Est 1984; **Acres** 1,270; **Hunters/yr** 400; **Type**
Public; **On Site** Lodging, Meals; **Shoots** Field;
Birds Pheasant; **Dogs** Avail/HDW

Ringnecks Unlimited
Rt. 1, Box 67A, Cresbard, SD 57435
(800) 645-3850 Jon Batteen Anytime
30 mi. NW of Redfield
Est 1976; **Acres** 3,000; **Type** Public; **On Site**
Lodging, Meals; **Shoots** Field; **Birds** Pheasant;
Dogs Avail/HDW; **Packages** 2 Days, 1-20 guns

Paul Nelson Farm
PHEASANT
◆ HUNTING ◆

A South Dakota Pheasant Hunting Experience
8,000 Acres of Prime Habitat

3-Day Premium Hunting Starting at $1,795
Includes everything except airfare

◆

95% Repeat Business
Specializing in corporate groups of up to 20

◆

HOST FARM - '91, '92, '93 South Dakota's Governor's Hunt

CALL Paul D. Nelson
◆ (605) 765-2469 ◆

P.O. Box 183 ◆ Gettysburg, SD 57442

Rocky Hills Hunting Club
PO Box 686, South Shore, SD 57263
(605) 756-4355 Vern Meyer
20 mi. from Watertown
Est 1994; **Acres** 975; **Type** Public; **On Site** Meals;
Shoots Field; **Birds** Dove, Pheasant; **Dogs**
Avail/HDW; **Packages** 1/2 Day

Rooster Roost Ranch

RR#2, Box 221, Mitchell, SD 57301
(605) 996-4676 Dean Strand 7-10pm
4 mi. SW of Mitchell
Est 1988; **Acres** 2,000; **Hunters/yr** 50; **Type**
Public; **On Site** Clubhouse, Lodging, Meals; **Shoots**
Field; **Birds** Dove, Pheasant, Huns, Ducks; **Dogs**
Avail/HDW; **Packages** 1 Day, 1-10 guns
○ NAGA/See Pg. 72

Light hunting pressure at Rooster Ranch–we will
not book over 80 guests in any season–results in
some of the most fantastic hunting you've ever experienced. By keeping things "small" we can offer
uncomparable personalized service, including excellent home cooked farm meals and extremely
comfortable lodging. Our spacious and clean kennels are at your disposal, if you'd like to hunt with
your own dogs. Other South Dakota operations are
larger, but none offers better hunting or more reasonable prices. Call today.

S&S Hunting
RR1, Box 64, Burke, SD 57523
(605) 775-2262 Mary Ann Shaffer Late evenings
160 mi. W of Sioux Falls
Est 1984; **Acres** 1,000; **Hunters/yr** 100; **Type**
Public, Member/Avail; **On Site** Clubhouse, Lodging,
Meals, Clays; **Shoots** Field; **Birds** Quail, Pheasant,
Chukar, Huns, Turkey, Prairie Chicken, Sharp Tail Grouse;
Dogs Avail/HDW; **Packages** 1 Day, 3-10 guns

South Dakota Pheasant Hunts
RR1, Box 260, Gary, SD 57237
(605) 272-5608 William E. Stone
90 mi. N of Sioux Falls
Est 1985; **Acres** 800; **Type** Public; **Shoots** Field;
Birds Dove, Pheasant, Ducks, Geese; **Dogs**
Avail/HDW; **Packages** 1 Day, 1-10 guns

South Dakota
Pheasant Safaris
PO Box 27, Pierre, SD 57501
(619) 296-8533 Darwin Dapper Early am
20 mi. E of Pierre
Est 1980; **Acres** 10,000; **Hunters/yr** 125; **Type**
Public, Member/Avail, Corp.; **On Site** Clubhouse,
Lodging, Meals, Clays; **Shoots** Field, Blinds; **Birds**
Pheasant, Huns, Prairie Chicken, Sharp Tail Grouse,
Ducks, Geese; **Dogs** Avail/HDW; **Packages** 3 1/2
Days, 4-16 guns
See Our Ad Across

HUNT WILD
SOUTH DAKOTA
PHEASANTS • DUCKS • GEESE

3 FULL DAYS OF HUNTING
$1950.00

Includes guides, accommodations, dogs, licenses, ammunition, gourmet meals, open bar, game cleaning and applicable taxes.
A first quality hunt with no itemized bill at days end.

Each day mallards over decoys on stock dams or out of our custom duck boats on big water, or Honker hunting from corn field pits. Pheasants and grouse at noon in cornfields, weed patches and tree strips. After hunting open bar, wines and outstanding dinners.

Private hunts for as few as 4 guns, for as large as 16.
A perfect corporate program.

SOUTH DAKOTA PHEASANT SAFARIS

P.O. Box 27, Pierre, SD 57501
(619) 296–8533
Brochures • Videos • References Available on Request

Stukel's
Birds
&
Bucks
OUTFITTERS & GUIDES

Stukel's Birds & Bucks

Rt. 1, Box 112W, Gregory, SD 57533
(605) 835-8941 Frank Stukel
90 mi. SE of Pierre
Est 1981; **Acres** 10,000; **Hunters/yr** 250; **Type**
Public; **On Site** Clubhouse, Lodging, Meals, Clays;
Shoots Field, Blinds; **Birds** Pheasant, Turkey, Sharp
Tail Grouse; **Dogs** Avail/HDW; **Packages** 2 Days,
up to 18 guns   ○ NAGA/See Pg. 72
○ Family Run Business   ○ Quality Clubhouse
○ Onsite Pro Shop   ○ Sporting Clays
○ Award Winning Habitat
See Our Ad Pg. 374

Swisher Hunting
RR2, Box 163, Groton, SD 57445
(605) 294-5860 Robert Swisher 11:30-1:30
25 mi. NE of Aberdeen Airport
Est 1986; **Acres** 2,000; **Hunters/yr** 150; **Type**
Public; **On Site** Clubhouse, Meals; **Shoots** Field;
Birds Dove, Pheasant, Huns, Ducks, Geese; **Dogs**
Avail/HDW; **Packages** 1/2 Day, 10-15 guns

Thunderstik Lodge
RR1, Box 10T, Chamberlain, SD 55459
(800) 888-1601 Chuck Ross M-F, 8-5
125 mi. W of Sioux Falls
Est 1988; **Acres** 8,000; **Hunters/yr** 300; **Type**
Public; **On Site** Clubhouse, Lodging, Meals; **Shoots**
Field, Blinds; **Birds** Pheasant, Ducks, Geese; **Dogs**
Avail/HDW; **Packages** 3 Days, 2-30 guns
○ NAGA/See Pg. 72

Tinker Kennels
3031 Sussex Pl., Pierre, SD 57501
(605) 224-5414 Bob Tinker
from Pierre
Est 1989; **Acres** 50,000; **Type** Public; **On Site**
Clubhouse, Lodging, Meals; **Shoots** Field, Blinds;
Birds Quail, Pheasant, Chukar, Huns, Turkey, Prairie
Chicken, Sharp Tail Grouse, Ducks, Geese; **Dogs**
Avail/HDW; **Packages** 1 Day, 1-5 guns

Valley West
Hunting Preserve

809 W. 10th St., Sioux Falls, SD 57104
(800) 424-2047 Daniel Stock/ Francis Phillips 8am-5pm
5 mi. W of Empire Mall at Sioux Falls
Est 1990; **Acres** 700; **Hunters/yr** 5,000; **Type**
Public, Member/Avail, Corp.; **On Site** Clubhouse,
Lodging, Meals, Clays; **Shoots** Field, Tower, Blinds;
Birds Pheasant; **Dogs** Avail/HDW; **Packages** 1/2
Day, 2-20 guns   ○ NAGA/See Pg. 72
See Our Ad Pg. 376

Wells Shooting Preserve
R1, Box 44, Oldham, SD 57051
(605) 854-3284 Dale E. Wells
65 mi. NW of Sioux Falls
Est 1945; **Acres** 1,100; **Hunters/yr** 600; **Type**
Public; **On Site** Clubhouse, Lodging, Meals; **Shoots**
Field; **Birds** Pheasant, Ducks, Geese; **Dogs**
Avail/HDW

Wild Flush, Inc.

RR2, Box 75, Waubay, SD 57273
(800) 599-2393 Mike Frederick 7am-7pm
20 mi. NW of Watertown
Est 1992; **Acres** 1,000; **Hunters/yr** 65; **Type**
Public, Member/Avail, Corp.; **On Site** Lodging,
Meals, Clays; **Shoots** Field, Blinds; **Birds** Dove,
Pheasant, Huns, Ducks, Geese; **Dogs** Avail/HDW;
Packages 1/2 Day, 1-20 guns   ○ NAGA/See Pg. 72
See Our Ad Pg. 373

Wild Wings
Box 149, Gregory, SD 57533
(605) 835-8391 Rick Johnson 9-5
160 mi. SE of Sioux Falls
Est 1987; **Acres** 3,000; **Hunters/yr** 200; **Type**
Public, Member/Avail; **On Site** Clubhouse, Lodging,
Meals, Clays; **Shoots** Field; **Birds** Pheasant, Turkey;
Dogs Avail/HDW; **Packages** 2 Days, 8-20 guns

Willow Creek Wildlife
HCR33, Box 24, Ft. Pierre, SD 57532
(605) 223-3154 Steve Stoeser Daytime
12 mi. W of Pierre
Est 1986; **Acres** 13,000; **Hunters/yr** 150; **Type**
Public, Member/Avail; **On Site** Clubhouse, Lodging,
Meals, Clays; **Shoots** Field, Blinds; **Birds** Dove,
Pheasant, Prairie Chicken, Sharp Tail Grouse, Geese;
Dogs Avail/HDW; **Packages** 1 Day, 1-20 guns

TENNESSEE

Arrowhead Hunt Club
PO Box 598, Whiteville, TN 38075
(901) 231-8684 Elmer Kahl
45 mi. E of Memphis
Est 1984; **Acres** 3,000; **Type** Public, Member/Avail;
On Site Clubhouse, Lodging, Meals, Clays; **Shoots**
Field, Tower, Driven; **Birds** Dove, Quail, Woodcock,
Pheasant; **Dogs** Avail/HDW; **Packages** 1/2 Day,
2-12 guns   ○ NAGA/See Pg. 72

Caryonah Hunting Lodge

Rt. 10, Box 264, Crossville, TN 38555
(615) 277-3113 Bobbie Jean Garrison 7am-10pm
14 mi. NW of Crossville — Off of I-40
Est 1950; **Acres** 2,000; **Type** Public; **On Site**
Clubhouse, Lodging, Meals; **Shoots** Field; **Birds**
Quail, Turkey; **Dogs** Avail; **Packages** 1 Day, 1-32
guns

Cedar Hill Shooting Preserve
714 S. Cumberland St., Morristown, TN 37814

(615) 587-6486 B.G. McFall/T. Newcomb
Acres 240; **Hunters/yr** 80; **Type** Public; **On Site**
Meals, Clays; **Shoots** Field; **Birds** Quail, Pheasant;
Dogs Avail

Crockett Pheasant Farm & Hunting
1213 Woodgate, Humboldt, TN 38343
(901) 784-5368 Van Holyfield After 5pm
75 mi. NE of Memphis
Est 1991; **Type** Public; **On Site** Clubhouse,Lodging,
Clays; **Shoots** Field; **Birds** Quail, Pheasant; **Dogs**
Avail/HDW; **Packages** 1/2 Day O NAGA/See Pg. 72

Deep Springs Sporting Clays & Hunting
850 Hid-A-Way, Dandridge, TN 37725
(615) 397-6617 Kerry Smith Anytime
15 mi. E of Knoxville
Est 1995; **Type** Public; **On Site** Clubhouse, Meals,
Clays; **Shoots** Field; **Birds** Quail, Pheasant; **Dogs**
Avail/HDW; **Packages** 1/2 Day, 1-5 guns

Dunaway Hunting & Fishing Club
600 Krystal Bldg., One Union Square, Chattanooga,
TN 37402
(615) 756-1202 Wilson P. Burton, Jr. 9 to 5
38 mi. N of Chattanooga
Est 1989; **Acres** 4,700; **Type** Member/Avail, Corp.;
On Site Clubhouse, Lodging, Clays; **Shoots** Field;
Birds Dove, Quail, Ruffed Grouse, Woodcock,
Pheasant, Turkey, Snipe; **Dogs** Avail/HDW;
Packages 1/2 Day, 1-2 guns

Estanaula Hunt Club
PO Box 26, Brownsville, TN 38012
(901) 772-9780 Harbert Mulherin
50 mi. NE of Memphis
Est 1977; **Acres** 6,000; **Type** Public; **On Site**
Clubhouse, Lodging, Meals, Clays; **Shoots** Field;
Birds Quail; **Dogs** Avail; **Packages** 1/2 Day

Falls Creek Hunt Club
HC69, Box 234, Spencer, TN 38585
(615) 946-2095 Frank Hanwright
85 mi. SE of Nashville **Est** 1989; **Acres** 280; **Type**
Public, Member/Avail; **On Site** Clubhouse, Lodging,
Meals, Clays; **Shoots** Field; **Birds** Quail, Pheasant,
Chukar; **Dogs** Avail/HDW

Goose Creek Hunting Preserve
659 Nicholson Rd., Jefferson City, TN 37760
(615) 397-7406 Tom Jenkins 6-9pm
35 mi. E of Knoxville
Est 1990; **Acres** 220; **Hunters/yr** 100; **Type**
Member/Avail; **Shoots** Field; **Birds** Quail, Pheasant;
Dogs HDW; **Packages** 1/2 Day, 1-3 guns

Grinders Switch Club
1608 Chickering Rd., Nashville, TN 37215
(615) 729-9732 Barry Claud M-F, 8-5
50 mi. SW of Nashville
Est 1990; **Acres** 2,000; **Type** Public, Member/Avail,
Corp.; **On Site** Clubhouse, Meals, Clays; **Shoots**
Field; **Birds** Dove, Quail, Pheasant; **Dogs**
Avail/HDW; **Packages** 1/2 Day, 2-16 guns

Hamilton's Resort
Rt. 1, Hornbeak, TN 38232
(901) 538-2325 Bonnie
80 mi. NE of Memphis **Est** 1945; **Acres** 1,300;
Type Public; **On Site** Lodging; **Shoots** Field, Blinds;
Birds Dove, Turkey, Snipe, Ducks, Geese; **Dogs** Avail;
Packages 1 Day, 2-30 guns

Honey Creek Hunting Preserve
Star Rt., Box 171, Allardt, TN 38504
(615) 879-9796 Royal D. Tompkins
87 mi. NW of Knoxville **Type** Public; **Shoots** Field;
Birds Quail, Pheasant, Chukar O NAGA/See Pg. 72

The Hunting Lodge
PO Box 381, Manchester, TN 37355
(615) 728-7260 Harry L. Taylor
75 mi. SE of Nashville
Est 1991; **Acres** 565; **Type** Public; **On Site**
Clubhouse, Lodging, Meals, Clays; **Shoots** Field;
Birds Quail, Pheasant, Chukar; **Dogs** Avail/HDW;
Packages 1/2 Day

Meadowbrook Game Farm
1600 Meadowbrook Dr., Westmoreland, TN 37186
(615) 888-2411 G.D. Denning
40 mi. N of Nashville
Est 1950; **Acres** 1,600; **Hunters/yr** 700; **Type**
Public, Member/Avail; **Shoots** Field; **Birds** Dove,
Quail, Pheasant, Chukar; **Dogs** Avail/HDW

Pheasant Creek Hunting Preserve
692 Huddleston Rd., Lascassas, TN 37085
(615) 286-2499 Jesse Dunaway Anytime
25 mi. E of Nashville **Acres** 410; **Type** Public,
Member/Avail; **On Site** Clubhouse, Clays; **Shoots**
Field, Tower; **Birds** Dove, Quail, Pheasant, Chukar,
Turkey, Ducks; **Dogs** Avail/HDW; **Packages** 1/2
Day, 1-12 guns O NAGA/See Pg. 72

Quail Valley Hunt Club
506 Bryant St., Shelbyville, TN 37160
(615) 685-4628 Jim Walker
50 mi. SE of Nashville
Est 1986; **Type** Public, Member/Avail, Corp.; **On
Site** Lodging, Clays; **Shoots** Field; **Birds** Quail,
Pheasant, Chukar; **Dogs** Avail/HDW; **Packages** 1/2
Day O NAGA/See Pg. 72

Quail Walk
1212 Evans Lane, Brownsville, TN 38012
(901) 772-3213 D. Clinton Evans
50 mi. NE of Memphis
Est 1990; **Acres** 200; **Hunters/yr** 200; **Type**
Public; **On Site** Clubhouse, Meals, Clays; **Shoots**
Field; **Birds** Quail, Pheasant, Chukar; **Dogs**
Avail/HDW; **Packages** 1/2 Day, 1-6 guns

Shaw Creek Shooting Preserve
2055 Burnett Rd., Williston, TN 38076
(901) 465-4530 Randy Reeves 9 to 5
29 mi. E of Memphis
Est 1988; **Acres** 900; **Type** Public; **On Site**
Clubhouse, Lodging, Clays; **Shoots** Field; **Birds**
Dove, Quail, Pheasant, Chukar; **Dogs** Avail/HDW;
Packages 1/2 Day, 2-9 guns

WINGS

TEXAS

74 Ranch Hunting Resort
5005 Riverway, Houston, TX 77056
(800) 874-7411 John Burdett 9am-5pm, cst
50 mi. S of San Antonio
Est 1987; **Acres** 27,000; **Hunters/yr** 100; **Type** Public, Member/Avail; **On Site** Clubhouse, Lodging, Meals, Clays; **Shoots** Field; **Birds** Dove, Quail, Turkey; **Dogs** Avail; **Packages** 1 Day
○ NAGA/See Pg. 72

Adobe Lodge Hunting Camp
4124 Sherwood Way, San Angelo, TX 76901
(915) 942-8040 Skipper Duncan
10 mi. SW of San Angelo
Est 1985; **Acres** 50,000; **Hunters/yr** 117; **Type** Public; **On Site** Clubhouse, Lodging, Meals; **Shoots** Field; **Birds** Turkey; **Dogs** Avail/HDW; **Packages** 31/2 Days, 1-8 guns

Blue Goose
HUNTING CLUB

Hunt the Texas Gulf Coast Prairies over large
white spreads for Snows, Blues, Ross,
Whitefronted, Lesser Canada Geese and Ducks.

Hunt Mexico for White Wing Dove and Quail.

All Hunts guided. Lodging, meals and
bird processing available.

Corporate Hunts our specialty
Over 40 years at the same location
Rated best by Texas Sportsman Magazine
Showcased on TNN *Great American Outdoors*
and *Classic Adventures*

For further information or reservations call or write:

JOHN FIELDS C/O BLUE GOOSE HUNTING CLUB
P.O. BOX M, Dept. W, ALTAIR, TEXAS 77412
PHONE: (409) 234-3597 FAX (409) 234-5188

Allen Ranches
574 Dana Lane, Houston, TX 77056
(713) 465-2298 Ranch Phone
100 mi. SW of Houston
Acres 1,000; **Type** Public, Member/Avail, Corp.;
On Site Clubhouse, Lodging, Clays; **Shoots** Field;
Birds Quail, Pheasant, Chukar; **Dogs** Avail/HDW;
Packages 1/2 Day, 2-20 guns
○ Bird Processing   ○ Loaner Guns
○ Bird Phone (512) 798-5768
○ Ranch Foreman (512) 798-4203
○ Serving Houston & San Antonio

L.D. Anderson
1802 Ave. Q, Lubbock, TX 79401
50 mi. SE of Lubbock
Acres 1,100; **Hunters/yr** 20; **Type** Member/Avail;
Shoots Field; **Birds** Pheasant, Chukar; **Dogs** Avail

B-Bar-B Ranch
Rt. 1, Box 457, Kingsville, TX 78363
(512) 296-3331 Luther or Patti Young
45 mi. SW of Corpus Christi
Est 1992; **Acres** 20,000; **Type** Public; **On Site** Clubhouse, Lodging, Meals, Clays; **Shoots** Field; **Birds** Dove, Quail, Turkey; **Dogs** Avail/HDW; **Packages** 1 Day, 4-16 guns

Bajio Ranch
PO Box 502, Fowlerton, TX 78021
(800) 528-8725 Warren Vecker
65 mi. S of San Antonio
Acres 600; **Type** Public; **On Site** Lodging; **Shoots** Field; **Birds** Quail; **Packages** 1 Day

Bar H Dude Ranch
Box 1191, Clarendon, TX 79226
(806) 874-2634 Frank Hommel
45 mi. SE of Amarillo
Acres 1,500; **Hunters/yr** 30; **Type** Public; **On Site** Lodging, Meals; **Shoots** Field, Blinds; **Birds** Dove, Quail, Chukar, Turkey; **Dogs** Avail

Bar K Hunting Lodge
10000 County Road 430, San Angelo, TX 76901
(915) 949-2229 Dale Bates
30 mi. W of San Angelo
Acres 5,000; **Type** Public; **On Site** Clubhouse, Lodging, Meals; **Shoots** Field; **Birds** Turkey; **Packages** 3 Days, 1-22 guns

Bay Prairie Outfitters
PO Box 35378, Houston, TX 77235
(800) 242-1374 Mike Ladnier
70 mi. SW of Houston
Type Public; **Shoots** Field, Blinds; **Birds** Dove, Ducks, Geese; **Dogs** Avail; **Packages** 1/2 Day, up to 4 guns

Big County Game Bird Farm
PO Box 1880, Abilene, TX 79604
(915) 677-0866 Norman Dozier
Type Public, Member/Avail; **Birds** Quail, Pheasant, Chukar

Black Creek Ranch

2523 Nacogdoches Rd., San Antonio, TX 78217
(210) 805-9600 Lee McClintick 9-5
58 mi. S of San Antonio
Est 1988; **Acres** 1,200; **Hunters/yr** 200; **Type**
Public; **On Site** Clubhouse, Lodging, Meals, Clays;
Shoots Field, Tower; **Birds** Dove, Quail, Pheasant,
Chukar, Huns, Turkey, Ducks; **Dogs** Avail/HDW;
Packages 1/2 Day, 2-16 guns ○ NAGA/See Pg. 72
See Our Ad Below

Blue Goose Hunting Club

PO Box M, Altair, TX 77412
(409) 234-3597 John R. Fields Anytime
50 mi. W of Houston
Est 1953; **Acres** 150,000; **Hunters/yr** 4,000;
Type Public; **On Site** Clubhouse, Lodging, Meals,
Clays; **Shoots** Field; **Birds** Dove, Quail, Pheasant,
Chukar, Ducks, Geese; **Dogs** Avail/HDW; **Packages**
1/2 Day, 4-100 guns
See Our Ad Across Left

Butch's Guide Service

2806 Patna, Katy, TX 77493
(713) 391-4381 Butch Waggoner
25 mi. W of Houston

Est 1970; **Acres** 9,000; **Hunters/yr** 1,500; **Type**
Public, Member/Avail; **On Site** Meals; **Shoots** Field;
Birds Dove, Quail, Pheasant, Chukar, Ducks, Geese;
Dogs Avail/HDW; **Packages** 1/2 Day

William Carl, Jr.

1640 Fountain View Dr., Houston, TX 77057
(713) 785-5788 W. Noble Carl Ext. 123
60 mi. SW of Houston
Acres 1,600; **Hunters/yr** 12; **Type** Member/Avail;
On Site Clubhouse, Lodging, Meals; **Shoots** Field,
Blinds; **Birds** Dove, Quail, Ducks, Geese

Caverhill Ranch

HCR81, Box 312, Junction, TX 76849
(915) 446-2448 John T. Fargason
100 mi. NW of San Antonio
Est 1987; **Acres** 640; **Hunters/yr** 30; **Type**
Public; **On Site** Clubhouse, Lodging; **Shoots** Field;
Birds Turkey; **Packages** 1/2 Day, 1-6 guns

Cedar Creek Ranch

Rt. 1, Box 84A, Rochelle, TX 76872
(915) 463-5547 Rawley Curry Anytime
30 mi. S of Brownwood
Est 1984; **Acres** 20,000; **Type** Public; **On Site**
Clubhouse, Lodging, Meals, Clays; **Shoots** Field;
Birds Dove, Quail, Turkey; **Dogs** Avail/HDW;
Packages 2 Days

Central Texas Hunts
Rt. 1, Box 52, Medina, TX 78055
(210) 589-7703 Tommy Thompson
55 mi. NW of San Antonio
Est 1982; **Acres** 100,000; **Type** Public; **On Site**
Lodging, Meals; **Shoots** Field; **Birds** Turkey

Central Texas
Shooting Reserve
Rt. 4, Box 288, Elgin, TX 78621
(512) 856-2200 Oscar Albert
40 mi. NE of Austin
Est 1988; **Acres** 500; **Hunters/yr** 350; **Type**
Public; **On Site** Clubhouse, Meals, Clays; **Shoots**
Field, Tower; **Birds** Quail, Pheasant, Chukar; **Dogs**
Avail/HDW; **Packages** 1/2 Day, 1-12 guns

Cinco Ranch
PO Box 55, El Indio, TX 78860
(210) 773-1131 Steve Robishaw
Type Public; **On Site** Lodging, Meals, Clays; **Birds**
Dove, Quail, Turkey; **Dogs** Avail

South   Coastal

Texas   Bend

- Exclusive hunts on 12,000 acres of private ranch
- Wild and release quail, dove, turkey, whitetail deer, feral hog
- Sporting clays and Quail Walk
- Dogs/handlers, guides, specially outfitted truck, 20 tower blinds
- Lake fishing, 9-hole golf course, 2 paved runways
- Spacious deluxe lodge, superb dining, open bar, lounge with fireplace, cable TV
- 45 minutes north of Corpus Christi

Call or Write for Brochure

Joan Rooke   P.O. Box 1035

(512) 543-4905   Refugio, TX 78377

Circle H Outfitters
2019 Cutter Dr., League City, TX 77573
(409) 935-9220 Scott & Gary Hickman 7am-10pm
45 mi. E of Houston
Est 1983; **Acres** 20,000; **Hunters/yr** 1,200; **Type**
Public, Member/Avail, Corp.; **On Site** Clubhouse,
Lodging; **Shoots** Field, Blinds, Boat; **Birds** Dove,
Quail, Snipe, Ducks, Geese; **Dogs** Avail/HDW;
Packages 1/2 Day, 1-40 guns

Circle Rocking N Ranch
PO Box 449, Texarkana, TX 75504
(903) 793-4647 Fred Norton
Shoots Field; **Birds** Quail

Clear Creek Gun Range
306 Crystal, League City, TX 77573
(713) 337-1722 Ernest Randall 1-8, T-Th, S/Su
20 mi. S of Houston
Est 1976; **Acres** 82; **Type** Public; **On Site**
Clubhouse, Meals, Clays;

Clear Creek Shooting Club
PO Box 744, Bellville, TX 77418
(409) 865-2689 David Charpiot 9-5
45 mi. NW of Houston
Est 1987; **Acres** 1,900; **Hunters/yr** 1,000; **Type**
Public; **On Site** Clubhouse, Lodging, Meals, Clays;
Shoots Field, Tower, Driven; **Birds** Dove, Quail,
Pheasant, Chukar; **Dogs** Avail/HDW; **Packages** 1/2
Day, 2-36 guns

Cold River Land & Cattle Co.
Rt. 2, Box 77C, San Juan, TX 78589
(210) 783-0870 Bobbie Brown Anytime
45 mi. NW of McAllen
Est 1971; **Acres** 13,000; **Hunters/yr** 200; **Type**
Public; **On Site** Clubhouse, Lodging, Meals, Clays;
Shoots Field; **Birds** Dove, Quail, Turkey; **Dogs**
Avail/HDW; **Packages** 2 Days, 2-24 guns

Cypress Valley Preserve
PO Box 162525, Austin, TX 78716
(512) 328-5279 Phillip C. Walker
25 mi. N of Austin
Est 1986; **Acres** 515; **Type** Member/Avail; **On
Site** Clubhouse, Lodging, Meals, Clays; **Shoots** Field,
Tower, Blinds; **Birds** Quail, Pheasant, Chukar, Ducks;
Dogs Avail/HDW; **Packages** 1/2 Day, 2-12 guns

Dancing Dogs Ranch & Lodge
PO Box 226, Wingate, TX 79566
(915) 743-2084 Patty or Bob Curnutte 8am-5pm
40 mi. SW of Abilene
Est 1988; **Acres** 7,000; **Hunters/yr** 100; **Type**
Public; **On Site** Clubhouse, Lodging, Meals, Clays;
Shoots Field; **Birds** Dove, Quail, Turkey, Ducks;
Dogs Avail/HDW; **Packages** 2 Days, 2-8 guns

Wayne or Jane Daniels
Rt. 5, Box 51952, Winnsboro, TX 75494
(903) 365-2610
120 mi. NE of Dallas
Acres 500; **Hunters/yr** 100; **Type** Public; **Shoots**
Field; **Birds** Quail; **Dogs** Avail

Deer Run Lodge

8307 Meadow Rd, Suite 2053, Dallas, TX 75321
(405) 367-2687 Mike Clancy
100 mi. NE of Dallas
Est 1991; **Acres** 6,000; **Type** Public, Member/Avail,
Corp.; **On Site** Clubhouse, Lodging, Meals, Clays;
Shoots Field, Blinds, Boat; **Birds** Dove, Quail,
Pheasant, Chukar, Turkey, Ducks; **Dogs** Avail/HDW;
Packages 1/2 Day, 1-50 guns
See Our Ad Pg. 350

Divin Hunting Services, Inc.

11303 El Sendero, San Antonio, TX 78233
(210) 646-6817 Mike Divin
55 mi. E of Laredo
Est 1976; **Acres** 21,000; **Hunters/yr** 200; **Type**
Public, Corp.; **On Site** Lodging, Meals, Clays;
Shoots Field; **Birds** Dove, Quail; **Dogs** Avail/HDW;
Packages 2 Days, 4-10 guns

Dolan Creek Ranches

PO Box 420069, Del Rio, TX 78842
(210) 775-3129 John Finegan after 6pm
150 mi. W of San Antonio
Est 1970; **Acres** 35,000; **Type** Public; **On Site**
Meals; **Shoots** Field; **Birds** Dove, Quail, Turkey;
Dogs Avail

Dos Vaqueros

PO Box 1035, Refugio, TX 78377
(512) 543-4905 Joan Rooke 9-5
45 mi. N of Corpus Christi
Est 1990; **Acres** 12,000; **Hunters/yr** 100; **Type**
Public; **On Site** Clubhouse, Lodging, Meals, Clays;
Shoots Field; **Birds** Dove, Quail, Turkey; **Dogs**
Avail; **Packages** 1/2 Day, 2-9 guns
See Our Ad Across Left

Double E Kennels

2863 Speegleville Rd., Waco, TX 76712
(817) 848-4658 Earl Elkins
20 mi. SW of Waco
Acres 600; **Hunters/yr** 50; **Type** Public; **Shoots**
Field; **Birds** Quail, Pheasant

Eagle Lake & Katy Prairie Outfitters

PO Box 129, Katy, TX 77492
(713) 391-6100 Larry Gore 8:30am-5:30pm
35 mi. W of Houston
Est 1977; **Acres** 40,000; **Type** Public,
Member/Avail, Corp.; **On Site** Clubhouse, Lodging,
Meals; **Shoots** Field, Blinds; **Birds** Dove, Pheasant,
Chukar, Ducks, Geese; **Dogs** Avail/HDW; **Packages**
1/2 Day, 1-100 guns

HUNTERS CLUB

PO Box 158, Mingus, TX 76463
(817) 672-5927 Dan Van Schaik
70 mi. W of Ft. Worth
Est 1993; **Acres** 4,000; **Type** Member/Avail, Corp.;
On Site Clubhouse, Lodging, Meals, Clays; **Shoots**
Field, Tower, Driven, Blinds; **Birds** Dove, Quail,
Pheasant, Chukar, Turkey, Ducks; **Dogs** Avail/HDW;
Packages 1/2 Day, 2-12 guns ○ NAGA/See Pg. 72

Eshleman-Vogt Ranch
PO Box 2442, Corpus Christi, TX 78403
(512) 888-4888 William T. Vogt, Jr. 8:30-5
100 mi. SW of Corpus Christi
Est 1984; **Acres** 25,000; **Hunters/yr** 200; **Type**
Public, Member/Avail, Corp.; **On Site** Clays; **Shoots**
Field; **Birds** Dove, Quail; **Dogs** Avail/HDW;
Packages 2 Days, 3-12 guns

Executive Outfitters
6956 Meadowbriar Lane, Dallas, TX 75230
(214) 638-9200 Richard R. Lee
Est 1964; **Type** Public; **On Site** Clubhouse,
Lodging, Meals, Clays; **Shoots** Field; **Birds** Dove;
Packages 2 Days

Flying Feathers
Rt. 1, Box 468C, Winnie, TX 77665
(409) 296-2348 Billy Ray Hickman
45 mi. E of Houston **Est** 1993; **Acres** 1,000;
Hunters/yr 900; **Type** Public, Member/Avail; **On
Site** Clubhouse, Meals, Clays; **Shoots** Field; **Birds**
Quail, Pheasant, Chukar; **Dogs** Avail/HDW;
Packages 1/2 Day, 1-8 guns ○ NAGA/See Pg. 72

GB Flyers
3221 Jack Beaver Rd., Santa Fe, TX 77517
(409) 925-2433 Greg Blackburn
20 mi. S of Houston
Est 1992; **Acres** 2,000; **Type** Public, Member/Avail;
On Site Clubhouse; **Shoots** Field; **Birds** Quail,
Pheasant, Chukar; **Dogs** Avail/HDW; **Packages** 1/2
Day, 1-30 guns ○ NAGA/See Pg. 72

Graves Hunting
Rt. 2, Box 136, Shelbyville, TX 75973
(409) 598-2751 Aubrey Graves
180 mi. E of Houston
Est 1989; **Acres** 800; **Type** Public; **Shoots** Field;
Birds Quail, Pheasant, Chukar; **Dogs** Avail/HDW;
Packages 1/2 Day, 1-30 guns ○ NAGA/See Pg. 72

Harper's Hunting Preserve
Rt. 2, Box 484 WC, Booker, TX 79005
(806) 435-3495 Gilbert & Clydeene Harper
130 mi. NE of Amarillo **Est** 1989; **Acres** 1,200;
Type Public; **Shoots** Field; **Birds** Dove, Quail,
Pheasant, Chukar; **Dogs** Avail/HDW; **Packages** 1/2
Day, 2-40 guns ○ NAGA/See Pg. 72

Hawkeye Hunting Club
PO Box 27, Center, TX 75935
(409) 598-2424 Jerry Waters 9-6pm
55 mi. SW of Shreveport, LA **Est** 1955; **Acres**
4,000; **Type** Member/Ltd, Corp.; **On Site**
Clubhouse, Lodging, Meals, Clays; **Shoots** Field,
Driven; **Birds** Quail, Pheasant, Chukar; **Dogs** Avail;
Packages 1/2 Day, 1-35 guns ○ NAGA/See Pg. 72

Herradura Ranch Inc.
PO Drawer 698, Cotulla, TX 78014
(210) 373-4492 David Schuster 9:30-4:30

Hickman's
Gamebird Hunting
PO Box 1871, Beeville, TX 78104
(512) 362-2473 Priscilla Hickman
60 mi. N of Corpus Christi
Est 1991; **Acres** 400; **Hunters/yr** 100; **Type**
Public, Member/Avail; **On Site** Clubhouse, Lodging,
Meals, Clays; **Shoots** Field; **Birds** Dove, Quail,
Pheasant, Chukar, Huns; **Dogs** Avail/HDW;
Packages 1/2 Day, 1-4 guns ○ NAGA/See Pg. 72
○ Bird Processing   ○ Family Recreation
○ Loaner Guns   ○ Brochure Available
○ Fishing   ○ Factory Ammunition
○ Family Run Business   ○ 90 Mi. So. of San Antonio

HCR67, Box 58C, Pleasanton, TX 78064
(210) 569-5555 Steve Hill 8-5, M-S
35 mi. S of San Antonio
Est 1994; **Acres** 900 **Type** Public; **On Site**
Clubhouse, Meals, Clays; **Shoots** Field, Blinds; **Birds**
Dove, Quail, Pheasant, Chukar, Ducks; **Dogs**
Avail/HDW; **Packages** 1/2 Day, 2-12 guns
○ Brochure Available   ○ World Class Sporting Clays
○ The Finest in South Texas Cuisine
○ Bass Fishing
○ Special events, private parties and corporate outings
○ A short 35 minute drive south of San Antonio!
Welcome to the Brush Country of South Texas,
where a new hunting adventure awaits you at Hill-
top Fish and Game Ranch. The very best native
gamebird hunting is made possible by combining
cultivated fields with authentic South Texas terrain.
To complement your outdoor experience, fishing >
and sporting clay shooting are available. A beautiful Texas sunset and the sounds of the wild will
round out a perfect sporting adventure just a short
35 minute drive south of San Antonio. Call today
for information and reservations.

Idania Hunter
Rt. 9, Box 1428, Sour Lake, TX 77659
(504) 279-0452
25 mi. W of Beaumont
Acres 2,000; **Hunters/yr** 40; **Type** Public,
Member/Avail; **On Site** Lodging, Meals, Clays;
Shoots Field, Blinds; **Birds** Dove, Quail, Pheasant,
Chukar, Ducks, Geese; **Dogs** Avail

The Inn at El Canelo
PO Box 487, Raymondville, TX 78580
(210) 689-5042 Ray Burdette
75 mi. S of Corpus Christi
Est 1990; **Acres** 11,000; **Type** Public; **On Site**
Clubhouse, Lodging, Meals, Clays; **Shoots** Field;
Birds Dove, Quail, Pheasant, Chukar, Turkey; **Dogs**
Avail/HDW; **Packages** 1/2 Day, 4-25 guns
○ NAGA/See Pg. 72

○ Airport Pickup	○ Bird Processing
○ Sporting Clays	○ Deer Hunting
○ Gourmet Meals	○ Brochure Available
○ Factory Ammunition	○ Quality Clubhouse
○ Family Run Business	○ Private Bedrooms

J&L Game Bird Farm
1176 US Hwy. 180 W., Rotan, TX 79546
(915) 776-2852 Jackie W. Etheredge 8-10pm
75 mi. NW of Abilene
Est 1990; **Acres** 19,000; **Hunters/yr** 400; **Type**
Public; **Shoots** Field; **Birds** Dove, Quail, Pheasant,
Chukar; **Dogs** HDW; **Packages** 1 Day, 1-5 guns
○ NAGA/See Pg. 72

Jenkins Ranch Dove Hunt
1803 West Crescent, Odessa, TX 79761
(915) 367-9592 Jon & Dolly Thomas
60 mi. W of Odessa
Est 1992; **Acres** 100,000; **Type** Public; **Shoots**
Field; **Birds** Dove; **Packages** 3 Days, 1-8 guns
See Our Ad Below

Pat Johnson's Wild Goose Hunting Club
2718 West Creek, El Campo, TX 77437
(409) 543-6242 Pat Johnson
70 mi. SW of Houston
Est 1982; **Acres** 30,000; **Hunters/yr** 1,200; **Type**
Public, Member/Avail; **On Site** Clubhouse, Lodging,
Meals, Clays; **Shoots** Field, Blinds; **Birds** Dove,
Quail, Pheasant, Snipe, Ducks, Geese; **Dogs**
Avail/HDW; **Packages** 1/2 Day, 3-35 guns

Joshua Creek Ranch

PO Box 1946, Boerne, TX 78006
(210) 537-5090 Ann Kercheville 9-6
25 mi. NW of San Antonio
Est 1990; **Acres** 1,000; **Hunters/yr** 500; **Type**
Public, Member/Avail; **On Site** Clubhouse, Lodging,
Meals, Clays; **Shoots** Field, Driven, Blinds; **Birds**
Dove, Quail, Pheasant, Chukar, Huns, Turkey, Ducks;
Dogs Avail/HDW; **Packages** 1/2 Day, 1-34 guns
O NAGA/See Pg. 72

O Hunting License	O Airport Pickup
O Bird Processing	O Deer Hunting
O Shooting Instruction	O Gourmet Meals
O Train Bird Dogs	O Loaner Guns
O Brochure Available	O On-Site Pro Shop
O Fishing	O Factory Ammunition

Shooting Instruction Available - See Pg. 182
See Our Ads Pgs. 383 & Across

KAT CREEK RANCH
Hunting Club & Sporting Clays
PO Box 987, Henderson, TX 75653
(903) 854-2232 Chester Martin
135 mi. SE of Dallas/Ft. Worth
Acres 1,200; **Type** Public, Member/Avail; **On Site**
Clubhouse, Meals, Clays; **Shoots** Field; **Birds** Quail,
Pheasant; **Dogs** Avail; **Packages** 1/2 Day
O NAGA/See Pg. 72

King Pheasant Farm & Hunting Preserve
1608 71st St., Lubbock, TX 79412
(806) 745-4003 Ray King
10 mi. W of Lubbock
Acres 640; **Hunters/yr** 100; **Type** Public; **Shoots**
Field; **Birds** Pheasant, Chukar; **Dogs** Avail;
Packages 1/2 Day

Krooked River Ranch
5 Squirrel Ridge, Wylie, TX 75098
(214) 442-3851 Steve Packer 9-5
200 mi. W of Dallas/Ft. Worth
Est 1985; **Acres** 80,000; **Hunters/yr** 350; **Type**
Public; **On Site** Clubhouse, Lodging, Meals, Clays;
Shoots Field, Blinds; **Birds** Dove, Quail, Turkey,
Ducks, Geese; **Dogs** Avail/HDW; **Packages** 2 Days,
1-25 guns

La Media Sportsman's Lodge
PO Box 319, Linn, TX 78563
(800) 437-3903 Jerry & Karen Pippen
110 mi. S of Corpus Christi

Type Public; **On Site** Clubhouse, Lodging, Meals,
Clays; **Shoots** Field; **Birds** Dove, Quail, Turkey;
Dogs Avail; **Packages** 1 Day O NAGA/See Pg. 72

LaPaloma Sporting Club
PO Box 160516, San Antonio, TX 78280
(210) 980-4424 Henry Burns 9am-Dark
20 mi. NE of San Antonio
Est 1987; **Acres** 70; **Type** Public, Member/Avail;
On Site Clubhouse, Meals, Clays; **Shoots** Field,
Driven; **Birds** Quail, Pheasant, Chukar; **Dogs**
Avail/HDW; **Packages** 1/2 Day, 2-4 guns

Lazy WJ Ranch
Rt. 5, Box 51952, Winnsboro, TX 75494
(903) 365-2610 Wayne or Jane Daniels After 6pm
120 mi. NE of Dallas
Est 1987; **Acres** 500; **Type** Public; **Shoots** Field;
Birds Quail; **Dogs** Avail/HDW; **Packages** 1/2 Day,
1-8 guns O NAGA/See Pg. 72

Jonathan Letz
Rt. 1, Box 71, Comfort, TX 78013
(210) 995-2120
11 mi. NW of San Antonio
Acres 7,000; **Hunters/yr** 30; **Type** Member/Avail;
On Site Clubhouse, Lodging; **Shoots** Field; **Birds**
Quail, Turkey; **Dogs** Avail

PO Box 200105, San Antonio, TX 78220
(210) 676-3317 Pat Moore/Sonny Hild 7am-8pm
132 mi. SW of San Antonio
Est 1993; **Acres** 4,000; **Hunters/yr** 100; **Type**
Public, Member/Avail, Corp.; **On Site** Clubhouse,
Lodging, Meals, Clays; **Shoots** Field, Driven, Blinds;
Birds Dove, Quail, Pheasant, Chukar, Huns, Turkey,
Ducks; **Dogs** Avail/HDW; **Packages** 1/2 Day, 2-15
guns

O Hunting License	O Airport Pickup
O Bird Processing	O Sporting Clays
O Shooting Instruction	O Gourmet Meals
O Hunting Jeeps	O Train Bird Dogs
O Fishing	O Factory Ammunition
O Quality Clubhouse	O 4,000 Ft. Landing Strip

Los Patos Lodge
18907 Tranquility Dr., Houston, TX 77346
(409) 286-5767 Forrest West Anytime
90 mi. E of Houston
Est 1964; **Acres** 45,000; **Type** Public,
Member/Avail; **On Site** Clubhouse, Lodging, Meals,
Clays; **Shoots** Field, Blinds; **Birds** Dove, Quail,
Snipe, Ducks, Geese; **Dogs** Avail/HDW; **Packages**
1/2 Day, up to 40 guns

Lynn Manor Hunting Preserve & Kennels
3808 Curry Rd., Manvel, TX 77578
(713) 489-0315 C.B. Watts/Glenda Watts

Joshua Creek Ranch: Hill Country's Best Kept Secret

By Bob Rivard
Deputy Managing Editor, San Antonio Light

WELFARE, Texas - Call me Buddy. Buddy Gough, Light Outdoors Editor, that is. For a day and night, I recently filled ol' Buddy's shoes while he was out of town inspecting ancient cave paintings, chasing giant, mutant bass or doing something that wouldn't sound much like work to you or me. I stepped into the breach.

My assignment: Explore Joshua Creek Ranch, a one-year-old scenic hunting and fishing preserve located on the Guadalupe River, in the company of Bill Morrill, noted wildlife biologist and owner of Wildlife Management, Inc. in Boerne.

I also took along John Maeckle, my father-in-law, as friend and witness in the event I caught any fish on the flies I recently learned to tie under master fly-tyer Pete Jones at the Tackle Box. John introduced me to the Texas outdoors and it only seemed fair to deal him into my new career as outdoor writer.

Buddy, ol' boy, you should have stayed in town. Joshua Creek is one of the Hill country's best kept secrets. It is hard to believe a 1,000 acre ranch this beautiful, this alive with fish and game, this secluded, sits only 45 minutes from my downtown office.

On another matter, Buddy, I owe you an apology. I have always thought you guys stretched the truth a little bit, if you know what I mean, but after the great hunting and fishing John and I enjoyed at Joshua Creek Ranch, I'm beginning to believe what I read. Why, we came away with a few stories of our own. But first the facts.

Deluxe Ranch

Joshua Creek Ranch is a deluxe, guest oriented fish and game ranch—"an outdoor recreation enterprise," in the words of Morrill—designed to serve a limited membership, and for a few more months, the occasional day fishers and hunters. Right now it's a great place to fish for rainbow trout at $25 a day, but the ranch's reputa-

Joe & Ann Kercheville at one of Joshua Creek Ranch's Driven Pheasant shoots.

tion is growing fast and the enterprise will shift to members only in October.

"We call it hunting like Granddad used to know", Morrill said.

Granddad was never so lucky.

Joe and Ann Kercheville, successful San Antonio business people and avid outdoorsmen themselves (the lodge's African trophies came from their honeymoon), own and operate Joshua Creek Ranch. They have set an ambitious goal for themselves in offering members a well managed highly serviced ranch resort at very competitive prices.

Success seems possible, even in this economy, with a strong business plan based on location, a guest oriented ambience, superb service and excellent game and habitat management.

Guaranteed Good Time

Joshua Creek Ranch is geared toward the family and corporations and offers a variety of activities for those who choose not to hunt or fish, including a world class sporting clays course, nature hikes, volleyball, croquet,canoeing, fishing or simply relaxing.

"A lot of people out there work very hard and simply do not have very much time for shooting and fishing or recreating", Ann Kercheville, our gracious host said over a superb lunch of homemade soup and pasta salad prepared by chef and director of member services Sue Wetmore. "We guarantee that every person has a very good time. We take care of every detail. We offer quality experience. I think the future of hunting in Texas, is this."

The ranch is an ideal balance of water, fields, pasture and hills, open spaces and thick cover. Half the ranch has been cleared of cedar, the other half remains thick with cedar and live oak.

Morrill was brought in to match the habitat with game and to make sure ideal conditions were achieved and maintained. The result is a balance that seems natural when experienced, but actually is the product of much work and understanding complex relationships up and down the food chain.

While the ranch offers traditional white tail deer and wild turkey hunting for an additional harvest fee, the emphasis here is on wing shooting: pheasant, chukar, and quail. Mallard duck and Hungarian partridge are also available.

Families and corporations can buy either

Professional guides and well trained dogs conduct walk-up shooting for upland birds.

fishing or hunting and fishing memberships and select the number and types of birds they will hunt during the season. Fishing and sporting clays are year round activities.

Hunting

I've visited two game shooting resorts in the past, and each one featured birds that

Traditional European Estate Shoots Just 25 Miles From San Antonio? Yes! At Joshua Creek Ranch

by Chuck Wechsler

When Joe and Ann Kercheville purchased Joshua Creek Ranch eight years ago, they set in motion plans for developing a world-class hunting preserve that would replicate the traditional estate shoots of Europe.

Ann explained: "Joe and I have shot in countries around the world. We've seen what it takes to provide a top-flight shooting experience, and we're determined to offer that to sportsmen over here--but at a greatly reduced cost."

If what wildlife artist Ron Van Gilder and I saw during our brief stay at Joshua Creek is any indication, they've succeeded in becoming a leader in stateside driven shoots. After a memorable morning of walk-up shooting, Ron and I watched three husbands and their wives shoot flighted mallards. The birds were released above a plunging wooded ravine, where the guns were stationed several hundred feet apart. Most of the mallards made a beeline toward a pond at the bottom of the canyon. Shooters on the slopes were challenged by birds that careened just above the treetops, while those along the valley floor had

to pick out their targets through small openings in the woodland canopy.

The next day's shoot was even more impressive. This time the guns were positioned over a picked cornfield at the base of a tree-covered bluff, where a string of beaters pushed pheasants into the air. A few of the birds sliced through the trees, but most climbed high above them, offering difficult, straight-up shots of forty yards or more. The limestone cliff was like a natural amphitheater, intensifying the sights and sounds of the hunt. All in all it was a wonderful spectacle and a challenging shoot, even for the best gunners.

Most driven shoots at Joshua Creek total about 400 birds, though as many as 650 have been presented in a single day. After completing the drives, the guides take the hunters down to the fields where they can gun the escaped birds over dogs.

Ann told us that she is able to set up a shoot with very little notice and carry it off in just one day. "For an American to plan a driven shoot in Europe , he'd have to set aside a week to ten days," she added. For more information about estate shoots and Joshua Creek's many other sporting amenities call Ann Kercheville at 210-537-5090. [A longer version of this article appeared in the March/April, 1994 issue of *Sporting Classics* Magazine.]

practically came when you called, embarrassing guides when they refused to flush. At Joshua Creek, the quail appear fully acclimated to their wooded cover. They flushed high and hard and flew strongly even on a second flush.

John, my father-in-law, is a robust 70 year old, but he has had all the hunting he wants and now limits himself to fly fishing. I, on the other hand, had never hunted quail with well trained pointers.

Morrill and I met up with guide James Barnes, a friendly 21 year old graduate of Comfort High School who also was a member of his school's nationally ranked range and pasture team. All day, in between shooting, I had the pleasure of Jim's tutoring on plants and flowers whose names have always eluded me. Silver leaf night shade was my favorite.

The morning started, predictably, with Morrill's Browning, 20-gauge functioning much better than my Beretta, 20-gauge. Whatever was wrong with my gun, it disappeared as the morning wore on, and I finished the quail hunt quite nicely. By the time we switched to chukar, and had walked the rows of trampled corn stalks once or twice, I was close to acting cocky.

Later in the day, while hunting pheasant in an old pea field on the edge of sloping woods, we paused to watch a pair of pointers work the field in tandem. It was a pleasure to watch the two, well trained dogs sweep through the high grass. Even if Morrill and I hadn't each knocked down a hen, watching the dogs would have made the trip worthwhile.

That night we dined on pheasant, again prepared by Chef Wetmore, and then retired to the flagstone patio for a view of a full moon and a long evening of stories..

I stayed up late in the lodge's great room, browsing the well stocked periodical table admiring spear points, measuring the enormous fireplace and wondering who built the lodge. We slept in one of the two bedrooms, each containing eight deluxe bunk beds, fireplaces and whirlpool baths.

The lodge, available to members or guests at $35 a night per person, inclusive of continental breakfast, seems ideal for family gatherings, company picnics or small corporate retreats.

Fly Fishermen catch rainbow trout in the brisk spring waters of Joshua Creek.

Fishing, too

The next morning we rose early to fish. Pete, it was an epiphany. The flies, that is, my flies, actually worked. They fooled the fish. At one point, fishing a deep, secluded blue hole located on the backside of Joshua Creek, John and I landed and released more than a dozen rainbow trout, all measuring 14 inches or more, in the space of 30 minutes. The trout fought and leapt and shimmered like wild rainbows. The Kerchevilles hope that the cool, spring fed blue hole and larger lake that cascades into the creek just below the old stone lodge will stay cool enough for the trout to survive and breed.

Another secret to divulge here, Buddy, we caught those fat rainbows below the surface on olive bodied woolly buggers, leadwing coachmen nymphs and a small green pupa. We failed, in the afternoon heat, to get the rainbows to rise to my dryflies, though the flies seemed to sit up and sail nicely. Joshua Creek Ranch, incidentally has to be about the southern most location in Texas offering rainbow trout.

Buddy, I wrote out a check for my birds and a couple of Joshua Creek caps and was handed back neatly packaged vacuum packed birds. I'm saving them for a backyard cookout, maybe with a few of my fellow editors, including the real outdoor editor.

[This article originally appeared in the *San Antonio Light, Outdoors,* April 28, 1991. For more information about Joshua Creek Ranch, call or write Ann & Joe Kercheville at P.O. Box 1946, Boerne, TX 78006, (210) 537-5090.]

Acres 1,800; **Type** Public; **On Site** Meals; **Shoots** Field; **Birds** Quail, Pheasant, Chukar, Ducks, Geese; **Dogs** Avail/HDW; **Packages** 1/2 Day, 2-4 guns

Mariposa Ranch-SK Corporation
Rt. 1, Box 33, Falfurrias, TX 78355
(512) 325-5752 Dan Sullivan/Robert King 8am-5pm
75 mi. SW of Corpus Christi
Est 1985; **Acres** 45,000; **Hunters/yr** 240; **Type** Public; **On Site** Clubhouse, Lodging, Meals, Clays; **Shoots** Field; **Birds** Dove, Quail; **Dogs** Avail; **Packages** 1 Day, 2-12 guns

Mesquite Hunts
5900 Dobbs Valley Rd., Millsap, TX 76066
(817) 325-0749
from Waco
Acres 80,000; **Type** Public; **Shoots** Field; **Birds** Quail; **Packages** 1 Day

More or Less Game Ranch
2626 N 2nd, Abilene, TX 79603
(915) 673-7208 Toad Leon
25 mi. S of Abilene
Acres 2,000; **Type** Public; **On Site** Clubhouse, Lodging, Meals, Clays; **Shoots** Field; **Birds** Dove, Quail, Pheasant, Turkey

Nail Ranch
Rt. 1, Box 106, Albany, TX 76430
(915) 762-2974 Craig Winters 8am-6pm
35 mi. NE of Abilene
Est 1900; **Acres** 57,000; **Hunters/yr** 400; **Type** Public; **On Site** Clubhouse, Lodging, Meals; **Shoots** Field; **Birds** Quail, Turkey; **Dogs** HDW; **Packages** 3 Days, up to 8 guns

Gene Naquin's
Fin and Feathered Safaris

Gene Naquin's Fin & Feathered Safaris
PO Box 1734, Laredo, TX 78044
(210) 724-4648 Gene Naquin
170 mi. S of San Antonio
Est 1980; **Acres** 15,000; **Type** Public; **On Site** Lodging, Meals; **Shoots** Field, Blinds; **Birds** Dove, Quail, Ducks, Geese; **Dogs** Avail/HDW; **Packages** 1 Day, 2-8 guns

HUNT SOUTH TEXAS & MEXICO - Quail, White-wing/Mourning Dove and Waterfowl hunting north and south of the Rio Grande. We hunt quail over 15,000 acres on several locations in South Texas–quail capital of the world. On a typical day we may move on the average 25 coveys per day–somedays more. Specialized hunting trucks smooth out the rugged terrain and our experienced guides and well-trained dogs produce the best quail hunts possible. Our dove and waterfowl hunts have to be experienced to be believed. Call or write today for a brochure or reservations.

Earl Nobles
Rt. 5, Box 430, Beaumont, TX 77713
(409) 866-1310 Earl H. Nobles
90 mi. NE of Houston
Type Public; **Shoots** Field; **Birds** Turkey

Jeff Pegg & Son Hunting
Rt. 1, Box 593-A, Springtown, TX 76082
(817) 748-2729 Jeff Pegg After 7pm
30 mi. W of Ft. Worth
Est 1990; **Acres** 500; **Type** Public, Corp.; **On Site** Clubhouse, Meals; **Shoots** Field, Tower, Blinds; **Birds** Dove, Quail, Pheasant, Chukar, Turkey, Ducks; **Dogs** Avail/HDW; **Packages** 1/2 Day, 2-15 guns

Possum Walk Ranch
Rt. 2, Box 174, Huntsville, TX 77340
(409) 291-1891 Buddy Smith 6am-9pm
70 mi. N of Houston
Est 1990; **Acres** 1,350; **Hunters/yr** 250; **Type** Public, Member/Avail, Corp.; **On Site** Clubhouse; **Shoots** Field, Tower; **Birds** Dove, Quail, Pheasant, Chukar; **Dogs** Avail/HDW ○ NAGA/See Pg. 72

Pringle Pheasant Farm & Hunting Area
PO Box 274, Girvin, TX 79740
(915) 652-8245 Burl or Frankie Pringle After 7pm
75 mi. SW of Midland/Odessa
Est 1986; **Acres** 160; **Hunters/yr** 100; **Type** Public; **On Site** Clubhouse, Meals; **Shoots** Field, Tower; **Birds** Dove, Quail, Pheasant, Chukar, Turkey; **Dogs** HDW; **Packages** 1/2 Day, 2-20 guns ○ NAGA/See Pg. 72

Quail Ridge Hunting Club
Rt. 1, Box 107, Spur, TX 79370
(806) 294-5333 Buddy Moore
60 mi. SE of Lubbock
Acres 20,000; **Type** Public; **On Site** Clubhouse, Lodging, Meals, Clays; **Shoots** Field; **Birds** Dove, Quail, Pheasant, Chukar, Turkey, Ducks, Geese; **Dogs** Avail

Rafter W Ranches
Box 944, Sonora, TX 76950
(915) 387-3377 Jack Wardlew
Type Public; **Shoots** Field; **Birds** Quail, Turkey

Raisin L Ranch
PO Box 1710, Pearland, TX 77588
(713) 485-2300 Darryl Lilie
79 mi. SW of Houston
Acres 640; **Hunters/yr** 600; **Type** Public; **On Site** Clubhouse, Lodging, Meals; **Shoots** Field; **Birds** Quail, Pheasant; **Dogs** Avail

Red Bluff Preserve
Rt. 2, Box 106B, Trent, TX 79561
(915) 235-4360 Eddy Mayfield After dark
30 mi. W of Abilene
Est 1990; **Acres** 1,700; **Type** Public, Member/Avail, Corp.; **On Site** Clubhouse, Meals, Clays; **Shoots** Field, Blinds; **Birds** Dove, Quail, Pheasant, Chukar; **Dogs** Avail/HDW; **Packages** 1/2 Day, 1-60 guns

Rio Paisano Ranch
PO Box 130, Riviera, TX 78379
(512) 294-5281 Casey Taub/Frank Horlock 7-5:30
55 mi. SW of Corpus Christi
Est 1978; **Acres** 10,000; **Hunters/yr** 100; **Type**
Public; **On Site** Clubhouse, Lodging, Meals, Clays;
Shoots Field, Driven, Blinds; **Birds** Dove, Quail,
Turkey, Ducks, Geese; **Dogs** Avail/HDW; **Packages**
3 Days, 1-18 guns

Riverside Farms
Rt. 3, Box 217-R, Hamilton, TX 76531
(214) 953-2850 Jill Bishop/Les Ethetton 8-5
120 mi. SW of Dallas
Est 1981; **Acres** 12,000; **Type** Public, Corp.; **On**
Site Clubhouse, Lodging, Meals, Clays; **Shoots** Field,
Driven, Blinds; **Birds** Dove, Quail, Pheasant, Chukar,
Huns, Turkey, Ducks; **Dogs** Avail; **Packages** 1/2
Day, up to 12 guns ○ NAGA/See Pg. 72
○ Airport Pickup   ○ Bird Processing
○ Sporting Clays
○ Hunting License/Loaner Guns
○ Exclusive 3 Day Pkg. for 12 Hunters
    with World Class Lodging

Robby Robinson Ranches
PO Box 274, Junction, TX 76849
(915) 446-3165 Robby Robinson
100 mi. NW of San Antonio
Est 1956; **Acres** 20,000; **Type** Public,
Member/Avail; **On Site** Lodging, Meals; **Shoots**
Field; **Birds** Turkey

Rustic Range
Rt. 2, Box 182, Slaton, TX 79364
(806) 828-4820 Dub Dillard 1-Sunset
11 mi. E of Lubbock
Est 1990; **Acres** 10; **Hunters/yr** 100; **Type**
Public; **On Site** Clubhouse, Clays; **Shoots** Tower;
Birds Quail, Pheasant, Chukar; **Dogs** HDW;
Packages 1/2 Day

SF Ranch
Rt. 4, Box 151-A, Comanche, TX 76442
(817) 842-5456 Steve M. Fleming Before 8 & after 5
100 mi. SW of Dallas
Est 1989; **Acres** 650; **Type** Public; **On Site** Clays;
Shoots Field; **Birds** Quail, Pheasant, Chukar; **Dogs**
Avail/HDW; **Packages** 1/2 Day, 1-4 guns
○ NAGA/See Pg. 72

Santa Anna Hunting Area
Rt. 1, Box 102A, Santa Anna, TX 76878
(915) 348-9267 John/Gerry Stearns 7am-10pm
60 mi. SE of Abilene
Est 1986; **Acres** 600; **Hunters/yr** 600; **Type**
Public; **On Site** Clays; **Shoots** Field; **Birds** Quail,
Pheasant, Chukar; **Dogs** Avail/HDW; **Packages** 1/2
Day, 1-30 guns ○ NAGA/See Pg. 72

W.S. Sherrill Waterfowl Hunting
1702 Garrett Court, Wharton, TX 77488
(409) 532-1789 W.S. Sherrill
45 mi. SW of Houston
Acres 40,000; **Type** Public; **On Site** Clubhouse,

Lodging, Meals, Clays; **Birds** Ducks, Geese; **Dogs**
Avail; **Packages** 1/2 Day, 4-30 guns

Southwest Safaris
PO Box 38, Campbellton, TX 78008
(210) 579-4808 R.P. Hodges Anytime
60 mi. S of San Antonio
Est 1987; **Acres** 30,000; **Hunters/yr** 400; **Type**
Public; **On Site** Clubhouse, Lodging, Meals, Clays;
Shoots Field, Blinds; **Birds** Dove, Quail, Turkey, Ducks;
Dogs Avail/HDW; **Packages** 2 Days, 2-12 guns

Southwest Sporting Clays
Rt. 5, Box 418-C, Texarkana, TX 75501
(903) 838-4000 John A. Woodman, Jr. 11am-7pm,
W-Su
10 mi. W of Texarkana
Est 1992; **Acres** 1,200; **Type** Public, Member/Avail;
Corp.; **On Site** Clubhouse, Lodging, Meals, Clays;
Shoots Field, Tower, Driven; **Birds** Dove, Quail,
Pheasant, Chukar, Ducks, Geese; **Dogs** Avail/HDW;
Packages 1/2 Day, 2-25 guns

Spanish Dagger Hunting Resort
PO Box 1325, Uvalde, TX 78802
(210) 278-2998 George Cooper
70 mi. W of San Antonio
Est 1987; **Acres** 2,000; **Type** Public; **On Site**
Lodging, Meals, Clays; **Shoots** Field, Driven; **Birds**
Dove, Quail, Pheasant, Chukar, Ducks; **Dogs**
Avail/HDW; **Packages** 1/2 Day ○ NAGA/See Pg. 72

Marvin Spiller
Rt. 2, Box 5-K, Bridgeport, TX 76426
(817) 683-4660
14 mi. from Decatur
Acres 850; **Hunters/yr** 12; **Type** Public; **Shoots**
Field; **Birds** Quail; **Dogs** Avail

Sporting Pheasants
Rt. 1, Box 56, Ivanhoe, TX 75447
(903) 664-4205 John Haynes
Type Member/Avail; **Birds** Pheasant ○ NAGA/ Pg. 72

Stasney's Cook Ranch
PO Drawer 1826, Albany, TX 76430
(915) 762-3695 Johnnie Hudman
30 mi. N of Abilene
Acres 22,000; **Hunters/yr** 400; **Type** Public; **On**
Site Clubhouse, Lodging, Meals, Clays; **Shoots** Field;
Birds Dove, Quail, Pheasant, Chukar, Turkey, Ducks;
Dogs Avail/HDW; **Packages** 2 Days, 2-8 guns

Sun Land Game Farm
910 W. 1st, Amarillo, TX 79116
(806) 374-8121 Dewayne Weatherly
Type Public; **On Site** Lodging; **Shoots** Field; **Birds**
Quail, Pheasant, Chukar ○ NAGA/See Pg. 72

T.G.R. Gamebird Preserve
6501 CR 118, Bullard, TX 75757
(903) 894-6320 Rob Martin
Type Public, Member/Avail; **On Site** Clays; **Shoots**
Field; **Birds** Quail, Pheasant, Chukar
○ NAGA/See Pg. 72

WINGS

Texas Rice Belt Hunt Club
PO Box 274, Garwood, TX 77447
David Ordonez
70 mi. SW of Houston
Est 1982; **Acres** 40,000; **Hunters/yr** 1,000; **Type** Public, Member/Avail; **On Site** Clubhouse, Clays; **Shoots** Field, Blinds; **Birds** Dove, Snipe, Ducks, Geese; **Dogs** Avail/HDW;**Packages** 1/2 Day, 4-40 guns

Texas Waterfowl Outfitters
22413 Katy Frwy., Katy, TX 77450
(800) 899-2650 Tony Hurst 9-5
20 mi. W of Houston
Est 1984; **Acres** 35,000; **Hunters/yr** 3,000; **Type** Public, Member/Avail, Corp.; **On Site** Lodging, Meals, Clays; **Shoots** Field, Tower, Driven, Blinds, Boat; **Birds** Dove, Quail, Pheasant, Chukar, Huns, Snipe, Ducks, Geese; **Dogs** Avail/HDW; **Packages** 1/2 Day, 1-100 guns

Texas-Oklahoma Quail Hunts
PO Box 464, Nocona, TX 76255
(817) 995-2210 John Cox
30 mi. N of Abilene/Oklahoma City, OK
Est 1984; **Acres** 150,000; **Hunters/yr** 300; **Type** Public; **On Site** Clubhouse, Lodging, Meals; **Shoots** Field; **Birds** Dove, Quail, Turkey; **Dogs** Avail/HDW; **Packages** 3 Days, 3-12 guns

Third Coast Outfitters
PO Box 1351, Bay City, TX 77404
(409) 245-3071 Bobby Hale 8am-8pm
78 mi. SW of Houston
Est 1986; **Acres** 40,000; **Type** Public, Member/Avail, Corp.; **Shoots** Field, Blinds; **Birds** Dove, Quail, Snipe, Ducks, Geese; **Dogs** Avail/HDW; **Packages** 3 Days, 1-35 guns

Thunderbird Ranch
768 South Main, Lumberton, TX 77657
(409) 755-7204 Lee Riston
5 mi. N of Beaumont
Type Public; **Shoots** Field; **Birds** Pheasant, Chukar; **Dogs** Avail

Tierra Colinas
Rt. 5, Box 162B, Weatherford, TX 76086
(817) 596-4827 Joe Bishop
30 mi. W of Dallas/Ft. Worth
Acres 1,200; **Type** Member/Avail, Corp.; **On Site** Clubhouse, Meals, Clays; **Shoots** Field; **Birds** Quail, Pheasant, Chukar, Huns; **Dogs** Avail/HDW; **Packages** 1/2 Day, 1-30 guns
O Bird Processing   O Kennel Bird Dogs
O Sporting Clays   O Shooting Instruction
O Quality Clubhouse

Top Flight Hunting Preserve
Rt. 1, Box 233, Beasley, TX 77417
(409) 387-2284 Leon Randermann anytime
30 mi. W of Houston
Est 1990; **Acres** 1,100; **Hunters/yr** 250; **Type** Public, Member/Avail, Corp.; **On Site** Clubhouse, Meals, Clays; **Shoots** Field; **Birds** Dove, Quail,

Pheasant, Chukar; **Dogs** Avail/HDW; **Packages** 1/2 Day, 2-24 guns

Torel Wildlife
PO Box 65 (Duval County), Freer, TX 78357
(512) 394-6684 B.R. Thompson After 7pm
65 mi. W of Corpus Christi
Est 1976; **Acres** 6,000; **Type** Public; **On Site** Clubhouse, Lodging; **Shoots** Field; **Birds** Dove, Quail, Turkey; **Dogs** HDW

PO Box 730, Corsicana, TX 75151
(903) 872-5663 Steve Stroube 8:30-4:30
55 mi. SE of Dallas
Est 1985; **Acres** 640; **Hunters/yr** 700; **Type** Public; **On Site** Clubhouse, Meals, Clays; **Shoots** Field, Tower; **Birds** Quail, Pheasant, Chukar, Huns; **Dogs** Avail/HDW; **Packages** 1/2 Day, 2-18 guns
O NAGA/See Pg. 72

Waterfowl Specialties, Inc.
PO Box 411, El Campo, TX 77437
(409) 543-1109 Terry Karstedt Anytime
74 mi. SW of Houston
Est 1984; **Acres** 60,000; **Hunters/yr** 2,000; **Type** Public; **On Site** Lodging, Meals; **Shoots** Field, Blinds; **Birds** Dove, Ducks, Geese; **Dogs** Avail/HDW; **Packages** 1/2 Day, 4-40 guns

Wild Wings Hunting Club
Rt. 4, Box 11, El Campo, TX 77437
(409) 543-6075 Lonnie Neel 6-10pm
60 mi. SW of Houston
Est 1976; **Acres** 40,000; **Hunters/yr** 1,000; **Type** Public; **On Site** Clubhouse, Lodging, Meals; **Shoots** Field; **Birds** Dove, Quail, Ducks, Geese; **Dogs** Avail/HDW; **Packages** 1/2 Day, up to 4 guns
O Hunting License   O Bird Processing
O Brochure Available   O Factory Ammunition
O Quality Clubhouse

Wing & Shot Shooting Resort
2209 Stroker Rd., Crosby, TX 77532
(713) 328-3439 Gus Holmelin
35 mi. NE of Houston
Acres 940; **Type** Public, Member/Avail; **On Site** Clubhouse, Lodging, Clays; **Shoots** Field, Blinds; **Birds** Dove, Quail, Pheasant, Chukar, Huns, Ducks, Geese; **Dogs** Avail; **Packages** 1/2 Day

Y.O. Ranch Onion Creek Lodge
, Mountain Home, TX 78025
(210) 640-3222 Bo Wafford
30 mi. S of Austin
Acres 5,000; **Type** Public; **On Site** Clubhouse, Lodging, Meals; **Shoots** Field; **Birds** Dove, Quail, Turkey; **Dogs** Avail

UTAH

4 Mile Hunting Club
PO Box 261, Mona, UT 84645
(801) 623-0704 Earl Sutherland
80 mi. S of Salt Lake City
Est 1992; **Acres** 1,900; **Hunters/yr** 1,100; **Type**
Public, Member/Avail; **On Site** Clubhouse, Lodging,
Meals, Clays; **Shoots** Field; **Birds** Quail, Pheasant,
Chukar; **Dogs** Avail/HDW; **Packages** 1/2 Day, 1-20
guns ○ NAGA/See Pg. 72

Beer Creek Farms
1085 E. 1050 S., Spanish Fork, UT 84660
(801) 798-6355 Bob Llewellyn
10 mi. S of Provo
Acres 387; **Type** Public; **On Site** Meals, Clays;
Shoots Field; **Birds** Quail, Pheasant, Chukar; **Dogs**
Avail/HDW ○ NAGA/See Pg. 72

Chicken Creek Hunting Club
PO Box 12, Levan, UT 84639
(801) 623-0656 Tom or Ryan Aagard
45 mi. S of Provo
Acres 3,800; **Hunters/yr** 200; **Type** Public,
Member/Avail; **Shoots** Field, Blinds; **Birds**
Pheasant, Chukar, Ducks, Geese; **Dogs** Avail

Diamond Bar Ranch
4832 W. 8800 S., Payson, UT 84651
(801) 465-9173 Jay or Ben Isaac 7am-10pm
20 mi. S of Provo
Est 1989; **Acres** 350; **Hunters/yr** 600; **Type**
Public, Member/Avail, Corp.; **On Site** Clays; **Shoots**
Field; **Birds** Pheasant, Chukar; **Dogs** Avail/HDW;
Packages 1/2 Day, 1-20 guns

Hatt's Ranch
Box 275, Green River, UT 84525
(801) 564-3224 Rey Lloyd Hatt
16 mi. SW of Green River
Est 1976; **Acres** 1,000; **Hunters/yr** 1,800; **Type**
Member/Avail; **On Site** Clubhouse, Meals, Clays;
Shoots Field; **Birds** Pheasant, Chukar, Huns; **Dogs**
Avail/HDW; **Packages** 1/2 Day ○ NAGA/See Pg. 72

L&R Bird Ranch
816 S. 600 E. Circle, St. George, UT 84770
(801) 628-7132 Lee Scott 5-10pm
34 mi. W of St. George
Est 1988; **Acres** 1,020; **Hunters/yr** 600; **Type**
Public; **On Site** Clubhouse, Clays; **Shoots** Field;
Birds Dove, Quail, Pheasant, Chukar; **Dogs**
Avail/HDW; **Packages** 1/2 Day, 1-25 guns
○ NAGA/See Pg. 72

Lakeview Pheasantry
1494 S. Carterville Rd., Orem, UT 84058
(801) 224-5223 Jerry Cross
Type Public, Member/Avail; **Shoots** Field; **Birds**
Quail, Pheasant, Huns, Turkey ○ NAGA/See Pg. 72

Mosida
PO Box 120, Elberta, UT 84626
(801) 667-3282 Lance
40 mi. S of Salt Lake City
Est 1986; **Acres** 2,700; **Hunters/yr** 60; **Type**
Member/Ltd; **On Site** Lodging, Meals; **Shoots**
Field, Blinds; **Birds** Pheasant, Chukar, Ducks, Geese;
Dogs HDW

Pheasant Grove Hunting Preserve
4230 North Hwy. 13, Corinne, UT 84307
(801) 744-2284 Ken Dillree
Type Public, Member/Avail; **Shoots** Field; **Birds**
Quail, Chukar, Turkey ○ NAGA/See Pg. 72

Pheasant Valley Hunting Club
16840 W. 12800 N., Howell, UT 84316
(801) 471-2245 Carlos Christensen Evenings
75 mi. N of Salt Lake City **Est** 1981; **Acres** 3,500;
Hunters/yr 1,250; **Type** Public, Member/Avail,
Corp.; **On Site** Clubhouse, Lodging, Clays; **Shoots**
Field; **Birds** Dove, Quail, Pheasant, Chukar, Huns,
Turkey; **Dogs** Avail/HDW ○ NAGA/See Pg. 72

Pleasant Valley Preserve
Rt. 3, Box 3736, Myton, UT 84052
(801) 646-3194 Phil & Keith Hicken Evenings
100 mi. E of Provo
Est 1987; **Acres** 3,000; **Hunters/yr** 2,500; **Type**
Public, Member/Avail, Corp.; **On Site** Clubhouse,
Lodging, Meals, Clays; **Shoots** Field; **Birds**
Pheasant, Chukar; **Dogs** Avail/HDW; **Packages** 1/2
Day, 1-40 guns ○ NAGA/See Pg. 72

River Hollow Hunting Club & Kennel
68 N. 3rd E., Hyrum, UT 84319
(801) 245-6150 Randy A. Burbank 4-10pm
70 mi. N of Salt Lake City
Est 1988; **Acres** 500; **Type** Public, Member/Avail,
Corp.; **On Site** Clubhouse; **Shoots** Field, Tower;
Birds Quail, Pheasant, Chukar; **Dogs** Avail/HDW;
Packages 1/2 Day ○ NAGA/See Pg. 72

Road Creek Rod & Gun Club
90 S. Main, Loa, UT 84747
(801) 836-2485 Mark Leavitt 1 mi. W of Loa
Acres 2,100; **Type** Public, Member/Avail; **On Site**
Lodging, Meals, Clays; **Shoots** Field, Blinds; **Birds**
Quail, Pheasant, Chukar, Huns; **Dogs** Avail

Rooster Valley Pheasants
855 North 300 West, Richfield, UT 84701
(801) 896-4868 Russ Peterson
2 mi. S of Richfield
Acres 2,000; **Hunters/yr** 500; **Type** Public,
Member/Avail; **On Site** Clubhouse, Lodging, Meals,
Clays; **Shoots** Field, Blinds; **Birds** Dove, Pheasant,
Chukar, Huns, Ducks, Geese; **Dogs** Avail

W.C. Flyers
1580 N. 5600 W., Corinne, UT 84307
(801) 744-2975 Scott Forsgren
50 mi. N of Salt Lake
Acres 466; **Type** Public, Member/Avail; **On Site**
Clubhouse; **Shoots** Field; **Birds** Quail, Pheasant;
Dogs Avail; **Packages** 1/2 Day, 1-20 guns
○ NAGA/See Pg. 72

WINGS

Wings Unlimited
PO Box 334, Wellington, UT 84542
(801) 637-2057 Dale Norton
100 mi. SE of Provo
Est 1990; **Acres** 1,200; **Hunters/yr** 600; **Type** Public, Member/Avail, Corp.; **On Site** Clubhouse, Meals; **Shoots** Field; **Birds** Quail, Pheasant, Chukar; **Dogs** Avail/HDW; **Packages** 1/2 Day, 2-20 guns
○ NAGA/See Pg. 72

VERMONT

Hermitage Inn
Coldbrook Rd., Wilmington, VT 05363
(802) 464-3511 Jim McGovern 9-5
25 mi. E of Bennington
Est 1980; **Acres** 200; **Hunters/yr** 50; **Type** Public, Member/Avail; **On Site** Clubhouse, Lodging, Meals, Clays; **Shoots** Field; **Birds** Pheasant; **Dogs** Avail/HDW; **Packages** 1/2 Day, 1-4 guns
○ NAGA/See Pg. 72

Seymour Lake Lodge
Rt. 111, Box 61, Morgan, VT 05853
(802) 895-2752 Dave & Sue Benware or
(800)-207-2752
12 mi. NE of Newport
Est 1921; **Acres** 10,600; **Type** Public; **On Site** Clubhouse, Lodging, Meals; **Shoots** Field, Blinds; **Birds** Ruffed Grouse, Woodcock, Pheasant; **Dogs** Avail/HDW; **Packages** 1 Day, 1-12 guns

Tinmouth Hunting Preserve
Box 556, Wallingford, VT 05773
(802) 446-2337 Rick Fallar 8am-5pm
70 mi. NE of Albany
Est 1977; **Acres** 800; **Hunters/yr** 500; **Type** Public, Member/Avail; **On Site** Clubhouse, Meals, Clays; **Shoots** Field, Tower, Driven; **Birds** Quail, Ruffed Grouse, Woodcock, Pheasant, Chukar, Ducks; **Dogs** Avail/HDW; **Packages** 1/2 Day, 1-25 guns
○ NAGA/See Pg. 72

Upland Sports of South Hero, Inc.
PO Box 260, South Hero, VT 05486
(802) 372-6648 Daniel Farnham
Type Public; **Shoots** Field; **Birds** Quail, Pheasant, Chukar ○ NAGA/See Pg. 72

The Vermont Sportsman
HCR70, Box 42, Morgan, VT 05853
(802) 895-4209 Bob/Maryann/Andy Beaupre
12 mi. E of Newport
Type Public; **On Site** Clubhouse, Lodging, Meals; **Shoots** Field; **Birds** Ruffed Grouse, Woodcock; **Dogs** HDW

VIRGINIA

Buffalo Creek Farms, Inc.
Rt. 1, Box 232, Lynch Station, VA 24571
(540) 297-6626 Robert & Ed Ott 8-5
36 mi. E of Roanoke
Est 1992; **Acres** 1,050; **Type** Public; **On Site** Clubhouse, Lodging, Meals, Clays; **Shoots** Field; **Birds** Quail, Pheasant, Chukar; **Dogs** Avail/HDW; **Packages** 1/2 Day, 1-8 guns ○ NAGA/See Pg. 72
See Our Ad Across Right

SHOOT THE BEST

CHARLES CITY
SPORTING CLAYS &
HUNTING PRESERVE

Charles City Hunting Preserve
501 Shirley Plantation Rd., Charles City, VA 23030
(804) 829-6270 Charles Carter
19 mi. SE of Richmond
Est 1994; **Acres** 1,000; **Type** Public; **On Site** Clubhouse, Meals, Clays; **Shoots** Field, Tower, Blinds; **Birds** Dove, Quail, Pheasant, Chukar, Ducks; **Dogs** Avail/HDW; **Packages** 1/2 Day, 1-10 guns
Charles City Hunting Preserve offers the novice to advanced shooter one of the most diverse hunting experiences in the DC area. We have guided and unguided tours, loaner guns and offer airport pickup from nearby Richmond International Airport. Our 1/2 day package includes 10 quail & 4 pheasants. For non-shooters and visitors, we have the lovely Shirley Plantation to roam and a gift shop to visit. Our sporting clays offers a terrific challenge with 45 stations. Please call for reservations: (804) 829-6270.

Eastern Shore Safaris
6276 Sturgis House Rd., Jamesville, VA 23398
(804) 442-6035 Tom Webb
40 mi. E of VA Beach
Est 1982; **Acres** 2,500; **Hunters/yr** 500; **Type** Public, Member/Avail; **On Site** Clubhouse, Lodging, Meals, Clays; **Shoots** Field, Blinds, Boat; **Birds** Dove, Quail, Woodcock, Ducks, Geese; **Dogs** Avail/HDW; **Packages** 1/2 Day, 2-100 guns

Falkland Farms
PO Box 1297, Halifax, VA 24558
(804) 575-1400 Tom Rowland 8-5
90 mi. SW of Richmond
Est 1991; **Acres** 7,700; **Hunters/yr** 150; **Type** Public; **On Site** Clubhouse, Lodging, Meals, Clays; **Shoots** Field, Driven, Blinds, Boat; **Birds** Dove, Quail, Turkey, Ducks; **Dogs** Avail/HDW; **Packages** 1 Day, 2-14 guns

Feathers-Fur & Fin Kennels
Rt. 1, Box 255, Keysville, VA 23947
(804) 568-3944 Bill Hall
50 mi. SE of Lynchburg
Acres 600; **Hunters/yr** 60; **Type** Public; **On Site**
Clubhouse, Lodging, Clays; **Shoots** Field, Blinds;
Birds Dove, Quail, Ducks; **Dogs** Avail

Forest Green Shooting Preserve
Forest Green Ln., PO Box 361, Spotsylvania, VA 22553
(540) 582-2566 Leory Hilsmier 8-8
60 mi. S of Washington, DC
Est 1989; **Acres** 380; **Type** Public, Member/Avail,
Corp.; **On Site** Clubhouse, Meals, Clays; **Shoots**
Field; **Birds** Dove, Quail, Pheasant; **Dogs**
Avail/HDW; **Packages** 1/2 Day, 1-4 guns
○ NAGA/See Pg. 72

Fort Lewis Lodge, Inc.
HCR03, Box 21A, Millboro, VA 24460
(540) 925-2314 John Cowden Evenings
65 mi. NE of Roanoke
Est 1988; **Acres** 3,200; **Type** Public; **On Site**
Clubhouse, Lodging, Meals; **Shoots** Field; **Birds**
Pheasant, Turkey; **Dogs** Avail/HDW; **Packages** 1/2
Day, 2-6 guns

Jonakin Creek Hunt Club
Rt. 1, Box 417, Gladehill, VA 24092
(540) 576-1223 Eddie Shelton
26 mi. S of Roanoke
Est 1990; **Acres** 1,200; **Type** Public, Member/Avail;
On Site Clubhouse; **Shoots** Field; **Birds** Quail;
Dogs Avail/HDW; **Packages** 1/2 Day, 2-12 guns

King Kennels & Shooting Preserve
PO Box 563, Rixeyville, VA 22737
(540) 937-4310 Naomi Ray
55 mi. SW of Washington, DC
Est 1936; **Acres** 123; **Type** Public; **Shoots** Field;
Birds Quail, Pheasant; **Dogs** Avail/HDW; **Packages**
1/2 Day, 1-6 guns

Lorraine Farms Shooting Preserve
Rt. 3, Box 282, Farmville, VA 23901
(804) 223-8233 Harry Lowry
65 mi. SW of Richmond
Type Public; **Shoots** Field; **Birds** Quail, Pheasant;
Dogs Avail; **Packages** 1 Day

Magnolia Shooting Preserve
101 Philhower Dr., Suffolk, VA 23434
(804) 539-6296 M. Dewey Howell
65 mi. SW of Norfolk
Est 1979; **Acres** 420; **Hunters/yr** 300; **Type**
Public, Member/Avail; **Shoots** Field; **Birds** Quail,
Pheasant, Chukar, Huns; **Dogs** Avail/HDW;
Packages 1/2 Day, 1-6 guns

Merrimac Farm
Hunting Preserve
14710 Deepwood Lane, Nokesville, VA 22123
(703) 594-2276 Dean N. McDowell
30 mi. SW of Washington, DC
Est 1971; **Acres** 296; **Type** Public, Member/Avail;
Shoots Field; **Birds** Quail, Pheasant, Chukar, Huns;
Dogs Avail/HDW; **Packages** 1/2 Day, 1-12 guns
○ NAGA/See Pg. 72

Mountain Empire Quail Ranch
Rt. 2, Box 550, Marion, VA 24354
(540) 646-5452 Fred Rupard
85 mi. SW of Roanoke
Acres 125; **Type** Public; **Shoots** Field; **Birds** Quail;
Dogs Avail

Old Coppermine Hunting Preserve
PO Box 450, Keysville, VA 23947
(804) 736-9495 J.W. Bolton
70 mi. SW of Richmond
Acres 5,400; **Hunters/yr** 200; **Type** Public;
Shoots Field; **Birds** Quail, Turkey

Orapax Plantation
3831 River Rd. W., Goochland, VA 23063
(804) 556-4856 Nancy Dykers 8 to 8
35 mi. NW of Richmond
Est 1987; **Acres** 675; **Hunters/yr** 500; **Type**
Public; **Shoots** Field, Tower; **Birds** Quail, Turkey;
Dogs HDW; **Packages** 1/2 Day, 1-4 guns
O NAGA/See Pg. 72

Piedmont Guides & Gunners, Inc.
Rt. 2, Box 12, Louisa, VA 23093
(540) 967-3647 Howard Scheurenbrand, Jr.
16 mi. E of Charlottesville
Acres 200; **Hunters/yr** 125; **Type** Public,
Member/Avail; **On Site** Clubhouse, Clays; **Shoots**
Field, Blinds; **Birds** Dove, Quail, Pheasant, Geese;
Dogs Avail; **Packages** 1/2 Day

Plain Dealing Hunting Preserve
Rt. 2, Box 72, Center Cross, VA 22437
(804) 443-4592 Ron Edwards Evening
100 mi. S of Washington, DC
Est 1983; **Acres** 280; **Type** Public, Member/Avail,
Corp.; **Shoots** Field, Tower, Driven; **Birds** Quail,
Woodcock, Pheasant, Turkey, Ducks; **Dogs**
Avail/HDW; **Packages** 1/2 Day, 2-12 guns

Primland

Rt. 1, Box 265-C, Claudville, VA 24076
(540) 251-8012 Johnny Lambert 8:30-5, M-F
60 mi. N of Greensboro
Est 1987; **Acres** 14,000; **Type** Public, Corp.; **On
Site** Clubhouse, Lodging, Meals, Clays; **Shoots** Field,
Tower, Driven; **Birds** Quail, Pheasant, Turkey, Ducks;
Dogs Avail/HDW; **Packages** 1/2 Day, 1-12 guns
See Our Ads Below Left & Across

Red Oak Ranch-Virginia Upland Outfitters
Red Oak Ranch, Hightown, VA 24444
(540) 468-2949 Ken Martin 8:30am-Dark
90 mi. NW of Roanoke
Est 1985; **Acres** 4,500; **Hunters/yr** 200; **Type**
Public; **On Site** Clubhouse, Lodging, Meals, Clays;
Shoots Field; **Birds** Turkey; **Dogs** Avail/HDW;
Packages 3 Days, 1-16 guns

Sundance Hunting
Preserve, Inc.
PO Box 91, Orlean, VA 22128
(540) 364-9525 Dave Bierlein
35 mi. W of Washington, DC
Est 1989; **Acres** 400; **Hunters/yr** 100; **Type**
Public; **On Site** Clubhouse; **Shoots** Field; **Birds**
Quail, Pheasant, Geese; **Dogs** Avail/HDW;
Packages 1/2 Day, up to 3 guns
O Airport Pickup   O Deer Hunting
O Shooting Instruction   O Brochure Available
O Fishing   O Quality Clubhouse
O Family Run Business

Primland Hunting Reserve...The Secret's Out

Long the "best kept secret" of a small group of discriminating sportsmen, Primland Hunting Reserve is emerging to take its place as one of the finest facilities of its type in the United States.

Located in the beautiful Blue Ridge Mountains of Patrick County, VA, the Reserve is easily reached from Greensboro, Winston-Salem, and Charlotte, NC, Richmond and Roanoke, VA and worth a trip from practically anywhere. And no wonder: Primland's combination of hunting--ranging from European Style Pheasant Shoots to Deer Hunts--sporting clays, and private dining lodging is difficult to match.

The pulse-quickening action of a traditional English pheasant shoot.

Upland Style Hunts

If Primland specializes in anything, it's fully guided upland style pheasant and quail hunts catered to the individual demands of the hunter, whether new to the sport or a "campaign" veteran. Primland's varied cover--grain and corn fields, thickets and forested ravines--are intensely managed to provide abundant game and ample shooting opportunities. Hunters may bring their own dogs or shoot over one of Primland's healthy and highly trained pointers, setters, brittanys, short hairs or labradors.

European Style Pheasant Shoots

Not long ago, you'd have to make the costly and time-consuming trip to Europe to experience the exhilaration of a traditional British pheasant shoot. No longer. The rolling hills and mountains of Primland's Estate creates a terrain almost custom designed for this type of challenging shoot. Each shooter is paired with a loader and moves from marked station to station aboard horse drawn wagons. Birds are pushed over the guns and retrievers pick up downed birds. Hardy and sporty flying ringnecks are released the day of the shoot and throughout the year and these birds, flying from 20 to 50 yards aloft, create challenging and competitive shooting. Loaders and dog handlers on the shoot are dressed in European style shooting attire--an added touch that lends air of authenticity.

Deer hunting and a unique released duck hunt round out Primland's hunting menu and trout fishing in one of the Estate's 3 ponds provides a thoroughly relaxing counterpoint to the pulse-quickening hunting available.

Sporting Clays--Rated Tops

Majestically laid out in the foothills of the Blue Ridge Mountains, Primland's 12 station sporting clays course was chosen one of the top 25 in the country by Esquire Magazine. Shooters traverse the 1 mile course on foot or golf cart and are challenged by simulated hunting shots. Primland also offers a fast and furious five stand clay game. At Primland, guests find either game a great way to spend quality time with friends, family, colleagues or clients.

Lodging and Dining

Virtually the only thing to challenge the sporting opportunities at Primland is the quality of its lodging and dining services. Captivating chalets and cabins, each different in character and most with majestic mountain or valley views, provide a welcome retreat for weary hunters.

Hunters and guests find their day in the field or on the sporting clays course punctuated by superb meals prepared by Primland's chef de cuisine and staff at a private restaurant located on the property. The restaurant's dining room will seat up to 100 people and is perfect for corporate meetings.

Primland Hunting Reserve offers something for everyone—individuals, families and corporations. Reservations are required, so make plans to visit soon. **Write Primland Hunting Reserve, Rt. 1, Box 265-C, Claudville, VA 24076; Fax 540-251-8244; or call 540-251-8012.**

Sussex Shooting Sports
Box 624 (Rt. 460), Waverly, VA 23890
(804) 834-3200 Bob Hall
35 mi. SE of Richmond
Est 1991; **Acres** 300; **Type** Public; **On Site**
Clubhouse, Clays; **Shoots** Field; **Birds** Quail, Ducks;
Dogs Avail/HDW; **Packages** 1/2 Day, 1-4 guns

Tulloch Farm at Gynnfield
PO Box 1408, Tampahanac, VA 22560
(804) 370-4975 Tom Tullidge
Acres 700; **Type** Public; **Shoots** Field, Blinds;
Birds Quail, Pheasant, Chukar, Ducks; **Dogs**
Avail/HDW; **Packages** 1/2 Day

Walnut Run Shooting Preserve
26233 Raccoon Ford Rd., Culpeper, VA 22701
(540) 423-1569 Don Taylor 7 to 9 pm
55 mi. SW of Washington, DC
Est 1989; **Acres** 170; **Hunters/yr** 80; **Type**
Member/Ltd; **Shoots** Field; **Birds** Quail, Pheasant;
Dogs Avail/HDW; **Packages** 1/2 Day, 2-6 guns

Windwood Farm
2014 Martinsburg Pike, Winchester, VA 22603
(540) 667-1045 Linwood R. Williamson 7 to 10 pm
Est 1986; **Acres** 166; **Hunters/yr** 200; **Type** Public;
On Site Clubhouse; **Shoots** Field; **Birds** Pheasant;
Dogs Avail/HDW; **Packages** 1/2 Day, 4-6 guns

WASHINGTON

Acme Hunting Club
3110 Standard Rd., Acme, WA 98220
(360) 595-2725 Jim Lallas
Type Public, Member/Avail; **On Site** Lodging, Clays;
Shoots Field; **Birds** Quail, Pheasant, Chukar, Ducks

Banks Lake Rod & Gun Club
HCR Box 357-A, Coulee City, WA 99115
(509) 632-5502 Jimmy Pitts 6-8am; 7-9pm
100 mi. W of Spokane **Acres** 17,000; **Type** Public,
Member/Avail, Corp.; **On Site** Clubhouse; **Shoots**
Field; **Birds** Dove, Quail, Pheasant, Chukar, Huns,
Ducks, Geese; **Dogs** Avail/HDW; **Packages** 1/2
Day, 1-10 guns o NAGA/See Pg. 72

Cooke Canyon Hunt Club
861 Cooke Canyon Rd., Ellensburg, WA 98926
(509) 968-4844 Ed Nestler, Pres.
115 mi. E of Seattle
Est 1991; **Acres** 1,400; **Hunters/yr** 300; **Type**
Member/Avail, Corp.; **On Site** Clubhouse, Clays;
Shoots Field, Blinds; **Birds** Quail, Pheasant, Chukar,
Turkey, Ducks; **Dogs** Avail/HDW; **Packages** 1/2
Day, 1-4 guns o NAGA/See Pg. 72

Goodnight's Hunting Preserve
345 Stegeman Rd., Bickleton, WA 99322
(509) 896-2923 Lawrence Goodnight Evenings
130 mi. NW of Portland, OR
Est 1990; **Acres** 1,800; **Type** Public, Member/Avail,
Corp.; **On Site** Clubhouse, Lodging, Meals, Clays;
Shoots Field; **Birds** Pheasant, Chukar; **Dogs**
Avail/HDW; **Packages** 1/2 Day, 3-20 guns

Landt Farms Shooting Preserve
W. 16308 Four Mound Rd., Nine Mile Falls, WA 99026
(509) 466-4036 Ellwood/Dolly Landt 6-9am, 4-9pm
10 mi. NW of Spokane
Est 1984; **Acres** 500; **Hunters/yr** 1,200; **Type**
Public, Member/Avail, Corp.; **On Site** Clubhouse,
Clays; **Shoots** Field; **Birds** Pheasant, Chukar;
Packages 1/2 Day o NAGA/See Pg. 72

Lincoln Creek Hunting Club
1401 Lincoln Creek Rd., Rochester, WA 98579
(360) 736-6609 Lorraine Smith Evenings
85 mi. SW of Seattle
Est 1962; **Type** Public; **On Site** Clubhouse, Clays;
Shoots Field, Blinds; **Birds** Pheasant, Ducks; **Dogs**
Avail/HDW; **Packages** 1/2 Day, up to 3 guns

Nate Johnson Hunting Club
1929 A Dry Slough Rd., Mount Vernon, WA 98273
(360) 445-6015 Nate Johnson
60 mi. N of Seattle
Est 1985; **Acres** 1,200; **Type** Public, Member/Avail;
Shoots Field, Blinds; **Birds** Pheasant, Ducks; **Dogs** HDW

North American Gamebird Hunt
Rt. 1, Box 71, Edwall, WA 99008
(509) 236-2241 Alan Burgess
45 mi. W of Spokane
Est 1993; **Acres** 800; **Type** Member/Avail;
Shoots Field; **Birds** Pheasant o NAGA/See Pg. 72

R&M Game Birds
& Sporting Clays
495 Fisher Hill Rd., Lyle, WA 98635
(509) 365-3245 Rodger L. Ford Anytime
80 mi. E of Vancouver, WA or Portland, OR
Est 1986; **Acres** 1,100; **Hunters/yr** 500; **Type**
Public, Member/Avail, Corp.; **On Site** Clubhouse,
Meals, Clays; **Shoots** Field; **Birds** Quail, Pheasant,
Chukar, Huns, Turkey; **Dogs** Avail/HDW; **Packages**
1/2 Day, 1-20 guns o NAGA/See Pg. 72

Reecer Creek
Gamebird Ranch
6623 196th SW, Lynnwood, WA 98036
(206) 776-0189 Claude Frable Anytime
12 mi. NW of Ellensburg
Est 1991; **Acres** 800; **Hunters/yr** 400; **Type**
Public; **On Site** Clubhouse, Lodging, Meals, Clays;
Shoots Field; **Birds** Quail, Pheasant, Chukar, Huns;
Dogs Avail/HDW; **Packages** 1/2 Day, 1-4 guns
o NAGA/See Pg. 72

WEST VIRGINIA

Kincheloe Pheasant Hunting Preserve
Rt. 2, Box 88A, Jane Lew, WV 26378
(304) 884-7431 Paul Hughes 8-10pm
123 mi. N of Charleston **Est** 1983; **Acres** 1,000;
Hunters/yr 2,000; **Type** Public, Corp.; **On Site**
Clubhouse, Lodging, Meals, Clays; **Shoots** Field;
Birds Dove, Quail, Ruffed Grouse, Woodcock,
Pheasant, Chukar, Turkey; **Dogs** Avail/HDW;
Packages 1/2 Day, 1-8 guns ○ NAGA/See Pg. 72

Prospect Hall Shooting Club
Rt. 1, Box 370, Kearneysville, WV 25430
(304) 728-8213 Kevin White 12 pm to 12 am
60 mi. NW of Washington, DC
Est 1985; **Acres** 400; **Hunters/yr** 500; **Type**
Member/Avail, Corp.; **On Site** Clubhouse, Lodging,
Meals, Clays; **Shoots** Field, Tower, Driven, Blinds;
Birds Dove, Quail, Pheasant, Chukar, Huns, Ducks;
Dogs Avail/HDW; **Packages** 1/2 Day, 2-24 guns
○ NAGA/See Pg. 72

WISCONSIN

Acorn Acres Hunting Club
E. 7920 Hoppe Rd., Spring Green, WI 53588
(608) 544-5451 Lester Schulenburg
Type Member/Avail, Corp.; **On Site** Clubhouse;
Shoots Field; **Dogs** Avail/HDW

Back Forty Hunting Preserve
N11055 Bandy Rd., Phillips, WI 54555
(715) 339-2823 Peter G. Jesunas After 6pm
150 mi. SE of Duluth, MN
Est 1992; **Acres** 120; **Type** Public, Member/Avail;
On Site Lodging, Meals; **Shoots** Field; **Birds** Quail,
Ruffed Grouse, Woodcock, Pheasant, Chukar; **Dogs**
Avail/HDW; **Packages** 1/2 Day, 1-6 guns

Bearskin Wildlife Reserve
8915 Church Rd., Harshaw, WI 54529
(715) 282-5362 John Hendrickson 7-9am, 6-10pm
130 mi. SE of Duluth, MN
Est 1984; **Acres** 400; **Type** Public; **Shoots** Field,
Driven; **Birds** Quail, Ruffed Grouse, Pheasant,
Chukar, Turkey, Ducks, Geese; **Dogs** Avail/HDW;
Packages 1/2 Day, up to 2 guns
○ NAGA/See Pg. 72

Big Rock Hunting Preserve
W15664 Chuck Rd., Gilman, WI 54433
(715) 668-5557 Chuck Birkenholz 7am or 7pm
60 mi. NE of Eau Claire
Est 1989; **Acres** 600; **Hunters/yr** 1,500; **Type**
Public, Member/Avail, Corp.; **On Site** Clubhouse,
Lodging, Clays; **Shoots** Field; **Birds** Quail, Ruffed
Grouse, Woodcock, Pheasant, Chukar; **Dogs**
Avail/HDW; **Packages** 1/2 Day, 1-20 guns
○ NAGA/See Pg. 72

Black Slough Conservation Club
59 Racine St., Menasha, WI 54952
(414) 722-4293 Dr. Vern Larsen
Est 1971; **Acres** 1,300; **Hunters/yr** 20; **Type**

Member/Ltd; **On Site** Clubhouse, Lodging, Clays;
Shoots Field, Blinds, Boat; **Birds** Pheasant, Ducks,
Geese; **Dogs** Avail/HDW ○ NAGA/See Pg. 72

Blonhaven Hunting Preserve
8006 N. John Paul Rd., Milton, WI 53563
(608) 868-3176 Jim Clark 7am-8pm
Est 1953; **Acres** 250; **Hunters/yr** 3,000; **Type**
Public, Member/Avail; **On Site** Clubhouse, Clays;
Shoots Field, Tower; **Birds** Pheasant, Chukar, Huns;
Dogs Avail/HDW; **Packages** 1/2 Day, 1-40 guns
○ NAGA/See Pg. 72

BURNETT GAME FARM & HUNT CLUB

4430 Imperial Dr., Brookfield, WI 5304b
(414) 781-9156 Bob Voit 8-8
60 mi. NW of Milwaukee
on the famed Horicon Marsh
Est 1964; **Acres** 6,800; **Hunters/yr** 130; **Type**
Member/Avail, Corp.; **On Site** Clubhouse, Lodging,
Meals, Clays; **Shoots** Field, Driven, Blinds, Boat;
Birds Quail, Woodcock, Pheasant, Chukar, Huns,
Ducks, Geese; **Dogs** Avail/HDW; **Packages** 1/2
Day, 2-8 guns

Cadens Kennels & Hunt Club
W2738 Scenic Dr., Campbellsport, WI 53010
(414) 533-8579 Dennis Brath 8-5pm
40 mi. NW of Milwaukee
Est 1989; **Acres** 600; **Hunters/yr** 120; **Type**
Public, Member/Avail, Corp.; **On Site** Clubhouse,
Lodging, Meals, Clays; **Shoots** Field, Tower, Blinds;
Birds Quail, Pheasant, Chukar, Huns, Geese; **Dogs**
Avail/HDW; **Packages** 1/2 Day, 1-25 guns

County Line Hunt Club
W7163 Grouse Dr., Portage, WI 53901
(608) 981-2691 Don Gneiser
40 mi. N of Madison **Est** 1992; **Acres** 145; **Type**
Public, Member/Avail, Corp.; **On Site** Clubhouse;
Shoots Field; **Birds** Pheasant; **Dogs** Avail/HDW;
Packages 1/2 Day, 1-6 guns

N5659 Popp Rd., Jefferson, WI 53549
(414) 674-3709 Peter Thomsen
30 mi. E of Madison
Est 1991; **Acres** 500; **Type** Public, Member/Avail,
Corp.; **On Site** Clubhouse; **Shoots** Field; **Birds**
Pheasant, Chukar; **Dogs** Avail/HDW; **Packages** 1/2
Day ○ NAGA/See Pg. 72
○ 40 Mi. West of Milwaukee

WINGS

Crooked Creek Hunt Club
W1896 Prairie Rd., Burlington, WI 53105
(414) 763-6597 John Parat 8am-8pm
5 mi. W of Lake Geneva
Est 1993; **Acres** 120; **Hunters/yr** 500; **Type**
Public, Member/Avail, Corp.; **On Site** Clubhouse;
Shoots Field; **Birds** Quail, Pheasant, Chukar, Huns;
Dogs Avail/HDW; **Packages** 1/2 Day, 1-12 guns
○ NAGA/See Pg. 72

E&E Game Farm
102 County Line Lane, Kewaskum, WI 53040
(414) 626-2820 Perry Etta
Type Public; **Shoots** Field; **Birds** Quail, Pheasant,
Chukar, Huns ○ NAGA/See Pg. 72

Eastman
Hunting Club, Inc.
527 Hillside Rd., Edgerton, WI 53534
(608) 884-6588 Tom Eastman
30 mi. S of Madison
Acres 700; **Type** Member/Ltd, Corp.; **On Site**
Clubhouse, Clays; **Shoots** Field; **Birds** Quail,
Pheasant, Chukar, Huns ○ NAGA/See Pg. 72
Eastman Hunting Club is an exclusive recreational
game farm. Membership is limited to minimize
crowding. A maximum of two new members are
accepted per year. At Eastman's, fields and hunting conditions are maintained to recreate the
rugged natural hunting of a bygone era. Only serious inquiries welcome.

David A. Eilertson
105 S. 7th St., LaCrosse, WI 54601
(608) 781-7519 David A. Eilertson 6:30-9:30pm
120 mi. SE of Minneapolis
Est 1984; **Acres** 165; **Hunters/yr** 30; **Type**
Member/Avail; **On Site** Clubhouse, Meals, Clays;
Shoots Field; **Birds** Pheasant; **Dogs** Avail/HDW;
Packages 1/2 Day, up to 6 guns

Fence Line Hunt Club
10759 W. 8 Mile Rd., Franksville, WI 53126
(414) 425-8112 Richard Prihoda
15 mi. SW of Milwaukee
Acres 105; **Type** Public, Member/Avail; **On Site**
Clubhouse; **Shoots** Field; **Birds** Quail, Pheasant;
Dogs HDW; **Packages** 1/2 Day, 1-4 guns ○
NAGA/See Pg. 72

Forest Ridge Hunt Club
PO Box 128, Glenwood City, WI 54013
(715) 265-4286 Tom Whitten
55 mi. NE of Minneapolis
Est 1990; **Acres** 1,600; **Type** Public, Member/Avail,
Corp.; **On Site** Clubhouse, Lodging, Meals; **Shoots**

Field; **Birds** Quail, Pheasant, Chukar; **Dogs**
Avail/HDW; **Packages** 1/2 Day, 1-30 guns

Fox Ridge Game Farm
8585 Valley Line Rd., Oconto Falls, WI 54154
(414) 846-2508 Bill or Kathy 7am-1pm
135 mi. N of Milwaukee
Est 1988; **Acres** 1,000; **Hunters/yr** 700; **Type**
Public, Member/Avail; **On Site** Clubhouse, Lodging,
Clays; **Shoots** Field, Tower; **Birds** Quail, Pheasant,
Chukar; **Dogs** Avail/HDW; **Packages** 1/2·Day, 1-6
guns ○ NAGA/See Pg. 72

Game Unlimited Hunting Club
871 Ct. Rd. E., Hudson, WI 54016
(715) 246-2350 Patrick Melloy 6am-10pm
20 mi. E of Minneapolis
Est 1963; **Acres** 1,000; **Type** Member/Avail, Corp.;
On Site Clubhouse, Lodging, Meals, Clays; **Shoots**
Field, Tower, Blinds; **Birds** Quail, Pheasant, Chukar,
Ducks; **Dogs** Avail/HDW

Geneva National Hunt Club
555 Hunt Club Court, Lake Geneva, WI 53147
(414) 245-7203 Bruce Kapanky 9-5, T-Su
45 mi. from Milwaukee
Est 1990; **Acres** 400; **Hunters/yr** 2,000; **Type**
Public, Member/Avail, Corp.; **On Site** Clubhouse,
Lodging, Meals, Clays; **Shoots** Field, Blinds, Boat;
Birds Quail, Woodcock, Pheasant, Chukar, Huns,
Snipe, Ducks, Geese; **Dogs** Avail/HDW; **Packages**
1/2 Day, 2-5 guns ○ NAGA/See Pg. 72

Ghost Lake Lodge
Rt. 7, Box 7450, Hayward, WI 54843
(715) 462-3939 Bill Gryzik
140 mi. NE of Minneapolis-St.Paul
Acres 900,000; **Type** Public; **On Site** Clubhouse,
Lodging, Meals; **Shoots** Field; **Birds** Ruffed Grouse,
Woodcock, Ducks; **Dogs** Avail/HDW; **Packages** 3
Days, 2-40 guns

Donald Gneiser
W7163 Grouse Rd., Portage, WI 53901
40 mi. N of Madison
Acres 145; **Type** Public, Member/Avail; **On Site**
Clubhouse; **Shoots** Field; **Birds** Pheasant; **Dogs** Avail

Golden Heritage Farms
5221 County Rd. N., Pickett, WI 54964
(414) 589-4852 Dic Schultz After 7pm
60 mi. NW of Milwaukee
Est 1985; **Acres** 82; **Hunters/yr** 50; **Type** Public,
Corp.; **On Site** Clubhouse, Meals, Clays; **Shoots**
Field, Blinds; **Birds** Pheasant, Ducks, Geese; **Dogs**
Avail/HDW; **Packages** 1/2 Day, 2-4 guns

Hawe Hunting Preserve
N2594 Blueberry Lane, Waldo, WI 53093
(414) 528-8388 Tom Hawe
35 mi. N of Milwaukee
Est 1950; **Acres** 700; **Type** Public, Member/Avail,
Corp.; **On Site** Clubhouse, Clays; **Shoots** Field;
Birds Quail, Woodcock, Pheasant, Chukar, Ducks;
Dogs Avail/HDW; **Packages** 1/2 Day, 2-20 guns
○ NAGA/See Pg. 72

Highland Hunt Club
N3041W Cty A, Cascade, WI 53011
(414) 528-8848 Mike or Joann Sommers 8-7, T-Su
50 mi. N of Milwaukee
Est 1989; **Acres** 291; **Type** Public, Member/Avail;
On Site Clubhouse, Meals; **Shoots** Field, Driven;
Birds Quail, Pheasant, Chukar, Huns; **Dogs**
Avail/HDW; **Packages** 1/2 Day, 1-4 guns
O NAGA/See Pg. 72

Isaacson's Pheasant Pharm
Rt. 1, Box 365, Sarona, WI 54870
(715) 635-9586 Sylvia & Scott Isaacson Anytime
85 mi. S of Duluth
Est 1988; **Acres** 200; **Type** Public; **Shoots** Field;
Birds Pheasant; **Dogs** Avail/HDW; **Packages** 1/2
Day, 2-4 guns O NAGA/See Pg. 72

J&H Game Farm
RR1, Box 221, Shiocton, WI 54170
(715) 758-8134 James or Joanne Johnson 8-6
27 mi. W of Green Bay
Est 1968; **Acres** 400; **Hunters/yr** 1,000; **Type**
Member/Avail, Corp.; **On Site** Clubhouse, Meals,
Clays; **Shoots** Field, Tower; **Birds** Quail, Pheasant,
Chukar; **Dogs** Avail/HDW; **Packages** 1/2 Day, 1-4
guns O NAGA/See Pg. 72

K 'N K Hi Lo, Inc.
N265 County "T", Endeavor, WI 53930
(608) 587-2696 Darwin Kottka
40 mi. N of Madison
Est 1963; **Acres** 700; **Type** Public, Member/Avail,
Corp.; **On Site** Clubhouse; **Shoots** Field; **Birds**
Pheasant; **Dogs** Avail/HDW

Kidder Game Farm
1582 Co. Cty. N., Milton, WI 53563
(608) 868-2376 Warren/Nancy/Clark 8am-10pm
30 mi. from Madison
Est 1960; **Acres** 300; **Type** Public; **Shoots** Field;
Birds Quail, Pheasant, Chukar, Turkey; **Dogs**
Avail/HDW; **Packages** 1/2 Day, up to 1 guns
O NAGA/See Pg. 72

Longshot Sportsman's Club
N8995 Townline Rd., Van Dyne, WI 54979
(414) 688-2314 John Eiden
75 mi. NW of Milwaukee
Est 1987; **Acres** 410; **Hunters/yr** 250; **Type**
Public, Member/Avail, Corp.; **On Site** Clubhouse,
Meals, Clays; **Shoots** Field, Driven, Blinds; **Birds**
Quail, Pheasant, Chukar, Ducks, Geese; **Dogs**
Avail/HDW; **Packages** 1/2 Day, 1-24 guns

Martin Fish & Game Farm
W10681 Hwy. 127, Portage, WI 53901
(608) 742-7205 Jim Martin
Type Public, Member/Avail; **Shoots** Field; **Birds** Quail,
Pheasant, Chukar, Huns, Ducks O NAGA/See Pg. 72

Mecan River Outfitters
Rt. 2, Box 103, Princeton, WI 54968
(414) 295-3439 Paul Harvey
45 mi. W of Oshkosh
Acres 400; **Hunters/yr** 600; **Type** Public,

Member/Avail; **On Site** Clubhouse, Lodging, Meals,
Clays; **Shoots** Field, Tower; **Birds** Pheasant, Chukar,
Turkey; **Dogs** Avail

Oak Hill Hunting Preserve
W8718 Forest Ave., Eldorado, WI 54932
(414) 921-2776 Paul Snider
50 mi. N of Milwaukee
Acres 500; **Type** Public, Member/Avail, Corp.; **On
Site** Clubhouse; **Shoots** Field; **Birds** Quail,
Pheasant, Chukar, Ducks, Geese; **Dogs** Avail/HDW
O NAGA/See Pg. 72

Oakwood Kennel & Game Farm
7149 Badger Lane, Allenton, WI 53002
(414) 488-5852 Ron or Dianne Norman 7am-7pm
30 mi. NW of Milwaukee
Est 1989; **Acres** 150; **Hunters/yr** 100; **Type**
Public, Member/Avail, Corp.; **On Site** Clubhouse,
Clays; **Shoots** Field, Blinds; **Birds** Quail, Pheasant,
Chukar, Huns, Ducks, Geese; **Dogs** Avail/HDW;
Packages 1/2 Day O NAGA/See Pg. 72

Our Farm
PO Box 108, Eastman, WI 54626
(608) 874-4556 Rudy Wendt
80 mi. W of Madison
Est 1992; **Acres** 278; **Type** Public, Member/Avail,
Corp.; **On Site** Clays; **Shoots** Field; **Birds** Quail,
Pheasant, Chukar, Huns, Turkey; **Dogs** Avail/HDW;
Packages 1/2 Day, 1-4 guns O NAGA/See Pg. 72

Palmquist's "The Farm"
N5136 River Rd., Brantwood, WI 54513
(800) 519-2558 Helen & JIm Palmquist
60 mi. N of Wausau
Est 1949; **Acres** 800; **Type** Public; **On Site**
Clubhouse, Lodging, Meals; **Shoots** Field; **Birds**
Ruffed Grouse, Woodcock, Ducks, Geese; **Dogs**
Avail/HDW

Pheasant City Hunt Club
R#1, Box 272, Markesan, WI 53946
(414) 324-5813 Bill/Debbie Scallon
65 mi. NW of Milwaukee
Est 1957; **Acres** 640; **Type** Public, Member/Avail,
Corp.; **On Site** Clubhouse, Lodging, Meals, Clays;
Shoots Field, Tower, Blinds; **Birds** Quail, Pheasant,
Chukar, Ducks, Geese; **Dogs** Avail/HDW; **Packages**
1/2 Day

Pheasant Retreat Game Farm
7617 Prellwitz Rd., Ripon, WI 54971
(414) 748-9427 Dick & Deb 6am-10pm
70 mi. NW of Milwaukee
Est 1983; **Acres** 527; **Type** Public, Member/Avail;
On Site Clubhouse; **Shoots** Field; **Birds** Quail,
Pheasant, Chukar; **Dogs** Avail/HDW
O NAGA/See Pg. 72

Jon & Gertrude Polcyn
N4028 Cty. C, Montello, WI 53949
(608) 297-7104 Jon Polcyn
8 mi. from Montello
Acres 567; **Type** Public; **Shoots** Field; **Birds** Quail,
Ruffed Grouse, Pheasant

WINGS

Quail Haven Hunt Club
Rt. 4, Box 821, Clintonville, WI 54929
(715) 823-6123 Michael K. Duffey 6:30-9am
35 mi. W of Green Bay
Est 1985; **Acres** 200; **Hunters/yr** 20; **Type**
Public; **On Site** Clubhouse, Clays; **Shoots** Field;
Birds Quail, Ruffed Grouse, Woodcock, Pheasant,
Chukar; **Dogs** Avail/HDW; **Packages** 1/2 Day, 2-4
guns

R&R Ranch
8923 Richfield Dr., Marshfield, WI 54449
(715) 676-3365 Steve Strong
6 mi. S of Marshfield
Est 1985; **Acres** 700; **Hunters/yr** 300; **Type**
Public, Member/Avail; **On Site** Clubhouse, Lodging,
Meals, Clays; **Shoots** Field; **Birds** Quail, Ruffed
Grouse, Pheasant, Chukar; **Dogs** Avail/HDW;
Packages 1/2 Day, 1-100 guns

Richford Game Club
Rt. 1, Box 107, Coloma, WI 54930
(715) 228-3052 Vern Slife/Debb Semrow
50 mi. N of Madison
Est 1987; **Acres** 80; **Hunters/yr** 75; **Type**
Member/Avail; **Shoots** Field; **Birds** Pheasant;
Dogs HDW; **Packages** 1/2 Day, up to 20 guns

River Wildlife
, Kohler, WI 53044
(414) 457-0134 Max Grube 7am-6pm
55 mi. N of Milwaukee
Est 1977; **Acres** 250; **Hunters/yr** 1,000; **Type**
Member/Avail, Corp.; **On Site** Clubhouse, Lodging,
Meals, Clays; **Shoots** Field; **Birds** Pheasant, Chukar,
Turkey; **Dogs** Avail/HDW; **Packages** 1/2 Day, 1-15
guns O NAGA/See Pg. 72

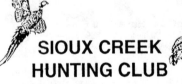

SIOUX CREEK HUNTING CLUB

PO Box 561, Chetek, WI 54728
(715) 237-2805 Jimmy Lane 12 Noon
80 mi. NE of Minneapolis
Est 1989; **Acres** 800; **Hunters/yr** 300; **Type**
Public, Member/Avail; **On Site** Clubhouse, Meals,
Clays; **Shoots** Field, Blinds; **Birds** Quail, Pheasant,
Chukar, Huns, Ducks; **Dogs** Avail/HDW; **Packages**
1 Day, 1-15 guns

O Airport Pickup	O Bird Processing
O Sporting Clays	O Gourmet Meals
O Train Bird Dogs	O Loaner Guns
O Brochure Available	O On-Site Pro Shop
O Factory Ammunition	O Quality Clubhouse
O Family Run Business	

Smoky Lake Reserve
1 Lake St., PO Box 100, Phelps, WI 54554
(715) 545-2333 Miriam Saucke 9-5, M-F
45 mi. NE of Rhinelander **Est** 1966; **Acres** 6,000;
Hunters/yr 100; **Type** Member/Avail, Corp.; **On
Site** Clubhouse, Lodging, Meals, Clays; **Shoots** Field,
Blinds; **Birds** Quail, Ruffed Grouse, Woodcock,
Pheasant, Chukar, Turkey, Ducks; **Dogs** Avail/HDW;
Packages 1/2 Day, 1-16 guns O NAGA/See Pg. 72

Spring Valley
Hunting Preserve
15201 Lang Rd., Orfordville, WI 53576
(608) 879-2628 Lyle Yaun 7am-9pm
15 mi. W of Janesville
Est 1985; **Acres** 130; **Hunters/yr** 400; **Type**
Public; **On Site** Clubhouse; **Shoots** Field; **Birds**
Quail, Pheasant; **Dogs** Avail/HDW; **Packages** 1/2
Day, 2-12 guns O NAGA/See Pg. 72

Strebig's Game Farm & Shooting Preserve
N 3215 CTHE, Medford, WI 54451
(715) 748-2883 Tim Strebig
50 mi. NW of Wausau
Est 1990; **Acres** 600; **Type** Public, Member/Avail,
Corp.; **On Site** Clubhouse; **Shoots** Field; **Birds**
Pheasant; **Dogs** Avail/HDW; **Packages** 1/2 Day
O NAGA/See Pg. 72

Summit Lake Game Farm
PO Box 810, Hayward, WI 54843
(715) 354-7241 John Treslley
75 mi. SE of Superior
Est 1990; **Acres** 5,000; **Hunters/yr** 1,500; **Type**
Public, Member/Avail, Corp.; **On Site** Clubhouse,
Lodging, Meals, Clays; **Shoots** Field, Blinds, Boat;
Birds Quail, Ruffed Grouse, Woodcock, Pheasant,
Chukar, Huns, Turkey, Ducks, Geese; **Dogs**
Avail/HDW; **Packages** 1/2 Day, 1-5 guns
ENJOY THE BEST HUNTING WISCONSIN HAS TO
OFFER! Summit Lake Game Farm is a sportsman's
paradise, a 5,000 acre game preserve. A 60 acre
private lake, numerous creeks, ponds and marshes
are found amidst the 5 square miles of woodlands.
Here sportsmen will find abundant deer, bear,
grouse, woodcock and upland birds. Upon arrival
at Summit Lake, we will provide you with everything you need to make your stay as enjoyable as
possible. We offer two lake-side lodges and one
right in the middle of the preserve. After the hunt,
relax in our Club House, nestled among towering
pines, and watch majestic bald eagles soar overhead. Quality upland bird hunts ensured. Fishing,
too. A pro shop, shooting instruction, dog training,
trap range and bird processing also available. Call
today for more information.

Tall Feathers Corporation
PO Box 37, Nashotah, WI 53058
(414) 781-2270 Barth Chudik
Type Member/Avail; **On Site** Lodging; **Shoots**
Field; **Birds** Pheasant, Chukar O NAGA/See Pg. 72

Tamarack Game Farm
N8745 Cty. Rd. G, Colfax, WI 54730
(715) 632-2346 Stan Lorenz Eve.
65 mi. E of Minneapolis, MN
Est 1987; **Acres** 240; **Hunters/yr** 25; **Type**
Public; **Shoots** Field; ; **Dogs** Avail/HDW;
Packages 1/2 Day, 1-8 guns o NAGA/See Pg. 72

Three Lakes Preserve
PO Box 440, Three Lakes, WI 54562
(715) 546-8289 Roger Devenport
Type Public; **On Site** Lodging; **Shoots** Field; **Birds**
Pheasant, Turkey o NAGA/See Pg. 72

Thunderbird Game Farm
W23119 Thunderbird Rd., Chilton, WI 53014
(414) 853-3030 Leonard Leberg
30 mi. S of Green Bay
Est 1967; **Acres** 400; **Type** Member/Avail,
Member/Ltd; **On Site** Clubhouse, Meals, Clays;
Shoots Field, Tower, Blinds; **Birds** Pheasant, Ducks,
Geese; **Dogs** Avail/HDW o NAGA/See Pg. 72

Top Gun Farms
N3249 Riverview Rd., Juneau, WI 53039
(414) 349-8128 David Fiedler 9-2
45 mi. NE of Madison
Est 1990; **Acres** 400; **Hunters/yr** 50; **Type**
Member/Avail, Corp.; **On Site** Clubhouse, Lodging,
Meals, Clays; **Shoots** Field, Driven, Blinds; **Birds**
Quail, Pheasant, Chukar, Huns, Ducks, Geese; **Dogs**
Avail/HDW; **Packages** 1/2 Day, 1-25 guns
o NAGA/See Pg. 72

Tumm's Pine View Game Farm
PO Box 240, Fall Creek, WI 54742
(715) 877-2434 James W. Tumm 7am-8pm
100 mi. SE of Minneapolis
Est 1988; **Type** Public; **On Site** Clubhouse;
Shoots Field; **Birds** Quail, Pheasant; **Dogs**
Avail/HDW; **Packages** 1/2 Day, 1-4 guns
o NAGA/See Pg. 72

Wern Valley Sportsmen's Club
S36W29903 Wern Way, Waukesha, WI 53188
(414) 968-2400 Steve Williams
20 mi. W of Milwaukee
Acres 700; **Type** Public, Member/Avail, Corp.; **On
Site** Clubhouse, Clays; **Birds** Quail, Pheasant, Chukar,
Huns; **Dogs** Avail/HDW o NAGA/See Pg. 72

Whispering Emerald Ridge Game Farm
N3952 640th St., Menomonie, WI 54751
(715) 235-1720 Mike Kettner/Bruce Olson anytime
60 mi. E of Minneapolis-St. Paul
Est 1989; **Type** Public; **On Site** Clubhouse, Clays;
Shoots Field; **Birds** Quail, Pheasant; **Dogs**
Avail/HDW; **Packages** 1/2 Day, 1-6 guns

Wild Wings Hunting & Fishing
N. 865 Hwy. W., Campbellsport, WI 53010
(414) 533-8738 Jim Coblentz 8-5
40 mi. N of Milwaukee
Est 1974; **Acres** 120; **Type** Public, Member/Avail,

Corp.; **On Site** Clubhouse, Meals, Clays; **Shoots**
Field; **Birds** Quail, Pheasant, Chukar; **Dogs**
Avail/HDW; **Packages** 1/2 Day, 1-50 guns

Willow Creek Ranch
N710 Bloomer Mill Rd., LaCrosse, WI 54601
(608) 788-8662 Kevin Churchill
Type Public; **On Site** Lodging, Clays; **Shoots** Field;
Birds Quail, Pheasant o NAGA/See Pg. 72

Wolf River Game Farm
Rt. 1, Box 247, Shiocton, WI 54170
(715) 758-8106 Dean Daebler
Type Public, Member/Avail; **Shoots** Field; **Birds**
Quail, Pheasant o NAGA/See Pg. 72

Woodland Pheasant Club
6799 Woodland Dr., Waunakee, WI 53597
(608) 849-5898 Lloyd Meinholz Evenings
10 mi. N of Madison
Est 1987; **Acres** 360; **Hunters/yr** 65; **Type**
Public, Member/Avail, Corp.; **On Site** Clubhouse;
Shoots Field; **Birds** Pheasant; **Dogs** Avail/HDW

Woods & Meadows Game Farm
Rt. 1, Warrens, WI 54666
(608) 378-4223 Scott Goetzka Evenings
100 mi. NW of Madison
Est 1972; **Acres** 1,055; **Hunters/yr** 400; **Type**
Public; **On Site** Clubhouse, Lodging, Clays; **Shoots**
Field; **Birds** Quail, Pheasant, Chukar; **Dogs**
Avail/HDW; **Packages** 1/2 Day, 1-12 guns
o NAGA/See Pg. 72

WYOMING

Bear Mountain Back Trails
PO Box 37, LaGrange, WY 82221
(307) 834-2281 Ellis or Linda Kessler
56 mi. NE of Cheyenne
Est 1987; **Acres** 2,000; **Type** Public, Member/Avail;
On Site Lodging, Meals, Clays; **Shoots** Field; **Birds**
Quail, Pheasant, Chukar; **Dogs** Avail/HDW;
Packages 1/2 Day, 2-10 guns o NAGA/See Pg. 72

Big Willow Pheasant Pharm
HC76, Box 47, Hawk Springs, WY 82217
(307) 532-3442 Dennis Simmons
Type Public, Member/Avail; **Shoots** Field; **Birds**
Quail, Pheasant, Chukar o NAGA/See Pg. 72

Canyon Ranch Gun Club
PO Box 282, Big Horn, WY 82833
(307) 674-9097 Jim Roach Evenings
15 mi. S of Sheridan
Est 1985; **Acres** 4,000; **Hunters/yr** 150; **Type**
Member/Ltd; **On Site** Clubhouse, Lodging, Meals,
Clays; **Shoots** Field, Driven; **Birds** Pheasant, Huns,
Turkey, Sharp Tail Grouse, Ducks; **Dogs** Avail/HDW;
Packages 1/2 Day, 4-8 guns o NAGA/See Pg. 72

WINGS

Clear Creek
Hunting Preserve
3004 Hwy. 14-16 East, Clearmont, WY 82835
(307) 737-2217 Doug Kauffman 7am-9pm
125 mi. N of Casper
Est 1980; **Acres** 700; **Hunters/yr** 800; **Type**
Public, Member/Avail, Corp.; **On Site** Clubhouse,
Lodging, Meals, Clays; **Shoots** Field, Tower, Blinds;
Birds Dove, Pheasant, Chukar, Huns, Sage Grouse,
Ducks, Geese; **Dogs** Avail/HDW; **Packages** 1/2
Day, 1-30 guns o NAGA/See Pg. 72

Clear Creek offers some of the finest Upland Game
Bird hunting in the Rocky Mountain region at the
foot of the Big Horn Mountains in secluded north-
eastern Wyoming. Our full-time conservationists
have worked for years cultivating habitats for our
Upland Game Bird hunting areas. Released in-
gnecked pheasants, Chukar and Hungarian par

rtridges supplement native stock. Whether you opt
for a morning, afternoon or all-day hunt, our experienced guides and well-trained bird dogs–Labradors,
pointers and Brittany Spaniels–work hard to make it
successful and pleasurable. Your birds can be
dressed and quick frozen after each hunt. Clear
Creek's excellent sporting clays course, including
Duck Tower, Grouse Butte, and Crazy Quail (skeet,
too), allows you to tune up before your hunt or simply enjoy an afternoon of recreation.

Milliron 2 Outfitting
1513 Culbertson, Worland, WY 82401
(307) 347-2574 Billy & Barbara Sinclair
160 mi. N of Casper, WY
Type Public; **Shoots** Field, Blinds, Boat; **Birds** Quail,
Pheasant, Chukar, Turkey, Sage Grouse, Ducks; **Dogs**
Avail

TAMAULIPAS, MEXICO

• *See Pg. 248 for "High Volume*
Wingshooting— Closer Than You Think", a
detailed article on hunting in Tamaulipas.

Arnoldo's Hunting Services
745 West Elizabeth, Brownsville, TX 78520
(210) 542-3571; in Mexico 011-52-131-67452
Contact Arnoldo Rodriquez
Birds Dove, Quail, Duck

Club Exclusive & Big Bass Tours
(800) 531-7500 Contact Rick Schroeder
Location 60 mi. S of San Fernando on Lake Guerrero
Birds Dove, Quail **U.S. Gateway** Car/van from
border **Airstrip** Yes **Agent** Bob Hallette
(713) 266-5515

Classic Adventure Group (Lodge #1)
PO Box 2186, Harlingen, TX 78557

(800) 447-6420 Dial Dunkin
Location 65 mi. S of San Fernando in Jimenez, Mex.
Est 1994 **Staff** 6-8 **Capacity** 8
Birds Dove **U.S. Gateway** Car/van from Harlingen
Airstrip Yes

Classic Adventure Group (Lodge #2)
PO Box 2186, Harlingen, TX 78557
(800) 447-6420 Dial Dunkin
Location 80 mi. N of San Fernando
Capacity Small **Birds** Duck, Geese, Quail
U.S. Gateway Car/van from Harlingen

Classic Adventure Group (Lodge #3)
PO Box 2186, Harlingen, TX 78557
(800) 447-6420 Dial Dunkin
Location 80 mi. SE of San Fernando on Lake Lorenzo
Capacity Medium **Birds** Duck, Geese, Quail
U.S. Gateway Car/van from Harlingen **Airstrip** No

Finca La Herradura Lodge
011-52-88-440944 Ruben Caballero
Location In San Fernando
Est 1989 **Staff** 20+ **Capacity** 12-30
Birds Quail, Doves, Duck, Geese **U.S. Gateway**
Car/van from Harlingen or McAllen **Airstrip** Yes
Agent Outdoor Sports Consultants; 800-992-5767;
Contact: Chuck Stankey; Bob Hallette (713) 266-5515

Gerald Glasco Kennels and Guide Service
RR7, Box 302, Marion, IL 62959
(618) 997-6583 Gerry Glasco
Birds Quail

Hacienda San Juan
c/o Outdoor Travel
1973 W. Gray, #9, Houston, TX 77019
(800) 533-7299 David Settles
Location 100 mi. S of San Fernando
Capacity 6-62 **Birds** Quail, Dove **U.S. Gateway**
Car/van from Harlingen **Airstrip** Yes

Laguna Vista Lodge
PO Box 44, Combes, TX 78535
(800) 274-4401   Roger Gerdes
Location   30 mi. E of San Fernando on Gulf Coast
Est 1989 **Staff** 10-12 **Capacity** 2-30
Birds Duck, Dove, Quail **U.S. Gateway** Car/van
from Harlingen or Brownsville **Airstrip** Yes

La Loma Lodge
c/o Sunbelt Hunting and Fishing
PO Box 3009, Brownsville, TX 78520
(800) 876-4868   Barry Batsell
Location Approx. 50 mi. W of San Fernando
Est 1993 **Staff** 12-14 **Capacity** 2-52
Birds Dove, Quail **U.S. Gateway** Car/van from
Brownsville or Harlingen **Airstrip** No
Agent   Rod & Gun Resources, Sporting Charters

La Marina del Rio
PO Box 720071, McAllen, TX 78504
011-52-132-70460, ext. 199 Cavi del Rio
Location   120 mi. SE of San Fernando on the Gulf
Coast at La Pesca
Est 1988 **Staff** 12-16 **Capacity** 2-24
Birds Duck, Geese, Quail, Dove, Turkey
U.S. Gateway Car/van from harlingen or McAllen
Airstrip Yes **Agent** Tex-Mex Hunting & Fishing;
(800) 284-1286; contact Bob Hallette

Loma Colorado Lodge
Box 202, Linn, TX 78563
(210) 380-2303   Philip Veale
Location   5 mi. E of San Fernando
Est 1986 **Staff** 12 **Capacity** 16
Birds Quail, Duck, Geese, Dove **U.S. Gateway**
Car/van from Harlingen or McAllen **Airstrip** Yes

Los Patos

PO Box 608, McAllen, TX 78505
(800) 375-4868 Fax: (210) 618-1037 Don Turner
Location 30 mi. E San Fernando
Est 1992 **Staff** 12 **Capacity** 12
Birds Duck, Geese
Car/van from McAllen, TX **Airstrip** Yes
Agent: Outdoor Adventures (owner/operator)
See Our Ad Pg. 251

Mescalero Outfitters Lodge
c/o Outdoor Mexico
PO Box 8520, Brownsville, TX 78520
(800) 635-1594   Danny Putegnat or Hector Sanchez
Location   60 mi S. of San Fernando
Est 1980 **Staff** 14-16 **Capacity** 22
Birds Dove, Quail, Geese **U.S. Gateway** Car/van
from Brownsville or Harlingen **Airstrip** Yes

Gene Naquin's
Fin and Feathered Safaris

Gene Naquin's Fin & Feathered Safaris

P.O. Box 1734, Laredo, TX 78044

(210) 724-4648 Gene Naquin
Location: Miquel Aleman
Est 1980
Birds Quail, Duck, Geese, Dove **U.S. Gateway**
Car/van from Laredo or McAllen **Airstrip** No
Hunting for over 25 years in Mexico, I have developed
a keen sense of what my guests are looking for in a
quality hunt—and I give it to them. We pride ourselves
in well-organized and enjoyable hunts. Short driving
distances between lodging and hunting areas are our
specialty. I am not a booking agent. I do not send you
to Mexico; I take you. Call me today for more
information.

No Le Hace Lodge
c/o Sports Resorts International
730 N. Post Oak Blvd., Suite 302, Houston, TX 77024
(713) 956-1628; 957-4396 Lloyd Fite
Location 20 mi E of San Fernando
Est 1968 **Staff** 14 **Capacity** 26
Birds Quail, Duck, Geese **U.S. Gateway** Car/van
from Harlingen **Airstrip** Yes **Agent** Detail Co.,
(800) 292-2213, contact Jeri Booth; LandsEnd
Expeditions, Inc., (216) 257-9403

No Le Hace Hacienda
c/o Sports Resorts International
730 N. Post Oak Blvd., Suite 302, Houston, TX 77024
011-52-131-71773 Lloyd Fite/Doug Johnson
Location 90 mi. SW of San Fernando on Lake Guerrero
Est 1977 **Staff** 12-14   18
Birds Quail, Dove **Airstrip** Yes **Agent** Detail
Co. & LandsEnd Expeditions

Operacion Las Palomas

PO Box 608, McAllen, TX 78505
(800) 375-4868 Fax: (210) 618-1037 Don Turner
Location San Fernando, 85 mi. S of McAllen, TX
Est 1987 Staff 30 Capacity 4-45
Birds Dove, Quail, Duck, Geese
Car/van from McAllen, TX **Airstrip** Yes
Agent: Outdoor Adventures (owner/operator)
See Our Ad Pg. 251

Rio Corona Lodge
Location 80 mi. S of San Fernando on Rio Corona
Est 1990 **Staff** 5 **Capacity** 10
Birds Quail **U.S. Gateway** Car/van from
Harlingen or McAllen **Airstrip** Yes **Agent** Detail
Co., (800) 292-2213, contact Jeri Booth

El Sargento Lodge
c/o Sunbelt Hunting & Fishing
PO Box 3009, Brownsville, TX 78520
(800) 876-4868 Eduarddo Lalo Maraboto
Location Approx. 60 mi. S of San Fernando
Est 1975 **Staff** 8-10 **Capacity** 2-12
Birds Quail **U.S. Gateway** Car/van from
Harlingen or Brownsville Airstirp No **Agent** Rod
& Gun Resources

South Padre Island Rod & Gun Club

S.E. Regional Headquarters
530 Lake Malone
Lewisburg, KY 42256
(800) 775-6343 Nat B. Nofsinger
**Location: 26 mi. fron San Fernanco on the Gulf
Coast at Los Elbanos Ranch**
Birds Dove, Quail, Duck, Geese **U.S. Gateway Plane
/van from McAllen/Harlingen Airstrip Yes
Agent Stafford & Stafford, (800) 383-0245,
contact Ron Stafford**

El Tejon Lodge
c/o Sunbelt Hunting & Fishing
PO Box 3009, Brownsville, TX 78520
(800) 876-4868 Barry Batsell
Location 18 mi. N of San Fernando
Est 1972 **Staff** 20-25 **Capacity** 2-24
Birds Quail, Geese **U.S. Gateway** Car/van from
Brownsville or Harlingen **Airstrip** No
Agent Rod & Gun Resources; Sporting Charters

El Tesoro Lodge
c/o BT Hunting
17319 Methil, Spring, TX 77379
(713) 251-3244 Bruno Taino
Location 2 mi. N of San Fernando
Est 1980 **Staff** 12-16 **Capacity** 2-26
Birds Quail, Dove, Duck **U.S. Gateway** Car/van
from Harlingen or Brownsville **Airstrip** Yes
Agent Bob Hallette (713) 266–5515

•*See Pg. 248 for "High Volume
Wingshooting— Closer Than You
Think", a detailed article on hunting
in Tamaulipas, Mexico.*

How to Use Wing & Clay's Sporting Clays, Trap & Skeet Directory

Near home or far away

Finding a place to shoot clays—especially when you're away from home—can be difficult. This is especially true of sporting clays. Dozens of new courses are coming on line monthly and even more are in the planning stages. Fortunately, you now have a copy of Wing & Clay to make the job easier and less time consuming.

Extensive listings

The heart of the Clays Directory is its extensive listings of sporting clay courses—some affiliated with the National Sporting Clays Association or Sporting Clays of America and yet other unaffiliated courses—across the country. A complete listing includes the operation's name, address and telephone number, a contact name, membership type, days and hours of operation, reservation policy (this information given in advertiser and enhanced listings only) , sporting clay course description, and the availability of trap, skeet, five stand, wobble traps, high towers and other clay games. [Look for detailed explanations in the numbered Typical Listing on the following page.]

The listings in each state begin with the sub-head **SPORTING & 5 STAND**, followed by an alphabetical listing of locations that offer sporting clays, five stand (or both) and in many instances trap, skeet or other clay games.

This year for the first time, the Clays directory section includes individual listings of locations that offer trap or skeet, but no sporting of five stand. Here listings follow the **TRAP & SKEET** sub-head in alphbetical order. The listings include the operation's name, address, telephone number, contact name and the number of trap and skeet fields at the location.

Your primary source

In short, the Clays Directory is your primary source of information on clay shooting opportunities anywhere in the country. Please use it at home and whenever you travel. And when you do, remember to say you "saw it in Wing & Clay." (Note: The information contained in the Clays section is provided by the operator or a reliable source, but is not verified by Wing & Clay. Call ahead to confirm listing data, before visiting a location.)

CLAY TARGETS

STANDARD
4 ¼ inches in diameter, 1 ⅛ inches thick; dome shaped; standard in trap and skeet.

ROCKET
4 ¼ inches in diameter; ⅝ inch thick; deceptive in flight; appears to float, but retains more velocity than the standard.

RABBIT
4 ¼ inches in diameter; ½ inch thick; rolls and bounces on the ground; thick rim, density prevent shattering on impact with ground.

BATTUE
4 ¼ inches in diameter; ⅜ inch thick; "flying razor blade," difficult to pick up edge-on; does rolls and wingovers.

MIDI
3 ½ inches in diameter, ⅞ inch thick; smaller size make it appear farther away than it actually is; retains initial velocity longer than other targets.

MINI
2 ⅜ inches in diameter, ⅝ inch thick; deceptive because small size makes it appear to be moving faster than it actually is; slows quickly because it's light.

TYPICAL LISTING

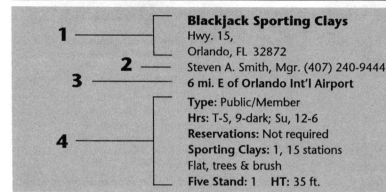

1 ——————⌐ **Blackjack Sporting Clays**
                  Hwy. 15,
            └—   Orlando, FL 32872
        2 —— Steven A. Smith, Mgr. (407) 240-9444
3 ———————— 6 mi. E of Orlando Int'l Airport

            ⌐ Type: Public/Member
               Hrs: T-S, 9-dark; Su, 12-6
               Reservations: Not required
4 ——————— **Sporting Clays:** 1, 15 stations
               Flat, trees & brush
            └ Five Stand: 1   HT: 35 ft.

HOW THE DIRECTORY IS ORGANIZED

Listings in Wing & Clay's Sporting Clay Directory are organized alphabetically first by state (followed by foreign listings). Within state, listings appear in alphabetical order by operation name, beginning with operations that offer sporting clays or five stand. These listings are followed by an alphabetical listing of locations within the state that offer trap or skeet.

1 CLAY SHOOTING LOCATION NAME & ADDRESS

2 CONTACT NAME(S) & TELEPHONE NUMBER: The name of the person and the telephone number to call when you're looking for information or making a reservation. When you call, please remember to tell the contact you saw the location's advertisement or listing in Wing & Clay

3 NEAREST MAJOR TOWN/CITY: Distance in miles and direction from a large city or town or ,in some cases, an airport ; intended to give you a better general idea of where the sporting clays course is located, especially if you are unfamiliar with an area.

4 PARTICULARS

Type Specifically, type of membership. That is whether the sporting clays course is open to the public (**Public**) or to members only—individual or corporate. "**Member**" usually means an annual fee is required. Public/Member means the club is a membership club that is also open to the public, though public access may be limited. (Contact the club directly for information on membership cost and availability and policies governing public access.)

Hours: The operating schedule of the sporting clays location—days and hours open. For

example: **T-Su, 9-dk** means that the operation is open Tuesday through Sunday from 9 a.m. to dusk or dark. Seasonal information is provided in some instances, space allowing. Always call ahead to confirm.

Reservations: (Information provided in enhanced listings only.) Course reservation policy, specifically whether they are: **Not Required, Recommended** or **Strongly Recommended.**

Sporting clays & terrain description: (Terrain and coverage information is found only in enhanced listings.) Number of sporting clays courses on the property, total number of shooting stations; topography (**Flat, Rolling, Hilly**) and coverage or foliage (**Light, Brush, Trees & Brush, Heavily Wooded**). A listing that reads "**Sporting Clays: 3, 36 stations, Mostly flat and heavily wooded**" means that the location has 3 courses with a total of 36 shooting stations that are laid out on flat, densely wooded land. (A station is defined as a position along the course at which a shooter receives a score.)

Clay shooting games & high tower: The availability of other clay shooting games or disciplines—**Trap, Skeet, Wobble Trap, Five Stand, Olympic Trap, Double Trap ,Universal Trench**—and whether the operation has a High Tower from which targets are thrown. A "**Y**" appearing after "**Skeet**" or "**Trap**" indicates that these games are available at the location; a number following these words (or **Five Stand**) indicates the number of shooting fields available for that particular game or discipline. "**HT**" indicates the presence of at least one High Tower at the location (whenever possible the height of the tallest tower is printed in the listing).

CLAY LOCATIONS
STATE/PAGE INDEX

ALABAMA

SPORTING & 5-STAND

Dixieland Plantation
PO Box 168
Hatchechubbee, AL 36858
Donald Dixon (334) 667-7876
25 mi. SW of Columbus, GA
Type: Public **Hrs:** 8am-5pm
Sporting: 1, 11 stations
Skeet: 1 **Five Stand:** 1 **HT**

Greenfield Hunting
Hwy. 4 West, PO Box 174
Pittsview, AL 36871
Rick Cunningham (334) 855-9118
25 mi. S of Columbus, GA
Type: Public
Hrs: S, 10-Dk; W/F, 2-Dk; Su, 1-Dk
Sporting: 11, 20 stations **HT:** 25'.

Mars Skeet Club
107 Parcus Rd., SE
Huntsville, AL 35803
Richard Sheppard (205) 544-7198
80 mi. N of Birmingham
Type: Member/Avail
Sporting: 1, 10 stations
Trap: 1 **Skeet:** 2

Mobile Shooting Center
710 Dykes Rd., Mobile, AL 36608
Sandra Green (334) 633-8629
3 mi. W of Mobile Airport
Type: Public **Hrs:** T-Su, 10-5
Sporting: 1, 8 stations
Trap: 1 **Skeet:** 5 **HT:** 40 ft.

Parches Cove
4415 Parches Cove Rd.
Union Grove, AL 35175
Houston Lindsay (205) 498-2447
20 mi. from Huntsville
Type: Public
Hrs: Call for information
Sporting: 1, 10 stations

Pine Ridge
Sporting Clays
PO Box K (Highway 23)
Ashville, AL 35953
John Godwin (205) 594-5505
35 mi. NE of Birmingham
Type: Public/Member
Hrs: S, 9-Dark; Su, 11-Dark;
Weekdays by appt.
Reservs: Recommended
Sporting: 1, 11 stations

Rockfence Station
4388 Chmbrs. Cty Rd. 160
Lafayette, AL 36862
Branch McClendon (800) 627-2606
95 mi. SW of Atlanta
Type: Public/Member

Hrs: Su-S, 8am-6pm
Reservs: Recommended
Sporting: 1, 14 stations
Trap: 1 **Skeet:** 1 **Five Stand:** 1
HT: 25 ft.
○ Factory Ammunition
○ On-Site Meals
○ Shooting Lodge
○ Formal Instructions
○ Golf Carts

Rocky Top Sporting Clays
135 Rogers Circle
Notasulga, AL 36866
Darsic Rogers (334) 887-9240
5 mi. N of Tallasse
Type: Public/Member **Hrs:** Su,
1-5; Other by appt; closed Jun./ July
Sporting: 1, 8 stations **HT:** 32 ft.

Selwood
Sporting Clays
706 Selwood Rd.
Alpine, AL 35014
Alan Hill (800) 522-0403
40 mi. SE of Birmingham
Type: Public/Member
Hrs: M-S, 8-dark
Reservs: Strongly recommended
Sporting: 2, 28 stations
Five Stand: 1 **HT:** 30 ft.
○ Loaner Guns
○ Factory Ammunition
○ On-Site Pro Shop
○ Shooting Lodge
○ Formal Instructions
○ Golf Carts

Seven Bridges
Sporting Clays, Inc.
Rt. 2, Box 633, Ramer, AL 36069
Quincy Stacey (334) 288-5150
10 mi. S of Montgomery
Type: Public/Member
Hrs: W-Su, 9-5
Reservs: Strongly recommended
Sporting: 2, 20 stations
Five Stand: 1 **HT:** 40 ft.

CLAYS

Tannehill Sporting Clays
PO Box 187, Woodstock, AL 35188
Hunter Faulconer (205) 938-3379
35 mi. S of Birmingham
Type: Public/Member
Hrs: W-S, 12-Dusk; Su, 1-Dusk
Sporting: 1, 12 stations
Five Stand: 5   **HT:** 60 ft.
Wobble Trap

Westervelt
Sporting Clays
PO Box 2362, Tuscaloosa, AL 35403
John C. Roboski (205) 556-3909
50 mi. SW of Tuscaloosa
Type: Public
Hrs: Booking required with 10 or
more; and hunt package
Reservs: Recommended
Sporting: 1, 7 stations
Trap: 1   **Skeet:** 1

Wheeler Station
1316 Stratford Rd., SE
Decatur, AL 35601
Scottie Letson (205) 637-6400
35 mi. W of Huntsville
Type: Public/Member
Hrs: M-F, by appt; S, 9-Dk; Su, 1-5
Sporting: 1, 13 stations
HT: 60 ft.

White Oak
Plantation
5215 B Cty. Road 10
Tuskegee, AL 36083
Matthew or Robert Pitman
(334) 727-9258
45 mi. E of Montgomery
Type: Public/Member
Hrs: M-Su, By Appt.
Reservs: Strongly recommended
Sporting: 1, 14 stations
Five Stand: 1   **HT:** 40 ft.
Wobble Trap
Shooting Instruction
Available - See Ad Pg. 154

TRAP & SKEET
Big Sky Skeet & Trap Club
PO Box 14396, Huntsville, AL 35802
Norman Lindsey (205) 586-1970
Hrs: W/F/S, 12-5; Su, 8-5
Trap: 2   **Skeet:** 4

Dixie Trap
315 West Fleming Rd.
Montgomery, AL 36105
Bill Parson (334) 288-5427
Trap: Y

Ft. Rucker Skeet Club
PO Box 620992
Ft. Rucker, AL 36362
Ralph Aaron (334) 347-8363
Hrs: S/Su/Holidays, 10-5
Trap: 1   **Skeet:** 6

Headland Skeet Club
2618 Denton Rd.,
Dothan, AL 36303
Ronald Bass (334) 793-3111
Hrs: S/Su, 12-6   **Skeet:** 2

Honey Do Retreat
Rt. 3, Box 346A
Enterprise, AL 36330
Harrell Howell (334) 293-2843
Hrs: By invitation   **Skeet:** 1

Muscle Shoals Skeet & Trap
PO Box 334, Florence, AL 35631
Charles Irwin (205) 757-1481
Hrs: Su, pm; Th/S
Trap: 5   **Skeet:** 3

Red Eagle Skeet & Trap
PO Box 280, Childersburg, AL 35044
Cecil Davenport (205) 378-6970
Hrs: S, all day; W/Su, 12-Dark
Trap: 1   **Skeet:** 6

Styx River Shooting Center
Box 1457, Robertsdale, AL 36567
Allen Ard (334) 964-7066
Type: Public/Member
Hrs: W-Su, 8-6:30
Trap: 2   **Skeet:** 2

War Eagle Gun Club
300 Mockingbird Lane
Auburn, AL 36830
John David Vedder (334) 826-6381
Hrs: By appt.   **Skeet:** 1

ALASKA

SPORTING & 5-STAND

Eagles' Ridge
Ranch
HC62, Box 5780
Delta Junction, AK 99737
Mike Crouch (907) 895-4329
100 mi. S of Fairbanks

Type: Public   **Hrs:** Su-S, 8-10
Reservs: Strongly recommended
Sporting: 2, 27 stations
HT: 50 ft.   **Wobble Trap**
○ Loaner Guns
○ On-Site Pro Shop
○ NSCA Certified Instructor
○ Visa & Mastercard Accepted
○ Meals, Lodging & RV Parking
   Available
○ Wingshooting Available (Apr. 1 -
   October 31)

Haines Sportsmans Assn.
PO Box 458, Haines, AK 99827
Bob Swinton (907) 766-2094
70 mi. N of Juneau
Type: Public/Member
Hrs: W, 7pm; other days by appt.
(clays proposed 6/95)
Sporting: 1   **Trap:** 1

Sporting Clays
of Alaska
PO Box 774547
Eagle River, AK 99577
Rick Allen (907) 688-2529
21 mi. N of Anchorage
Type: Public/Member
Hrs: Summer: 9am-9pm; Winter:
Daylight hours
Reservs: Strongly recommended
Sporting: 1, 15 stations
HT: 35 ft.

TRAP & SKEET
Eielson Skeet Club
PO Box 55785,
North Pole, AK 99705
Frank Garzelnick (907) 377-1328
Hrs: S/Su, 12-5; T, 5-9
Trap: 1   **Skeet:** 1

Fairbanks Trap Club
Box 71447, Fairbanks, AK 99707
John D. Hartwick (907) 457-6116
6.5 mi. N of Fairbanks
Type: Public   **Hrs:** W/Th, 6-9;
12-5   **Trap:** 5

Izaak Walton Recreation
Box 670650, Chugiak, AK 99567
Mac McCord (907) 688-2809
21 mi. N of Anchorage
Type: Public
Hrs: W-F, 1-10; F, 5-10; S/Su, 10-6
Trap: 12   **Skeet:** 4

Nanook Skeet & Trap
Box 1041, Delta Junction, AK 99737
Michael W. Koke (907) 873-1240
Hrs: T-F, 11-7; S/Su, 10-6
Trap: 1 **Skeet:** 4

Valdez Sportsmens Club
PO Box 1921, Valdez, AK 99686
Club Manager (907) 835-9503
Type: Public
Hrs: W, 6-9; Su, 12-9 (May-Oct)
Trap: Y

ARIZONA
SPORTING & 5-STAND

Arizona
Hunt Club
PO Box 1021, Mayer, AZ 86333
Kent Henry (520) 632-7709
65 mi. N of Phoenix
Type: Public/Member
Hrs: T-Su, 8-5
Reservs: Strongly recommended
Sporting: 1, 10 stations **HT:** 55 ft.
○ Factory Ammunition
○ On-Site Snack Bar
○ Rental Guns Available
○ Shooting Instruction Available
○ Pheasant/Chukar Hunting
   Oct.-March

Ben Avery Public R&P
Box 1555, Black Canyon Stage #1
Phoenix, AZ 85001
Lloyd Van Sickle (602) 582-8313
Sporting: 1 **Trap:** Y **Skeet:** Y

Bird Busters of Payson, Inc.
606 N. Hideway Cir.
Payson, AZ 85541
Ernest Rogers (602) 474-9781
Hrs: W & Sat., 8-3 or by appt.
Sporting: 1 **Skeet:** 1

Black Canyon Trap & Skeet
49 West McLellan
Phoenix, AZ 85013
Jack August (602) 258-1901
20 mi. N of Phoenix
Type: Public/Member
Hrs: W/Th/F, 1-10; S/Su, 8-5
Sporting: 1, 10 stations
Trap: 19 **Skeet:** 15

Double Adobe
5057 West Double Adobe Rd.
McNeal, AZ 85617
Mike McNeeley (602) 364-4000
90 mi. SE of Tucson
Type: Public **Hrs:** Daily, 9-6
Sporting: 1, 15 stations
Trap: 3 **HT:** 40 ft. **Wobble Trap**

Long Meadow Preserve
HC30, Box 1030
Prescott, AZ 86301
Jim Puntenney (602) 778-9563
20 mi. NW of Prescott
Type: Public/Member
Hrs: F-Su, 8-4 **Sporting:** 1, 5 sta.

Phoenix Trap & Skeet Club
12450 W. Indian School Rd.
Litchfield Park, AZ 85340
Don Brown (602) 935-2691
10 mi. W of Phoenix
Type: Public/Member
Hrs: W, 1-10; Th/S/Su, 10-5
Sporting: None
Trap: 48 **Skeet:** 10 **Five Stand:** 1
Wobble Trap

River's Edge
Sporting Retreat
HC1, Box 742
Benson, AZ 85602
Norm Crawford (520) 212-4868
70 mi. E of Tucson
Type: Public/Member
Hrs: Yr. Round, Th-M, 7:30-5:30
Reservs: Strongly recommended
Sporting: 1, 12 stations

Tucson Trap & Skeet Club
PO Box 13086, Tucson, AZ 85732
Geoff Shepard (602) 883-6426
8 mi. W of Tucson
Sporting: None
Trap: 22 **Skeet:** 14 **Five Stand:** 2

TRAP & SKEET
Bullhead City Gun Club
Box 1026, Bullhead City, AZ 86430
Flint Swassand (602) 754-2606
Hrs: W/Su, 9-Noon
Trap: 4 **Skeet:** 1

Casa Grande Trap Club
1320 N. Arbor
Casa Grande, AZ 85222
Sam Stedman (602) 836-8300
Trap: 10

Davis-Mont. AFB Rod/Gun
355 MWRSS/MWRO,
3775 S. 5th St.
Davis-Monthan AFB, AZ 85707
James E. Bunch (602) 750-3736
Hrs: S/Su, 8-12; T/Th, 4-7
Skeet: 1

Flagstaff Clay Target Shooters
PO Box 2456, Flagstaff, AZ 86004
Toby Johnson (520) 526-9409
Trap: 5 **Skeet:** 2

Ft. Huachuca Skeet & Trap
Box 334, Ft. Huachuca, AZ 85613
Charlie L. Cornett (602) 538-8013
Hrs: W-Su, 10-6 **Trap:** 5 **Skeet:** 4

Garden Canyon Trap Club
27 W. Kayeton Dr.
Sierra Vista, AZ 85635
Rod Ritter (602) 533-7085
Hrs: W/F, 11-7; Th, 11-9; S/Su, 10-6
Trap: 4

Phantom Skeet & Trap
8427 N. 17th Pl. Phoenix, AZ
Barney C. Fagan (602) 856-3928
Hrs: Su, 12-4 **Skeet:** 2

Pleasant Valley Trap Club
PO Box 294, Young, AZ 85554
Pat Meredith (602) 462-3205
Trap: 4

Prescott Gun Club
PO Box 1881, Prescott, AZ 86302
Frank Otvos (520) 772-9539
Hrs: T/Th/S/Su, 12-5
Trap: 5 **Skeet:** 2

Sedona Sportsmens Club
PO Box 2552, Sedona, AZ 86339
Jim Sullivan (602) 282-7787
Hrs: Su, 1-5; others by appt.
Skeet: 2

Yuma Trap & Skeet Club
PO Box 11789, Yuma, AZ 85366
Hrs: S, 9-2; Su, 12-4
Trap: 5 **Skeet:** 21

ARKANSAS
SPORTING & 5-STAND
Blue Rock Sportsman Club
PO Box 6612, Sherwood, AR 72116
Blanchard Causey (501) 374-5275
1 mi. SE of Little Rock
Type: Public/Member
Hrs: S/Su, 1-5 **Sporting:** None
Skeet: 4 **Five Stand:** 1

Cordell Game Birds, Inc.
Rt. 2, Box 334-1
Malvern, AR 72104
John Fowler (501) 332-3215
50 mi. SW of Little Rock
Type: Public/Member
Hrs: (W) T-Su, 7-Dark; (S) T-S, 8-5
Sporting: 1, 14 stations
Trap: 1 **Skeet:** 2

Crowley Ridge
Shooting Resort
112 SFC 434
Forrest City, AR 72335
Dale Horton (501) 633-3352
42 mi. W of Memphis, TN
Type: Public/Member
Hrs: Su-S **Reservs:** Strongly
recommended
Sporting: 1, 13 stations
HT: 30 ft. **Wobble Trap**

CLAYS

Drake's Landing
Rt. 1, Box 177, Tichnor, AR 72166
Tommy Turner (800) 548-4389
45 mi. SE of Stuttgart
Type: Public   **Hrs:** 7 days/week;
by appt.   **Sporting:** 1

Grandview Plantation
PO Box 201, Columbus, AR 71831
Charles Butler (501) 983-2526
120 mi. SW of Little Rock
Type: Public/Member
Sporting: 1, 15 stations   **HT**

Great Guns
20492 Raceway Rd.
Harrisburg, AR 72432
Steve Skillern (501) 578-9700
60 mi. NW of Memphis, TN
Type: Public/Member
Hrs: W-Su, 10-Dark
Reservs: Recommended
Sporting: 2, 23 stations
Five Stand: 1   **HT:** 40 ft.
○ On-Site Meals
○ Golf Carts
○ Rental Guns
○ Pro Shop/Instruction
○ Archery, Pistol & Rifle Ranges
○ 1/2 hr. West of I-55

Hawk's Range Sporting
PO Box 589, Foreman, AR 71836
Paul Hawkins, Jr. (501) 542-7350
30 mi. W of Texarkana
Type: Public/Member
Hrs: S/Su, 10-6; W, 4-Dk; & appt.
Sporting: 1, 20 stations   **HT:** 25 ft.

Miriah
Sporting Clays
PO Box 88, Wesley, AR 72773
Mike & Theresa Carfagno
(501) 456-2533
20 mi. E of Fayetteville
Type: Public/Member
Hrs: M-F, 8-4; Sa/Su 8-5
Reservs: Recommended
Sporting: 1, 25 stations   **HT:** 50 ft.
○ Full Service Conference Facilities
   Available
○ On Site Fishing & Camping
○ 3 Station Practice Course
○ Shooting Instruction
○ Rental Guns Available

Nevada Gamebirds
Rt. 1, Box 171, Buckner, AR 71827
Karl Salb (501) 899-2902
100 mi. S of Little Rock
Type: Public
Hrs: M-F, 1-7; S/Su, 10-7
Sporting: 1, 10 stations
Skeet: 1   **HT:** 40 ft.

Pajaro Gun Club
3424 S. Houston,
Ft. Smith, AR 72903
Don Barksdale (501) 785-2891
Sporting: 1 **Trap:** 1 **Skeet:** 3

Point Remove WMA, Inc.
PO Box 133, Hattieville, AR 72063
Scott Kaufman (501) 354-0136
60 mi. NW of Little Rock
Type: Public/Member
Sporting: 2, 10 stations
Trap: 1 **Skeet:** 1 **Five Stand:** 1
HT: 60 ft.

Quail Ridge Sporting Clays
8821 North Lake Ln.
Hackett, AR 72937
Randy Jacobs (501) 638-8156
135 mi. W of Little Rock
Type: Public/Member
Hrs: S/Su, 9-4
Sporting: 1, 26 stations

Sand Creek Sporting Clays
Rt. 2, Box 218-A
Lockesburg, AR 71846
Randy Goldman (501) 289-3373
40 mi. N of Texarkana
Type: Public/Member
Hrs: By appt.
Sporting: 1, 16 stations   **WT**
Sanders LaGrue Hunt Club
PO Box 171, Humphrey, AR 72073
Charles Sanders, Sr.
(501) 673-2796
50 mi. SE of Little Rock
Type: Public
Hrs: Call for appt.
Sporting: 2, 16 stations
Skeet: 1   **HT:** 60 ft.

Thunder Valley Sptg. Clays
PO Box 2401, Batesville, AR 72501
John Clouse (501) 793-6350
80 mi. NE of Little Rock
Type: Public
Hrs: Th, 4-Dark; S/Su, 9-Dark
Sporting: 1, 12 stations
Skeet: 1 **HT:** 24 ft. **Wobble Trap**

TRAP & SKEET

Barkman Gun Club
PO Box 118, Friendship, AR 71942
John Fowler (501) 384-5357
Hrs: M-F, 8-5   **Skeet:** 1

Malloy Sportsman Club
Box 1878 , El Dorado, AR 71731

Bud Albritton (501) 862-5141
Trap: 1 **Skeet:** 1

Remington Gun Club
Rt. I-40 & Remington Rd.
Lonoke, AR 72086
Billy Crutchfield (501) 676-2677
Hrs: W/Th, 2-6:30; S/Su, 1-5:30
Trap: 5 **Skeet:** 4

Twin Lakes Gun Club, Inc.
Box 199, Mountain Home, AR 72653
John McKinney (501) 425-7640
Hrs: 8-Sundown **Trap:** 1 **Skeet:** 1

West Poinsett Gun Club
PO Box 336, Weiner, AR 72479
Lloyd Wofford (501) 684-2271
Hrs: Su, 1-6 (Apr-Oct)
Trap: 2 **Skeet:** 2

CALIFORNIA

SPORTING & 5-STAND

5 Dogs Range, Inc.
20238 Woody Rd.
Bakersfield, CA 93308
David Olds (805) 399-7296
18 mi. NE of Bakersfield
Type: Public/Member
Hrs: W-S, by appt; Su, 8-Dark
Sporting: 1, 10 stations **HT:** 50 ft.

6B Sportsman's Club
3100 West Gaffery Rd.
Tracy, CA 95376
Paul Bogetti (209) 832-5672
10 mi. SE of Tracy
Type: Public **Hrs:** W-Su, 8am-5pm
Sporting: 1, 10 stations
Five Stand: 1

Angeles Shooting Club
12651 Little Tujunga Canyon Rd.
San Fernando, CA 91342
Jim Petersen (818) 899-2255
Type: Member/Avail
Sporting: 1, 15 stations

Antelope Valley/
Whiteside's Sporting Clays
45408 160th St., W.
Lancaster, CA 93536
David Whiteside (805) 724-1291
60 mi. N of Los Angeles
Type: Public/Member
Hrs: W-Su, 10-Dusk; Otherby appt.
Reservs: Recommended
Sporting: 1, 15 stations
Trap: 1   **HT:** 300 ft.
See Our Ad Across

BIRDS LANDING

Sporting Clays
PO Box 5, Birds Landing, CA 94512
Dan Cirillo (707) 374-5092
60 mi. NE of San Francisco
Type: Public/Member
Hrs: W/S/Su, 9-5 by appt.
Reservs: Recommended
Sporting: 1, 15 stations
Five Stand: 1
O Napa Valley's Closest Sporting
   Clays
O 60 Mi. NE of San Francisco
O 45 Mi. SW of Sacramento
O 5-Stand, Pro Shop & Corporate
   Events
O Call for Info & Reservations
   (707) 374-5092

Black Point Game Bird Club
7711 Lakeville Hwy.
Petaluma, CA 94954
Mike Sutsos (707) 763-0076
25 mi. N of San Francisco
Hrs: W/S/Su, 10-4
Sporting: 1, 5 stations **HT:** 30 ft.

Camanche Hills Hunting Preserve
2951 Curran Rd.
Ione, CA 95640
Larry L. Skinner (209) 763-5270
40 mi. S of Sacramento
Type: Public
Hrs: Year round; Closed Tuesdays
Reservs: Recommended

Sporting: 1, 10 stations **Trap:** 1
O Factory Ammunition
O Easy Drive From San Francisco
O On-Site & Close By Meals
O One of the Most Challenging
   Courses in CA
O See Our Listing CA Wings Section

Carr Creek Sporting Clays
PO Box 1502, Hayfork, CA 96041
Steve Beck (916) 628-5888
Type: Public **Hrs:** S/Su
Sporting: 1, 16 stations

Circle HH Sporting Clays
HCR#1, Box 512, Nipton, CA 92364
Fred Hymes (702) 642-9405
84 mi. S of Las Vegas, NV
Type: Public/Member
Hrs: F-Su, 8-6; others by appt.
Sporting: 1, 6 stations **Trap:** 1

Clear Creek Sports Club
3971 Keefer Rd., Chico, CA 95926
Bob Henman (916) 343-9263
45 mi. N of Sacramento
Type: Public/Member
Sporting: 1

Coyote Valley Sporting Clays
1000 San Bruno Avenue
Morgan Hill, CA 95037
Tom Ebert (408) 778-3600
15 mi. S of San Jose
Type: Public/Member
Hrs: W-F - 10 to 5; S/Su - 8 to 5
Reservs: Recommended
Sporting: 2, 22 stations
Trap: 1 **Skeet:** 1 **Five Stand:** 1
O Loaner Guns
O On-Site Pro Shop
O Formal Instructions

Creekside Pheasant Club
Box 3640, Pkfield Rt.
San Miguel, CA 93451
Larry Hamilton (805) 463-2349
115 mi. NW of Los Angeles
Type: Member/Avail
Sporting: 1, 5 stations **Trap:** Y

Dibble Hills Sporting Clays
Rt. 2, Box 22, Adin, CA 96006
Scott Weigand (916) 299-3508
100 mi. E of Redding
Type: Public
Hrs: S/Su, 9-6; Weekdays by appt.
Sporting: 1, 11 stations **HT:** 35 ft.

Fresno Trap & Skeet Club
5195 N. Humboldt
Kerman, CA 93630
Joe Young (209) 846-8750
15 mi. S of Fresno
Type: Public **Hrs:** 7 days/wk, 9-5
Sporting: 1, 10 stations
Trap: 13 **Skeet:** 10 **Five Stand:** 1
Wobble Trap

Green Head Hunting Club
PO Box 552, Pine Valley, CA 91962
(619) 473-8668
26 mi. E of San Diego
Type: Public/Member
Hrs: W/Th/F, noon; S/Su, all day
Sporting: 1, 10 stations
Trap: Y **Skeet:** Y

Hooker Creek
16110 Basler Rd., Cottonwood, CA
Roger Harris (916) 547-3481
30 mi. SW of Redding
Type: Public/Member
Hrs: M/F/S/Su, 10-Dark by appt.
Sporting: 1, 18 stations **HT:** 120 ft.

Humbolt Trap & Skeet
PO Box 3642, Eureka, CA 95502
Glenn Peake (707) 839-9947

Hrs: Su, 10-3 **Sporting:** None
Trap: 4 **Skeet:** 2 **Five Stand:** 1

Hunter's Retreat/
Palm Springs
Sporting Clays
67-555 Hwy. 111, C115
Cathedral City, CA 92234
(619) 324-0099 or (619) 321-1817
**5 mi. E of Downtown Palm
Springs**
Type: Public, Public/Member
Hrs: W-Su/& by app't
Reservs: Recommended
Sporting: 1, 10 stations
O Factory Ammunition
O On-Site Pro Shop
O Formal Instructions
O Rental Guns
O Full Service Gun Shop - Gunsmith
  & Gunfitting Service
O Indoor Handgun Range
O The Only Sporting Clays Course
  in Palm Springs!

Knowles Ranch
Sporting Clays
PO Box 982,Willows, CA 95988
Tom Knowles (916) 934-5595
75 mi. N of Sacramento
Type: Public/Member

Hrs: W/F/S/Su, By Appt. All Day
Reservs: Strongly recommended
Sporting: 2, 20 stations
Five Stand: Y   **HT:** 40 ft.
See Our Ad Pg. 413

Miramar Trap & Skeet Club
Box 82181, San Diego, CA 92138
Harvey Fischer (619) 278-3173
Type: Public/Member
Hrs: W/S/Su, 8-5; F, 11-4
Sporting: 1, 5 stations **Trap:** 10
Skeet: 8 **Wobble & Olympic Trap**

Moore-N-Moore
Sporting Clays
12651 N. Little Tujunga Cyn Rd.
San Fernando, CA 91342
Pat & Cory Moore (818) 890-4788
15 mi. NE of Los Angeles
Type: Public/Member
Hrs: W/Th, 12-9; F, 12-5; S/Su, 9-5
Reservs: Recommended
Sporting: 1, 12 stations
Five Stand: 1   **HT:** 100 ft.
O Factory Ammunition
O On-Site Pro Shop
O Formal Instructions
O Organized Leagues
O Gunsmith Service
O Gun Fitting

Pachmayr International
Shooting Sports Park
831 N. Rosemead Blvd.
S. El Monte, CA 91733
(818) 579-5201
20 mi. SE of Los Angeles
Type: Public
Hrs: T/W/Th, 12-9; F, 3-9; S/Su, 8-5
Reservs: Not required
Sporting: 1, 10 stations
Trap: 14 **Skeet:** 8   **HT:** 45 ft.
Wobble Trap   Olympic Trap
O Loaner Guns
O On-Site Pro Shop
O Formal Instructions
O Gunsmith Service
O Gun Fitting

Pacific Rod & Gun Club
PO Box 3276, Daly City, CA 94015
Secretary (415) 876-2380
SW of Corner in San Francisco
Type: Public/Member
Hrs: W/S/Su & some holidays, 11-5
Sporting: 1, 5 stations
Trap: 7 **Skeet:** 6 **Five Stand:** 1
Wobble Trap

Potter Valley Sportsmen's
6950 Hwy. 20, Ukiah, CA 95482
Jim Guntly (707) 485-5188

50 mi. N of Santa Rosa
Type: Public/Member
Hrs: 1st & 3rd Sun./mo. (10-dark);
Sporting: 1, 12 stations

Mike Raahauge
Shooting Enterprises
5800 Bluff St., Norco, CA 91760
Mike Raahauge (909) 735-2361
35 mi. E of Los Angeles
Type: Public/Member
Hrs: W/F, 11-6; S/Su, 9-6
Reservs: Not required
Sporting: 2, 10 stations
Trap: 1 **Skeet:** 1 **HT:** 75 ft.
See Our Ad Across Left

Red Bank
Ale & Quail
Gamebird Club
PO Box 627, Red Bluff, CA 96080
Jim or Melodi Byrne
(916) 527-6199
170 mi. N of San Francisco
Reservs: Strongly recommended
Sporting: 1, 20 stations
See Our Ad Right

Redlands Trap & Skeet
PO Box 2231, Redlands, CA 92373
Margaret Yochem (909) 792-5780
55 mi. E of Los Angeles
Type: Public **Hrs:** W, 9-10pm; Th,
5-10; F, 12-5; S/Su, 9-5
Sporting: 1, 5 stations
Trap: 12 **Skeet:** 6 **Five Stand:** 1

SPORTING CLAY**S**
RIVER ROAD
"Golf with a Shotgun"

River Road
Sporting Clays
PO Box 3016, Gonzales, CA 93926
Bruce Barsotti (408) 675-2473
30 mi. NE of Carmel-Monterey
Peninsula
Type: Public/Member
Hrs: T-Su, 9-5 **Reservs:**
Recommended
Sporting: 3, 45 stations **Trap:** 1
Skeet: 1 **Five Stand:** Y **HT:** 60 ft.
○ Loaner Guns
○ Factory Ammunition
○ On-Site Pro Shop
○ On-Site Meals
○ Shooting Lodge
○ Formal Instructions
○ Golf Carts
○ Gunsmith Service
○ Gun Fitting
○ Overnight Accommodations

ROCK SPRINGS RANCH — PAICINES, CALIFORNIA

Rock Springs
Ranch
11000 Old Hernandez Rd.
Paicines, CA 95043
Ken Range (800) 209-5175
75 mi. S of San Jose
Type: Public
Hrs: Daily, 8am-5pm
Reservs: Strongly recommended
Sporting: None
Five Stand: 1
See Our Ad Pg. 267

Sacramento
Valley Shooting
Center
Box 1407, Sloughhouse, CA 95683
Walt Mansell (916) 952-3780
30 mi. SE of Sacramento
Type: Public/Member
Hrs: Weekends only, 8-5
Reservs: Not required
Sporting: None
Trap: 5 **Skeet:** 2 **Five Stand:** 1

Sun Mountain Sportsman
Box 283, Coarse Gold, CA 93644
Vivian Phelan (209) 683-3669
30 mi. N of Fresno
Type: Public/Member
Hrs: Th-Su, 10-5
Sporting: 1, 12 stations
Trap: 3 **Wobble Trap**

CLAYS

Target Tossers
5350 Otay Valley Rd.
San Ysidro, CA 92073
Chip Enniss (619) 661-1400
10 mi. S of San Diego
Type: Public
Hrs: W/Th, 12-10; S/Su, 9-5
Reservs: Not required
Sporting: 1, 10 stations
Trap: 5 **Skeet:** 1 **HT:** 40 ft.

Timbuctoo Sporting Estate
PO Box 357, Smartville, CA 95977
Randy Rigdon (916) 639-2200
50 mi. NW of Sacramento
Type: Public
Hrs: Daily by appt.
Sporting: 1, 12 stations

United Sportsmen Inc.
4700 Evora Rd., Concord, CA
94522
Jill Sawyers (510) 676-1963
30 mi. E of San Francisco
Type: Public/Member
Hrs: S/Su, 10-6; W/Th, 3-10
Sporting: None
Trap: 12 **Skeet:** 5 **Five Stand:** 1

Veale Pheasant Club
PO Box 277 Knightsen, CA 94548
John Mass, III (510) 625-6000
50 mi. E of San Francisco
Type: Public **Hrs:** T-Su, 8-6:30
Sporting: 1, 5 stations **HT:** 50 ft.

West Valley Sportsmen's
PO Box 257, Gustine, CA 95322
Robert Kloepfer (209) 634-1547
80 mi. SE of San Francisco
Type: Public/Member
Hrs: W-Su
Sporting: 1, 10 stations
Trap: Y **Skeet:** Y **Five Stand:** 1
HT: 40 ft.

Winchester Canyon
PO Box 3306
Santa Barbara, CA 93130
Tony Urwick (805) 965-9890
90 mi. NW of Los Angeles
Type: Public/Member
Hrs: Trap/Skeet, S/Su/W, 10-4;
Clays 1st Sun. of month
Sporting: 1, 30 stations
Trap: 3 **Skeet:** 1 **HT:** 60 ft.
Wobble Trap

Yolo Sportsmen's Assn.
PO Box 82, Woodland, CA 95776
Phil DeCarlo (916) 662-2349
Hrs: 9-Dark
Sporting: 1 **Trap:** 4 **Skeet:** 1

TRAP & SKEET
Barstow Gun Club
16152 Pamela St.
Victorville, CA 92392
Allen Seymour (619) 247-2299
Type: Public/Member
Hrs: T, 6-10; Su, 10-5
Trap: 4 **Skeet:** 1 **Wobble Trap**

Coon Creek Trap & Skeet
5393 Waltz Rd., PO Box 460
Lincoln, CA 95648
George Ahart (916) 539-8544
Hrs: T/Th/S/Su, 10-Dark
Trap: 8 **Skeet:** 2

EAFB Rod & Gun Activity
650 ABW/MWRO, 210 Adams Way
Edwards AFB, CA 93524
Debbie Nygren (805) 277-3182
Hrs: T/Th, 10-8; S/Su, 9-6
Trap: 6 **Skeet:** 2

Edwards AFB R&GC
6500 ABW/SSRO
Edwards AFB, CA 93523
Bruce Jones
Type: Member/Avail
Hrs: T/Th, 10-8; S/Su, 9-6
Trap: 6 **Skeet:** 2

Fraternal Order of Eagles
16287-24 1/2
Chowchilla, CA 93610
H.K. Crow (209) 665-1723
Hrs: S, 1-5 **Trap:** 2

Kern County Gun Club
2818 China Grade Loop
Bakersfield, CA 93308
Paul Mooney (805) 871-9977
Hrs: W/F, 3-9; Su, 9-3
Trap: 6 **Skeet:** 4

Los Cazadores Gun Club
PO Box 6700, Oxnard, CA 93030
Jim Lupold (805) 482-8443
Hrs: Su, 10-5 **Trap:** 1

Newman Swamp Rats Trap
& Skeet Club
806 Orestimba Rd.
Newman, CA 95360
George Siler (209) 523-8423
Type: Public/Member
Hrs: M-F, 8-5 **Trap:** 5

Novato Trap Club
PO Box 482, Novato, CA 94948
Woody Hoke (415) 897-9712
Hrs: Th, 6-10; Su, 9-3
Trap: 9

Peterseи Productions, Inc.
17501 Pomona Rincon Rd.
Chino, CA 91710
Wayne Moulton (714) 597-4794
Hrs: W/F, 11-5; Th, 11-9; S/Su, 8-5
Trap: 9 **Skeet:** 5

Prado Tiro Olympic
Shooting Park
3180 Milton St.
Pasadena, CA 91107
Steve Lakatos (818) 796-6754

Redding Gun Club
PO Box 991765CT #3
Redding, CA 96099
Gerald Stankey (916) 549-4652
Hrs: W, 3-Dark; S/Su, 1-Sundown
Trap: 5 **Skeet:** 1

Sacramento Trap Club
3701 Fulton Ave.
Sacramento, CA 95821
Charlette Shaw (916) 484-9889
Type: Public/Member
Hrs: W, 11-7; S, 11-4; Su, 12-4
Trap: 10

San Benito Co Skeet & Trap
4351 Pacheco Pass Hwy.
Hollister, CA 95023
Dan Lanini (408) 637-2310
Trap: 1 **Skeet:** 1

San Gabriel Valley Gun
4001 Fish Canyon Rd.
Duarte, CA 91010
Richard Phillips (818) 358-9906
Hrs: T/W/F, 10-4; S/Su, 8:30-4:30
Trap: 1 **Skeet:** 4

San Joaquin Valley R&G
1169 Beverly Dr., #40
Lemoore, CA 93245
John Cortner (209) 998-4072
Hrs: Su, 9-4; W, 6-8
Trap: 1 **Skeet:** 2

Santa Maria Trap Club
3150 Telephone Rd., PO Box 867
Santa Maria, CA 93456
Club Manager (805) 295-6673
Hrs: Su, 9am; W, 5:30-Dark
Trap: 8 **Skeet:** 1

Stockton Gun Club
4343 N. Ashley Lane
Stockton, CA 95205
C.W. Shay (209) 931-6803
Type: Public/Member
Hrs: S/Su, 11-5; W, 12-10
Trap: 20 **Skeet:** 7

Stockton Trap & Skeet Club
4832 Granada Ln.
Linden, CA 95236
Francine Haines (209) 931-0323
Hrs: 8-6
Trap: 20 **Skeet:** 7

Tulare County Trap Club
8601 W. Roosevelt
Visalia, CA 93291
Club Manager (209) 651-2525
Hrs: Su, 9am; W, 5:30-Dark
Trap: 6 **Skeet:** 1

Vado Del Rio Skeet/Trap
11110 Red Cedar Dr.
San Diego, CA 92131
Anthony Erbacher (714) 725-4832
Hrs: W-Su, Daylight Hrs.
Trap: 2 Skeet: 2

Vandenburg Rod & Gun
537 Venus Ave.
Lompoc, CA 93436

Levi Lee H. Miller, Jr.
(805) 734-8232
Hrs: M-S, 11-1
Trap: 1 Skeet: 1

Wingmaster Gun Club
12600 Bell Ave.
Wasco, CA 93280
Bud Cashen (805) 758-2100
Trap: 1 Skeet: 1

Say You Saw It In...
Black's
WING & CLAY

If shotgunning is your sport, you can help it grow and prosper.

Use the information you find in Wing & Clay when you're planning hunts, clay shoots or buying shotgun related equipment and services.

Tell your shotgunning friends and associates how helpful you find Wing & Clay, and encourage them to get a copy of their own.

Also, tell the many companies found in the book—including the hundreds of hunting preserves and clay shooting locations in the Wings and Clays sections—that you benefited from seeing the information in their listings and advertisements.

In short, don't forget to say:
"I saw it in Wing & Clay."

Thank you.

COLORADO

SPORTING & 5-STAND

American Sporting Clay
Road 53, Kiowa, CO 80117
Clay Blyth (303) 621-2841
30 mi. SE of Denver
Type: Public/Member
Hrs: F-Su, 9-4
Sporting: 1, 10 stations HT: 25 ft.

Aurora Gun Club
Gun Club Rd., Aurora, CO 80041
Jake Bechtel (303) 366-9030
from I70 E. of Aurora, Ex. 289 S.,
2 mi. of I70
Type: Public/Member
Hrs: M-F (Members); S/Su, 9-3
Sporting: 1, 10 stations Trap: 5

Bang-A-Away Gun Club
17629 Weld County Rd. 5
Berthoud, CO 80513
Bill Voigt (303) 535-4538
45 mi. N of Denver
Type: Public/Member
Hrs: T-Su, 8:30-4:30
Sporting: 2, 10 stations
Trap: 1

Broadmoor
Shooting Grounds
4570 Cheyenne Mt. Zoo Rd.
Colorado Springs, CO 80906
Jack Bath, Jr. (719) 635-3438
3 mi. SW of Colorado Springs
Type: Public
Hrs: M-F, 12-4; S/Su, 10-4; closed 12/1-4/1
Reservs: Strongly recommended
Sporting: 2, 15 stations
Trap: 2 Skeet: 2

Cherry Creek Sporting
10325 C.R. 250
Durango, CO 81301
Rob Conaty (303) 247-2250
28 mi. from Durango
Type: Public/Member
Hrs: April-Nov., by appt.
Sporting: 1, 11 stations HT

Chipeta Guest Ranch
1938 Hwy. 133
Paonia, CO 81428

CLAYS

Larry Mautz (303) 929-6260
70 mi. W of Aspen
Type: Public **Hrs:** Su-S, call for resrv.
Sporting: 1, 10 stations **HT:** 12 ft.

Glenarm Sporting Clays
68202 Trout Rd.
Montrose, CO 81404
C. Courtney Antrim
(970) 249-6490
60 mi. S of Grand Junction
Type: Public
Hrs: Daily by appt.
Sporting: 1, 12 stations

Glenwood Springs Gun Club
Box 2362,
Glenwood Springs, CO 81602
Linden Burnsworth (303) 945-5346
5 mi. SW of Glenwood Springs
Type: Public/Member
Hrs: Th, 4:30-Dark; S, 9-5
(Spring/Summer/Fall)
Sporting: 2, 10 stations
Trap: 3 **Skeet:** 1 **HT:** 100 ft.
Wobble Trap

High Country Game Birds
33300 County Rd. 25
Elizabeth, CO 80107
Todd Pederson (303) 646-3315
35 mi. SE of Denver
Type: Public/Member
Hrs: Year Round
Sporting: 1, 10 stations

Izaak Walton League of America
450 Francsville Rd.
Colorado Springs, CO 80929
Bill Jacobs/William Bell
(719) 683-4420
Type: Public/Member
Sporting: 1, 10 stations
Trap: 5 **Five Stand:** 1

Mt. Blanca Game Bird & Trout
PO Box 236, Blanca, CO 81123
Bill Binnian (719) 379-3825
150 mi. SW of Colorado Springs
Type: Public/Member
Hrs: M-Su, 7-10 (June-Dec); W-Su, 7-10 (Feb-May)
Reservs: Recommended
Sporting: 1, 10 stations
Skeet: 1 **HT:** 35 ft. **Wobble Tr.**
See Our Ad Above

R&T Gun Club
9912 Downing, Thornton, CO 80229
Dave Redell (303) 452-4777
100 mi. NE of Denver
Type: Public/Member
Hrs: Weekends, 8-dark
Sporting: 1, 10 stations
Trap: 1 **HT:** 40 ft. **Wobble Trap**

Renegade Gun Club, Inc.
3570 Weld County Road #23
Fort Lupton, CO 80621
Dick Chikuma (303) 857-6000
20 mi. N of Denver
Type: Public/Member
Hrs: S/Su, 9-5; W, 1pm
Reservs: Strongly recommended
Sporting: 3, 20 stations
Five Stand: 1 **HT:** 30 ft.
Wobble Trap

ROCKY MOUNTAIN ROOSTERS INC.°

Colorado's Finest Private Pheasant Hunting Preserve And Sporting Clays Range

Rocky Mountain Roosters
PO Box 10164
Colorado Springs, CO 80932
Brett M. Axton (719) 635-3257
35 mi. E of Colorado Springs
Type: Public/Member
Hrs: Su-S, by rsv. only
Reservs: Strongly recommended
Sporting: 1, 10 stations
Wobble Trap

Rocky Ridge Hunting Club
633 Gait Circle
Ft. Collins, CO 80524
Michael Moreng (303) 221-4868
55 mi. N of Denver
Type: Public/Member
Hrs: Proposed 4/96
Sporting: 1
Trap: Y

SPORTHAVEN LTD.

SPORTHAVEN, LTD.
50500 E. 72nd Ave.
Bennett, CO 80102
David A. Lincoln, Jr.
(303) 644-3030
20 mi. NE of Denver
Type: Public/Member
Hrs: S-Su, all day; W-F afternoons
& by app't.
Reservs: Recommended
Sporting: 1, 30 stations
HT: 35 ft.
○ On-Site Pro Shop
○ Visa/Mastercard Accepted
○ Tower Ht. 35 ft.
○ Denver's Most Complete
   Sporting Facility
○ Closed Monday/Tuesday

Vail Rod & Gun Club
PO Box 1848, Vail, CO 81658
M. Murphy/J. Jouflas
(970) 926-3472
120 mi. W of Denver
Type: Public/Member
Hrs: Th-Su, 9-5 (Oct-Mar); Daily,
10-5 (June-Sep)
Sporting: 1, 18 stations
HT: 100 ft.

Valhalla-Bijou Inc.
450 County Rd. 133
Bennett, CO 80102
Rich Cummings (303) 644-4300
20 mi. E of Denver
Type: Member/Avail
Hrs: By appt. only
Sporting: 1, 10 stations
HT: 30 ft.

Western Colorado Sporting
2510 Wintergreen Dr.
Grand Junction, CO 81504
Jim Lander, VP (970) 245-0403
30 mi. E of Grand Junction
Type: Public/Member
Hrs: Sat., 10-5; call for appt.
Sporting: 1, 15 stations
HT: 125 ft.

TRAP & SKEET
Buckeye Trap Range
6255 WCR#74
Windsor, CO 80524
Tim or Lisa Brough (303) 686-5210
Type: Public/Member
Hrs: S/Su, 10-4; T, 4-9
Trap: 6   **Skeet:** 2   Wobble Trap

Cactus Flats Club
16154 Hwy. 115
Florence, CO 81226
Jim Vendetti (719) 372-3726
Type: Public/Member
Hrs: W, 4:30-Dk; Su, 11-Dk (Winter)
Trap: 5

Colorado West Gun Club
2913 Hwy. 92
Hotchkiss, CO 81419
Gerhart L. Stengel (303) 872-3748
Hrs: Call for appt.
Trap: 1   **Skeet:** 1

Cortez Trap Club
PO Box 48, Cortez, CO 81321
Pat Woosley (303) 565-7396
Hrs: Th, 6-10; Su, 1-5
Trap: 8

Delta Trap Club
PO Box 1061Delta, CO 81416
John Lowe (308) 874-4980
Type: Public
Hrs: W, Eve. League; Su, 11-2:30
Trap: 9

ENT Gun Club
PO Box 14002
Peterson AFB, CO 80914
Bob Tate (719) 596-7688
Hrs: Th/S/Su, 10-5
Trap: 8   **Skeet:** 7

Grand Junction Trap Club
PO Box 334,
Grand Junction, CO 81502
Al Strecker (303) 245-0780
Hrs: T, 7-10; Su, 1-4
Trap: 4   **Skeet:** 1

Haxton Gun Club
12350 RD 11
Haxton, CO 80731
Rod Ham (303) 774-7504
Type: Public/Member
Trap: 2

Mile Hi Shooting Park
1745 Co Hwy. 7, Erie, CO 80516
Ida L. Wiens (303) 665-9991
Hrs: T-Th, 3-6; S/Su, 10-4
Trap: 16   **Skeet:** 2

Northern Colorado R&G
2207 Suffolk St.
Fort Collins, CO 80526
Donald Carlson
Hrs: 2nd & 4th Su, 9am
Trap: 1   **Skeet:** 1

OTC Olympic Shooting Club
1 Olympic Plaza
Colorado Springs, CO 80909
Randy Moeller (719) 578-4882
Olympic Trap   Double Trap

Tri Service Sportsmans Club
7664 W. Ontario Place
Littleton, CO 80123
Mike Gutirrez (303) 340-9889
Hrs: W/S/Su, 9-3 **Trap:** 1   **Skeet:** 4

USA Shooting
One Olympic Plaza
Colorado Springs, CO
Randy Moeller (719) 578-4883
Trap: 4   **Skeet:** 4

Watkins Skeet Club
PO Box 21, Watkins, CO 80137
Felix Lopez (303) 366-6970
Trap: 10   **Skeet:** 6

CONNECTICUT

SPORTING & 5-STAND
Bristol Game & Fish Assoc.
PO Box 175, Bristol, CT 06010
James Strecker (203) 879-9938
75 mi. NE of New York
Type: Public/Member
Hrs: S, 9-1
Sporting: 1, 20 stations
Trap: 4   **Skeet:** 1

Guilford Sportsmans Assoc.
PO Box 286, Guilford, CT 06437
D. Summerton/T. Altieri
(203) 457-9931
Type: Member/Avail
Hrs: 9-Dark
Sporting: 1, 7 stations
Trap: 2   **Skeet:** 2   **Five Stand:** 1

Ledyard Sportsmen's Club
PO Box 156, Ledyard, CT 06339
Donna & Steve Reynolds
(401) 596-3909
100 mi. S of Boston
Type: Member/Avail
Hrs: Su-S
Sporting: 1, 6 stations
Trap: 1   **Skeet:** 2

Markover Game Farm &
Hunting Preserve
719 Cook Hill Rd.
Danielson, CT 06239
Kevin Olsen (203) 774-4116
75 mi. SW of Boston, MA
Type: Public
Hrs: Su-S, by appt.
Sporting: 1, 6 stations

TRAP & SKEET
Fairfield Co. Fish & Game
53 Wood Ave.,
Trumbull, CT 06611

CLAYS

William Morey (203) 426-9400
Trap: 5 **Skeet:** 5

Fin Fur & Feather Club
PO Box 81,
North Windham, CT 06256
Frank Mauri (203) 455-9516
30 mi. E of Hartford
Type: Member/Avail
Hrs: M-F, 11-Dark; S/Su, 9-Dark
Trap: 1 **Skeet:** 8

Hamden Fish & Game
PO Box 5619
Hamden, CT 06518
S. Amendola (203) 281-9440
Hrs: Su, 9:30-2:30
Trap: 4 **Skeet:** 4

Hartford Gun Club
157 S. Main St.
East Granby, CT 06026
Chuck Hazelett (203) 658-1614
Hrs: S/Su, 12-5; T/Th, 4-8
(May-Sept. 1)
Trap: 12 **Skeet:** 6

Mukluk Skeet Club
RD7, #502, Norwich, CT 06360
Hervey LaLiberte
Hrs: S, 1-4; W, 5-Dark
Skeet: 2

Niantic Sportsmen's Club
4 York Ave., Niantic, CT 06357
Belinda Gribosky (203) 739-5322
Hrs: Su-F, 10-Dusk; S, 10-3
Skeet: 2

Northfield Rod & Gun Club
PO Box 639, Watertown, CT 06795
Pauline Kalita
Trap: 2

Nutmeg Skeet Club
26 A Golden Hill St.
South Norwalk, CT 06854
Howard Altman

Pahquioque Rod & Gun
615 S. Salem Rd.
Ridgefield, CT 06877
Fran Redman (203) 792-5222
Type: Public **Hrs:** T, 3-Dark
Trap: 4

Quaker Hill Rod & Gun
33 Converse Place
New London, CT 06320
Kirt M. Webster (203) 848-8387
Hrs: Su-S, 9-Dusk
Trap: 1 **Skeet:** 2

Seymour Fish & Game
34 Stoddard St.
Seymour, CT 06483
Raymond P. Manzolla
(203) 881-0788
Hrs: T/Th, 3:30-9; Su, 9:30-3
Trap: 2 **Skeet:** 2

DELAWARE

SPORTING & 5-STAND

**Eagle Wing Skeet &
Sporting Clays**
729 Bradford St.
Dover AFB, Dover, DE 19904
Carl Barnes (302) 678-1212
Type: Public
Hrs: W, 3:30; Su, 9:30-4:30
Sporting: None
Skeet: 3 **Five Stand:** Y

Ommelanden Range
1205 River Rd.
New Castle, DE 19720
Michael Friel (302) 323-5333
35 mi. SE of Philadelphia
Type: Public
Hrs: T-S, 9-4; Su, 9-12; Th, 4-9
Sporting: 1, 28 stations
Trap: 6 **Skeet:** 2 **Five Stand:** 1
HT: 45 ft.

Owens Station
RD1, Box 203
Greenwood, DE 19950
Bill Wolter (302) 349-4434
75 mi. E of Washington, DC
Type: Public
Hrs: T-S, 9-dusk; Su, 10-4
Sporting: 3, 43 stations
Five Stand: 1 **HT:** 60 ft.
Wobble Trap

TRAP & SKEET

Dupont Fish and Game
701 Faun Rd.
Newark, DE 19711
E.J. Hackman (302) 366-2484
Hrs: Varies
Trap: 5 **Skeet:** 5

Wilmington Trapshooting
PO Box 9203
Newark, DE 19714
Thelma E. Clagett (302) 738-6600
Trap: 14 **Skeet:** 2

FLORIDA

SPORTING & 5-STAND

BIG D
• PLANTATION •

Sporting Clays
Rt. 15, Box 1760
Lake City, FL 32024
Charlie Parnell (800) 437-4441
70 mi. W of Jacksonville
Type: Public **Hrs:** Tu-S, 10-Dusk
Reservs: Recommended

Sporting: 1, 20 stations
HT: 40 ft. **Wobble Trap**
○ Loaner Guns
○ Factory Ammunition
○ On-Site Meals
○ Organized Leagues
○ Golf Carts

Blackjack
Sporting Clays
Hwy. 15, Box 721412
Orlando, FL 32872
Steven A. Smith, Mgr.
(407) 240-9444
6 mi. E of Orlando Int'l. Airport
Type: Public/Member
Hrs: T-S, 9-Dark; Su, 12-6
Reservs: Recommended
Sporting: 1, 15 stations
Five Stand: 1 **HT:** 35 ft.
See Our Ad Pg. 423

Bonnette Hunting & Fishing
5309 Hood Rd.
Palm Beach Gardens, FL 33418
Tom Shephard (407) 626-5180
70 mi. N of Miami
Type: Member/Avail
Hrs: M/T/Th/F, 10-6; S/Su, 10-5
Sporting: 1, 12 stations
Trap: 5 **HT**

Bradford Sportsmen's
S.W. 106th St.
Graham, FL 32042
Patrick B. Welch (904) 964-8721
15 mi. N of Gainesville
Type: Member/Avail
Hrs: W, 12-Sundown; S/Su,
9-Sundown
Sporting: 3, 24 stations **HT**

Coon Bottom Gun Club
2995 Lake Bradford Rd.
Tallahassee, FL 32310
Willis L. Heath (904) 539-0293
Hrs: W/S/Su, 1-Dark
Sporting: None
Skeet: 3 **Five Stand:** 1

Double WW
Sporting Clays
1200 Cassat Ave.
Jacksonville, FL 32205
Ken Branham (904) 266-1121
12 mi. SW of Jacksonville
Type: Public
Hrs: W/F, noon-dusk; S/Su, all day
Reservs: Not required
Sporting: 2, 36 stations
Five Stand: 1   **HT:** 40 ft.
O Factory Ammunition
O NSCA Certified Instructor
O Dove Tower Game
O Plantation Quail Hunts
O Just 8 mi. off I-10 West

Everglades
Sporting Clays
4750 CR951 Florida Sports Park
Naples, FL 33962
Susan Branco (813) 793-0086
3 mi. S of I75 Exit 15
Type: Public/Member
Hrs: W/F, 10-4; S/Su, 9-3
Reservs: Strongly recommended
Sporting: 1, 16 stations
HT: 30 ft.
O Loaner Guns
O Factory Ammunition
O On-Site Pro Shop
O Shooting Lessons Available
O 30 mi. South of Ft. Myers

Gator Skeet & Trap Club
5202 NE 46th Ave.
Gainesville, FL 32609
Wayne Pearce (904) 372-1044
60 mi. SW of Jacksonville
Type: Public/Member
Hrs: W/S/Su, 1:30-7
Sporting: None
Trap: 9 **Skeet:** 4 **Five Stand:** 1
HT: 40 ft.   **Olympic Trap**

Indian River T&S Club
699 17th St.
Vero Beach, FL 32960
Annette Skaggs (407) 231-1783
100 mi. SE of Orlando
Type: Member/Avail
Hrs: W/Su, 1-5
Sporting: 1, 10 stations
Trap: 1 **Skeet:** 2 **Five Stand:** 1
HT: 35 ft.

Iron-Wood Super Wobble
PO Box 1949, Lake City, FL 32056
Nickey Jackson (904) 963-3508
60 mi. W of Jacksonville
Type: Public/Member
Sporting: 1, 5 stations
Wobble Trap

J&R Hunting
Preserve
8400 SW Fox Brown Rd.
Indiantown, FL 34956
Joe or Liz O'Bannon
(407) 597-4757
30 mi. NW of West Palm Beach
Type: Public/Member
Hrs: Anytime, by reservation
Reservs: Strongly recommended
Sporting: 1, 13 stations **HT:** 12 ft.
O Factory Ammunition

O Hunt Packages Available
O Large Private Groups Welcome
O Shooting Lessons Available
O Rental Guns Available
O 30 miles NW of Palm Beach

Jacksonville Gun Club
12125 New Berlin Rd.
Jacksonville, FL 32226
Richard Lacey (904) 272-5609
5 mi. NE of Jacksonville
Type: Public **Hrs:** W-Su, 1-Dark
Sporting: None
Trap: 4 **Skeet:** 5 **Five Stand:** 1

Jennings Bluff
Rt. 2, Box 4250
Jennings, FL 32053
Troy Tolbert (904) 938-5555
65 mi. NE of Tallahassee
Type: Public **Hrs:** By Appt.
Sporting: 1, 8 stations

SPORTING CLAYS
10 Stations, 2 Hightowers

5 miles south of I-75, Exit 78
13 miles N of Gainesville on Rt. 441
65 miles SW of Jacksonville

Farm Land & Open Woods

SHOOT
IN THE
SHADE!

Call Or Write For Information:
Jack Baier
Hours: Wed. - Sun., 9 am to 6 pm
Reservations Recommended
904-462-5303
Rt. 3, Box 221, Highway 441
Alachua, FL 32615

Palm Beach
Sporting Clays at Bonnette's Hunting & Fishing Club
5309 Hood Rd.
Palm Beach Gardens, FL 33418
Warren H. Woody (407) 622-7300
15 mi. N of West Palm Beach Airport **Type:** Public/Member
Hrs: Tu-Su, 9-dusk
Reservs: Strongly recommended
Sporting: 1, 12 stations   **HT:** 40 ft.

See Our Ad Below

TRAP&SKEET CLUB

2950 Pierson Rd.
West Palm Beach, FL 33414
Joe Fordham (407) 793-8787
7 mi. W of Palm Beach Int'l Airport
Type: Public/Member
Hrs: W, 1 to 10; S/Su, 10 to 5
Reservs: Recommended
Sporting: 1, 10 stations

Trap: 20 **Skeet:** 5 **Five Stand:** 1
HT: 30 ft. **Olympic Trap**
○ Loaner Guns
○ Int'l. Olympic Bunker Trap
○ Quality New & Used Shotguns
○ Outstanding Snack Bar
○ Shooting Lessons Available
○ Complete Pro Shop

Polk County Skeet & Trap
151 Racepit Rd.
Winter Haven, FL 33880
Al Schweizer (813) 299-4853
40 mi. SW of Orlando
Type: Public
Hrs: W/Su, 1-6; Th, 6-10; S, 9-6
Sporting: 2, 10 stations
Trap: 7 **Skeet:** 5   **Wobble Trap**

Port Malabar Rifle & Pistol
PO Box 060307
Palm Bay, FL 32906
Rick Pepin (407) 777-6405
Hrs: Call for info
Sporting: 1 **Trap:** 2 **Skeet:** 2

Shoal River Gun Club
PO Box 1293, Crestview, FL 32536
Jim Griffin (904) 689-1997
6 mi. E of Crestview
Type: Public/Member
Hrs: T-S, 9-6; Su, 1-6
Sporting: 1, 10 stations
Trap: 1 **Skeet:** 1

Silver Dollar Trap Club
17000 Patterson Rd.

Odessa, FL 33556
Edna Mollohan (813) 920-3231
15 mi. NE of Tampa
Type: Public/Member
Hrs: W/S/Su, 10-6 (Summer); T-Su, 10-6 (Winter)
Sporting: 0 **Trap:** 26 **Five Stand:** 1

South Florida Sporting Clays @ Markham
16001 W. State Rd. 84
Sunrise, FL 33326
Steve Fischer (305) 389-2005
12 mi. W of Ft. Lauderdale
Type: Public/Member
Hrs: T-Su, 12-5; S/Su, 9-5; F/S/Su, by appt (Clays)
Sporting: 1, 12 stations
Trap: 5 **Skeet:** 5 **Five Stand:** 1
HT: 40 ft.

Southmere Sporting Clays
PO Box 0276, Mims, FL 32754
Janice Mitchell (407) 383-8556
Sporting: 1

Spaceport Gun Club
PO Box 540995
Merritt Island, FL 32954
Al Luther (407) 459-2605
8 mi. S of Kennedy Space Center
Type: Public/Member
Hrs: W/Su afternoons (5-Stand)
Sporting: 1, 28 stations
Trap: 4 **Skeet:** 5 **Five Stand:** 1
HT: 27 ft.

Sporting Clays
of Tampa Bay
PO Box 16998, Tampa, FL 33687
Jay Lusk (813) 986-7888
70 mi. SW of Orlando
Type: Public/Member
Hrs: W/S/Su, 8-6
Reservs: Recommended
Sporting: 2, 20 stations
Skeet: 1 **Five Stand:** 1   **HT:** 50 ft.

Telegraph
Cypress Field Club
45501 Bermont Rd. (CR74)
Punta Gorda, FL 33982
Tom McGavern (813) 575-0550
30 mi. N of Ft. Myers
Type: Public/Member
Hrs: Winter: Th-Su, 9-dark; Summer: Th-S, 8-12, 4-dark
Reservs: Strongly recommended
Sporting: 2, 30 stations
Trap: 1 **Skeet:** 1 **Five Stand:** 1
○ On-Site Pro Shop
○ NSCA Instructors Available
○ Fax: (813) 573-0544
See Our Ad Pg. 424

Allen Smith
Shooting Sports, Inc.
Orlando World Shooting Center at Lake Nona

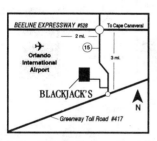

Welcome to Blackjack Sporting Clays, located just 2 miles east of Orlando International Airport. Visit Blackjack and shoot its challenging 15-station fully automated course, designed by Bob Edwards and general manager, Steven A. Smith. International Five-Stand and FITASC are also available.

Blackjack offers many amenities to the public and its members including a *Lodge Style Clubhouse, Beretta Loaner Guns, Gunsmith Service and Golf Carts.* Factory ammunition is available at the *On-site Pro Shop.*

Shooting instruction, available daily from certified, resident instructors, is supplemented by clinics held throughout the year by touring instructors.

Visit Blackjack Sporting Clays whenever you are in Orlando. Ask about our Special Packages for area attractions. Call today for reservations and membership information:

407-240-9444
Blackjack Sporting Clays • Orlando World Shooting Center
P.O. Box 721412 Orlando, FL 32872

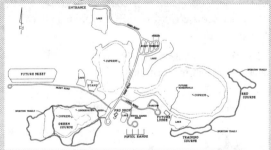
Trail Glades Range/Tamiami Pk
10901 SW 24th St.
Miami, FL 33165
Janie Clark (305) 226-1823
18 mi. W of Miami
Type: Public **Hrs:**
Sporting: 1, 10 stations
Trap: 6 **Skeet:** 5 **HT:** 25 ft.

Trail Trap and Skeet Club
6915 SW 139th Pl.
Miami, FL 33193
Fred Azan (305) 386-9479
Hrs: M-F, 12-Sundown; S/Su,
9-Sundown
Sporting: None
Trap: 2 **Skeet:** 5 **Five Stand:** 1

Turkey Run Gun Clubs
Rt. 3, Box 221, Alachua, FL 32615
Jack Baier, Mgr. (904) 462-5303
13 mi. N of Gainesville
Type: Public **Hrs:** W-Su, 9-6
Reservs: Recommended
Sporting: 1, 10 stations
HT: 25 ft.

See Our Ad Pg. 421

TRAP & SKEET

Cecil Field Skeet Club
MWR Dept., PO Box 109
Jacksonville, FL 32215
Thomas Beets (904) 778-5181

Chairscholars Foundation
17000 Patterson Rd.
Odessa, FL 33556
Hugo A. Keim (813) 920-2737
Hrs: 9-4
Trap: 4 **Skeet:** 2

Imperial Polk County Skeet & Trap Club
PO Box 1915
Winter Haven, FL 33880
(813) 299-4853
Hrs: W/S/Su, 1-5; Th, 6:30-10:30
Trap: 6

Key West Skeet Club
2108 Harris Ave.
Key West, FL 33040
Johnnie Yongue (305) 294-1394
Hrs: Su, 9-3; W, 4:30-Sundown
Skeet: 2

Keystone Heights Skeet
1403 Ree St., Starke, FL 32091
Janet Kimutis (904) 964-8804
Hrs: W, 7-11
Skeet: 1

Li Bi Ho Gun Club
Rt. 3, Box 475
Perry, FL 32347

Henry Lee (904) 838-7131
Hrs: W, 3-9; S/Su, 1-9
Trap: 1 **Skeet:** 1

MacDill AFB Skeet & Trap
PO Box 6825
MacDill AFB, FL 33608
Linda Carter (813) 830-5299
Trap: 2 **Skeet:** 2

Mayport Skeet Club
11049 Jean Ribault Ct.
Jacksonville, FL 32225
Kenneth L. Krueger
(904) 270-5627
Hrs: W, 3-5; Su, 12-5
Skeet: 1

Orange Bend Skeet Club
PO Box 492810
Leesburg, FL 34749
B. Murray Tucker, Jr.
(904) 787-3157
Hrs: Varies **Skeet:** 1

Orange County Trap & Skeet
10955 Smith-Bennett Rd.
Orlando, FL 32811
D. Cain/T. Forrest (407) 351-1230
Type: Public/Member
Hrs: W, 12-10; Th, 12-6; S/Su 10-6
Trap: 9 **Skeet:** 4

Palatka Skeet & Trap Club
PO Box 1546, Palatka, FL 32177
Roy Dear (904) 325-5425
Hrs: W-Su, 1-Dark
Skeet: 7

Palm Beach Gun Club
3001 S.W. 10th St.
Pompano Beach, FL 33069
David Humble (305) 425-7800

Patrick Skeet & Trap Range
320 Maple Dr.
Satellite Beach, FL 32937
Adrian Troy (407) 773-4863
Hrs: W, 3-7; S/Su, 12-5
Trap: 1 **Skeet:** 4

Port of the Islands
25000 Tamiami Trail East
East Naples, FL 33999
Russ Howard (813) 394-8666
90 mi. NW of Miami
Type: Public **Hrs:** W/Su, 9-4
Trap: 3 **Skeet:** 5

Skyway Trap & Skeet Club
3200 74th Ave., N.
St. Petersburg, FL 33702

Richard Gamble (813) 526-8993
70 mi. SW of Orlando
Type: Public **Hrs:** W, 12- 9:30;
S/Su, 12- 6; Th, 5-9
Trap: 8 **Skeet:** 2

St. Augustine Rod & Gun
PO Box 877, St. Augustine, FL
32085
Fred H. Bozard, Jr. (904) 829-6011
Trap: 1 **Skeet:** 5

Sunshine Gun Club
5781 SW Markel St.
Palm City, FL 34990
Ed Traylor
Hrs: Not Open the Public
Trap: 1 **Skeet:** 1

Tyndall AFB Trap & Skeet
4014 Par Dr.,
Panama City, FL 32404
Msgt. Tim Ross (904) 283-3855
Hrs: W/F, 3-7; S, 9-5; Su, 11-5
Trap: 2 **Skeet:** 3

GEORGIA

SPORTING & 5-STAND

Ashburn Hill
PO Box 128, Moultrie, GA 31776
F.R. Pidcock, III (912) 985-1507
60 mi. S of Tallahassee
Type: Public
Hrs: Su-S, Oct. thru March
Sporting: 1, 9 stations
Trap: 1 **Skeet:** 1 **HT:** 60 ft.

**Barksdale Bobwhite
Plantation Sporting Clays**
Rt. 4, Longstreet Rd., P.O. Box 851
Cochran, GA 31014
Ronnie·Wright (912) 934-6916
35 mi. S of Macon
Type: Public/Member
Hrs: Yr Round; M-S, 9-9; Su, 1-9
Sporting: 1, 11 stations
Skeet: 1 **Five Stand:** 1 **HT:** 50 ft.

Bevy Burst
Rt. 2, Box 245, Edison, GA 31746
Kathy Gray (912) 835-2156
40 mi. SW of Albany
Type: Public **Hrs:** By appt.
Sporting: 1, 9 stations

Boggy Pond Plantation
1084 Lanier Road
Moultrie, GA 31768
Mack W. Dekle, Jr. (912) 985-5395

55 mi. NE of Tallahassee, FL
Type: Public
Hrs: October 1 thru March 31st
Sporting: 1, 14 stations
HT: 50 ft.

Boll Weevil Plantation
4264 Thompson Bridge Rd.
Waynesboro, GA 30830
Al McClain (706) 554-6227
35 mi. S of Augusta
Type: Public
Hrs: M-S, 9-Dark; Su, 1-Dark
Sporting: 1, 24 stations

Cat Creek Sporting Clays
N. Main St., PO Box 52
Pavo, GA 31778
Buddy Lewis (912) 859-2075
30 mi. W of Valdosta
Type: Public **Hrs:** W-Su
Sporting: 1, 14 stations
Five Stand: 1 **Wobble Trap**

Cherokee Gun Club
PO Box 941, Gainesville, GA 30503
(404) 531-9493
45 mi. NE of Atlanta
Type: Member/Avail
Hrs: By appointment
Sporting: 1, 15 stations
Trap: 3 **Skeet:** 3 **Five Stand:** 1
HT: 12 ft.

Climax Clays
PO Box 248, Climax, GA 31734
Eugene Oviatt (912) 246-3214
2 mi. S of Climax
Type: Public/Member
Hrs: M-S, by appt.
Sporting: 1, 15 stations **Skeet:** 1

Forest City Gun Club
9203 Ferguson Ave.
Savannah, GA 31406
Carl Cole (912) 354-0210
1 mi. SE of Savannah
Type: Member/Avail
Hrs: W/S/Su, 2-8
Sporting: 1, 14 stations
Trap: 22 **Skeet:** 42 **Five Stand:** 1
HT: 45 ft.

Griffin Gun Club
988 Stormy Lane
Jonesboro, GA 30236
Larry Lyskowinski (404) 228-4872
Type: Member/Avail
Sporting: None
Trap: 1 **Skeet:** 4

Gun Swamp Country Club
PO Box 4116
Eastman, GA 31023
Lister Harrell (912) 374-5097
5 mi. E of Eastman
Type: Public **Hrs:** By Appt. Only
Sporting: 1, 22 stations
HT: 60 ft.

Llewellin's Point Hunting Preserve & Kennel
4897 Salem Rd.
Pine Mountain, GA 31822
Floyd Clements (800) 636-9819
70 mi. SW of Atlanta
Type: Public/Member
Hrs: T-F, 2-9; S, 10-8; Su, 2-8
Reservs: Recommended
Sporting: 2, 20 stations
Trap: 4 **Skeet:** 4 **Five Stand:** 1
HT: 50 ft.

See Our Ad Across

Manbone Run
270 Trinty Rd.
Whigham, GA 31797
Julian Knight (912) 762-4315
10 mi. NW of Cairo
Type: Public **Hrs:** S/Su, 9-6
Sporting: 2, 20 stations
Five Stand: 2 **HT:** 30 ft.

The Meadows Nat'l. Gun
PO Box 377, Smarr, GA 31086
Cliff M. Evans (912) 994-9910
Type: Member/Avail
Sporting: 1, 17 stations
HT: 50 ft. **Wobble Trap**

Millcreek Hunting Preserve
PO Box 131, Rincon, GA 31326
William Exley/Jesse (912) 826-4968
15 mi. N of Savannah

Type: Public/Member
Hrs: Su-S, Dawn-Dusk
Sporting: 1, 25 stations

Myrtlewood Hunting/ Sporting Clays
Box 199, Thomasville, GA 31799
Bob or John (912) 228-0987
55 mi. S of Albany
Type: Public
Hrs: M-Sa, daylight to dusk
Sporting: 1, 24 stations
HT: 35 ft. **Wobble Trap**

Ocmulgee River Gun Club
169 Marcar Rd., Macon, GA 31206
Kenny Sassiter (912) 788-7989
Type: Public/Member
Hrs: W/Th/S/Su, 2-Dark
Sporting: None
Trap: 1 **Skeet:** 6 **Five Stand:** 1

Outback Gun & Bow Club
Rt. 1, Box 1815,
Hazlehurst, GA 31539
Rhonwyn Dawson (912) 375-0765
100 mi. S of Macon
Type: Public/Member
Hrs: T-S, 9:30-Dark; Su, 1:30-6
Sporting: 1, 30 stations
HT: 40 ft.

Pine Hill Plantation
255 Kimbrel Rd.
Colquitt, GA 31737
G.J. Kimbrel, III (912) 758-6602
60 mi. NW of Tallahassee
Sporting:

Pinetucky Skeet & Trap Club, Inc.
2676 Gordon Hwy.
Augusta, GA 30909
Dan Mumpower (706) 592-4230
135 mi. E of Atlanta

Type: Public
Hrs: W/Th/F, 2-10; S/Su, 12-10
Reservs: Recommended
Sporting: 1, 12 stations
Trap: 4 **Skeet:** 5 **Five Stand:** 1
HT: 60 ft.
See Our Ad Below

Quail Creek
PO Box 2846
Valdosta, GA 31604
Chuck May (912) 244-6558
80 mi. NE of Tallahassee
Type: Member/Avail
Hrs: (S), Daily 8-9; (W), S, 10-6; Su, 1-6
Sporting: 1, 10 stations
Skeet: 1 **HT:** 35 ft. **Wobble Trap**

Quail Ridge Preserve
Rt. 3, Box 387-C
Douglas, GA 31533
Francis Fountain (912) 384-0025
140 mi. NE of Tallahassee
Type: Public **Hrs:** By Appt.
Sporting: 1, 12 stations

Quailridge Plantation
PO Box 155
Norman Park, GA 31771
Edwin Norman (912) 985-5011
70 mi. N of Tallahasse, FL
Type: Public
Hrs: Oct. 1 thru March 31
Sporting: 1, 4 stations
Trap: 1

Shirahland Plantation
Rt. 1, Box 340, Camilla, GA 31730
Ray Shirah (912) 294-4805
25 mi. S of Albany
Type: Public/Member
Hrs: Th 3-8; S 1:30-8; & by appt.
Sporting: 1, 10 stations
Five Stand: 1 **HT:** 66 ft. **Wobble Trap**

South River Gun Club
5205 Hwy. 212
Covington, GA 30209
Frank Churney (404) 786-3752
30 mi. E of Atlanta
Type: Public/Member
Hrs: W, 11-9; T-F, 11-7; S/Su, 9-6
Sporting: None
Trap: 9 **Skeet:** 5
Five Stand: 1 **HT**

Southpoint Plantation
PO Box 4309, Albany, GA 31706
Darryl E. Pinkston (912) 888-6598
20 mi. NW of Albany
Type: Public **Hrs:**
Sporting: 1, 6 stations

At Callaway Gardens

Llewellin's Point Gun Club & Sporting Clays at Callaway Gardens offers the premier clay shooting experience in Georgia. Two world-class sporting clays courses, trap & skeet fields and 5-stand sporting clays offer a wide array of shooting challenges.

In addition, certified instructors are available to assist novices and experienced gunners alike improve their skills. Rental guns, factory ammunition and a fully stocked, on-site pro shop complete the "picture perfect" clay shooting experience.

Llewellin's Point is also a world-renowned hunting preserve. Its staff of hunting professionals grew up hunting quail, and have put themselves and an excellent kennel of experienced Llewellin setters at your disposal. There's nothing they'd rather do than put you over an exploding covey of quail. No matter what your level of expertise, Llewellin's Point guides can outfit and guide you to a great day's hunting.

And there's more. Guests of the Club enjoy accommodations ranging from the 345-room inn at Callaway Gardens to 2-bedroom cottages or 4-bedroom villas, the ultimate in privacy and elegance. There are seven restaurants to choose from, all offering their unique brand of Southern fare. Fly fishing, golf and tennis, too! Easily accessible by car, only 70 miles south of Atlanta and just 2 miles off I-185. Or fly in by private plane to our 5,000 ft. paved, lighted airport.

Call Today For Information, Reservations Or A Color Brochure:

800-636-9819

4897 Salem Road • Pine Mountain, GA 31822

Starrsville Plantation
283 Bo Jones Rd.
Covington, GA 30209
Nathan V. Hendriks, III
(404) 787-1366
30 mi. E of Atlanta
Type: Public
Hrs: Daily, 8:30-5; Year Round
Sporting: 3, 6 stations
Trap: 1   HT: 45 ft.

**Tannenwood-A Hunting &
Shooting Preserve**
PO Box 130,
Davidsboro, GA 31018
Chad Tanner (912) 348-4931
60 mi. SW of Augusta
Type: Public/Member
Hrs: W, 9-til; Su, 1-til
Sporting: 1, 10 stations
Five Stand: 1

Wolf Creek Sport Shooting
3070 Merk Rd., SW
Atlanta, GA 30349
Dan Mitchell (404) 346-8382
2 mi. SW of Atlanta
Type: Public
Hrs: T-F, 1 to 9; S/Su, 10 to 5
Sporting: 3, 10 stations
Trap: 19 Skeet: 19 Five Stand: 1
HT: 40 ft.

TRAP & SKEET

Athens Rifle Club
1131 Hollow Creek Lane
Watkinsville, GA 30677
Henry A. Burkes (404) 549-0936
Hrs: Su, 2-5
Trap: 1 Skeet: 2

Burke Co. Rifle/Pistol Club
394 D. Knight Rd.
Waynesboro, GA 30830
Calvin Highsmith
Hrs: Upon Request
Skeet: 1

Chickasaw Rod & Gun Club
PO Box 191, Pelham, GA 31779
R.G. Rogers, Sr. (912) 294-8240
Hrs: Appt. only
Skeet: 6

Elbert Co. Gun Club
Rt. 2, Box 644, Carlton, GA 30627
Mike Metternick (706) 213-0098
Hrs: W, 5; Su, 1-6
Trap: 1 Skeet: 2

Flint Skeet & Trap Club
PO Box 70058, Albany, GA 31707
Jack M. Jones (912) 432-6603
Hrs: W-S, 3-9
Trap: 1 Skeet: 5

Floyd County Wildlife
909 Holland Rd., SW
Rome, GA 30161

Marvin Wright (706) 234-7879
Trap: 1 Skeet: 1

Fort Benning-US Army Base
US Army Marksmanship Unit
Fort Benning, GA 31905
Burl Branham (706) 545-7916
Olympic Trap

Little River Gun Club
174 Folds Rd., Carrolton, GA 30116
Clifford Jiles, Sr. (404) 832-9553
Hrs: Su, 1-6
Trap: 1 Skeet: 2

Moultrie Gun Club
Rt. 1, Box 516,
Moultrie, GA 31768
Royce Brooks
Hrs: Su, 2-5; Sat. on request
Skeet: 2

Ora Gun Club
PO Box 211, Statesville, GA 31648
Leo L. Miller (912) 559-7025
Trap: 1 Skeet: 1

Pickens Co. Sportsmans
PO Box 822, Jasper, GA 30143
Don Hendrix   Skeet: 1

RPM Gun Club
PO Box 40, Coleman, GA 31736
Billy Moore (912) 732-3416
Hrs: S/Su, 2-7
Skeet: 1

Robins Skeet & Trap Range
2669 Hwy. 127,
Kathleen, GA 31047
Alan Ray (912) 926-4500
Hrs: W, 5-9; S/Su, 11-5 (Nov-Mar)
Trap: 1 Skeet: 3

Sea Island Gun Club
PO Box 30296
Sea Island, GA 31561
Fred D. Missildine (912) 638-3611
45 mi. N of Jacksonville, FL
Type: Public Hrs: Daily, 2:30-4
Trap: 1 Skeet: 3

HAWAII

SPORTING & 5-STAND

Maui Trap & Gun Club
PO Box 963, Ulupalakua, HI 96790
Sam King (808) 572-0689
Sporting: None

Papaka Sporting Clays, Maui
1295 So. Kihei Rd., #3006
Kihei, Maui, HI 96753
Dave Barnes (808) 879-5649
5 mi. S of Makena
Type: Public/Member
Hrs: By app't. only; 7 days: 9 - dusk
Sporting: 1, 30 stations
Trap: Y Five Stand: 1   HT: 90 ft.

**Westside Sporting Clays
Kapalua**
2600 Liaholo Pl., Kihei, HI 96753
Mickey Hewitt (808) 669-SHOT
Type: Public Hrs: Su-S, 9-Dark
Sporting: 1, 6 stations
Skeet: 1

TRAP & SKEET

Big Island Trap Club
PO Box 10645, Hilo, HI 96721
Garrett Zane (808) 969-3750
Hrs: S/Su Trap: 4

Koko Head Skeet Club
96-1225 Waihona St.
Pearl City, HI 96782
Patrick Nolan (808) 455-4444
Hrs: S/Su, 8-4
Skeet: 2

Schofield Club
1825 Fern St., #A1
Honolulu, HI 96826
Iris Kano

IDAHO

SPORTING & 5-STAND

Blaine County Gun Club
Box 2940, Ketchum, ID 83340
Mike Riedel (208) 788-2681
7 mi. S of Sun Valley
Type: Public
Hrs: W/S/Su, 10-3; Th/F, 3-7
Sporting: 1, 8 stations
Trap: 1 Skeet: 1 Five Stand: 1
HT: 50 ft.

Idaho Gamebirds
Rt. 1, Box 1212
Homedale, ID 83628
Jim Davenport (208) 337-4826
40 mi. W of Boise
Type: Public/Member
Hrs: Open daily; dawn to dark
Sporting: 1, 12 stations
HT: 30 ft.

Idaho Sporting Clays
Rt. 1, Box 1212
Homedale, ID 83628
Jim Davenport (208) 337-4826
Type: Public
Hrs: M-F, 2-7; S/Su, 9-Dark
Sporting: 1, 9 stations

Skyline Gun Club, Inc.
6888 W. Arco Hwy-PO Box 50774
Idaho Falls, ID 83405
W.R. Lloyd (208) 525-8575
185 mi. E of Boise
Type: Public Hrs: S/Su, 12-5
Sporting: 1, 11 stations
Trap: 9 Skeet: 1 Five Stand: 1
Wobble Trap

Hunting Club & Clays

Rt. 2, Box 14A
Homedale, ID 83628
George Hyer (208) 337-4443
40 mi. W of Boise
Type: Public/Member
Hrs: Daily
Reservs: Strongly recommended
Sporting: 1, 14 stations
HT: 38 ft.

Teton Ridge Guest Ranch
200 Valley View Rd.
Tetonia, ID 83452
Albert Tilt (208) 456-2650
40 mi. NW of Jackson Hole, WY
Type: Member/Avail
Hrs: (Summer) Daily, 2-6
Sporting: 2, 15 stations
HT: 60 ft.

Tews Ranches
745 N. 550 W.
Shoshone, ID 83352
Rusty or Carla Tews
(208) 886-2100
50 mi. S of Sun Valley, ID
Type: Public/Member
Hrs: S/Su, 10-Dark
Sporting: 1, 10 stations
HT: 47 ft.

TRAP & SKEET

Boise Gun Club
PO Box 2293
Boise, ID 83701
Abe Wilson (208) 342-0892
Hrs: Su, 12-5; W, 5-10
Trap: 14 **Skeet:** 2

CDA Skeet & Trap Club
PO Box 1281
Coeur D'Alene, ID 83816
John Bainter (208) 772-2275
Hrs: Th, 12-9; S, 9-9; Su, 9-4
Trap: 4 **Skeet:** 4

Caldwell Gun Club
Box 1363
Caldwell, ID 83605
R.W. Murphey (208) 459-2616
Hrs: T, 6-10; S, 12-5
Trap: 6

MHAFB Trap & Skeet Range
366 SV/SVRT, 710 Trap Dr.,
Bldg. 2222
Mtn. Home, ID 83648
Harley Lekvold (208) 828-6093
Hrs: W-S, 11-8; Su, for reg. shoots
Trap: 7 **Skeet:** 3

Pleasant Valley Skeet Club
2703 Smith Ave., Boise, ID 83702
Don Mues (208) 336-3018
Hrs: By appt. **Skeet:** 1

Skeet Farm
1165 Miller Rd.
Lewistown, ID 83501
Gary Schwank (208) 743-5622
Hrs: By appt. only
Skeet: 1

St. Maries Gun Club
323 10th St., St. Maries, ID 83861
Robert Grieser (208) 245-4101
Type: Public
Hrs: Dec-April, Sundays 10-3
Trap: 3

ILLINOIS

SPORTING & 5-STAND

Best Shot Sporting Clays
2610 Willow Grove Rd.
Harrisburg, IL 62946
Alan Pulliam (618) 268-4629
Type: Public/Member
Hrs: S, 9-Dusk; Wkdys by appt.
Sporting: 2, 20 stations
HT: 40 ft.

Bloomington Gun Club
RR2, Box 96, Colfax, IL 61728
Tracey Robertson (309) 724-8516
Hrs: W/Th, 12-10; F/S/Su, 8-10
Sporting: 2
Trap: 2 **Skeet:** 2

Callahan Ranch Hunting
RR#1, Box 7A, Montrose, IL 62445
Tom & Dana Thull (217) 924-4412
100 mi. NE of St. Louis, MO
Type: Public **Hrs:** Su-S, 8-Dusk
Sporting: 2, 20 stations
Trap: 1

Darnall Shooting Center

RR3, Box 274,
Bloomington, IL 61704
Ron Darnall (309) 379-4331
8 mi. W of Bloomington
Type: Public/Member
Hrs: T/W/Th, 9-9; F/S/Su, 9-6
Reservs: Not required
Sporting: None
Trap: 5 **Skeet:** 3 **Five Stand:** 1
HT: 30 ft.
○ Rental Guns
○ Indoor/outdoor rifle & pistol
   range
○ Fully stocked Pro and Gun Shop
○ Gunsmith on duty 6 days a week
○ Just 8 mi. west of I-55

Diamond S Sporting Clays
27211 Townline Rd.
Tremont, IL 61568
Cory Stowell (309) 449-5500
120 mi. SW of Chicago
Hrs: Th/Su, 8-5:30
Sporting: 1

Garden Plain Hunt Club
7737 Long Rd., Fulton, IL 61252
Curt Ebersohl (309) 887-4439
120 mi. W of Chicago
Type: Public/Member
Hrs: Su-S, 8-Dusk
Sporting: 1, 15 stations

Grizzle's Gamebirds
RR#2, Brighton, IL 62012
Terry Grizzle (618) 372-8672
30 mi. NE of St. Louis, MO
Type: Public
Hrs: Call for reserv.
Sporting: 1, 10 stations **HT:** 10 ft.

Hopewell Views Hunting
Rt. 2, Rockport, IL 62370
Rick Wombles (217) 734-9234
85 mi. NW of St. Louis, MO
Type: Member/Avail
Sporting: 1

Hot Shot Sporting Clays, Ltd.
4945 State Rt. 156
Waterloo, IL 62298
Steve King (618) 939-3015
Hrs: By Appt.
Sporting: 1, 13 stations

Hunting Unlimited
RR4, Box 98, Mt. Sterling, IL 62353
Larry Hanold (217) 289-3366
35 mi. E of Quincy
Type: Public/Member
Hrs: 8-5, by app't
Sporting: 2, 15 stations
Trap: 1 **HT:** 50 ft.

Knights Prairie Hunt Club/MacKenzie Kennels
Rt. 1, Box 142,
McLeansboro, IL 62859
Gerry MacKenzie (618) 736-2690
90 mi. SE of St. Louis
Type: Public/Member
Sporting: 1

Millbrook Hunting Club

7519 Finnie Rd.
Newark, IL 60541
Dick Carlson (708) 553-5407
60 mi. SW of Chicago
Type: Member/Avail
Hrs: Su-S, by appt.
Reservs: Strongly recommended
Sporting: 1, 14 stations

CLAYS

Nishkawee Preserve
21887 Pigeon Rd.
Morrison, IL 61270
Norman F. Spencer (815) 772-3394
140 mi. W of Chicago
Type: Public/Member
Hrs: 4/16-9/20; 8-5 daily by app't
Sporting: 1, 10 stations
HT: 16 ft.

North Pike Hunting Club
RR2, Griggsville, IL 62340
Donovan Baldwin (217) 236-3131
60 mi. W of Springfield
Type: Public/Member
Hrs: S/Su, 8-5; Wkdys by Appt.
Sporting: 1, 13 stations
Trap: Y

Northbrook Sports Club
PO Box 766, Grayslake, IL 60030
Art Moldenhauer (708) 223-5700
40 mi. NW of Chicago
Type: Public/Member
Hrs: W, 12-5; Th, 12-10; S/Su, 10-5
Sporting: 1, 10 stations
Trap: 12 **Skeet:** 12 **Five Stand:** 1
Olympic Trap   Double Trap

Oakmount
Game Club
30808 N. Darrell Rd.
McHenry, IL 60050
Peter Reiland, Jr. (815) 385-2144
45 mi. NW of Chicago
Type: Public
Hrs: W-S, 9-5; Su, 10-5
Reservs: Strongly recommended
Sporting: 1, 18 stations
HT: 55 ft.

Olde Barn Sporting Clays
RR2, Box 143A, Rt. 130
Oakland, IL 61943
B.C. McQueen (217) 346-3211
85 mi. E of Springfield
Type: Public
Hrs: Th/F/S/Su, 8:30-5; M/T/W
by appt.
Sporting: 2, 20 stations
HT: 40 ft. **Wobble Trap**

Otter Creek
Hunting Club
Rt. 3, Box 125G
Jerseyville, IL 62052
Mike Runge (618) 376-7601
40 mi. NE of St. Louis, MO
Type: Public/Member
Hrs: M-F, by appt; S/Su, 8-?
Reservs: Recommended
Sporting: 2, 27 stations
Trap: Y **Skeet:** Y **Five Stand:** 1
Wobble Trap
○ Bird Brain operated 5-Stand,
   lighted for evening shooting
○ Skeet and Trap Fields; Rifle &
   pistol range for members.
○ Shooting Instructor on Staff.
○ Leagues/Corporate Shoots–with
   Hog Roasts.
○ Monthly tournaments. NSCA
   Member. 60 mi. SW of
   Springfield, IL.

Pheasant Valley Hunt Club
R#1, Box 360
Bunker Hill, IL 62014
Sharon Wilkinson (618) 585-3956
30 mi. NE of St. Louis, MO
Type: Public/Member
Hrs: W-Su, 9am-dusk
Sporting: 1, 10 stations
Five Stand: 1   **HT:** 40 ft.

Pinewood Hunt Club
RR#1, Box 36
Beaverville, IL 60912
Wayne DeYoung (815) 435-2314
55 mi. S of Chicago
Type: Member/Avail
Hrs: 8am-7pm
Sporting: 1, 25 stations

Rend Lake Trap Field
Rt. 3, Box 242, Benton, IL 62812
Tom Winn (618) 629-9920
Type: Public **Hrs:**
Sporting: 1, 10 stations
Trap: 10 **Skeet:** 1   **Wobble Trap**

Richmond Hunting Club
Hwy. 173, Rt. 12
Richmond, IL 60071
Mike Daniels (815) 678-3271
50 mi. NW of Chicago
Type: Public/Member
Hrs: Su-S, 8-5
Sporting: 1, 10 stations
Trap: 3   **HT:** 25 ft.

Sand Prairie Farms
185 Rogers Rd., Ohio, IL 61349
Tom Yucus (815) 376-6641
90 mi. W of Chicago
Type: Public/Member
Hrs: M-S, Dawn-Dusk, year-round
Sporting: 1, 10 stations
Trap: 1

Sandy Creek
Ranch
RR# 2, Box 244
Winchester, IL 62694
Clubhouse (217) 927-4223
60 mi. N of St. Louis
Type: Public/Member
Hrs: M-F, by appt; S/Su, 9-Dusk
Reservs: Not required
Sporting: 3, 25 stations
HT: 30 ft.
○ Alt. Phone: (217) 886-2540;
   Steve Wheeler
○ 2, 10-station walking courses; 1
   5-station tower course
The Ranch consists of 1,000
contiguous acres of upland
terrain in West Central Illinois.
Located 60 miles from
Springfield, St. Louis and Quincy,
it lies just two miles off the
Illinois River in Green and Scott
counties. We offer sporting
clays, big game bow hunting,
upland game hunting, dog
training, kennels, a shooting
lodge and campsite.

Seneca Hunt Club
PO Box 824, Seneca, IL 60098
Larry Higdon (815) 357-8080
60 mi. SW of Chicago
Type: Public/Member
Hrs: T-Su, 8-4:30
Sporting: 4, 15 stations
Five Stand: 1   **HT:** 45 ft.

Smokin' Gun Hunt Club
Box 392, RR1, Hamilton, IL 62341
Darrin Miller (217) 847-2227
100 mi. NW of Springfield
Type: Public/Member
Hrs: T/W/Th, 4-9; Su, appt; S, 12-9
Sporting: None
Trap: 2 **Skeet:** 1 **Five Stand:** 1

St. Charles Sportsmen Club
8N365 Shady Lane
Elgin, IL 60123
Robert Scherf (708) 365-9881
25 mi. W of Chicago
Type: Public/Member
Hrs: Th, 6pm-10pm; Su, 9:30-1
Sporting: 1, 10 stations
Trap: 7 **Skeet:** 1

Streamline Sporting Clays
Rt. 1, Box 204, Percy, IL 62272
Ron Doering (618) 497-2539
50 mi. SE of St. Louis, MO
Type: Member/Avail
Hrs: S/Su, 10-4; Weekdays by Appt.
Sporting: 1, 10 stations

Tamarack Farm Hunt Club
7210 Keystone Rd.
Richmond, IL 60071
Dick Hendricksen (815) 678-4506
40 mi. NW of Chicago
Type: Member/Avail
Hrs: Group Resrv. Only
Sporting: 1, 10 stations
Trap: Y **Five Stand:** 1
Wobble Trap

Timberview Lakes Sporting Clays
23200 North 2000 Rd.
Bushnell, IL 61422
Ken Stone (309) 772-3609
30 mi. S of Galesburg
Type: Public **Hrs:**
Sporting: 2, 25 stations

Trail of Tears Sports Resort
Rt. 1, Old Cape Rd.
Jonesboro, IL 62952
Ron & Deb Charles (618) 833-8697
15 mi. NE of Cape Girardeau
Type: Public/Member
Hrs: Yearly
Sporting: 2, 10 stations

Upland Bay Hunt Club
Rt. 173 & Lakeview 4218
Richmond, IL 60071
Steve Warner (815) 678-4411
50 mi. NW of Chicago
Type: Public/Member
Sporting: 1, 10 stations **HT:** 40 ft.

UPLAND HUNT CLUB
& SPORTING CLAYS
14755 Edson Rd.
Davis Junction, IL 61020
Mike McInerney, Mgr. (815) 874-7444
55 mi. W of Chicago
Type: Public/Member
Hrs: Daily by reservation
Reservs: Strongly recommended
Sporting: 5, 30 stations
HT: 35 ft.

Wild Cat Run
961 Hawns Rd., RR1, Box 46
Keithsburg, IL 61442
David McCaw (800) 484-9611
30 mi. SW of Moline
Type: Public
Hrs: S/Su, 8-Dark; others by appt.
Sporting: None
Five Stand: 1

X Sporting Clays
Rt. 3, Box 165
Pana, IL 62557
James Eck (217) 562-5272
45 mi. SE of Springfield
Type: Public
Hrs: S/Su, 8:30-5; M-F, By Appt.
Sporting: 1, 10 stations
Trap: 2   **HT:** 30 ft. **Wobble Trap**

TRAP & SKEET
Brittany Shooting Park
RR2, Box 224,
Bunker Hill, IL 62014
Larry Mohr (618) 362-6265
Hrs: T/S, 6-11; Su, 12-6
Trap: 9 **Skeet:** 3

Decatur Gun Club
PO Box 3062, Decatur, IL 62525
Mike Turner (217) 877-0400
Hrs: S, 11-4; Th, 5-9; Su, 9-4
Trap: 9 **Skeet:** 8

Edgewood Shooting Park
1008 W. Madison St.
Auburn, IL 62615
James Ketchum (217) 438-6327
Type: Public
Hrs: Th, 6-10; Su, 1-4 **Trap:** Y

Edwardsville Gun Club
PO Box 557, Edwardsville, IL 62025
Chuck Malmgren (618) 656-2875
Hrs: Th, 7-10; S/Su, 1-5
Trap: Y

Effingham Co. Sportsman's
306 S. 8th St., Altamont, IL 62411
David Miller (217) 342-3951
Trap: 2 **Skeet:** 2

Frankfort Sportsmans Club
1008 S. Kolin Ave.
Oaklawn, IL 60453
John Newgren (815) 469-9887
Hrs: W/F, 6-10:30; Su, 10-4
Trap: 4

Hi-Lo Club, Inc.
47 Fox Court, Mahomet, IL 61853
Wayne R. Cluver (217) 495-3576
Hrs: S/Su, 10-4; W, 4-6 (Summer)
Trap: 2 **Skeet:** 2

Highland Pistol/Rifle Club
1910 Olive St., Highland, IL 62249
Wes Stueber (618) 654-5971
Hrs: M-F, 6-10; S/Su, 12-5
Trap: 5 **Skeet:** 1

Hilldale
18 N. 681 Rt. 31,
Dundee, IL 60118
Fred Lawrence (708) 428-2816
Hrs: F, 1-Dark; S/Su, 10-6
Trap: 4 **Skeet:** 4

Illinois State Trap Assn.
624 Lakeview, E. Peoria, IL 61611
Roger Rocke (309) 699-6202
Type: Public **Hrs:** S/Su
Trap: Y **Skeet:** Y

Jacksonville Sportsmens
1850 Mound Rd.
Jacksonville, IL 62650
Robert Hall
Type: Public/Member
Trap: Y

Knollwood Gun Club
37W461 Heritage Dr.
Batavia, IL 60510
Paul Moecher (708) 553-7585
Hrs: Su, 10-3
Skeet: 3

Marble Gun Club
RR5, Box 285A, Danville, IL 61832
Todd Marble (217) 431-3014
Trap: 4 **Skeet:** 1

McHenry Sportsmen's Club
N. Weingart Rd. @ Rolling Ln.
McHenry, IL
Harvey Scharlau (708) 894-9135
Hrs: S, 1-5; 2nd & 4th Sun, 10-4
Trap: 4

New Boston Gun Club
403 SE 3rd Ave., Box 208
Aledo, IL 61231
(309) 582-5327
Type: Public
Hrs: 1st Sunday/month
Trap: 5

Oak Park Country Club
PO Box 109, Oak Park, IL 60303
Tom Geraghty (708) 456-7600
Hrs: S, 10-2; Su, 9-3 (Nov-Mar)
Trap: 1 **Skeet:** 2

Olin Gun Club
427 Shamrock St.
East Alton, IL 62024
Cindy R. Wattles
Trap: 2 **Skeet:** 4

CLAYS

Palos Sportsman's Club
24038 S. Harlem
Frankfort, IL 60423
Robert Osterberg (815) 469-4446
Hrs: W, 12-Dusk; S/Su, 9-5
Trap: 4 Skeet: 5

Peoria Skeet & Trap Club
1305 Charlotte, Pekin, IL 61554
Bill Durbin (309) 822-8146
Type: Public/Member
Hrs: Th/S/Su, 11-5
Trap: 10 Skeet: 10

Quincy Gun Club
4607 Woodland Trail
Quincy, IL 62301
Denny Dedert (217) 224-5819
Type: Public/Member
Hrs: T/Th, 5pm; S/Su, Noon
Trap: 5 Skeet: 4

Rockford Country Club
4439 Applewood Ln.
Loves Park, IL 61111
Mike Arduino (815) 968-3055
Type: Member/Avail
Hrs: Last Su. in March, 9-4
Trap: 1 Skeet: 2

Rockford Skeet Club
641 Amphitheater, Unit 3
Rockford, IL 61107
James E. Gaddis (815) 874-9900
Hrs: S/Su, 1-5
Trap: 1 Skeet: 3

Scott AFB Rod & Gun Club
D#9 Meadowbruck La.
Belleville, IL 62221
Kevin Pellone (618) 256-2052
Hrs: Th, 5-10; S, 10-3; Su, 12-5
Trap: 2 Skeet: 3

Shoot N Cuss Gun Club
RR3, Box 9
Danville, IL 61832
Robert H. Smalley (217) 446-3659
Hrs: Su, morn; Wed., eve.
Trap: 1 Skeet: 1

Voorhees Street Gun Club
R1, Box 191, Westville, IL 61883
John Kocurek (217) 267-2510
Hrs: S/Su, 9-3
Trap: 1 Skeet: 1

West Chicago Gun Club
Box 104, West Chicago, IL 60185
Jack Anderson (708) 231-9862
Hrs: Th, 7-10; Su, 9-1; M, 7-10
Trap: 2 Skeet: 1

X-Line Gun Club
1157 Pheasant, Bradley, IL 60915
Jack or Jan Miller (815) 932-0877
Type: Public
Hrs: T/F, 6pm; S, 11-3; Reg. Shoots
Trap: 9

INDIANA

SPORTING & 5-STAND

Back 40 Sporting Clays
9442 Beech Rd.
Bourbon, IN 46504
Larry Mioster (219) 342-4665
45 mi. W of Fort Wayne
Type: Public/Member
Hrs: S/Su, 9-Dark; M-F, by appt.
Sporting: 2, 20 stations
HT: 20 ft.

Bearcreek
Sporting Clays
R4, Box 268-A (500 North)
Portland, IN 47371
John Lawrence (219) 726-8646
40 mi. S of Fort Wayne
Type: Public/Member
Hrs: M-F, call for hrs; S/Su, 8-dark
Reservs: Not required
Sporting: 3, 45 stations
Skeet: 1 HT: 25 ft.
○ Factory Ammunition
○ On Site Gun Shop & Pro Shop
○ Less than 1/2 mi. off U.S. 27

Bush Country
Sporting Clays, Inc.
RR#1, Box 111
Campbellsburg, IN 47108
Trent & J.D. Bush (812) 755-4760
55 mi. NW of Louisville, KY
Type: Public
Hrs: S/Su, 8-Dark; M-F, by appt.
Reservs: Not required
Sporting: 1, 11 stations HT: 35 ft.

Located in beautiful southern Indiana, this is one of the most challenging courses in the State. Designed by John Cochran, it represents the true meaning of sporting clays. Come try your luck at our well-known "Birds from Hell" station (it keeps you shooting). Refreshments, shells, reloading supplies, etc. available at our clubhouse.

Question or problem?
Give Wing & Clay a call
9 am - 5 pm E.S.T.
and we'll try to help. Our
number is: (908) 224-8700.

Clear Creek Sporting Clays
7944 W. Country Rd. 100 North
Danville, IN 46122
Jay Dee Mendenhall
(317) 539-2869
25 mi. W of Indianapolis
Type: Public
Hrs: W-S, 10-Dusk; Su, 1-Dusk
Sporting: 3, 15 stations HT: 40 ft.

Evansville Gun Club
RD#2, Box 89D
Haubstadt, IN 47639
Ron Eberhard (812) 768-6370
15 mi. N of Evansville
Type: Public/Member
Hrs: T/W/Th, 12-9; S/Su, 8-4
Sporting: 1, 14 stations
Trap: 9 Skeet: 2 Five Stand: 1
HT: 35 ft. Olympic Trap Double
Trap Universal Trench

Graham Creek
Sporting Clays
3700 E. Private Rd., #390S
N. Vernon, IN 47265
George Cummins (812) 873-2529
70 mi. S of Indianapolis
Type: Public
Hrs: S/Su, 9-5; M-F, by appt.
Reservs: Recommended
Sporting: 3, 11 stations
Wobble Trap

Graham Creek offers sporting clays shooters 3 courses, pro-shop, picnic area and course instruction. Beginner or pro can enjoy shooting the two 100 target eleven stations. Woodlands I and II designed by Jon Kruger winds through heavily wooded rolling terrain with crushed stone paths. One FITASC style course, Meadows offer a variety of long crossing targets and wide spread pairs. Drop the family at adjoining Broomsage Ranch to enjoy swimming, fishing, paddle boats, water slide, hiking, camping and dining. Call today for more information and reservations.

Hard Scrabble
PO Box 1313, Warsaw, IN 46580
Roy Gregory (219) 566-2511
40 mi. SW of Fort Wayne
Type: Public
Hrs: S, 9-3; Wkdays. by appt.
Sporting: 3, 33 stations HT: 40 ft.

The Hollow
Sporting Clays & Hunting Preserve
4611 Morningside Dr.
Bloomington, IN 47408
Jim Burhans, Owner/Operator
(317) 795-3999
40 mi. SW of Indianapolis
Type: Public
Hrs: Daily, 8-Dark; Year Round
Reservs: Recommended
Sporting: 2, 30 stations
Trap: 1 **Skeet:** 1 **Five Stand:** 1
HT: 60 ft.
○ Chosen One of the Top 25 Courses in the U.S. by Esquire Sportsman Magazine
○ Shoot "The Humbler". Free Shooting & Hunting Instruction. Handicapped Accessible
○ Large, modern clubhouse and excellent food. TV-lounge. Pro Shop. Rental Guns.
○ Outstanding Hunting Preserve: Season 9/1 - 4/30. See listing& ad in Indiana Wings Section
○ Located in Cloverdale, IN, 40 mi. SW of Indianapolis off I-70

Indian Creek Shooting Ctr
5950 Gun Club Rd., NE
Georgetown, IN 47122
Wanda Seitz (812) 951-3031
15 mi. W of Louisville, KY
Type: Public/Member
Hrs: M/W/F, by appt., 1st, 3rd & 5th Weekends
Sporting: 1, 11 stations
Trap: 4

Indiana Gun Club
14926 E. 113th St.
Fortville, IN 46040
Veldon Smith (317) 485-6540
8 mi. NE of Indianapolis
Type: Public
Hrs: W, 12-10:30; Th/F, 12-6; S/Su, 10-6
Sporting: 1, 12 stations
Trap: 23 **Skeet:** 6 **Five Stand:** 1

Lost River
Game Farm
PO Box 82, Orleans, IN 47452
Bob Hudelson (812) 865-3021
75 mi. S of Indianapolis
Reservs: Strongly recommended

Sporting: 2, 18 stations
HT: 32 ft.
○ 45 mi. west of Louisville
○ Family owned and operated
○ 2 Courses: 10 station tower course and 8 station walking course
○ Upland Hunting, too! See our ad in Indiana Wings section.

Quail Ridge
Sportsman's
PO Box 515, Aurora, IN 47001
Brian E. Lane (812) 926-4999
35 mi. W of Cincinnati
Type: Public/Member
Hrs: W-Su, 9-dusk
Reservs: Strongly recommended
Sporting: 1, 15 stations
HT: 60 ft.

Scott County Sporting
3331 E. Harrod Rd.
Scottsburg, IN 47170
Patricia Lytle (812) 794-2382
10 mi. NE of Scottsburg
Type: Public
Hrs: S/Su, 9-Dusk; M-F, by appt.
Sporting: 1, 10 stations

Springer Run Hunting
PO Box 816
New Albany, IN 47151
Tony Thomas (812) 739-4848
3 mi. N of Levenworth
Type: Public
Hrs: S/Su, 9-5; Wkdays by appt.
Sporting: 1, 11 stations
Five Stand: 1 **HT:** 15 ft.

Sugar Creek
Sporting Clays
RR2, Box 413
Mitchell, IN 47446
Dale Waldbieser (812) 849-2296
40 mi. S of Bloomington
Type: Public
Hrs: S/Su, 10-Dark; W/Th/F, 8-Dark by appt.
Reservs: Recommended
Sporting: 2, 20 stations
Trap: 2 **Skeet:** 2
○ Loaner Guns
○ Less than 1 hour from Louisville, KY
○ Just 35 minutes off I-65

West Creek Shooting
15547 W. 169th Ave.
Cedar Lake, IN 46303
Randy or Patty Lukasik
(219) 696-6101
50 mi. SE of Chicago
Type: Public/Member

Hrs: Su-S, 9am & 1pm
Sporting: 2, 15 stations
HT: 40 ft.

Wild Wing Sporting Center
RR1, Box 1,
Center Pointe, IN 47840
James Andrews (812) 986-2828
20 mi. E of Terre Haute
Type: Public
Hrs: W-Su, 8:30-5; M/T, By appt.
Sporting: 1, 15 stations
Trap: 1 **HT:** 45 ft.

TRAP & SKEET
Chain O Lakes Gun Club
1601 Kings Court
Mishawaka, IN 46544
Art Horvath (219) 259-7333
Type: Public/Member
Hrs: S/Su, 1-5
Trap: 5 **Skeet:** 3

Columbus Gun Club
3939 S. 525E, Columbus, IN 47203
Don Schnier (812) 377-5849
Hrs: Th, 4-9 **Trap:** 3

Crooked Creek
Conservation
8656 Fox Ridge La.
Indianapolis, IN 46256
Greg Hoffman
Hrs: S/Su, 12-5 (Summer); T/Th, 5-8

Deer Creek Conservation
6203 S. 375 East
Jonesboro, IN 46938
Toni or Jim Ehle (317) 677-8281
Type: Public/Member
Hrs: S, 6; 1st Su/month-Reg. 11am
Trap: 5 **Wobble Trap**

Evansville Izaak Walton
4266 Bethany Church Rd.
Boonville, IN 47601
Howard Shrode (812) 897-2746
Hrs: S-Th, 8-10
Trap: 2 **Skeet:** 2

Fall Creek Valley CC
2306 Nichol Ave.
Anderson, IN 46016
Thomas Daily (317) 644-0421
Type: Public/Member
Hrs: Reg. Trap, 2nd Sun; Practice, T, 6pm (Apr-Nov)
Trap: 4

Frontier Gun Club
RR2, Box 235
Roachdale, IN 46172
Steve Smith (317) 522-2084
Type: Public/Member
Hrs: 2nd & 3rd S/Su, 10-6
Trap: 13

Fulton County Gun Club
3916 N. Meridian Rd.
Rochester, IN 46975

CLAYS

Don E. Cain (219) 223-2072
Type: Public/Member
Hrs: F, 6:30-11pm; 2nd, 4th & 5th
Sundays, 9:30am **Trap:** 4

**Henry County
Conservation Club**
PO Box 35, New Castle, IN 47362
Gil Lee (317) 533-6602
Type: Public/Member
Hrs: Th, 6pm-11pm; Su, 10-2; ATA
Shoot 1st Sun/month
Trap: 4   **Wobble Trap**

I U Skeet Range
HPER Bldg., Room 290
Bloomington, IN 47405
Jack Mills (812) 855-0244
Hrs: Su, 12-5
Trap: 2   **Skeet:** 2

Indiana State Trap Assn.
PO Box 121, Orleans, IN 47452
Velton Smith (317) 485-6540
Type: Public/Member
Hrs: W, 12-10; Th/F/S/Su, 10-6
Trap: 23   **Skeet:** 6

Kingen Gun Club
5190 N. 500 W.
McCordsville, IN 46055
Dennis Kingen (317) 335-3781
Hrs: W/S, 11-5
Trap: 19

Oakwood Gun Club
RR2, Box 736,
Wheatfield, IN 46392
Dave Glissman (219) 956-4615
Hrs: W, 5:30-10:30; S, 10-3
Trap: 4

Purdue Trap & Skeet Club
IPIA 268B Agad Bldg.
Purdue Univ.,
W. Lafayett, IN 47907
Charles Rhykerd (317) 494-8459
Hrs: Wkends during school,
college only
Trap: 2   **Skeet:** 1

St. Joe Valley Conservation
7222 State Rd. #8
Butler, IN 46721
Tom or Shirley Bassett
(219) 337-5234
Type: Public/Member
Hrs: 1st Su/mo. W, 12-8 (June-Aug)
Trap: 5   **Skeet:** 1

Vincennes Gun Club
PO Box 538, Vincennes, IN 47591
Robert V. Bierhaus (812) 882-0990
Type: Public/Member
Hrs: Th, 6-11
Trap: 4   **Skeet:** 1

Wallace Traps
R#1, Box 95, Hillsboro, IN 47949
Charles Bryant (317) 397-3568

Type: Public
Hrs: 4th Sunday, April-Sept.
Trap: 5

White River Gun Club
3221 29th St., Bedford, IN 47421
Robert Snyder (812) 275-3697
Type: Public/Member
Hrs: 1st & 3rd Sun/month
Trap: 5

IOWA

SPORTING & 5-STAND

Arrowhead Hunting Club
3529 170th St.
Goose Lake, IA 52750
Gloria Mullin (319) 577-2267
165 mi. E of Des Moines
Type: Public/Member
Hrs: By Appt.
Sporting: 1, 5 stations
Trap: 5

Black Hawk Sporting Clays
2407 Valley High Dr.
Cedar Falls, IA 50613
Mike Grieger (319) 266-7262
90 mi. NE of Des Moines
Type: Public
Hrs: Su, 9-5; W, 4-Dark
Sporting: 1, 8 stations
Trap: 1   **Skeet:** 1   **HT:** 45 ft.

Flood Creek
1545 Fool Hill La.
Nora Springs, IA 50458
Mike Kelsey (515) 395-2694
120 mi. N of Des Moines
Type: Public/Member
Hrs: W, 5-dark; Su, 11-5
Sporting: 1, 12 stations **HT:** 80 ft.

HATS/SC, Inc.
3703 Rohret Rd.
Iowa City, IA 52240
James C. Rogers (319) 645-2093
Hrs: T/Th, 4-10; S, 10-6; Su, 12-6
Sporting: 1, 10 stations
Trap: 6   **Skeet:** 2

Hawkeye Area T.S. & SC
PO Box 75, Tiffin, IA 52340
Jim Rogers (319) 645-2093
95 mi. NE of Des Moines
Type: Public
Hrs: T/Th, 4-10; Su, 12-6; S, 10-6
Sporting: 1
Trap: 7   **Skeet:** 2   **HT:** 50 ft.

Hunter's Knob Gun Club
623 Pershing St.
St. Charles, IA 50240
Daryl Brown (515) 297-2250
25 mi. S of Des Moines
Type: Public
Hrs: Th, 6-Dark, 1st & 3rd Wkends
Sporting: 1, 11 stations

**Kruger
Clay World**
RR1, Box 213,
St. Ansgar, IA 50472
Jon Kruger (515) 736-4893
20 mi. NE of Mason City
Type: Public
Hrs: M/Th/F, 5; S/Su, 1-5; T, 5-Dark
Reservs: Not required
Sporting: 1, 16 stations
Trap: 1   **Skeet:** 1   **Five Stand:** 1
Wobble Trap

*Shooting Instruction
Available - See Pg. 163*

**Bill Kuntz's
Oakwood Sporting
Resort**
RR#2, Box 69
Sigourney, IA 52591
Bill Kuntz (800) 432-3290
40 mi. SW of Iowa City
Type: Public **Hrs:** By Appt.
Reservs: Recommended
Sporting: 1, 10 stations
HT: 40 ft.

Lazy H Hunting Club
RR#2, Woodbine, IA 51579
Murray Hubbard (712) 647-2877
45 mi. NE of Omaha/Co. Bluffs
Type: Public/Member
Hrs: S/Su, 9-dk; Wkdays, by appt.
Sporting: 1, 27 stations
HT: 90 ft.

New Pioneer Gun Club
PO Box 219, Waukee, IA 50263
Jeff Brammer (515) 987-4415
7 mi. W of Des Moines
Type: Public/Member
Hrs: W/Th, 1-6; S/Su, 10-5
Sporting: 1, 10 stations
Trap: 4   **Skeet:** 6   **HT:** 65 ft.

Outpost Clays Range
Rt. 1, Box 211
Logan, IA 51546
Bob Spencer (712) 644-2222
30 mi. N of Omaha, NE
Type: Public
Hrs: Su-S, by appt.
Sporting: 1, 10 stations
Trap: 1   **HT:** 100 ft.

Quad City Skeet & Trap
1603 Central Ave.

Bettendorf, IA 52722
Duane Sassen (319) 324-8097
140 mi. E of Des Moines
Type: Public/Member
Hrs: Su, 10-5; S, 1-5; T, 4-10
Sporting: 1, 13 stations
Trap: 3 **Skeet:** 5 **Five Stand:** 1
HT: 40 ft.

Shell Rock Area Sportsmens Club
PO Box 12, Shell Rock, IA 50670
Ernest W. Ramige (319) 885-6521
20 mi. NW of Waterloo
Type: Public/Member
Hrs: Twice a month by appt.
Sporting: 1, 5 stations

Southern Iowa Sporting
RR2, Box 91, Moulton, IA 52572
Bruce Burgher (515) 642-3256
70 mi. SE of Des Moines
Type: Public
Hrs: Weekends & Evenings by appt.
Sporting: 1, 10 stations
HT: 30 ft.

Spring Run
Box 8364A, Spirit Lake, IA 51360
Marty Loos (712) 336-0882
85 mi. E of Sioux Falls
Type: Public **Hrs:** By appt.
Sporting: 1, 10 stations
Trap: Y

Timber Ridge
RR1, Box 203A
Castana, IA 51010
Richard Bumann (712) 353-6517
90 mi. N of Omaha, NE
Type: Public **Hrs:** By appt. only
Sporting: 1, 10 stations

Triple H Ranch Hunting Preserve
16365 70th Avenue
Burlington, IA 52601
Keith A. Hoelzen (319) 985-2253
140 mi. SE of Des Moines
Type: Public
Hrs: S/Su, 9-5; M-F, by Appt.
Reservs: Strongly recommended
Sporting: 2, 15 stations
Five Stand: 1   **HT:** 60 ft.

Wing & Clay makes a great gift for your favorite shotgunner! A gift that he or she will use throughout the year. Why not order one now? Or order a dozen and give 'em to your business colleagues or shooting buddies. Call: 800-224-9464 to order.

TRAP & SKEET

Ames Izaak Walton League
1804 Northwestern
Ames, IA 50010
Martin Simpson (512) 233-1105
Hrs: W, 6:30-11:30; Su, 3-5
Trap: 2 **Skeet:** 1

Marion Co. Sportsmens
926 128th Ave.
Knoxville, IA 50138
Stephen C. Coon (515) 828-7392
Hrs: W, 6pm (TR); Th, 6pm (SK)
Trap: 4 **Skeet:** 2

Marshall Gun Club
812 Washington
Marshalltown, IA 50158
Allen Huseboe (515) 752-1760
Type: Public/Member
Hrs: Su, 1pm; T/W/Th, 5pm
Trap: Y **Skeet:** Y

Otter Creek Sportsmens
PO Box 31, Hiawatha, IA 52233
Joanne DeLong
Type: Public/Member
Hrs: T/Th, 5-9:30; S, 12-4; Su, 12-5
Trap: 6 **Skeet:** 1

Pella Trap Range
906 W. South, Knoxville, IA 50138
Karl Crook (515) 842-6078
Hrs: Th, 5pm **Trap:** 4

Stockdale Gun Club
RR2, Box 42, Ackley, IA 50601
Dale Stockdale (516) 648-4779
Type: Public/Member
Hrs: By request, resrv.;
ATA Shoots May-Sept. **Trap:** Y

Tri-State Gun Club
Box 336, Montrose, IA 52639
Glen Van Pelt
Type: Public/Member
Hrs: T/W, 5-9pm; S/Su, 12:00
Trap: Y

KANSAS

SPORTING & 5-STAND

4500 E. 117th North
Sedgwick, KS 67135
Todd Beers (316) 744-8366
10 mi. N of Wichita
Type: Public/Member
Hrs: W/Th/F, 2-9; S/Su, 9-9
Reservs: Recommended
Sporting: 1, 8 stations **Trap:** 5
Skeet: 5 **Five-Stand:** 1 **HT:** 35'

Capital City Gun Club
PO Box 332, Topeka, KS 66604
Jim McKee (913) 478-4682
8 mi. W of Topeka
Type: Public/Member
Sporting: 1
Trap: 2 **Skeet:** 4 **Five Stand:** 1

Cedar Hill Gun Club & Sporting Clays
918 E. 1650 Rd., Baldwin, KS 66006
Mary Watson (913) 843-8213
30 mi. SW of Kansas City
Type: Public/Member
Hrs: S/Su, 10-5; M-F, By Appt.
Reservs: Strongly recommended
Sporting: 1, 13 stations
Trap: 5 **Five Stand:** 1
Wobble Trap
○ Loaner Guns
○ Factory Ammunition
○ On-Site Meals
○ Organized Leagues
○ Golf Carts

Cimarron Sporting Clays
Box 575, Cimarron, KS 67835
Gavin Unruh (316) 855-7050
180 mi. E of Wichita
Type: Public/Member
Hrs: Su, 1-6; Other days by appt.
Sporting: 1, 8 stations
HT: 30 ft.

Claythorne Lodge
R1, Box 13, Hallowell, KS 66725
Sam or Frieda Lancaster
(316) 597-2568
150 mi. S of Kansas City
Type: Public/Member
Hrs: W/S/Su, 9-dusk; Others
by reserv.
Reservs: Recommended
Sporting: 2, 19 stations
Trap: 1 **Skeet:** 1   **HT:** 65 ft.
Wobble Trap

Cokeley Farms
RR1, Box 149, Delia, KS 66418
Will Cokeley (913) 771-3817
22 mi. NW of Topeka
Type: Public/Member
Hrs: M/T/F, by Appt;
W/Th/S/Su, 9-Dk
Sporting: 2, 11 stations
HT: 35 ft. **Wobble Trap**

Doug's Trap & Skeet
8601 Monticello Rd.
Lenexa, KS 66227
Doug Montis (913) 422-5063
10 mi. S of Kansas City, MO

Type: Public/Member
Hrs: T/F, 2-11; S/Su, 10-5
Sporting: 1, 10 stations
Trap: 5 **Skeet:** 3   **HT:** 40 ft.
Wobble Trap

Elkhorn Ranch
Rt. 1, Box 113
Fredonia, KS 66736
Lee White (316) 378-2306
80 mi. E of Wichita
Type: Public
Hrs: Su, 9-5; Other days by appt.
Sporting: 1, 18 stations
HT: 35 ft. **Wobble Trap**

Flint Oak
Rt. 1, Box 262
Fall River, KS 67047
Pete Laughlin (316) 658-4401
75 mi. E of Wichita
Type: Public/Member
Hrs: T-S, 10-dusk; Su, 10-5
Reservs: Recommended
Sporting: 2, 5 stations
Trap: Y **Skeet:** Y   **HT:** 157 ft.
See Our Ad Below

Fossil Creek Sporting Clays
PO Box 811, Russell, KS 67665
Jack Yost (913) 483-6456
70 mi. W of Salina
Type: Public/Member
Hrs: Varies, call to check days &
hours of operation
Sporting: 1, 10 stations

Geary County F&G Club
1519 Hale Dr.
Junction City, KS 66441
Easy Ed Augustine (913) 238-8727
60 mi. W of Topeka
Type: Public

Hrs: Su, 1-5; T, 6-10; W/S, 1-5 (S)
Sporting: 1, 13 stations
Trap: 3

Horseshoe Bend Sporting Clays
PO Box 121, Hoxie, KS 67740
Pat Foster (913) 675-2150
200 mi. E of Denver
Type: Public/Member
Hrs: S/Su, 9-5; Other days by appt.
Reservs: Recommended
Sporting: 1, 10 stations
HT: 50 ft.
○ Factory Ammunition
○ On-Site Pro Shop
○ On-Site Meals
○ Shooting Lodge
○ RV Hook Ups

Kansas Field & Gun Dog
8601 Monticello Rd., Lenexa, KS
Doug Montis (913) 422-5063
Hrs: T/F, 5-11; S/Su, 10-5
Sporting: 1, 10 stations
Trap: 6 **Skeet:** 3

Lil' Toledo Lodge
Rt. 4, Box 117, Chanute, KS 66720
Ron King (316) 244-5668
100 mi. SW of Kansas City
Type: Public/Member
Hrs: S/Su, 9-4
Reservs: Recommended
Sporting: 1, 18 stations
Skeet: 1 **Five Stand:** 1 **HT:** 27 ft.
Wobble Trap
See Our Ad Pg. 435

Locust Point
Gun Club
RR 2, Box 122, Lyndon, KS 66451
Doug Koehler (913) 828-3406
25 mi. S of Topeka
Type: Public/Member
Hrs: S-Su, 8-dark; Evenings by app't
Reservs: Recommended
Sporting: 2, 10 stations
Skeet: Y **Five Stand:** 1
HT: 50 ft.

Marais des Cygnes
2103 E. 15th St., PO Box 811
Ottawa, KS 66067
Georgia Blacketer (913) 242-7468
45 mi. SW of Kansas City, MO
Type: Public/Member
Hrs: M/Th/S/Su, 10am-5pm
Sporting: 1, 10 stations
Trap: 1 **Wobble Trap**

Michael Murphy
& Sons
6400 S.W. Hunter Rd.
Augusta, KS 67010
Daryl Banmister (316) 775-2137
15 mi. E of Wichita
Type: Public
Hrs: W/F/Su, pm; S, am/pm
Reservs: Recommended
Sporting: 1, 10 stations
Skeet: 1 **Five Stand:** 1 **HT:** 35 ft.
Wobble Trap
Shooting Instruction
Available - See Pg. 169

Pleasant Valley
Rt. 1, Box 88, Sawyer, KS 67134
Carolyn & David Keller
(316) 594-2238
70 mi. SW of Wichita
Type: Public
Hrs: S/Su, 10-5; Weekdays by appt.
Sporting: 1, 12 stations
Wobble Trap

Quail Valley
Sporting Clays & Hunt Club
16501 NW 72nd, RR1, Box 134
Moundridge, KS 67107
Mike & Greg Stucky
(316) 345-8367

35 mi. NW of Wichita
Type: Public
Hrs: S, 9-Dusk; Su, 1:30-Dusk;
W, 4:30-Dusk
Reservs: Not required
Sporting: 1, 13 stations
HT: 35 ft. **Wobble Trap**

Ravenwood
Hunting Preserve & Sporting Clays
10147 SW 61 St.
Topeka, KS 66610
Ken Corbet (913) 256-6444
50 mi. W of Kansas City
Type: Public/Member
Hrs: M-F; by appt; S/Su; 9-Dark
Reservs: Recommended
Sporting: 1, 20 stations
HT: 50 ft. **Wobble Trap**
See Our Ad Above

Rohrer's Sporting Clays
RR1, Box 45, Troy, KS 66087
Sandy Rohrer (913) 985-2635
15 mi. W of St. Joseph
Type: Public
Hrs: S, 10-5; Su, 1-5; M-F, by appt.
Sporting: 2, 15 stations

Starbirds Sporting Clays
Rt. 1, Box 149, Delia, KS 66418
Gary Starbird (913) 771-3141
Hrs: W-Su, 9-Dusk
Sporting: 1

Sullivan Sand and Sage
3019 North Road G
Ulysses, KS 67880
Shane Sullivan (316) 356-3924
200 mi. W of Wichita
Type: Public
Hrs: By Reservations
Sporting: 1, 12 stations

Walnut Ridge Hunting
RR1, Box 35A, Walnut, KS 66780
Mike or Barb Duling
(316) 354-6713
120 mi. S of Kansas City
Type: Public **Hrs:**
Sporting: 1, 13 stations

Windridge Sporting Clays
8601 Monticello Rd.
Lenexa, KS 66227
Doug Montis (913) 422-5063
4 mi. W of Lenexa
Type: Public/Member
Hrs: S/Su, 10-5; T/F, 3-Dark
Sporting: 1, 10 stations
Trap: 4 **Skeet:** 3 **HT**

TRAP & SKEET
Ark Valley Gun Club
PO Box 781553
Wichita, KS 67278
Patrick H. Streiff (316) 776-0809
Hrs: Varies
Skeet: 3

Beech Gun Club
9709 East Central
Wichita, KS 67201

CLAYS

Dean Hilton (316) 676-8133
Trap: 3 **Skeet:** 3

Cadmus Skeet Range
12604 High Dr.
Leawood, KS 66209
Harry Wilber (913) 491-5496
Type: Member/Avail
Hrs: By invitation
Skeet: 1

Coffeyville Sportsmans
701 Lincoln, Coffeyville, KS 67337
Wes Stewart (316) 251-0637
Hrs: S, 8-12
Trap: 1 **Skeet:** 1

Dodge City Gun Club
PO Box 181, Dodge City, KS 67801
Club Manager
Type: Public/Member
Trap: Y

**Ft. Leavenworth
Skeet/Trap Club**
33650 187th St.
Leavenworth, KS 66048
(913) 651-8132
Hrs: S/Su, 12-5; W, 12-3:30;
Th, 5-8:30
Trap: 1 **Skeet:** 4

Kansas Skeet Shooting Assn.
400 W. 8th, Suite 412
Topeka, KS 66603
Whitney Damron (913) 233-4512
Type: Public/Member
Hrs: S/Su, 12-4
Trap: 2 **Skeet:** 4   **Wobble Trap**

**Kansas Trapshooters Assn.
Trap Park**
PO Box 133, Kanopolis, KS 67454
Luke Seitz (913) 472-5266
Hrs: T, 6:30-10
Trap: 20

Kinsley Gun Club
115 Sunnyside Dr.
Lewis, KS 67552
Frank O'Brien (316) 324-5693
Type: Public **Hrs:** W, Evening
Trap: 5

Liberal Gun Club
1210 N. Cain, Liberal, KS 67901
Bud Perry (316) 624-5810
Hrs: T/Th, 6-7; Sun, 1
Trap: 5 **Skeet:** 1

Prairie Dog Trap Range
PO Box 59, Norton, KS 67654
Bruce Reeves (913) 877-5545
Type: Public **Hrs:** Tues. eve.
Trap: 5 **Skeet:** 1

**Rawlins County
Sportsmans Assn.**
PO Box 162, Atwood, KS 67730
Scott W. Carlson (913) 626-3700
Type: Public/Member

Hrs: S/Su, by appt.
Trap: 2 **Skeet:** 1

Salt City Trap Park
203 N. 5th, Box 256
Sterling, KS 67579
Glenn Gable (316) 278-3301
Type: Public
Hrs: Th, 5-9; Su, 1-5 **Trap:** 5

Tuttle Creek Trap Park
1712 Ranser Rd.
Manhattan, KS 66502
Charles A. Lamaster
(913) 539-4392
Hrs: Th, 7pm; Su, 1;30
Trap: 4

Wheatbelt Gun Club
RR2, Russell, KS 67665
Loren Keil (913) 483-3459
Hrs: W, 5pm **Trap:** 2

KENTUCKY

SPORTING & 5-STAND

**Blue Grass Skeet &
Sporting Clays Club**
125 Handys Bend Rd., Box 1496
Lexington, KY 40591
Bob Brimener (606) 858-4060
Type: Public/Member
Hrs: Varies Su-S: 8-9 (Summer)
Sporting: 1, 10 stations
Trap: 6 **Skeet:** 1

Bush Road Sporting Clays
888 Bush Rd.
Cadiz, KY 42211
Robert Bush (502) 522-6193
90 mi. NW of Nashville, TN
Type: Public
Hrs: S, 9-Dark; Su, 12-Dark;
Wkdays by appt.
Sporting: 2, 20 stations
Skeet: 1   **HT**

Deer Creek Outfitters
P.O. Box 39
Sebree, KY 42455
Tim Stull (502) 835-2424
140 mi. SW of Louisville
Type: Public/Member
Hrs: Open daily by app't
Sporting: 1, 10 stations

Flush-A-Covey
1403 Ealy Branch Rd.
Owingsville, KY 40360
E. Wells/M. Miller (606) 674-6554
40 mi. E of Lexington
Type: Public
Hrs: S/Su, 8-dusk; Wkdays by appt.
Sporting: 2, 27 stations **Trap:** 2

Grassy Lake Lodge
PO Box 319, Wickliffe, KY 42087
Greg Joles (502) 462-3595

32 mi. SW of Paducah
Type: Public/Member
Sporting: 1

Hammond
**Sycamore Hill
Sporting Club**
70 Three Lick Rd.
Harrodsburg, KY 40330
W.C. Hammond (606) 366-9198
35 mi. W of Lexington
Type: Public
Hrs: S, 8-5; Su/W, 12-5;
Other by appt.
Reservs: Recommended
Sporting: 1, 14 stations
Five Stand: Y

Hummin' Birds Sporting
9110 Wall Rd., Utica, KY 42376
Tom O'Daniel (502) 785-9429
Type: Member/Avail
Hrs: S, 10-Dusk; Su, 1-Dusk
Sporting: 1, 10 stations

Jackson Purchase Gun Club
Rt. 1, Box 724, Ridgeland Dr.
Mayfield, KY 42066
William R. Miller (502) 247-2903
Type: Public/Member
Hrs: Th, 5:30-10; Su, 12-Dark
Sporting: 1, 5 stations
Trap: 4 **Skeet:** 2

Jefferson Gun Club
660 Gun Club Rd.
Brooks, KY 40109
Greg Meeks (502) 957-4661
10 mi. S of Louisville
Type: Public/Member
Hrs: S/Su, 12-6; T/W/Th, 4-9
Sporting: 1, 25 stations
Trap: 9 **Skeet:** 9 **Five Stand:** 2
HT: 50 ft.

223 Highland Ave.
Cynthiana, KY 41031
Larry Ritchie (606) 234-2511
35 mi. NE of Lexington
Type: Public
Hrs: M/T/W/F, by Rsrv; S, 9-Dusk;
2nd & 4th Su, 12-Dusk
Reservs: Recommended
Sporting: 2, 27 stations
Trap: 2   **HT:** 14 ft.

Shoot Fire Sportsman's Farm
290 Koostra Rd.
Bowling Green, KY 42101
Kent Koostra (502) 781-9545
60 mi. N of Nashville
Type: Public
Hrs: M-F, by appt; S, 9-dusk;
Su, 1-dusk
Reservs: Recommended
Sporting: 2, 15 stations
Trap: Y **Skeet:** Y **Five Stand:** 1
HT: 50 ft.

Shooter's Sporting Clays
11958 Big Bone Rd.
Union, KY 41091
Jim McHale (606) 384-1022
35 mi. S of Cincinnati on I-71 in KY
Type: Public/Member
Hrs: S, 9-Dusk; Su, 10-Dusk; Wkdys by resrv. only
Reservs: Strongly recommended
Sporting: 2, 20 stations **HT:** 60 ft.
○ On I-71, less than 1/2 hr. from I-75
○ 50 Target English Sporting (2 trap combos)
○ 5 Station/5 Trap Practice Field
○ Factory Ammo/Rental Guns & Golf Carts
○ KY Club Phone, Wkends, 606-643-3411

Sugar Creek Sporting Clays
RR2, Box 413
Mitchell, KY 47446
Dale Waldbieser (812) 849-2296
40 mi. S of Bloomington
Type: Public
Hrs: S/Su, 10-Dk; W/Th/F, 8-Dk by app't
Reservs: Recommended
Sporting: 2, 20 stations
Trap: 2 **Skeet:** 2

TRAP & SKEET
Ashland Gun Club
PO Box 422, Ashland, KY 41105
Louis Clark
Hrs: Th, 4-Dark; Su, 9-Dark
Skeet: 4

Calvert City Gun Club
Rt. 2, Box 419
Calvert City, KY 42029
Milton Stevenson (502) 395-5676
Hrs: Th, night; Sun, afternoon
Skeet: 2

Chief Paduke Gun Club
1501 Martin Luther King
Paducah, KY 42001
Tommy Lynn (502) 443-6313
Hrs: W, 4-9; S/Su, 12-9
Trap: 2 **Skeet:** 4

Ft. Knox Skeet Club
Bldg. 9333 French Range
Ft. Knox, KY 40121
Outdoor Recreation
(502) 624-7754
Type: Public
Hrs: W, 12-6; F/S/Su, 10-5
Trap: 2 **Skeet:** 4

Knob Creek Range
690 Richey Lane
West Point, KY 40177
Kenny Sumner (502) 922-4457
18 mi. S of Louisville
Type: Public
Hrs: M/T/Th, 7pm; Su, 1pm
Trap: 1

Lloyd Area Skeet Club
Box 272, Crittenden, KY 41030
Harry R. Rieder (606) 428-2323
Hrs: W, 7-11; Su, 1-5 (Yr round)
Skeet: 3

Powder Ridge
PO Box 436, Warsaw, KY 41095
Bill Eckler (606) 567-4113
Hrs: S/Su, 12-6
Skeet: 1

Pulaski Outdoorsmen Trap
1010 Hwy. 39,
Somerset, KY 42502
Charles Reed (606) 678-5843
Type: Public/Member
Hrs: T, Nights; Su, Afternoons
Trap: 2 **Skeet:** 2

LOUISIANA

SPORTING & 5-STAND
Fort Polk Recreational
PO Box 3909
Fort Polk, LA 71459
Jim Callaway (318) 531-6591
120 mi. S of Shreveport
Type: Public
Hrs: F, 2-50; S/Su, 10-5
Sporting: 1, 5 stations
Skeet: 2

Hill Country Plantation
272 Dunleith Drive
Dunleith, LA 70047
Owen Brennan (800) 986-4868
50 mi. E of New Orleans
Type: Public
Hrs: Tu-Su, 11-dark
Reservs: Recommended
Sporting: 2, 20 stations
HT: 100 ft. **Wobble Trap**

Jean LaFitte Shooting Ctr.
2304 Constance Lane
Lake Charles, LA 70605
Clem Myers (318) 478-2672
Hrs: W-Su, 2-Dark
Sporting: 1, 10 stations
Trap: 1 **Skeet:** 7 **Five Stand:** 1

Natchitoches Shooting Range
1421 Washington Ave.
Natchitoches, LA 71457
Louis F. "Pop" Hyams, Jr.
(318) 352-2785
6 mi. NE of Natchitoches
Type: Public/Member
Hrs: S/Su/Bank Holidays,
9am-9pm; W/Th/F, 2pm-9pm
Reservs: Recommended
Sporting: 1, 30 stations
Trap: 1 **Skeet:** 1 **Five Stand:** 1
HT: 40 ft.

Pin Oak Mallards
Rt. 5, Box 126, Rayville, LA 71269
Ace Cullum (800) 259-3827
15 mi. E of Monroe
Type: Public/Member
Sporting: 1, 10 stations

Shreveport Gun Club
4435 Meriwether Rd.
Shreveport, LA 71118
Robert LaBorde (318) 686-9810
1 mi. W of Shreveport
Type: Public/Member
Hrs: W, 3-Dark; S/Su, 1-Dark
Sporting: None
Trap: 9 **Skeet:** 1 **Five Stand:** 1
Wobble Trap

Wild Wings
Rt. 2, Box 26,
Downsville, LA 71234
Steve Bryan (318) 982-7777
75 mi. NE of Shreveport
Type: Public/Member

CLAYS

Hrs: W/Th/F/Su, 1-6; S, 9-6
Sporting: 1, 10 stations
Five Stand: 1   **HT:** 40 ft.

TRAP & SKEET

Arcadia Gun Club Inc.
1975 Third St., Arcadia, LA 71001
Greg Thomas (318) 263-8693
Type: Public
Hrs: Su, 1pm; Th, 3pm
Trap: 2 **Skeet:** 2

Bayou Boeuf Skeet Range
PO Box 488, LeCompte, LA 71346
Wade Jones (318) 776-9301
Skeet: 2

Bogalusa Skeet Club
106 Suzanne St.
Bogalusa, LA 70427
Paul Capo (504) 748-9173
Hrs: Su, 1-Dark
Skeet: 5

Florida Parishes Skeet
107 E. Mulberry St.
Amite, LA 70422
Nick Brocato (504) 748-8025
60 mi. NW of New Orleans
Hrs: W/S/Su, 2-Dark
Skeet: 6

Hunters Run Gun Club, Inc.
4412 Byron St.
Baton Rouge, LA 70805
Thomas J. Root (504) 387-3507
Hrs: W-Su, 10-7
Trap: 1 **Skeet:** 5

Lafayette Gun Club
PO Box 93043
Lafayette, LA 70509
Edward Francez (318) 234-2203
Hrs: Call for appt.
Skeet: 1

Pine Hills Gun Club
PO Box 1293
West Monroe, LA 71294
Jim Steele, III (318) 396-1495
Hrs: Su, 1-Sundown; Th,
4:30-Sundown
Trap: 2 **Skeet:** 2

South Louisiana Gun Club
6615 Argonne Blvd.
New Orleans, LA 70124
Sammy Centanni (504) 436-9901
Hrs: W/Th, 1-Dark; S/Su, 1-6
Trap: 3 **Skeet:** 5

*Need an extra copy of
Wing & Clay? Ordering
by phone is a breeze.
Call: 800-224-9464
and, please, have a
major credit card handy.*

MAINE

SPORTING & 5-STAND

The Bradford Camps
PO Box 499
Patten, ME 04765
Dave Youland (207) 746-7777
75 mi. W of Presque Isle
Type: Public **Hrs:** Daily
Sporting: 1, 10 stations

Foggy Ridge
PO Box 211
Warren, ME 04864
Jim Olmsted (207) 273-2357
80 mi. NE of Portland
Type: Public/Member
Hrs: M-S, day hrs; Su, after 9am
Sporting: 1, 20 stations

Hermon Skeet & Trap Club
80 Wiley St., Bangor, ME 04401
Marty Drew (207) 945-3113
10 mi. W of Bangor
Type: Public/Member
Hrs: Su, 9-1; W, 1-Dark
Sporting: None
Trap: 1 **Skeet:** 1 **Five Stand:** 1

Presque Isle Fish & Game
PO Box 375
Presque Isle, ME 04769
Bill Norsworthy (207) 764-0162
160 mi. N of Bangor
Type: Public/Member
Hrs: Su, 9-3; W, 5-Dk
Sporting: None
Trap: 1 **Skeet:** 1 **Five Stand:** 1

Scarborough Fish & Game
PO Box 952
Scarborough, ME 04070
Brad Varney (207) 865-4825
10 mi. S of Portland
Type: Public/Member
Hrs: Clays-1st Sun. of month, 9-5;
call for tr/sk times
Sporting: 1, 15 stations
Trap: 9 **Skeet:** 3

Sheepscot Ridge Sporting Club
Box 185
Wiscasset, ME 04578
David Laemmle (207) 882-5033
38 mi. E of Portland
Type: Public/Member
Hrs: S/Su, by appt.
Sporting: 1, 22 stations
HT: 20 ft.

TRAP & SKEET

Arnold Trail Sportsmans
PO Box 330, Litchfield, ME 04350
C. Andre Charron
Hrs: Su, 10-4
Trap: 1 **Skeet:** 3

Durham Rod & Gun Club
288 US Rt. 1, N.,Freeport, ME 04032
Peter MacDonald (207) 665-9409
Hrs: Su, 11-5; W, nigh (Summer)
Trap: 1 **Skeet:** 1

Richmond Gun Club
Reed Rd., Richmond, ME 04357
Leland Smith (207) 737-2620
Type: Public **Hrs:** Tues. Nights
Trap: 9 **Skeet:** 1

Windham Gorham R&G Club
Great Falls Rd., Gorham, ME 04107
David LaRose/Joe Hall
Type: Public **Hrs:** T, 4-Dk; Su, 9-1
Trap: 4

MARYLAND

SPORTING & 5-STAND

Alexander Sporting Farms
13503 Alexander Rd.
Golt, MD 21637
James/Samuel Alexander
(410) 928-3549
5 mi. N of Millington
Type: Public
Hrs: S-Su, 10-6; Others by appt.
Sporting: 1, 44 stations **HT**

Chesapeake Clays

16090 Oakland Rd. (Rt. 312,
Bridgetown)
Henderson, MD 21640
Bill Connors (410) 758-1824
65 mi. NE of Washington, DC
Type: Public **Hrs:** Su-S, 9am-6pm
Reservs: Recommended
Sporting: 1, 25 stations **HT:** 100 ft.
See Our Ad Pg. 441

Del-Mar-Va Sporting Clays
23501 Marsh Rd.
Mardela Springs, MD 21837
Bryon Richardson (410) 742-2023
75 mi. SE of Washington, DC
Type: Public
Hrs: 7 days a week, 9-5
Sporting: 2, 4 stations **Five Stand:** 1

Fairs Regulated
Shooting Area & Sporting Clays
1605 Old Virginia Rd.
Pocomoke City, MD 21851
Ray Fair (410) 957-1749
30 mi. S of Salisbury
Type: Public
Hrs: W-F, 1; S/Su, 9-5; Closed M/T
Reservs: Not required
Sporting: 1, 25 stations
HT: 40 ft.

Gunsmoke
Sporting Clays
Bethel Rd.(Mail: 860 Bent Tine Rd.)
Willards, MD 21874
Richard Laws (410) 835-2324
18 mi. W of Ocean City
Type: Public
Hrs: Su-S, starting @ 8am
Reservs: Not required
Sporting: 1, 15 stations **HT**
○ Loaner Guns
○ Factory Ammunition
○ On-Site Pro Shop
○ Formal Instructions
○ Organized Leagues
○ Gary Phillips, Shooting Instructor

Hopkins Game Farm
PO Box 218
Kennedyville, MD 21645
George or Patti (410) 348-5287
35 mi. E of Baltimore
Type: Public **Hrs:** Year Round
Sporting: 3
Five Stand: 1   **HT**

J&P Hunting
Lodge, Inc.
1105 Benton Corner Rd.
Sudlersville, MD 21668
John George, Jr. (410) 438-3832
20 mi. W of Delaware
Type: Public **Hrs:** T-Su, 10-4
Reservs: Recommended
Sporting: 1, 14 stations
Five Stand: 1   **HT:** 30 ft.

National Capital S&T
16700 Riffleford Rd.
Darnestown, MD 20849
Manager (301) 948-2266
Type: Public/Member
Hrs: T/Th, 4-9; S/Su/Holiday, 10-4
Sporting: None
Trap: 9 **Skeet:** 9 **Five Stand:** 1

Pintail Point Farm
511 Pintail Point Farm Lane
Queenstown, MD 21658
Carol Johnson or Bob Burris
(410) 827-7029
[listing continued>]

Eastern Shore, 20 mi. E. of Bay
Bridge
Type: Public/Member
Hrs: T/Th, 10-9; W/F/S/Su, 10-4
Reservs: Recommended
Sporting: 1, 13 stations **HT:** 35 ft.
○ Loaner Guns
○ Factory Ammunition
○ On-site Panoramic view clubhouse
○ New Course on Maryland's
   Eastern Shore
○ See our Ad & Listing in Maryland
   WINGS section

Prince George's
County Trap & Skeet
10400 Goodluck Rd.
Glen Dale, MD 20769
Mark Biggins (301) 577-7178
5 mi. E of Washington, DC
Type: Public
Hrs: M&F, 10-5; T/W/Th, 1-8:30;
S/Su, 10-5 **Reservs:** Not required
Sporting: 1, 23 stations
Trap: 9 **Skeet:** 13 **Five Stand:** 1
HT: 45 ft. **Olympic & Double Trap**
See Our Above

The East Coast's
Finest Hunting Lodge

Lodging Available
at the Mansion
or

World Class Sporting Clays Range
Trophy Whitetail Hunting
Pheasant, Quail, Waterfowl,
and Dove Hunts
Individual or Corporate
Packages

HUNT
CHESAPEAKE
INNS

your choice of these
elegant Inns

1-800-787-INNS
1-410-758-1824

Top Gun Sporting Clay, Inc.
4633 Ocean Gateway (Rt. 50)
Vienna, MD 21869
Bill Murphy (410) 376-3394
50 mi. E of Bay Bridge
Type: Public
Hrs: 7 days a week, 8:30-Dark
Sporting: 1, 16 stations
Five Stand: 1   **HT:** 60 ft.

Tuscarora Gun Club
5694 Glen Rock Dr.
Frederick, MD 21790
John R. Ortaldo (301) 874-2620
10 mi. SW of Frederick
Type: Public
Hrs: Th, Eve. (Apr-Sept); Reg.
Shoots Sun.
Sporting: 2, 10 stations
Trap: 9 **Skeet:** 1   **Wobble Trap**

TRAP & SKEET

Andrews Rod & Gun Club
PO Box 857
Clinton, MD 20735
Kenneth Crump (301) 981-5985
Hrs: W, 1-5; S/Su, 9-5
Trap: 1 **Skeet:** 3

Cambridge Skeet/Gun Club
5420 White Hall Rd.
Cambridge, MD 21613
Gloria Creighton (410) 228-8199
Hrs: Th, 5-8; Su, 11-6
Trap: 1 **Skeet:** 3

Carroll County Gun Club
8009 Windsor Mill Rd.
Baltimore, MD 21244
Don Kirk (410) 655-5223
Type: Public
Hrs: W/F, 6pm; S-Noon; Other
shoots, please call
Trap: 9

Loch Raven Skeet/Trap
PO Box 6846
Towson, MD 21204
Fritz Tepel (410) 252-3851
Hrs: W, 12-7; Th, 12-9; F, 12-6;
S/Su, 10-6
Trap: 7 **Skeet:** 7

Maryland State Sportsmens
3332 Woodside Ave.
Baltimore, MD 21234
Gene Mullinix (410) 665-9185
Trap: 28

Millington Sportsmens Assn.
335 N. Ferry Point Rd.
Pasadena, MD 21122
Ohmer Webb, Jr. (410) 360-1013
Type: Member/Avail
Trap: 22

North American R&G Club
669 Westwood St.
Hagerstown, MD 21740

Donald Armstrong, II
(717) 739-4440
Hrs: T-F, 11-11; S, 8-11; Su, 6-11
Trap: 2 **Skeet:** 1

Potomac River Gun Club
Box 264, Indian Head, MD 20640
Larry A. Buckley (301) 743-6986
Hrs: T/Th, 4-9; Su, 9-4
Trap: 2 **Skeet:** 2

Salisbury Gun Club
PO Box 4061, Salisbury, MD 21801
John Lee Taylor (301) 749-0337
Hrs: W/F, 12-Dark; S/Su, 9-Dark
Trap: 2 **Skeet:** 7

Sanner's Lake Sportsmans
PO Box 1300 ,
Lexington Park, MD 20653
Vernon Gray (301) 863-5850
Hrs: 9-sunset
Skeet: 1

Sudlersville Skeet Club
935 Coon Box Rd.
Centerville, MD 21617
Marvin Coppage (410) 438-3880
Hrs: Su, 1-5
Trap: 1 **Skeet:** 4

Synepuxent Gun Club
PO Box 724, Berlin, MD 21811
Roger Taylor (410) 641-0326
Type: Public
Hrs: W, 6-10pm; Su, 1-4pm
Trap: 5

Talbot Rod & Gun Club
F28132 Pleasant Valley Dr.
Easton, MD 21601
John K. Waters (301) 822-9754
Hrs: W, 4-7; Su/Su, 11-5
Trap: 1 **Skeet:** 6

**Thurmont Con. &
Sportsmans Club**
13404 Rabbit Run Terrace
Union Bridge, MD 21791
John R. Dodd, Sr. (301) 898-9093
Trap: 16

MASSACHUSETTS

SPORTING & 5-STAND

Angle Tree Stone R&G
PO Box 1243 (Kelly Blvd.)
N. Attleboro, MA 02761
James Bolton (508) 695-0902
40 mi. SW of Boston
Type: Public/Member
Hrs: S/Su, 12-4
Sporting: 1, 10 stations
Trap: 1 **Skeet:** 2

Cape Cod's Sporting Clays
PO Box 3157
Waquoit, MA 02586
Lenny Rentel (508) 540-2851

60 mi. SE of Boston
Type: Public **Hrs:** Sunday, 9-3
Sporting: 1, 12 stations
Trap: 1 **Skeet:** 2

Fall River Rod & Gun Club
PO Box 571
Fall River, MA 02723
Gus Yankopoulos (508) 673-4535
40 mi. S of Boston
Type: Public/Member
Hrs: T/Th/S/Su, 10-5
Sporting: 1, 6 stations
Trap: 2 **Skeet:** 2

Falmouth Skeet Club
PO Box 157
Waquoit, MA 02536
Stuart Gifford (508) 540-3177
Hrs: W/S, 1-4; Su, 9-1
Sporting: 1, 10 stations
Trap: 1 **Skeet:** 2

Fin Fur & Feather Club
25 Mallard Rd.
Needham, MA 02192
Richard Lyons (508) 376-2977
20 mi. W of Boston
Type: Public/Member
Hrs: S/Su, 11-4 (Nov-Apr);
12-4 (May-Oct)
Sporting: None
Trap: 2 **Skeet:** 2 **Five Stand:** 1

Hamilton Rod & Gun Club
Hamilton Rd., PO Box 954
Sturbridge, MA 01566
John O'Leary (508) 867-8426
50 mi. W of Boston
Type: Public
Hrs: S, 10-4; Su, 11-4; & by appt.
Sporting: 1, 13 stations
Trap: 4

Lissivigeen
Spooner Rd.
Barre, MA 01005
Kevin J. Coakley (413) 477-8783
55 mi. W of Boston
Type: Public/Member
Hrs: 9/15-3/31, Su-S, 8-4:30pm
Reserv: Strongly recommended
Sporting: 1, 5 stations
Five Stand: 5

Springfield Sportsmen's
179 Birch Rd.
Longmeadow, MA 01106
Dick Haskins (413) 267-9652
75 mi. from Boston
Type: Public **Hrs:** T/S/Su, 9-5
Sporting: 1, 8 stations
Trap: 1 **Skeet:** 3 **Five Stand:** 1

Stockbridge Sportsmen's
Rt. 102, Box 6
Stockbridge, MA 01262

Robert Otten (518) 828-2133
30 mi. E of Albany, NY
Type: Public/Member
Hrs: W/Th, 5-Dark; S/Su, 9-12
Sporting: None
Skeet: 2 **Five Stand:** 1
HT: 500 ft.

Walpole Sportsmen's Assn.
PO Box 91
Walpole, MA 02081
Barry Parker (508) 668-6919
30 mi. W of Boston
Type: Public/Member
Hrs: Th, 5-Dark; Su, 11-3
Sporting: 1, 15 stations
Trap: 4 **Skeet:** 1   **HT:** 30 ft.
Wobble Trap

TRAP & SKEET

Danvers Fish & Game Club
3 Judith Rd.
Peabody, MA 01960
Charlie Parziale (508) 774-9541
Trap: 2 **Skeet:** 2

**The Eight Point
Sportsmen's Club**
PO Box 235, Sterling, MA 01564
Richard Hewett (508) 278-3095
Hrs: Su/T, 1-4; Th, 6-9; S, 1-5
Trap: 2 **Skeet:** 1

Franklin Co. League Sportsmen
19 James St.,
Greenfield, MA 01301
Dr. Norman Pike (413) 773-8750
Hrs: S/Su, Noon-5; W, 5-Dusk
Trap: 4 **Skeet:** 2

Holbrook Sportsmen's Club
PO Box 275, Holbrook, MA 02343
Arthur Lavallee (617) 767-4971
Hrs: W, 6-9; S, 12:30-4; Su, 9-3
Trap: 4

Hopkinton Sportsmens
95 Lumber St.
Hopkinton, MA 01748
Shaun Smith (508) 435-3838
Hrs: T, 6-9; Su, 10-2
Trap: 1 **Skeet:** 2

Ludlow Fish & Game Club
36 Shumway SE
Amherst, MA 01002
John Stanley (413) 583-4055
Trap: 1 **Skeet:** 7

Marshfield Rod & Gun Club
127 Heathstone Way
Hanover, MA 02039
Nick Kanavos (617) 837-2942
Hrs: S/Su, 10-2 **Skeet:** 1

Martha's Vineyard R&G Club
PO Box 1799
Edgartown, MA 02539
Harold Green (508) 693-8116
2.5 mi. NE of Edgartown

Type: Member/Avail
Hrs: Su, 12-5
Trap: 1 **Skeet:** 1

Massapoag Sportsmens
42 Bear Hill Rd.
Sherborn, MA 01770
Michael F. Murphy (617) 784-5856
Hrs: Su, 10-3; S, 12-3
Trap: 1 **Skeet:** 3

Minute Man Sportsmans Club
Box 212, Burlington, MA 01803
Andy Greene (617) 272-7169
Hrs: W/Su, 12-Sunset; S, 10-Sunset
Trap: 14 **Skeet:** 10

Nauset Rod & Gun Club
83 Fortune Farrow Way
Brewster, MA 02651
Ronald P. Goguen (508) 896-6758
Hrs: Su, 9:30-1; W, 1-3:30;
S, 9:30-11 **Skeet:** 2

North Leominster R&G
PO Box 25, Leominster, MA 01453
George W. Makrianis
(508) 840-6322
18 mi. N of Worcester
Type: Public/Member
Hrs: Th, 6-10; Su, 9-1
Sporting: 1, 11 stations
Trap: 6 **Skeet:** 3

Old Colony Sportsmens
PO Box 523, Pembrooke, MA
02359
Nancy Allen (617) 293-9980
Hrs: S/Su, 10-3; W, Afternoons
Trap: 1 **Skeet:** 2

Riverside Gun Club
48 Crestwood Lane
Marlboro, MA 01752
Lenny O'Reilly (508) 562-2404
Hrs: Daily, 9-9
Trap: 2 **Skeet:** 2

Royalston Fish & Game
New Boston Rd.
S. Royalston, MA 01331
Roy Smith, Jr. (508) 249-9687
Hrs: S, 1-5; W, 6-9
Trap: 8

Scituate Rod & Gun Club
Box 321, N. Scituate, MA 02060
Hugh Scott (617) 545-1510
Hrs: W, 6-9; Su, 12-6
Skeet: 1

Sheffield Sporting Club
PO Box 1033
Sheffield, MA 01257
Wayne Palmer (413) 229-8766
Hrs: W, 5-8; Su, 9-1
Trap: 1 **Skeet:** 2

Shirley Rod & Gun Club
28 Rodman Ave.
Shirley, MA 01464

Richard Pontbriand (617) 425-4039
Hrs: W, 6-9; Su, 1-6
Trap: 2

Singletary Rod & Gun Club
11 Wesley Dr.
Leicester, MA 01524
Frank Laureyns (617) 987-8783
Hrs: W, 6:30-10; S, 1-5
Trap: 6

MICHIGAN

SPORTING & 5-STAND

Alpena
Sportsman Club
4260 M-32 West
Alpena, MI 49707
Frank Malenski (517) 354-2582
3.5 mi. W of Alpena
Type: Public/Member
Hrs: S, 9-3; Su, 9-4;
W (Summer), 3-6
Reservs: Recommended
Sporting: 1, 11 stations

Bald Mountain Gun Range
2500 Kern Rd.,
Lake Orion, MI 48360
Larry Woo (810) 814-9193
30 mi. N of Detroit
Type: Public
Hrs: S/Su, 10-6; W, 1-Dark; M/T,
12-Dark
Sporting: 1, 12 stations
Trap: 3 **Skeet:** 4 **Five Stand:** 1

Bay County Conservation
2985 Cadillac Dr.
Bay City, MI 48706
Val Syring (517) 631-9944
85 mi. NW of Detroit
Type: Public/Member
Hrs: M/W, 4-9; S/Su, 11:30-5
Sporting: 1, 10 stations
Trap: 2 **Skeet:** 4   **HT:** 20 ft.

Big Creek Shooting
PO box 369, Mio, MI 48647
Steven Basl (517) 826-3606
130 mi. NE of Grand Rapids
Type: Public/Member
Hrs: Su-S, Sunup-Sundown
Sporting: 1, 7 stations
Trap: 1 **Skeet:** 1   **HT:** 15 ft.

Blendon Pines
8455 88th Ave.,
Zeeland, MI 49464
Arvin Boersema (616) 875-7000
20 mi. SW of Grand Rapids
Type: Public/Member
Hrs: W,9-6;Th, 2-6;S, 8-4; Tu & Fr
by app't

CLAYS

Reservs: Recommended
Sporting: 1, 10 stations
Five Stand: 1   **HT:** 30 ft.

Brule
Sporting Clays
397 Brule Mt. Rd.
Iron River, MI 49935
Steve Polich (800) 362-7853
6 mi. S of Iron River
Type: Public
Hrs: Tues. pm; S/Su, 9-5;
Others by appt.
Reservs: Recommended
Sporting: 3, 45 stations **HT:** 60 ft.
○ Call 1-800-DO BRULE
○ Stay & Shoot Packages
○ $89 Lodging 200 Targets
○ Guns & Ammo Sale & Rent
○ Lodge & Meals

Capital Area Sportsman's
7534 Old River Trail
Lansing, MI 48917
Dave Blankenburg (517) 321-3155
5 mi. from Lansing
Type: Public/Member
Hrs: S, 10am; W, 5-8; Su, 10-2
Sporting: 1, 15 stations
Trap: 1 **Skeet:** 2 **Five Stand:** 1
HT: 12 ft.

Cedar Rod
& Gun Club
10030 S.W. Bay Shore Dr.
Traverse City, MI 49684
Sterling L. Chamberlain
(616) 946-5288
17 mi. NW of Traverse City
Type: Public/Member
Hrs: T, 6:30-10; W, 10-8; F,
6:30-10; S, 10-4
Reservs: Recommended
Sporting: 1, 20 stations
Trap: 2 **Skeet:** 1 **Five Stand:** 1

18000 Basswood Rd.
Three Oaks, MI 49128
George W. Daniels (616) 756-6600
50 mi. SE of Chicago
Type: Public/Member
Hrs: Su-S, 9am-Dusk
Reservs: Strongly recommended
Sporting: 1, 16 stations
Skeet: Y **Five Stand:** 1 **HT:** 65 ft.

Detroit Gun Club
2775 Oakley Park Rd.
Walled Lake, MI 48390
Scott Behnke (810) 624-9647
20 mi. NW of Detroit
Type: Member/Avail
Hrs: W, 1-dark; S/Su, 10-dusk
Sporting: 1, 13 stations
Trap: 9 **Skeet:** 10
Five Stand: 1 **HT**

Detroit Sportsmen's
56670 Jewell
Shelby Twp., MI 48315
Karen Peterson (810) 739-2210
15 mi. N of Detroit
Type: Public/Member
Hrs: S/Su, 10-4 (Clays); W/Th, 4-9;
S/Su, 10-5 (Tr/Sk)
Sporting: 1, 14 stations
Trap: 5 **Skeet:** 5 **Wobble Trap**

Fenton
Lakes Clays
1140 Butcher Rd.
Fenton, MI 48430
Al Roy (517) 548-4566
50 mi. NW of Detroit
Type: Public
Hrs: W, 3-8:30; Su, 10-5
Reservs: Not required
Sporting: 2, 15 stations
Trap: 1 **Skeet:** 1 **HT:** 25 ft.

Flat River Conservation
332 S. Greenville Rd., PO Box 424
Greenville, MI 48838
Ed Skinner (616) 754-9855
8 mi. N of Greenville
Type: Public/Member
Hrs: Su, 10-4; Closed 11/15-1/15
Sporting: 2, 24 stations
Trap: 2 **Skeet:** 1 **Five Stand:** 1
HT: 25 ft.

Genesee Sportsmans Club
8208 N. Seymour Rd.
Flushing, MI 48532
Robert Ballard (810) 639-5100
Type: Public/Member
Hrs: W, 5-9; S/Su, 10-4
Sporting: 2
Trap: 4 **Skeet:** 4

Grand Blanc Huntsman's
9046 S. Irish Rd.
Grand Blanc, MI 48439
H.V. Burrow (810) 636-7261
5 mi. SE of Grand Blanc
Type: Public/Member
Hrs: S/Su, 9-5; W, 9-10
Sporting: 1, 13 stations
Trap: 4 **Skeet:** 4

Hunter's
Creek Club
675 Sutton Rd.
Metamora, MI 48455
Charlie Mann (810) 664-4307
30 mi. N of Detroit
Type: Member/Avail
Hrs: Daily, except Monday
Reservs: Strongly recommended
Sporting: 1, 10 stations
Trap: 1 **Skeet:** 1 **HT:** 70 ft.
Wobble Trap
See Our Ad Pg. 315

Hunter's Ridge
Hunt Club
3921 Barber
Oxford, MI 48371
David M. Fischer (810) 628-4868
50 mi. NE of Detroit
Type: Public
Hrs: W/F, 2-6; S/Su, 9-6
Reservs: Strongly recommended
Sporting: 2, 10 stations
Trap: 1 **Skeet:** 1 **HT**
Wobble Trap

The Huntsman Hunt Club
3166 Havens Rd.
Dryden, MI 48428
Nora M. Tebben (810) 796-3962
40 mi. N of Detroit
Type: Member/Avail
Sporting: 2, 15 stations
Wobble Trap

Kent County Conservation
8461 Conservation NE
Ada, MI 49301
Manager (616) 676-1056
8 mi. E of Grand Rapids
Type: Public/Member
Hrs: T/Th, 4-10; S/Su, 10-5
Sporting: 1, 12 stations
Trap: 5 **Skeet:** 5 **Wobble Trap**

Lapeer County Sportsmens
1213 Lake George Rd.
Attica, MI 48455
Bill Behnke (810) 724-6579
25 mi. E of Flint
Type: Public/Member
Hrs: Su, 10-5; T, 4-10
Sporting: 1, 16 stations
Trap: 5 **Skeet:** 2 **Five Stand:** 1

Lost Arrow Hunting Preserve
1749 Bomanville Rd.
Gladwin, MI 48624
Avery Sterling (517) 345-7774
15 mi. NE of West Branch
Type: Public **Hrs:**
Sporting: 1

Lucky Feather Game Farm
2040 N. Pittsford Rd.
Hillsdale, MI 49242
Hal Bennett (517) 523-2050
80 mi. SW of Detroit
Type: Public
Hrs: Su-S, daylight hours; yearly
Sporting: 1, 9 stations
HT: 55 ft.

Mid-Upper Peninsula Shooters
765 White Ave.
Ishpeming, MI 49849
Brett W. French (906) 486-4526
Type: Public/Member
Hrs: Varies
Sporting: 1, 10 stations
Trap: 3 **Skeet:** 2

Monterey Sporting Clays
2726 134th Ave.
Hopkins, MI 49328
James Spray (616) 793-7400
25 mi. SW of Grand Rapids
Type: Public/Member
Hrs: M-Th, 10-Dark; S, 9-6
Sporting: 2, 25 stations
Five Stand: Y **HT:** 30 ft.

North Ottawa Rod & Gun
15596 Pine St.
Grand Haven, MI 49417
Forrest Palmer (616) 842-9711
Hrs: W, 5-9; S/Su, 9-2
Sporting: None
Trap: 4 **Skeet:** 4 **Five Stand:** 1

Orchard Hill Sporting Clays
PO Box 463
Escanaba, MI 49829
Mike Gierke (906) 466-2887
4 mi. SW of Bark River
Type: Public
Hrs: Su-S, 10am-Dusk
Sporting: 1, 8 stations

PGW Haymarsh Hunt Club
9215 Jefferson Rd.
Lakeview, MI 48850
Bud Gummer (517) 352-6727
50 mi. N of Grand Rapids
Type: Public **Hrs:** Flexible
Sporting: 2, 11 stations
Trap: 1 **Five Stand:** 1

Pere Marquette Sporting Clays
PO Box 3
Chase, MI 49623
Greg Bishop (616) 832-9055
6 mi. W of Reed City
Type: Public

Hrs: F, 4-Dark; S/Su, 9-Dark;
Others by appt.
Sporting: 1, 5 stations

Pointe Mouillee Shooting
10670 US Turnpike
South Rockwood, MI 48179
Michael Winter (313) 379-3820
Type: Public/Member
Hrs: W-Su, 10-9
Sporting: None
Trap: 2 **Skeet:** 5 **Five Stand:** 1
Wobble Trap

Rolling Hills
17025 McKenzie St.
Marcellus, MI 49067
Curt Johnson (616) 646-9164
60 mi. SW of Grand Rapids
Type: Public
Hrs: Su-S, call for appt.
Sporting: 1, 10 stations

Saginaw Gun Club, Inc.
PO Box 6054
Saginaw, MI 48603
Cora Gorsuch (517) 781-2260
70 mi. NW of Detroit
Type: Public/Member
Hrs: Th, 12-9; S/Su, 12-5
Sporting: 1, 10 stations
Trap: 4 **Skeet:** 4
Five Stand: 1 **HT**

South Haven Rod & Gun
68611 8th Ave.
South Haven, MI 49090
Geary Garvison (616) 637-8001
120 mi. W of Detroit
Type: Public/Member
Hrs: S/Su, 10-5
Sporting: 1
Trap: Y

Southern Michigan Gun Club
51640-35 1/2 St.
Paw Paw, MI 49079
Norm Rushing (616) 657-4620
Hrs: Th, 5-10; Su, 9-2
Sporting: None
Trap: 2 **Skeet:** 4 **Five Stand:** 1

Stoney Point Sporting Clays
12013 Grover Rd.
Hanover, MI 49241
Mark Nastally (800) 319-6222
14 mi. SW of Jackson
Type: Public
Hrs: S/Su, 9-6; Wkdays by appt.
Sporting: 1, 11 stations

Sugar Springs Sporting
1491 W. Sargeant Rd.
Gladwin, MI 48624
Lou Dallas (517) 426-2645
Type: Public
Hrs: S/Su, 9-3 by appt.
Sporting: 1
Five Stand: 1 **Wobble Trap**

Thundering Aspens
4421 N. 5 1/2 Rd.
Mesick, MI 49668
Greg Wright (616) 885-2420
110 mi. N of Grand Rapids
Type: Public/Member
Hrs: Varies, Year Round
Sporting: 1, 10 stations

Top Gun Hunt Club
1937 68th St.
Fennville, MI 49408
George Vuillemot (616) 543-3351
35 mi. SW of Grand Rapids
Type: Public **Hrs:** By appt. only
Sporting: 1

Whisky River
Hunt Club
4555 Cambria Rd.
Hillsdale, MI 49242
Mike Damman (517) 357-4424
80 mi. SW of Detroit
Type: Public/Member
Hrs: S/Su, 9-6; Weekdays by Appt.
Reservs: Strongly recommended
Sporting: 2, 10 stations **HT:** 35 ft.
See Our Ad Pg. 317

Willow Lake Sportsmen's
51704 U.S. 131
Three Rivers, MI 49093
Hal Standish (616) 279-7124
65 mi. S of Grand Rapids
Type: Member/Avail
Hrs: Su-S, 8:30-dark
Sporting: 1, 8 stations **HT:** 20 ft.

Wycamp Lake Camp
c/o 5484 Pleasantview Rd.
Harbor Springs, MI 49740
Dirk Shorter (616) 537-4830
150 mi. NE of Grand Rapids
Type: Public/Member
Hrs: Apr-Nov, Daily by appt.
Sporting: 2, 32 stations **HT:** 150 ft.

TRAP & SKEET

Barry County Conservation
PO Box 14, Hastings, MI 49058
Sam Sobey (616) 945-9058
Hrs: S, 1-6   **Trap:** 4

Battle Creek Gun Club
416 Glendale Ave.
Battle Creek, MI 49017
Robert D. Hall (616) 965-1370
Type: Public/Member
Hrs: Su, 10-3; Th, 4:30-Dusk
Trap: 4 **Skeet:** 3

Berrien Co. Sportsmans
PO Box 325, St. Joseph, MI 49085
George V. Nichols (616) 429-3792
Hrs: Su, 10-2; T, 7-9; S, 1
Trap: 4 **Skeet:** 2

CLAYS

Cass City Gun Club
263 S. Main St.
Pigeon, MI 48755
Ronald L. Snider (517) 872-5395
Hrs: W, 5-10; Su, 11-5
Trap: 2 Skeet: 1

Elk Rapids Sportsman Club
PO Box 705
Elk Rapids, MI 49629
Michael Locke (616) 264-5250
Hrs: W, 2-5; Su, 10-5
Trap: 1 Skeet: 2

Gun River Skeet & Trap Inc.
620 11th St., PO Box 151
Plainwell, MI 49080
Robert O. Link (616) 685-5280
Hrs: W/F, 6-9; Su, 9-12
Trap: 3 Skeet: 4

Iosco Sportsmens Club
1170 Bischuff Rd.
East Tawas, MI 48730
Neal R. Miller (517) 362-5963
Type: Public/Member
Hrs: M/Th; Eve.; Su, 1pm
Trap: 2

Lost Lake Woods Assn.
4243 Lost Lake Trail
Lincoln, MI 48742
James B. Henderson
(517) 736-8197
Hrs: F/S/Su, 10-6 (Apr-Oct)
Trap: 1 Skeet: 2

Manistique Rifle & Pistol
Rt. 2, Box 2826
Mainistique, MI 49854
Jim Creighton (906) 341-2124
Type: Public/Member
Trap: 4 Skeet: 2

Michigan Trapshooting Assn.
1534 W. Service Rd.
Mason, MI 48854
Ben Johnston (517) 676-2295
Trap: 40

Mid-Up Shooters Inc.
125 N. Pansy St.
Ishpeming, MI 49849
James E. Frounfelter
(906) 475-4957
Hrs: W, Eve. (S); Sa., noon (W)
Trap: 3 Skeet: 2

Nawakwa Hunt & Gun Club
116 Chesterfield
Bloomfield Hills, MI 48304
Howard Confer (517) 848-2751
Trap: 1 Skeet: 2

*Remember your hearing
protection. Remember
your eye protection.
Remember to say:
"I saw it in Wing & Clay."*

Northport Point
107 Northcott Dr.
Northport, MI 49670
Gerard Jacobson (616) 386-5075
Hrs: 3 Afternoons/wk, 2-5
Trap: 1 Skeet: 1

Oak Hill Gun Club
238 N. Grant, Portland, MI 48875
Dan Pline (517) 647-7303
Hrs: Su, 10; M/W, 6:30-11
Trap: 3 Wobble Trap

Portage Lake Sportsmen
RR1, Box 37, Houghton, MI 49931
Bill Hockings (906) 482-5311
Type: Public/Member
Hrs: W, 6-9 Trap: 2

Reed City Sportsman Club
Rt. 1, Box 135,
Reed City, MI 49677
Gary A. Sweet (616) 832-4481
Trap: 1 Skeet: 2

Seaway Gun Club
3400 West Bard Rd.
Muskegon, MI 49445
John Hughes (616) 766-3428
Hrs: W, 5-10; Su, 10-3
Trap: 7 Skeet: 4

St. Joseph Co. Conservation
1007 N. Lakeview Ave.
Sturgis, MI 49091
James Terrell (616) 467-7128
Hrs: Su, 9-1
Trap: 4 Skeet: 1

Wayne County Sportsmans
14115 Burns,
Southgate, MI 48195
Ty Cobb (313) 941-9688
Hrs: W, 12-10; S/Su, 10-6
Trap: 3 Skeet: 4

MINNESOTA

SPORTING & 5-STAND

A Wild Acres Hunting Club
HC83, Box 108
Pequot Lakes, MN 56472
Mary Ebnet (218) 568-5024
150 mi. N of Minneapolis
Type: Public
Hrs: Daily by appt; 9:30-Dk
Sporting: 1, 8 stations

American Heritage
Rt. 2, Box 131
Eagle Bend, MN 56446
Don/Sue Ellwanger
(218) 738-5143
140 mi. NW of Minneapolis
Type: Public/Member
Sporting: 1, 13 stations
Trap: 1

Caribou Gun Club
Shooting Preserve
Rt. 1, Box 26, Le Sueur, MN 56058
Randy Voss-Earl Voss
(612) 665-3796
55 mi. SW of Minneapolis-St. Paul
Type: Public/Member
Hrs: Su-S, daylight-dark
Reservs: Strongly recommended
Sporting: 2, 31 stations
Trap: 3 Skeet: 1 HT: 175 ft.
○ Loaner Guns
○ Factory Ammunition
○ On-Site Pro Shop
○ On-Site Meals
○ Shooting Lodge
○ Formal Instructions
○ Organized Leagues

Central Minnesota Gun
3030 12th St., SE
St. Cloud, MN 56304
Dick Berger (612) 252-5630
Type: Public
Hrs: M/Th, 9-9:30; T/W/F,
12-5:30; S, 9-4, Su
Sporting: 1, 13 stations
Trap: 14 Skeet: 1

Charlie's Hunting Club
RR1, Box 173
Danvers, MN 56231
Jim Langan (612) 567-2276
115 mi. W of Minneapolis
Type: Public Hrs: T-Th, 12-dark
Sporting: 1, 10 stations
Trap: 1 HT: 50 ft. Wobble Trap

Clear Creek
Outdoors
2250 Hwy 23, Wrenshall, MN 55797
Patrick LaBoone (218) 384-3670
6 mi. SW of Duluth
Type: Public/Member
Reservs: Strongly recommended
Sporting: 1, 14 stations HT: 35 ft.
*Shooting Instruction
Available - See Pg. 167*

Crookston Gun Club
RR1, Box 259
Crookston, MN 56716
Myron Uttermark (218) 281-5143
70 mi. N of Fargo
Type: Public/Member
Hrs: M/W, 6:30-Dk; Some Wkends
Sporting: 1, 10 stations
Trap: 3 HT: 40 ft. Wobble Trap

Dalton Hunting
RR1, Box 290
Dalton, MN 56324
Dick Henkes (218) 589-8523

60 mi. SE of Fargo
Type: Public
Hrs: 12-Dark, 7 days by appt.
Sporting: 1, 20 stations
Trap: 1 **Skeet:** 1 **HT:** 40 ft.
Wobble Trap

Dead Horse Creek
RR 2, Box 103
Frazee, MN 56544
Chris Wacker (218) 334-4868
180 mi. NW of Minneapolis
Type: Public/Member
Sporting: 1, 20 stations

Federal Shooting Sports Center
16128 Varialite St., NW
Anoka, MN 55303
Jack McKusick (612) 421-3741
Type: Public
Hrs: M-Th, 6-9; Su, 12-4; & By Appt.
Sporting: None
Trap: 9 **Skeet:** 1 **Five Stand:** 1

Fort Thunder PSC
RR3, Box 30
Perham, MN 56573
Leroy Atkinson (218) 346-6083
170 mi. NW of Minneapolis
Type: Public
Hrs: Su, 1-5; M/W, 5-dusk
Trap: 5 **Skeet:** 5 **Five Stand:** 1
HT: 85 ft.

H&R Shooting Preserve
34934 140th Ave.
Avon, MN 56310
David J. Raab (612) 356-7427
75 mi. NW of Minneapolis
Sporting: 1

Horse Barn & Hunt Club
RR1, Box 103
Lakefield, MN 56150
Brent Rossow (507) 662-5490
20 mi. NE of Iowa Great Lakes
Type: Public/Member
Hrs: W-Su, 1-Sunset or by appt.
Sporting: 1, 10 stations **HT:** 40 ft.

Johnson Enterprises
Rt. 3, Box 45, Canby, MN 56220
Roger D. Johnson (507) 223-7992
N of Canby
Type: Public/Member
Hrs: Fri. & Sat.
Sporting: 1, 13 stations
Trap: 1 **HT:** 20 ft.

Lac Qui Parle Hunting
RR5, Box 68,
Montevideo, MN 56265
Steve Baldwin (612) 269-9769
110 mi. W of Minneapolis
Type: Public/Member
Hrs: S/Su, 9-Dk; Others by appt.
Sporting: 1, 15 stations
Trap: 1 **Skeet:** 1 **HT:** 100 ft.

Don Le Blanc
Rt. 5, Box 228,
Little Falls, MN 56345
Don/Marge Le Blanc
(612) 745-2522
85 mi. NW of Minneapolis
Type: Public/Member
Hrs: Daily, dawn to dusk by appt.
Sporting: 1, 22 stations
HT: 60 ft.

LeBlanc Rice Creek
Rt. 5, Box 213
Little Falls, MN 56345
Gregg LeBlanc (612) 745-2451
85 mi. N of Minneapolis
Type: Public **Hrs:** Su-S
Sporting: 2, 25 stations
Trap: 3 **HT:** 30 ft.

Little Moran Hunting Club
Rt. 1, Pheasant Valley Rd.
Staples, MN 56479
Steve Grossman (218) 894-3852
130 mi. NW of Minneapolis
Type: Public
Hrs: Daily by appt.
Sporting: 3, 30 stations
Five Stand: 1 **HT:** 80 ft.

Lock & Load Hunting Club
Rt. 1, Box 44A
Middle River, MN 56737
Dan Rantanen (218) 222-3714
210 mi. NW of Duluth
Type: Public/Member
Hrs: Daily by appt.
Sporting: 1, 10 stations
Trap: 3

Major Ave. Hunt Club
11721 Major Ave.
Glencoe, MN 55336
Gerald G. Martin (612) 864-6025
45 mi. W of Minneapolis
Type: Public
Hrs: Daily, 8am-Dark
Sporting: 2, 22 stations
HT: 50 ft. **Wobble Trap**

Maple Island Hunt Club
425 Hamm Bldg.
St. Paul, MN 55102
Maurice Grogan (612) 439-2405
NE of St. Paul
Type: Public/Member
Hrs: By reservation
Sporting: 1, 10 stations
Trap: Y **HT:** 25 ft.

Metro Gun Club
10601 Naples St., NE
Blaine, MN 55434
Loren Hentges (612) 786-5880
Hrs: M-Th, 10-9:30; F-Su, 10-5
Sporting: None
Trap: 14 **Skeet:** 6 **Five Stand:** 1

Minneapolis Gun Club
20006 Judicial Rd.
Prior Lake, MN 55372
Jerry Hazel (612) 469-4386
Type: Public/Member
Hrs: T/W/Th, 12-Dark; F, 12-4;
S/Su, 10-4
Sporting: None
Trap: 10 **Skeet:** 7 **Five Stand:** 1
Wobble Trap

MINNESOTA

HORSE & HUNT
CLUB

Minnesota Horse & Hunt
2920 220th St.
Prior Lake, MN 55372
Terry Correll (612) 447-2272
25 mi. SW of Minneapolis-St. Paul
Type: Public/Member
Hrs: T-Su, 9am-Dusk; M, 12-Dusk
Reservs: Recommended
Sporting: 3, 18 stations
Trap: 2 **Skeet:** 2 **HT:** 65 ft.
Wobble Trap

Misty Meadows
HC9, Box 439
Detroit Lakes, MN 56501
Steve Laine (218) 847-4680
16 mi. E of Detroit Lakes
Type: Public **Hrs:** Su-S, 8-Dark
Sporting: 2, 24 stations
Trap: 1

North Creek Sporting Clays
RR1, Box 146
Lakefield, MN 56150
Ted Pehlman (507) 662-6703
70 mi. E of Sioux Falls, SD
Type: Public
Hrs: W, 4-Dk; S/Su, 1-5; & by appt.
Sporting: 1, 9 stations

Oak Point
RR3, Box 44-A
Wadena, MN 56482
Don Dykhoff (218) 631-4467
Type: Public **Hrs:**
Sporting: 1

Peaceful Acres Sporting Clays
RR2, Slayton, MN 56172
Leroy Kalass (507) 836-6188
20 mi. S of Marshall
Type: Public/Member
Hrs: Open 7 Days a Week
Sporting: 1, 8 stations

CLAYS

Pleasant Acres
RR3, Box 144
New Ulm, MN 56073
Lester Zwach (507) 359-5770
70 mi. SW of Minneapolis
Type: Public Hrs: T-Su, 9-dark
Sporting: 1, 22 stations
Trap: 1 Five Stand: 5 HT: 70 ft.

Ringneck Ridge
Rt. 1, Box 319
Motley, MN 56466
John Jacklitch (218) 575-2913
100 mi. N of Minneapolis
Type: Public
Hrs: Everyday, 9-dusk
Sporting: 1, 10 stations HT: 27 ft.

Royal Flush Shooting Club
Rt. 5, Box 228
Little Falls, MN 56345
Bob Schneider (612) 745-2522
85 mi. NW of Minneapolis
Type: Public/Member
Hrs: Daily, by appt. only
Sporting: 1, 12 stations
Trap: 1 HT: 60 ft.

Rum River Pheasant Club
30925 CR 5 NW
Princeton, MN 55371
Rick Johnson (612) 389-2316
45 mi. N of Minneapolis
Type: Public/Member
Hrs: Daily, 3:30-Dark by appt.
Sporting: 2, 13 stations Trap: 3

Shooters
Rt. 1, Box 135A
Marshall, MN 56258
Steven Peterson (507) 336-2560
9.5 mi. E of Marshall
Type: Public Hrs: S/Su, 10-6
Sporting: 1, 16 stations

South St. Paul Rod & Gun
600 Gun Club Road
South St. Paul, MN 55075
Bob Haselberger (612) 455-7249
5 mi. S of St. Paul
Type: Public/Member
Hrs: T/W/Th, 4-dark; Sa/Su, 10-4
Reservs: Recommended
Sporting: 1, 13 stations
Trap: 4 Skeet: 3 HT: 40 ft.

Ten Mile Creek Htg Preserve
Rt. 1, Box 85
Dunnell, MN 56127
Michael Honnette (507) 695-2524
140 mi. SW of Minneapolis
Sporting: 1, 8 stations

Udovich Guide Service
12503 Sethers Rd.
Gheen, MN 55771

Dennis Udovich (218) 787-2237
225 mi. N of Minneapolis
Type: Public/Member
Hrs: Apr-Sept, W/Th, 2-Dark;
Su, 1-Dark Sporting: 1

Valhalla Hunt Club
RR1, Albert Lea, MN 56007
Gary Pestorious (507) 377-7225
85 mi. S of Minneapolis
Type: Public/Member
Hrs: Daily by appt.
Sporting: 1, 20 stations HT: 80 ft.

Viking Valley Hunt Club
Rt. 1, Box 198
Ashby, MN 56309
Les Bensch (218) 747-2121
140 mi. NW of Minneapolis
Type: Public/Member
Hrs: 10-7 & by appt.
Sporting: 1, 23 stations HT: 80 ft.

Wild Marsh Sporting Clays & Hunting Preserve
13767 CR3
Clear Lake, MN 55319
Debbie Mortensen (612) 662-2021
60 mi. NW of Minneapolis
Type: Public/Member
Hrs: S, 11-3; Su, 10-3; W/Th,
4:30-Dark & appt.
Sporting: 1, 40 stations HT: 38 ft.

Wild Wings of Oneka
9491 152nd St., N.
Hugo, MN 55038
J. Hughes/G. Schulte
(612) 439-4287
15 mi. NE of Minneapolis-St. Paul
Type: Member/Avail
Hrs: Th/S/Su (Mid-Aug. thru
Mid-April)
Sporting: 2, 20 stations
Trap: 1 HT: 80 ft.

Windsor Fields
6835 Hilda Rd.
Tower, MN 55790
Richard Kronmiller (218) 741-5837
75 mi. N of Duluth
Type: Public/Member
Hrs: T-Su, 8-dusk by appt.
Sporting: 2, 30 stations
HT: 40 ft.

TRAP & SKEET

3M Trap & Skeet Club
280 Hill Top Ct.
N. St. Paul, MN 55109
Dick Raths (612) 459-8240
Hrs: T-Th, 4-8 Trap: 4 Skeet: 2

Albany Sportsmans Club
32496 Ironwood Dr.
St. Joseph, MN 56374
Jim Moeller (612) 845-4271
Hrs: Su, 1-8 (May-Sept); T/W, 6-Dk
Trap: 4 Skeet: 2

Becker Co. Sportsmens
PO Box 415
Detroit Lakes, MN 56501
Archie Wiedwitsch (218) 847-3743
Hrs: T/Th, 6:30
Trap: 5

Bricelyn Sportsmens Club
PO Box 351, Bricelyn, MN 56014
Arden Lium (507) 653-4487
Type: Public/Member
Hrs: Th, 6pm-11pm
Trap: Y

Golden Eagle Gun Club
2612 S. Broadway
Alexandria, MN 56308
Art Thompson (612) 763-5315
Type: Public/Member
Trap: 5 Skeet: 1

Grand Rapids Gun Club
Box 217, Bovey, MN 55709
Dick Sturk (218) 326-3348
Type: Public
Hrs: T/W/Th, 12-Dark
Trap: 9

Lester Prairie Sportsmens
227 N. Maple St.
Lester Prairie, MN 55354
Ed Mlynar (612) 395-2258
Hrs: Mid-April-August, Wed. night
& reg. targets
Trap: 5

Owatonna Gun Club
PO Box 12, Owatonna, MN 55060
Mike Belina
Type: Public/Member
Trap: 9

MISSISSIPPI

SPORTING & 5-STAND

Bad Rabbit Sporting Clays
PO Box 677,
West Point, MS 39773
Robert Harrell (601) 494-1800
170 mi. SE of Memphis
Type: Public Hrs: by app't only
Sporting: 1, 5 stations
HT: 15 ft.

Capitol Gun Club
PO Box 12973
Jackson, MS 39236
R. Kelly Kyle (601) 362-0653
Hrs: S/Su, 1-Sundown; Th,
3-Sundown
Sporting: 1, 7 stations
Trap: 5 Skeet: 5

Daybreak Sporting Clays
134 Lilac Dr., Leland, MS 38756
John/Debra Ingram
(601) 686-9013

14 mi. S of Greenville
Type: Public **Hrs:** By Appt. Only
Sporting: 1, 12 stations
Five Stand: 1 **HT:** 30 ft.

Dunn's Shooting Grounds

Rt. 3, Box 39D4
Holly Springs, MS 38635
Stephen Pannell (601) 564-1111
35 mi. SE of Memphis
Type: Public
Hrs: S, 9-5; Su, 1-5; Wkdays by app't
Reservs: Recommended
Sporting: 1, 10 stations
○ Factory Ammunition
○ On-Site Meals
○ Shooting Lodge
○ Plantation Style Quail Hunts
   Available
○ Shooting School

Get Away Place
8176 Hwy. 84 E.
Waynesboro, MS 39367
Dan Young (601) 735-5764
125 mi. SE of Jackson
Type: Public/Member
Sporting: 1

Hill Country Plantation

1488 Bowie Rd.
Carriere, MS 39426
Owen Brennan (800) 986-4868
50 mi. E of New Orleans
Type: Public
Hrs: Tu-Su, 11-dark
Reservs: Recommended
Sporting: 2, 20 stations
HT: 100 ft. **Wobble Trap**

Kearney Park Shooting
151 Ergon Rd.
Flora, MS 39071
Chuck Boyer (601) 879-3249
10 mi. N of Jackson
Type: Public
Hrs: M-Sa, 8-5 (Apr-Oct/Min. 6 shooters)
Sporting: 1, 11 stations
HT: 40 ft.

Natchez Flyway
338 N. Palestine Rd.
Natchez, MS 39120
Terry Wagoner (601) 442-0136
80 mi. SW of Jackson
Type: Public **Hrs:** By appt. only
Sporting: 1, 10 stations

Ol' Place Sporting Clays
Rt. 5, Box 360
Lucedale, MS 39452
Joel Fike (601) 947-4726
45 mi. W of Mobile, AL
Type: Public
Hrs: S/Su, by appt.
Sporting: 1, 20 stations

Plantation Sporting Clays
PO Box 1082
Picayune, MS 39466
T. Knight/M. Walker (601) 798-6919
50 mi. N of New Orleans
Type: Public/Member
Sporting: 1, 18 stations
HT: 30 ft.

Rolling Hills Sporting Clays
440 Hickory Grove Rd.
Dalesville, MS 39326
Derek D. Sevier (601) 681-8459
6 mi. E of Meridian
Type: Public
Hrs: M-F, by appt; S/Su, 12-Dark
Sporting: 1, 10 stations

TRAP & SKEET

CBR Skeet Range
209 Canal St.
McComb, MS 39648
Milton Burris (601) 684-4781
Skeet: 2

Coast Rifle & Pistol Club
217 Ashley Place
Ocean Springs, MS 39564
James L. Guernsey (601) 875-3858
Skeet: 2

Columbus Trap & Skeet
149 Alabama Ave.
Columbus AFB, MS 39701
Steven Barbour (601) 434-5085
Hrs: To be determined
Trap: 1 **Skeet:** 1

Gulfport Skeet & Trap Club
3740 8th Ave.
Gulfport, MS 39501
Greg M. Lawrence (601) 868-5971
Trap: 2 **Skeet:** 2

Lake Gep Skeet Club
1 Stonesthrow
Laurel, MS 39440
W.M. Deavours (601) 426-3729
Hrs: W, 1-5; S, 9-noon
Skeet: 2

Little Black Creek Gun Club
504 9th Ave.,
Lumberton, MS 39455
Brent Crider **Hrs:** S/Su, 12-Dark
Skeet: 1

North Delta Gun Club
1130 Pk. Ln., Clarksdale, MS 38614
Buford Hopper (601) 624-4321
Hrs: By Appt. **Skeet:** 1

Starkville Gun Club
PO Box 383, Starkville, MS 39759
Gary Bunner (601) 323-3542
Hrs: Th, 6-10; Su, 2-6
Trap: 2 **Skeet:** 4

MISSOURI

SPORTING & 5-STAND

B&C Game Farm
RFD1, St. Catherine, MO 64677
Jeff Sayre (816) 258-2973
110 mi. NE of Kansas City
Type: Public/Member
Sporting: 1, 10 stations **HT**

Baker's Acres Sporting
Ex. 68, Interstate 35
Pattonsburg, MO
Ken or Sean Baker (816) 387-7915
68 mi. N of Kansas City
Type: Public
Hrs: S, 10-6; Su, 1-5; Wkdays by appt.
Sporting: 1, 15 stations

Big River Hunting Club
PO Box 30
Fletcher, MO 63030
(314) 452-3511
33 mi. SW of St. Louis
Type: Member/Avail
Hrs: M-F, 8-6; S/Su, 8-5
Sporting: 1, 7 stations **HT**

Blackhawk Valley Hunting Preserve

Rt. 1, Box 118
Old Monroe, MO 63369
Mickey Palmer (314) 665-5459
40 mi. NW of St. Louis
Type: Public/Member
Hrs: Su-S, 9-5; others by app't
Reservs: Strongly recommended
Sporting: 2, 12 stations **HT:** 30 ft.

CLAYS

Boot Hill Sporting Clays
2531 NE JC Penney Dr.
Hamilton, MO 64644
Ray Evans (816) 583-2275
62 mi. NE of Kansas City
Type: Public
Hrs: S, by appt; Su, 1-6
Sporting: 1, 10 stations

BrownFeather
3460 St. Hwy. N
Clever, MO 65631
Dan Dover (417) 743-2527
15 mi. SW of Springfield
Type: Public/Member
Hrs: S, 10-6; Su, 1-6; & by appt.
Sporting: 1, 10 stations

Cedar Creek
Rod & Gun Club
RR#6, Box 96
Columbia, MO 65202
Ralph D. Gates (314) 474-5804
13 mi. NE of Columbia
Type: Public/Member
Hrs: Su, 11-10; Th, 5-10; S, by
resrv.; T, 12noon-10pm
Reservs: Not required
Sporting: 2, 22 stations
Trap: 6 Skeet: 6 Five Stand: 1
HT: 45 ft.
○ Loaner Guns
○ Factory Ammunition
○ On-Site Meals
○ Formal Instructions
○ Golf Carts

Devil's Ridge
Sporting Clays
209 NW 1771
Kingsville, MO 64061
Jim Hatch (816) 597-3703
30 mi. SE of Kansas City
Type: Public/Member
Hrs: S/Su, 10-6; other times
by appt.
Reservs: Recommended
Sporting: 1, 11 stations
HT: 70 ft.

Geode Hollow
RR2, Box 23A
Revere, MO 63465
Wilbur Himes (816) 754-6347
60 mi. NE of Hannibal
Type: Public
Hrs: Su-S, by reservation
Sporting: 1, 13 stations
HT: 30 ft.

Kansas City Trapshooters Assn.
6420 N.E. 176th St.
Smithville, MO 64089
Gary Norris (816) 532-4427

30 mi. N of Kansas City
Type: Public/Member
Hrs: W, 5-10; S/Su, 11-5
Sporting: None
Trap: 8 Skeet: 2 Five Stand: 1
Wobble Trap

Lake of the Ozarks
Sporting Clays
Rt. 70, Box 964
Camdenton, MO 65020
Jason Chappell (314) 873-3566
9 mi. N of Camdenton
Type: Public/Member
Hrs: Su-S, 9-5
Reservs: Strongly recommended
Sporting: 1, 10 stations
○ Loaner Guns
○ Factory Ammunition
○ Shooting Lodge

Malinmor Sporting Estate
RR4, Box 108
Eolia, MO 63344
Rick Merritt (314) 324-3366
60 mi. N of St. Louis
Type: Member/Avail
Hrs: 7 Days, 8-6; by appt. only
Sporting: 2, 10 stations
Trap: 1 Skeet: 1

Midway Farms, Inc.
700 County Road 404
Fayette, MO 65248
Lee Myers (816) 248-3838
125 mi. E of Kansas City
Type: Public
Hrs: For Corporate Groups &
Individuals by Resrv. Only
Sporting: 2, 10 stations
HT: 20 ft.

New London Hunting Club
& Shooting Preserve
Rt. 1, Box 269a
New London, MO 63459
Steve & Pam Swon (314) 985-7477
88 mi. N of St. Louis
Type: Public/Member
Hrs: By reservation
Sporting: 1, 10 stations
Trap: 1 Five Stand: Y HT: 36 ft.

Newcastle Hunt Club
3100 Broadway, #711
Kansas City, MO 64111
Larry Carter (816) 931-9551
75 mi. NE of Kansas City
Type: Public Hrs: S/Su, Noon-5
Sporting: 1, 9 stations

Ozark Shooters
PO Box 6518, Hwy. 65
Branson, MO 65616
Peggy M. Siler (417) 443-3093
25 mi. S of Springfield

Type: Public Hrs: Su-S, 10-dark
Sporting: 2, 10 stations
Trap: 5 Skeet: 2 HT: 80 ft.
Wobble Trap

Pin Oak Hills
RR1, Chillicothe, MO 64601
Doug or Scott Luetticke
(816) 646-6069
85 mi. NE of Kansas City
Type: Public
Hrs: M-F, by Res.; S/Su, 10-5
Sporting: 1, 10 stations
Trap: 1 HT: 40 ft.

Rockbridge Gun Club
Box 100, Rockbridge, MO 65741
Ray Amix (417) 679-3619
80 mi. S of Springfield
Type: Public Hrs: 7 Days, 8-8
Sporting: 1, 10 stations
Trap: 1 HT: 30 ft. Wobble Trap

Show-Me Safaris
PO Box 108
Summersville, MO 65571
Mark Hampton (417) 932-4423
30 mi. S of Rolla
Type: Public Hrs: Hours by appt.
Sporting: 1, 6 stations

Sorenson's S.C. &
Preserve Hunting
1703 Hwy. DD
Defiance, MO 63341
Tom, Kay or T.J. Sorenson
(314) 828-5149
19 mi. W of St. Louis
Type: Public
Hrs: Su-S, by appt.
Reservs: Strongly recommended
Sporting: 1, 22 stations

St. Louis Skeet & Trap Club
18854 Franklin Rd.
Pacific, MO 63026
Patricia Gardner (314) 257-4210
Type: Public/Member
Hrs: T/Th, 3-9; S/Su, 10-4
Sporting: None
Trap: 5 Skeet: 7 Five Stand: 1
Olympic Trap & Double Trap
Universal Trench

Twin Lakes
Sporting Club
Rt. 1, Box 203, Mexico, MO 65265
Wally Feutz (314) 581-1877
110 mi. NW of St. Louis
Type: Public/Member
Hrs: S/Su, 9-dark
Reservs: Strongly recommended
Sporting: 1, 18 stations
HT: 10 ft.

United Sportsmen's Club
4750 Henwick Lane
Jefferson City, MO 65109
Don Balkenbush (314) 761-4946
2 mi. W of Jefferson City
Type: Public/Member
Hrs: W, 6-9 (Summer); Su, 1-4
Sporting: 1, 22 stations
Trap: 2 **Skeet:** 2 **HT:** 25 ft.

White Oak Ranch
RR1, Box 169, Edina, MO 63537
Bill Ingalls (816) 397-2451
50 mi. NW of Qunicy, IL
Type: Public **Hrs:** By appt.
Sporting: 1, 16 stations

Wildwood Hunting & Sporting Clays
RR1, Box 143
Houstonia, MO 65333
Bill Wall (816) 879-4451
100 mi. SE of Kansas City
Type: Public
Hrs: S, 10-Dk; Su, 1-Dk;
Others by appt.
Sporting: 1, 10 stations
HT: 60 ft.

Wings - St. Albans
PO Box 49
St. Albans, MO 63073
Gale Oertli (314) 458-6523
35 mi. W of St. Louis
Type: Member/Avail
Hrs: M-Su, 9-6
Sporting: 1, 10 stations
Trap: 1 **Skeet:** 1 **HT:** 32 ft.

TRAP & SKEET

Falcon Skeet Club
PO Box 122, Belton, MO 64012
Cliff Walker (816) 322-0815
Hrs: Th, 3-9; S/Su, 10-5
Trap: 1 **Skeet:** 2

Ft. Leonard Wood Rod/Gun Club
PO Box 876, Bldg. 498
Ft. Leonard Wood, MO 65473
Stan Harris (314) 336-3502
Hrs: W-F, 4-8; S/Su, 12-6
Trap: 1 **Skeet:** 2

Joplin Skeet & Trap Club
Rt. 7, Box 559
Joplin, MO 64801
Roger Brown (417) 781-1101
Trap: 1 **Skeet:** 2

KCTA Public Shooting Park
6420 NE 176th St.
Smithville, MO 64809
Lynn & Cindy Gipson
(816) 532-4427
Type: Public
Hrs: W, 5-10; S/Su, 11-5
Trap: 7 **Skeet:** 2

Mississippi Valley Gun Club
613 Country Club Dr.
Hannibal, MO 63401
Leo Harrison (314) 221-8237
Type: Public/Member
Trap: Y **Skeet:** Y

Missouri Trap Association
Rt. 1, Box 396
Linn Creek, MO 65052
B.J. Wilson (314) 346-2449
Hrs: T, 1; W-S, 1-5
Trap: 40

Poplar Bluff Gun Club
PO Box 4175
Poplar Bluff, MO 63901
J.L. Costin
Hrs: S/Su, 1-5:30
Trap: 1 **Skeet:** 2

Settle's Ford Gun Club
PO Box 353, Adrian, MO 64720
Dan Clifton (816) 297-2440
Type: Public/Member
Hrs: T, 7:30
Trap: 1 **Skeet:** 1

Springfield Rod & Gun
Rt. 2, Box 278
Springfield, MO 65802
Don Young (417) 833-2199
Trap: 2 **Skeet:** 3

Wright City Gun Club
57 Quiet Village Dr.
Foristell, MO 63348
Bob Overstreet (314) 639-5306
Type: Public/Member
Hrs: T/Th, 6-10; S, 12-5
Trap: 5

MONTANA

SPORTING & 5-STAND

Big Sky Sporting Clays
PO Box 10, Polson, MT 59860
Dick Mandeville (406) 883-2000
4 mi. NW of Polson
Type: Public/Member
Hrs: W/Th, 12-6; Fr-Su), 10-6pm
Reservs: Recommended
Sporting: 2, 33 stations
Five Stand: 1
See Our Ad Below

Diamond J Guest Ranch
PO Box 577W, Ennis, MT 59729
Felipe Acosta (406) 682-4867
60 mi. SW of Bozeman
Type: Public **Hrs:** By Appt.
Reservs: Strongly recommended
Sporting: 1, 7 stations
Trap: 1 **Skeet:** 1 **HT:** 40 ft.
See Our Ad Pg. 330

Eagle Nest Lodge
PO Box 470, Hardin, MT 59034
Nick Forrester (406) 665-3799
45 mi. S of Billings
Type: Public **Hrs:** By Appt.
Sporting: 1, 5 stations

Fetch Inn Hunting Preserve
PO Drawer 1429
Hamilton, MT 59840
Tom Fox (800) 854-6732

BIG SKY SPORTING CLAYS

Sporting Clays
Instruction
Fun Shoots
Tournaments
Ammunition
Open to the Public
Memberships Available
Hunting Preserve

Polson, Montana

LOCATED IN THE BEAUTIFUL FLATHEAD VALLEY OF MONTANA

Club House and Sporting Clays Course 3 1/2 Miles on Irvine Flats Road • Polson, Montana
(406) 883-2000 or (406) 887-2465

150 mi. SW of Great Falls
Type: Public
Hrs: Mid April '93 Opening
Sporting: 1, 10 stations   **HT**

Gallatin
Sporting Clays
PO Box 3483, Bozeman, MT 59772
Sam Robinson (406) 388-1346
W of Bozeman
Type: Public/Member
Hrs: (3/1-10/1), Tu, 5-9; Sa,
12-dusk; by app't
Reservs: Strongly recommended
Sporting: 1, 12 stations
HT: 80 ft.

Missoula Trap & Skeet Club
1225 Rogers, Missoula, MT 59802
Gene Clawson, Jr. (406) 549-4815
Type: Public/Member
Sporting: None
Trap: 18 **Skeet:** 5 **Five Stand:** 1
Olympic Trap

Perry Hunts & Adventures
Box 355, Fort Benton, MT 59442
Loran A. Perry (406) 633-5336
40 mi. NE of Great Falls
Type: Public **Hrs:** Every Day
Sporting: 1, 10 stations
HT: 30 ft.

Stillwater Shooting Preserve
1141 Church Dr.
Kalispell, MT 59901
Brian Tutvedt (406) 755-1959
10 mi. NW of Kalispell
Type: Public
Hrs: Call for schedule
Sporting: 1, 13 stations

Z Bar Z Sporting Clays
5760 Timber Trail
Helena, MT 59601
Zane Drishinski (406) 278-7713
12 mi. NE of Helena
Type: Public/Member
Hrs: Th-S, Daylight-Dark
Sporting: 1, 10 stations

TRAP & SKEET
Beaverhead Gun Club
436 S. Dakota
Dillon, MT 59725
Henry Greitl (406) 683-4923
Type: Public/Member
Hrs: W, 6-Dark May-Sept.
Trap: 5

Billings Rod & Gun Club
2519 Hancock
Billings, MT 59102
Billy D. Williams (406) 259-0006
Hrs: Su, 11-4
Trap: 1 **Skeet:** 4

Duck Shack Skeet Club
Box 2005, Missoula, MT 59806
Jack Gordon (406) 549-0782
Skeet: 1

Flathead Valley Clay Target
Box 537, Kalispell, MT 59903
(406) 752-4452
Type: Public/Member
Hrs: Sunday days; Wed. evenings
Trap: Y

Great Falls Trap & Skeet
1208 Ave. B NW
Great Falls, MT 59404
Jerry R. Lane (406) 453-5032
Type: Public/Member
Hrs: W, 4-9; Su, 11-3
Trap: 14

Havre Trap Club
Box 605, Havre, MT 59501
Dave Peterson (406) 265-3076
Type: Public/Member
Hrs: W, 6-close; Su, 1-5
Trap: 5

Lewiston Trap & Skeet Club
Box 1141, Lewistown, MT 59457
Type: Public/Member
Hrs: W, 6-Dark; Su, 1-5
Sporting: 1, 1 station
Trap: 5 **Five Stand:** 1

Manhattan Wildlife Assn.
9715 Cougar Dr.
Bozeman, MT 59715
Clay Fracchiolla (406) 586-5705
Hrs: W, 7-10; Su, 1-4 (Winter)
Trap: 5 **Skeet:** 2

Sun River Skeet Club
Box 1494, Great Falls, MT 59403
Wm. David Manix (406) 761-9035
Hrs: Su, 10-4; T, 6:30-10;
Th, league   **Skeet:** 5

NEBRASKA

SPORTING & 5-STAND
Can-Hunt
Rt. 1, Seward, NE 68434
Todd Halle (402) 588-2448
60 mi. SW of Omaha
Type: Public/Member
Hrs: Daily by appt.
Sporting: 1, 12 stations
Five Stand: 1 **HT:** 30 ft.

Cedar Hills Range
1809 R St., Tekamah, NE 68061
Jay Fred Bacon (402) 374-1254
2 mi. W of Tekamah-Hwy. 32
Type: Public/Member
Hrs: M/T, Eve; W/Th/F, by appt;
S/Su, 9-6
Sporting: 1, 40 stations
Trap: 1 **HT:** 70 ft.

Grand Island Sporting
PO Box 1117
Grand Island, NE 68802
John Hoffman (308) 382-7133
3.5 mi. S of Grand Island
Type: Public/Member
Hrs: Call for hours; Su, 1:30-5:30
Sporting: 1, 10 stations
Skeet: 4 **HT:** 30 ft.

Honore Hilltop
1605 North E Rd.
Phillips, NE 68865
Nina/John Honore (402) 886-2215
130 mi. W of Omaha
Type: Public
Hrs: Su, 1-5; during week by resrv.
Sporting: 1, 10 stations
HT: 55 ft.

Hunt Nebraska
PO Box 317, Arapahoe, NE 68922
Johnny Hemelstrand
(800) 486-8632
180 mi. W of Lincoln
Type: Public
Hrs: S/Su, 8am-Dusk; & by appt.
Sporting: 1, 10 stations

Nebraska One Box
Sporting Clays
Box 394, Broken Bow, NE 68822
Matt Lyne (308) 872-6131
65 mi. NW of Kearney
Type: Public **Hrs:** Su, 1-6
Sporting: 1, 6 stations
HT: 45 ft.

Sand Prairie Preserve
Box 94, Alliance, NE 69301
William or Bev Lore
(308) 762-2735
6 mi. SE of Alliance
Type: Public
Hrs: T-Su, 9-4 (All Year)
Sporting: 1, 8 stations
Five Stand: 1

Sportsman's Ranch
Sporting Clays
40212 CR #9
Morrill, NE 69358
Steve Decker (308) 247-3370
1.5 mi. S of Morrill
Type: Public **Hrs:** By appt. only
Sporting: 1, 10 stations

Sumac Sporting Clays
PO Box 189
Homer, NE 68030
Don Albertson (712) 251-1882
17 mi. SE of Sioux City
Type: Public
Hrs: S/Su, 10-4; W, 4-Dark
Sporting: 1, 18 stations

TRAP & SKEET

Beatrice Gun Club
PO Box 44
Beatrice, NE 68310
Greg Penner (402) 766-4265
Type: Public/Member
Hrs: W, 6-9; Su, 1-4:30
Trap: 4 Skeet: 1

Cozad Gun Club
818 Lake Ave.
Gothensburg, NE 69138
Nancy Sitorius (308) 784-4159
Type: Public/Member
Hrs: 6 Registered Shoots (Apr-Oct)
Summer League Shoots
Trap: 4

Fremont Izaak Walton Gun Club
2108 Donald, Fremont, NE 68025
Keith Nieman (402) 721-5874
Type: Public Hrs: Tues., 6-8
Trap: 5

H.A. Koch Trap & Skeet
6802 Harrison
Omaha, NE 68157
Gilbert Johnson (402) 331-1249
Hrs: S/Su, 12-5; W, 4-9; T-F, 4-9
Sporting: 1 Trap: 13 Skeet: 6

Lincoln County Wildlife
310 E. 4th St.
North Platte, NE 69101

Cliff Reed (308) 532-6972
Type: Public/Member
Hrs: W/F, 4-Dark (Apr-Sept)
Sporting: 1, 5 stations
Trap: 9 Skeet: 5

Lincoln Trap & Skeet Club
2027 Ranger Circle
Lincoln, NE 68521
Gary Riecke
Type: Public Trap: 9 Skeet: 6

Valley Trap Range
10303 N. 51st Court
Omaha, NE 68152
Dan Linblad (402) 571-6878
Type: Public/Member
Hrs: Th, 6:15-Dark April-Aug.
Trap: 9

NEVADA

SPORTING & 5-STAND

The Capital City Gun Club
PO Box 1422
Carson City, NV 89702
Chip Garofalo (702) 849-2979
4 mi. NE of Carson City
Type: Public
Hrs: W-Su, call for hrs; Mon. & Nat'l. Holidays
Sporting: 1, 5 stations
Trap: 8 Skeet: 1 Five Stand: 1
Wobble Trap

Carson Valley Clays
PO Box 1217
Minden, NV 89423
Steve Stratton (702) 782-3303
15 mi. S of Carson City
Type: Member/Avail
Hrs: Daily
Sporting: 2, 20 stations
Trap: 1

COTTONWOOD CLAYS GUN CLUB

Cottonwood Clays Gun Club
155 Horseshoe Circle
Reno, NV 89506
Rick Moore (702) 342-0333
6 mi. E of Reno
Type: Public/Member
Hrs: W/F, Noon to Dark; S/Su, 10-Dark & by app't
Reservs: Not required
Sporting: 1, 10 stations
Trap: 4 Skeet: 1 Five Stand: 1

Las Vegas
Gun Club
9400 Tule Springs Rd.
Las Vegas, NV 89131
Steve Carmichael (702) 645-5606
Type: Public/Member
Hrs: Th-T, 9-5; W, 9-10
Sporting: 1, 5 stations
Trap: 30 **Skeet:** 1
See Our Ad Above

Remember your hearing
protection. Remember
your eye protection.
Remember to say:
"I saw it in Wing & Clay."

LAS VEGAS, NEVADA

Nellis Trap &
Skeet Club
PO Box 9745
Nellis AFB, NV 89101
Robert Gilmore (702) 652-1937
10 mi. N of Las Vegas
Type: Public
Hrs: W/S/Su, 9-4; Th, 6pm-10pm
Reservs: Not required
Sporting: None
Trap: 6 **Skeet:** 12 **Five Stand:** 1

The Oasis Arvada
Ranch Gun Club
(formerly Peppermill) PO Box 360
Mesquite, NV 89024
Jimmie Hughes (800) 621-0187
77 mi. NE of Las Vegas, NV
Type: Public/Member
Hrs: Su-S, 8am-Dusk
Reservs: Not required
Sporting: 2, 12 stations
Trap: 2 **Skeet:** 2 **Five Stand:** 1
HT: 120 ft.
O Loaner Guns
O Factory Ammunition
O On-Site Pro Shop
O Shooting Lodge
O Formal Instructions
O Golf Carts
See Our Ad Pg. 453

Perdiz
Sports Shooting
PO Box 735, Eureka, NV 89316
Jerry White (702) 237-7027
112 mi. N of Elko
Type: Public/Member
Hrs: Daily, by appt.; Open wk. ends
Reservs: Strongly recommended
Sporting: 1, 10 stations
Trap: 2 **Five Stand:** 1

Red Hills Hunting Preserve
PO Box 493,
Gardnerville, NV 89410
Jack DeMars (702) 266-3856
60 mi. S of Reno
Type: Public/Member
Hrs: 9/15-3/31, T-Su, 8-8;
4/1-9/14, W-Su, 8-6
Sporting: 1, 10 stations **Trap:** 1

Sage Hill
Clay Sports
11500 Mira Loma Rd.
Reno, NV 89511
Rich & Darlene Bullard
(702) 851-1123
12 mi. SE of Reno
Type: Public/Member
Hrs: W/Th, 12-10; F, 12-6; S/Su, 10-6
Reservs: Not required
Sporting: 1, 15 stations **Trap:** 30
Skeet: 6 **Five Stand:** 1 **HT:** 25 ft.
See Our Ad Left

TRAP & SKEET

Flying Saucer Trap Club
PO Box 1373
Lovelock, NV 89419
Larry Vonsild (702) 273-2207
Type: Public/Member
Hrs: Sundays
Trap: Y

Lander Gun Club
310 Bastian 191 15
Battle Mountain, NV 89820
Robert Fox (702) 635-2732
Type: Public
Hrs: Seasonal (scheduled on
request)   **Trap:** 3

Spring Creek Association
451 E. Spring Crk. Pkwy.
Elko, NV 89801
Sherri Tervort (702) 753-6295
15 mi. from Elko
Type: Public **Hrs:** W, 4-9; Su, 9-4
Trap: 16

Spring Creek Trap & Skeet
451 E. Spring Creek Pkwy.
Elko, NV 89801
Dwayne McPhearson
Type: Public/Member
Trap: 12 **Skeet:** 3

Winnemucca Trap Club
Box 1413, Winnemucca, NV 89445
Pete Valdon (702) 623-3074
Type: Public **Hrs:** Su at 1pm
Trap: 5

NEW HAMPSHIRE

SPORTING & 5-STAND

20th Skeet & Sportsmens
116 Goffstown Rd.
Hooksett, NH 03106
Mark Sandler (603) 485-5414
8 mi. N of Manchester
Type: Public/Member
Hrs: W/S/Su, 9-5; Others by appt.
Sporting: 1, 20 stations **Trap:** 1
Skeet: 2 **Five Stand:** 1

Chester Rod & Gun Club
PO Box 337, Chester, NH 03036
Ed Fallon (603) 887-4629
14.5 mi. NE of Derry
Type: Public **Hrs:** Varies, Call
Sporting: 1, 10 stations **HT:** 10 ft.

Grafton County
PO Box 1071, Lebanon, NH 03766
Norm Lorrey (603) 448-3506
105 mi. NW of Boston
Type: Public/Member
Hrs: Th/S/Su
Sporting: 1, 15 stations
Trap: 2 **HT:** 55 ft.

Green Mountain Kennels Hunting Preserve
RR1, Box 438F
Center Ossipee, NH 03814
David Bardzik (603) 539-2106
50 mi. NE of Concord
Type: Public
Hrs: Call for hours
Sporting: 1 **Five Stand:** 1

Kinnicum Fish & Game
PO Box 191, Candia, NH 03034
Mark Trombley (603) 483-0894
60 mi. N of Boston
Type: Public/Member
Hrs: Su, by appt. only; T, 6-Dark
Sporting: 1, 15 stations
Trap: 1 **HT:** 25 ft.

Major Waldron Sportsmen's Assoc.
PO Box 314, Route 9
Barrington, NH 03825
Lester Waterhouse (603) 742-6866
5 mi. W of Dover
Type: Public/Member
Hrs: S, 9-3; Su, 9-Noon; T/W, 6-9
Reservs: Not required
Sporting: 2, 14 stations
Trap: 3 **Skeet:** 2 **Five Stand:** 2
HT: 12 ft.

SKAT
PO Box 137,
New Ipswich, NH 03071
Tony Haigh (603) 878-1257
50 mi. NW of Boston
Type: Public/Member
Reservs: Strongly recommended
Sporting: 5, 70 stations
Trap: 1 **Skeet:** 1   **HT:** 110 ft.
O Loaner Guns
O Factory Ammunition
O On-Site Pro Shop
O On-Site Meals
O Formal Instructions

The Timberdoodle Club
One Webster Hwy.,
Temple, NH 03084
Randall Martin (603) 654-9510
55 mi. NW of Boston
Type: Member/Avail
Hrs: By Appointment
Reservs: Strongly recommended
Sporting: 2, 14 stations
Five Stand: 2   **HT**
O On-Site Pro Shop
O Gunsmith Service

Shooting Instruction
Available - See Pg. 178

TRAP & SKEET

Cheshire County F&G Club
PO Box 233, Ferry Brook Rd.
Keene, NH 03431
Richard Clark (603) 358-6829
Type: Public/Member
Hrs: S, 10-2; W, 4:30-Dark
Trap: 2

Horseshore Fish & Game
PO Box 147, Nashua, NH 03061
Richard Gath (603) 424-9646
Skeet: 1

Pelham Fish and Game
Simpson Mill Rd.,
Pelham, NH 03076
Peter H. Tomaini (603) 472-5624
Type: Public/Member
Hrs: T/Th, 4-9; S/Su, 10-3
Trap: 9 **Skeet:** 2

NEW JERSEY

SPORTING & 5-STAND

Belleplain Farms Sporting Clays
346 Handsmill Rd.
Belleplain, NJ 08270
Nick Germaino (609) 861-2345
50 mi. SE of Philadelphia
Type: Public **Hrs:** S/Su/W, 8-8
Reservs: Recommended
Sporting: 2, 15 stations **HT:** 25 ft.
O Shooting Lodge
O Gun Rental Available

Big Spring Sporting Clays
RD#3, Box 591, Sussex, NJ 07461
(201) 875-3373
50 mi. NW of New York City
Type: Public **Hrs:** W-Su, 8-4
Sporting: 5, 10 stations **HT:** 40 ft.

Buckshorn Sportsmen Club
507 Friendship Rd.
Salem, NJ 08079
Tom Hess (609) 935-4659
40 mi. SW of Philadelphia
Type: Public/Member
Hrs: Su, 9-4
Reservs: Not required
Sporting: 1, 19 stations **HT:** 30 ft.

CLAYS

Buttonwood Game Preserve
810 Harmony Station Rd.
Phillipsburg, NJ 08865
Gail & Frank Vargo (908) 454-8377
60 mi. W of New York
Type: Public
Hrs: W/Th/F, 9-5 by app't;
Sa, 9-5; Su, 1-5
Sporting: 1, 13 stations

Cedar Creek Sportsman's
1910 E. Main St.
Millville, NJ 08332
Tom Kates (609) 825-5051
40 mi. S of Philadelphia
Type: Public/Member
Hrs: S/Su, open at 8:30 am
Sporting: 1, 17 stations HT: 30 ft.

Central Jersey Rifle & Pistol
PO Box 710, Jackson, NJ 08527
Frank Pipoli (908) 928-9334

5 mi. W of Toms River
Type: Member/Avail
Hrs: Open daily to membership
Sporting: None
Trap: 5 Skeet: 4 Five Stand: 1

**Giberson's
Red Wing
Sporting Clays**
317 Sooys Landing Rd.
Port Republic, NJ 08241
Clem Giberson (609) 652-1939
15 mi. NW of Atlantic City
Type: Public/Member
Hrs: W-Su, 9-5
Reservs: Recommended
Sporting: 1, 20 stations HT: 25 ft.
See Our Ad Below

**M&M
Hunting Preserve**
Hook & Winslow Rds.
Pennsville, NJ 08070
Anthony Matarese (609) 935-1230
25 mi. SW of Philadelphia
Type: Public
Hrs: T-Su, 8-5; (Reservations T-F)
Reservs: Recommended
Sporting: 1, 25 stations HT
See Our Ad Pg. 457

Oak Lane Farms
Dutch Mill Rd.,
Piney Hollow, NJ 08344
John Scavelli (609) 697-2196
30 mi. N of Atlantic City
Type: Public/Member
Sporting: 1

Quinton Sportsman's Club
PO Box 397, Quinton, NJ 08072
Don Ives (609) 935-9843
30 mi. SW of Philadelphia
Type: Public/Member
Hrs: Su, 8-3:30; F, 6-11
Sporting: 1, 12 stations
Trap: 3 Skeet: 2 Five Stand: 1
HT: 30 ft.

**Thunder Mountain
Trap & Skeet**
PO Box 164, Mansion Dr.
Ringwood, NJ 07456
Rob Landberg (201) 962-6377
35 mi. NW of New York City
Type: Public
Hrs: W/Th/F, 1-10; S/Su, 9-6
Reservs: Not required
Sporting: None
Trap: 4 Skeet: 4 Five Stand: 1
O Loaner Guns
O Factory Ammunition
O On-Site Pro Shop
O On-Site Meals
O Organized Leagues
O Gunsmith Service

West Creek Sporting Clays
Stipson Island Rd., Eldora, NJ 08270
George Campbell (609) 861-2760
55 mi. SE of Philadelphia
Type: Public
Hrs: Oct. 1-May 15; 7 days/week,
8-4:30; please confirm
Sporting: 2, 36 stations
Trap: 1 Skeet: 1 Five Stand: 1
HT: 60 ft.

TRAP & SKEET

Englishtown Gun Club
11509 Old Bridge Rd.
Englishtown, NJ 07725

John Starace (201) 446-9825
Hrs: M, 1-9; T, 1-pm; S/Su, 9-4
Trap: Y **Skeet:** Y

Farmers Sportsman Club
225 Ellis Rd., Milford, NJ 08848
Norbert McGuire, Jr.
(908) 996-4862
Hrs: F, 7-10 **Trap:** 3

Farmingdale Gun Club
Box 642, Farmingdale, NJ 07727
Eugene Salomon (908) 938-2189
Trap: 3

Lenape Park Trap & Skeet
407 Robins St., Roselle, NJ 07203
Mike DePaola (908) 276-0225
Type: Public **Hrs:** S/Su, 12-5
Trap: 2 **Skeet:** 2

Pine Belt Sportsman's Club
Ave. C & Sooy Place Rd.
Vincentown, NJ 08088
Harold Stevenson, Jr.
(609) 859-2631
Hrs: W, Eve.
Trap: 12 **Skeet:** 3

Pine Valley Gun Club
18 Ivanhoe Dr.,
Robbinsville, NJ 08691
Melvina Tindall (609) 767-2661
Hrs: Sat; 2nd, 4th, 5th Sun.
Trap: 8

Say you "Saw it in Wing & Clay" whenever you contact a company listed in these pages about a product or service.

NEW MEXICO

SPORTING & 5-STAND

Chaparral Sporting Clays
Rt. 1, Box 72G, Deming, NM 88030
Shaun Reynolds (505) 546-9767
60 mi. W of Las Cruces
Type: Public/Member
Hrs: 1st Sat. of month; 2nd Sun. of month; & by appt.
Sporting: 1, 15 stations
Trap: 1 **HT:** 30 ft.

Chile County Sporting Clays
PO Box 252, Hatch, NM 87937
Jimmy Lytle (505) 267-4366
37 mi. S of Truth or Consequences
Type: Public
Hrs: Every 3rd weekend of month; Labor Day
Sporting: 1, 10 stations

Holloman Rod & Gun Club
495 SUS/SURO
Holloman AFB, NM 88330
Recreation Director (505) 475-7398
13.5 mi. W of Alamogordo, NM
Type: Public
Hrs: W, 12-7; S/Su, 9-4
Sporting: 1, 10 stations
Trap: 2 **Skeet:** 2 **Five Stand:** 1

Los Alamos Sportsmen's Club
1362 Trinity Dr., Suite D-2563
Los Alamos, NM 87544
Paul Cook (505) 672-3669
35 mi. N of Santa Fe
Type: Public/Member **Hrs:** M-eve.;
Sporting: 1, 10 stations
Trap: 1 **Skeet:** 1

NRA Whittington Center
Box 700, Raton, NM 87740
Mike Ballew (505) 445-3615
Type: Public **Hrs:** M-F, 8am-5pm
Sporting: 1, 12 stations
Trap: 11 **Skeet:** 2

Sandia Skeet Club
2430 Juan Tabo NE, Suite 150
Albuquerque, NM 87112
Garrett Donovan (505) 846-0196
Hrs: S/Su, 10-4; W, 3-Dark
Sporting: None
Skeet: 4 Five Stand: 1

Tinnin Hunt Club
PO Box 1885
Albuquerque, NM 87103
Tom Tinnin (505) 384-5163
45 mi. S of Albuquerque
Type: Public Hrs: Su-S
Sporting: 1, 10 stations
Five Stand: 1 HT: 20 ft.
Wobble Trap

Vermejo Park Ranch
PO Drawer E, Raton, NM 87740
Jim Baker (505) 445-3097
170 mi. NE of Santa Fe
Type: Public
Hrs: June 1st thru Mid-December
Reservs: Strongly recommended
Sporting: 1, 10 stations
Skeet: 1
See Our Ad Pg. 457

TRAP & SKEET
4 Corners Trap Club, Inc.
Box 693, Farmington, NM 87499
Joseph Stotts (505) 334-2143
Type: Public/Member
Hrs: Sun, 2pm
Trap: 4

Chaparral Skeet Club
HCR31, Box 1318B
Roswell, NM 88201
Gary Damron (502) 623-9191
Type: Public/Member
Hrs: Su, 1-5; W, 5-7 (Summer)
Skeet: 4

Four Corners Trap Club
Box 693, Farmington, NM 87499
Joe Stotts (503) 334-2143
Hrs: Su, 1pm; W, 5pm
Trap: 4

Roadrunner Trap Club
201 Plainview Dr.
Alamogordo, NM 88310
Sid Anderson (505) 437-7632
Type: Public/Member
Hrs: Su, 1pm Trap: 10

South West Shot Gunners
PO Box 36086
Fort Bayard, NM 88036
Fred Selders (505) 537-2744
Type: Public/Member
Hrs: Tues. & Sat. Trap: 2

Truth or Consequences Trap
PO Drawer 1470
Truth or Consequences, NM 87901
Jim Stubblefield (505) 743-6860
Trap: 8

NEW YORK
SPORTING & 5-STAND
Batavia Rod & Gun Club
1 Elmwood, Batavia, NY 14020
Paul Levins (716) 343-2656
35 mi. E of Buffalo
Type: Public/Member
Hrs: S/Su, 8-3; Other times by appt.
Reservs: Strongly recommended
Sporting: 1, 22 stations
Trap: 2 HT: 70 ft. Wobble Trap

Bath Rod & Gun Club
PO Box 764, Bath, NY 14810
Bob Wagner (607) 522-3712
4 mi. E of Bath
Type: Public
Hrs: Trap/Skeet-Su, 8-1; W, 5;
Clays-Su 1pm; M-S, appt.
Sporting: 2, 12 stations
Trap: 2 Skeet: 3

Bellmore Rod & Gun Club
PO Box 324, Bellmore, NY 11710
Warren Busch
12 mi. NE of Roscoe
Type: Member/Avail
Hrs: By Appt.
Sporting: 1 Trap: 1

Binghamton Gun Club, Inc.
235 Main St.,
Johnson City, NY 13790
Emil Misata (607) 797-3313
5 mi. E of Binghamton
Type: Public/Member
Hrs: Twice a Month
Sporting: 1, 10 stations
Trap: 2 Skeet: 4 Five Stand: 1

Brookhaven
Rt. 25, Box 405, Ridge, NY 11961
Al Marelli (516) 924-5091
Type: Public Hrs: W-Su, 9-5
Sporting: 1, 10 stations
Trap: 5 Skeet: 4

Buffalo Shooting Club
563 W. Ferry, Buffalo, NY 14222
James O'Brien (716) 849-2111
Type: Public/Member
Hrs: Sat 11-3,Sun 9-1,
We/Th 4:30-9:30
Sporting: None
Trap: 9 Skeet: 2 Five Stand: 1
Automatic Ball Trap

Cabin Range
Clay Fields
3580 Lockport-Olcott Rd.
Lockport, NY 14094
Doug Thompson (716) 751-9084
30 mi. N of Buffalo
Type: Public
Hrs: S/W/Su, 9-Dk; other by appt.
Reservs: Not required
Sporting: 3, 35 stations
Trap: 1 Skeet: 2 Five Stand: 1
HT: 30 ft.

Catskill Pheasantry & Sporting Clays
PO Box 42, Long Eddy, NY 12760
Alex Papp (914) 887-4487
100 mi. NW of New York City
Type: Public Hrs: Su-S, 9-5
Reservs: Recommended
Sporting: 1, 12 stations
Skeet: 1

Cayuga County Sportsmen's Assn.
RD2, Rockefeller Rd.
Auburn, NY 13021
Roger Button (315) 252-2031
25 mi. SW of Syracuse
Type: Public/Member
Hrs: Su, 9-3:30
Reservs: Not required
Sporting: 1, 17 stations
Trap: 1 Skeet: 2 Five Stand: 1

Cedar Hill Shooting Preserve
21 Marlin Hill Rd.
Germantown, NY 12526
Bernie Mortellaro (518) 828-9360
30 mi. S of Albany
Type: Public
Hrs: Every day, 10-dark
Reservs: Strongly recommended
Sporting: 1, 18 stations
HT: 30 ft. Wobble Trap

Chemung Shooting Preserve
115 Lilac Dr.,
Horseheads, NY 14845
Pat Colligan (607) 739-9238
70 mi. S of Syracuse
Type: Public/Member
Sporting: 1, 10 stations
Trap: 2 Skeet: 2

Crosswinds Sporting Clays
RD2, Box 242, Co. Rt. 29 South
Oswego, NY 13126
Tom Daniels (315) 343-4734

42 mi. NE of Syracuse
Type: Public/Member
Hrs: By reservation only
Sporting: 5, 30 stations **HT:** 30 ft.

East Mountain
Shooting Preserve
150 McCarthy Rd.
Dover Plains, NY 12522
Victor D'Avanzo (914) 877-6274
80 mi. N of New York City
Type: Public **Hrs:**
Reservs: Recommended
Sporting: 1, 10 stations **HT:** 35 ft.
○ Factory Ammunition
○ Shooting Lodge
○ Formal Instructions

Eldred Preserve
PO Box 111, Rt. 55
Eldred, NY 12732
Lou Monteleone (914) 557-8316
90 mi. NW of New York City
Hrs: W-M, 11-4
Reservs: Recommended
Sporting: 1
Five Stand: Y
○ Factory Ammunition
○ Private Motel & Restaurant
○ Deer & Turkey Hunting - Trout & Bass Fishing
○ Hunting & Fishing Guide Service
○ Family Recreation
○ Visa/Mastercard/Discover Accepted

Friar Tuck Inn
Sporting Clays
4858 Rt. 32, Catskill, NY 12414
Ross Caridi (800) 832-7600
150 mi. N of New York City
Type: Public/Member
Hrs: S/Su, 10-6
Reservs: Recommended
Sporting: 1, 20 stations
See Our Ad Pg. 461

Hamburg Rod & Gun Club
PO Box 187, Hamburg, NY 14075
Mike Gusek (716) 648-2236
16 mi. S of Buffalo
Type: Public/Member
Hrs: W/F, 6pm-9pm; S/Su, 10-3
Sporting: 1, 20 stations
Trap: 5 **Skeet:** 5
Five Stand: 1 **HT**

Hendrick-Hudson F&G Club
252 Palmer Rd.
E. Greenbush, NY 12061
Arthur Milanese (518) 674-5184
13 mi. E of Albany
Type: Public/Member
Hrs: Su, 9-1; W, 5-Dark (May-Sept)
Sporting: 1, 15 stations
Trap: 2 **Skeet:** 4 **HT**
Automatic Ball Trap

Horton Brook Shooting
846 Horton Brook Rd.
Roscoe (Horton), NY 12776
Joe or Joann Bracco
(607) 498-5852
8 mi. W of Roscoe
Type: Public **Sporting:** 1

Ilion Fish & Game Club
319 1st Ave.
Frankfort, NY 13340
Edward J. Freedman
(315) 894-2938
12 mi. W of Utica
Type: Public/Member
Hrs: W, 4-8 (Apr-Sept); Su, 9-1 (Sept-Apr)
Sporting: 1, 10 stations
Trap: 4 **Skeet:** 6 **HT:** 40 ft.

Indian Mountain Lodge
PO Box 774, Pine Plains, NY 12567
Joseph L. Blank (518) 789-6801
100 mi. N of Manhattan
Type: Public/Member
Hrs: Open all week, 8-5
Sporting: 1, 12 stations
Skeet: 1 **HT:** 35 ft.

Ischua Valley Sporting Clays
9 First Ave., Franklinville, NY 14737
Bill Atwater (716) 676-5230
7 mi. NW of Franklinville
Type: Public/Member
Hrs: S/Su, 8-4; Wkdays by appt.
Sporting: 1, 14 stations **Trap:** 2

Kayaderros Fish & Game
600 Charlton Rd.
Ballston Spa, NY 12020
Ken DeLano (518) 399-4481
4.5 mi. W of Saratoga Springs
Type: Public/Member
Hrs: By Resrv.
Sporting: 1, 15 stations
Trap: 2 **Skeet:** 1

Mid Hudson Trap & Skeet
411 N. Ohioville Rd.
New Paltz, NY 12561
Hugh Davis (914) 255-7460
75 mi. N of New York
Type: Public **Hrs:** W-Su, 10-5
Sporting: 1, 15 stations
Trap: 4 **Skeet:** 7 **Five Stand:** 1

Millbrook
Shooting School & Preserve Ltd.
RR1, Box 193A
Millbrook, NY 12545
Charles Schneible (914) 677-5756
70 mi. N of New York City
Type: Public
Hrs: By appointment
Reservs: Strongly recommended
Sporting: 1, 12 stations
Five Stand: 1 **HT:** 75 ft.
○ Formal Instructions
○ FITASC
Shooting Instruction Available - See Pg. 166

Nine Partners Pheasant Farm
RR#3, Box 47
Millbrook, NY 12545
Jonathan L. Wicker (914) 677-3114
80 mi. N of New York City
Type: Public/Member
Hrs: Su-S, 9-4; Reservations only
Sporting: 1, 25 stations
Trap: 1 **Wobble Trap**

North Fork
Preserve, Inc.
5330 Sound Ave. (Mail: 349 Pennys Rd.)
Riverhead, NY 11901
Brett Jayne or Robert H. Krudop
(516) 369-1728
70 mi. E of New York
Type: Member/Avail
Hrs: Daily, 9-Dark by appt.
Reservs: Strongly recommended
Sporting: 1, 10 stations
Skeet: 1 **HT:** 40' **Wobble Trap**
Exclusive Sportsman's Club on Eastern Long Island has limited owner/memberships available. Facilities include sporting clays, FITASC, skeet, excellent upland game and cover, deer, bass ponds, clubhouse and tennis courts. Non- member, private and corporate shoots and functions may be arranged. Call: North Fork Preserve:
(516) 369-1728 (days);
(516) 722-3152 (evenings).

Oneonta Sportsmen's Club
Wasson Rd., Oneonta, NY 13820
Dennis Van Deusen
(607) 433-0515
60 mi. SW of Albany
Type: Public/Member
Hrs: W, 5-Dark; Su, 8-Dark
Sporting: 1, 13 stations
Trap: 2 Skeet: 3   HT: 30 ft.

Painted Post Field & Stream
PO Box 325, Corning, NY 14830
Lloyd Hurd (607) 936-4912
5 mi. W of Corning
Type: Public/Member
Hrs: 9-Dark, 1st & 3rd Sat.
Sporting: 1, 20 stations
Skeet: 1

Pathfinder Fish & Game
PO Box 194, Fulton, NY 13069
Robert Weldin (315) 593-7281
Hrs: S, 10-5; Su, Noon-6; M-F, 6-10
Sporting: None
Trap: 7 Five Stand: 1

**Pawling
Mountain Club**
PO Box 573, Pawling, NY 12564
Gary Hall (914) 855-3825
80 mi. N of New York City
Type: Member/Avail
Sporting: 1, 15 stations
Five Stand: 1   HT: 90 ft.
Wobble Trap
*Shooting Instruction
Available--See Pg. 175*

Peconic River Sportsmans
RFD 389 River Rd.
Manorville, NY 11949
Sid Miller (516) 727-5248
Hrs: W/S/Su, 11-5

Sporting: 1, 14 stations
Trap: 5 Skeet: 5

Quigg Hollow Hunting Club
3130 Quigg Hollow Rd.
Andover, NY 14806
Rod & Phyllis Walker
(607) 478-5222
90 mi. S of Rochester
Type: Public/Member
Hrs: Daylight-Dark
Sporting: 1, 13 stations

Ramapough Sportsmens
45 Treetop Circle
Nanuet, NY 10954
Mark L. Dorfman (914) 426-0590
Hrs: W-Su, 10-7
Sporting: None
Skeet: 2 Five Stand: 1

**Rochester Brooks
Gun Club**
Box 289, 926 Honeoye Falls Rd. #6
Rush, NY 14543
Thomas Dobbins (716) 533-9913
15 mi. S of Rochester
Type: Member/Avail
Hrs: W, 9-10; S/Su, 9-5
Reservs: Not required
Sporting: 1, 25 stations
Trap: 16 Skeet: 14 Five Stand: 1
HT: 70 ft. Automatic Ball Trap
O Factory Ammunition
O Formal Instructions
O Pistol & Rifle Range

Salmon Creek Sportsmen's
Scipio-Venice Town Line Rd.
Scipio Center, NY 13147
Gerry Shook (315) 364-6778
15 mi. S of Auburn
Type: Public/Member
Hrs: Su, 9-2

Sporting: 1, 23 stations
Trap: 1   HT: 40 ft.

**Serendipity Farms
Sporting Clays**
12201 Rt. 62, Lawtons, NY 14091
George Bogner/Vince Lorenz
(716) 337-9828
25 mi. S of Buffalo
Type: Public/Member
Hrs: W/Sa/Su, 9-5; otherS by app't
Reservs: Not required
Sporting: 2, 18 stations
HT: 65 ft.
O Factory Ammunition
O Formal Instructions
O On-Site Clubhouse
O Brand New 2nd Course in 1995!
O See our listing in NY Wings
  Section

**Stonegate
Hunting Preserve**
262 A Beattie Rd.
Rock Tavern, NY 12575
James Filardi (914) 496-9811
55 mi. N of New York City
Type: Public/Member
Hrs: M-F, 9-4 by reserv; S/Su, 9-4
resv. not required
Reservs: Recommended
Sporting: 2, 10 stations HT: 30 ft.
See Our Ad Below

Suffolk Trap
& Skeet Range
165 Gerrard Rd., PO Box 181
Yaphank, NY 11980
Richard DeMott (516) 924-4490
60 mi. E of New York City
Type: Public   **Hrs:** W/Th,
10-Dark; T/F/S/Su, 10-6 (Summer)
Reservs: Not required
Sporting: 1, 10 stations
Trap: 11 **Skeet:** 5 **Five Stand:** 1
HT: 30 ft.

T-M-T Hunting Preserve
RR1, Box 297, School House Rd.
Staatsburg, NY 12580
Thomas F. Mackin (914) 266-5108
55 mi. N of New York City
Type: Public **Hrs:** By Appt.
Sporting: 1, 10 stations

Taconic Trap Club
Rt. 82, PO Box 132
Salt Point, NY 12578
Jeff or Ted Philipbar (914)
266-3788
70 mi. N of New York City
Type: Public/Member
Hrs: Rsrv. only
Reservs: Recommended
Sporting: 1, 12 stations
Trap: 9 **Skeet:** 1
See Our Ad Below

Tamarack Preserve Ltd.
RR#1, Box 111B
Millbrook, NY 12545
Bob Vanecek (914) 373-7084
85 mi. N of New York
Type: Member/Avail
Hrs: Weekdays by appt., 9-5
Sporting: 1, 18 stations
HT: 120 ft.

Tioga County Sportsman's
PO Box 598
Oswego, NY 13827
Mike Pasquale (607) 687-1418
15 mi. W of Binghamton
Type: Public/Member
Hrs: By Schedule
Sporting: 1, 12 stations
Trap: 4 **Skeet:** 1 **Five Stand:** 1
HT: 75 ft.

Tonawanda Sportsman
5657 Killian Rd.
Tonawanda, NY 14120
Robert Guyder (716) 692-2161
10 mi. N of Buffalo
Type: Public/Member
Hrs: W, 6-10; S, 12-3; Su, 10-3
Sporting: 1, 18 stations
Trap: 9 **Skeet:** 6

Trenton Fish & Game Club
Wood Rd., Box 113
Holland Patent, NY 13354
William Swarts (315) 337-8516
10 mi. N of Utica
Type: Public/Member

Hrs: Trap: Su, 9am; Clays: 7/22,
8/19, 9/16, 10/21
Sporting: 1, 10 stations
Trap: 1

**West Branch Angler &
Sportsman's Resort**
PO Box 102
Deposit, NY 13057
Jim Serio, Gen. Mgr.
(607) 467-5525
Type: Public **Hrs:**

Whale Back
Farms Shooting
Preserve &
Sporting Clay
PO Box 301
Canandaigua, NY 14424
R. Bruce Lindsay (800) 923-4868
40 mi. SE of Rochester
Type: Public/Member
Hrs: Daily by reserv.; Corp. groups
welcome
Reservs: Strongly recommended
Sporting: 2, 15 stations
HT: 35 ft.

Whale Back's championship
course at 2,200 feet above sea
level overlooks beautiful
beautiful Canandaigua Lake
1,500 feet below! Most of the
New York state championship
for SCA carts and organized
leagues. Corporate groups
welcome. Call 800-923-4868,
Mon-Fri; or R. Bruce Lindsay,
800-861-6208 all other times.

Whispering Pines Hideaway
548 Townline Rd.
Lyons, NY 14489
Charlie Buisch (315) 946-6170
30 mi. E of Rochester
Type: Public/Member
Hrs: S/Su, 9-4; & by appointment
Sporting: 1, 23 stations
HT: 80 ft.

Wild Woods Sporting Clays
RR8, Box 105A
Oswego, NY 13126
Rhonda Driscoll (315) 342-1296
6 mi. E of Oswego
Type: Public
Hrs: M-F, by rsrv; S/Su, 9-2
Sporting: 2, 10 stations
Trap: 1 **Skeet:** 1

Wilderness Sporting Clays
Old Baker Rd., Box 746
Arkville, NY 12406
Joseph Lombardino
(914) 586-2766
45 mi. NW of Kingston
Type: Public/Member

Hrs: Su-S, 9am-Dusk
Sporting: 1, 16 stations
HT: 30 ft.

TRAP & SKEET

Bridgeport Rod & Gun
PO Box 117, Bridgeport, NY 13030
(315) 699-3313
Hrs: Su   **Trap:** 12

Calverton Shooting Range
395 Nugent Dr.,
Calverton, NY 11933
George L. Schmelzer
(516) 727-9881
E of Riverhead
Type: Public
Hrs: Daily, 8:30-5:30
Trap: 10

Central Square Forest Fish
6736 Lehigh Rd.
Pulaski, NY 13142
Thomas A. Whitaker
(315) 298-6701
Type: Public/Member
Hrs: M/T, Evenings; S/Su,
Trap: 6

Clifton Park Fish & Game
Eaglemore Rd.,
Clifton Park, NY 12866
Dennis Conrad (518) 371-9869
Type: Public   **Hrs:** T, 6-10
Trap: 3

Conesus Lake Sportsmens Club
Stonehill Rd., Lakeville, NY 14480
Dana Driscoll (716) 346-6527
Type: Member/Avail
Hrs: T/W/Th, Eve; S/Su, 12
Trap: 4   **Skeet:** 4

DeWitt Fish & Game Club
PO Box 21, DeWitt, NY 13214
Steven Kawryga (315) 446-1190
Automatic Ball Trap

Fur, Fin & Feathers
PO Box 323, Elmira, NY 14902
Dennis Wieland (607) 733-3943
Trap: 1   **Skeet:** 2

Hudson Falls Fish & Game
Box 332, Hudson Falls, NY 12839
Andrew B. Collins
Hrs: T/Th, 4-9; Su, 8-1
Skeet: 2

Jamestown Skeet/Trap
PO Box 337, Lakewood, NY 14750
Rick Sanders (716) 763-9700
Hrs: Th, 7-10
Trap: Y   **Skeet:** 2

Need an extra copy of
Wing & Clay? Ordering
by phone is a breeze.
Call: 800-224-9464
and, please, have a
major credit card handy.

Lost Pond Club
47 Fair St., Norwich, NY 13815
James J. McNeil (607) 336-5678
Trap: 1   **Skeet:** 5

Medina Conservation Club
10381 Ridge Rd.
Medina, NY 14103
Howard Robinson
Trap: 1   **Skeet:** 2

Mumford Sportsmens Club
3256 Ellen Pl.,
Caledonia, NY 14423
William P. Taylor (716) 538-2341
Type: Public/Member
Hrs: Varies   **Trap:** 4

New Paltz Rod & Gun Club
PO Box 363, New Paltz, NY 12561
Edward Kara (914) 255-7586
Type: Public/Member
Trap: 2

New York Trapshooting Assn.
116 Kimry Moor
Fayatteville, NY 13066
Robert Spence (315) 637-4827
Trap: 24

Newark Rod & Gun Club
140 Dell St., Newark, NY 14513
Craig Parsons (315) 331-0623
Hrs: M/T, 5; W/F, 10-3; Su, 9-1
Trap: 4   **Skeet:** 4

Olean Rod & Gun Club
1209 Washington St.
Olean, NY 14760
C.E. "Bud" Johnson (716) 933-6190
Hrs: Su, 9-3; W, 5-10
Trap: 2   **Skeet:** 2

Ontario Rod & Gun Club
28 Ridge Rd. West
Rochester, NY 14615
Bill Palermo, Jr. (716) 458-5398
Type: Public/Member
Hrs: T, 4-9   **Trap:** 4

Outlet Gun Club Inc.
Box 8009, W. Webster, NY 14580
Curtis J. Graham (716) 377-4851
Hrs: S/Su, 9-5
Trap: 4   **Skeet:** 4

Pine Tree Point Gun Club
46963 Carnegie Bay Rd.
Alexandria Bay, NY 13607
W. G. Lanterman Jr. (315) 482-3911
Type: Public
Hrs: W/S, 12-9; Su, 9-9
Trap: 2   **Skeet:** 4

The Plattsburgh Rod & Gun
284 Pleasant St.
Peru, NY 12972
Dominick F. Ciampo
Hrs: Su, 12-Dk (W); W, 5-Dk; S/Su
Trap: 3   **Skeet:** 3

Portville Conservation Club
High St., Cres, NY 14721
Gordon Harmon
Hrs: Weekends   **Trap:** 1

Randolph Rod & Gun Club
87 Main St., Randolph, NY 14772
Arnold E. Towers (716) 358-6606
Type: Public   **Hrs:** W, 6; S, 10-5
Trap: 4   **Skeet:** 2

Red Creek Conservation
PO Box 449, Haminbal, NY 13074
Mark Cole (315) 754-6459
Hrs: Th, 6-9; S/Su, 12-6; By appt.
Trap: 1   **Skeet:** 2

Saraspa Rod & Gun Club
PO Box 22,
Greenfield Center, NY 12833
Thomas Law (518) 893-2682
Hrs: T/W, 6-9
Skeet: 1

Sodus Bay Sportsman Club
Box 106, Sodus Point, NY 14555
Pat O'Neil (315) 483-0051
Hrs: W, Eve; Sun, 10-2
Trap: 2   **Skeet:** 2

Staten Island Sportsmens Club
Box 45, Staten Island, NY 10314
Vince Ricciardi (718) 448-1155
Hrs: S/Su, 8; W, 6
Trap: 4

Sullivan Trail Rod/Gun
118 John St.,
Horseheads, NY 14845
Mike Moses (607) 739-1814
Type: Public/Member
Hrs: W, 4:30-Dark; Su, 8:30-1:30
Trap: 2   **Skeet:** 2

Tri-State Rod & Gun Club
N. Orange St., Box 801
Port Jervis, NY 12771
Eddy Cohen
65 mi. NE of New York City
Type: Public/Member
Hrs: Su, 12-4; T, 5-9 (Apr-Oct)
Trap: 2

Victor Rod & Gun Club
PO Box 1323
Fairport, NY 14450
Andy Nolan (716) 924-4427
Hrs: Th, 5-10; Su, 9-12
Trap: 1   **Skeet:** 3

Williamson Rod & Gun
PO Box 175, Williamson, NY 14589
Robert L. Carr
Hrs: Su, 9-1; Th, 5
Trap: 1   **Skeet:** 2

Wood & Brook Sportsmens
44 Brookedge Rd.
Depew, NY 14043
Dale Wittig (716) 937-4061
Hrs: Varies   **Trap:** 2

CLAYS

NORTH CAROLINA

SPORTING & 5-STAND

Adams Creek
Gun Sports
6240 Adams Creek Rd.
Havelock, NC 28532
Rusty/June Bryan (919) 447-6808
115 mi. SE of Raleigh near Morehead City
Type: Public/Member
Hrs: By appt.
Reservs: Recommended
Sporting: 1, 27 stations
Skeet: 1   **HT:** 35 ft.

Apple Wood Sporting Clays
Rt. 2, Box 363
Hendersonville, NC 28792
John Laughter (704) 697-3757
40 mi. S of Asheville
Type: Public
Hrs: W/F/S, 9-6; Su, 1-6
Sporting: 1, 10 stations

Catawba Sporting Clays
1809 Brenner Ave.
Salisbury, NC 28144
Drew Arey/Todd Swicegood
(704) 642-1710
30 mi. N of Charlotte
Type: Public/Member
Hrs: T-F, 12-Dusk; S, 9-Dusk; Su, 1-Dusk; M/T, by appt.
Sporting: 1, 14 stations
Five Stand: 1   **HT:** 30 ft.

Central Carolina Sporting
PO Box 1101, Biscoe, NC 27209
Bill Robbins (910) 428-2529
60 mi. NE of Charlotte
Type: Public
Hrs: M-F, by appt; W, 12-5; S, 9-5; Su, 12-5
Reservs: Recommended
Sporting: 1, 10 stations

Charlotte Rifle & Pistol Club
P.O. Box 11183
Charlotte, NC 28220
Jim Bogart (704) 843-2915
15 mi. S of Charlotte
Type: Public/Member
Hrs: Sa/Su, 12-5:30
Sporting: None
Trap: 1 **Skeet:** 2 **Five Stand:** 1

Contentnea Creek Hunting Preserve-Kennels-Clays
Rt. 1, Box 202
Hookerton, NC 28530
S.M.Gray/Bob Steed/Gary Tripp
(919) 747-8302
60 mi. SE of Raleigh
Type: Public/Member
Hrs: M-F, 10-Dk; S, 9-Dk; Su, 1-Dk
Sporting: 3, 10 stations
Skeet: 1 **Five Stand:** 2
Wobble Trap

Deep River
Sporting Clays, Inc.
3420 Cletus Hall Rd.
Sanford, NC 27330
Bill Kempffer (919) 774-7080
28 mi. SW of Raleigh
Type: Public/Member
Hrs: W-S, 10-6; Su, 1-6 & by resrv.
Reservs: Recommended
Sporting: 4, 18 stations
HT: 35 ft.
O On-Site Pro Shop
O Rental Guns
O Corporate Meeting Facilities
O Only 35 Minutes South of Raleigh/Durham/Chapel Hill
O Four Certified Instructors on Staff
Shooting Instruction Available - See Pg. 158

Durham County Wildlife
Rt. 1, Box 213, Hopson Rd.
Morrisville, NC 27560
Bill Fleeman (919) 477-1782
Type: Public/Member
Hrs: Su, 1-6; W, 6-9
Sporting: None
Trap: 4 **Skeet:** 4 **Five Stand:** 1

Fairview
Hunting Preserve
8004 Concord Hwy.
Monroe, NC 28110
E.L. Connor (704) 753-4004
10 mi. N of Monroe
Type: Public
Hrs: M-F, 2-6; S, 9-6; Su, 1-6
Reservs: Not required
Sporting: 1, 35 stations
Trap: 2   **HT:** 30 ft.

Hunters' Pointe
Sporting Clays, Inc.
506 Decoy Drive
Washington, NC 27889
Scott/David Downs
(919) 975-2529
20 mi. E of Greenville
Type: Public
Hrs: W/Th/F/Su, 12-6; S, 9-6; M/T, by appt.
Reservs: Not required
Sporting: 2, 45 stations
Five Stand: 1   **HT:** 45 ft.
Wobble Trap
O On-Site Pro Shop
O Formal Instructions
O Golf Carts
O Rental Guns Available
O Visa & Mastercard Accepted
O NSCA 5-Stand with Bird Brain Controller

Pecan Grove Sporting Clays
Rt. 2, Box 154, Ayden, NC 28513
Jerry T. Gibson (919) 746-2527
7 mi. SE of Greenville
Type: Public
Hrs: M-F, appt. only; S, 9-6; Su, 12:30-6
Sporting: 2, 25 stations
HT: 30 ft.

Pender Co.
Gun Club
239 N. Channel Haven Dr.
Wilmington, NC 28409
Allan Snyder (919) 791-3182
28 mi. NW of Wilmington
Type: Public/Member
Hrs: W/S/Su, 10-Dark
Reservs: Not required
Sporting: 1, 15 stations
Trap: 2 **Skeet:** 1

Powell Farm Sporting Clay
Rt. 2, Box 241-C
Shawboro, NC 27973
Marsha Powell (919) 232-3092
45 mi. S of Norfolk, VA
Type: Public

Hrs: W/Th/F/Su, 1-Dark; S, 9-Dark
Sporting: 1, 21 stations   HT: 40 ft.

Qualla Farm
Sporting Clays, Inc.
PO Box 1771
Maggie Valley, NC 28751
Jeff Phillips/John Leatherwood
(704) 926-8500
30 mi. W of Asheville
Type: Public/Member
Hrs: F, 1-6; S, 10-6; Su, 1-6;
(Summer, W, 1-6)
Reservs: Recommended
Sporting: 1, 22 stations
Five Stand: 1   HT: 18 ft.
Wobble Trap

Rowan County Wildlife
PO Box 612, Salisbury, NC 28145
Joe W. Earley (704) 636-8662
2 mi. SW of Salisbury
Type: Public/Member
Hrs: W, 5-8:30pm; S/Su, 2-8:30pm
Sporting: 1, 13 stations
Trap: 8 Skeet: 8

Shane's
Sporting Clays
6319 A Hwy. 158
Summerfield, NC 27358
Shane Naylor (910) 643-7168
12 mi. N of Greensboro
Type: Public/Member
Hrs: M-S, 8-7; Su, 1-4
Reservs: Strongly recommended
Sporting: 2, 25 stations   HT: 115'

Shooters Sporting Club
PO Box 93, Turnerburg, NC 28688
Buck Nooe (704) 546-5400
40 mi. N of Charlotte
Type: Public/Member
Sporting: 1, 13 stations
Skeet: 1 Five Stand: 1

Smoke Rise Field Club
PO Box 1069, Cashiers, NC 28717
John H. Druffel (704) 743-5799
40 mi. SW of Ashville

Type: Member/Avail
Hrs: W/Su, 1-5; S, 10-5
Sporting: 1, 16 stations
Trap: 1 Skeet: 2

Wiccacon Gun Club
Box 385, Harrellsville, NC 27942
R.C. Kennington (919) 356-2912
Hrs: W/S, 1-7
Sporting: None
Skeet: 2 Five Stand: 1

Wintergreen Hunting
Box 981, Bladenboro, NC 28320
Boyce White (919) 648-6171
85 mi. S of Raleigh
Type: Public Hrs:
Sporting: 1, 10 stations
HT: 40 ft.

Yadkin Point
Shooting Preserve & Kennels
PO Box 313, Advance, NC 27006
Howell W. Woltz (910) 998-9518
10 mi. W of Winston-Salem
Type: Public/Member
Reservs: Recommended
Sporting: 3, 22 stations
Five Stand: 1   HT: 30 ft.
Yadkin Point offers 3 sporting
clays courses. Summer hours:
April 1 - Sept. 30; Wed-Fri., 12-7;
Sat., Open all day. Winter hours:
Oct. 1 - Mar. 31; Mon-Sat.,
8:30-6:30. Also:
O Guided quail hunts--wagon
   style or on foot
O Bird dog training
O Bird dogs for sale
O Lodging and food available on
   grounds
O Bird cleaning available

TRAP & SKEET
Alamance Wildlife Club
125 Frissell Dr.
Whitsett, NC 27377
Mike Pittard (910) 376-6739
Hrs: Th, 7-10; Su, 2-5
Trap: 2 Skeet: 1

Bostic Gun Club
PO Box 632, Ellenboro, NC 28040
Mike Billingsley
Trap: 3 Skeet: 1

Buccaneer Gun Club
1017 Robert E. Lee Dr.
Wilmington, NC 28412

Fred G. Welfare (910) 675-6605
Hrs: Varies
Trap: 1 Skeet: 1

Buncombe Co. Wildlife
PO Box 530, Tuxedo, NC 28784
Bob Schultz/Ron Wilson
(704) 628-2838
Type: Public/Member
Hrs: W/S/Su, 1-6
Trap: 2 Skeet: 2

Carolina Clay Target Club
PO Box 7372,
Greensboro, NC 27417
Kerry B. Ward (910) 294-2569
Hrs: S, 8-Dark; Su, 1-Dark
Trap: 1 Skeet: 1

Cleveland Skeet Inc.
131 Appian Way
Shelby, NC 28150
D. Scott McIntyre (704) 487-7532

Crow Hill Farms Skeet
PO Box 819, Beaufort, NC 28516
Warren J. Davis (919) 728-4080
Hrs: By appt. Skeet: 1

Gastonia Skeet and Trap
PO Box 174B, Gastonia, NC 28053
Kieffer Gaddis (704) 866-6734
Type: Public Hrs: W/F/S/Su, 1-6
Trap: 2 Skeet: 2

Horseshoe Neck Gun Club
Rt. 5, Box 2409
Lexington, NC 27292
Henry Grubbs (704) 956-2111

Morganton Skeet Club
105 Jacksons Run
Morganton, NC 28655
Ethan Frankin (704) 438-5359
Hrs: W, 4-7; Su, 2-6
Skeet: 2

Ocean Skeet Club
219 Channel Dr., Cape Canteret
Swansboro, NC 28584
Otis H. Johnston (919) 393-8543
Hrs: Call for appt.
Skeet: 1

Old Hickory Gun Club
PO Box 7984
Rocky Mount, NC 27804
Louis A. Levy (919) 977-3231
Hrs: W/F/S/Su, Afternoon
Trap: 1 Skeet: 5

Piedmont Gun Club
Rt. 5, Box 25
Rutherfordton, NC 28139
Buddy Lawing (704) 286-4361
Type: Public/Member
Hrs: Sat., by appt.
Trap: 3

San-Lee Gun Club
5104 Jefferson Davis Hwy.

CLAYS

Cameron, NC 28326
Paul Turbeville, Jr. **Skeet:** 1

Watauga Gun Club
PO Box 2316, Boone, NC 28607
Randy Jones (704) 264-0843
Type: Member/Avail
Hrs: Open all day
Trap: 4

NORTH DAKOTA

SPORTING & 5-STAND

Dakota Hunting Club
PO Box 13623
Grand Forks, ND 58208
George Newton (701) 775-2074
12 mi. SW of Grand Forks
Type: Public
Hrs: Spring/Summer/Fall, 10-6;
Winter, 1-4
Sporting: 2, 10 stations
HT: 60 ft.

J.T's Sporting Clays
17425 Highway 11
Fairmont, ND 58030
Jeff Trom (701) 474-5598
60 mi. S of Fargo
Type: Public
Hrs: S/Su, 9-Dk; Wkdays by appt.
Sporting: None
Trap: 1 **Skeet:** 1 **Five Stand:** 1

Minot Gun Club
1004 4th Ave., NW
Minot, ND 58701
Anthony Bennett (701) 838-7472
Hrs: T-Th, 6-10; Su,12-6
Sporting: 1, 8 stations
Trap: 13 **Skeet:** 2

P.K.'s Sporting Clays
2307 11th St. S.
Fargo, ND 58103
Peter Knoff (701) 293-1873
10 mi. E of Fargo
Type: Public **Hrs:** Su-S, 9-Dark
Sporting: 1, 21 stations **HT:** 35 ft.

The Shooting Park, Inc.
4333 167th Ave., SE
Horace, ND 58047
John/Joyce Nelson (701) 282-3805
Type: Public
Hrs: Su-Th, 2-Dark (Apr-Oct)
Sporting: None
Trap: 13 **Skeet:** 3 **Five Stand:** 1
Wobble Trap

TRAP & SKEET

Buffalo City Gun Club
Box 1052, Jamestown, ND 58402
Jeffrey A. Seher (701) 251-2250
Hrs: Th, 6-10; F, 1x/month
Trap: 4

Capital City Gun Club
2100 Industrial Park
Bismark, ND 58502
Darold Asbridge (701) 258-0252
Type: Public
Hrs: T-Th, 6pm-10pm (Apr-Sept)
Trap: 14 **Wobble Trap**

Northwest Gun Club
1108 2nd Ave., E.
Williston, ND 58801
R.C. Koch (701) 572-2935
Type: Public/Member
Hrs: T-Th, 7pm (Summer)
Trap: 4

Tri County Trap & Wildlife
Box 94, Winbledon, ND 58492
Bruce Meikle (701) 435-2406
Hrs: M, 6-9
Trap: 1 **Skeet:** 1

A&A Shooting & Hunting
12006 Fenstermaker
Garrettsville, OH 44231
Al or Joe Spolarich (216) 548-8753
40 mi. E of Cleveland
Type: Public/Member
Hrs: W/S/Su, 8-5; also by appt.
Sporting: None
Trap: 2 **Skeet:** 2 **Five Stand:** 1

OHIO

SPORTING & 5-STAND

Anderson's Sporting Clays
237 Cockrell's Run Rd.
Lucasville, OH 45648
Ed Anderson (614) 259-5211
85 mi. N of Columbus
Type: Public/Member
Hrs: Th, 4:30-Dark; S/Su,
8:30-Dark; Others by appt.
Sporting: 1, 43 stations
Five Stand: 1

Avon Sportsman Club
Box 181
Avon, OH 44011
Larry Hocking (216) 937-9006
10 mi. W of Cleveland
Type: Public
Hrs: W, 6-10pm; S/Su, 9-3
Reservs: Not required
Sporting: None
Trap: 1 **Skeet:** 1 **Five Stand:** 1
From Cleveland-Rt. 90 West to
Bradley Road exit, south to
Detroit Rd., west to Lear-Nagle
Rd., south to Swartz Rd., east to
Williams Ct., & south to end of
Williams Ct.

Beaver Creek Club
48430 Cooper Foster Park Rd.
Amherst, OH 44001
Tim Keller (216) 988-8884
35 mi. W of Cleveland
Type: Member/Avail
Hrs: 7 days a week, 9-5
Sporting: 2, 17 stations
Trap: 1 **Skeet:** 1 **Five Stand:** 1
HT: 50 ft.

Brier Oak Sporting Clays
State Rt. 113, Bellevue, OH 44811
Kevin or Denise Schaeffer
(419) 483-4953
65 mi. SW of Cleveland
Type: Public
Hrs: S/Su, 8-6; M/W/Th/F, 8-5,
by appt.
Reservs: Recommended
Sporting: 2, 38 stations
HT: 30 ft.
○ Organized Leagues
○ Ammunition for Sale
○ Formal Instruction by Reservation
○ Easy Access between Exts. 6A
Ohio Tpke. State Rt. 113

Buckeye Valley Sporting Clays
12360 Shellbeach Rd.
Thornville, OH 43076
Robert Worrell (614) 467-2868
30 mi. E of Columbus
Type: Public/Member
Hrs: S/Su, 9-6; M-F, By Appt.
Reservs: Not required
Sporting: 2, 10 stations
Trap: 1 **HT:** 35 ft.
○ Factory Ammunition
○ Shooting Lodge
○ Formal Instructions
○ Organized Leagues
○ Gunsmith Service

Cherrybend Pheasant Farm
2326 Cherrybend Rd.
Wilmington, OH 45177
Mary Hollister (513) 584-4269
40 mi. NE of Cincinnati
Type: Public/Member
Hrs: Wkdays by resrv.;
Wkends, 9-Dark
Sporting: 2, 16 stations

Conneaut Creek Club
2265 Harcourt Dr.
Cleveland, OH 44106
H.F. Biggar, III (216) 368-1565
70 mi. NE of Cleveland
Type: Member/Avail
Hrs: Private Club; Reservation only
Sporting: 1, 12 stations

Elkhorn Hunt Club
4146 Klopfenstein Rd.
Bucyrus, OH 44820
Samuel A. Ballou (419) 562-6131
55 mi. N of Columbus
Type: Public/Member
Hrs: M-F, by Appt; S/Su, 9-6
Sporting: 1, 10 stations
Trap: Y **Skeet:** Y

Evick's Shotgun Sports
70183 Maynard Rd.
St. Clairsville, OH 43950
John Evick (614) 695-6948
10 mi. W of Wheeling, WV
Type: Public
Hrs: Su-S, by appt.
Sporting: 1, 15 stations

Grand Valley Ranch
10198 Penniman Rd.
Orwell, OH 44076
Glenn Rex (216) 437-6440
40 mi. E of Cleveland
Type: Public/Member
Hrs: W/Th/F, 9-5; S/Su, 9-4;
& by app't.
Sporting: 1, 9 stations
Trap: 2 **HT:** 25 ft.

Hidden Haven
Shooting Preserve
9257 Buckeye Rd.
Sugar Grove, OH 43155
Ronald Blosser (614) 746-8568
50 mi. SE of Columbus
Type: Public/Member
Hrs: Daily, 9am-Dark; Hunting
hours-appt. only
Reservs: Not required
Sporting: 10, 9 stations
Trap: 1 **HT:** 70 ft.
O Loaner Guns
O Factory Ammunition
O On-Site Pro Shop
O On-Site Meals
O Shooting Lodge
O Formal Instructions
O Organized Leagues
O Golf Carts
O 5-Stand Sporting-FITASC

Highfield Shooting Sports Club
8575 Carson Rd.
Fultonham, OH 43738
Daniel C. Miller (614) 849-3144
40 mi. E of Columbus
Type: Public
Hrs: S-Su, 9-5; W, 4-dusk
Sporting: 2, 20 stations   **HT:** 54 ft.

Hill 'N Dale Club
3605 Poe Rd., Medina, OH 44256
Terry L. Eicher (216) 725-2097
50 mi. S of Cleveland
Type: Member/Avail
Hrs: T-S, 8-5; Su, 10-5
Reservs: Strongly recommended
Sporting: 1, 30 stations
Skeet: 1   **HT:** 45 ft.
O Factory Ammunition
O On-Site Pro Shop
O On-Site Meals
O Formal Instructions NSCA
   Level I & II

Lone Dove Sporting Clays
8780 Bunker Hill Rd., SW
Port Washington, OH 43837
Jerry A. Wilson (614) 498-6266
75 mi. NE of Columbus
Type: Public
Hrs: Su, 9-5; M-S, by appt.
Sporting: 2, 10 stations

Lost Bird Sporting Clays
3344 Harrison Rd.
Fredericksburg, OH 44627
Fred Mowerer/Art Opliger
(216) 695-3621
15 mi. SE of Wooster
Type: Public
Hrs: M-S, daylight-dark; Su, 10-6
Sporting: 1, 20 stations

Mad River
Sportsman's Club
1055 County Rd. 25
Bellefontaine, OH 43311
Tony Stratton, Mgr.
(513) 593-8245
45 mi. NW of Columbus
Type: Member/Avail
Hrs: T-S, 9-5; Su, 12-5
Reservs: Strongly recommended
Sporting: 1, 16 stations
Trap: 1
O Loaner Guns
O Factory Ammunition
O On-Site Pro Shop
O Shooting Lodge
O Gunsmith Service
O Gun Fitting
Shooting Instruction
Available - See Pg. 160
& Our Ad Above

Marietta Gun Club
RR1, Box 312B
Vincent, OH 45784
Victor A. Rutter, Jr. (614) 678-2631

CLAYS

80 mi. SE of Columbus
Type: Public/Member
Hrs: T, 6-9; Su, 1-5
Sporting: None
Trap: 8 **Skeet:** 2 **Wobble Trap**

Medusa Sporting Clays
5515 Centennial Rd.
Sylvania, OH 43560
Skip Weiss (419) 531-4759
10 mi. W of Toledo
Type: Public/Member
Hrs: Su, 10-5; S, 9-5
Sporting: 1, 14 stations
Trap: 2 **Skeet:** 2

Miami Valley Skeet Club
9292 Cincinnati Columbus Rd.
Cincinnati, OH 45241
George Quigley (513) 779-7177
4 mi. S of Dayton
Type: Public/Member
Hrs: S/Su, 12-Dark
Sporting: None
Trap: 1 **Skeet:** 5 **Five Stand:** 1
HT: 40 ft.

Middletown Sportsmen's Club
6943 Michael Rd.
Middletown, OH 45042
Darryl Landwehr (513) 422-5112
5 mi. NW of Middletown
Type: Public/Member
Hrs: W/S/Su, 12-7 (Non-Mmbrs);
T/Th/Su, 10-Dark (Mmbrs)
Sporting: 1, 10 stations
Trap: 20 **Skeet:** 2

Milford Gun Club
400 Marietta Ave.
Terrace Park, OH 45174
Tim Langner (513) 248-0401
15 mi. E of Cincinnati
Type: Public/Member
Hrs: S/Su, 11-5; W, 2-Dark
Sporting: None
Trap: 2 **Skeet:** 2 **Five Stand:** 1

Oak Shade Sport Shooting
16747 County Rd. L
Wauseon, OH 43567
Ann Lange (419) 337-2529
25 mi. W of Toledo
Type: Public/Member
Hrs: M-F, by appt; S/Su, 9-5
Sporting: 2, 16 stations

Ottawa Sporting Clays
Box 327, Port Clinton, OH 43452
Lorie Little (419) 635-2530
50 mi. W of Cleveland
Type: Public
Hrs: W/S/Su, 10-4; Anyday by
reserv. of 8
Sporting: 1, 14 stations **HT:** 40 ft.

The Outback Inc.
PO Box 308, Brinkhaven, OH 43006
Larry Pollard (216) 377-5477

Type: Public/Member
Hrs: W-Su, 10am-7pm
Sporting: 1, 30 stations

Paw Paw Creek
Rt. 2, Box 173C
Lower Salem, OH 45745
Gary Pontius (614) 585-2214
85 mi. SE of Columbus
Type: Public/Member
Hrs: M-F, by appt; S/Su, 9-Dark
Sporting: 2, 48 stations **HT:** 50 ft.

Pheasant Recreation Inc.
18376 London Rd.
Circleville, OH 43113
Jack E. Carpenter (614) 477-1587
25 mi. S of Columbus
Type: Public/Member
Hrs: Year Round
Sporting: 1, 10 stations

Pheasant View Farm
11625 Beloit Snodes Rd.
Beloit, OH 44609
Bob Anderson & Brian Galbraith
(216) 584-6828
55 mi. SE of Cleveland
Type: Public/Member
Hrs: T-F, 9:00-7; S/Su, 9:00-9:00
Reservs: Recommended
Sporting: 3, 32 stations
HT: 75 ft. **Wobble Trap**
o International Trap Field

Portage Sporting Clays
6821 W. Little Portage Rd.
Oak Harbor, OH 43449
Bill O'Neal (419) 732-3209
5 mi. from Port Clinton
Type: Public
Hrs: S/Su, 9-4; other days by appt.
Sporting: 1, 10 stations
Skeet: 5 **HT:** 25 ft.

Ringneck Ridge
1818 Cty. Rd. 74
Gibsonburg, OH 43431
Rick Bowser (419) 637-2332
85 mi. W of Cleveland
Type: Public/Member
Hrs: Su-S, call for reservations
Sporting: 1, 15 stations
Five Stand: 1

Scioto River Hunting Club
17226 St. Rt. 235
Waynesfield, OH 45896
Mary Zirkle (513) 464-6560
60 mi. NW of Columbus
Type: Public **Hrs:** T-Su, 8-Dark
Sporting: 2, 16 stations
Skeet: 1 **HT:** 35 ft.

Shooter's Sporting Clays
2827 Gilbert Ave.

Cincinnati, OH 45206
Jim McHale (513) 961-1454
35 mi. S of Cincinnati
Type: Public/Member
Hrs: S, 9-Dusk; Su, 10-Dusk;
Weekdays by appt. only
Sporting: 2, 20 stations **HT:** 60 ft.

The Shooting Challenge
PO Box 12, Sullivan, OH 44880
Art & Cheryl Lundquist
(419) 736-2529
10 mi. N of Ashland
Type: Public
Hrs: M, 3-9; T, 12-5; W/Th, 12-9;
F, 12-7; S, 8-9
Sporting: 3, 48 stations
Five Stand: 1 **HT:** 35 ft.

Toledo
Trap & Skeet Club
3150 N. Berkey Southern Rd.
Berkey, OH 43504
Jim Fletcher (419) 829-5101
**from State Rt. 295 @ Central
Ave. (US 20)**
Type: Public **Hrs:** T/W, 5-10;
Th/F, 12-10; S/Su, 10-6
Sporting: None
Trap: 4 **Skeet:** 3 **Five Stand:** 1

WR Hunt Club
5690 CR237, Clyde, OH 43410
Robert or Betty Wright
(419) 547-8550
50 mi. W of Cleveland
Type: Public/Member
Hrs: T-Su
Reservs: Strongly recommended
Sporting: 1, 20 stations **HT**

Wrestle Creek
Game Club
23605 Fairmont - CR180
Waynesfield, OH 45896
Jim Hardin (419) 568-2867
12 mi. SE of Lima
Type: Public **Hrs:** Su-S, 9am-6pm
Reservs: Not required
Sporting: 2, 17 stations **Skeet:** 1
o Loaner Guns
o Factory Ammunition
o Organized Leagues
o Golf Carts
o Gunsmith Service

TRAP & SKEET

Adams Conservation Club
39 Derbyshire Rd.
Toledo, OH 43615
Steve Schultz (419) 865-8314
Hrs: S/Su, 12-4
Trap: 4 Skeet: 4

Airport Gun Club
1884 Martinsburg Rd.
Utica, OH 43080
Frank Lanuzza (614) 653-3712
Type: Public
Hrs: W, 3-10; Th, 12-10; S/Su, 10-5
Trap: 9 Skeet: 1 Wobble Trap

Amateur Trapshooting Assn.
601 W. National Rd.
Vandalia, OH 45388
David D. Bopp (513) 898-4638
Type: Member/Avail
Hrs: M-F, 8-4:30 Trap: 100

The Camargo Club
8605 Shawnee Run Rd.
Indian Hill, OH 45243
C. Douglas Postler

Clinton Co. Sportsmen
231 Cedar Woods Dr.
Hillsboro, OH 45133
Thomas Birkhimer/Dave Young
(513) 393-6946
Type: Public/Member
Hrs: Sundays
Trap: 2 Skeet: 2

Coldstream Country Club
400 Asbury Rd.
Cincinnati, OH 45255
Michael J. Haehnle (513) 231-3900
Hrs: S/Su, 9:30-3
Skeet: 1

Columbiana Co. F&G Protect Assn.
20821 #16 School Rd.
Wellsville, OH 43968
David Peterson (216) 532-3253
Type: Public
Hrs: W, 6-10:30; F, 7-10; Su, 12-4
Trap: 4

Erie Skeet Club of Ohio
PO Box 608, Norwalk, OH 44857
Gary Kalizewski (419) 668-5710
Hrs: By appt.
Skeet: 1

Fairfield Sportsmens Assn.
5696 West Fork Rd.
Cincinnati, OH 45247
Charles Wentzel (513) 574-8315
Type: Public/Member
Hrs: Su, 12-5; T, 7pm-9:30pm; F,
7pm-11pm; Su,10-2(Skt)
Trap: 6 Skeet: 2 Olympic Trap
Double Trap Automatic Ball
Trap

Great Eastern Trap Club
PO Box 55, State Rt. 515
Walnut Creek, OH 44687
Sue Kaufman (216) 893-2930
Type: Public
Hrs: Sptg. Clays by appt.
Trap: 10

Greene County Fish & Game Club
PO Box 64, Xenia, OH 45385
Bob Akers
Type: Public/Member
Hrs: Th, 6-11; 1st & 3rd Sun, 12-5
Trap: 4

Greenville Sportsmens Club
906 N. State Line Rd.
Masury, OH 44438
Dick Cameron (412) 588-9994
Hrs: W/S/Su, 10-5
Trap: 1 Skeet: 3

Hambden Orchard Club
8245 Belle Vernon Dr.
Novelty, OH 44072
Henry Vavrick (513) 341-2212
Hrs: S, 10-4
Skeet: 1

Hawthorne Valley Skeet
6090 Cochran Rd.
Solon, OH 44139
John P. Lennon (216) 248-6515
Hrs: Su, (Sept. 1-June 1)
Skeet: 1

Huber Heights Rod & Gun
4210 N. Hyland Ave.
Dayton, OH 45424
Bill Colwell (513) 236-6159
Type: Public/Member
Hrs: F, 6-10; Su, 12-5
Trap: 3

Hunting Valley Gun Club
6090 Cochran Rd.
Solon, OH 44139
John Lennon (216) 246-6515
Hrs: S, 10-4
Skeet: 1

Indian Hill Shooting Club
6053 Sebright Ct.
Cincinnati, OH 45230
Tom Kanis (513) 831-0994
Hrs: S/Su, 12-5; T/Th, 7-10:30
Trap: 1 Skeet: 1

Inidan Hill Shooting Club
6053 Sebright Court
Cincinnati, OH 45230
Tom Kanis (513) 831-0994
Hrs: S/Su, 12-5; T/Th, 7-10:30
Sporting: 1, 10 stations
HT: 15 ft.

JMS Shooting Center
293 Hopewell Dr.
Powell, OH 43065

Mike McGuire (614) 848-3232
3 mi. W of Delaware
Type: Public/Member
Hrs: W, 4-10; S/Su, 10-4
Trap: 5 Skeet: 2 Wobble Trap

Jackson County Trap & Gun
117 North High St.
Jackson, OH 45640
Rick Smith (614) 286-3245
Trap: 1

Jaqua Trap Club
900 E. Bigelow Ave.
Findlay, OH 45840
George Ranzau (419) 422-0912
Hrs: Sat, noon
Trap: 18

Logan County F&GC
4494 Co Rd. 43
Bellefontaine, OH 43311
John Kerr (515) 585-5676
Hrs: Sat. eve. Trap: 4

Lowellville Rod & Gun Club
2515 South Ave.
Youngstown, OH 44502
Ronald F. Lysowski (216) 536-8143
Type: Public/Member
Hrs: Th, 6-10pm Trap: 2

Lynchburg Lions Gun Club
9186 Smarthill Ln. Rd.
Hillsboro, OH 45133
John Condo (513) 764-1314
Hrs: Th, 4:30-10; S, Noon-9
Trap: 2

Mapleton Gun Club
5330 Grandvale St., NE
East Canton, OH 44730
Dale Wardle (216) 488-0682
Type: Public/Member
Hrs: Th, 7pm; S/Su, per reg.
schedules Trap: 5

Mentor Harbor Yacht Club
D5330 Coronado Dr.
Mentor, OH 44124
William Bozarth (216) 951-0155
Hrs: S/Su, 12-5 (Nov-Apr)
Skeet: 1

Mid State Gun Club
1385 Putnam Rd.
Clarksburg, OH 43115
Ed Fulton (614) 998-2103
Type: Public/Member
Hrs: S/Su, 10-8; W/F, eve.
Trap: 2 Skeet: 2

Minerva Sportsman Club
9247 Arrow Rd.
Minerva, OH 44657
Greg Hole (216) 863-1839
Type: Member/Avail
Hrs: S, 5pm-11:30pm (trap shoot
open to public)
Trap: 2

CLAYS

**Mision Guillermo
de Concrecion**
PO Box 672, Norwalk, OH 44875
Bill Newcomer (419) 663-3129
Hrs: S/Su, 2-5
Skeet: 1

Newport Sportsmen Club
6377 SR 66
Fort Loramie, OH 45845
Wally Meyer (513) 295-2579
Type: Public/Member
Hrs: Th, 5-11; S/Su, 9-7
Trap: 5

**Northwest Ohio
International**
Co. Rd. #3 & C
Swanton, OH 43558
Joseph Rusin, M.D. (419) 867-8884

Ohio State Trap Assn.
6010 Opossum Run Rd.
Grove City, OH 43123
Hugh L. McKinley (614) 877-9936
Hrs: 8-6 (during State trap shoot)
Skeet: 52

Paulding Co. F&G Club
PO Box 158, Paulding, OH 45879
Steve Sprow   Trap: 2

Sandhill Skeeters
3883 Sandhill Rd.
Bellevue, OH 44811
Sue Parks (419) 483-2230
Hrs: By appt.
Skeet: 1

Sportsman's Haven Gun Club
14695 E. Pike Rd.
Cambridge, OH 43725
Brent Umberger
Type: Member/Avail
Trap: 1 Skeet: 1

Sportsmen's Shooting Center
1232 Chelmsford St., NW
North Canton, OH 44720
J.E. Doebereiner (216) 875-8081
Hrs: T/Th, 6:30-10:30; Su, 1-5
Trap: 4 Skeet: 8

Urbandale Gun Club
7655 Lakeshore Blvd.
Madison, OH 44057
Helen Cone (216) 298-3200
Trap: 4

Vienna Fish & Game Club
631 N. Turner Rd.
Youngstown, OH 44451
C.D. Jones   Type: Public
Hrs: W/Su, 1-5 Year Round
Trap: 4

Williams County Gun Club
214 N. Platt St.
Montpelier, OH 43543
Rob Heller (419) 485-3176

Type: Public/Member
Hrs: S, 9-2; T, 9-9; F, 6-10
Trap: 3 Skeet: 1

Wright Patterson AFB Rod/Gun
PO Box 752, Fairborn, OH 45324
Ed Hock (513) 257-3935
Type: Member/Avail
Hrs: S/Su, 12-6; W, 2-8
Trap: 5 Skeet: 5

Youngstown Country Club
201 E. Commerce St.
Youngstown, OH 44503
Stephen T. Bolton (216) 759-1040
Hrs: S/Su, 11-4
Trap: 1 Skeet: 2

OKLAHOMA

SPORTING & 5-STAND

ADA Skeet & Trap Club
2504 Kirby Dr.
Ada, OK 74820
Larry Drennan (405) 332-5286
Type: Public/Member
Hrs: Th/S/Su, afternoons
Sporting: None
Trap: 4 Skeet: 4 Five Stand: 1
Wobble Trap

Bartlesville Sportsmen's
PO Box 391, Bartlesville, OK 74005
L.M. Winkler (918) 333-2583
Type: Public/Member
Hrs: M/T/Th, 6:30-9; T/Th/Su;
9-12; S, 8:30-11:30
Sporting: 1, 5 stations
Trap: 1 Skeet: 2

Cedar Creek Sporting Clays
Rt. 1, Box 138A
Geary, OK 73040
Robert Rinehart (405) 884-5530
45 mi. W of Oklahoma City
Type: Public
Hrs: W, 4-Dark; S/Su, 12-Dark
(Summer); Others by appt.
Sporting: 1, 12 stations
Trap: 1

The Cimarron
Junction Land &
Cattle Co. Sporting
Clays
PO Box 50, Ringwood, OK 73768
Timothy J. Crowley (405) 883-4999
120 mi. W of Tulsa
Type: Public
Hrs: S/Su & Holidays, call for hrs.
Reservs: Strongly recommended
Sporting: 1, 12 stations HT: 60 ft.

Melot's Sportsman Club
8900 W. Memorial Rd.
Oklahoma City, OK 73142

Max Melot (405) 721-4394
10 mi. NW of Oklahoma City
Type: Public/Member
Hrs: W/S/Su, 12-7
Sporting: 1, 10 stations

Oklahoma City
Sporting Clays
24-100 North Hiwassee
Arcadia, OK 73007
Jim & Bobbie Jolly (405) 396-2661
10 mi. NE of Oklahoma City
Type: Public/Member
Hrs: W-S, 9-Dark; Su, 10-Dark
Reservs: Recommended
Sporting: 1, 20 stations
Five Stand: 1   HT: 40 ft.

Shawnee Twin Lakes Trap
& Sporting Clays
704 SW 27th
Moore, OK 73160
Tom Batt (405) 793-9021
10 mi. W of Shawnee
Type: Public/Member
Hrs: Th, 5:30-9; S, 12-5; Scheduled
Sun. Shoots
Sporting: 1, 10 stations
Trap: 4

Southern Ranch Hunting
Rt. 2, Box 75, Chandler, OK 74834
Dean Caton (918) 377-4226
45 mi. NE of Oklahoma City
Type: Public/Member
Hrs: W/S/Su, 9-5 (W); Daily, 9-6 (S)
Sporting: 2, 24 stations
Five Stand: 1   HT: 50 ft.
Wobble Trap

Wichita Mountains
Sporting Clays
Rt. 2, Box 85,
Geronimo, OK 73543
Shelby Kervin (405) 248-1947
Hrs: S, 10-6; Su, Noon-6; Wkdays
by appt.
Sporting: 1

Woods & Water
Rt. 1, Box 319
Catoosa, OK 74015
Doug Fuller (918) 266-5551
6.5 mi. E of Tulsa
Type: Public/Member
Hrs: W-Su, 12-Sunset; S, 9-Sunset
Reservs: Not required
Sporting: 1, 13 stations
Five Stand: 1   HT: 60 ft.
Wobble Trap
See Our Ad Pg. 471

TRAP & SKEET

Bird Island Gun Club
2042 The Coves
Afton, OK 74331
M. Kinderman (918) 782-2722
Hrs: W/S/Su, 1-4
Trap: 1 Skeet: 1

Comanche Skeet & Trap
1010 NW 75th
Lawton, OK 73505
Frank Hays (405) 353-2540
Hrs: S/Su, 12-6; W, 4-6:30
Trap: 1 Skeet: 5

Enid Elks Gun Club
PO Box 3791, Enid, OK 73702
Darrell Scott (405) 874-2551
Hrs: W, 7-11; Su, 1-6
Trap: 4

Hobart Gun Club
Rt. 2, Box 14, Hobart, OK 73651
Brent Hancock (405) 726-5240
Hrs: Su, 1-6
Trap: 1 Skeet: 2

O.T.A. Shooting Park
Rt. 2, Box 162AA
El Reno, OK 73036
Kenneth Jantzen (405) 422-4111
20 mi. W of Oklahoma City
Type: Public
Hrs: T/Th, 4-10; W/S/Su, 12-7
Trap: 18 Skeet: 8

Oil Capital Rod & Gun Club
6225 E. 24th St.
Tulsa, OK 74114
H.D. Conklin (918) 835-3379
Type: Public/Member
Hrs: Th/S/Su, 1:30-Evening
Trap: 4 Skeet: 5

Oklahoma City Gun Club
609 N. Juniper Ave.
Midwest City, OK 73130
James Hansen
Hrs: Su, 8:30-1; 2nd & 4th Sat., 9-1
Trap: 1 Skeet: 2

Sooner Skeet Club
308 Country Lane
Midwest City, OK 73130
Charlie Duncan
Hrs: Upon request
Skeet: 1

Tahlequah Gun Club
Rt. 3, Box 784
Tahlequah, OK 74464
Hal C. Sammons (918) 456-4749
Hrs: Registered Shoot Dates Only
Trap: 4

Tulsa Gun Club
PO Box 580411, Tulsa, OK 74158
Harold W. Radke, Jr.
(918) 272-0262
Hrs: S/Su/W/F, 1-6
Trap: 5 Skeet: 4

OREGON

SPORTING & 5-STAND

B&B Clay Sports
PO Box 1686
Klamath Falls, OR 97601
David Bleha (503) 892-0352
6 mi. W of Klamath Falls
Hrs: S/Su, 12-Dark
Sporting: 1, 12 stations
Trap: 1 Skeet: 2

Cottage Grove-Eugene
81078 N. Pacific Hwy.
Cresswell, OR 97426
Gary (503) 942-2021
110 mi. S of Portland
Type: Public/Member
Hrs: T, 5-11; Su, 9-5
Sporting: 1, 10 stations
Trap: 13 Skeet: 2 HT: 35 ft.

Great Basin Game Birds
PO Box 575, Burns, OR 97720
Lance Okeson (800) 646-0058
95 mi. SE of Portland
Type: Public/Member
Sporting: 1, 10 stations

Great Expectations Hunting Preserve
HC82, Box 234
Kimberly, OR 97848
Jerry Russell (503) 934-2117
70 mi. NW of John Day
Type: Public/Member
Hrs: Aug. 1-March 31;
Daylight to Dark
Reservs: Strongly recommended
Sporting: 1, 12 stations
See Our Ad Pg. 353

Hulse Pheasant & Sporting Clay Ranch
60277 Tygh Ridge Rd.
Dufur, OR 97021
Mike & Debbie Hulse
(503) 467-2513
100 mi. E of Portland
Type: Public
Hrs: Daily, Dawn-Dusk
Reservs: Strongly recommended
Sporting: 1, 10 stations

JCSA Trap & Skeet Club
7407 Highland Ave.
Grants Pass, OR 97526
Ron Tripp (503) 476-2040
Sporting: None
Trap: 1 **Skeet:** 4 **Five Stand:** 1

Jefferson State Shooting
2057 Gettle St.
Klamath Falls, OR 97603
John Juniel (503) 882-0944
235 mi. S of Portland
Type: Public **Hrs:** April-Sept.
Sporting: 1, 10 stations
Five Stand: 1

Josephine County Sporting
7407 Highland Ave. (I-5)
Grants Pass, OR 97526
Ronald Tripp (503) 476-2040
320 mi. S of Portland
Type: Public/Member
Hrs: Su-S, 8-Dark

Sporting: 1, 5 stations
Trap: 1 **Skeet:** 4 **HT:** 25 ft.
Wobble Trap

Muddy Creek Sporting Club
29499 Buchanan Rd.
Corvallis, OR 97333
Don Hamblin (503) 753-9679
22 mi. N of Eugene
Type: Public/Member
Hrs: By Appointment
Reservs: Strongly recommended
Sporting: 1, 34 stations
Skeet: 1 **Five Stand:** 2   HT: 72 ft.
○ Factory Ammunition
○ Certified Shooting Instructors
○ Corporate Shoots/Catering
  Available
○ Night Shooting
○ 3 High Towers/Innovative Target
  Presentation

Noble Sporting Adventures
Rt. 2, Box 185-X
Milton-Freewater, OR 97862
Don Noble (503) 558-3675
235 mi. E of Portland
Type: Public **Hrs:** Year Round
Sporting: 1, 10 stations

Pheasant Ridge, Inc.
80420 Ross Rd.
Tygh Valley, OR 97063
Steve Pierce (503) 544-2183
120 mi. E of Portland
Type: Public/Member
Hrs: M-Su, 9-6, by resv. only
Sporting: 3, 27 stations
Skeet: 1   HT **Wobble Trap**

R&M Game Birds
Hood River, OR
Rodger Ford (509) 365-3245
80 mi. E of Vancouver, WA
Type: Public
Hrs: Year round, daylight-dark
Sporting: 1, 15 stations **HT:** 85 ft.

Salem Trap & Skeet Club
6181 Concomly Rd, NE
Jervais, OR 97026
Bill Lacefield (503) 792-3431
10 mi. N of Salem
Type: Public/Member
Hrs: W/Th, 12-9; F, 12-6; S/Su, 9-6
Sporting: 1, 13 stations
Trap: 22 **Skeet:** 6

Snake River Sportsmen
PO Box 1028
Ontario, OR 97914
Gary McClellan (503) 889-9232
50 mi. NW of Boise
Type: Public/Member
Hrs: Th, 5:30-dark; Su, 1-dark

Sporting: 1, 15 stations
Trap: 4 **Skeet:** 1 **HT:** 50 ft.
Wobble Trap

TREO Ranches
Rt. 1, Box 3171
Heppner, OR 97836
Phil Carlson (503) 676-5840
180 mi. E of Portland
Type: Public
Hrs: Daily by appt.
Reservs: Strongly recommended
Sporting: 1, 8 stations
See Our Ad Pg. 355

Tri-County Gun Club
13050 S.W. Tonquin Rd.
Sherwood, OR 97140
Joseph J. Dunn (503) 625-7318
18 mi. S of Portland
Type: Public/Member
Hrs: Su, 11-4; T/Th, 6:30-9:30
Reservs: Not required
Sporting: 1, 14 stations   **Trap:** 4
Skeet: 2 **Five Stand:** 1   **Wobble**
Trap   Automatic Ball Trap

TRAP & SKEET

Baker Trap Club
Baker, OR 97814
Ken Dunleavy (503) 523-6415
Type: Public/Member
Hrs: Th, 7-11pm   **Trap:** 4

Hillsboro Trap & Skeet
33295 NW Wren Rd.
Hillsboro, OR 97123
Linda Lorence (503) 648-2972

Willamette Valley Sportsmens
Box 14, Corvallis, OR 97339
James I. Harris (503) 752-8491
Hrs: S/Su, 12-5; T/Th, 5:30
Skeet: 3

PENNSYLVANIA

SPORTING & 5-STAND

All Seasons T&S Club
PO Box 787, DuBois, PA 15801
Fred Frantz (814) 583-5732
7 mi. SE of DuBois
Type: Public
Hrs: Su, 9-4; Wed. evenings, 5:30-8
Sporting: 2, 20 stations
Trap: 2 **Skeet:** 2   **HT:** 40 ft.

Angus Conservation & Hunting Farms
RD#1, Box 260
Latrobe, PA 15650

Jay Angus (412) 423-4022
35 mi. E of Pittsburgh
Type: Public/Member
Sporting: 1 **Trap:** Y **Skeet:** Y

Atglen Sportsmen's Club
PO Box 35, Parkesburg, PA 19365
Rick Beck (610) 286-5681
15 mi. E of Lancaster
Type: Public/Member
Hrs: W, 6pm-9pm; Su, 10-4 on the
1st, 3rd & 5th Sun.
Sporting: 1, 24 stations **HT:** 28 ft.

Big Pine Hunting Club
PO Box 45, Prompton, PA 18456
George Rabtzow (908) 362-9008
20 mi. NE of Scranton
Type: Public/Member
Hrs: Week Ends by Appt.
Sporting: 1

**Mr. Britt's Game Farm &
Sporting Clays**
PO Box 925, RD2
Homer City, PA 15748
John A. Boris (412) 479-9813
45 mi. E of Pittsburgh
Type: Public/Member
Hrs: M-S, 9am-Dusk; Su, 10am-Dusk
Sporting: 1, 15 stations **HT:** 40 ft.

The Busted Flush

RD#3, Shreve Rd., Box 57
Titusville, PA 16354
Jim Berry/Ken Mulford
(814) 827-4030
80 mi. N of Pittsburgh
Type: Public/Member
Hrs: M-F, by appt; S/Su, 9-dark
Reservs: Recommended
Sporting: 1, 18 stations
HT: 30 ft.
O Loaner Guns
O Factory Ammunition
O On-Site Meals
O Formal Instructions
O Organized Leagues

Cacoosing
Gun Club

PO Box 293, Birdsboro, PA 19508
Jack Babb (610) 856-1453
5 mi. SE of Reading
Type: Public/Member
Hrs: W, 9-2; Th, 3-Dark; S, 9-4; Su,
8:30-Dark
Reservs: Not required
Sporting: 1, 12 stations
Trap: 1 **Skeet:** 2   **HT:** 50 ft.
Wobble Trap

Carlisle Fish & Game Assoc.
Box 157, Rt. 641
Carlisle, PA 17013

Ben Barrouk (717) 938-2043
10 mi. SW of Harrisburg
Type: Public/Member
Hrs: S, 9-3
Sporting: 1, 25 stations
Trap: 5 **Skeet:** 2

Castlewood Rod & Gun
PO Box 7411
New Castle, PA 16101
Robert Saunders (412) 924-9010
5 mi. E of New Castle
Type: Public **Hrs:** Su, 9-4
Sporting: 1, 18 stations
Trap: 2   **HT:** 30 ft.

Chestnut Ridge
RD 6, Box 310-6
Latrobe, PA 15650
Mike Mahady (412) 539-2070
35 mi. E of Pittsburgh
Type: Public/Member
Hrs: S/Su, 9-5
Sporting: 2, 35 stations
Skeet: 2   **HT:** 60 ft.

Country Clays
2071 Baus Rd.
E. Greenville, PA 18041
Joe Andreoli (215) 679-6181
39 mi. NW of Philadelphia
Type: Public **Hrs:** T-Su, 9-Dark
Sporting: 1, 22 stations
Trap: 1 **Skeet:** 1

Critter Path Sporting Clays
3191 Wheelertown Rd.
Waterford, PA 16441
Mike Wise (814) 796-2658
12 mi. S of Erie
Type: Public
Hrs: S/Su, 9-5; Wkdys by appt
Sporting: 1, 12 stations **HT:** 20 ft.

Eagle Mountain
Box 4086, Williamsport, PA 17701
Mark P. Palmer (717) 327-9275
.5 mi. W of Williamsport
Type: Public **Hrs:** By resrv.
Sporting: 1, 14 stations
HT: 25 ft.

CLAYS

Elstonville Sportsmen
3133 Pinch Rd.
Manheim, PA 17545
Brad Deppen (717) 665-6354
20 mi. N of Lancaster
Type: Public/Member
Hrs: W, 4-9; Su, 9-3; Trap, Th, 5-9
Sporting: 1, 12 stations
Trap: 3 HT: 20 ft.

Endless Mountains
RD#2, Box 55
Montrose, PA 18801
Jeff Scavazzo (717) 553-2659
18 mi. S of Binghamton
Type: Public/Member
Hrs: M-F, 12-Dark; S/Su, 10-5
Sporting: 1, 12 stations

Factoryville
Sportsmen's Club
PO Box 331
Factoryville, PA 18419
Wade Stackhouse (717) 836-4350
15 mi. NW of Scranton
Type: Public/Member
Hrs: W, 4pm-Dusk (summer); S/Su, 9am-Dusk
Reservs: Not required
Sporting: 1, 26 stations
Trap: 2 Five Stand: 1 HT: 30 ft.
○ Factory Ammunition
○ On-Site Meals
○ Organized Leagues
○ Golf Carts
○ Shooting Lodge/Clubhouse
○ Handicap Accessible
○ Clubhouse Phone: (717) 378-2593
○ Call (717) 378-CLUB for Upcoming Events
○ Just 1 hr. from Rt. 80/Delaware Water Gap

Forest Hill Sporting Club
RD#2, Box 389
Mifflinburg, PA 17844
John B. Punako (717) 966-9419
35 mi. NW of Harrisburg
Type: Public
Hrs: Su-S, by appt.
Sporting: 1, 10 stations
Skeet: 1 Five Stand: 1 HT: 20 ft. Wobble Trap

Greater
Pittsburgh
Gun Club
RD1. Bulger, PA 15019
Tex Freund (412) 796-9111
18 mi. W of Pittsburgh
Type: Public/Member
Hrs: W/Th, 6-10; S/Su, 10-6 & Appt.

Reservs: Recommended
Sporting: 2, 15 stations
Trap: 4 Skeet: 3

Hillside
Hunting Preserve &
Sporting Clays
PO Box 56, Berlin, PA 15530
James Scurfield (814) 267-4484
60 mi. SE of Pittsburgh
Type: Public/Member
Hrs: Su-S, til dark (closed Mon)
Reservs: Recommended
Sporting: 4, 100 stations
Trap: 1 HT Wobble Trap
○ Loaner Guns
○ Factory Ammunition
○ On-Site Pro Shop
○ On-Site Meals
○ Shooting Lodge
○ Organized Leagues
○ Golf Carts
See Our Ad Pg. 473

Hollidaysburg Sportsmen's
RD#2, Box 259, Tyrone, PA 16686
Jimmie Miller (814) 742-8784
75 mi. E of Pittsburgh
Type: Public
Hrs: Th, evenings; Su
Sporting: 2, 10 stations
Trap: 1 Skeet: 6 Five Stand: 2
HT: 65 ft.

Indian Run Country
Rt. 2, Centerville, PA 16404
Dave Stutzman (814) 967-2635
85 mi. N of Pittsburg
Type: Public/Member
Sporting: 1

JDZ Game Farm
RD#2, Box 75
Watsontown, PA 17777
John Zaktansky (717) 649-5881
70 mi. SW of Scranton
Type: Public/Member
Hrs: Sept. thru April, no Sundays
Sporting: 1, 5 stations

Langhorne Rod & Gun Club
909 Bristol Pk., Apt. F6
Croydon, PA 19021
Vincent G. Tomes, III
(215) 968-9973
Type: Public/Member
Hrs: Th, 6-10; ATA Shoots
Sporting: None
Trap: 4 Five Stand: 1
Wobble Trap

Lappawinzo Fish & Game
12 Redwood Dr.
Northampton, PA 18067
Andrew J. Hensel, Jr.
(610) 262-9904

7 mi. N of Allentown
Type: Public/Member
Hrs: Year Round, 9-Dark; Reserv.
for sptg. clays
Sporting: 1, 12 stations
Trap: 6 Skeet: 2

Laurel Springs
Hunt-Fishing Club
RD#2, Box 162
Rockwood, PA 15557
Richard Sager (814) 352-8803
60 mi. SE of Pittsburgh
Type: Public/Member, Member/Avail
Hrs: Daily 8-dusk; closed Tu
Reservs: Recommended
Sporting: 1, 18 stations
Trap: 1 Skeet: 1 HT: 75 ft.
○ Loaner Guns
○ On-Site Meals
○ Shooting Lodge
○ NSCA Certified Instructor
○ 5 Minutes from Seven Springs Resort

Lawrence Co. Sportsmen's
RD3, Harbor Rd.
New Castle, PA 16105
Scott Rennie (412) 652-9260
Hrs: Su, 12-4; Th eve.
Sporting: 1, 10 stations
Trap: 1 Skeet: 3 Five Stand: 1

Lehigh Valley Sporting Clays
2750 Limestone St.
Coplay, PA 18037
Fred Durham, III (610) 261-9616
4 mi. N of Allentown
Type: Public
Hrs: W/Th/F, 10:30-Dk; S/Su, 9-Dk
Sporting: 1, 15 stations
Five Stand: 1

Martz's Gap View
RR#1, Box 85, Dalmatia, PA 17017
Don Martz (800) 326-8442
38 mi. N of Harrisburg
Type: Public Hrs: M-S, 8-5
Sporting: 1, 9 stations
Wobble Trap

McCrea's
Sporting Clays
155 Hays Road,
Fenelton, PA 16034
Joe McCrea (412) 445-3855
40 mi. N of Pittsburgh
Type: Public
Hrs: S-Su, 9-5; weekdays by app't
Reservs: Not required
Sporting: 1, 29 stations
HT: 35 ft.

**Game Bird
Hunting
September
thru April.**

THE WARRINGTON CLUB

- Comfortable facilities with a gracious atmosphere.
- Complete pro shop.
- Located two hour drive from Philadelphia and Washington D.C.

Discover

The

SPORTING CLAYS

- Well balanced and challenging course.
- Beautifully landscaped.
- Certified class II instructor for beginners and those who wish to improve their skills.

Oley Valley Fish & Game
PO Box 257, Oley, PA 19547
Donald Hoffman (610) 779-1317
6 mi. E of Redding
Type: Public/Member
Hrs: Clays–Tues & every 4th Sun;
TR/SK, Wed. eve.
Sporting: 1, 12 stations
Trap: 2 **Skeet:** 1

PAL Sporting Clays
524 Main St., #105
Honesdale, PA 18431
Robert K. Pierce (914) 763-5117
Sporting:

Pinewood Hunter Clays
Box 436, RD3
Kutztown, PA 19530
Jack Herbein (610) 683-5232
40 mi. NW of Philadelphia
Type: Public/Member
Hrs: Su-S, by appt. only
Sporting: 3, 45 stations
Five Stand: 1   **HT:** 100 ft.

The Preserve
& Shooting School
Rt. 209 S. (Box 1325)
Milford, PA 18337
Neil Chadwick (717) 296-2354
75 mi. W of New York City
Type: Public/Member
Hrs: M/W/Th/F, 10-Dk; S/Su, 9-Dk
Reservs: Recommended
Sporting: 3, 12 stations
Shooting Instruction
Available - See Pg. 176

Reading Regulated
Hunting &
Sporting Clays
RD1, Box 220A
Birdsboro, PA 19508
Buzzy Williams (610) 856-7671
42 mi. NW of Philadelphia
Type: Public **Hrs:** Su-S
Reservs: Strongly recommended
Sporting: 1, 30 stations
Trap: 1   **HT:** 50 ft.
o Factory Ammunition
o Shooting Lodge
o Golf Carts

Rock Ridge Hunting Pre-
serve & Game Farm
RD#3, Box 77M
Pine Grove, PA 17963
Gregory Fedechko (717) 345-8900
50 mi. NE of Harrisburg
Type: Public **Sporting:** 1, 13 sta.

Rolfe Beagle Club
HC 2, Box 83
Portland Mills, PA 15853
L.H. Goephert (814) 772-4322
130 mi. NE of Pittsburgh
Type: Public, Public/Member
Hrs: Su for Sporting Clays only
Sporting: 1, 8 stations
Trap: 1 **Skeet:** 1

Rural Sportsmens Assn.
1090 South Rt. 100
Trexlertown, PA 18087
Arthur Nevin (215) 536-7835
40 mi. NW of Philadelphia
Type: Public
Hrs: S/Su, 12-5; others by appt.
Sporting: 1, 5 stations
Trap: 5 **Skeet:** 3 **Five Stand:** 1
HT: 20 ft.

Shenecoy Sportsmen
PO Box 75,
McConnelstown, PA 16660
Mark A. Kane (814) 627-4003
4 mi. S of Huntingdon
Type: Public/Member
Hrs: Su, 10-5 (Sk & Tr); Sptg. Clays,
One Sunday/month
Sporting: 1, 10 stations
Trap: 2 **Skeet:** 16

Sporting Clays at Pip Inn
HC6, Box 6474, Blooming Grove Rd.
Blooming Grove, PA 18428
Larry Erdman (717) 665-7003
20 mi. W of Milford
Type: Public **Hrs:** F/S/Su, 9-5
Sporting: 1, 20 stations
Five Stand: 1   **HT:** 35 ft.

Spruce Hollow
Hunting Farms, Ltd.
RD#2, Box 353
Kunkletown, PA 18058
Junie & Cindy Kuehner
(610) 826-5134
70 mi. NE of Philadelphia
Type: Public
Hrs: 7 days a week by appt.
Reservs: Strongly recommended
Sporting: 1, 11 stations

Sunset Hill Shooting Range
RD#1, Box 59,
Henryville, PA 18332
Anton Bonifacic, Jr.
(717) 629-3981
80 mi. N of Philadelphia

Type: Public
Hrs: All year, 10-5
Sporting: 1 **Trap:** 1

Susquehanna Valley
Box 8, RD2, McClure, PA 17841
S. Kirby Bubb or Todd Musser
(800) 338-7389
20 mi. S of Lewistown
Type: Public
Hrs: M/T/Th, 10-4; S, 9-4
Sporting: 1, 20 stations

TNT Shooting Grounds
PO Box 236,
Waltersburg, PA 15488
Thomas Stewart (412) 677-2609
40 mi. S of Pittsburgh
Type: Public/Member
Hrs: Su-S, 8am-Dark
Sporting: 1, 20 stations

Thunder Ridge Sporting Clays
Cummings Creek Rd., RD#2
Lawrenceville, PA 16929
Bill Appel (717) 827-2529
20 mi. SE of Corning, NY
Type: Public/Member
Hrs: W/S/Su, 8am-Dusk
Sporting: 2, 17 stations
HT: 35 ft.

Thundering Pines
RD3, Box 15B
Shelocta, PA 15774
Ron Anthony (412) 726-5140
8 mi. W of Indiana, PA
Type: Public/Member
Hrs: Su-S, 9-5; Reserv. required M-F
Sporting: 2, 40 stations   **HT:** 80 ft.

Timberline
Sporting Clays
3725 Warmspring Rd.
(PO Box 203)
Chambersburg, PA 17201
Harold L. Cover, Jr. (717) 369-3966
60 mi. S of Harrisburg
Type: Public/Member
Hrs: Su, 8:30-3:30
Reservs: Not required
Sporting: 1, 12 stations
Trap: 4
o Less than 15 minutes from
  Exit 6, I-81

The Warrington Club
400 Yeager Rd.
Wellsville, PA 17365
Reservations (717) 741-7214
15 mi. S of Harrisburg
Type: Member/Avail
Hrs: Daily Except Sunday,
8-Dark - Year Round
Reservs: Recommended
Sporting: 1, 7 stations
Trap: 1 **Skeet:** 1
○ 100 miles north of Washington, DC
○ Alt. Phone: (717) 432-0643 - Terry Laird
○ Beautiful Grounds - 3 Towers
○ Class II Instruction Available

See Our Ad Pg. 475

**Warriors Mark
Shooting Preserve**
RD1, Box 464
Warriors Mark, PA 16877
Eric Gilliland (814) 632-6680
18 mi. SW of State College
Type: Public/Member
Hrs: M, by appt; T-Th, 12-7; F-Su, 9-7
Sporting: 5, 25 stations
Trap: Y **Skeet:** Y **Five Stand:** Y
HT: 40 ft.

**Western Penn.
Sportsmen's Club**
5730 Saltsburg Rd.
Murrysville, PA 15668
Al Crookston (412) 327-9918
Hrs: Th, 5:30-10; S, 10-2;
Sporting: 1, 13 stations
Trap: 9

TRAP & SKEET

7-H Skeet Club
RD1, Box 51, Patton, PA 16668
Roy Holtz (814) 674-8241
Hrs: W/F, 7:30-9:30
Trap: 1 **Skeet:** 4

B&L Skeet Club
RD#3, New Bethlehem, PA 16242
Darl L. Emings (814) 275-1111
Hrs: T, 6 **Skeet:** 3

Bradford Gun Club
PO Box 381, Bradford, PA 16701
Mike Schuler (814) 368-6245
Hrs: W, 5-8:30; Su, Noon-5
Trap: 8

Bucks County Fish & Game
Turk Rd., Doylestown, PA
Edward S. Yanchok
(908) 753-2365
Type: Public/Member
Hrs: 3rd & 4th Sunday, 11-5
Trap: 8

Clairton Sportsmen's Club
412 Coal Valley Rd.
Clairton, PA 15025
Ed Stanton (412) 233-4411
Hrs: W, 6:30-9:30
Trap: 8 **Skeet:** Y

Cocalico Sportsman Assn.
1000 Thompson Ave.
Annville, PA 17003
Larry Smith (717) 336-2997
Hrs: W, 5-9; S/Su, 12-4
Trap: 3 **Skeet:** 2

Delaware Co. Field & Stream
7310 Malvern Ave.
Philadelphia, PA 19151
Barry Greenberg (610) 872-9728
Hrs: 9-Sunset
Trap: 5 **Skeet:** 3

**Delaware County
Sportsmens Assn.**
168 Fox Rd., Media, PA 19063
Nino Campagna (215) 676-6585
Type: Public
Hrs: 2nd, 4th & 5th Sundays, Wed. eve., April-Sept.
Trap: 5

Erie Skeet Club of PA
1215 E. 31st, Erie, PA 16504
Brad Gregory (814) 838-3601
Hrs: W, 5-10; S, 12-5; Su, 9-2:30
Trap: 1 **Skeet:** 3

Fayette Gun Club
PO Box 295, Uniontown, PA 15401
Richard Barron (412) 438-9126
Type: Public/Member
Hrs: Su, 1-5; W, 6-9 (Summer)
Trap: 8 **Skeet:** 1

Ford City SA
RD2, Box 186, Ford City, PA 16226
John C. Novak (214) 763-3136
Type: Public
Hrs: W, 12-4; F, 6-11
Trap: 2

Greater Jackson Sptsmn.
RD#1, Box 450
Mineral Point, PA 15942
Terry L. Crouse (814) 749-9773
Type: Public
Hrs: T, 5:30-11 (Apr-Sept); Su, 1-5 (Oct-Mar) **Trap:** 4

Greencastle Sportsman's Assn.
Box 193, Greencastle, PA 17225
Joe Carbaugh (717) 597-7280
60 mi. SW of Harrisburg

Type: Public/Member
Hrs: F, 6:30-9:30 & scheduled
shoots **Trap:** 5

Harrisburg Hunters & Anglers
6611 Hunters Run Rd.
Harrisburg, PA 17111
George Miller (717) 545-6834
Hrs: Sunrise to Sunset
Trap: 2 **Skeet:** 2

Hegins Trap Club
819 Chestnut St.
Hegins, PA 17938
Wayne C. Stutzman
(610) 682-9577
Type: Public
Hrs: S, 12-5; 1 Sun. per mo.
Trap: 4

Irem Temple Gun Club
RD5 Country Club Rd.
Dallas, PA 18612
Alan Mellner (717) 675-1134
Type: Public/Member
Hrs: 2nd & 4th Sun., 12-5
Trap: 2

Keystone Sportsmen Assn.
311 Lyons Ave.
Williamsport, PA 17701
Roy H. Belcher, III (717) 546-5779
Hrs: Th, 5-10 **Trap:** 5

Library Sportsmens Assn.
RR1, Box 84B
Finleyville, PA 15332
Arthur Benevento (412) 835-9822
Hrs: 9-1 **Trap:** 5 **Skeet:** 2

Lower Providence R&G Club
PO Box 12, Phoenixville, PA 19460
A. Gazzillo (610) 666-9934
Hrs: F, 5-10; 3rd & 5th Sun, 11
Trap: 4

Mahonig Sportsmen Assoc.
Rt. 224, Hillsville, PA 16132
James Gardella (412) 667-7855
Trap: 2

Meadville Sportsman's Club
789 Williamson Rd.
Meadville, PA 16335
Jeff McNany (814) 336-4240
Hrs: Su, 1-4; W, 6-9
Trap: 2 **Skeet:** 2

Millvale Sportsmens Club
170 Sunnyhill Rd.
Wexvord, PA 15090
Karl Borgman (412) 935-9963
Hrs: W, Eve; Su, Afternoons
Trap: 4

New Holland Rod & Gun
59 Blaine Ave., Leola, PA 17540
Franklin D. Bair (717) 354-7814
Type: Public/Member
Hrs: 1st Sat. of month, 11-3
Trap: 5

CLAYS

North End Rod & Gun Club
6401 Schantz Rd.
Allentown, PA 18104
Freeman Kline, Jr. (610) 395-0140
Type: Public
Hrs: Fri. nights practice; Registered
shoots   **Trap:** 7

Northside Sportsmans Assn.
Mt. Pleasant Rd.
Warrendale, PA 15086
Jim Mandera (412) 935-9884
Type: Public/Member
Hrs: W, 6-11pm; Su, 10-3
Trap: Y **Skeet:** Y

Northumberland Point Twp. SA
RD2, Northumberland, PA 17857
Neil Mertz (717) 473-3272
Hrs: W, Eve.   **Trap:** 8 **Skeet:** Y

Ontelaunee Rod & Gun
PO Box 134, Lykens, PA 17048
Allen Chubb, Jr. (717) 453-7245
Olympic Trap

Oxford Gun Club
Box 222, Nottingham, PA 19362
Ted Wallace (610) 932-9213
Type: Public **Hrs:** Th, 5:30pm
Trap: 5

Paradise Shooting Center
Box 188, Rt. 940 East
Cresco, PA 18236
Joe Harrington (717) 595-3660
Hrs: M-S, 10-5; Su, 12-5
Trap: 2 **Skeet:** 2

Philipsburg Rod & Gun
102 Windsor St.,
Philipsburg, PA 16866
Ned Holdren (814) 342-3225
Type: Public
Hrs: W, 6-10 (Apr-Nov); Su, 1-5
Trap: 5   **Wobble Trap**
Automatic Ball Trap

Pocono-Slate Belt Shooting
RD1, Box 1420
Bangor, PA 18013
Stanley T. Miller (610) 588-4970
Hrs: Th, 4-8   **Trap:** 6

Richland Shotgun Club
3838 Shepard Rd.
Gibsonia, PA 15044
Raymond W. Russ (814) 498-2708
Type: Public **Hrs:** S/Su, 9-Dark
Trap: 1

Rosedale Sportsmen's Assn.
211 Glenfield Dr.
Pittsburgh, PA 15235
William D. Straub (412) 274-6686

Hrs: 1st Sat. of month; Th, 2-10
Trap: 4 **Skeet:** 3

Sandy Lake Sportsmans
118 Cole Rd.,
Sandy Lake, PA 16145
Carl Johnson (412) 376-3129
Hrs: W, 5-8 (Apr-Oct); S, 12-2;
Su, 10-1 **Skeet:** 3

Sewickley Heights Gun Club
400 Morgan Center
Butler, PA 16001
Timothy J. Cowan (412) 741-6160
Hrs: Weekends only
Trap: 1 **Skeet:** 2

South End Gun Club
205 Schweitz Rd.
Fleetwood, PA 19522
Richard Hamilton (610) 682-6647
Type: Public
Hrs: Every Wed. morn; ATA 2nd &
4th Sun., Mar-Oct **Trap:** 12

The Spruce Hollow Club
Box 4296, RD#4
Pottsville, PA 17901
Sheldon Gitman (717) 385-2975
Olympic Trap Double Trap

Tarentum Dist.Sportsmens
120 Crescent Hill Dr.
Sarver, PA 16055
Paul McConville
Hrs: Su-Th, 5:30-9; S, 1:30-3; (Win)
S/Su, 1:30-3
Trap: 2 **Skeet:** 3

Valley Gun & Country Club
PO Box 327, Elysburg, PA 17824
Andrew C. Long (717) 672-3130
Trap: 48

Valleyview Gun Club
RD2, Box 162N, Boyers, PA 16020
Don or Tony Mahafkey
(412) 776-2106
Hrs: ATA Every S/Su, 10-5
Trap: 4

Victory Hill Gun Club
124 Erivest Ave.
Monongahela, PA 15063
Frank Hillman (412) 258-9871
Type: Public/Member
Hrs: T, 6-11
Trap: 5   **Wobble Trap**

Washington Sportsman's Assn.
15 Wabash Ave.,
Morgan, PA 15064
Francis V. Kosmacki, III
(412) 222-0651
Hrs: Th, 6-11   **Trap:** 5 **Skeet:** 2

RHODE ISLAND

SPORTING & 5-STAND

Addieville East Farm
200 Pheasant Dr.
Mapleville, RI 02839
Geoff Gaebe (401) 568-3185
20 mi. N of Providence
Type: Public/Member
Hrs: Su-S, 7am-Dark
Reservs: Recommended
Sporting: 3, 55 stations
HT: 105 ft.
○ Loaner Guns
○ Factory Ammunition
○ FAX: (401) 568-3009

Peace Dale
441 Rose Hill Rd.
Peace Dale, RI 02879
Richie Frisella (401) 789-3730
20 mi. S of Providence
Type: Public **Hrs:** Su-S, 9-dusk
Sporting: 6, 150 stations **HT:** 40'

Wallum Lake Rod & Gun
200 Brook Rd., Harrisville, RI 02830
Paul Fetschke (401) 568-7171
Type: Public/Member
Hrs: S/Su, Noon 'til dark;
Weekdays by reserv.
Sporting: 2
Trap: 9 **Skeet:** 2 **Five Stand:** 1

SOUTH CAROLINA

SPORTING & 5-STAND

Back 40 Wing & Clay
4671 Timrod Rd.,
Bethune, SC 29009
Grady Roscoe (803) 475-4408
53 mi. NE of Columbia
Type: Public/Member
Hrs: M-Su, 8-Sundown
Reservs: Recommended
Sporting: 2, 20 stations
Wobble Trap
○ One of the Best Courses in the
Southeast!
○ Special Weekend

Camping/Shooting/Fishing Packages
O Just 49 miles east of I-77
O 25 miles from I-20
O Major Credit Cards Accepted

Back Woods
Quail Club
Rt. 3, Box 253F
Georgetown, SC 29440
Dave Lemmen (803) 546-1466
20 mi. W of Georgetown/Myrtle Beach
Type: Public/Member
Hrs: Open 7 days/week; 7am-dark
Reservs: Recommended
Sporting: 1, 15 stations
Trap: 2 **Skeet:** 2 **Five Stand:** 1
O Loaner Guns
O Factory Ammunition
O On-Site Pro Shop
O Shooting Lodge
O Organized Leagues
O Lighted trap, skeet & 5-stand fields

Bostick Plantation
PO Box 728, Estill, SC 29918
Joe Bostick (803) 625-4512
50 mi. N of Savannah, GA
Type: Public **Hrs:**
Sporting: 1

Boykin Mill Sporting Clays
73 Boykin Mill Rd.
Boykin, SC 29128
Whit Boykin (803) 424-4731
6 mi. S of Camden
Type: Public/Member
Hrs: Su, 2-6; other days by appt.
Sporting: 1, 14 stations

Brays Island Plantation
PO Box 30, Sheldon, SC 29941
Owner Services (803) 846-3100
50 mi. SW of Charleston
Type: Member/Avail
Hrs: Su, 12-6; M-S, 8-6
Sporting: 4, 37 stations
HT: 62 ft. **Wobble Trap**

Broxton Bridge
Plantation
PO Box 97, Hwy. 601
Ehrhardt, SC 29081
Jerry Varn, Jr. (800) 437-4868
60 mi. W of Charleston
Type: Public
Hrs: Anytime by appt.
Reservs: Strongly recommended
Sporting: 2, 47 stations
HT: 65 ft. **Wobble Trap**
O Loaner Guns
O Factory Ammunition
O On-Site Pro Shop
O On-Site Meals
O Shooting Lodge
O Formal Instructions
O Organized Leagues
O Golf Carts
See Our Ad Pg. 363

Carolina Sporting Clays
Rt. 3, Box 455-H
Nichols, SC 29581
Sam Thomas (803) 392-1401
105 mi. E of Columbia
Type: Public
Hrs: M-F, by appt; S, 9:30-Dusk; Su, 12:30
Sporting: 1, 10 stations
Trap: 1 **Skeet:** 1 **Wobble Trap**

Greenville Gun Club
111 Shaftsbury Rd.
Clemson, SC 29631
Ed Prater (803) 277-6154
8 mi. S of Greenville
Type: Member/Avail
Hrs: W, 4-Dusk; S/Su, 1-Dusk
Sporting: 1, 11 stations
Trap: 3 **Skeet:** 4 **Five Stand:** 1
HT: 35 ft.

Harris Springs Sporting Clays
PO Box 278, Cross Hill, SC 29332
Jake Rasor/Ted Avant
(803) 677-3448
45 mi. SE of Greenville
Type: Public/Member
Hrs: Th/F/S, 10-Dark; other days by appt.
Sporting: 1, 14 stations
Skeet: 1

Hermitage Farm
Shooting Sports
PO Box 1258, Camden, SC 29020
J.B. Cantey, III (803) 432-0210
35 mi. S of Columbia
Type: Public/Member
Hrs: T-S, 9-6; Su, 1-6
Sporting: 1, 10 stations
Skeet: 1 **Five Stand:** 1

Little River
Plantation
Sporting Clays
PO Box 1129, Abbeville, SC 29620
Jim & John Edens (803) 391-2300
80 mi. NW of Columbia
Type: Public/Member
Hrs: M-S, 8-Dark; Su, 1-Dark
Reservs: Recommended
Sporting: 1, 14 stations [Cont'd>]

CLAYS

Five Stand: Y   **HT:** 35 ft.
○ Loaner Guns
○ Factory Ammunition
○ On-Site Pro Shop
○ Formal Instructions
○ Custom Ear Plugs
○ 14 Stations

Mill Creek
Sporting Clays, Inc.
PO Box 6613 (957 Longwood Rd.)
Columbia, SC 29260
Bob Murphy (803) 695-0637
2.5 mi. SE of Columbia
Type: Public/Member
Hrs: Th/F/Su, 1-Dk; S, 10-Dk
Reservs: Not required
Sporting: 1, 13 stations
Five Stand: 1   **HT:** 22 ft.

Moore's Sporting Clays
2290 Martin Rd.
Hickory Grove, SC 29717
Doug Moore (803) 925-2064
45 mi. SW of Charlotte, NC
Type: Public
Hrs: M/T, by appt; W-S, 10-Dk;
Su, 1:30-Dk
Sporting: 2, 26 stations

Myrtle Beach Indoor
Shooting Range
3432 Hwy. 501 W PO Box 25
Plantation Sq.
Myrtle Beach, SC 29577
Ted Gragg (803) 236-4344
14 mi. NW of Myrtle Beach
Type: Public
Hrs: T/W/S, 9-6; M/Th/F, by appt.
Sporting: 2, 16 stations   **HT:** 30 ft.

Okatie Gun Club
at Hilton Head
Rt. 1, Box 67A
Bluffton, SC 29910
Rose Vires (803) 757-5180
15 mi. W of Hilton Head
Type: Public/Member
Hrs: M/Tu, 9-6; W/Th, closed;
F/Sa, 9-6; Su, 12-6
Reservs: Recommended
Sporting: 1, 15 stations
Trap: 1   **HT:** 50 ft.
○ Loaner Guns
○ Factory Ammunition
○ On-Site Pro Shop
○ Rifle/Pistol Range
○ 3-D Archery Range

River Bend
Sportsman's Resort
PO Box 279, Fingerville, SC 29338
Ralph N. Brendle (803) 592-1348
15 mi. NW of Spartanburg
Type: Public/Member
Hrs: W/F, 1-8; S, 8:30-8; Su, 2-6
Reservs: Strongly recommended
Sporting: 1, 10 stations
Skeet: 1   **Five Stand:** 1   **HT:** 40 ft.
○ Loaner Guns
○ Factory Ammunition
○ On-Site Pro Shop
○ On-Site Meals
○ Shooting Lodge
○ Formal Instructions

Singletree
Rt. 1, Box 564, Clinton, SC 29325
C.C. May (803) 833-2618
55 mi. NW of Columbia
Type: Public
Hrs: Call for reservations
Sporting: 1, 6 stations   **Skeet:** 1

South Carolina
Outdoor Shooting Ctr.
371 Cedar Branch Rd.
Windsor, SC 29856
Richard Sherman (803) 648-5132
17 mi. E of Augusta, GA
Type: Public/Member
Hrs: W, 12-10; Th/F, 12-7;
S, 9-7; Su, 1-7
Reservs: Recommended
Sporting: 2, 32 stations
Trap: 6   **Skeet:** 4   **Five Stand:** Y
HT: 125 ft.

See Our Ad Pg. 479

South Carolina Waterfowl
PO Box 450, Pinewood, SC 29125
David Watson (803) 551-4610
Sporting: 1   **Five Stand:** 1

Spartanburg Gun Club
PO Box 779
Whitestone, SC 29386
Eddie Glance (803) 474-2628
Type: Public/Member
Hrs: T-Su, 11-Dark
Sporting: 1, 13 stations
Trap: 9   **Skeet:** 4   **Wobble Trap**

Tinker Creek Sporting Clays
Rt. 2, Box 76, Williston, SC 29853
Gregg or Roger Bates
(803) 266-4840
40 mi. E of Augusta, GA
Type: Public/Member
Hrs: S/W, 9-Dark; Other by reserv.
Sporting: 6, 45 stations
HT: 60 ft.

Triangle Gun Club
Rt. 3, Box 883
Newberry, SC 29108
Allen Morrison (803) 276-8679
35 mi. NW of Columbia
Hrs: W/S/Su, 1-6
Sporting: None
Trap: 1   **Skeet:** 2   **Five Stand:** 1

Wagon Trail
P.O. Box 141, Gable, SC 29051
Thomas Durant (803) 495-2529
50 mi. E of Columbia (5 mi. east of
Sumter on U.S. Rt. 378)
Type: Public/Member
Hrs: Sa, 9-6; weekdays by app't
Sporting: 1, 15 stations

TRAP & SKEET

Beaufort Skeet Club
2910 4th St., Beaufort, SC 29902
Wayne Anderson (803) 522-7783
Hrs: Su, 9-5:30
Skeet: 1

Mid-Carolina Gun Club
Box 237, Orangeburg, SC 29115
Monty Smith (803) 534-4437
Trap: 1   **Skeet:** 5

Pageland Wildlife Action
515 Griggs St.,
Pageland, SC 29728
Richard Pigg
Type: Public/Member
Trap: 2   **Skeet:** 2

Partridge Creek
Trap/Skeet Club
4004 Rantowles Ct.
Ravenel, SC 29470
Charles Riding, Jr. (803) 873-7291
Hrs: Not open to public
Skeet: 4

Polk County Gun Club
107 Hotel Hill Dr.
Landrum, SC 29356
Randall Arthur (704) 863-4445
Type: Public/Member
Hrs: Su-S, 10-6
Trap: 2   **Skeet:** 1

School House Skeet & Trap
PO Box 363, Pamplico, SC 29583
Jimmy Ard (803) 493-3028
Hrs: 4-10
Trap: 1   **Skeet:** 1

Shaw Rod & Gun Club
R3, Box 315R
Sumter, SC 29154
Fred L. Samuel (803) 668-2492
Hrs: S/Su, 1-7; W, 7-10
Trap: 1   **Skeet:** 2

SOUTH DAKOTA

SPORTING & 5-STAND

Aberdeen Gun Club
721 S. State, Aberdeen, SD 57401
Jerry Brick (605) 225-6383
Type: Public/Member
Hrs: T/Th, 1-9; S/Su, 1-5 (May-Sept)
Sporting: 1, 13 stations
Trap: 9   Wobble Trap

Dakota Ridge
RR2, Box 67, Altamont, SD 57226
Charles Shomaker (605) 874-2813
95 mi. N of Sioux Falls
Type: Public
Hrs: Su-S, 10:30-sunset; Sept-March
Sporting: 1

Dakota Sporting Clays
PO Box 369, Jefferson, SD 57038
Jim Langstraat (605) 966-5399
15 mi. NW of Sioux City, IA
Type: Public/Member
Hrs: T/Th, 5-dusk; Su, 9-4
Sporting: 1, 16 stations

Funkrest Dakota Skat
RR3, Box 167, Madison, SD 57042
Don or Bonnie Funk
(605) 256-3636
50 mi. NW of Sioux Falls
Type: Public/Member
Hrs: Su-S, 9-dk; Others by appt.
Sporting: 1, 10 stations
HT: 40 ft.

Ghost Town Sporting Clays
45778 278th St., Parker, SD 57053
Steve Naatjes (605) 647-5691
24 mi. SW of Sioux Falls
Type: Public/Member
Hrs: S/Su, 12-5
Sporting: 1, 12 stations
HT: 30 ft.

Hunters Pointe Shooting Club
45743 260th St.
Humboldt, SD 57035
Tony Bour (605) 363-6489
22 mi. W of Sioux Falls
Type: Public/Member
Hrs: T-W-T, 1-8; S-Su 9-5
Reservs: Strongly recommended
Sporting: 6, 60 stations
HT: 60 ft. Wobble Trap
O Loaner Guns
O On-Site Pro Shop
O Formal Instructions
O Organized Leagues
O Golf Carts

James Valley Sporting Clays
Rt. 1, Box 39, Utica, SD 57067
Harold Klimisch (605) 364-7468
55 mi. SW of Sioux Falls
Type: Public Hrs: Year round
Sporting: 1, 10 stations

Paul Nelson Farm
119 Hilltop Dr., PO Box 183
Gettysburg, SD 57442
Paul Nelson (605) 765-2469
65 mi. NE of Pierre
Type: Public Hrs:
Sporting: 1
See Our Ad Pg. 375

Pearson's Hunting Adventures
HC74, 256, Forestburg, SD 57314
Marvin R. Pearson (612) 935-2514
16 mi. SE of Huron
Type: Public Hrs: By appt. only
Sporting: 1, 5 stations
HT: 60 ft.

Stukel's Birds & Bucks
Rt. 1, Box 112
Gregory, SD 57533
Frank Stukel (605) 835-8941
90 mi. SE of Pierre
Type: Public
Hrs: 6/1-12/30, daylight hours
Sporting: 1, 7 stations

Valley West Shooting Complex
809 W. 10th St.,
Sioux Falls, SD 57104
Daniel Stock (800) 424-2047
5 mi. W of Empire Mall/Sioux Falls
Type: Public/Member
Hrs: Year Round-7 days/wk
Sporting: 2, 14 stations
Trap: 2 Skeet: 2
Five Stand: 1   HT: 80 ft.

Willow Creek
HCR33, Box 24
Ft. Pierre, SD 57532
Steve Stoeser (605) 223-3154
12 mi. W of Pierre
Type: Public
Hrs: M-F, Sun-up - Sunset; S/Su,
Noon-Sunset
Sporting: 2, 15 stations   HT

TRAP & SKEET

Crooks Gun Club
Box 427, Sioux Falls, SD 57101
Bob Felber (605) 543-5481
Type: Public/Member
Hrs: T-F, 1-5; W/Th, Nights; Su, 1-5
Trap: 13 Skeet: 2   Wobble Trap

Devel County Ikes
512 5th St. West, Box 143
Clear Lake, SD 57226
Lewis J. Shelsta (605) 874-2384

Type: Public/Member
Hrs: S/Su, by appt; T, 5:30
Trap: 2 Skeet: 1

Mitchell Gun Club
421 W. 4th Ave.
Mitchell, SD 57301
Jerry Opbroek
Type: Public   Trap: 9

Rapid City Trap Club
9206 S. Hwy. 79
Rapid City, SD 57702
Jim White (605) 341-4412
Type: Public/Member
Hrs: T/Th, 5-10pm; Su, open
shooting Trap: 9

Sioux Falls Gun Club
PO Box 944, Sioux Falls, SD 57005
Jerry Vander Esch (605) 332-9558
Hrs: T, 6-9   Trap: 8

TENNESSEE

SPORTING & 5-STAND

Arrowhead Hunt Club
PO Box 598, Whiteville, TN 38075
Elmer Kahl (901) 231-8684
45 mi. E of Memphis
Type: Public Hrs: S, 8:30-Dark;
Su, 12:30-Dark; Weekdays by appt.
Sporting: 1, 9 stations

The Barn Gun Club
PO Box 664, Brentwood, TN 37024
Albert L. Menefee, Jr.
(615) 293-2141
Sporting: 1, 10 stations
Trap: 2 Skeet: 2

Crockett Hunting Preserve
1213 Woodgate
Humboldt, TN 38343
Van Holyfield (901) 784-5368
13 mi. NW of Humboldt
Type: Public Hrs: W/S/Su, 1-Dark
Sporting: 1, 15 stations
Trap: 1 Skeet: 1

**Deep Springs Sporting
Clays & Hunting Preserve**
850 Hid-A-Way,
Dandridge, TN 37725
Kerry Smith (615) 397-6617
15 mi. E of Knoxville
Type: Public Hrs:
Sporting: 1, 20 stations

**Dunaway Hunting &
Fishing Club**
600 Krystal Bldg., One Union
Square, Chattanooga, TN 37402
Wilson P. Burton, Jr.
(615) 756-1202
38 mi. N of Chattanooga
Type: Member/Avail
Hrs: Anytime by appt.
Sporting: 1, 14 stations HT

Eagle Skeet Club
446 Lee Hollow Rd.
Indian Mound, TN 37079
Veronica Tucker (502) 798-9958
Hrs: S/Su, 12-4 Sporting: None
Trap: 1 Skeet: 3 Five Stand: 1

Estanaula Hunt Club
PO Box 26, Brownsville, TN 38012
Harbert Mulherin (901) 772-9780
50 mi. NE of Memphis
Type: Public Hrs: 10/15-3/15
Sporting: 1

Falls Creek Hunt Club
HC69, Box 234
Spencer, TN 38585
Frank Hanwright (615) 946-2095
85 mi. SE of Nashville
Type: Public/Member
Hrs: Daily by appt.
Sporting: 1, 8 stations HT: 20 ft.

Grinders Switch Club
1608 Chickering Rd.
Nashville, TN 37215
Barry Claud (615) 729-9732
50 mi. SW of Nashville
Type: Public/Member
Hrs: W-Su, 8-5
Reservs: Strongly recommended
Sporting: 5, 40 stations
HT: 80 ft. Wobble Trap
See Our Ad Below

Happy Springs Sporting Clays
4350 Happy Springs Rd.
Red Boiling Springs, TN 37150
Gary McCarter (615) 699-3414
80 mi. NE of Nashville
Type: Public/Member
Hrs: S, 8-Dark; Su, 1-Dark
Sporting: 1, 10 stations
HT: 25 ft.

The Hunting Lodge
Box 381, Manchester, TN 37355
Harry L. Taylor (615) 728-7260
75 mi. SE of Nashville
Type: Public Hrs: By appt. only
Sporting: 1, 25 stations

Memphis Sport Shooting
PO Box 97, Brunswick, TN 38119
Jim Norris (901) 867-8277
10 mi. N of Memphis
Type: Member/Avail
Hrs: W-Su, 12-Dark
Sporting: 1, 8 stations
Trap: 5 Skeet: 5 HT: 41 ft.

Montlake Public Shooting
2009 Mowbray Pike
Soddy Daisy, TN 37379
Carl N. Poston (615) 332-1195
Type: Public Hrs:
Sporting: 1, 25 stations
Trap: 4 Skeet: 5

Nashville Gun Club
PO Box 90131, Nashville, TN 37209
Jeff Carrigan (615) 742-1101
3 mi. W of Nashville
Type: Public/Member
Hrs: W-Su, 10-Dusk
Sporting: 2, 20 stations
Trap: 4 Skeet: 4
Five Stand: 1 HT: 25 ft.

Northeast Tennessee Raceway & Sporting Clays
Jearoldstown Rd.
Greeneville, TN 37745
Nick Vigiano (615) 234-9412
45 mi. NE of Dollywood
Type: Public
Hrs: We/Fr, 12-dark; Sa/Su 9-dark
Sporting: 2, 30 stations
Skeet: 1 Five Stand: 1
HT: 25 ft.

Shaw Creek
2055 Burnett Rd.
Williston, TN 38076
Randy Reeves (901) 465-4530
29 mi. E of Memphis
Type: Public Hrs:
Sporting: 1, 13 stations

Short Creek Sporting Clays
191 County Rd. 50
Athens, TN 37303
Charles Daniel (615) 745-5463
55 mi. N of Chattanooga
Type: Public Hrs: W/S/Su
Sporting: 1, 22 stations
HT: 25 ft. Wobble Trap

Smoky Mountain Sports Club
4286 Miser Station Rd.
Lousiville, TN 37777
Jeff Smith (615) 995-9291
20 mi. S of Knoxville
Type: Public/Member
Hrs: M/T, by appt; W-F, 12-Dusk;
S, 11-Dusk; Su, 1-Dusk
Reservs: Not required
Sporting: 1, 10 stations
Trap: 2 Skeet: 2 Five Stand: 1
HT: 30 ft.
O Loaner Guns
O Factory Ammunition
O On-Site Pro Shop
O Formal Instructions
O Organized Leagues

Southgate Public Shooting
Rt. 1, Box 211B, Lavinia, TN 38348
E.V. Hillard (901) 783-3845
N of Jackson
Type: Public/Member
Hrs: Su-S, Noon-Dark
Sporting: 1, 24 stations
Trap: 5 Skeet: 5

Upper Cumberland Sports
R#3, Box 195-C, Crossville, TN 38555
Roy South (615) 484-1624
60 mi. W of Knoxville
Type: Public
Hrs: S, 9-Dusk; Su, 12-Dusk
Sporting: 2, 40 stations **HT:** 30 ft.

TRAP & SKEET

Bend of the River Trap Club
2880 Standing Stone Hwy.
Cookeville, TN 38501
Charles Pardue (615) 526-1136
Type: Public/Member
Hrs: S, 9-6 **Trap:** 1 **Skeet:** 1

Big Springs Sporting Club
8890 Big Springs Rd.
Christiana, TN 37037
Tommy Jackson (615) 890-6360
39 mi. E of Nashville
Type: Public
Hrs: Tu-Sa, 10-7; Su, 12-7
Trap: 2 **Skeet:** 2   **HT:** 40 ft.
Wobble Trap

Brownsville Skeet Range
10 Owen, Brownsville, TN 38012
Walter R. Powell (901) 772-1862
Hrs: T/Th, 6-10; Su, 1-6
Skeet: 3

Cedar City Gun Club
1212 Rosewood Tr.
Mt. Juliet, TN 37122
Tom Grimaldi (615) 444-0104
Type: Public/Member
Hrs: S/Su, 12-Dark
Trap: 2 **Skeet:** 2

Cleveland Skeet Club
PO Box 685, Cleveland, TN 37311
Todd Korn (615) 479-7426
Skeet: 1

Dyersburg Gun Club
114 Main St., Newbern, TN 38059
John Uitendaal (901) 627-3398
Type: Public
Hrs: Wed. afternoons (Apr-Aug)
Trap: 1 **Skeet:** 2

Henry Horton Skeet League
637 Scenic Dr., Lewisburg, TN 37091
Charles W. Rogers (615) 364-2093
Hrs: W-Su, 12-Dark
Trap: 9 **Skeet:** 5

Hog Heaven Gun Club
560 Hwy. 113,
White Pine, TN 37890
Wade Frazier/Anne Koella
(615) 674-2282
30 mi. from Gatlinburg
Type: Public/Member
Hrs: F&S, Noon-Dark; Su, 1-Dark;
Others by appt.
Trap: 6 **Skeet:** 1 **Five Stand:** 1

Maury County Gun Club
1514 Galloway St.
Columbia, TN 38401
Claude Mays (615) 381-3006
Skeet: 3

Mill Road Gun Club
Rt. 7, Box 7590
Manchester, TN 37355
B.J. Yates (615) 728-3585
Hrs: Su, 1-Dark **Trap:** 1 **Skeet:** 3

Morristown Trap Club
302 Fleming Dr.
Morristown, TN 37814
Tommy Cope (615) 581-3444
Hrs: M, 5-10; S, 1-10 **Trap:** 4

Nashville Gun Club
2323 Mt. Juliet Rd.
Mt. Juliet, TN 37122
Sam Jennings (615) 834-4214
Type: Public/Member
Hrs: T-Su, 11-Dk **Trap:** 9 **Skeet:** 5

Orion Gun Club
7195 Renda, Millington, TN 38053
Howard Terry (901) 873-5665
Hrs: W, 4-6; S, 12-6; Su, 1-6
Trap: 1 **Skeet:** 1

Tennessee State Trap. Assn.
3912 Hillshire Dr.
Antioch, TN 37013
Joseph Nevins (615) 361-7785
Hrs: W-Su   **Trap:** 8

TEXAS

SPORTING & 5-STAND

Abilene Gun Club
PO Box 1213, Abilene, TX 79604
Harold Powell (915) 692-9002
Hrs: T-Th, 4-Dark; S/Su, 1-Dark
Sporting: None
Trap: 4 **Skeet:** 4 **Five Stand:** 1

Alpine
Sporting Clays
5482 Shelby Rd.,
Ft. Worth, TX 76140
Jack Johnson (817) 478-6613
12 mi. SE of Ft. Worth
Type: Public **Hrs:** Daily, 8-Dark
Reservs: Not required
Sporting: 1, 14 stations
Trap: 2 **Skeet:** 3 **Five Stand:** 1
HT: 25 ft.
O Loaner Guns
O Factory Ammunition
O On-Site Pro Shop
O Formal Instructions
O Golf Carts
O Gunsmith Service
O Gun Fitting

Amarillo Gun Club
PO Box 30064
Amarillo, TX 79120
C. Moss/D. Rhoads (806) 372-0678
Type: Public/Member
Hrs: W/Th/F, 3-Dark; S/Su, 12-Dark
Sporting: 1, 5 stations
Trap: 14 **Skeet:** 5 **Five Stand:** 1
HT: 30 ft.

American Shooting Centers
16500 Westheimer Pkwy.
Houston, TX 77082
Bill Bacon (713) 556-1597
17 mi. W of Houston
Type: Public/Member
Hrs: W/Th/F, 12-7; S/Su, 9-7
Reservs: Not required
Sporting: 2, 15 stations
Trap: 2 **Skeet:** 7 **Five Stand:** 2
HT: 100 ft.

Arlington Sportsman Club
3021 Pecan Circle
Bedford, TX 76021
Bryan Cullen (817) 473-0581
15 mi. S of Dallas/Ft. Worth
Type: Member/Avail
Sporting: 1, 10 stations
Trap: 1 **Skeet:** 5   **HT**

Black Creek Ranch
2523 Nacogdoches Rd.
San Antonio, TX 78217
Lee McClintick (210) 805-9600
58 mi. S of San Antonio
Type: Public
Hrs: Daily by appt.
Sporting: 1, 20 stations **HT:** 66 ft.

Blue Goose
PO Box M, Altair, TX 77412
John R. Fields (409) 234-3597
50 mi. SW of Houston
Type: Public
Hrs: By Reservation Only
Sporting: 1, 10 stations **HT:** 60 ft.

Brown Dog Sporting Clays
Box 157, Elysian Fields, TX 75642
Ronnie or Kenneth Mericle
(903) 633-2334
17 mi. SE of Marshall
Type: Public
Hrs: M-F, by appt; S, 10-Dusk;
Su, 1-Dusk
Sporting: 1, 16 stations **HT:** 35 ft.

CLAYS

Caney Creek Sporting Clays
1702 Garrett Court
Wharton, TX 77488
W.S. Sherrill (409) 532-1789
45 mi. SW of Houston
Type: Public Hrs: By Appt.
Sporting: 1, 8 stations

Capitol City
Trap/Skeet Club
PO Box 141277, Austin, TX 78714
Bill Bellinghausen (512) 272-4707
8 mi. E of Austin
Type: Public/Member
Hrs: W-Su, Noon-Dark
Reservs: Recommended
Sporting: 1, 10 stations
Trap: 3 Skeet: 4 Five Stand: 1
HT: 45 ft.

Carter's Country Shooting
6231 Treaschwig Rd.
Spring, TX 77373
Billy Carter, Jr. (713) 443-8393
10 mi. N of Houston
Type: Public
Hrs: Open 7 Days a Week
Sporting: None
Trap: 1 Skeet: 1 Five Stand: 1

Champion Lake
Gun Club
5615 Hiltonview,
Houston, TX 77086
Jonathan Handy (713) 893-5868
15 mi. N of Houston
Type: Public/Member
Hrs: T/W/Th/F 11-dark;
S/Su, 9-Dark
Reservs: Strongly recommended
Sporting: 2, 20 stations
HT: 40 ft.
O Loaner Guns
O Factory Ammunition
O Formal Instructions
O Organized Leagues

Clear Creek Gun Range
306 Crystal, League City, TX 77573
Ernest Randall (713) 337-1722
20 mi. S of Houston
Type: Public
Hrs: T/W/Th, 1-8; S/Su, 9-8
Sporting: 2, 11 stations

Trap: 3 Skeet: 5 Five Stand: 1
HT: 90 ft.

Cypress Valley Preserve
PO Box 162525
Austin, TX 78716
Phillip C. Walker (512) 328-5279
25 mi. N of Austin
Type: Member/Avail
Hrs: (S) T-Th, 12-Dk; S/Su, 9-Dk;
(W) T-Su, 9-Dk
Sporting: 1, 18 stations
HT: 100 ft. Wobble Trap

Dallas Gun Club
3601 IH-35 South, PO Box 292848
Lewisville, TX 75029
Ann Myers (214) 462-0043
15 mi. N of Dallas/Ft. Worth
Type: Member/Avail
Hrs: W-F, 12-10; S/Su, 10-10
Sporting: 1, 10 stations
Trap: 5 Skeet: 8 Five Stand: Y
HT: 120 ft.

Dos Vaqueros
PO Box 1035, Refugio, TX 78377
Joan Rooke (512) 543-4905
45 mi. N of Corpus Christi
Type: Public, Member/Avail
Hrs: Year round, except July/Aug.
Sporting: 1, 5 stations

HUNTERS CLUB
Elk Castle Hunters Club
PO Box 158, Mingus, TX 76463
Dan Van Schaik (817) 672-5927
70 mi. W of Ft. Worth
Type: Public
Hrs: 9-4pm; Closed Mondays
Reservs: Strongly recommended
Sporting: 2, 18 stations
Skeet: 1

Elm Fork Shooting Park
10751 Luna Rd., Dallas, TX 75220
Dennis Reed (214) 556-0103
Type: Public
Hrs: (Sum) T-F, 12-7; S/Su, 9-7;
(Win) T/S/Su
Sporting: None Trap: 4 Skeet: 6
Five Stand: 1

Fort Bliss Rod & Gun Club
PO Box 6118, Fort Bliss, TX 79916
Thomas J. Piasecki (915) 568-2983
from El Paso
Hrs: Closed Mondays
Sporting: 1, 5 stations
Trap: 3 Skeet: 2

Greater Houston Gun Club
PO Box 97, Missouri City, TX 77459
Curt Sporull (713) 437-6025
10 mi. S of Houston
Type: Public/Member
Hrs: W-Su, 9-Dark
Sporting: None
Trap: 10 Skeet: 8 Five Stand: 1
HT: 20 ft.

Hawkeye Hunting Club
PO Box 27, Center, TX 75935
Jerry Waters (409) 598-2424
55 mi. SW of Shreveport, LA
Type: Member/Avail
Hrs: By Appt.
Sporting: 1, 10 stations
Trap: 1

Herradura Ranch Inc.
PO Drawer 698, Cotulla, TX 78014
David Schuster (512) 373-4492
95 mi. W of Corpus Christi
Type: Public Hrs:
Sporting: 1, 7 stations
Trap: 1 Skeet: 1

HILLTOP
FISH&GAME
R A N C H

Hilltop Fish & Game Ranch
HCR67, Box 58C
Pleasanton, TX 78064
Steve Hill (210) 569-5555
35 mi. S of San Antonio
Type: Public Hrs: M-Sa
Reservs: Strongly recommended
Sporting: 3, 11 stations
O Sporting Clays Course designed
　by Terry Howard, Olympic Gold
　Medalist
O Guided Upland Hunts with dogs
　available
O Bass Fishing
O Lodging and the finest in South
　Texas cuisine
O Just a short 35 minute drive from
　San Antonio!

The Inn
at El Canelo
Box 487, Raymondville, TX 78580
Ray Burdette (210) 689-5042
75 mi. S of Corpus Christi
Type: Public
Hrs: S, 8-12 & by resrv.
Reservs: Strongly recommended
Sporting: 1, 10 stations
Trap: 1 HT: 30 ft.

Joshua Creek Ranch
PO Box 1946, Boerne, TX 78006
Ann Kercheville (210) 537-5090
25 mi. NW of San Antonio
Type: Public/Member
Hrs: T-Su, 9am-7pm
Reservs: Strongly recommended
Sporting: 1, 30 stations
Wobble Trap
○ Loaner Guns
○ Factory Ammunition
○ On-Site Pro Shop
○ On-Site Meals
○ Shooting Lodge
○ Formal Instructions
○ Organized Leagues
See Our Ad Pg. 387

Kat Creek Hunting Club & Sporting Clays
PO Box 987, Henderson, TX 75653
Chester Martin (903) 854-2232
135 mi. SE of Dallas/Ft. Worth
Type: Public/Member
Hrs: Su, 1-Dk; S, 10-Dk;
Wkdys by Appt.
Sporting: 1, 12 stations
Five Stand: Y **HT:** 65 ft.
Wobble Trap

Kleberg County T&S
823 South 24th St.
Kingsville, TX 78363
Ronald Lewis (512) 595-8505
Type: Public
Hrs: W, 6-10; F, 6-11; Su, 1-8
Sporting: None
Trap: 2 **Skeet:** 2 **Five Stand:** 1
Wobble Trap

Krooked River Ranch
5 Squirrel Ridge
Wylie, TX 75098
Steve Packer (214) 442-3851
200 mi. W of Dallas/Ft. Worth
Type: Member/Avail
Hrs: By Appt. **Sporting:** 1, 6 sta.
Trap: 1 **Skeet:** 1

La Media Sportsman's
PO Box 319, Linn, TX 78563
Jerry & Karen Pippen
(800) 437-3903
110 mi. S of Corpus Christi
Type: Public   **Sporting:** 1
Trap: Y **Skeet:** Y

LaPaloma Sporting Club
PO Box 160516
San Antonio, TX 78280
Henry Burns (210) 980-4424
20 mi. NE of San Antonio
Type: Public/Member
Hrs: W-Su, 9am-dark
Sporting: 2, 20 stations
Skeet: 1 **Five Stand:** 1 **HT:** 55 ft.

Loma Blanca Ranch
1300 S. University Dr., #410
Fort Worth, TX 76107
Greg Williamson (817) 396-4570
15 mi. SW of Ft. Worth
Type: Member/Avail
Hrs: Reservation only
Sporting: 1, 12 stations **HT:** 50 ft.

Lone Star Sporting Clays
Rt. 1, Box 241A
Glen Rose, TX 76043
Mike K. Lewellen (817) 897-2918
60 mi. SW of Ft. Worth
Type: Public/Member
Hrs: W, 3-Dark; S/Su, 11-Dusk;
other days by appt.
Sporting: 1, 15 stations

Los Cuernos Ranch
PO Box 200105
San Antonio, TX 78220
Pat Moore (210) 676-3317
132 mi. SW of San Antonio
Type: Public/Member
Hrs: W-Su, 8-Dark; Call for resrv.
Reservs: Strongly recommended
Sporting: 1, 10 stations
○ Loaner Guns
○ Factory Ammunition
○ On-Site Pro Shop
○ On-Site Meals
○ Shooting Lodge
○ Formal Instructions
○ 4,000 Ft. Runway Lighted

McGuire Lodge
PO Box 42, Seminole, TX 79360
Terry Cox (915) 758-3640
160 mi. S of Amarillo
Type: Public **Hrs:** Su-S
Sporting: None
Trap: 1 **Five Stand:** 1

NSCA - National Gun Club
5931 Roft Rd.,
San Antonio, TX 78253
Mike Hampton (210) 688-3371
20 mi. NW of San Antonio
Type: Public
Hrs: Special Events Only
Sporting: 3, 36 stations
Trap: 16 **Skeet:** 40 **Five Stand:** 2
HT Wobble Trap

Northwest Texas Field & Stream
Box 4280, Wichita Falls, TX 76308
Cliff Wurster (817) 322-4845
130 mi. W of Dallas
Type: Public/Member
Hrs: W, 5-9; S, 8-Close; Su, 1-6
Sporting: 1, 10 stations
Trap: 2 **Skeet:** 2 **HT:** 20 ft.

One in One Hundred
1228 FM 421,
Lumberton, TX 77657
John Stockwell (409) 755-9903
10 mi. N of Beaumont
Type: Member/Avail
Hrs: W-F, 1-dark; S/Su, 8-dark
Sporting: 1, 10 stations
Trap: 2 **Skeet:** 3 **Wobble Trap**

P.S.C. Shooting Club
2027 Sieber, Houston, TX 77017
Richard Busing (713) 585-0068
25 mi. S of Houston
Type: Member/Avail
Hrs: S/Su, (Winter); S/Su/T/Th,
(Summer) **Sporting:** None
Trap: 1 **Skeet:** 1 **Five Stand:** 1

Paris Skeet & Trap Club
PO Box 164, Paris, TX 75460
Bill Gossman (903) 785-2155
Type: Public/Member
Hrs: S/Su, 12-Dark
Sporting: 1, 6 stations
Trap: 1 **Skeet:** 3

Possum Walk Ranch
Rt. 2, Box 174,
Huntsville, TX 77340
Buddy Smith (409) 291-1891
70 mi. N of Houston
Type: Public/Member
Hrs: Oct-Mar, daily by appt;
Apr-Sep, wkends by appt.
Sporting: 1, 11 stations
Trap: 1 **Skeet:** 1 **HT:** 90 ft.

Prairie Creek Sporting Clays
Rt. 5 - 112 Allen Dr.
Kilgore, TX 75662
Steve Brown (903) 845-6431
94 mi. W of Dallas
Type: Public **Hrs:** Th/F,
1:30-Dark; S/Su, 8:30-Dark;
M/T/W, by appt.
Sporting: 1, 10 sta. **Five Stand:** 1
HT: 30 ft. **Wobble Trap**

Red Bluff Shooting Preserve
Rt. 2, Box 106B, Trent, TX 79561
Ed Mayfield (915) 235-4360
10 mi. E of Sweetwater
Type: Public/Member
Hrs: Su-S, by resrv.
Sporting: 2, 15 stations
HT: 90 ft.

CLAYS

Riverside Farms
Rt. 3, Box 217-R
Hamilton, TX 76531
Jill Bishop/Les Ethetton
(817) 386-8921
150 mi. SW of Dallas/Ft. Worth
Type: Public
Hrs: Su-S, by appt.
Sporting: 1, 10 stations
Trap: 2 **Skeet:** 2   HT

Rustic Range Sporting Clays
Rt. 2, Box 182, Slaton, TX 79364
Dub Dillard (806) 828-4820
11 mi. E of Lubbock
Type: Public
Hrs: S, 11-Sunset; Su, 1-Sunset
Sporting: 1, 10 stations
HT: 22 ft.

San Antonio Gun Club
928 E. Contour
San Antonio, TX 78212
Mike Valerio (512) 828-9860
Type: Public/Member
Sporting: None
Trap: 5 **Skeet:** 8 **Five Stand:** 1

Silver Lake Gun Club
3300 Euless South Main
Euless, TX 76040
Cliff Mycoskie (817) 355-1311
4 mi. SW of DFW Airport
Type: Public/Member
Hrs: W/F, 12-Dark; S/Su, 9-Dark;
Other days by appt.
Reservs: Recommended
Sporting: 1, 15 stations
Trap: 1 **Skeet:** 2 **Five Stand:** 1
Wobble Trap
○ On-Site Pro Shop
○ Formal Instructions
○ Centrally located to Dallas/Ft.
   Worth
○ Corporate Outings
○ Excellent Fishing
○ Lighted Skeet Field
○ Friendly Staff

Southwest Sporting Clays
Rt. 5, Box 418-C
Texarkana, TX 75501

John A. Woodman (903) 838-4000
10 mi. W of Texarkana
Type: Public/Member
Hrs: W-Su, 11am-Dusk
Sporting: 2, 18 stations
Trap: 1 **HT:** 45 ft. **Wobble Trap**

Spanish Dagger
PO Box 1325, Uvalde, TX 78802
George Cooper (210) 278-2998
70 mi. W of San Antonio
Type: Public
Hrs: T/W, Eve; Others by appt.
Sporting: 1, 6 stations
HT: 35 ft. **Wobble Trap**

Sporting Clays International of Dallas
Rt. 1, Box 118
Allen, TX 75002
John Holiski/Lynn Carley
(214) 727-1998
15 mi. NE of Dallas/Ft. Worth
Type: Public/Member
Hrs: W-F 11 - dark; Sat/Sun 9 - dark
Reservs: Not required
Sporting: 2, 18 stations
Trap: 1 **Five Stand:** 1

Shoot pheasant like the British, red-legged partridge like the Spaniards, grouse like the Vermonters and many, many more. Our sporting clays can simulate the thrill of hunting these favorites. Hone your hunting skills as you walk with us along the beautiful and serene Rowlett Creek. Come for the "Ultimate Shooting Experience": Wed/Thurs/Fri, 11am; Sat/Su, 9am. We have CORPORATE OUTINGS available, call for information and reservations, (214) 727-1998; FAX: (214) 727-6420.
See Our Ad Left

TargetMaster
1717 S. Jupiter Rd.
Garland, TX 75042
Thomas Mannewitz
(214) 442-4565
15 mi. NE of Dallas/Ft. Worth
Type: Member/Avail
Hrs: T-Su **Sporting:** 1, 14 stations
Five Stand: 1 **HT:** 45 ft.
Wobble Trap

Texas Waterfowl Outfitters
22413 Katy Frwy.
Katy, TX 77450
Tony Hurst (800) 899-2650
20 mi. W of Houston
Type: Public/Member
Skeet: Y

Three Amigos Sporting Clays
Rt. 4, Box 64, El Campo, TX 77437
Jay Harris (409) 543-9475
60 mi. SW of Houston
Type: Public **Hrs:** Daily by appt.
Sporting: 1, 10 stations **HT:** 40 ft.

Tierra Colinas
Rt. 5, Box 162B,
Weatherford, TX 76086
Joe Bishop (817) 596-4827
20 mi. W of Dallas/Ft. Worth
Type: Public **Hrs:** By appt. only
Sporting: 1, 12 stations

Top Flight
Rt. 1, Box 233, Beasley, TX 77417
Leon Randermann (409) 387-2284
30 mi. W of Houston
Type: Public/Member
Hrs: Oct.-March, by appt.
Sporting: 1, 8 stations

Tyler Gun Club
PO Box 6945, Tyler, TX 75711
Steve Fry (903) 597-3345
80 mi. SE of Dallas/Ft. Worth
Type: Public/Member
Hrs: W, 4-Dark; S/Su, 2-Dark
Sporting: 1, 5 stations
Trap: 5 **Skeet:** 4 **Five Stand:** 1
HT: 30 ft.

Upland Bird Country
PO Box 730, Corsicana, TX 75151
Steve Stroube (903) 872-5663
55 mi. SE of Dallas
Type: Public
Hrs: Tues., after 5 or Sat., by resrv.
Sporting: 1, 10 stations
Skeet: 1 **HT:** 60 ft. **Wobble Trap**

Waco Gun Club, Inc.
7209 Airport Rd., Waco, TX 76708
Stan Nesmith (817) 753-2651
1 mi. NW of Waco
Type: Public/Member
Hrs: W-Su, 1:30-Dark
Sporting: None
Trap: 6 **Skeet:** 17
Five Stand: 1 **HT:** 30 ft.

West Texas Sportsman's
PO Box 14214, Odessa, TX 79768
Pete Wrenn (915) 561-9379
10 mi. E of Midland
Type: Public/Member
Hrs: T-Su, 10-Dusk
Sporting: 1, 12 stations
Trap: 2 **Skeet:** 1 **Five Stand:** 1
HT: 45 ft.

Westside Shooting Grounds
1627 N. Hearthside
Richmond, TX 77469
Jay Herbert (713) 371-2582
20 mi. W of Houston
Type: Member/Avail
Hrs: W-Su, 9-Dark
Sporting: 1, 14 stations
Skeet: 1 **HT:** 120 ft.

Windwalker Farm
4202 Dawn Circle
Midland, TX 79707
Ralph Cramer (915) 694-2311
17 mi. NE of Midland
Type: Public/Member
Hrs: T-F, 1-Dark; S/Su, 10-Dark
Sporting: 1, 10 stations
HT: 90 ft. **Wobble Trap**

TRAP & SKEET

Arrowhead Gun Club
Rt. 1, Box 134
College Station, TX 77845
Jim E. Broome (409) 690-0276
Hrs: T-Su, 10-Sunset
Trap: 2 **Skeet:** 3

Austin Skeet Range
5700 Avenue F, Austin, TX 78752
Stanley S. Castano (512) 272-8437
Hrs: 9-Dark
Trap: 1 **Skeet:** 2

Bandera Gun Club
Rt. 1, Box 506, Bandera, TX 78003
J.M. Clements (512) 796-4610
Hrs: W-F, 3-Dk; S, 8-Dk; Su, 1-Dk
Trap: 1 **Skeet:** 1

Bexar Community Shooting Range
Rt. 2, Box 73A, Marion, TX 78124
Jennifer Winkelmann
(512) 420-2182
Type: Public/Member
Hrs: T/Th/F/Su, 12-Dark; S, 9-Dark
Trap: 2 **Skeet:** 2 **Wobble Trap**

Callahan 4-H Shooting Sports
Rt. 2, Box 204, Clyde, TX 79510
Terry Ellis (915) 529-3652
Hrs: S/Su, 1-6 **Skeet:** 1

Corpus Christi Trap & Skeet
Box 7117, Corpus Christi, TX 78467
Richard Appleman (512) 852-1212
Hrs: W/F, 3-Dk; Th, 3-12;
S/Su, 9-Dk
Trap: 4 **Skeet:** 5

Creekwood Gun Club
PO Box 327, Groveton, TX 75845
Tommy Walton (409) 588-2181
Hrs: Th, 2-6; S/Su, 9-8
Trap: 1 **Skeet:** 3

Desoto Gun Club
PO Box 726, Desoto, TX 75123
Mike Hatch (214) 576-3338

10 mi. S of Dallas
Hrs: W, 6-9; S/Su, 12-Dark
Trap: 3 **Skeet:** 6

El Paso Trap Club
9817 Alameda Ave.
El Paso, TX 79927
Earl Scripture (915) 859-7325
Hrs: W, 2-5; S/Su, 10-5
Trap: 6

Fort Worth Trap & Skeet Club
Rt. 17, Box 283B
Ft. Worth, TX 76126
Stan Peterson (817) 244-9878
Hrs: W/Th/Su, 1-7; S, 10-7
Trap: 10 **Skeet:** 6

Ft. Hood Skeet & Trap Club
401 Roy Reynolds Dr.
Harken Heights, TX 76543
Bill Crossan (817) 532-2422
Hrs: S/Su, 10-Dark (Win),
10-6 (Sum)
Trap: 2 **Skeet:** 3

Graham Gun Club
PO Drawer 270
Graham, TX 76450
Kevin Stephens (817) 549-4758
Hrs: Various Wkends
Trap:

Grand Prairie Gun Club
PO Box 530274
Grand Prairie, TX 75053
Mike Vestal (214) 641-9940
Hrs: W/S/Su, afternoons
Trap: 2 **Skeet:** 3

Hill Country Gun Club
3009 Fawn Ridge
Fredericksburg, TX 78624
Don E. Landers (210) 997-6745
Hrs: Su/W, 1-Dark
Trap: 1 **Skeet:** 1

Hot Wells Skeet Range
PO Box 8, Cypress, TX 77429
Dallas Lamar (713) 373-0232
Skeet: 4

Iowa Park Gun Club
Box 368, Iowa Park, TX 76367
Terry Brogdon (817) 592-9557
Hrs: 4th Wkend of Month
(Feb-Aug) **Trap:** 4

LaBota Skeet & Trap Club
14426 Mines Rd.,
Laredo, TX 78041
Lester W. Early (512) 723-6328
Hrs: W, 5-12; S/Su, 1-12
Skeet: 2

Lackland Rod & Gun Club
37 MWRSS/MWBR, 5325 Military Dr.
Lackland AFB, TX 78236
Steve L. Strunk (512) 674-7831
Hrs: M-Th, 4-9; S, 9-1; Su, 1-6
Trap: 1 Skeet: 2
Olympic Trap

The Metro Gun Club
4601 Kelvin St.
Houston, TX 77005
Louis Poutous (713) 524-9074
10 mi. S of Houston
Type: Public Hrs: S/Su, all day
Trap: 2

Midland Shooters Assn.
PO Box 60704
Midland, TX 79711
Gordon Marcum (915) 563-5116
Hrs: W/Th/S/Su, 10-Dark
Trap: 16 Skeet: 6

Mission Skeet & Trap Club
PO Box 251, Mission, TX 78572
Joe L. Harris
Hrs: Su, 2-6; W, 5-7
Trap: 1 Skeet: 3

Mount Vernon Gun Club
PO Box 982,
Mt. Vernon, TX 75457
E.C. Withers (903) 537-4536
Hrs: Private
Skeet: 1

Nacogdoches Skeet Club
3734 Tudor,
Nacogdoches, TX 75961
Robert Akins (409) 564-5455
Hrs: T/Th/S/Su
Skeet: 1

Orange Gun Club Inc.
355 Glenwood, Vidor, TX 77662
Dennis Hawthorn (409) 883-5622
Hrs: Daylight
Skeet: 1

Randolph Skeet & Trap
12 MWRSS/MWR, 415 B St., E.
Randolph AFB, TX 78150
David Wheeless (210) 652-2064
Hrs: S/Su, 10-2; W, 5-8
Trap: 1 Skeet: 2

Rockdale Gun Club
Box 506, Rockdale, TX 76567
W.P. Hogan (512) 446-6669
Hrs: 10am, except Wed.; also
night shooting
Trap: 1 Skeet: 1

Rockwall Gun Club
1404 Fernwood Dr.
Mesquite, TX 75149
Rodonna Wolfe (214) 288-5676
Type: Member/Avail
Hrs: S/Su, 1-Dark; W, 5-Dark
Trap: 2 Skeet: 3

Sands Skeet Club
PO Box 181228
Corpus Christi, TX 78480
Steve Foshee

Stonehill Shooting Ranch
PO Box 21, Marble Falls, TX 78654
Cindi Darragh (512) 693-5296
Hrs: W/F, 1-Dark; S/Su, 9-Dark
Trap: 1 Skeet: 2

Tejas Gun Club
1214 Old Tyler Rd.
Nacogdoches, TX 75961
Linda M. Pronge (409) 560-2774
Type: Public/Member
Hrs: F, 4-9; Su, 12-9
Trap: 3 Skeet: 1

Texoma Trap Club
506 Oxford Dr.
Sherman, TX 75090
Bob Overturf (903) 892-1992
Hrs: W/Th, 1-6; Su, 8-6
Trap: 9

Uvalde Gun Club
PO Box 5291, Uvalde, TX 78802
Carl Dee Castellaw
Trap: 1 Skeet: 1

Victoria Gun Club
PO Box 4116, Victoria, TX 77903
Don Keeney
Hrs: 9-10 Trap: 1 Skeet: 1

UTAH

SPORTING & 5-STAND

Cache Valley Hunter Ed Ctr
780 E. 350 So.
Hyrum, UT 84319
Lloyd Johnson (801) 245-4000
Hrs: W/Th, 6-9:30; S/Su, 10:30-3
Sporting: None
Trap: 4 Skeet: 2 Five Stand: 1

**Castle Country
Sportsmen's Club**
3679 S. 180 W.
Price, UT 84501
Robert Migliori, Sr. (801) 637-7841
35 mi. S of Price
Type: Public/Member
Hrs: 7 Days/Wk; AM-Dusk
Sporting: 1, 12 stations
Trap: 1

Goshen Dam Sporting Clays
11609 W. Hwy. 6
Goshen, UT 84633

Kris Morgan (801) 667-3574
60 mi. S of Salt Lake City
Type: Public Hrs: Seasonal
Sporting: 3, 25 sta. Trap: 1

Goshute Sporting Clays
PO Box 187, Goshen, UT 84633
Ron Christensen (801) 667-3390
60 mi. S of Salt Lake City
Type: Public Hrs: S/Su, 9:30-5
Sporting: 1, 8 stations

Hatt's Ranch
Box 275, Green River, UT 84525
Rey Lloyd Hatt (801) 564-3224
16 mi. SW of Green River
Type: Public/Member
Hrs: T-Su, 9-5pm
Sporting: 1, 5 stations

Holladay Gun Club
PO Box 17304
Holladay, UT 84117
Dart Dowsett (801) 277-1426
10 mi. SE of Salt Lake City
Type: Public
Hrs: S/Su/Holidays; Wkdys by Appt.
Sporting: 1, 14 stations
Trap: 5 Skeet: 3 HT: 60 ft.

Pheasant Valley
16840 W. 12800 N.
Howell, UT 84316
Carlos Christensen (801) 471-2245
75 mi. N of Salt Lake City
Type: Public/Member
Hrs: Daily by reservation
Sporting: 2

TRAP & SKEET

Bonneville Trap & Skeet
2100 S. 6000 West
Salt Lake City, UT 84120
Fred Kuhn (801) 972-9853
Hrs: W, 7pm; S/Su, 10am
Trap: 16

Cedar City Trap Club
844 W. Mt. View Dr.
Cedar City, UT 84720
Jack Matheson (801) 586-8921
Type: Public/Member
Hrs: S, 11am (Win); W, 6pm (Sum)
Trap: 4

Golden Spike Trap Club
Box 771, Brigham City, UT 84302
Earl Kerkove (801) 723-3427
Hrs: Th, 7pm; Su, Noon Trap: 4

Heber Valley Gun Club
215 Little Sweden Rd.
Heber City, UT 84032
Lynn Luke (801) 654-1356
Hrs: W, 7pm; Su, Noon Trap: 6

Helper Gun Club
Rt. 1, Box 121, Helper, UT 84526
Bill Curtice (801) 637-1086
Hrs: S/Su, 10 Trap: 6

Hill Rod & Gun Club
Box 187, Clearfield, UT 84015
Robert D. Walker (801) 777-6767
Hrs: Su, 11-4; T, 4-7; Th, 3-6; S,10-2
Trap: 3 **Skeet:** 4

Magna Gun Club
2964 Continental Cr.
Salt Lake City, UT 84118
Jim Hardy (801) 250-9818
Hrs: S/Su, 10am **Trap:** 6

Ogden Gun Club
1577 Burton Ct., Ogden, UT 84403
Ralph McEntire (801) 782-3556
Hrs: W, 6pm; Su, 10am
Trap: 4

Provo Gun Club
591 E. 200 North
Pleasant Grove, UT 84062
David Adamson (801) 785-9283
Hrs: W, 7pm; S/Su, 10am
Trap: 6

The Salt Lake Gun Club
208 S. Redwood Rd.
North Salt Lake City, UT 84054
Larry Mitchell (801) 298-7516
5 mi. N of Salt Lake City
Type: Public/Member
Hrs: S/Su, 8-Dk; Others by appt.
Trap: 18 **Skeet:** Y **Wobble Trap**

Spanish Fork Gun Club
PO Box 352,
Spanish Fork, UT 84660
Mike Palfreyman (801) 489-3945
Type: Public/Member
Hrs: Call for info **Trap:** 13

Vernal Rod & Gun Club
PO Box 35, Vernal, UT 84078
Gail Herrmann (801) 789-2727
Hrs: S/Su, 10am **Trap:** 10

VERMONT

SPORTING & 5-STAND

Bull's-Eye Sporting Center
RR2, Box 4140, Barre, VT 05641
David & Nancy Brooks
(802) 479-2534
7 mi. W of Barre
Type: Public **Hrs:** Su-S
Sporting: 1, 30 stations **HT:** 30 ft.

Hermitage Inn
Coldbrook Rd.,
Wilmington, VT 05363
Jim McGovern (802) 464-3511
25 mi. E of Bennington
Type: Public **Hrs:** Daily, 10-3
Reservs: Recommended
Sporting: 1, 15 stations
Wobble Trap

North Country Sportsmen's
PO Box 5598,
Essex Junction, VT 05452
Keith Turman (802) 878-0330
6 mi. E of Burlington
Type: Public/Member
Hrs: Su, 9-4 year round; W, 5-Dark
summer only
Sporting: None
Trap: 2 **Five Stand:** 1 **Wobble Trap**

Tinmouth Hunting Preserve
Box 556, Wallingford, VT 05773
Rick Fallar (802) 446-2337
70 mi. NE of Albany
Type: Public/Member
Hrs: Daily Year Round by Appt.,
10am & 1pm
Sporting: 1, 16 stations **HT:** 75 ft.

TRAP & SKEET

Barre Fish & Game Club
PO Box 130, Barre, VT 05651
Byrond Moyer (802) 479-1266
Hrs: 8-Dusk
Skeet: 2

Underhill Rod & Gun Club
RD2, Box 3090
Fairfax, VT 05454
Burt McGowan (802) 849-6155
Hrs: T/Th, 5-Dark; Su, 9-5
Trap: 2 **Skeet:** 3

VIRGINIA

SPORTING & 5-STAND

Buffalo Creek Sporting Club
Rt. 1, Box 232
Lynch Station, VA 24571
Robert & Ed Ott (540) 297-6626
36 mi. E of Roanoke
Type: Public/Member
Hrs: S/Su, 8-7
Reservs: Strongly recommended
Sporting: 4, 40 stations
Trap: 1 **Skeet:** 1 **Five Stand:** 2
HT: 200 ft.

Bull Run Shooting Center
7700 Bull Run Dr.
Centreville, VA 22020
Gene Hutsky (703) 830-2344
30 mi. S of Washington, DC
Type: Public

Hrs: S/Su, 9-6; Weekdays, 4-9:30
Sporting: None
Trap: 13 **Skeet:** 5 **Five Stand:** 1

Cavalier Sporting Clays
9 Chase Gayton Dr., #1124
Richmond, VA 23233
Henry Baskerville (804) 740-5263
30 mi. W of Richmond
Type: Public
Hrs: Th/Su, 1-Dark; Other times by appt.
Reservs: Not required
Sporting: 4, 40 stations
Five Stand: 6 **HT:** 80 ft.
Wobble Trap

SHOOT THE BEST

Charles City Sporting Clays & Hunting Preserve
501 Shirley Plantation Rd.
Charles City, VA 23030
Charles Carter (804) 829-6270
19 mi. SE of Richmond
Type: Public
Hrs: W-F, 1-6; S/Su, 9-5; other
times by reserv.
Reservs: Recommended
Sporting: 2, 45 stations **HT:** 35 ft.

Cumberland State Forest
Rt. 1, Box 250
Cumberland, VA 23040
Lewis Martin (804) 492-9526
40 mi. W of Richmond
Type: Public
Hrs: W-S, 8:30-5:30; Su, 1-5:30
Sporting: 1, 10 stations

Eastern Shore Safaris
6276 Sturgis House Rd.
Jamesville, VA 23398
Tom Webb (804) 442-6035
40 mi. E of VA Beach
Type: Public/Member
Hrs: W-S, by appt; Su, 11-Dark
Sporting: 1, 60 stations
HT: 50 ft.

Falkland Farms
PO Box 1297, Halifax, VA 24558
Tom Rowland (804) 575-1400
85 mi. SW of Richmond
Type: Public
Hrs: Year Round by Reservation
Sporting: 1, 13 stations

Flying Rabbit
PO Box 1234, 1015 Greystone St.
Harrisonburg, VA 22801
Gregory Weaver (540) 432-3969
95 mi. SW of Washington, DC
Type: Public
Hrs: T-F, 5-Dk; S, 8-Dk; Su, 1-Dk
Sporting: 1, 11 stations

Forest Green Shooting
Forest Green Ln., PO Box 361
Spotsylvania, VA 22553
Leroy & Shirley Hilsmier
(540) 582-2566
60 mi. S of Washington, DC
Type: Public/Member
Hrs: Course Proposed 1995
Sporting: 1, 8 stations

Franklin Skeet & Trap Club
108 Tanyard Rd.
Rocky Mount, VA 24151
Dan Heckman (540) 483-5608
7 mi. S of Rocky Mount
Type: Member/Avail
Hrs: W, 4-Dark; Su, 1-Dark
Sporting: 1, 13 stations
Trap: 2 **Skeet:** 5 **Wobble Trap**

Ft. Lee Outdoor Recreation
Bldg. P-15014, Ft. Lee, VA 23801
Ltc. Pat Knutson (804) 765-2210
Hrs: W-Su, 12-Dark
Sporting: None
Trap: 4 **Skeet:** 3 **Five Stand:** 1

HOMESTEAD.
1766

The Homestead
PO Box 2000,
Hot Springs, VA 24445
David C. Judah, Club Mgr.
(540) 839-7787
75 mi. N of Roanoke
Type: Public/Member
Hrs: Year round: Apr-Nov, 10-5:30;
Nov-Apr, 10-5
Reservs: Recommended
Sporting: 2, 24 stations
Trap: 2 **Skeet:** 4 **Five Stand:** 1

Shooting Instruction
Available - See Pg. 174
& Our Ad Pg. 51

Oceana Skeet & Trap
Bldg. SR-6, NAS Oceana
Virginia Beach, VA 23460
Reb Nantz (804) 433-2875
Type: Public
Hrs: T/Th/F, 3-8; W, 11-10;
S/Su, 10-7
Sporting: None
Trap: 4 **Skeet:** 5 **Five Stand:** 1

Old Forge Outdoors, Inc.
104 Elizabeth Page
Williamsburg, VA 23185
Gerald H. Felix (804) 220-8544
20 mi. SE of Richmond
Type: Public
Hrs: M/T, by appt; W/F, 9-Dark;
S/Su, 9-Dark or appt.
Sporting: 2, 50 stations   **HT:** 40 ft.

**Piedmont Guides &
Gunners, Inc.**
Rt. 2, Box 12
Louisa, VA 23093
Howard Scheurenbrand, Jr.
(540) 967-3647
16 mi. E of Charlottesville
Type: Public/Member
Hrs: By appt.
Sporting: 1, 5 stations

Primland
Rt. 1, Box 265-C
Claudville, VA 24076
Johnny Lambert (540) 251-8012
60 mi. N of Greensboro
Type: Public **Hrs:** W-S, 8-5
Sporting: 1, 15 stations
See Our Ad Pg. 397

Quail Ridge
Sporting Clays
Rt. 3, Box 116A
Lexington, VA 24450
R. Chris Salb (540) 463-1800
45 mi. N of Roanoke
Type: Public
Hrs: W-M, 9am-1/2 hr. befo.. dusk
Reservs: Strongly recommended
Sporting: 1, 17 stations
o Loaner Guns
o On-Site Pro Shop
o NSCA & NRA Certified Instructor
   Available
o 5 mi. S of Junction Interstates
   I-81 & I-64
o Corporate & Fundraising Shoots

Shady Grove Kennel
And
Hunting Preserve
And
Sporting Clays

Shady Grove
Sporting Clays
11986 Lucky Hill Rd.
Remington, VA 22734
Neil Selby (540) 439-2683
45 mi. SW of Washington, DC
Type: Public/Member
Hrs: Su-S, 8-dark
Reservs: Recommended
Sporting: 2, 30 stations
Five Stand: 1   **HT:** 30 ft.

Sussex Shooting Sports
Box 624 (Rt. 460)
Waverly, VA 23890
Bob Hall (804) 834-3200
35 mi. SE of Richmond
Type: Public/Member
Hrs: T-F, 1-Dk; S/Su 9-Dk,
& by resrv.
Sporting: 2, 20 stations
HT: 35 ft. **Wobble Trap**

Thompson Valley
PO Box 4285, Richlands, VA 24641
J.E. Cooper (540) 988-5770
100 mi. W of Roanoke
Type: Public/Member
Hrs: W-Su, By appt.
Sporting: 2, 14 stations
HT: 30 ft.

Virginia-Carolina Shooting
Rt. #4, Box 379
Ridgeway, VA 24148
Walter E. Prillaman, Jr.
(540) 956-4778
38 mi. N of Greensboro, NC
Type: Public
Hrs: By Appointment
Sporting: 1, 12 stations

Walnut Hill Shooting Center
PO Box 177, Caret, VA 22436
Ruther Allen (804) 443-9229
7 mi. N of Tappahannock
Type: Public
Hrs: F, 10-7; S/Su, 9-7; M-Th, & appt.
Sporting: 1, 12 stations
HT: 12 ft.

TRAP & SKEET
Arlington Fairfax Izaak Walton
10521 Judicial Dr., #307
Fairfax, VA 22030
Allen H. Sachsel (703) 631-4497
Hrs: S, 10-5; Su, 12-5; W, 2-6
Trap: 4 **Skeet:** 3

Arrowhead Gun Club
734 Huston St.,
Chase City, VA 23924
Milton H. Mills (804) 372-3810
Hrs: Su, 1-Dark
Trap: 1 Skeet: 10

Brushy Mountain Club, Inc.
Rt. 4, Box 304, Gretna, VA 24557
Oscar Shelton
Hrs: Su, 1-Dark   Skeet: 5

Dunbrooke Hunt Gun Club
Rt. 1, Box 597
Tappahannock, VA 22560
Malcolm E. Courtney
(804) 443-3221
Hrs: W, 6-9 & Reg. Shoots
Trap: 1

Fredericksburg Rod & Gun
7301 Muscoe Pl.
King George, VA 22485
Ray L. Harding (540) 898-9595
Hrs: 7-10
Trap: 1 Skeet: 10

Halifax County Gun Club
PO Box 693,
South Boston, VA 24592
William N. Currie (804) 753-2375
Hrs: S/Su, 2-6   Skeet: 4

Izaak Walton S&T Club
5100 Charles City Rd.
Charles City, VA 23030
Jim Wallace (804) 966-7313
Trap: 5 Skeet: 12 Five Stand: 1

Langley Skeet Club
Box 728, Langley AFB, VA 23665
Lorna L. Clough (804) 766-3840
Hrs: S/Su, 12-6; W, 4-Dark
Trap: 1 Skeet: 2

Page Valley Sportsmens Club
Rt. 2, Box 214, Luray, VA 22835
James Mozisek (540) 778-1757
Hrs: Anytime to members; most
Sun. afternoons
Trap: 1 Skeet: 2

Piedmont Sportsman Club
HC6, Box 106, Banco, VA 22711
Kathy Moscoe (702) 832-5266
Hrs: Su, afternoon; Th, evening
Trap: 2 Skeet: 3

Portsmouth-Norfolk Co. Izaak
2533 Hanover Lane
Chesapeake, VA 23321
Tad S. Fischer (804) 484-0287
Hrs: S/Su, 2-6
Trap: 1 Skeet: 5

Quantico Shooting Club
PO Box 212, Quantico, VA 22134
SSGT Kirk N. Reider
(703) 640-6336
Hrs: Weekends   Skeet: 2
Oylympic Trap

Shenandale Gun Club
2975 Morris Mill Rd.
Staunton, VA 24401
Judith Stoner (540) 337-7800
Trap: 2 Skeet: 2

WASHINGTON

SPORTING & 5-STAND

**Boeing Employees
Dog/Gun Club**
26326 197th Place, SE
Kent, WA 98042
Bill Hardrath (206) 872-9960
Hrs: T, 4-8; Su, 10-2
Sporting: None
Trap: 4 Skeet: 3 Five Stand: 1

Bremerton Trap & Skeet
4956 State Hwy. 3 SW
Port Orchard, WA 98366
Al Paulus (206) 674-2438
60 mi. W of Seattle
Type: Public/Member
Hrs: W, 7-10; Su, 11-4
Sporting: 1, 17 stations
Trap: 5 Skeet: 6 Five Stand: 1
HT: 63 ft.

Evergreen Sportsmen Club
12736 Marksman Rd., SW
Olympia, WA 98512
Peter Strobl (206) 357-9080
25 mi. S of Olympia
Type: Public/Member
Hrs: S, 10-4; Th, 6-10; other
days by appt.
Sporting: 1, 10 stations
Trap: 36 Skeet: 1   HT: 20 ft.

Goodnight's Sporting Clays
PO Box 79, Bickleton, WA 99322
Lawrence Goodnight
(509) 896-2923
130 mi. NW of Portland, OR
Hrs: 7 days a week by appt.
Sporting: 1, 10 stations HT: 50 ft.

Landt Farms
W. 16308 Four Mound Rd.
Nine Mile Falls, WA 99026
Ellwood Landt (509) 466-4036
10 mi. NW of Spokane
Type: Public/Member
Hrs: Su-S, by appt.
Sporting: 1, 14 stations
HT: 50 ft.   Wobble Trap

Northwest Adventure Ctr
PO Box 33156
Fort Lewis, WA 98433
Norman Neubert (206) 967-7056
8 mi. S of Tacoma
Type: Public
Hrs: Special Events Only; W, 11-1;
Su/Su, 10:30-3:30
Sporting: 1, 10 stations

Trap: 2 Skeet: 4 Five Stand: 2
HT: 25 ft.

Pomeroy Gun Club
PO Box 532, Pomeroy, WA 99347
Elton Brown (509) 843-1460
100 mi. S of Spokane
Type: Public Hrs:
Sporting: 1, 10 stations
Trap: 2

R&M Game Birds
495 Fisher Hill Rd.
Lyle, WA 98635
Rodger Ford (509) 365-3245
80 mi. E of Vancouver, WA
Type: Public
Hrs: Year round, daylight-dark
Reservs: Strongly recommended
Sporting: 1, 15 stations
HT: 85 ft.

Rimrock Sporting Clays
Rt. 1, Box 10B
Uniontown, WA 99179
John Moehrle (509) 229-3287
20 mi. N of Lewiston
Type: Public
Hrs: S-Su, by appt.
Sporting: 1, 30 stations

Spokane Gun Club
19615 E. Sprague Ave.
Greenacres, WA 99016
Philip Kimere (509) 926-6505
10 mi. E of Spokane
Type: Public/Member
Hrs: W, 1-9; S/Su, 11-4 & by appt.
Sporting: 1, 5 stations
Trap: 18 Skeet: 8 Five Stand: 1

Sumner Sportsman Assoc.
15711 96th St. East
Puyallup, WA 98372
Jim Peterson (206) 848-9519
20 mi. N of Tacoma
Type: Public/Member
Hrs: SC; 2nd Sat, 10-til; TR/Sk, Su,
10-4; T, 7-10
Sporting: 1, 6 stations
Trap: 6 Skeet: 1 Five Stand: 1

Sun Valley Shooting Park
1452 Suntargets Rd.
Moxee, WA 98936
Rangemaster (509) 576-0866
14 mi. E of Yakima
Type: Public
Hrs: W-Su, 8am-Dusk
Sporting: 1, 10 stations
Trap: 1 Skeet: 1 Five Stand: 1

Sunnydell Shooting
292 Dryke Rd.
Sequim, WA 98382
Chuck Dryke (206) 683-5631
60 mi. W of Seattle

CLAYS

Type: Public
Hrs: Daily, 10-Dark
Sporting: 1, 22 stations
Trap: 2 **Skeet:** 2 **HT:** 100 ft.

Tacoma Sportsmen's Club
16409 Canyon Rd., E.
Puyallup, WA 98373
Dorie Jones (206) 537-6151
Hrs: T/Th, 6-10; Su, 10-4
Sporting: 1, 20 stations
Trap: 6 **Skeet:** 5

Turkey Ridge
1565 Evans Cutoff Rd.
Evans, WA 99126
Deryl Ruston (509) 684-2735
88 mi. N of Spokane
Type: Public
Hrs: By Reservation Only, 9-5:30
Sporting: 1, 10 stations

WCW, AKA Kenmore Gun Ranges
1031 228th SW
Bothell, WA 98071
Vic Alverez
35 mi. NE of Seattle
Type: Public/Member
Hrs: T/Th, 5-9; W, 12-5; S/Su, 10-5
Sporting: None
Trap: 4 **Five Stand:** 1

Wildlife Committee of Washington
1031 228th SW
Bothell, WA 98021
Charles Fulwood (206) 481-8685
30 mi. NE of Seattle
Type: Public/Member
Hrs: T&Th, 5-9; W, 12-7; S, 10-7; Su, 10-5
Sporting: 1, 10 stations
Trap: 4 **Five Stand:** 1

Winter Hawk
6362 Hwy. 291
Nine Mile Falls, WA 99026
Gary Scheinost (509) 276-5150
14 mi. NW of Spokane
Type: Public/Member
Hrs: Su-S, by appt.
Sporting: 1, 25 stations

TRAP & SKEET

NAS Whidbey Island Trap/Skeet
2250 W. Darvic Pl.
Oak Harbor, WA 98277
JC Fitzgerald (206) 257-5539
Hrs: W, 4-7; S/Su, 12-4 (Sum), 11-2 (Win)
Trap: 3 **Skeet:** 3

Renton Fish & Game Club
17500 SE 144th St.
Renton, WA 98059
(206) 226-1563
Universal Trench

Wenatchee Gun Club
1303 N. Devon Ave.
E. Wenatchee, WA 98802
Steve Repp (509) 884-6490
Hrs: Su, 10-4
Trap: 5 **Skeet:** 2

WEST VIRGINIA

SPORTING & 5-STAND

Prospect Hall
Rt. 1, Box 370
Kearneysville, WV 25430
Kevin White (304) 728-8213
60 mi. NW of Washington, DC
Type: Member/Avail
Hrs: 7 days a week, by appt.
Sporting: 1, 20 stations
Trap: 1 **Skeet:** 1 **HT:** 80 ft.

Warrior Trail Sporting Clays
Rt. 2, Box 167B
Terra Alta, WV 26764
Andrew P. Serdich (304) 789-2422
15 mi. W of Deep Creek Lake, MD
Type: Public/Member
Hrs: Su-S, all daylight hours
Reservs: Strongly recommended
Sporting: 1, 26 stations
HT: 50 ft.

Westlance Arms, Inc.
1610 Jones Spring East Rd.
Hedgesville, WV 25427
Mark T. Ewing (304) 754-7100
21 mi. S of Hagerstown
Type: Public
Hrs: Su-S, by resrv.
Sporting: 1, 10 stations
Trap: 1

TRAP & SKEET

Brooke County S&FA
1715 Main St.,
Wellsburg, WV 26070
Eugene Elcesser (304) 737-2243
Hrs: W, 6pm; Su, 1pm
Trap: 2

Paris Sportsman Club
269 Penco Rd.
Weirton, WV 26062
Bill King (304) 723-1151
Type: Public
Hrs: W, 5pm; Su, 2pm; July-Aug. 4pm **Trap:** 3

Piney Ridge Skeet & Trap
Rt. 1, Box 305, Weston, WV 26452
Bobby Cayton (304) 269-4227
Hrs: T/Th, 6-9; Su, 1-6
Trap: 1 **Skeet:** 2

Sportsman's Gun Club
2 Charlotte Lane
Scott Depot, WV 25560
David M. McClave (304) 757-9738
Hrs: S/Su, 1-5; W, 6-9
Trap: 4 **Skeet:** 2

Sportsmens & Farmers Assn.
190 Shangra-La lane
Wellsburg, WV 26070
John Platt (304) 737-1807
Hrs: W, 5:30; Su, 1 **Trap:** 10

WISCONSIN

SPORTING & 5-STAND

Acres for Recreation
6999 Retreat Rd., PO Box 24
Shawano, WI 54166
Barry Fredrich (715) 526-6055
35 mi. NW of Green Bay
Type: Public/Member
Hrs: Mar-Sep, 12-Dk; Others by appt.
Sporting: 1, 10 stations
Trap: 4 **HT:** 32 ft.

Big Rock Hunting Preserve
W15664 Chuck Rd.
Gilman, WI 54433
Chuck Birkenholz (715) 668-5557
60 mi. NE of Eau Claire
Type: Public/Member
Hrs: Su-S, 8-5 by appt.
Sporting: 1, 10 stations

Cadens Kennels & Hunt Club
W2738 Scenic Dr.
Campbellsport, WI 53010
Dennis Brath (414) 533-8579
40 mi. NW of Milwaukee
Type: Public/Member
Hrs: M-S, 8-5
Sporting: 1, 13 stations

Cassville Conservation Club
201 W. Dewey,
Cassville, WI 53806
Robert Bohringer (608) 725-5293
Type: Public **Hrs:** T, 5pm
Sporting: None
Trap: 3 **Five Stand:** 1

Cur-San's Clays
RR1, Box 87, Hancock, WI 54943
Curt & Sandy Dollar
(715) 228-5151
60 mi. N of Madison
Type: Public
Hrs: S/Su, 10-5; M/Th, 4:30-Dark; other times by appt.
Sporting: 1, 11 stations
Trap: 1 **HT**

F&R Sporting Clays
6431 Pleasant Hill Dr.
West Bend, WI 53095
Brett Richson (414) 675-6196

15 mi. S of Plymouth
Type: Public
Hrs: S/Su, call for hours
Sporting: 1, 13 stations

Fox Ridge Game Farm
8585 Valley Line Rd.
Oconto Falls, WI 54154
Bill or Kathy (414) 846-2508
135 mi. N of Milwaukee
Type: Public/Member
Hrs: By appt.
Sporting: 1, 9 stations
HT: 50 ft.

Game Unlimited
871 Ct. Rd. E., Hudson, WI 54016
Patrick Melloy (715) 246-2350
20 mi. E of Minneapolis
Type: Public
Hrs: M/W, S/Su, 9-6
Sporting: 3, 18 stations
Trap: Y   **HT:** 55 ft.

Gateway Gun Club
Box 596, Land O'Lakes, WI 54540
John Muir (715) 547-3321
from Land O'Lakes
Type: Public/Member
Hrs: M-Su, by appt.
Sporting: 1, 20 stations **Trap:** 4

Geneva National Hunt Club
555 Hunt Club Ct.
Lake Geneva, WI 53147
Bruce Kapanky (414) 245-7205
40 mi. N of Milwaukee
Type: Public/Member
Hrs: T-Su, 1-6
Sporting: 1, 10 stations **HT:** 52 ft.

J&H Game Farm
RR1, Box 221, Shiocton, WI 54170
James or Joanne Johnson
(715) 758-8134
27 mi. W of Green Bay
Type: Public/Member
Hrs: Tu-Su, 8-dark; by appt.
Reservs: Strongly recommended
Sporting: 3, 30 stations
HT: 30 ft.
O Loaner Guns
O Factory Ammunition
O On-Site Pro Shop
O On-Site Meals
O Shooting Lodge
O Formal Instructions
O Home of the 1993 NSCA State
  Shoot
O Host to '95 Field & Stream Jeep
  Classic

Lake Mills Conservation Club
PO Box 222, Lake Mills, WI 53551
Lee Braatz (414) 648-5758
25 mi. E of Madison
Type: Public/Member

Hrs: SC: call for schedule;
Trap: Th, 6-9
Sporting: 1, 12 stations
Trap: 3   **HT:** 12 ft.

Longshot
Sportsman's Club
N8995 Townline Rd.
Van Dyne, WI 54979
John Eiden (414) 688-2314
75 mi. NW of Milwaukee
Type: Public
Hrs: W, 3-7; S/Su, 10-2 (Summer);
Su, 10-2 (Winter)
Reservs: Strongly recommended
Sporting: 1, 10 stations

Luxenburg Sportsman Club
PO Box 160, Luxenburg, WI 54217
Jay Cravillion (414) 845-5510
20 mi. E of Green Bay
Type: Public **Sporting:** 1
Trap: 1 **Five Stand:** 1

Mayville Gun Club
PO Box 31, Mayville, WI 53050
Phil Nogalski/Gary Steinbach
(414) 387-9996
45 mi. NW of Milwaukee
Type: Public/Member
Hrs: Call for current schedule
Sporting: 1, 10 sta. **Trap:** 5   **HT**

North Shore Winchester
3109 Hwy. 41,
Franksville, WI 53126
Thomas V. Joerndt (414) 835-1112
Type: Public **Hrs:**
Sporting: 1, 9 stations
Trap: 6 **Skeet:** 4

Our Farm
PO Box 108, Eastman, WI 54626
Rudy Wendt (608) 874-4556
80 mi. W of Madison
Type: Public/Member
Hrs: M-F, by reservation; S/Su, 10-5
Sporting: 1, 10 stations

Ozaukee Co. Fish & Game
PO Box 12, Newburg, WI 53060
Roger Perlewitz (414) 692-9923
Sporting: 1

Pheasant City Hunt Club
R#1, Box 272,
Markesan, WI 53946
Bill Scallon (414) 324-5813
65 mi. NW of Milwaukee
Type: Public
Hrs: Su, 10-5; M/Th, 5-Dark
Sporting: 2, 16 stations **HT:** 45 ft.

Quail Haven Hunt Club
Rt. 4, Clintonville, WI 54929
Michael K. Duffey (715) 823-6123
35 mi. W of Green Bay

Type: Public **Hrs:** By Appt.
Sporting: 1, 10 stations

R&R Ranch
8923 Richfield Dr.
Marshfield, WI 54449
Steve Strong (715) 676-3365
6 mi. from Marshfield
Type: Public/Member
Hrs: Su-S, with reservations
Sporting: 1, 16 station **HT:** 30 ft.

Ripon Clays
Box 543, County Hwy. FF
Ripon, WI 54971
David Tabbert (414) 748-3453
70 mi. NW of Milwaukee
Type: Public/Member
Hrs: W; 5:30-Dark; 1st Su of
Month, May-Sep, 10-4
Sporting: 1, 8 stations
Trap: 2   **HT:** 30 ft. **Wobble Trap**

River Wildlife
Kohler, WI 53044
Max Grube (414) 457-0134
55 mi. N of Milwaukee
Type: Member/Avail
Sporting: 1, 5 stations
Trap: Y **Five Stand:** Y

Rivers Edge Sporting Clays
R2, Box 181,
Chippewa Falls, WI 54729
Robert D. Buss (715) 723-5865
10 mi. N of Eau Claire
Type: Public **Hrs:** By appt. only
Sporting: 1, 12 stations **HT:** 25 ft.

Shooters Sporting Club
RR2, Box 2344
Soldiers Grove, WI 54655
John Generalski (608) 538-3200
60 mi. NW of Madison
Type: Public **Hrs:** Su-S, by appt.
Sporting: 1, 10 stations

Sioux Creek
Hunting Club
PO Box 561, Chetek, WI 54728
Jimmy Lane (715) 237-2805
80 mi. NE of Minneapolis
Type: Public/Member
Hrs: S/Su, 8-4; T/Th, 12-Dark; W/F,
by appt.
Reservs: Not required
Sporting: 2, 22 stations **HT:** 45 ft.
O Loaner Guns
O Factory Ammunition
O On-Site Pro Shop
O On-Site Meals
O Shooting Lodge
O Organized Leagues
O Golf Carts
O Crazy Quail Course
O 4 miles from Highway 53

CLAYS

Smoky Lake Reserve
1 Lake St., PO Box 100
Phelps, WI 54554
Miriam Saucke (715) 545-2333
45 mi. NE of Rhinelander
Type: Member/Avail
Hrs: As requested
Sporting: 1, 10 stations
Trap: 1 **Skeet:** 1

Summit Lake
Game Farm
PO Box 810
Hayward, WI 54843
John Treslley (715) 354-7241
75 mi. SE of Superior
Type: Public/Member
Hrs: Th-T, 10-6; W, 12-8; Mem.
Day - Labor Day
Reservs: Strongly recommended
Sporting: 1, 15 stations
Trap: 1   **HT:** 55 ft. **Wobble Trap**

Top Gun Farms
N3249 Riverview Rd.
Juneau, WI 53039
David Fiedler (414) 349-8128
45 mi. NE of Madison
Type: Public/Member
Hrs: S/Su, 10-4; Th, 3:30-Dark;
other by resrv.
Sporting: 1, 20 stations
Trap: 1 **Five Stand:** 1   **HT:** 20 ft.

Trout & Grouse
11110 110th St.
Kenosha, WI 53142
Andrew Burrows (414) 857-7232
60 mi. N of Chicago
Type: Public
Hrs: T-S, 10-5:30; Su, 12-5;
Closed June-Aug.
Sporting: 1, 35 stations **HT:** 30 ft.

Wausau Skeet & Trap Club
PO Box 2154
Wausau, WI 54402
Roger Retzinger (715) 875-7227
135 mi. N of Madison
Type: Public/Member
Hrs: Th, 5-9 (May-Aug)
Sporting: 1, 10 stations
Trap: 3 **Skeet:** 3 **Five Stand:** 1
HT: 40 ft.

Wern Valley
S36W29903 Wern Way
Waukesha, WI 53188
Brian Johnson (414) 968-2400
20 mi. W of Milwaukee
Type: Public/Member
Hrs: Sat., 9-3; W, 4:30-Sunset
(May-Sept)
Sporting: 1, 10 stations **HT:** 60 ft.

Whispering Emerald Ridge
Game Farm
N3952 640th St.
Menomonie, WI 54751
Mike Kettner/Bruce Olson
(715) 235-1720
60 mi. E of Minneapolis-St. Paul
Type: Public   **Hrs:** By appt.
Sporting: 1, 13 stations **HT:** 45 ft.

Woodhollow Sporting Clays
517 Copeland Ave.
La Crosse, WI 54603
Roger Wendling (608) 784-0482
11 mi. N of LaCrosse
Type: Public/Member
Hrs: Sun. only (May-Sept); by appt.
Sporting: 3, 20 stations
Skeet: 1 **Five Stand:** 1   **HT:** 120'

Woods & Meadows
Rt. 1, Warrens, WI 54666
Scott Goetzka (608) 378-4223
100 mi. NW of Madison
Type: Public
Hrs: S, w/o appt; Su-F, appt. only
Sporting: 2, 22 stations **HT:** 30 ft.

TRAP & SKEET

Ashley Shooting Club
605 16th St., Mosinee, WI 54455
Glen Grabski
Hrs: Su-T, 6-9 (Apr-Nov)
Trap: 4 **Skeet:** 1

Beaver Dam
Conservationists
206 Hamilton St.
Beaver Dam, WI 53916
Mike Connaughty (414) 887-1575
Type: Public/Member
Hrs: W, 7-10; Su, 10-2
Trap: 9

Daniel Boone Conservation
W 158 N 8315 Steven Mac Dr.
Menomonee Falls, WI 53051
Bob Ehrgott (414) 628-1328
Hrs: W-Th, 5-9
Trap: 5 **Skeet:** 1

Brown County Sportsmens
3180 Bayview Dr.
Green Bay, WI 54311
Robert Trotman (414) 434-9930
Hrs: S, afternoons; Su, mornings
Trap: 6 **Skeet:** 6

Cudahy Sportsmen's Club
PO Box 243
Cudahy, WI 53110
Ron Applebee (414) 747-9284
Type: Public/Member
Hrs: T/W, 6:30pm-10pm
Trap: 8

Darien Sporting Goods
N2669 Hwy. 14
Darien, WI 53114

David E. Ennis (414) 724-3433
Type: Public   **Hrs:** T-Su, 9-6
Trap: 4

Eau Claire Rod & Gun Club
PO Box 1572, Eau Claire, WI 54702
Robert Webber (715) 832-4391
Type: Public
Hrs: Nights, 6-9:30; Su, 12-4
Trap: 7 **Skeet:** 1

Faskells Gun Club
Hwy. 54 West,
New London, WI 54961
Peter Ziebell (414) 596-2100
Hrs: Weekdays by appt.
Trap: 8 **Skeet:** 6

Fox Valley Huntsmen Club
PO Box 2983, Oshkosh, WI 54903
Rick Sebora (414) 685-6335
Type: Public/Member
Hrs: S, 10-3 (all year); M/Th,
5-9 (April-Aug)
Trap: 6

Hodag Sports Club
4340 Aberdean Rd.
Rhinelander, WI 54501
Don Minder (715) 362-2784
Type: Public/Member
Hrs: W/Th, 5-9; S, 12-5
Trap: 5 **Five Stand:** 2

Hudson Rod, Gun &
Archer Club
PO Box 83, Hudson, WI 54016
(715) 386-9955
Hrs: T/Th, Noon-8 (Summer);
Su, 1-4 (Winter)
Trap: 8

Janesville Conservation Club
4370 Milton Ave.
Janesville, WI 53546
Ron Morse (608) 756-4647
Type: Public/Member
Hrs: S, 10-4 (Jan-Apr); W, 10-2;
5-9 (Apr-Oct)   **Trap:** 8

Lafarge Trapshooting Assn.
109 E. Main St., PO Box 67
Lafarge, WI 54639
La Verne Campbell (608) 625-2180
Type: Public **Hrs:** Th, 7pm-11pm
Trap: 4

Lakeview Trap & Sport
S80 W. 14401 Schultz Lane
Muskego, WI 53150
Loreen L. Klauser (414) 422-9025
Type: Public
Hrs: T/Th, 6-9:30; W, 3-9:30; F,
3-7:30; S/Su, 11-3:30
Trap: 4

Manitowoc Gun Club
PO Box 201, Manitowoc, WI 54221
Joseph J. Koneczka
(414) 758-2727

Hrs: Th, 6-10; Su, 9-2
Trap: 5 **Skeet:** 2

Middleton Sportsmen's Club
7910 Airport Rd.
Middleton, WI 53562
Roger Pasch (608) 836-1118
Hrs: Su, 1-4; Th, 7-9:30
Trap: 2 **Skeet:** 1

Mosinee Sportsmans Alliance
977 Rocky Ridge Rd.
Mosinee, WI 54455
Douglas K. Davis, Pres.
(715) 693-6587
1 mi. NW of Mosinee
Hrs: Th, 5:30-8:30pm (Apr-Sep)
Trap: 4

Muscoda Sportsmens League
430 Beech St.,
Muscoda, WI 53573
Virgil Bomkamp (608) 739-3634
Type: Public/Member
Hrs: W, 6-10; S/Su, 10-4
Trap: 6

Oshkosh Gun Club
PO Box 425, Oshkosh, WI 54901
Mike Kobussen (414) 231-0682
Hrs: 9-Dark, year round
Trap: 2 **Skeet:** 2

Sauk Prairie Trap & Skeet
E. 11102 Sauk Prairie Rd.
Prairie Du Sac, WI 53578
Bill Skinner (608) 643-4844
30 mi. N of Madison
Type: Public
Hrs: W, 6-10; S, 12-5
Trap: 6 **Skeet:** 6

Sheboygan Falls Conservation
914 Linden St.,
Cleveland, WI 53015
Thomas Steinbeck (414) 467-2970
Hrs: Su, 11-4
Trap: 4 **Skeet:** 2

Van Dyne Sportsmens Club
PO Box 8, Van Dyne, WI 54979
Dick Baier (414) 688-2433
Hrs: Su, 1-4; T, 6-10; Th, 9-12& 6-10
Trap: 4 **Skeet:** 1

Waukesha Gun Club
Box 1509, Waukesha, WI 53187
Gary Schaetzel (414) 547-9785
Hrs: T/Th, 4-9; W, 10-10; S, 12-3:30; Su, 9-1
Trap: 29 **Skeet:** 5

Westgate Sportsman Club
4909 Sportsman Dr.
Eau Claire, WI 54701
Dennis Freid (715) 832-4548
5 mi. W of Eau Claire
Type: Public/Member
Trap: 2

WYOMING

SPORTING & 5-STAND

Canyon Ranch Gun Club
PO Box 282, Big Horn, WY 82833
Jim Roach (307) 674-9097
15 mi. S of Sheridan
Type: Member/Avail
Sporting: 1

Clear Creek Hunting & Sporting Clays
3004 Hwy. 14-16 East
Clearmont, WY 82835
Doug Kauffman (307) 737-2217
140 mi. N of Casper
Type: Public/Member
Hrs: Su-S, daylight-dark
Sporting: 1, 10 stations
Skeet: 1 **HT:** 100 ft.
Wobble Trap

Cody Shooting Complex
1385 Sherdian Ave.
Cody, WY 82414
John J. Gibbons (307) 587-9556
180 mi. NW of Casper
Type: Public
Hrs: Su, 10am; W, 5-Dark (May-Sept); Su, 10am (Sep-Apr)
Sporting: 4, 40 stations
Trap: 5 **Skeet:** 3

HF Bar Ranch
1301 Rock Creek Rd.
Saddlestring, WY 82840
Richard Platt (307) 684-2487
180 mi. N of Casper
Type: Public
Hrs: Daily by Appt.
Sporting: 4, 33 stations
Trap: 1 **HT:** 80 ft.

Pinedale Sporting Clays
PO Box 1191, Pinedale, WY 82941
Steve Griggs (307) 367-2893
Sporting: 1

Sheridan County
44 Fort Rd., Sheridan, WY 82801
Robert L. Prill (307) 672-6450
Type: Public/Member
Hrs: Su, 10-3; W/Th, 5-9 (Summer)
Sporting: 1, 5 stations
Trap: 14 **Skeet:** 1 **Wobble Trap**

TRAP & SKEET

Buffalo Trap & Skeet
647 N. Desmet,
Buffalo, WY 82834
Terry Barnhart (307) 684-9287
Type: Public/Member
Hrs: 5/15-9/1; Summer,
T/Th Evenings **Trap:** 3 **Skeet:** 1

Casper Skeet Club
3532 E. 23rd St.,
Casper, WY 82609

Roland Kessler (307) 234-6958
Hrs: T, 5-7; Su, 12-4
Trap: 1 **Skeet:** 3

Cheyenne Municipal T&S
Box 1065, ,Cheyenne, WY 82003
Thomas Gasser (307) 634-2504
Hrs: W, 5-9; Su, 9-3
Trap: 9 **Skeet:** 2

Heart Mountain R&G Club
211 Grand, Powell, WY 82435
Bob Hammond (307) 754-5577
Hrs: Varies **Trap:** 2 **Skeet:** 1

Jackson Hole Trap Club
PO Box V, Jackson, WY 83001
Dean K. Bark (307) 733-5067
Hrs: W, 6pm; Su, 1:30pm
Trap: 8

Laramie Trap Club
PO Box 669, Laramie, WY 82070
Tony Classi (307) 742-3068
Type: Public/Member
Hrs: W, 5:30-9:30; Su, 11-2;
Call for other times **Trap:** 14

Niobrara Sportsmens Club
PO Box 1344, Lusk, WY 82225
Club Manager (307) 334-3318
Type: Public/Member
Hrs: Th, 5pm **Trap:** 5

Rocky Mt. Gun Club
13940 Grady, Casper, WY 82601
Joy Trim (307) 265-6403
Type: Public/Member
Hrs: W, 5-8; Su, 1-5 **Trap:** 14

Sweetwater Trap Club
1304 Virginia St.
Rock Springs, WY 82901
Robert Bettolo (307) 362-3286
Type: Public/Member
Hrs: W, 6pm; Su, 1pm
Trap: 9

White Mountain Trap Club
505 P St., Rock Springs, WY 82901
Rick Carrillo (307) 362-2619
Type: Public/Member
Hrs: Th, 6-Dark; April-Aug.
Trap: 2

DOMINICAN REPUBLIC

Casa de Campo Shooting Center
PO Box 140,
LaRomana, Dominican Republic
Hermogenes Guerrero
(809) 523-3333
3 mi. W of La Romana
Type: Public/Member
Hrs: Su-S, 8-5
Sporting: 7, 110 stations
Trap: 1 **Skeet:** 1 **Five Stand:** 3
HT: 110 ft.

CLAYS

Make extra copies of this helpful Trip Planner Form and use them when you call a sporting clays, trap or skeet location to get information or make reservations.

SPORTING CLAYS TRIP PLANNER

LOCATION NAME: _____ W&C LISTING PAGE: _____

TELEPHONE: _____

CONTACT NAME: _____

DATE (DAY) & SQUAD TIME: _____

DOES LOCATION SELL AMMO?: ❑ Yes ❑ No If yes, gauge sold: ❑ 12 ❑ 20 ❑ 28

COST _____ PAYMENT: ❑ Cash ❑ Check ❑ Credit Card

OTHER CLAY GAMES AVAILABLE: _____

DIRECTIONS: _____

**Remember Your Eye Protection! Remember Your Ear Protection!
Remember to Say...You Found Them In Wing & Clay!**

SPORTING CLAYS TRIP PLANNER

LOCATION NAME: _____ W&C LISTING PAGE: _____

TELEPHONE: _____

CONTACT NAME: _____

DATE (DAY) & SQUAD TIME: _____

DOES LOCATION SELL AMMO?: ❑ Yes ❑ No If yes, gauge sold: ❑ 12 ❑ 20 ❑ 28

COST _____ PAYMENT: ❑ Cash ❑ Check ❑ Credit Card

OTHER CLAY GAMES AVAILABLE: _____

DIRECTIONS: _____

**Remember Your Eye Protection! Remember Your Ear Protection!
Remember to Say...You Found Them In Wing & Clay!**

SPORTING CLAYS TRIP PLANNER

LOCATION NAME: _____ W&C LISTING PAGE: _____

TELEPHONE: _____

CONTACT NAME: _____

DATE (DAY) & SQUAD TIME: _____

DOES LOCATION SELL AMMO?: ❑ Yes ❑ No If yes, gauge sold: ❑ 12 ❑ 20 ❑ 28

COST _____ PAYMENT: ❑ Cash ❑ Check ❑ Credit Card

OTHER CLAY GAMES AVAILABLE: _____

DIRECTIONS: _____

**Remember Your Eye Protection! Remember Your Ear Protection!
Remember to Say...You Found Them In Wing & Clay!**

Make extra copies of this helpful Trip Planner Form and use them when you call a sporting clays, trap or skeet location to get information or make reservations.

SPORTING CLAYS TRIP PLANNER

LOCATION NAME: _____ W&C LISTING PAGE: _____

TELEPHONE: _____

CONTACT NAME: _____

DATE (DAY) & SQUAD TIME: _____

DOES LOCATION SELL AMMO?: ❏ Yes ❏ No If yes, gauge sold: ❏ 12 ❏ 20 ❏ 28

COST _____ PAYMENT: ❏ Cash ❏ Check ❏ Credit Card

OTHER CLAY GAMES AVAILABLE: _____

DIRECTIONS: _____

Remember Your Eye Protection! Remember Your Ear Protection!
Remember to Say...You Found Them in Wing & Clay!

SPORTING CLAYS TRIP PLANNER

LOCATION NAME: _____ W&C LISTING PAGE: _____

TELEPHONE: _____

CONTACT NAME: _____

DATE (DAY) & SQUAD TIME: _____

DOES LOCATION SELL AMMO?: ❏ Yes ❏ No If yes, gauge sold: ❏ 12 ❏ 20 ❏ 28

COST _____ PAYMENT: ❏ Cash ❏ Check ❏ Credit Card

OTHER CLAY GAMES AVAILABLE: _____

DIRECTIONS: _____

Remember Your Eye Protection! Remember Your Ear Protection!
Remember to Say...You Found Them in Wing & Clay!

SPORTING CLAYS TRIP PLANNER

LOCATION NAME: _____ W&C LISTING PAGE: _____

TELEPHONE: _____

CONTACT NAME: _____

DATE (DAY) & SQUAD TIME: _____

DOES LOCATION SELL AMMO?: ❏ Yes ❏ No If yes, gauge sold: ❏ 12 ❏ 20 ❏ 28

COST _____ PAYMENT: ❏ Cash ❏ Check ❏ Credit Card

OTHER CLAY GAMES AVAILABLE: _____

DIRECTIONS: _____

Remember Your Eye Protection! Remember Your Ear Protection!
Remember to Say...You Found Them in Wing & Clay!

Make extra copies of this helpful Trip Planner Form and use them when you call a hunting preserve or outfitter to get information or make reservations.

HUNTING PRESERVE TRIP PLANNER

PRESERVE NAME: _____ **W&C LISTING PAGE:** _____

TELEPHONE: _____

CONTACT NAME: _____

TYPE OF HUNT: ❑ Field ❑ Tower ❑ Blind ❑ Driven ❑ Boat
TYPE OF BIRD: ❑ Quail ❑ Pheasant ❑ Chukars ❑ Ducks
 ❑ Huns ❑ Dove ❑ Other:

DIFFICULTY OF HUNT: ❑ Easy ❑ Moderate ❑ Difficult

LENGTH OF HUNT/STAY: _____

DATES & TIME: _____
_____

KEY QUESTIONS: Ammunition? _____
 License requirements? _____
 Special group requirements? _____
 Guides and dogs? _____

DIRECTIONS: _____

HELP US GROW! WHEN YOU CALL, SAY YOU FOUND THEM IN WING & CLAY.

HUNTING PRESERVE TRIP PLANNER

PRESERVE NAME: _____ **W&C LISTING PAGE:** _____

TELEPHONE: _____

CONTACT NAME: _____

TYPE OF HUNT: ❑ Field ❑ Tower ❑ Blind ❑ Driven ❑ Boat
TYPE OF BIRD: ❑ Quail ❑ Pheasant ❑ Chukars ❑ Ducks
 ❑ Huns ❑ Dove ❑ Other:

DIFFICULTY OF HUNT: ❑ Easy ❑ Moderate ❑ Difficult

LENGTH OF HUNT/STAY: _____

DATES & TIME: _____
_____

KEY QUESTIONS: Ammunition? _____
 License requirements? _____
 Special group requirements? _____
 Guides and dogs? _____

DIRECTIONS: _____

HELP US GROW! WHEN YOU CALL, SAY YOU FOUND THEM IN WING & CLAY.

Make extra copies of this helpful Trip Planner Form and use them when you call a hunting preserve or outfitter to get information or make reservations.

HUNTING PRESERVE TRIP PLANNER

PRESERVE NAME: _____ W&C LISTING PAGE: _____

TELEPHONE: _____

CONTACT NAME: _____

TYPE OF HUNT: ❑ Field   ❑ Tower   ❑ Blind   ❑ Driven   ❑ Boat
TYPE OF BIRD: ❑ Quail   ❑ Pheasant ❑ Chukars ❑ Ducks
               ❑ Huns   ❑ Dove   ❑ Other:

DIFFICULTY OF HUNT: ❑ Easy   ❑ Moderate   ❑ Difficult

LENGTH OF HUNT/STAY: _____

DATES & TIME: _____
_____

KEY QUESTIONS: Ammunition? _____
                  License requirements? _____
                  Special group requirements? _____
                  Guides and dogs? _____
DIRECTIONS: _____

HELP US GROW! WHEN YOU CALL, SAY YOU FOUND THEM IN WING & CLAY.

HUNTING PRESERVE TRIP PLANNER

PRESERVE NAME: _____ W&C LISTING PAGE: _____

TELEPHONE: _____

CONTACT NAME: _____

TYPE OF HUNT: ❑ Field   ❑ Tower   ❑ Blind   ❑ Driven   ❑ Boat
TYPE OF BIRD: ❑ Quail   ❑ Pheasant ❑ Chukars ❑ Ducks
               ❑ Huns   ❑ Dove   ❑ Other:

DIFFICULTY OF HUNT: ❑ Easy   ❑ Moderate   ❑ Difficult

LENGTH OF HUNT/STAY: _____

DATES & TIME: _____
_____

KEY QUESTIONS: Ammunition? _____
                  License requirements? _____
                  Special group requirements? _____
                  Guides and dogs? _____
DIRECTIONS: _____

HELP US GROW! WHEN YOU CALL, SAY YOU FOUND THEM IN WING & CLAY.

Make extra copies of this helpful Trip Planner Form and use them when you call a hunting preserve or outfitter to get information or make reservations.

HUNTING PRESERVE TRIP PLANNER

PRESERVE NAME: _____ W&C LISTING PAGE: _____

TELEPHONE: _____

CONTACT NAME: _____

TYPE OF HUNT: ❏ Field ❏ Tower ❏ Blind ❏ Driven ❏ Boat
TYPE OF BIRD: ❏ Quail ❏ Pheasant ❏ Chukars ❏ Ducks
              ❏ Huns ❏ Dove ❏ Other:

DIFFICULTY OF HUNT: ❏ Easy ❏ Moderate ❏ Difficult

LENGTH OF HUNT/STAY: _____

DATES & TIME: _____
_____

KEY QUESTIONS: Ammunition? _____
               License requirements? _____
               Special group requirements? _____
               Guides and dogs? _____

DIRECTIONS: _____

HELP US GROW! WHEN YOU CALL, SAY YOU FOUND THEM IN WING & CLAY.

HUNTING PRESERVE TRIP PLANNER

PRESERVE NAME: _____ W&C LISTING PAGE: _____

TELEPHONE: _____

CONTACT NAME: _____

TYPE OF HUNT: ❏ Field ❏ Tower ❏ Blind ❏ Driven ❏ Boat
TYPE OF BIRD: ❏ Quail ❏ Pheasant ❏ Chukars ❏ Ducks
              ❏ Huns ❏ Dove ❏ Other:

DIFFICULTY OF HUNT: ❏ Easy ❏ Moderate ❏ Difficult

LENGTH OF HUNT/STAY: _____

DATES & TIME: _____
_____

KEY QUESTIONS: Ammunition? _____
               License requirements? _____
               Special group requirements? _____
               Guides and dogs? _____

DIRECTIONS: _____

HELP US GROW! WHEN YOU CALL, SAY YOU FOUND THEM IN WING & CLAY.

SHOTGUNNER'S SOURCE INDEX

Buying a new shotgun?

That's great! But with over 68 companies manufacturing and importing shotguns for the U.S. market, how do you go about finding the right gun for you? Easy! The perfect place to start the buying process is in **Wing & Clay**. Turn to the following sections to begin:

SHOTGUN MANUFACTURERS & IMPORTERS   Page 184

You'll find detailed information on the 68 different shotgun companies and importers serving the U.S. market. Company and individual contact names, addresses, telephone and fax numbers. Brand names, models, price ranges and the country in which the shotguns are manufactured. And cross-references to a score of informative advertisements.

SHOTGUNS/NATIONAL DEALERS   Page 197

31 of the best shotgun dealers in the country—stocking thousands of shotguns—are just a phone call away with this valuable section. Use it to check prices and availability. Locate "hard to find" items. Order by mail or phone.

SHOTGUN TRADE NAME & MANUFACTURERS CHART   Page 183

Know the shotgun name but not the maker? This chart will help you find the manufacturer, importer or distributor of almost every gun available in the U.S.

WING & CLAY'S GUARANTEED DISTRIBUTION 60,000 COPIES

Double-Barrel Distribution Targeted to Meet the Advertising Needs of the Shotgun Industry.

At WING & CLAY your needs as an advertiser come first. That's why, unlike magazines and other periodicals, WING & CLAY offers you a chance to reach an audience of 60,000 prospects with a one-time buying decision that works for you for a full 12 months!

Double-Barrel Distribution

WING & CLAY's distribution provides advertisers with maximum impact at minimum cost.

How? By delivering a selective audience of avid sportsmen and blanket coverage of shotgun trade and industry groups. This unique, "double-barrel" distribution system works like this:

SPORTSMEN - 40,000 COPIES

☐ **Wingshooters** - WING & CLAY delivers thousands of copies to avid sportsmen whose names are gathered from top-flight hunting publications and catalogs. Other wingshooters receive copies at hunting/wildlife conservation group dinners and celebrity hunts; or purchase them at retail locations through direct response ads in leading shotgunning publications.

☐ **Sporting Clays Enthusiasts** - A copy of WING & CLAY is sent to every member of the major sporting clays associations—NSCA, SCA, and NESCA. WING & CLAY also works with numerous organizations, including the state-wide sporting clays associations, the Women's Shooting Sports Foundation, and sponsors of charitable shoots to reach new and experienced shooter who rely heavily on WING & CLAY when they are buying shotgun related equipment.

SHOTGUN TRADE & INDUSTRY GROUPS - 20,000 COPIES

☐ **Club & Range Operators** - 5,127 Copies are sent to the operators of all hunting preserves, sporting clays courses, trap and skeet locations, and shooting schools in WING & CLAY's comprehensive private and published databases.

☐ **Retail Gun Dealers** - No one has more influence on an individual sportsman's buying decision than the gun counter sales person. That's why over 11,000 highly-targeted, "yellow page" storefront gun dealers nationwide receive a special *Gun Counter* edition of WING & CLAY—drilled through the corner so that it can be secured for easy reference.

☐ **Professional Sporting Goods Buyers** Over 2,400 copies of WING & CLAY are distributed to these professionals who are responsible for buying millions of dollars worth of guns, ammo and shooting supplies annually

☐ **Sporting Goods Wholesalers & Sales Representatives** - This relatively small but influential group—serving the needs of both manufacturers and retailers— receives copies of WING & CLAY.

☐ **Shotgun Industry Executives** - Individual copies are sent to executives culled from WING & CLAY's own SHOTGUNNER'S SOURCE database. Avid sportsmen in their own right, this key group of executives are a "must hit" target for the advertiser trying to build product awareness and sway industry opinion.

☐ **Outdoor Writers & Editors** - The sporting press plays an important role in influencing the buying and shooting habits of America's sportsmen. Consequently, copies of WING & CLAY are sent to all members of the Outdoor Writers Association of America and to hundreds of independent journalists at hunting and shooting publications.

THE SHOTGUNNER'S SOURCE

WINGS - HUNTING PRESERVES

A nationwide guide to hunting preserves. Begins on page 194

CLAYS - SPORTING, TRAP & SKEET

A nationwide guide to sporting clays, trap & skeet shooting locations. Begins on page 328

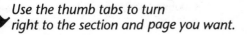

*Use the thumb tabs to turn
right to the section and page you want.*